FUNDAMENTALS OF

ENGINEERING DRAWING

AND

AUTOCAD

FUNDAMENTALS OF
ENGINEERING DRAWING
AND
AUTOCAD

For
B.Tech/Diploma Students
According to Latest Syllabus of M.D.(Rohtak) UPTU (Lucknow)

By

Mohd. Parvez
B.T.E (New Delhi)
J.M.I New Delhi, A.M.U (Aligarh)

THIRD EDITION

GALGOTIA
Publications Pvt. Ltd.
5, Ansari Road, Darya Ganj, New Delhi-110002
Phone: 23263334, 23288134 Fax: 23281909
e-mail: agmgppl@gmail.com, gppl@indiatimes.com

FUNDAMENTALS OF ENGINEERING DRAWING AND AUTOCAD

IMPORTANT
Author and Publisher would welcome suggestions for the improvement of the book or pointing out of any misprint.

First Edition : 2005
Second Edition : 2008
Third Edition : 2010
Reprint: 2015
ISBN: 978-81-7515-611-1

Typesetting at :C
Sara Assignments, 96-B, DDA Flats, Mansarover Park, Shahdara, Delhi-110032

Published by :
Suneel Galgotia for Galgotia Publications Pvt., Ltd.
5, Ansari Road, Daryaganj, New Delhi-110002.

Printed at : Earam Offset Printers, Delhi-110053
Phone : 011-22182218

Dedicated to my wife
who has
given moral support in the preparation of this book

PREFACE TO THE THIRD EDITION

I am thankful to the readers who have made this book so popular that within such a short time, the second edition had to be revised incorporate of valueable suggestions received from the readers and also cover the latest syllabus of U.P. Technical University (Lucknow), M.D. Unversity (Rohtak), B.T.E. (New Delhi).

In this improved edition, many solved problems have been added including two new chapters viz, geometrical construction and plane of projections. Since AutoCAD is playing an important role in modern industry, therefore special attention has been given to the latest version of AutoCAD 2010.

I express my heartiest and the most sincere thanks to Mr. J.A Siddiqui Chairman, AL–Falah School of Engg. & Tech. Faridabad, Mr. Malkhan Singh, Incharge (Part-time Diploma Engg.), G.B. Pant Polytechnic, New Delhi, Prof S.M Mahmood, University polytechnic J.M.I, New Delhi and Mr. Mohd. Razi Assistant Prof. AL–Falah School of Engg. & Tech. Faridabad.

Thanks are also due to Mr. Irfan Hayat O.S.D & Member of governing body AFSET FBD, Mr. Hilal Uddin (Librarian), Delhi College of Tech. & Management Palwal (Haryana), Mr. Karmachandra Kushwaha (Production) Galgotia Publications and Mr. Naushad, Galgotia Publication.

I sincerely invite the users comments and suggestions for improving this book.

MOHD PARVEZ

PREFACE

This book is intended to fulfill the needs of B.Tech/Diploma in civil, Mechanical and Electrical Engineering. It furnishes all relevant details on the subject in a manner that it can cover to the requirements of all Diploma Engineering students, especially Board of Technical Education Delhi, University Polytechnic A.M.U. Aligarh, University Polytechnic J.M.I New Delhi-25. The object of this book is not only to train a Engineering student in such a manner that he/she acquires a good style of draftsmanship, but also to give him the basic knowledge of the treatment of simple to complicated problems in design and drawing by geometrical methods and to develop in him/her an orderly imagination essential to all concerned with practical constructive work.

As this book is intended to be in the subject, it contains a very large number of worked out problems covering every phase of the subject presented in a simple, understandable and compact form. To be in line with ISO, first angle projection has been followed in this book. However, few problems on third angle projection have also been included in it.

Today drawings are prepared quickly through software packages. That is why knowledge of AutoCAD is a must. However the fundamentals of engineering drawing must be very clearly understood. We have tried to present the subject matter in simple language with examples so that students can grasp the finer points easily. The book has been written keeping in view the difficulties of a beginner in the subject of Engineering Drawing. We are quite hopeful that this book will serve its purpose very well for young and building engineers.

Thanks are due to Mr. J.A. Siddiqui Chairman, Al-Falah School of Engineering & Techonology, Faridabad and Mr. Malkhan Singh, Incharge (Part-time Diploma Engg.), G.B. Pant Polytechnic, New Delhi for their help. My thanks are to Mr. Suneel Galgotia who took all the initiative of publishing the book. I would like to express my special thanks to Mr. Karmachandra Kushwaha, (Production), Mrs. M. Jayanthi and Mr. Naushad Akber, Galgotia Publications acknowledge for their sincere efforts to publish this book.

MOHD PARVEZ

CONTENTS

PART–I: GEOMETRICAL DRAWING

PART–II: MECHANICAL ENGINEERING DRAWING

PART–IV: AUTOCAD

PART I

GEOMETRICAL DRAWING

1

DRAWING INSTRUMENTS AND THEIR USES

1.1 INTRODUCTION

Engineering drawing known as the language of engineers is widely used means of communication among the designer, engineers, draftsmen and craftmen in the industry. The translation of ideas into practice without the use of graphic language is really beyond imagination. The word graphics means dealing with the expression of ideas by drawing lines or curves on a surface.

Like other languages, the drawing is also a language that can be learned and used like other languages. Basically, engineering drawing is the graphic language of engineers. It is a graphic representation of thinking, planning and language of every technical person who uses to communicate his ideas clearly to the other engineers.

Before starting, manufacturing or construction work, product to be developed or plan of housing society, is firstly drawn on a rough paper. The purpose of these drawing is to define physical shape completely and accurately of particular object by means of lines and other useful informations regarding the object.

In an age of automation engineering drawing has greatly enhanced. Without the fundamental knowledge of technical drawing the student would not success in industry. There are many uses of engineering drawing in practical field, especially in modern industries.

Application: Engineering drawing is widely used in machines, automobiles, aeronautics, chemical, marine, electronics, computer and in electrical engineering which gives the correct shape and size along with the dimensional tolerances for understanding of component.

In civil and architecture, engineering drawing is used to draw the plan and elevation of buildings, and structure work.

The application of engineering drawing in electrical, electronics, instrumentation and computer science are usually to prepare electrical wiring drawing, printed circuit board drawing, installation drawing, process drawing and pictorial drawing.

1.2 DRAWING INSTRUMENTS

Drawing instruments are used to prepare drawings easily and accurately. A neat and clean drawing is prepared with the help of good quality of drawing instruments. The students must know the proper use of drawing instruments.

The following instruments are commonly used for the preparation of engineering drawing:

1. Drawing board
2. Drawing sheet
3. Mini drafter/Drafting machine/Tee square

4. Set squares (45° and 30°–60°)
5. Drawing instrument box containing:
   (i) Large compass
   (ii) Bow compass
   (iii) Large divider
   (iv) Bow divider
   (v) Inking pen
   (vi) Lead
6. Pencils/Mechanical pencil (Ejector type)
7. Cello tape
8. Eraser
9. French curve
10. Circle master
11. Knife cutter
12. Duster (a piece of cloth)
13. Sand paper
14. Drawing note book.

1.3 USES OF DRAWING INSTRUMENTS

(1) Drawing Board: Drawing board is used for fixing the drawing sheet by means of cello tape as shown in Fig. 1.1. It should be made of well seasoned soft wood of yellow pine. This wood is free from knots and oily grains. Its surface should be perfectly smooth. Drawing boards are available in different sizes in the market. As per IS 1444:1989 the sizes of drawing boards are given in Table 1.1

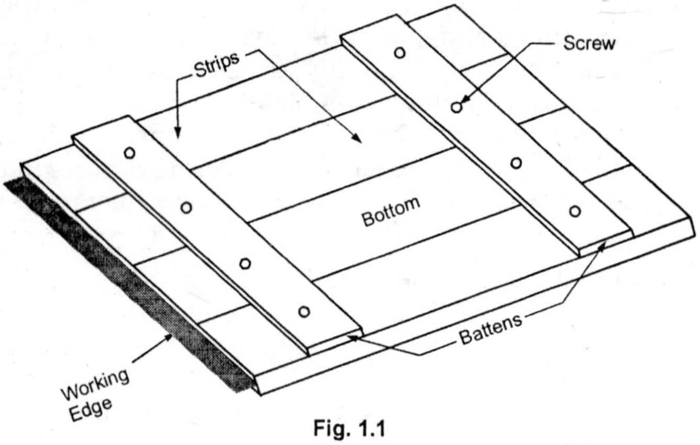

Fig. 1.1

Table 1.1 Drawing Board Size

S.No.	*Designation*	*Size (in mm)*
1.	B_0	1500 × 1000 × 25
2.	B_1	1000 × 700 × 25
3.	B_2	700 × 500 × 15
4.	B_3	500 × 350 × 15
5.	B_4	350 × 250 × 15

For the use of engineering colleges **B2(700 × 500 × 15)** size of drawing board is recommended.

(2) Drawing Sheet: Drawing sheets are available in many varieties in the market. Generally drawing sheets are produced in A_0 size and the other sizes can be obtained by cutting the A_0 size sheet as shown in Fig 1.2.

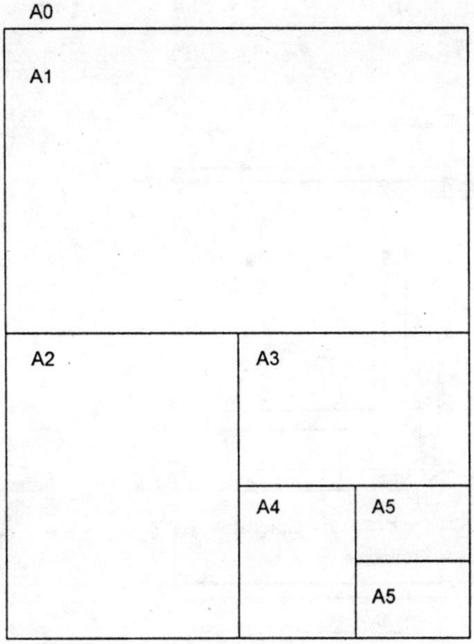

Fig. 1.2

There are six standard sizes for drawing sheets specified by the Indian Standard Institution. The preferred sizes of the sheet as selected from IS 10711:1983 are given in Table 1.2.

Table 1.2 Drawing Sheet Size

S.No.	*Designation*	*size (in mm)*
1.	A_0	841 × 1189
2.	A_1	594 × 841
3.	A_2	420 × 594
4.	A_3	297 × 420
5.	A_4	210 × 297
6.	A_5	148 × 210

For the practice of engineering students $\mathbf{A_2}$ **(420 × 594)** size of drawing sheet is recommended.

(3) Mini Drafter: The function of mini drafter has the combined advantages of tee-square, set square, scale and protractor as shown in Fig. 1.3. It is mounted at the left end on the drawing board by means of a Knob.

It consist of two blades always parallel to their original position, fixed on a circular disc in such a way that they can be moved freely on circular disc, which act as a protractor.

The bigger version of this mini drafter is known as drafting machine, which is permanently fixed on a large drawing board, as shown in Fig. 1.4.

Mini drafter is commonly used by the college students and draftsmen in the design department.

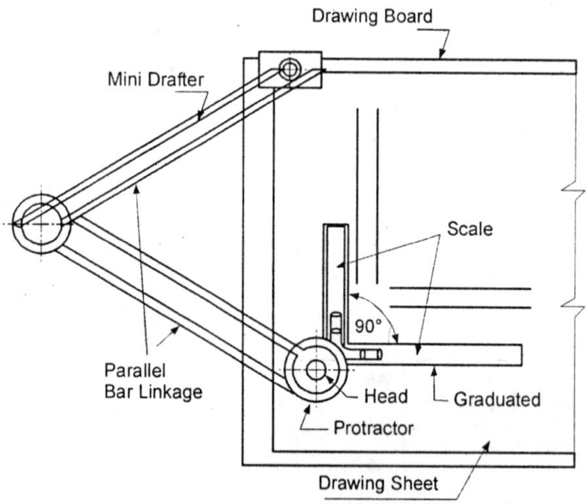

Fig. 1.3

Fig. 1.4 Drafting Machine

Care of Instruments

- Zero of adjustable circular disc marking should coincide when its blade are in horizontal and vertical positions.
- Fixed end should not move with the movement of the blades of mini drafter.

Tee-square : The tee-square should be made of well seasoned hard wood, such as teak as shown in Fig. 1.5.

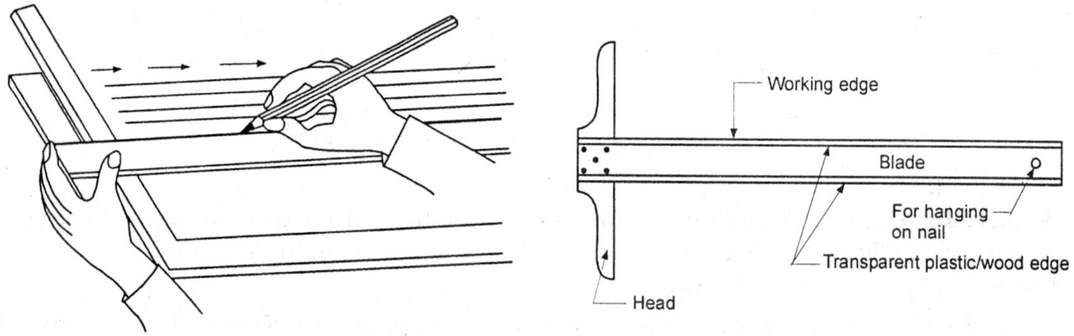

Fig. 1.5

It consists of two parts, stock and the blade which are joined together at a right angle to each other by means of screws. The stock is placed along the working edge of the drawing table, which is always on the left side of the students, and slides on it when ever required. It is used to draw horizontal lines and parallel lines. The clear length of the blade should be more than the drawing board length. It is also available in plastic material in the market.

Care in handling of tee-square

- Clean the blade with cloth to remove pencil graphite lead.
- It should always be kept on drawing board, even when not in use.
- Lower edge of tee-square should not be used for drawing horizontal lines.

(4) Set-squares: Set-squares are used in combination for drawing all straight lines except the horizontal lines which are usually drawn with *T*-square as shown in Fig. 1.6.

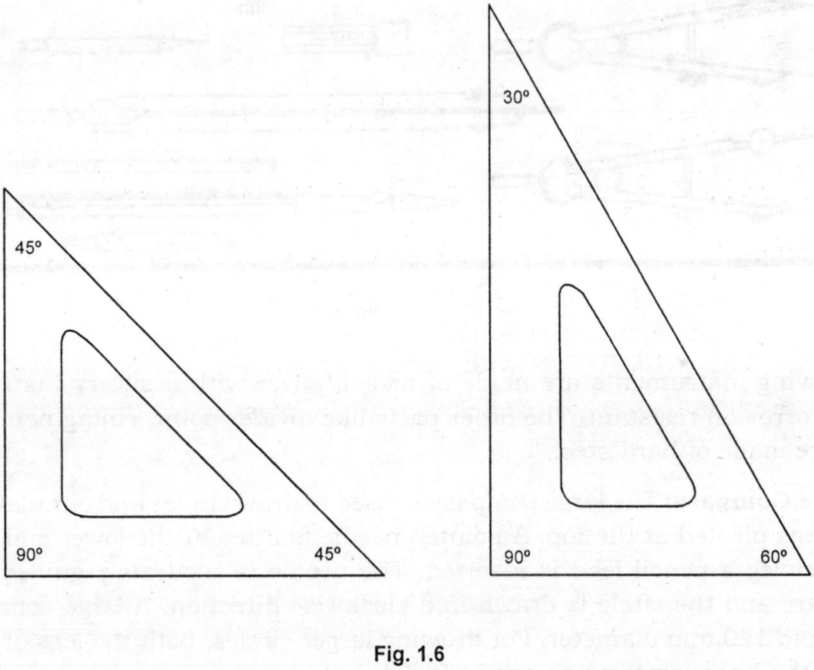

Fig. 1.6

It is made of transparent sheet of celluloid or plastic material in various sizes. They are available in the shape of triangle with one right angle corner. The set-square of 45° triangle and 30°-60° triangle of 200 mm and 250 mm length are available in the market for ordinary work. Two set-squares used simultaneously along with the tee-square produce lines for making angles of 15°, 30°, 45°, 60°, 75°, 90° and 105° etc. A circle can be divided in 6, 8, 12 and 24 parts using set-squares. Hatching lines are also drawn by set squares.

1.4 DRAWING INSTRUMENT BOX

A standard set of drawing instrument box is used by engineering students, containing large compass, bow compass, large divider, bow divider, inking pen and pencil lead etc. as shown in Fig. 1.7.

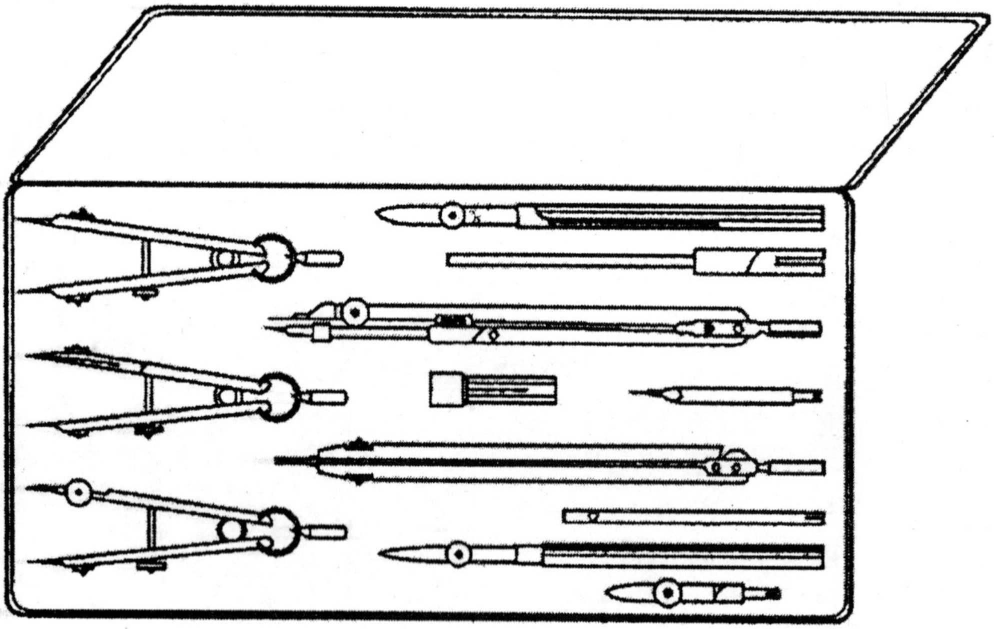

Fig. 1.7

Drawing instruments are made of nickel, silver with a silvery lustre on the surface and is corrosion resistant. The other parts like divider point, ruling pen, nibs and spring parts are made of hard steel.

(i) Large Compass: The large compass is used to draw circles and circular arcs. It consists of two legs pivoted at the top. A pointed needle is fitted at the lower end of one leg, while the other leg a pencil lead is inserted. The needle is accurately guided into position at the centre and the circle is drawn in a clockwise direction. A large compass can draw a circle upto 120 mm diameter. For drawing larger circles, both the legs of the compass are bent at the knee joints as shown in Fig. 1.7 (i).

The needle point of the compass should not be pressed too much otherwise a hole is produced on the drawing sheet as well as in the drawing board. For better working of the compass, the leg containing lead of pencil should be shorter than the needle point.

(ii) Bow Compass: A bow compass is used for drawing small circles and arcs upto 25 mm diameter. This compass is used by structural engineers when a large number of small circles of the same diameter are to be drawn as shown in Fig. 1.7(ii).

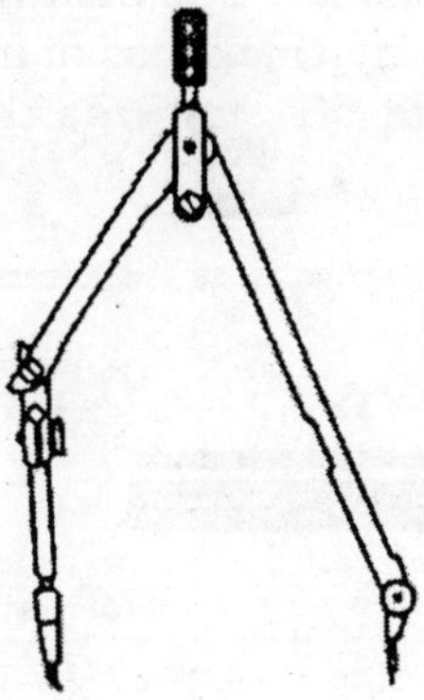

Fig. 1.7 (i)

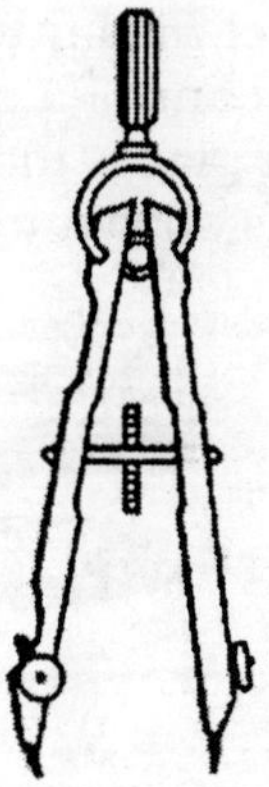

Fig. 1.7 (ii)

iii) Large Divider: The divider is used for dividing straight lines and circles into desired ıumber of equal parts as shown in Fig. 1.7 (iii).

It is also used for transfering distance from one part of drawing to another part of the łrawing. It has two legs, with steel points at both the lower ends instead of pencil point.

iv) Bow Divider: The bow divider is used for dividing small circles or arcs and number of small equal distances as shown in Fig. 1.7 (iv).

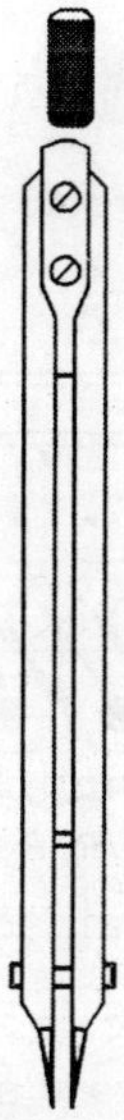

Fig. 1.7 (iii)

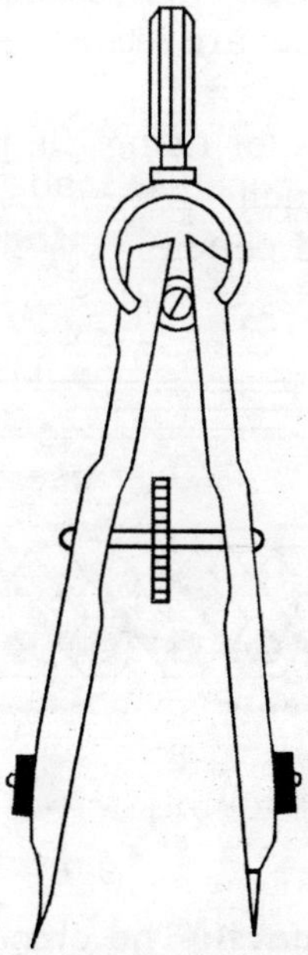

Fig. 1.7 (iv)

(v) Inking Pen: This instrument is used for inking drawing of straight and curved lines. It consists of a pair of steel nibs fitted to a metal holder. The distance between nibs of a pen can be adjusted by means of a screw to gives any thickness of a line. The inking pen should be kept in vertical plane, inclined slightly at 60°, towards the direction in which the line is being drawn, as shown in Fig. 1.7(v)

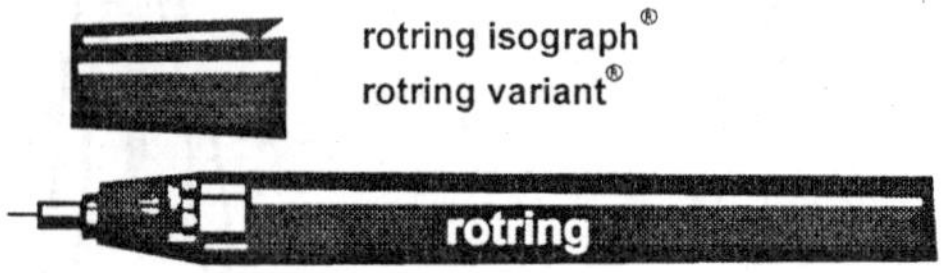

Fig. 1.7 (v)

(vi) Drawing Pencils: Drawing pencils are used for preparing the drawing of an object. The quality, neatness and accuracy of the drawing depends upon the quality of the pencil used.

Pencils are made of graphite mixed with varying quantities of clay to produce different degree of hardness covering with ordinary wood. Various grades of the pencil to be used depend upon the type of the lines required as shown in Fig. 1.8.

It is available in a variety of grades 9H, 8H, 7H and 6H (hard) 5H and 4H (medium hard) 3H and 2H (medium), H and F (medium soft), HB, B, 2B to 6H (very soft). Engineering students use HB pencil to draw extra thick lines e.g. border line, title block lines etc. H pencil is used to draw thick lines e.g.: visible lines, cutting plane lines, short break lines and lettering or dimensioning. 2H pencil is used to draw thin lines e.g., centre line, hidden lines etc. and 3H pencil is used to draw faint lines, or guide lines.

Engineering students are recommended to use Kohinoor and Apsara brand pencils for better result.

There are two ways for using the pencil to prepare the drawing:

(a) Chisel edge pencil

(b) Conical pointed pencil.

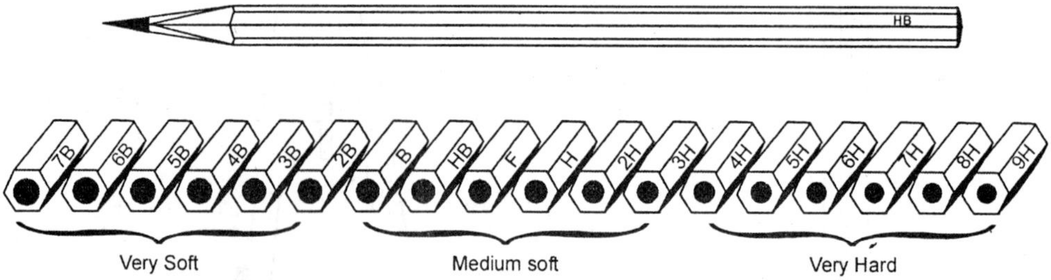

Fig. 1.8 Different Grades of Pencils

(a) Chisel edge pencil: The chisel edge pencil is used to draw straight lines. It is used to obtain uniform thickness of line as shown in Fig. 1.9 (i).

(b) Conical pointed pencil: The conical pointed pencil is used for general work e.g.: lettering, dimensioning and drawing circles and arcs. Do not use a pencil less than 75 mm and cut the wood of pencil at the opposite end of grade marking as shown in Fig. 1.9(ii).

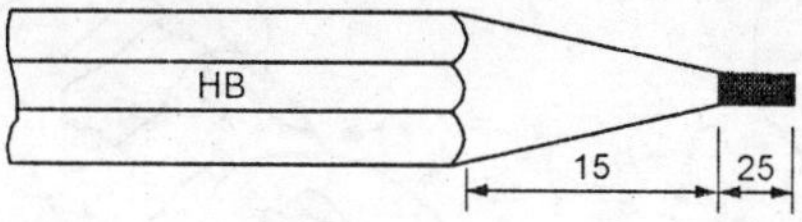

Fig. 1.9 (i)

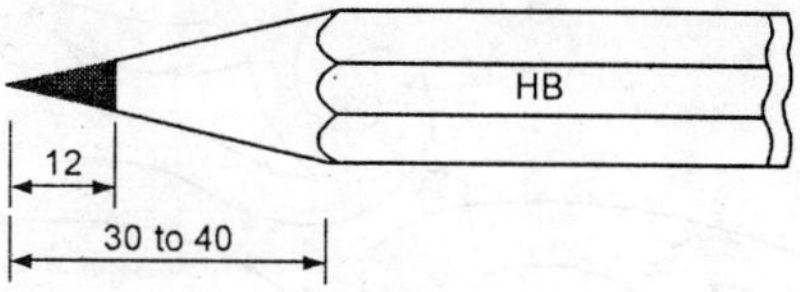

Fig. 1.9 (ii)

1.5 OTHER MISCELLANEOUS INSTRUMENTS

(i) Cello Tape: Cello tape is used for fixing the drawing sheet on the drawing board, before starting the work. It is made of transparent material and available in rolls of varying sizes and length.

(ii) Eraser: A soft colourless and good quality of rubber is used for erasing or rubbing unnecessary lines in the drawing. Frequent use of rubber should be avoided and rubbing should be dusted off by dusting cloth as shown in Fig. 1.10 (i).

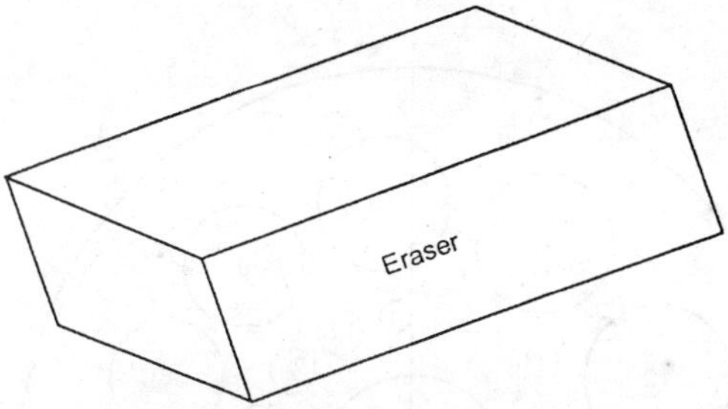

Fig. 1.10 (i)

(iii) French Curve: French curve is used to draw irregular curves and arcs in the drawing. It is made of transparent plastic material and available in different shapes and sizes. Its edge must be perfectly smooth as shown in Fig. 1.10(ii).

(iv) Circle Master: Circle master is used to draw of small size circles which are not possible to draw by compass. It consist of different size of circles. It is also used to increase the speed of drafting. It is made of plastic material in various sizes and different colours as shown in Fig. 1.10 (iii).

(v) Knife Cutter: A knife cutter is used to remove the wood on a pencil and leaving the exposed lead for sharpening. The sharp blade of stainless steel with plastic handle is joined together by means of brass rivet as shown in Fig. 1.10 (iv).

(vi) Duster: Duster is used for cleaning of drawing sheet as well as drawing instruments etc. Preferably it should be a towel cloth or a handkerchief. The eraser crumbs formed after the use of eraser should be removed with the help of duster.

Fig. 1.10 (ii)

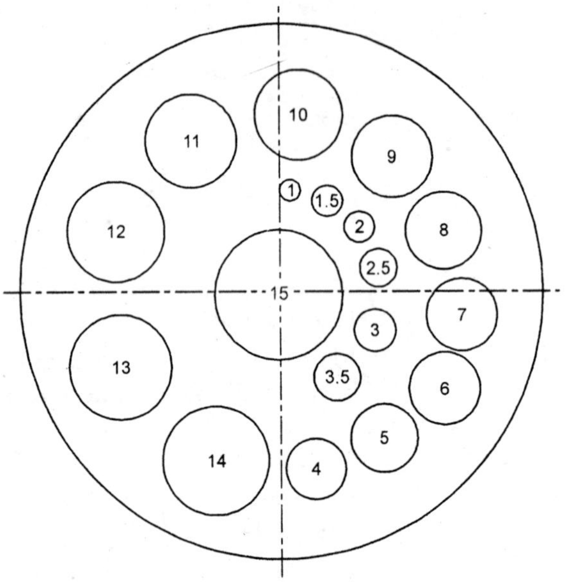

Fig. 1.10 (iii)

(vii) Sand Paper: Sand paper is used to sharpening the pencil point. Zero number sand paper is used for this purpose as shown in Fig. 1.10 (v). Avoid sharpening the pencils on the drawing board.

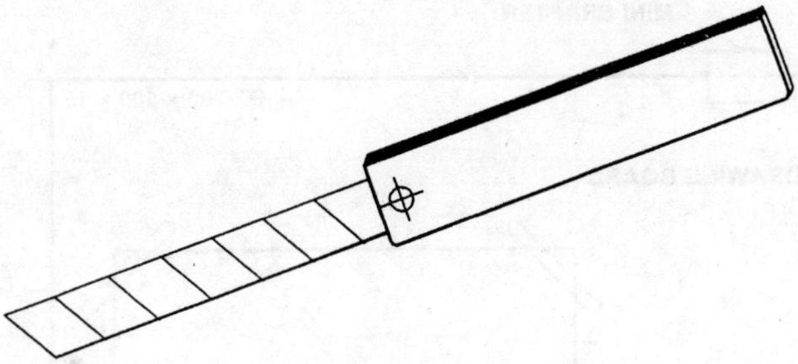

Fig. 1.10 (iv)

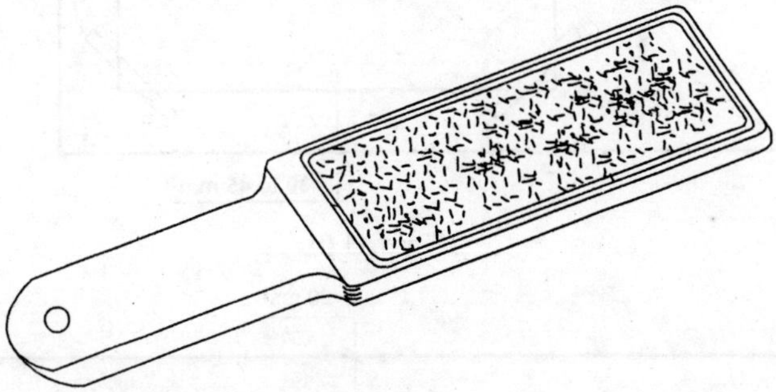

Fig. 1.10 (v)

(viii) Small Size Drawing Notebook: A sketch book is used to draw free hand sketching of various types of objects in the class room as shown in Fig. 1.10 (vi).

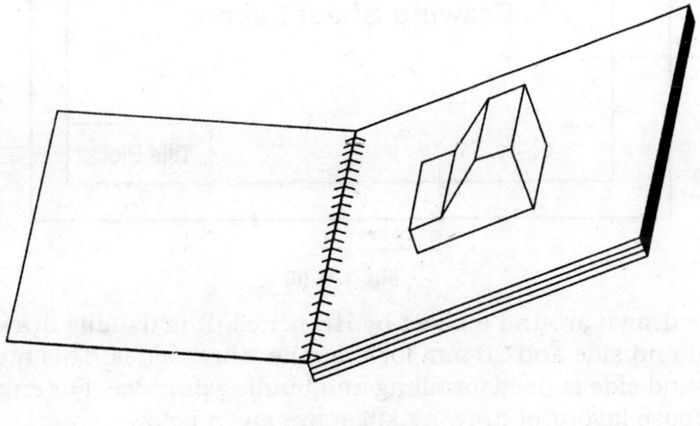

Fig. 1.9 (vi)

1.6 LAYOUT OF DRAWING SHEET

The layout of drawing sheet is an important function of engineering drawing. The engineering student must know the standard rules for the selection of suitable scale, margin space, title block and part list etc. on the drawing sheet as shown in Fig. 1.11 (i). Fig. 1.11 (ii) shows a typical layout of a drawing sheet, size A_2, according to IS 46 : 2003.

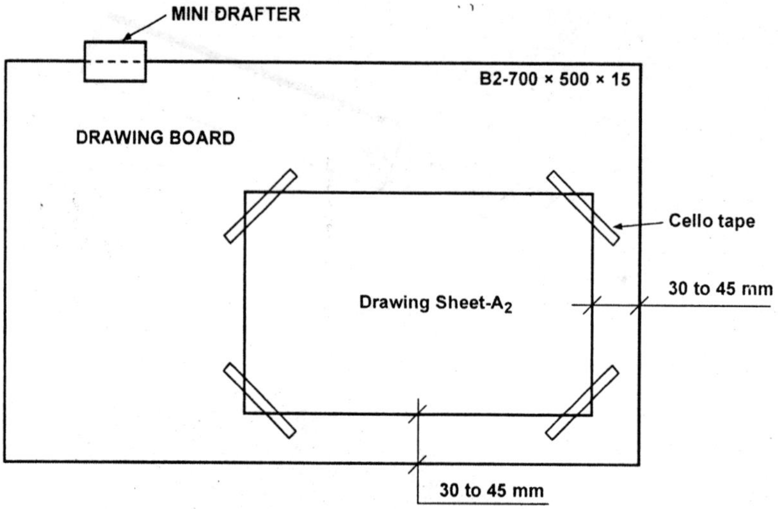

Fig. 1.11 (i)

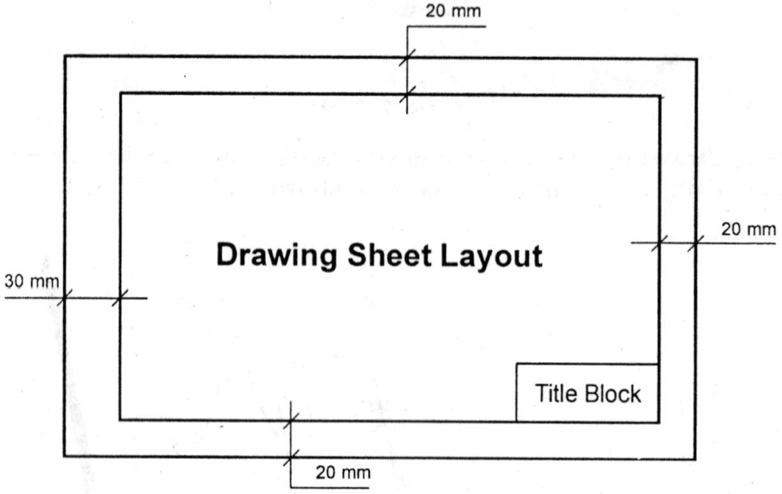

Fig. 1.11 (ii)

The border line is drawn around a sheet by HB pencil. It is usually drawn at a distance of 30 mm from left hand side and 20 mm for the other three sides. This more space which is kept on the left hand side is used for filling and binding purpose. For engineering students and practice purpose layout of drawing sheet are given below.

1.7 TITLE BLOCK

Different types of title blocks are used in industrial as well as in colleges. For all sizes of drawing sheets 65 × 185 mm size of title block is commonly used.

The title block provides the following information:

- Name of the institute or firm:
- Title of drawing:

- Sheet No:
- Scale:
- Symbol (1st angle or 3rd angle projection):
- Class:
- Starting date:
- Drawn by:
- Roll No:
- Completion date:

The different types of title blocks are shown in Fig. 1.12.

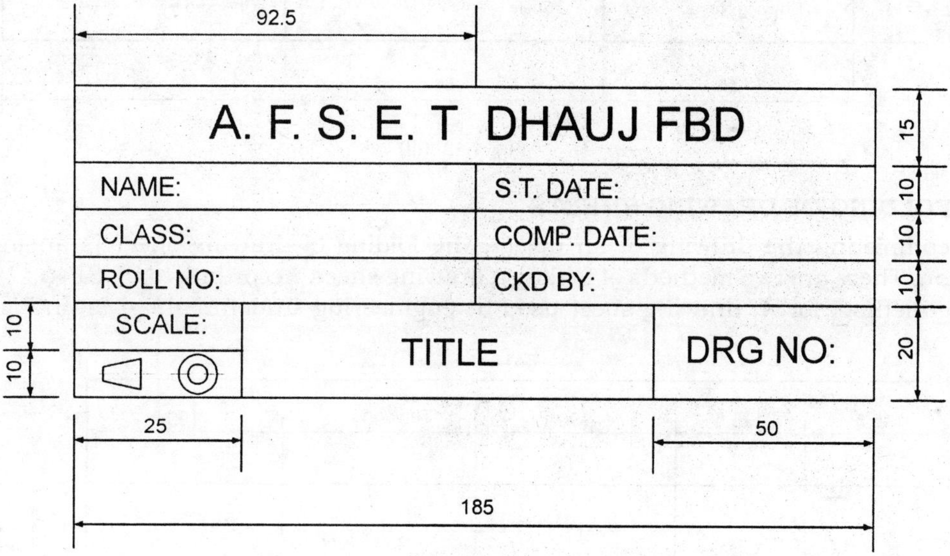

Fig. 1.12 (i)

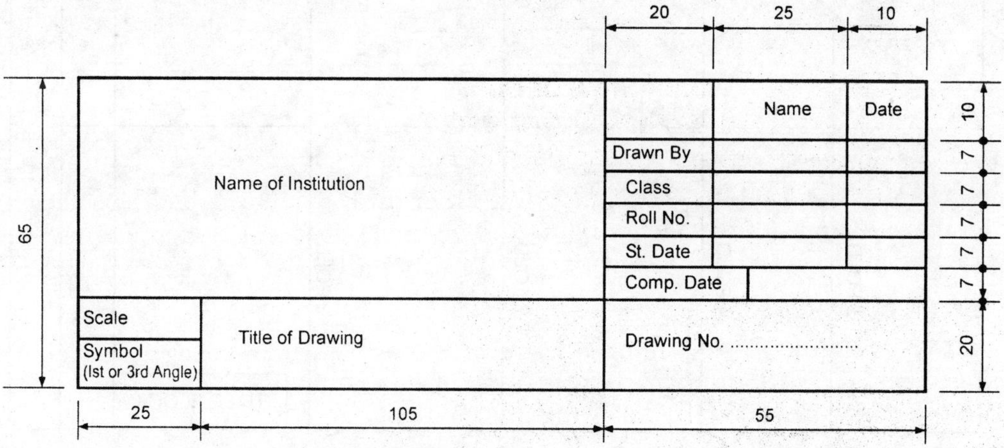

Fig. 1.12 (ii)

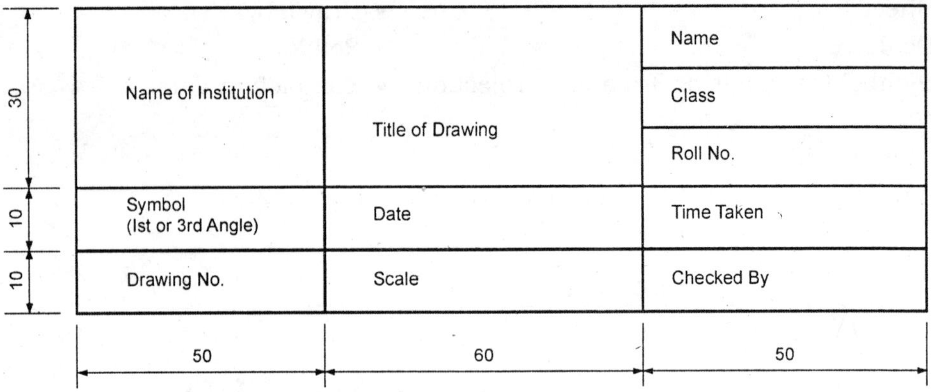

Fig. 1.12 (iii)

1.8 FOLDING OF DRAWING SHEETS

After completing the drawing of an object, the folding of drawing sheet is an important function. There are two methods of folding a drawing sheet. According to IS: SP46 : 1998, the folding method, for A_1 drawing sheet used by engineering students are given in Fig. 1.13.

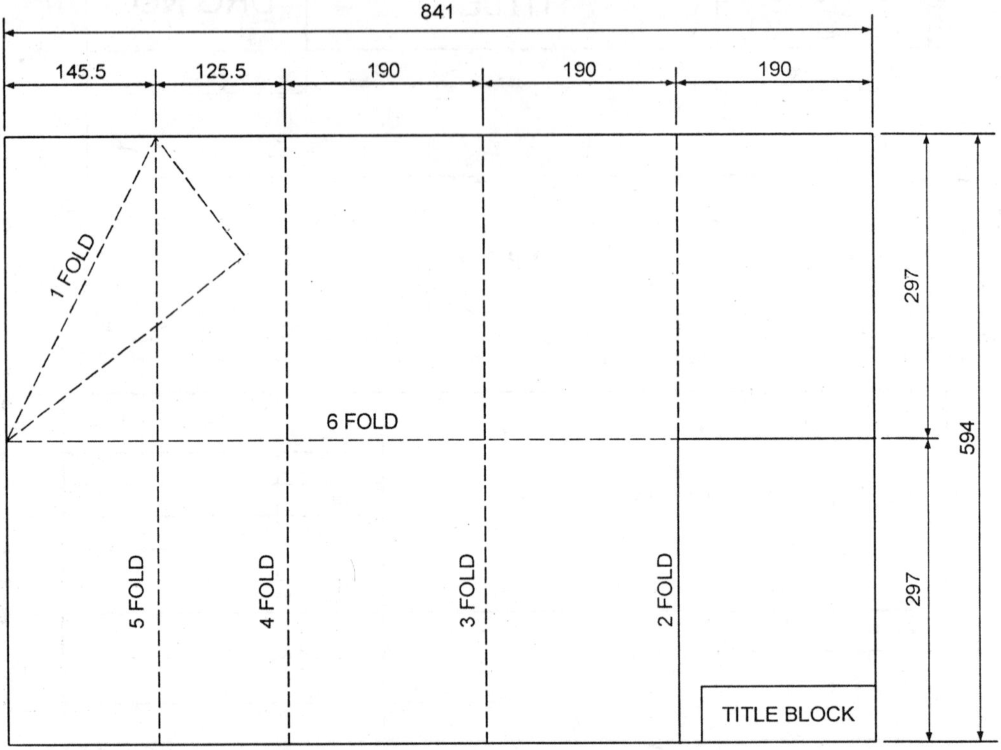

Folding marks on a drawing sheet of size A_1 (Method Ist)

Fig. 1.13 (i)

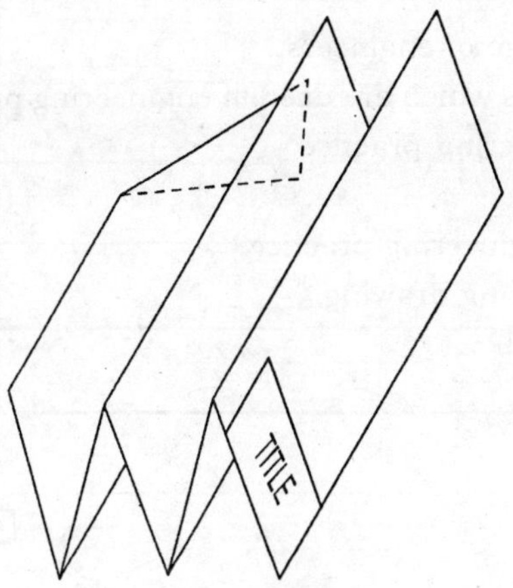

LENGTHWISE FOLDING

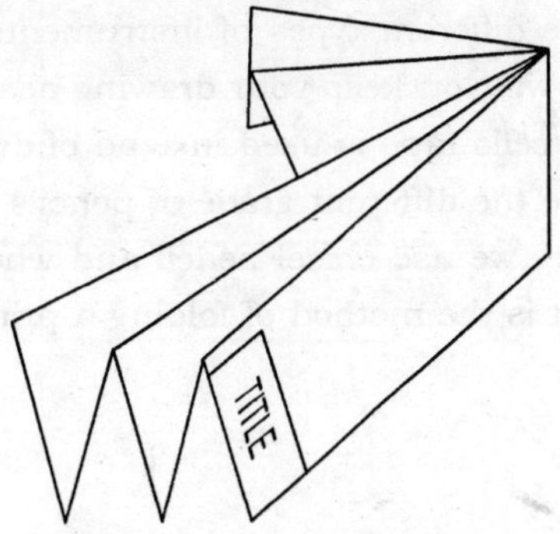

CROSSWISE FOLDING

Fig. 1.13 (i)

SHEET - A-1. 594 × 841

FOLDING DIAGRAM (Method IInd)

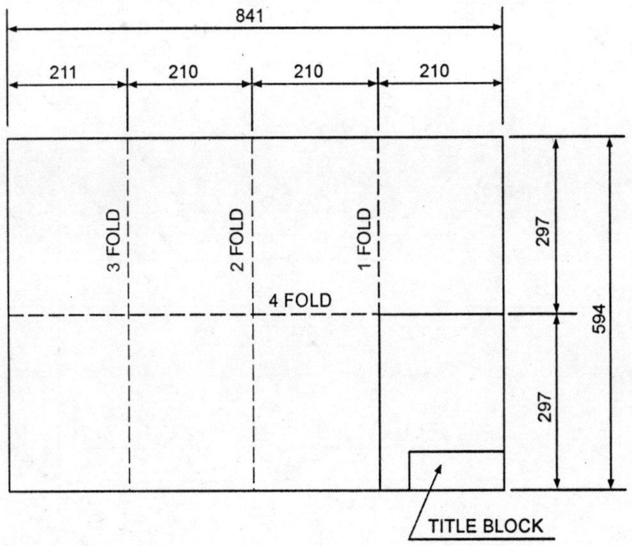

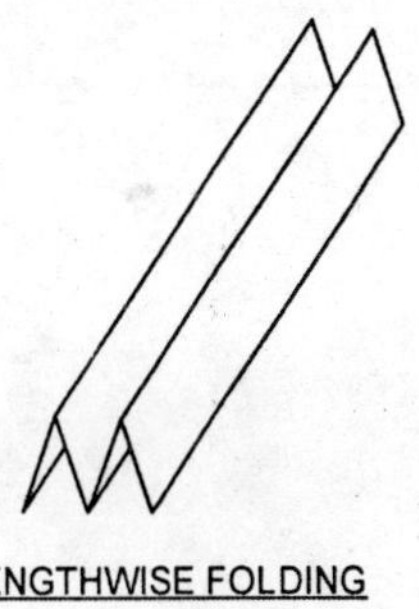

LENGTHWISE FOLDING

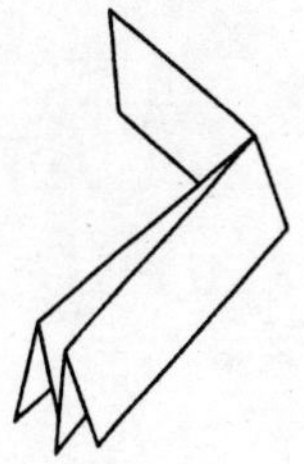

CROSSWISE FOLDING

Fig. 1.13 (ii)

EXERCISE

1. Explain, "engineering drawing is the graphic language of engineers."
2. What are the various standard sizes of drawing boards which are used in engineering practice?
3. Name different types of instruments used in engineering practice.
4. How will you keep your drawing neat and clean?
5. Why cello tape is used instead of drawing pin in engineering practice?
6. Name the different grade of pencils used in engineering drawing.
7. Where we use chisel pencil and where conical pencil?
8. What is the method of folding a print?

❑❑❑

2

TYPES OF LINES AND FREE HAND SKETCHING

2.1 LINES

Different types of lines are used for different purposes in engineering drawing as described by S.P. 46-1988 which are known as an "ALPHABET OF LINES".

The following types of lines should be used as given below in Table 2.1 & 2.2.

Table 2.1

S. No.	TYPES OF LINES	DESCRIPTION	THICKNESS OF LINE IN MM	GRADE OF PENCIL
1.		Border line	0.8	HB
2.		Visible line	0.6	H
3.		Center line	0.3	2H
4.		Hidden line	0.3	2H
5.	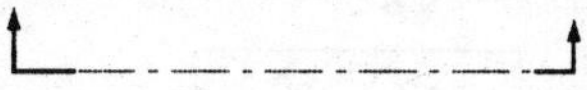	Cutting plane line	0.6	H
6.		Short break line	0.6	H
7.		Long break line	0.3	2H
8.	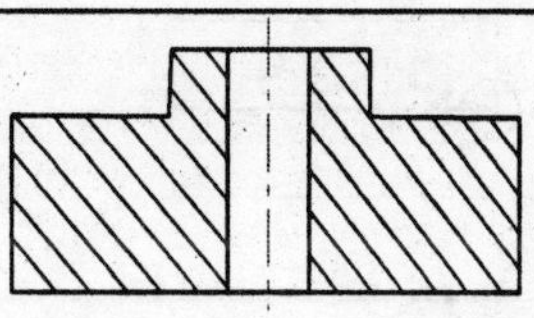	Section line	0.3	2H
9.		Dimension line	0.3	2H
10.		Extension line	0.3	2H
11.		Leader line	0.3	2H

Detailed description and uses of various lines are given below:

Table 2.2 Different Types of Lines

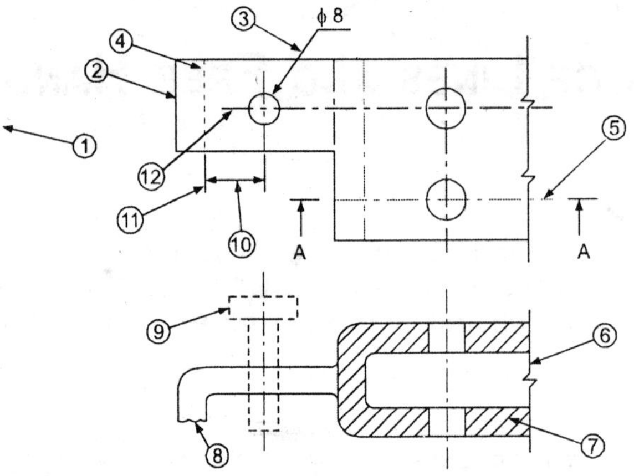

1.	BORDER LINE
2.	VISIBLE LINE
3.	LEADER LINE
4.	HIDDEN LINE
5.	CUTTING PLANE LINE
6.	LONG BREAK LINE
7.	SECTION LINNING
8.	SHORT BREAK LINE
9.	ADJACENT PARTS. ALTERNATE POSITION OR REPEAT LINE
10.	DIMENSION LINE
11.	EXTENSION LINE
12.	CENTRE LINE

2.2 TYPES OF LINES

(*i*) **Border Line:** It is a thick continuous line used to draw boundary lines of the drawing sheet and title block lines at the bottom of drawing sheet.

(*ii*) **Visible Line:** Out lines of parts in finished drawing is represented by thick lines. It is a continuous line which is also known as object line.

(*iii*) **Centre Line:** Centre line is used to locates the centre of arcs, circles and cylindrical objects. It should be thin, long and short dashes are evenly spaced in a proportion of 4 : 1 to 6 : 1.

(*iv*) **Hidden Line:** Hidden lines are used, where viewing surface of an object is not visible. Hidden line is represented by short dashes evenly spaced.

(*v*) **Cutting plane line:** Cutting plane line is thin and long chain line which is thick at the ends. Cutting planes are designated by capital letters, with arrows indicating the direction for viewing section. It is just like a centre line.

(*vi*) **Short Break Line.** Short break line is drawn free hand for short breaks. It may be used on both details and assembly drawing. It is a thick curved line.

(*vii*) **Long Break Line.** Long break line represented by thin ruled straight lines with evenly spaced free hand zig-zag, is used to shortening of long parts, which are same throughout.

(*viii*) **Section Line.** Section line indicates plane cut in section view. These lines are usually drawn at an angles of 45° to the axis, with a spacing of 2 mm for small size drawing and 3 mm for large size drawings.

(*ix*) **Dimension Line.** Dimension line should be terminated by arrow head touching the extension lines on both ends. It is thin continuous line broken in the centre to insert the dimension.

(*x*) **Extension Line.** Extension lines projected from the out lines of the object and are usually perpendicular to the dimension line at a distance 2 mm from the out line of object.

(*xi*) **Leader Line.** Leader line is containing numerals indicating size of objects, is 3 mm long. The angle of leader line is not less than 30°.

2.3 FREE HAND SKETCHING

Ability of free hand sketching is an essential part of the equipment of every engineer. Free hand sketching is used by the engineers as the first steps to the preparation of a scale drawing i.e., a drawing drawn with the aid of instruments.

In other words, the drawing prepared without the use of instruments is known as free hand sketching. An engineer expresses his/her ideas initially in the form of sketches which are later converted into drawing. In training, as in professional work, time can be saved by working freehand instead of with instruments, because with this method more problems can be solved in an allotted amount of time. A freehand drawing is always made in correct proportion without the use of scale. Freehand sketching is never drawn too small. Drawing free hand is, of course, an excellent exercise in accuracy of observation. A good sketching should be achieved by continuous practice. The following instruments are required for free hand sketching:

(*i*) Pencil (A sharp conical pointed pencil)
(*ii*) Eraser
(*iii*) Paper.

2.4 SKETCHING STRAIGHT LINES

1. Horizontal Lines: Horizontal lines are drawn from left to right neatly. The pencil is hold with freedom and not too close to the lead point. Horizontal lines are drawn with the hand shifted to the position as shown in Fig. 2.1. Using a wrist motion for short lines and a forearm motion for longer lines.

Following procedures are used for drawing horizontal lines:

(*i*) Mark the starting and end point of the lines.
(*ii*) Position the arm for trial movement from left to right and hold the pencil at about

30 mm distance from the lead point.

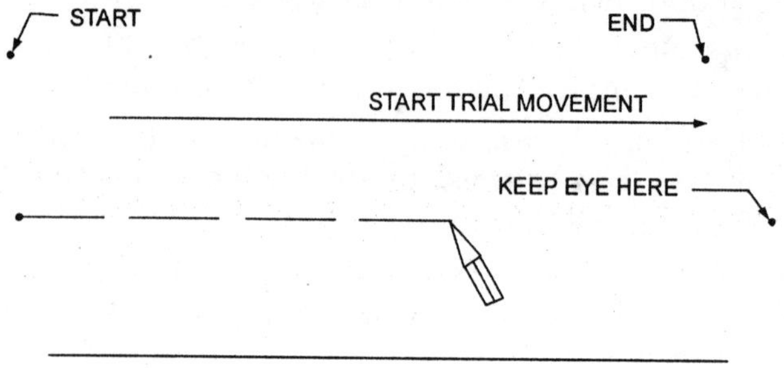

SKETCHING HORIZONTAL LINES

Fig. 2.1

(*iii*) Keep your eyes on the end point to which the line is to follow and sketch it with short and very light strokes.

(*iv*) Finally darken the line in a single stroke of pencil in correct direction as in Fig. 2.1.

2. Vertical Lines: Vertical lines are drawn in a similar way as to sketching of horizontal lines except the direction of pencil movement. Vertical lines are drawn downward with a finger movement in a series of overlapping strokes as shown in Fig. 2.2.

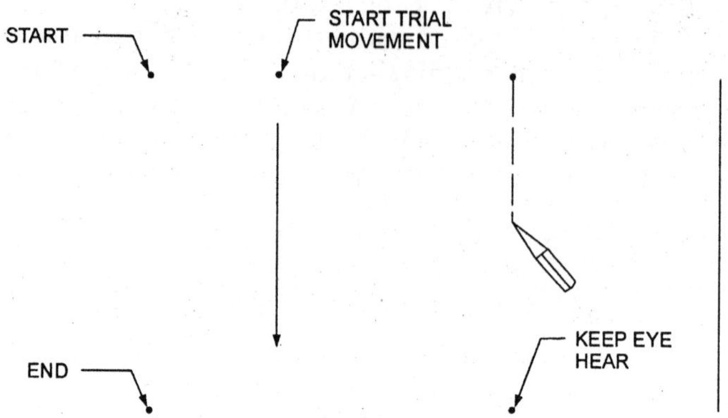

SKETCHING VERTICAL LINES

Fig. 2.2

3. Inclined Lines: Inclined lines running downward from right to left are drawn with the same movements as vertical lines, but the paper may be turned and the line is drawn vertically. When the position is more horizontal then the vertical, the lines should be sketched as horizontal lines and the lines are always drawn from left to right as shown in Fig. 2.3.

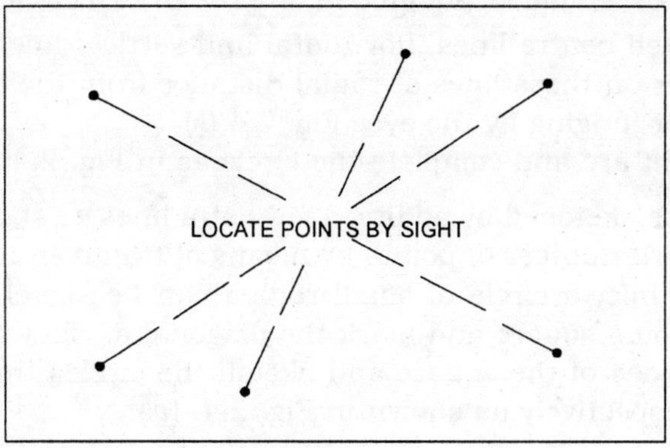

Fig. 2.3

2.5 SKETCHING CIRCLES

Circle can be drawn by marking the radius on each side of the centre lines. A more accurate method of sketching the circles is to locate a number of points through which the curve should pass as shown in Fig. 2.4.

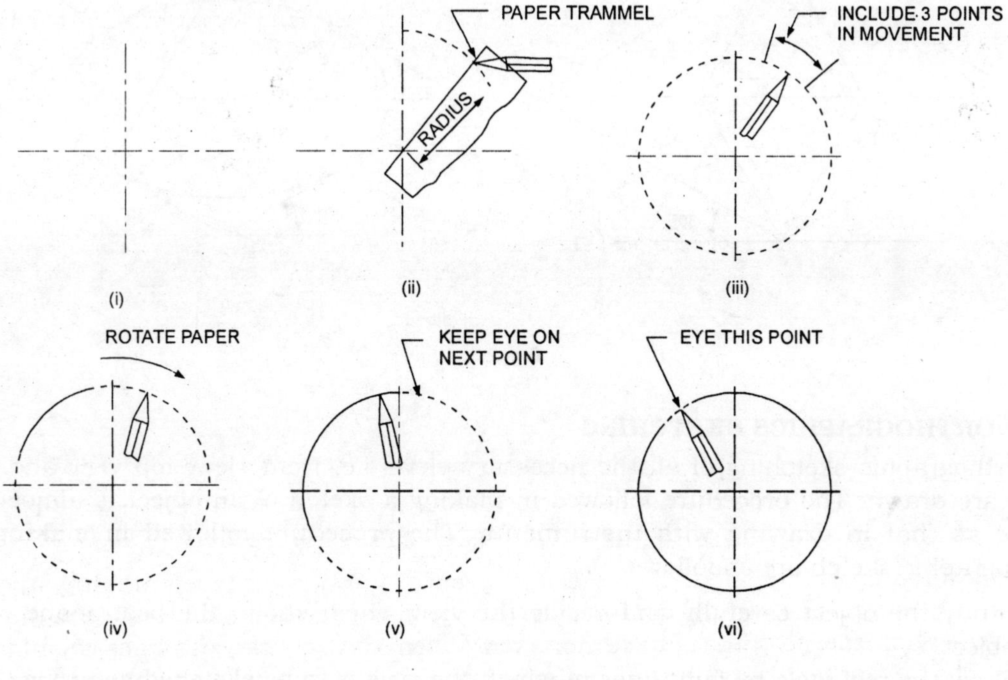

Fig. 2.4

Following procedures should be adopted in order to drawn circles.

1. First of all sketch centre lines, horizontal and vertical lines.
2. Mark the points on these lines at radial distance from the centre by using paper as a trammer or judging by the eyes Fig. 2.4 (*ii*)
3. Sketch first light arc and complete the circle as in Fig. 2.4 (*iii*).

Large circles may be sketched by adding a few extra lines as shown in fig. 2.4. (*iv*). An easier method is to mark number of points by means of trammer and complete the circle as described above. While, a circle of small radius can be sketched with in a square. Sketch the circumscribing square and mark the diagonal as shown in fig. 2.4. (*v*). Mark the mid-point of the sides of the square and sketch the circles through these points to complete the circles respectively as shown in Fig. 2.4. (*vi*).

2.6 SKETCHING ELLIPSES

To sketch an ellipse, firstly remember that an ellipse has a centre, through which all its diameters pass. The largest diameter is called the major axis and shortest diameter is called the minor axis. The ellipse is symmetrical in shape about both of these axes. Sketch one fourth of the ellipse by drawing arc as shown in Fig. 2.5. (*i*), (*ii*) and then complete the ellipse.

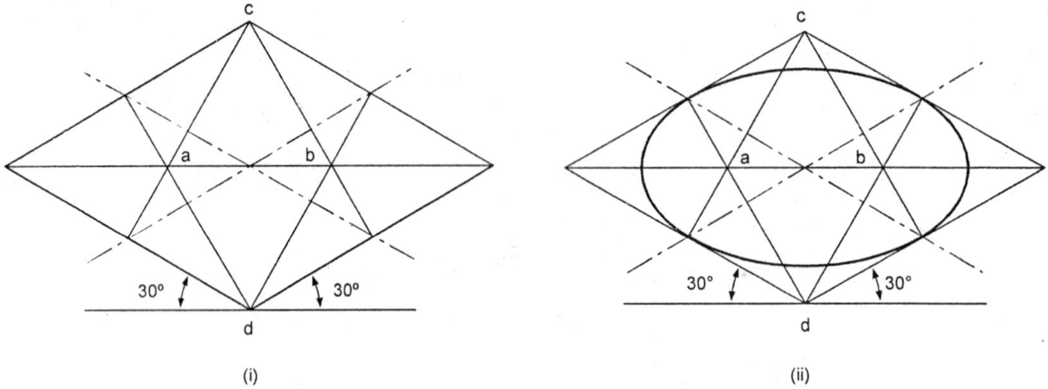

Fig. 2.5

2.7 ORTHOGRAPHICS SKETCHING

In Orthographic sketching of all the necessary views i.e. front view, top view and side view are drawn. The procedure followed in making a sketch of an object is almost the same as that in drawing with instruments. The procedure followed in making an orthographic sketch are as follows:

1. Study the object carefully and decide the view which shows the best shape of an object.
2. Draw the rectangle by faint lines in which the view is to be sketched as in Fig. 2.6.
3. Sketch the centre lines and hidden lines of an object if required by faint or construct lines.

4. Complete all the views of an object and rub the construction lines.
5. Dimensioning the object and add the notes where required and complete the drawing.

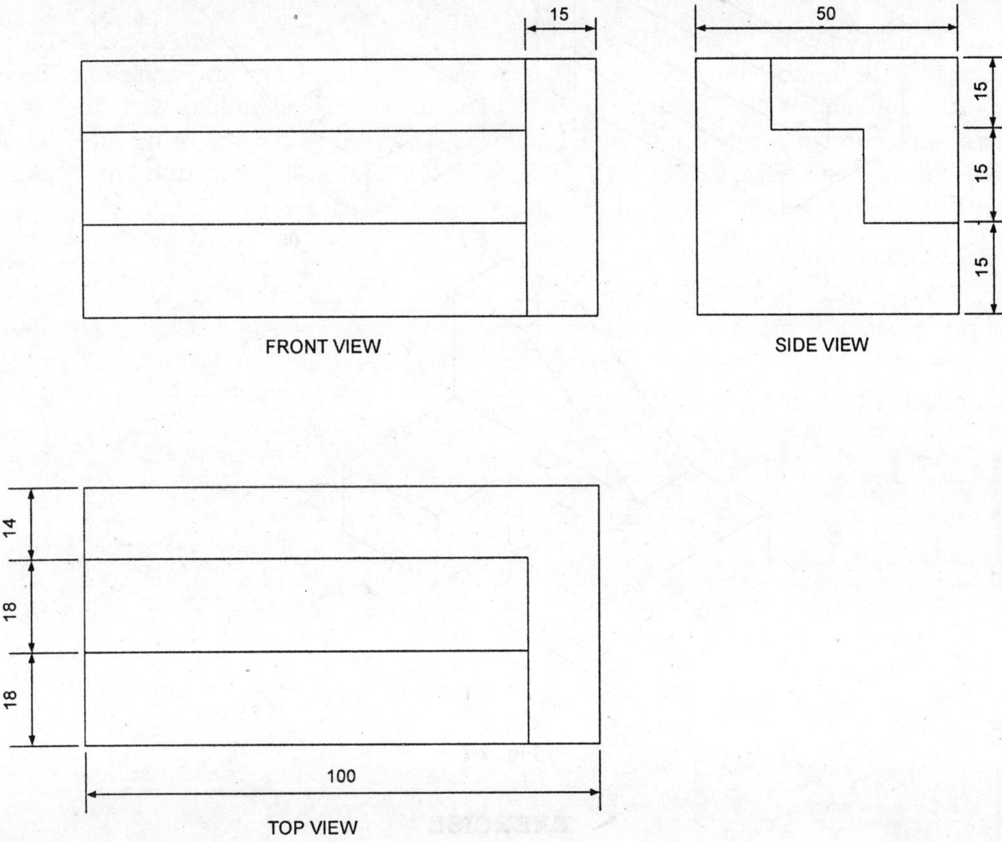

Fig. 2.6

2.8 SKETCHING OF ISOMETRIC

The isometric sketches are prepared on a plain paper. Use the box method to draw the isometric sketches. The following procedure should be followed for making the isometric sketches.

1. Study the orthographic view carefully and decide the position in which it should be drawn.
2. Draw the orthographic view in a box, to give length, breadth and height.
3. Lay off the isometric lines and darken the required lines.
4. Sketch the required hidden lines.
5. Add the necessary dimensions, notes etc. as shown in Fig. 2.7.

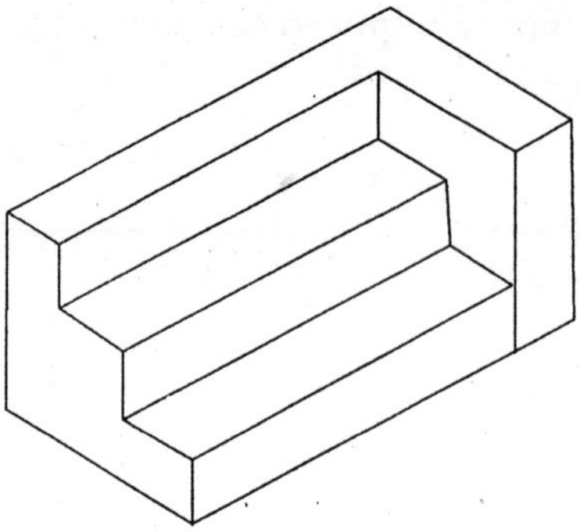

(i)

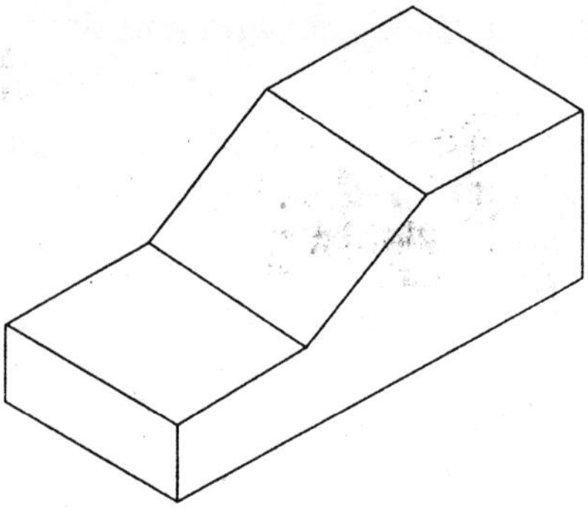

(ii)

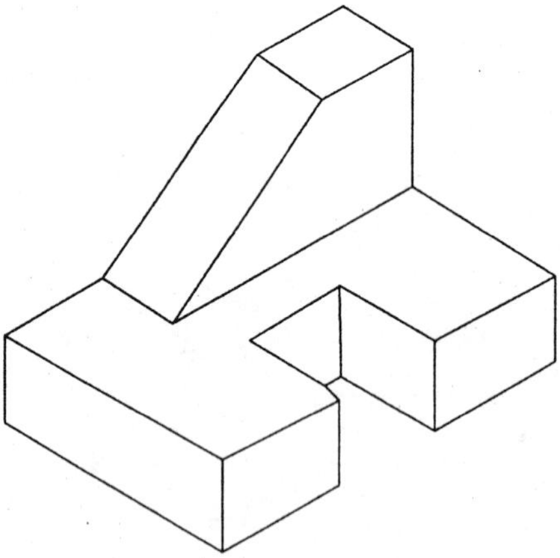

(iii)

Fig. 2.7

EXERCISE

1. Describe the various types of lines used in engineering drawing.
2. What do you mean by gradation of lines and gradation of pencils?
3. Define section line with the help of neat sketches.
4. What do you mean by free hand sketching?
5. What are the uses of free hand sketching?
6. Which type of pencil and paper are required for free hand sketching.
7. Give the methods of sketching of triangles and rectangles.
8. Explain the different steps taken for making an isometric sketch.
9. What are the important rules of free hand sketching?

❑❑❑

3

LETTERING AND METHODS OF DIMENSIONING

3.1 LETTERING

Lettering is an important part of engineering drawing which provides the complete information about size of an object and appearance required. Writing of titles, sub-titles, dimensions and other relative details on drawing should be lettered with freehand. A good practice of freehand lettering improves the quality of drawing and is also executed neatly, uniformly and rapidly. The use of instruments for lettering consumes more time as compared with freehand lettering. Both the vertical (up-right) and sloping (italic) letters can be lettered freehand as well as by instruments. Capital letters should be used for all purpose except where lower case letters are accepted in international usage for abbreviations. A good practice of lettering is required which may be achieved by continuous efforts.

Normally two types of lettering are commonly used by engineers which are:

1. Single-stroke letters
2. Double-stroke letters.

But another important type of lettering is gothic style of lettering which is commonly used by draftsman as well as engineering students for writing title block and other features. It may be performed with single stroke without lifting the pencil.

Note:

- The letters and numerals should be kept clean of the lines. Words may be underlined where preferred.
- Time is an important factor for engineers, therefore lettering should be in plain and simple style.

3.2 SINGLE-STROKE LETTERS

Single stroke letters are used universally in engineering drawing. The Bureau of Indian standards ISO 9609 : 2001/ ISO 3098-0 : 1997 replaced by SP: 46-2003 also recommended the use of single stroke letters. The term "Single stroke" means the uniform width of letter is obtained in single stroke of pencil. Single stroke letters are of two types:

(*i*) Single-stroke vertical letters.
(*ii*) Single-stroke inclined letters.

(*i*) Single-stroke vertical letter: Single stroke vertical letters and numerals are written in a vertical upward direction without the use of drawing instruments as shown in Fig. 3.1. For writing the single-stroke vertical letters and numerals, first draw the faint guide lines at a distance equal to the height of letters. These guide lines should be drawn by light grade pencil (2H). The height of letters and numerals are written in 1.8, 2.5, 3.5, 5, 7, 10, 14 and 20 mm. The ratio of height to width is 7 : 4 for single-stroke vertical letters except A, M and W which is of 7 : 5 ratio. The ratio of height to width of all the numerals are also written in 7 : 4 except 1. There is no hard and fast rule for spacing between two letters. Generally the gap between two letters is taken as one unit. The spacing between two words is generally taken as 1 to 1.5 times their height and spacing in between two sentences is twice the height of letters as shown in Fig. 3.2.

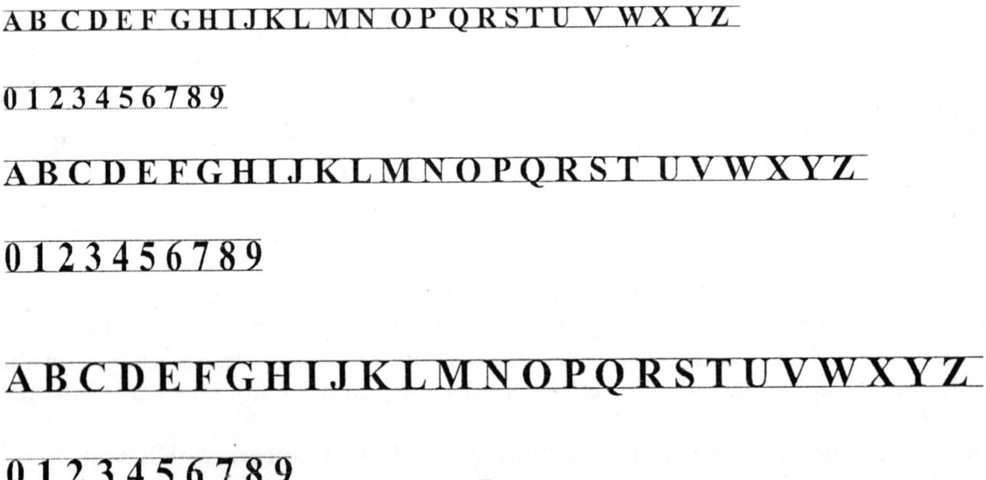

(i)

(II)

Fig. 3.1

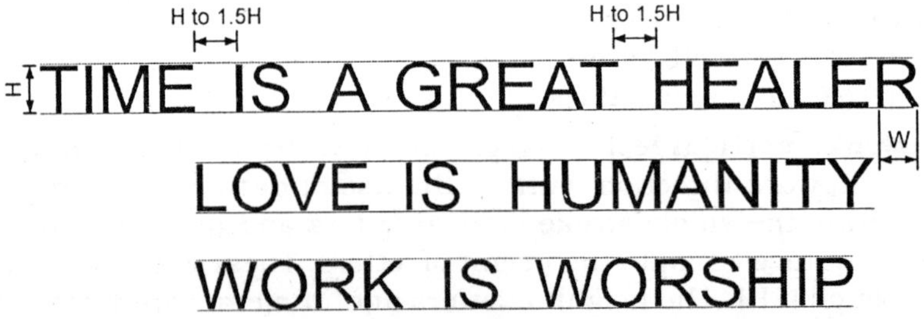

Fig. 3.2

***(ii)* Single-stroke Inclined lettering.** Many draftsmen use the inclined letters in preference to the vertical letters. The order and direction of the strokes are the same as in the vertical form. These inclined letters and numerals are written at an inclination of 75° from right towards left as recommended by SP 46 : 2003 as shown in Fig. 3.3. H grade pencil is preferred for freehand inclined lettering and numerals. The height of letters and numerals are same as described in single stroke vertical letters. The same ratio of height to the width and spacing are used as we used in single-stroke vertical letters.

Fig. 3.3

3.3 DOUBLE-STROKE LETTERS

The letters and numerals which are completed in double stroke of the pencil with a uniform thickness in between the stokes is known as double stroke letters and numerals. For drawing double stroke gothic letters and numerals, a square grid is constructed with light lines (2H-chisel tip pencil). The height of the grid is taken equal to the height of letters as shown in Fig. 3.4. The ratio of height to width is 7 : 5 for double stroke letters.

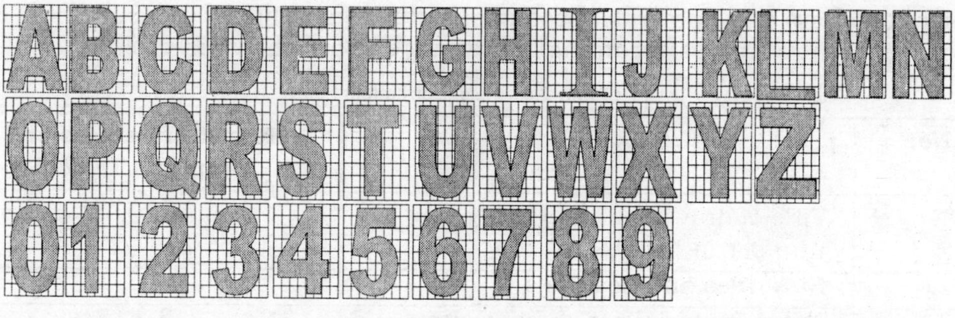

Fig. 3.4

3.4 LOWER CASE LETTERS

The lettering in which the alphabets are small uniform letters is called as a lower case gothic letters, such as *a, b, c, d, e ... z.* These letters are written free hand. The method of writing the vertical and inclined types lower case letters are shown in Fig. 3.5.

a b c de f g h i j k l m n o p q r s t u v w x y z

a b c d e f g h i j k l m n o p q r s t u v w x y z

a b c d e f g h i j k l m n o p q r s t u v w x y z

(i)

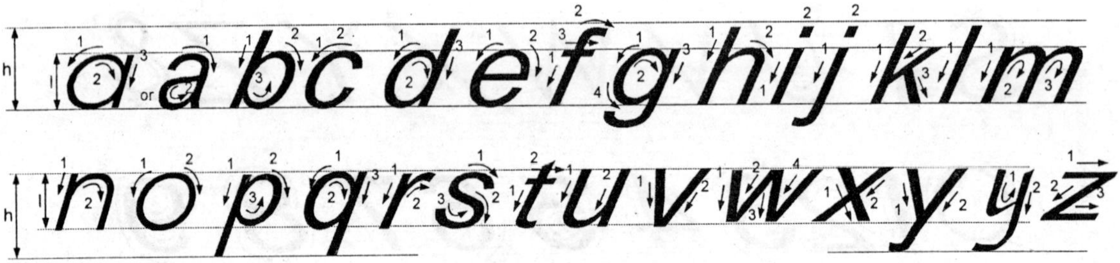

Fig. 3.5

For writing the lower case letters, three horizontal lines are drawn and dividing the desired height in the ratio 2 : 5, keeping the upper division 2 and the lower on 5. The lower-case letters are extensively used in architectural drawing and in map drawing etc. The standard height for lower lettering and numerals are 3.5, 7, 10 and 20 mm according to B.I.S.

3.5 THE HEIGHT OF LETTERS AND NUMERALS

The height of letters and numerals recommended by IS 9609 (Part O) : 2001/ISO 3098-0 : 1997 for different purposes according to drawing size are shown in table 3.1:

Table 3.1 Height of Letters

S.No.	Purpose	Height of Letters and Numerals in MM
1.	Title of drawing and drawing number in title block	6, 8, 10, 12
2.	Sub-titles and headings	3, 4, 5, 6
3.	Notes, material list, dimensioning and the tolerances	2, 3, 4, 5

3.6 COMPRESSED AND EXTENDED LETTERS

It is often desirable to decrease or increase the width of the letters to fill in a certain space.

(i) Normal Letters: Normal letters are written in 7 : 4 ratio as per IS 9609 (Part O) : 2001/ ISO 3098-0 : 1997 as shown in Fig. 3.6. (*i*).

DRAWING (Normal)

(i)

(ii) Compressed Letters: Sometime letters are compressed due to non-availability of space. Therefore, letters narrower than normal letters of same height are called compressed letters as shown in Fig. 3.6. (*ii*).

DRAWING (Compressed)

(ii)

(iii) Extended Letters. Some letters are extended for filling the extra space. Therefore, letters which are wider are called extended letters as shown in Fig. 3.6. (*iii*).

D R A W I N G (Extended)

(iii)

Fig. 3.6

3.7 INSTRUMENTAL SINGLE-STROKE LETTERING

Instrumental single-stroke lettering is used with the height of 35 mm and 70 mm in the ratio of 7 : 4. The art of writing letters and numerals from A to Z and 0 to 9 with the help of instruments is known as instrumental single stroke lettering. In instrumental single stroke lettering all types of instruments such as, compass, pencil and minidrafter etc. are used. It is always better than single-stroke free hand lettering, if there is enough time to use the instrument as shown in Fig. 3.7.

Fig. 3.7

3.8 METHODS OF DIMENSIONING

It is the art of describing the size of an object by supplying the complete information stating length, breadth, height, angle, arcs, size and position of holes etc. Lines, symbols, figure and notes are used for this purpose.

The elements of dimensioning are the projection lines or extension lines, dimension lines, leader lines etc. as shown in Fig. 3.8. The dimension without any unit is considered in mm.

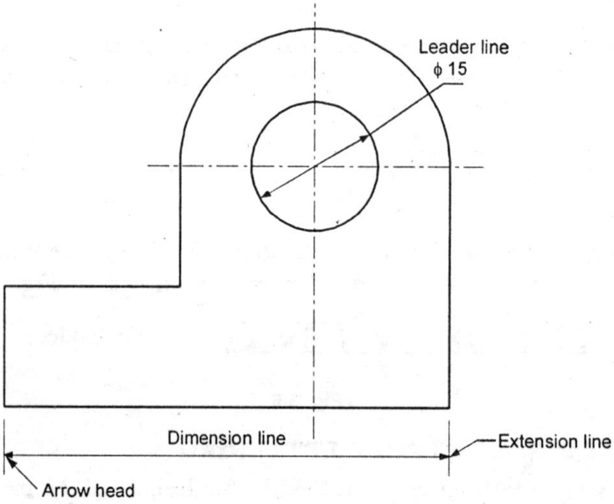

Fig. 3.8

3.9 NOTATION OF DIMENSIONING

The notation of dimensioning consists of arrow heads, leader lines, dimension lines, extension lines, symbols, notes etc. According to IS: SP 46-2003 these notations are explained below.

(1) Arrowheads: They should be of isosceles triangular shape, the length of which is three times of its width (w). It is placed at each end of dimension line by touching the extension line. The space between arrowheads is filled up with HB pencil as shown in Fig. 3.9.

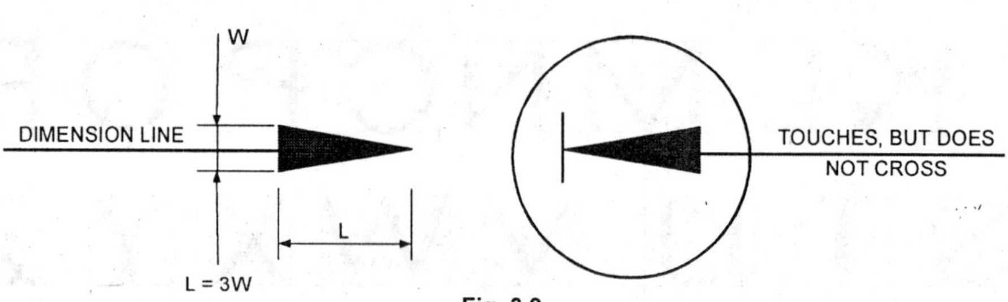

Fig. 3.9

(2) Leader Line. A leader line is a thin continuous line connecting notes and terminated by an arrow heads touching the line to be pointed out at an angle of 30° or 45°. The straight horizontal line of about 3 mm is used for writing dimensions or notes as shown in Fig. 3.10.

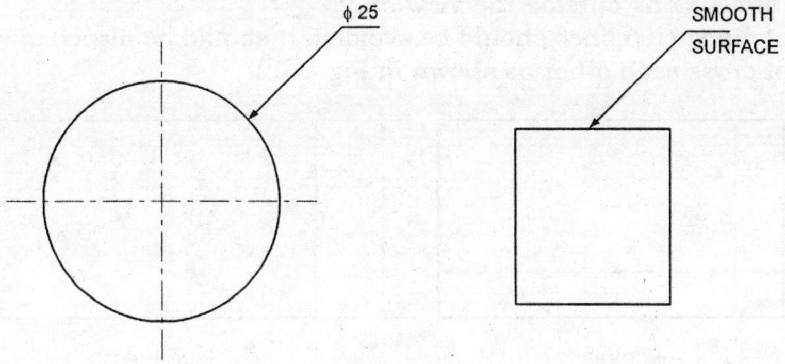

Fig. 3.10

(3) Dimension Line. A dimension line is a thin continuous line. It should be terminated by arrow heads touching the extension lines on both ends. Dimension lines are light lines as shown in Fig. 3.11.

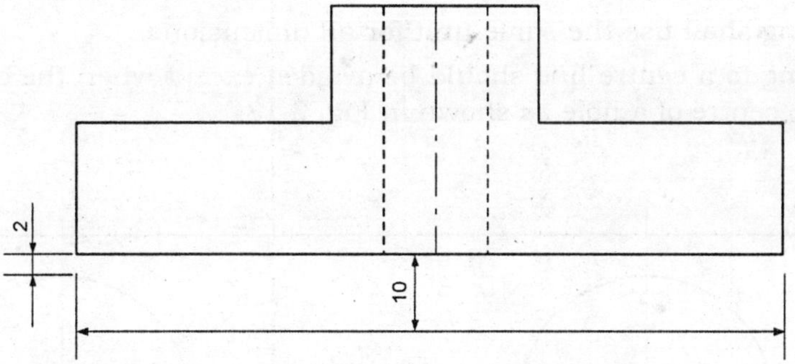

Fig. 3.11

(4) Extension Lines. An extension line is a thin continuous line, extended from the outline of the objects.

The extension line extends about 3 mm beyond the dimension line and the gap between an outline and the extension line is about 2 mm as shown in Fig. 3.11

(5) Symbols: The symbols are used in dimensioning for representation some marks on the drawing, which save the time are given below:

1. To represent diameter of a circle ϕ
2. To represent radius of a circle *R*
3. To represent square. □

3.10 GENERAL PRINCIPLES OF DIMENSIONING

According to IS:SP46-2003 following principles of dimensioning are recommended:

1. Each feature is dimensioned and positioned only once.
2. All the necessary dimensions of the parts must be written on drawing sheet to show the correct functioning of each part.
3. Avoid the unnecessary dimensioning, every dimension should be given in one view only. Avoid to repeat in second view.
4. Each feature is dimensioned and positioned where its shape shows.
5. Dimension should be given in the view which shows relative feature, more clearly.

6. Mark the dimensions outside the view only.
7. Crossing of dimension lines should be avoided. It should be placed in such a way that they do not cross each other as shown in Fig. 3.12.

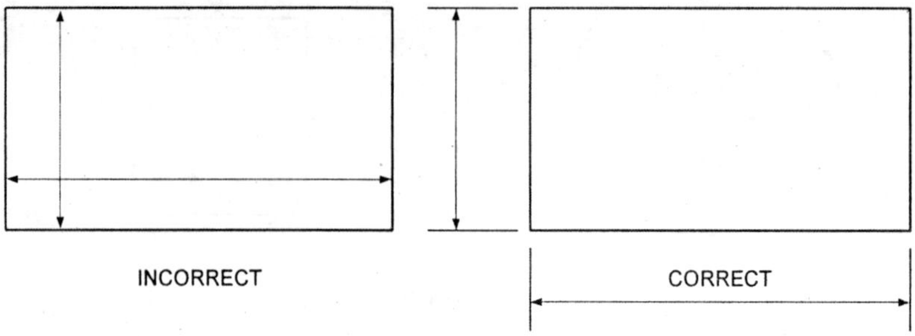

Fig. 3.12

8. Dimension should not be placed too close to each other.
9. Each drawing shall use the same unit for all dimensions.
10. Dimensioning to a centre line should be avoided except when the centre line passes through the centre of a hole as shown in Fig. 3.13.

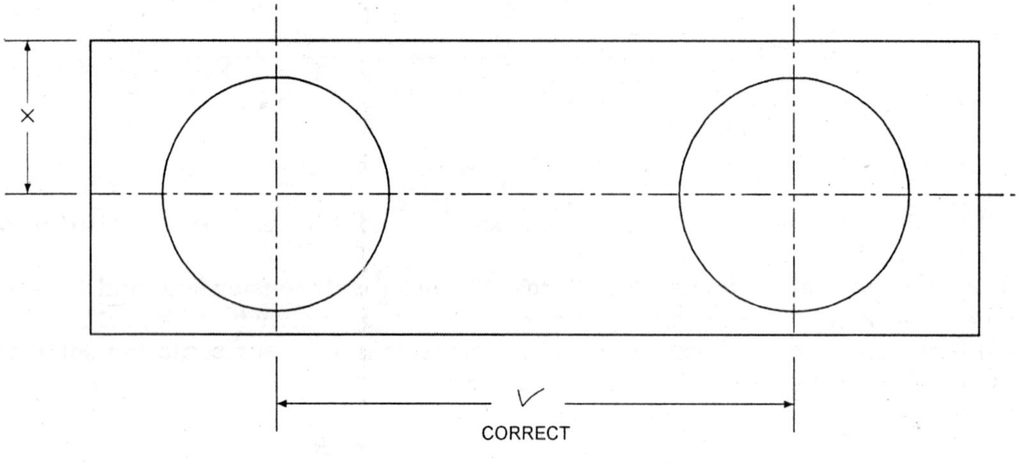

Fig. 3.13

11. Dimensioning for narrow space are shown in Fig. 3.14.

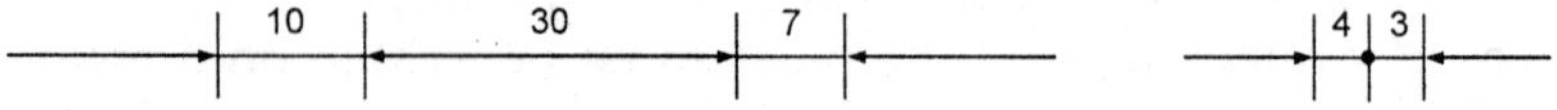

Fig. 3.14

12. Dimension should be taken from visible outline instead of hidden lines as shown in Fig. 3.15.

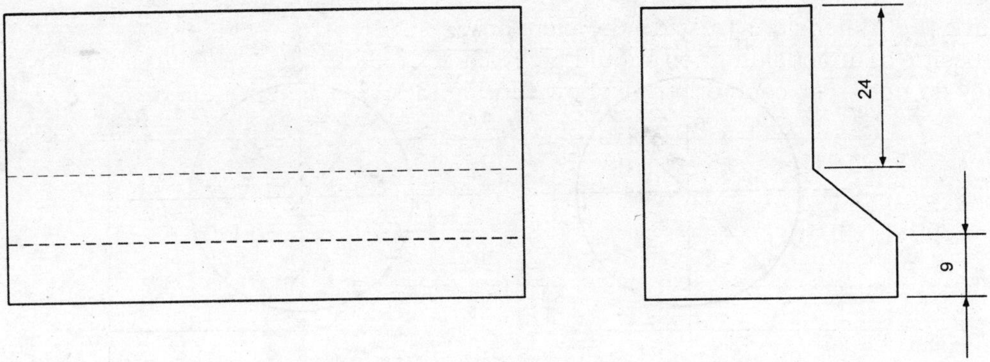

Fig. 3.15

13. Avoid the crossing of dimension lines with extension lines as shown in Fig. 3.16.

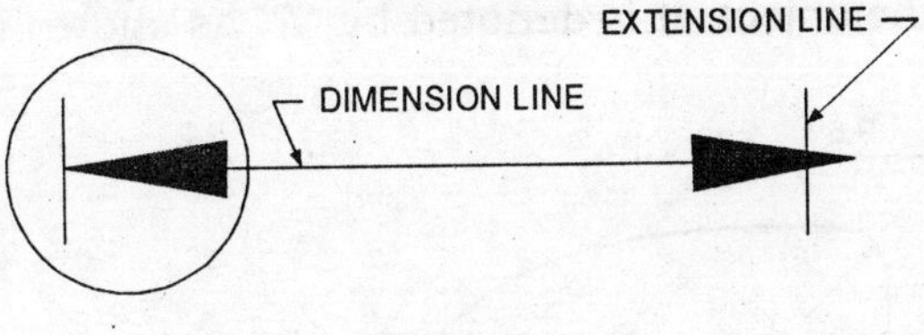

Fig. 3.16

14. Production and inspection methods should not be specified on the drawing unless they are essential.

3.11 DIMENSIONING TECHNIQUES FOR COMMON FEATURES

1. **Circles:** Circles of different sizes should be dimensioned and diameter should be denoted by "ϕ", as per IS; SP46–2003 as shown in Fig. 3.17.

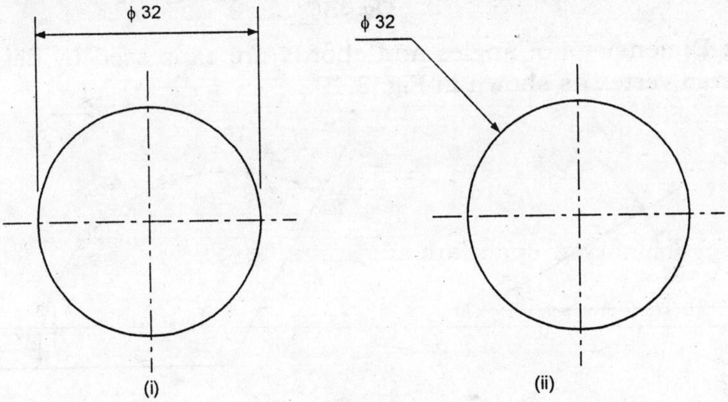

Fig. 3.17.

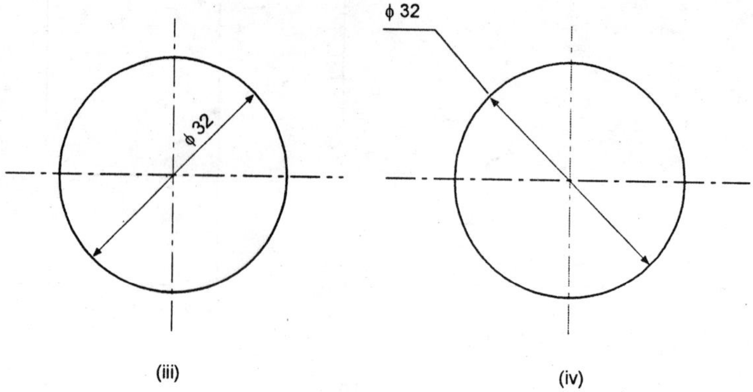

Fig. 3.17

2. **Arcs:** Arcs should be deminsioned by their radius which is shown preferably outside the line of the object. It is denoted by "*R*" as shown in Fig. 3.18.

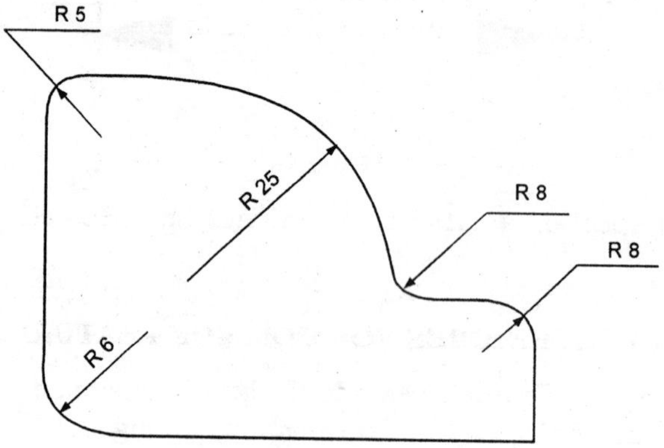

Fig. 3.18

3. **Angles:** Dimensions of angles and chords are expressed by degrees, on the arc swing from vertex as shown in Fig. 3.19.

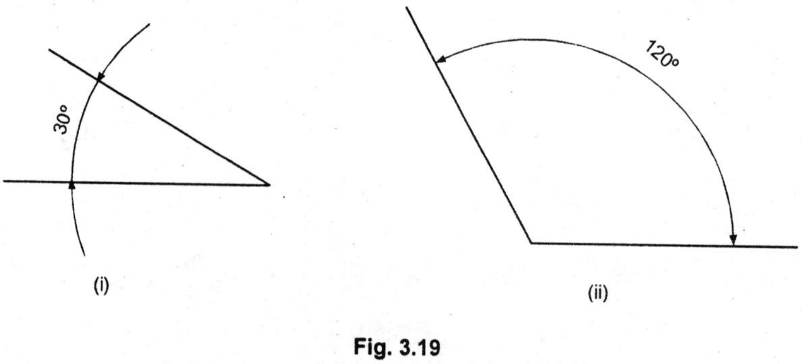

Fig. 3.19

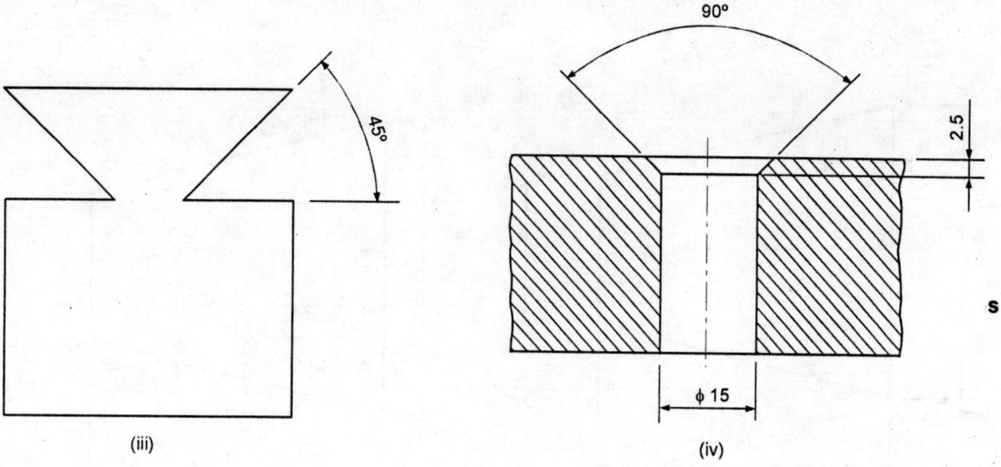

Fig. 3.19

4. Chamfers: Chamfers may be dimensioned by notes as shown in Fig. 3.20.

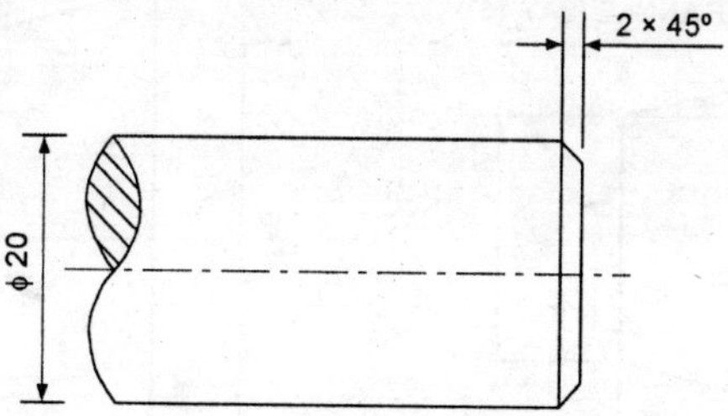

Fig. 3.20

5. Holes: The methods of dimensioning holes are shown in Fig. 3.21.

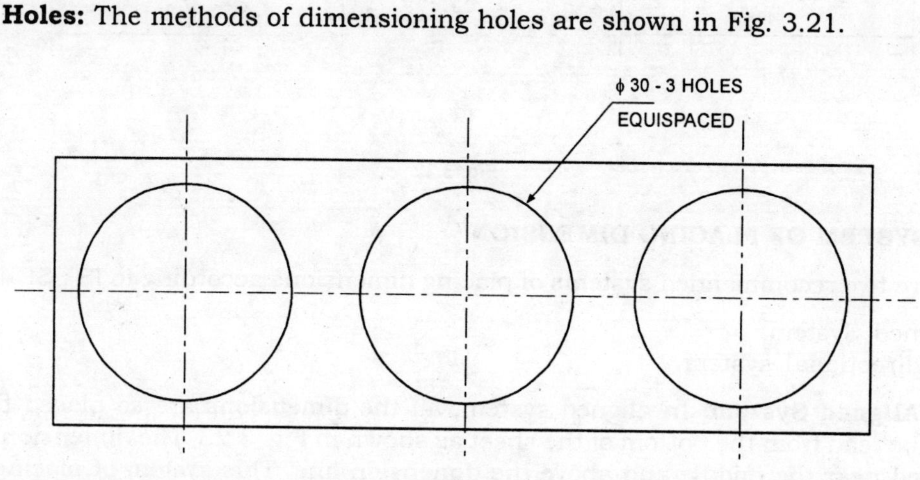

Fig. 3.21

6. Tapers: Dimensioning of tapered objects are shown in Fig. 3.22.

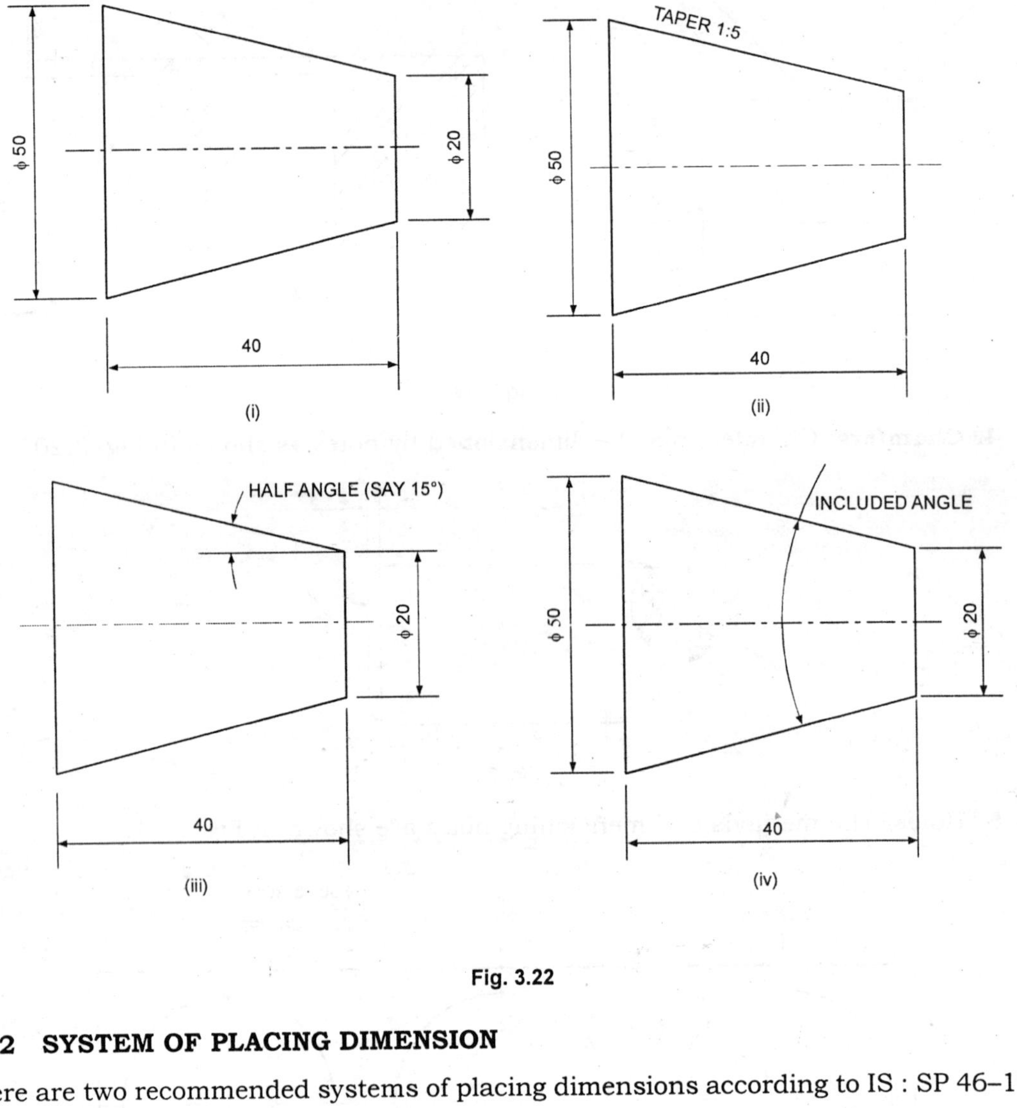

Fig. 3.22

3.12 SYSTEM OF PLACING DIMENSION

There are two recommended systems of placing dimensions according to IS : SP 46–1988.

1. Aligned System,
2. Unidirectional system.

(1) Aligned System: In aligned system, all the dimensions are so placed that they should be read from the bottom of the sheet as shown in Fig. 3.23. The dimensions should be placed near the middle and above the dimension line. This system of placing dimension is commonly used in small size drawings.

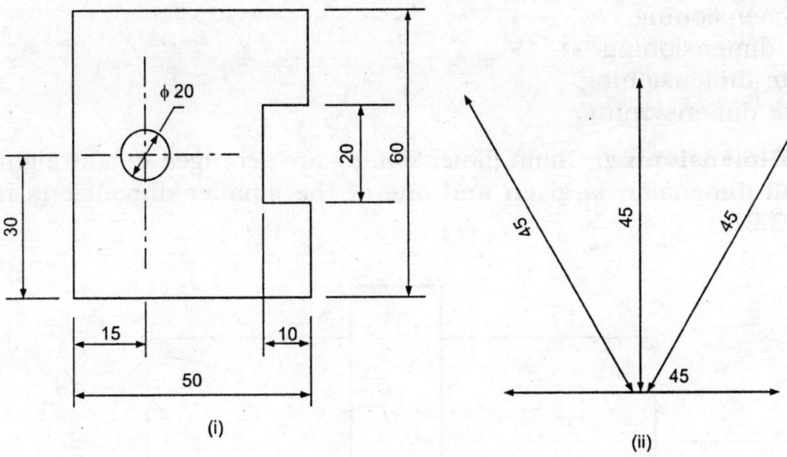

Fig. 3.23

(2) Unidirectional System: In this system all dimension are so placed that they may be read from bottom of the sheet. In this system dimension lines are broken near the middle for inserting the dimensions as shown in Fig. 3.24. The system has advantage in on large size drawing. For example, aircrafts drawing and automobiles drawing etc.

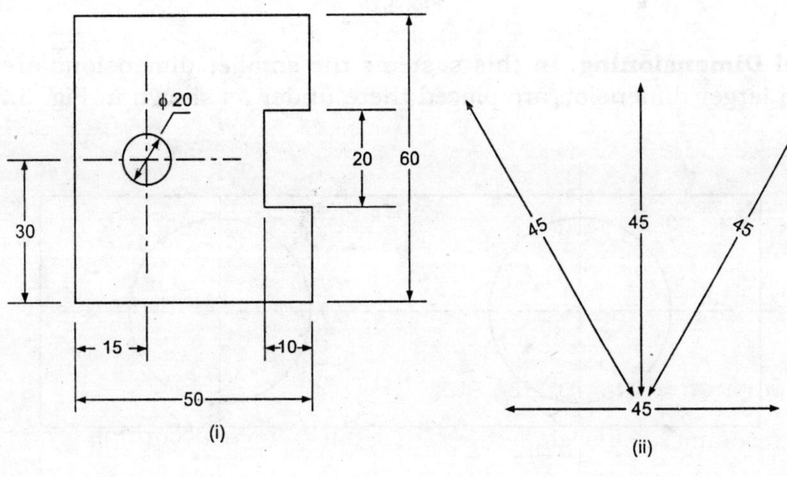

Fig. 3.24

3.13 ARRANGEMENT OF DIMENSIONS

Generally, dimensions in a series may be given on the views in any one of the following arrangements:

1. Chain dimensioning.
2. Parallel dimensioning.
3. Combined dimensioning.
4. Co-ordinate dimensioning.
5. Progressive dimensioning.

1. Chain Dimensioning: Chain dimensioning are arranged in a straight line. In this system, overall dimension is given and one of the smaller dimensions is omitted as shown in Fig. 3.25.

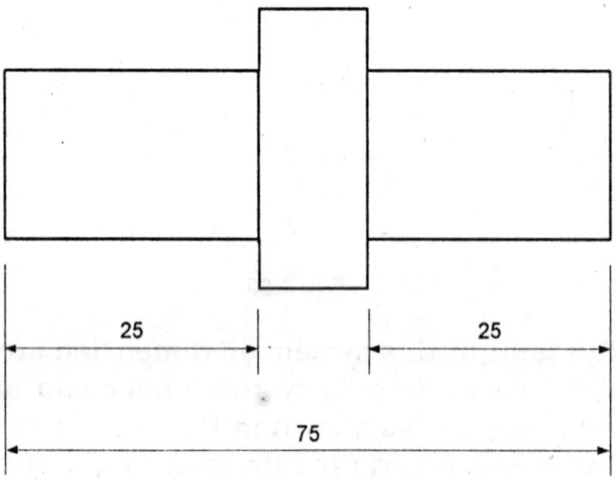

Fig. 3.25

2. Parallel Dimensioning. In this systems the smaller dimensions are placed near the object and larger dimension are placed there under as shown in Fig. 3.26.

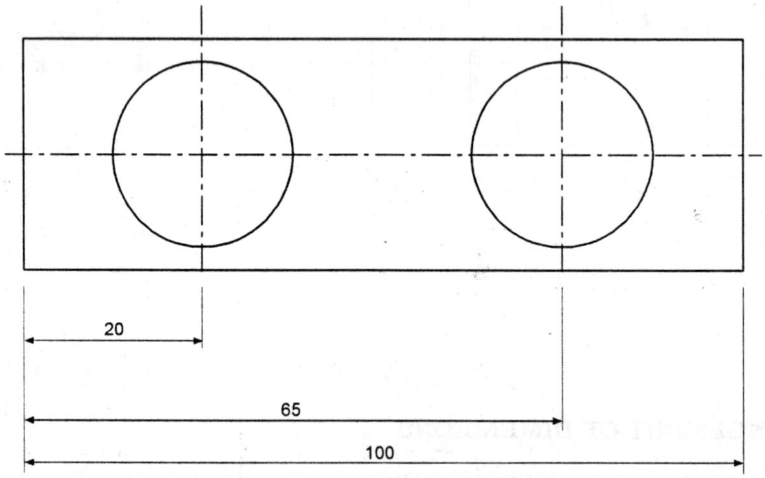

Fig. 3.26

3. Combined dimensioning. In this system the combination of chain dimensioning and parallel dimensioning are used together as shown in Fig. 3.27.

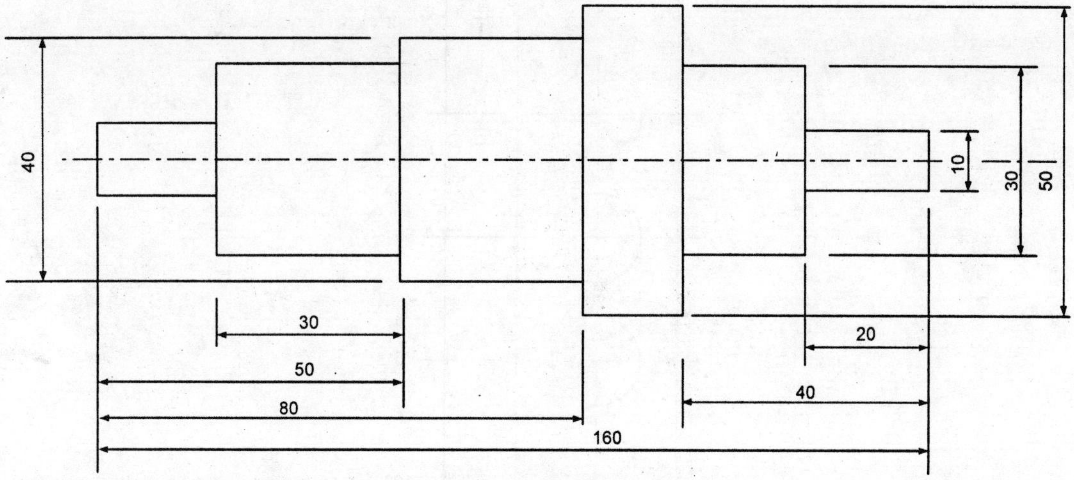

Fig. 3.27

4. Co-ordinate Dimensioning. In this system, group dimensions are shown separately from the drawing as shown in Fig. 3.28 and Table 3.2.

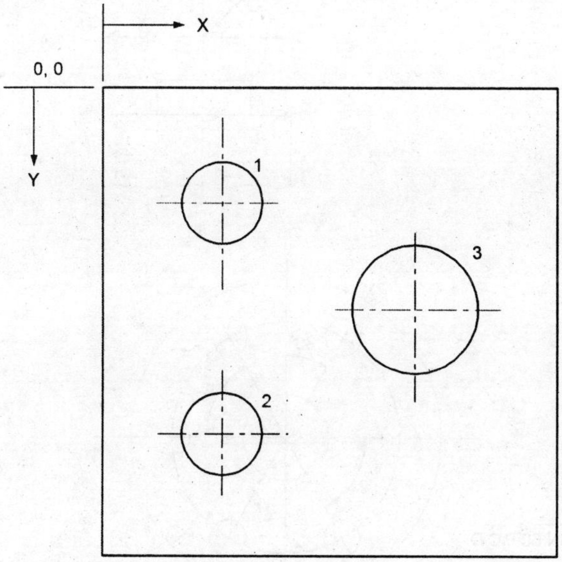

Table 3.2

	1	2	3
X	20	20	40
Y	20	45	30
ϕ	15	15	20

Fig. 3.28

5. Progressive dimensioning. In this arrangement, one datum point is selected which reads as zero as shown in Fig. 3.29.

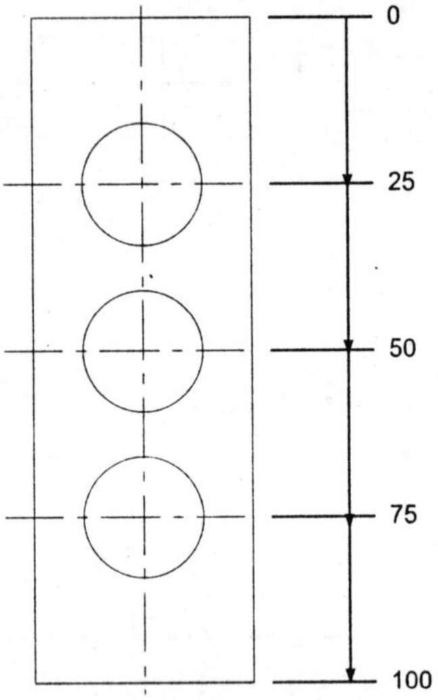

Fig. 3.29

Note: Dimensioning of square, sphere and pitch circle are shown in Fig. 3.30.

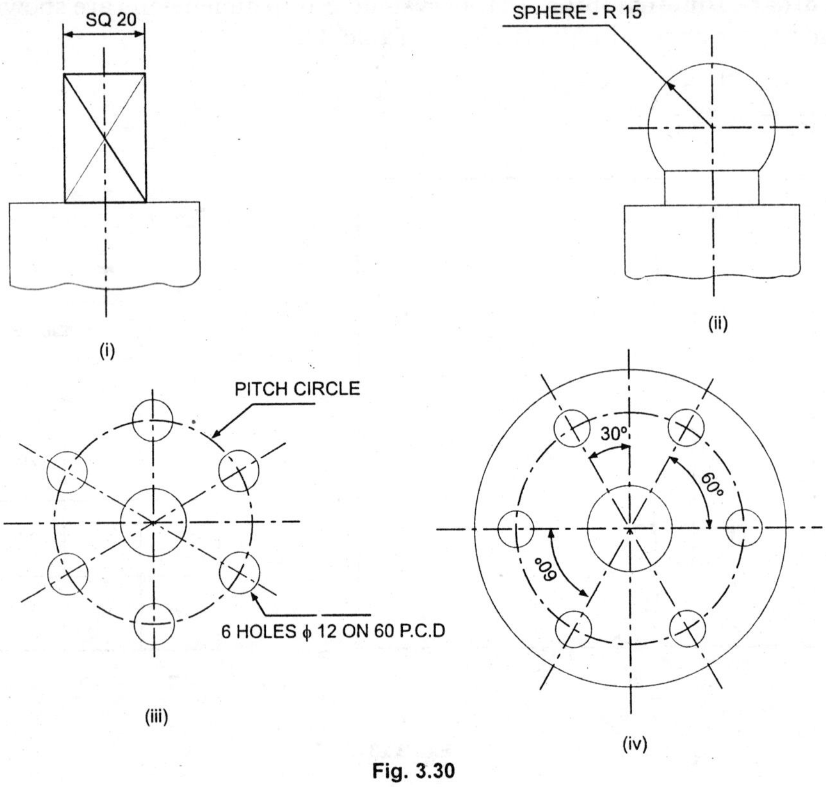

Fig. 3.30

Table 3.3 Shows correct and Incorrect dimensioning

Table 3.3

	CORRECT	INCORRECT	REASONS FOR INCORRECT
(i)	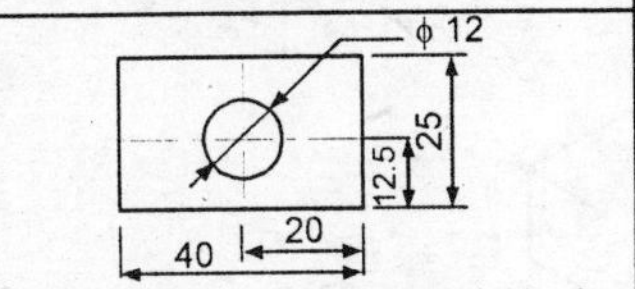 Dimensions should be placed outside view	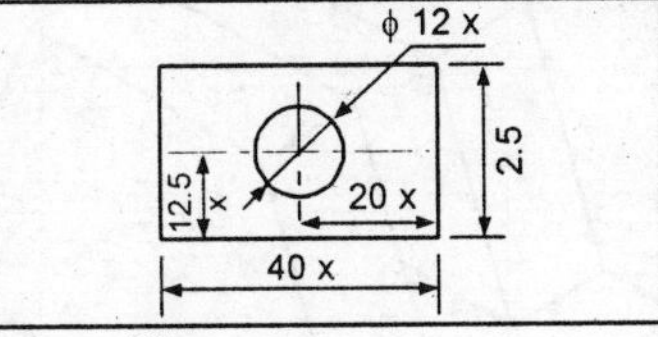	1. Arrow head not proportionate. 2. Hole dimension shown in figure. Leader line not ends horizontally. 3. Dimension '40' is too close.
(ii)	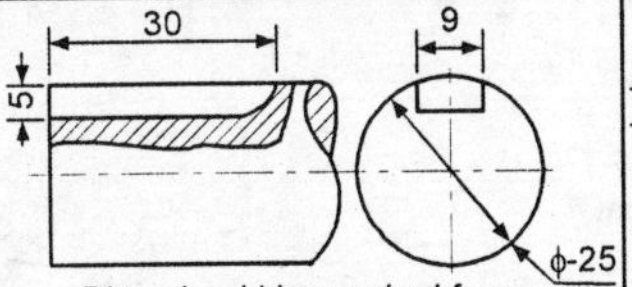 Dim, should be marked from visible outlines	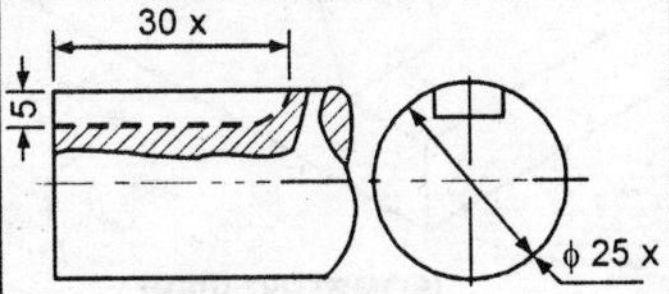	1. A key-way is shown with dotted line where the dimensions are placed. 2. Leader line for the shaft diameter is drawn horizontal touching the boundary line.
(iii)	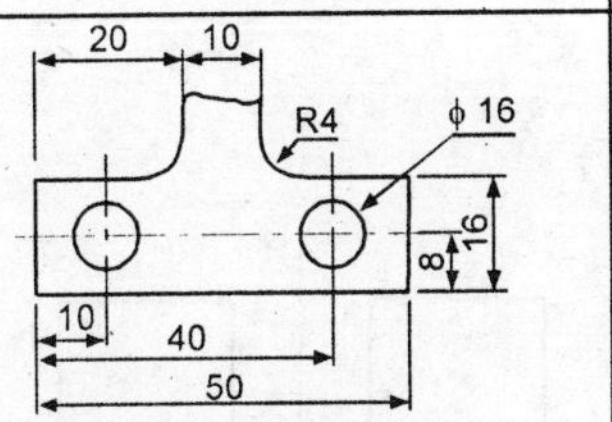 Dimensions should be given from the outlines (finished surfaces) or a centre line of a hole	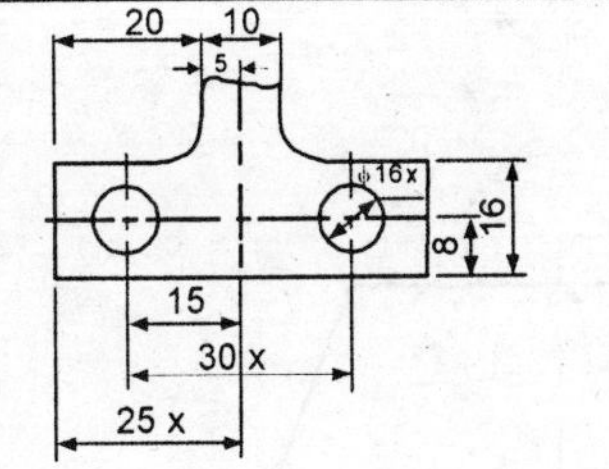	1. Dimensions are given from the mid-line of the object. 2. Dimensions of holes are shown inside the figure. 3. Dimensions are shown in vertical line. 4. Smaller dimensions (25 mm) precedes the larger dimensions (30 mm) 5. Fillet radius is not shown.
(iv)	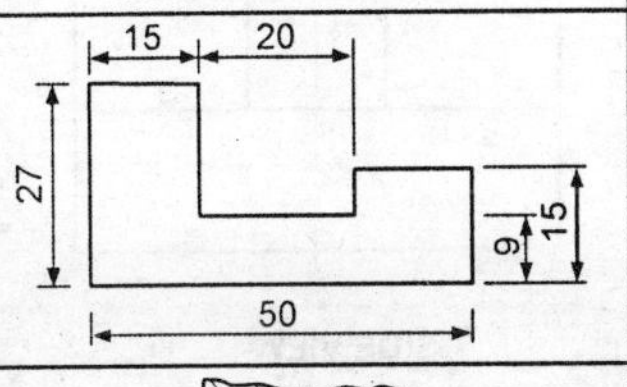	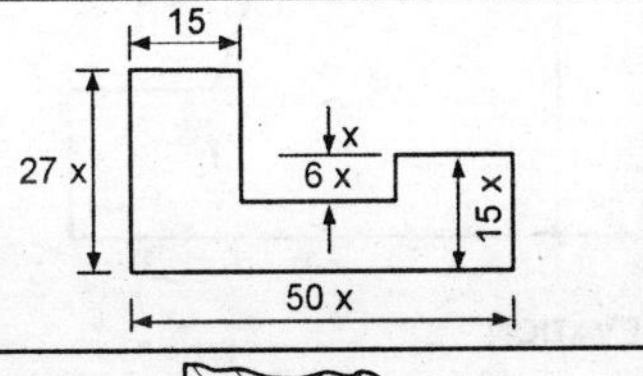	1. Dimension lines are used as extension. 2. Dimensions are placed inside the view. 3. Dimension 27 and 50 not written according to aligned system.
(v)	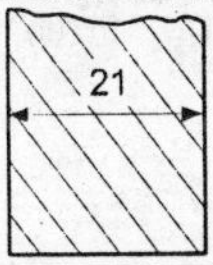	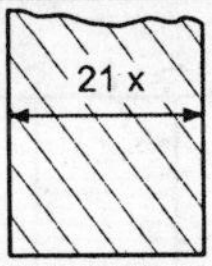	Section-lines overlap the dimension 21.
(vi)	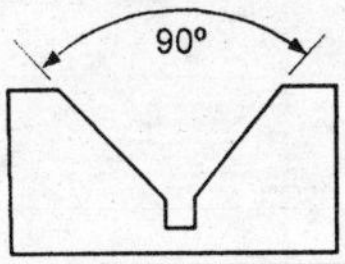	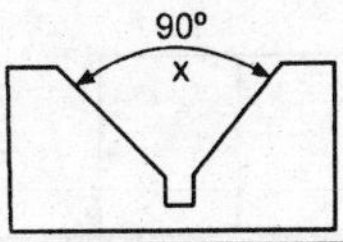	The outlines of the object are used as the extension lines.
(vii)	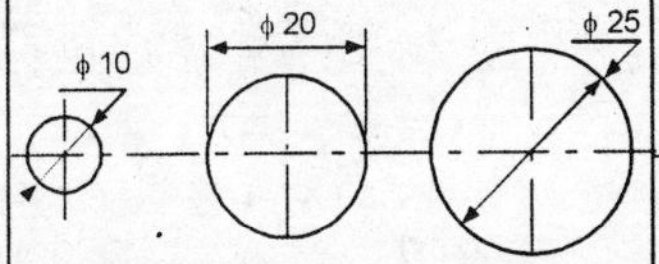	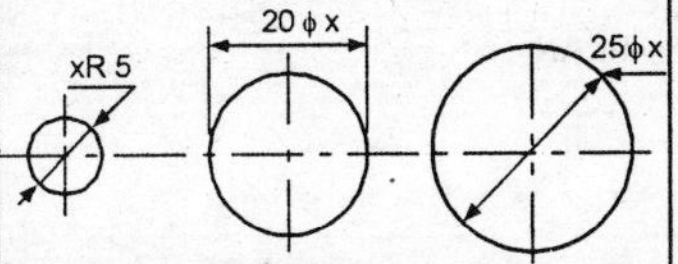	1. Smaller circle is designated with radius. 2. Convention 'ϕ' for diameter is placed after dimension. 3. Leader has arrow and it is drawn horizontal.

Problem 1. Figs. 3.31 (*i*) and (*ii*) show the pictorial and orthographic views of an object. Complete the dimension of a given object.

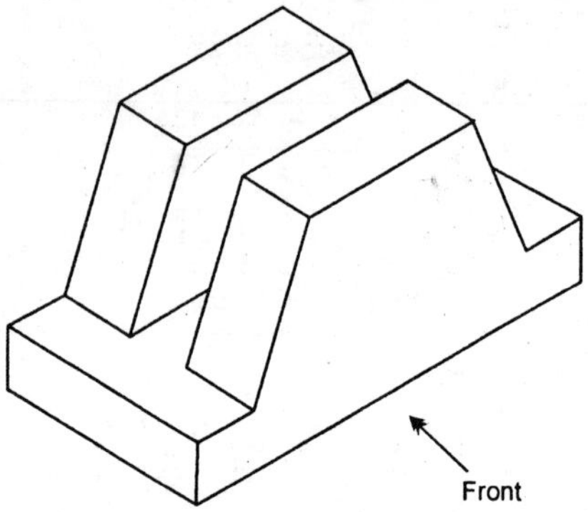

ISOMETRIC VIEW

(I)

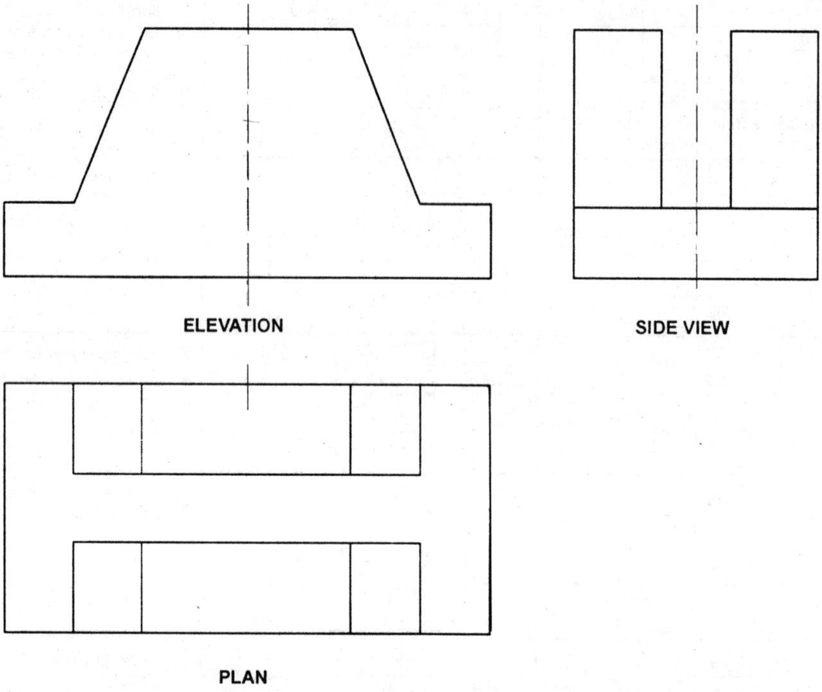

(ii)

Fig. 3.31

Solution. See Fig. 3.32

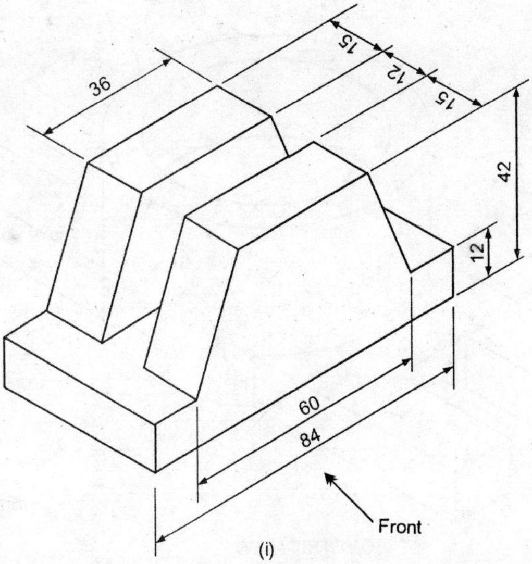

(i)

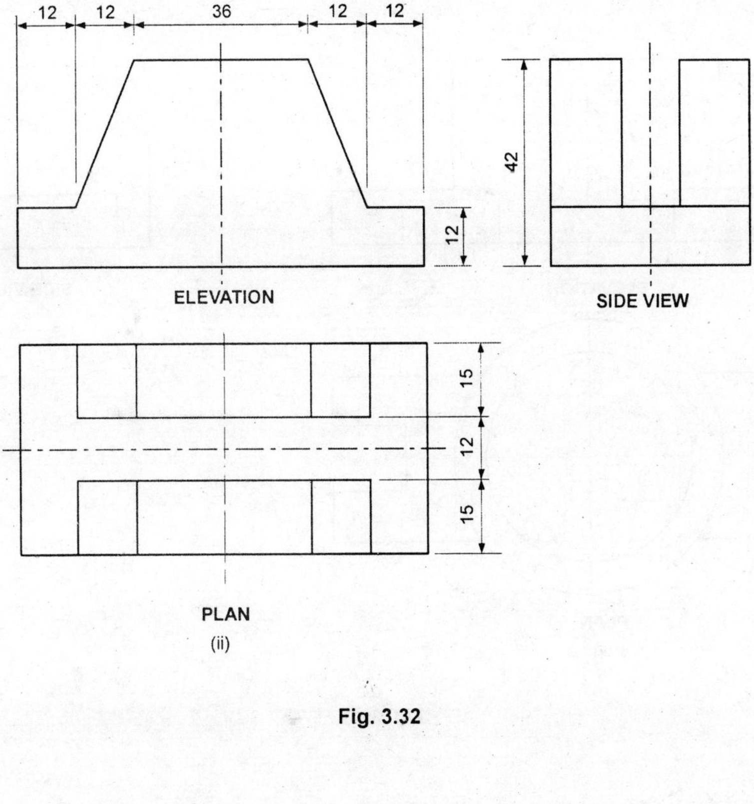

(ii)

Fig. 3.32

Problem 2: Figs. 3.33 (i) and (ii) show the isometric view and orthographic view of an object. Complete the dimensioning of given object.

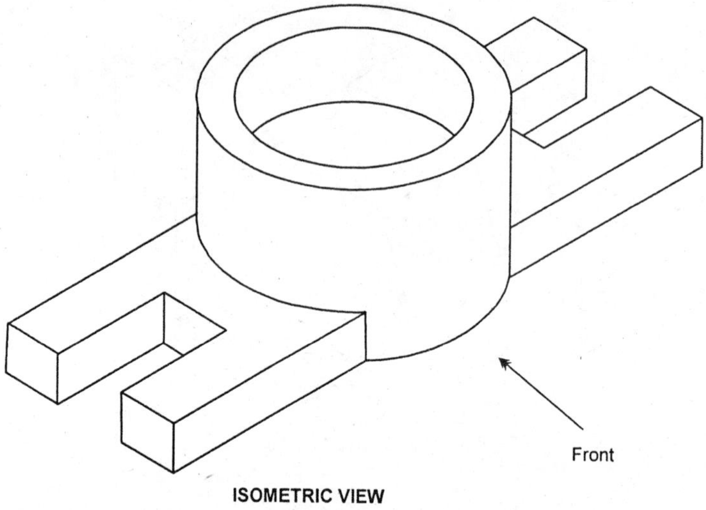

(i)

Fig. 3.33

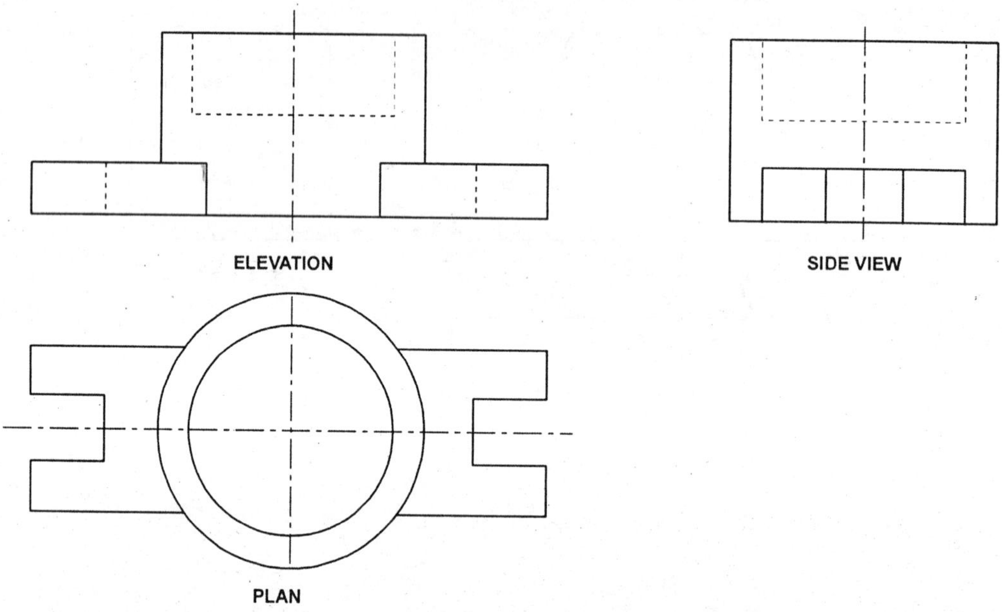

(ii)

Fig. 3.33

Solution: See Fig. 3.34.

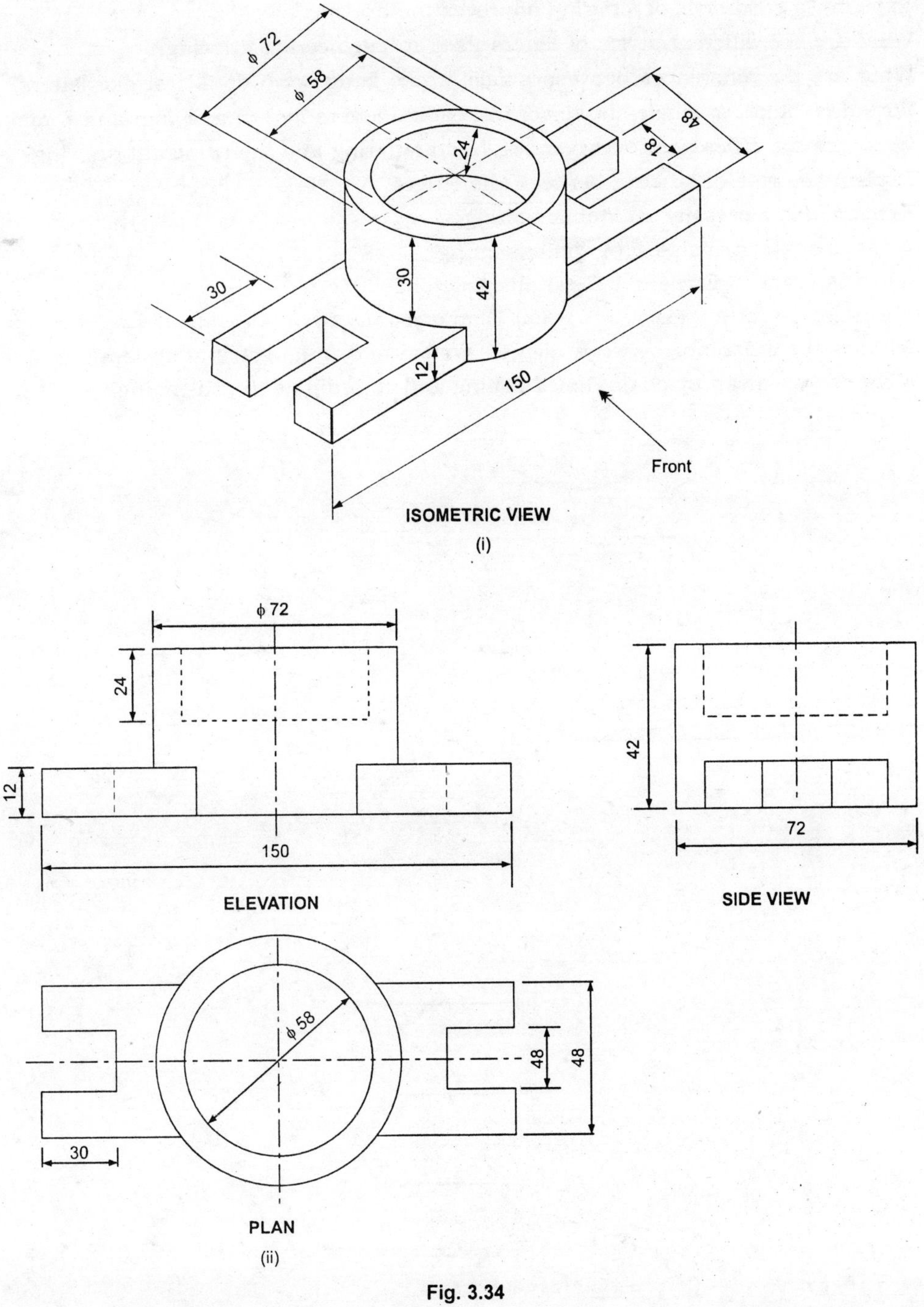

Fig. 3.34

EXERCISE

1. State the main requirements of lettering in engineering drawing.
2. Explain, “a good style of lettering improves the drawing”.
3. What are the different styles of letters used in engineering drawing?
4. What are the differences between single stroke letters and double stroke letters?
5. Write free hand, in single-stroke vertical capital letters in 3 mm, 5 mm and 8 mm.
6. What are the differences between free hand lettering and instrumental drawing?
7. Explain the rule of spacing between the letters.
8. Explain the necessity of dimensioning.
9. What are the principles of dimensioning?
10. What is leader? Explain by suitable sketch.
    (*i*) Holes (*ii*) Angles (*iii*) Diameter (*iv*) Radius
11. What is the difference between aligned system and unidirectional system?
12. What do you mean by chain dimensioning and co-ordinate dimensioning?

❑❑❑

4

GEOMETRICAL CONSTRUCTION

4.1 INTRODUCTION

Geometry is the basis of all technical drawings. The knowledge of the principles of geometric construction and its applications are essential to an engineering aid. As a engineer, we must be able to draw various types of lines. In a line drawing, a line may be a straight line, a circle, an arc of circle, a circular curve etc. This chapter provides information as well as deal with the drawing of polygons and non-circular curves like ellipse, parabola and hyperbola.

4.2 TERMS USED IN GEOMETRICAL CONSTRUCTION

Definitions:

(1) SURFACE

A surface has length and breadth but no thickness as shown in Fig 4.1.

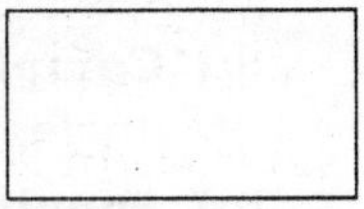

Fig. 4.1

(2) POINT

A point is that which has position but has no magnitude. It is simply represented by a small dot as shown in Fig. 4.2.

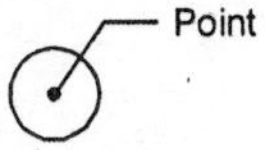

Fig. 4.2

(3) LINE

A line is that which has length but no thickness e.g., the boundary of a surface is a line.

(*i*) **Straight line:** The shortest distance between two points is known as straight line as shown Fig. 4.3.

(*ii*) **Curved line:** A curved line is that which does not lie in straight direction or no where straight as shown in Fig. 4.4.

(*iii*) **Parallel lines:** Parallel lines are those lines, which are equal distance apart and never meet to each other, if they produce in any direction as shown in Fig. 4.5.

Fig. 4.3

Fig. 4.4

Fig. 4.5

(4) ANGLE

An angle is formed between two intersecting lines, drawn from the same point as shown in Fig. 4.6.

(*i*) **Right angle:** A right angle is the inclination between two perpendicular lines or an angle of 90° as shown in Fig. 4.7.

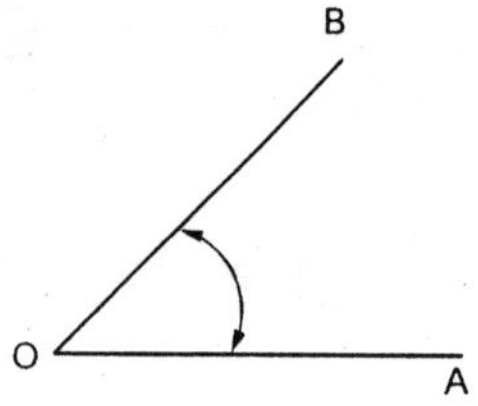

Fig. 4.6

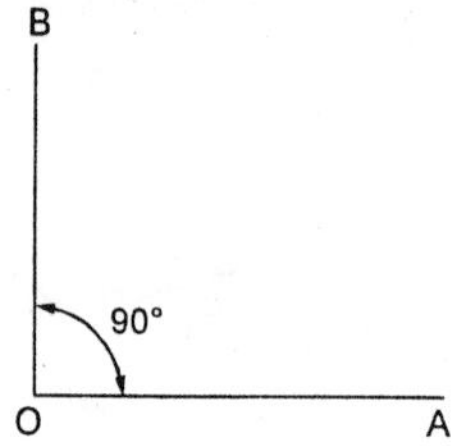

Fig. 4.7

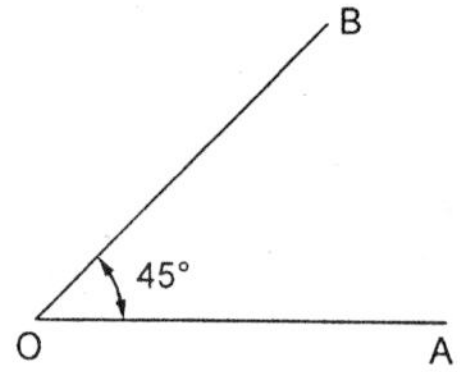

Fig. 4.8

(*ii*) **Acute angle:** An angle which is less than a right angle then it is known as acute angle as shown in Fig. 4.8.

(*iii*) **Obtuse angle:** An angle which is greater than a right angle then it is known as obtuse angle as shown in Fig. 4.9.

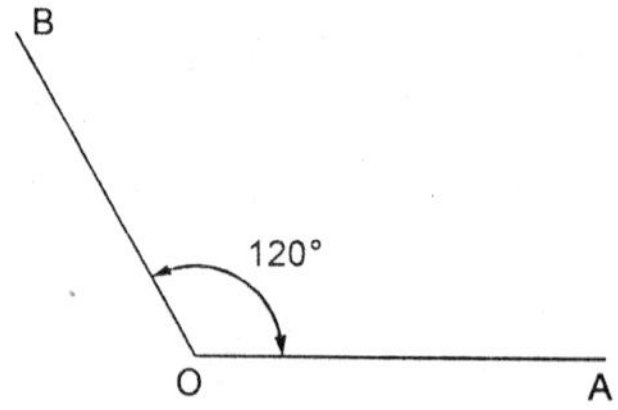

Fig. 4.9

(*iv*) **Reflex angle:** An angle which is greater than two right angles then it is known as reflex angle as shown in Fig. 4.10.

(*v*) **Complementary angles:** If the sum of two adjacent angles is equal to one right angle, they are known as complementary angles as shown in Fig. 4.11.

(*vi*) **Supplementary angles:** If the sum of two adjacent angles is equal to two right angles, they are known as supplementary angles as shown in Fig. 4.12.

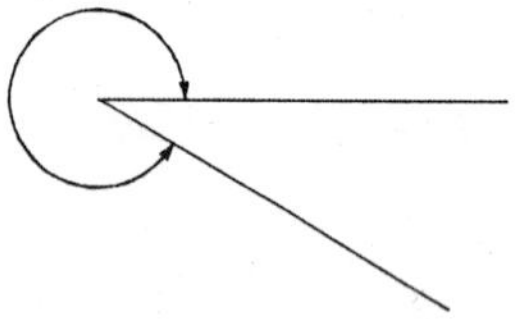
Fig. 4.10

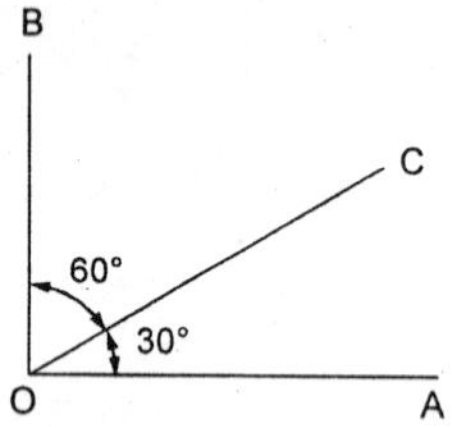

Fig. 4.11

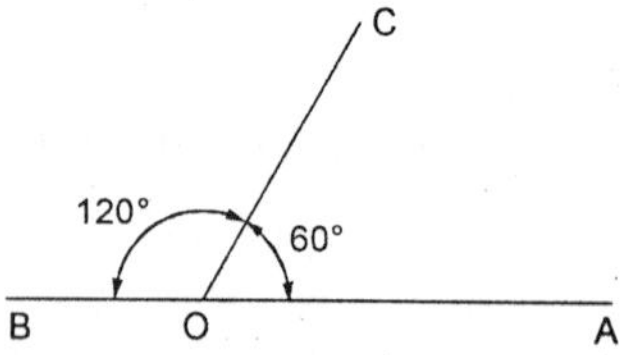

Fig. 4.12

4.3 POLYGON

A polygon is a plane figure bounded by more than four sides. If the sides and angles of a polygon are equal, then it is known as a regular polygon and if they are unequal, then it is known as an irregular polygon. The sum of external angles of a regular polygon is 360° and each external angle is $\frac{360^\circ}{N}$. Where N is the number of sides.

Polygons are named according to the number of their sides and angles are given below:

(*i*) **Pentagon:** A polygon having five equal sides then it is known as a pentagon as shown in Fig. 4.13.

(*ii*) **Hexagon:** A polygon having six equal sides, then it is known as hexagon as shown in Fig. 4.14.

(*iii*) **Heptagon:** A polygon having seven equal sides, then it is known as heptagon as shown in Fig. 4.15.

(*iv*) **Octagon:** A polygon having eight equal sides, then it is known as octagon as shown in Fig. 4.16.

(*v*) **Nonagon:** A polygon having nine equal sides, then it is known as nonagon as shown in Fig. 4.17.

(*vi*) **Decagon:** A polygon having ten equal sides, then it is known as decagon as shown in Fig. 4.18.

(*vii*) **Undecagon:** A polygon having eleven equal sides, then it is known as undecagon as shown in Fig. 4.19.

(*viii*) **Duodecagon:** A polygon having twelve equal sides, then it is known as duodecagon as shown in Fig. 4.20.

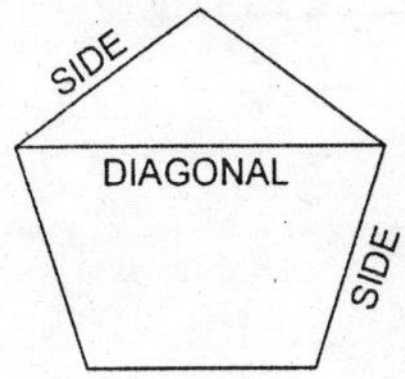

Fig. 4.13

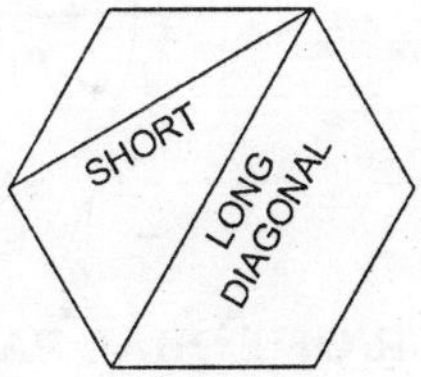

Fig. 4.14

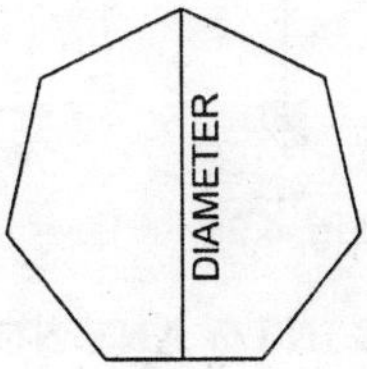

Fig. 4.15

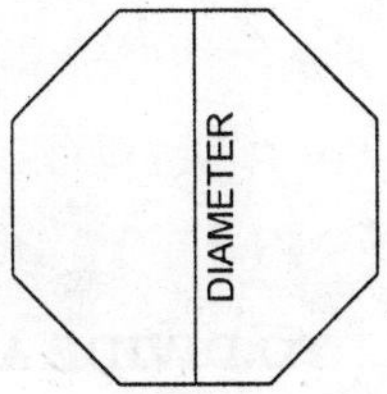

Fig. 4.16

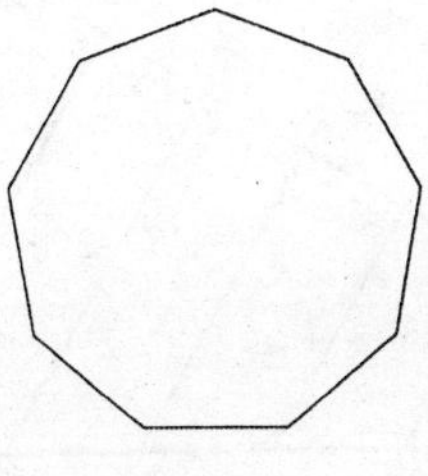
Fig. 4.17

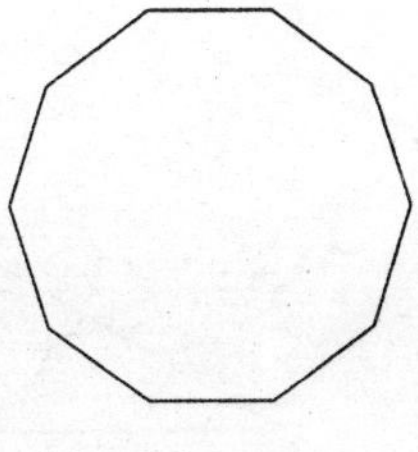
Fig. 4.18

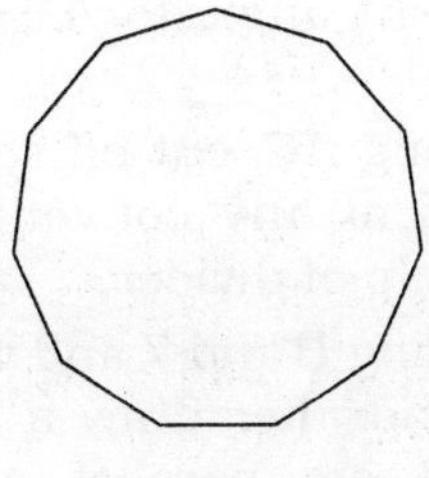
Fig. 4.19

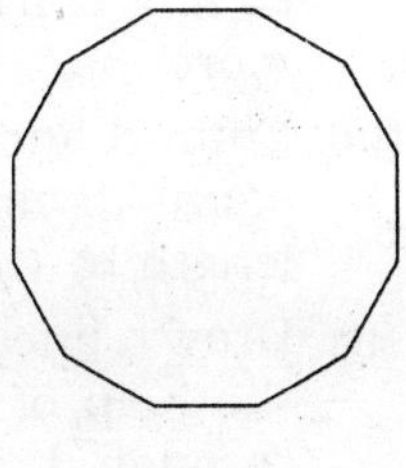
Fig. 4.20

4.4 BISECTING A STRAIGHT LINE

Problem 1. To bisect a given straight line.

Solution. (*i*) Let *AB* be a given straight line. With centre *A* and radius greater than half *AB*, draw an arcs on both the sides of *AB*.

(*ii*) With centre *B* and the same radius, draw an arcs on both the sides of *AB*, intersecting the previous arcs at *C* and *D*.

(*iii*) Draw a line joining *C* and *D* intersecting *AB* at *E*.

(*iv*) Then *CD* bisects the line *AB* at *E*. Thus, $AE = EB = \frac{1}{2}AB$ as shown in Fig. 4.21.

Problem 2. To draw a perpendicular to given line from a given point within.

Solution. (*i*) Let *AB* be a given line and *P* is the point in it.

(*ii*) With *P* as a centre, draw an arc cutting *AB* at *C* and *D* at any convenient radius R_1.

(*iii*) With any radius R_2 greater than R_1 and centres *C* and *D*, draw an arcs intersecting each other at *O* as shown in Fig. 4.22.

(*iv*) Draw a line joining *P* and *O*. Then the line *PO* is the required perpendicular.

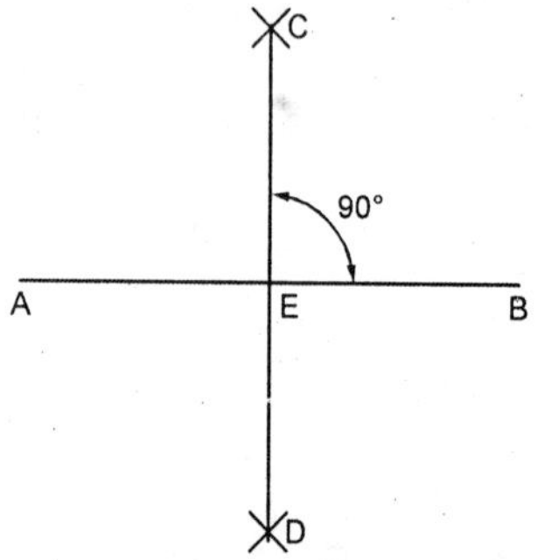

Fig. 4.21

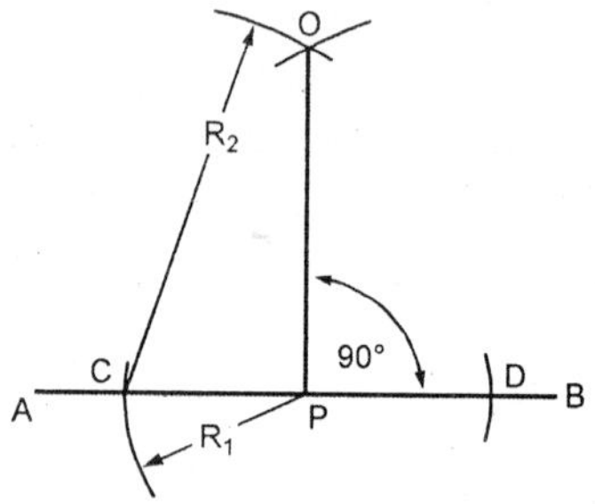

Fig. 4.22

4.5 TO DIVIDE A LINE INTO ANY NUMBER OF EQUAL PARTS

Problem 3. Divide a given line of 90 mm length into seven equal parts.

Solution. (*i*) Draw a line *AB* of 90 mm length, and divide into seven equal parts.

(*ii*) Draw a line *AC* of any length inclined at any convenient angle to *AB* (say more than 30°).

(*iii*) From *A* and along *AC*, cut-off seven equal divisions of any convenient length by the help of divider.

(*iv*) Draw a line joining *B* and 7 and with the help of minidrafter draw a line through 1, 2, 3, etc. parallel to *B7* intersecting *AB* at points 1′, 2′, 3′ ... etc. into seven equal parts as shown in Fig. 4.23.

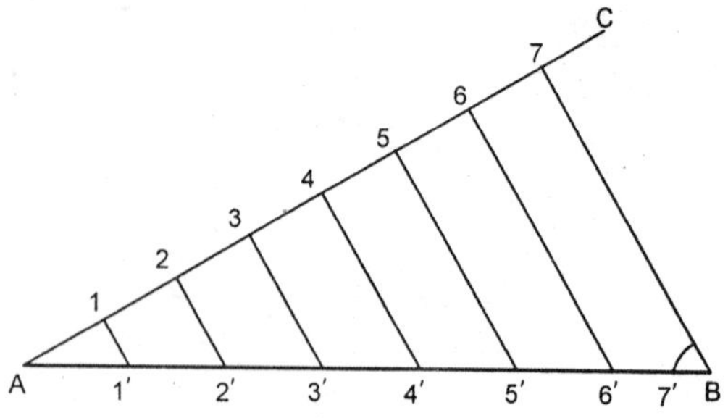

Fig. 4.23

4.6 TO BISECT AN ANGLE BETWEEN TWO GIVEN LINES

Problem 4. To bisect a given angle between two lines

Solution. Let *ABC* be the given angle, is to be bisect.

(*i*) With *B* as a centre and with any convenient radius, draw an arc cutting *AB* and *BC* at *D* and *E* as shown in Fig. 4.24.

(*ii*) With centres *D* and *E*, taking any convenient radius, draw an arcs intersecting each other at *O*.

(*iii*) Draw a line joining *B* and *O*, then *BO* is the bisector of the angle *ABC* as shown in Fig. 4.24.

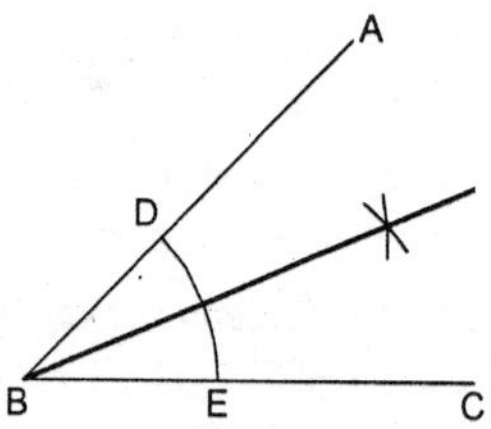

Fig. 4.24

4.7 TO DRAW AN ARCS TANGENTIAL TO LINES

Problem 5. To draw an arc of given radius touching two straight lines perpendicular to each other. Taking *R* is the radius of arc.

Solution. Let *AB* and *AC* be the given lines and *R* is the given radius

(*i*) With centre *A* and given radius *R*, draw an arcs to cut *AB* at *M* and *AC* at *N*.

(*ii*) With *M* and *N* as a centres and radius *R*, draw an arcs intersecting each other at *O*.

(*iii*) With *O* as a centre and the same radius *R*, draw the required tangent arc as shown in Fig. 4.25.

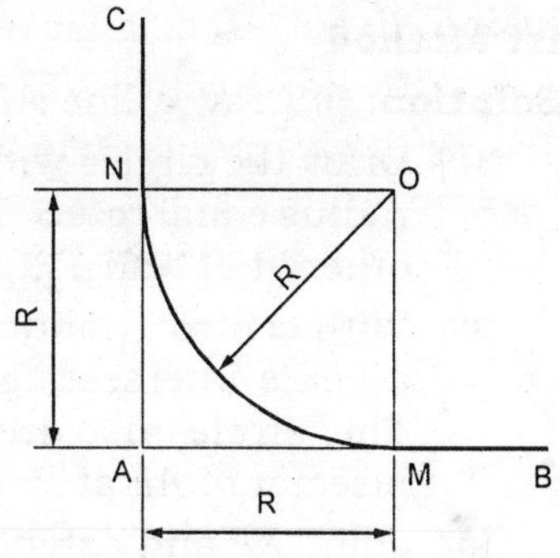

Fig. 4.25

Problem 6. To draw an arc touching two given straight lines which make an acute angle between them. Taking radius of arc is equal to *R*.

Solution. Let *AB* and *AC* be the given lines and *R* is the given centre.

(*i*) Draw a line *PQ* parallel to and at a distance equal to *R* from *AB*.

(*ii*) Draw a line *EF* parallel to and at a distance of *R* from *AC*, meeting *PQ* at *O*.

(*iii*) With *O* as a centre and *R* as a radius draw the tangent arc as shown in Fig. 4.26.

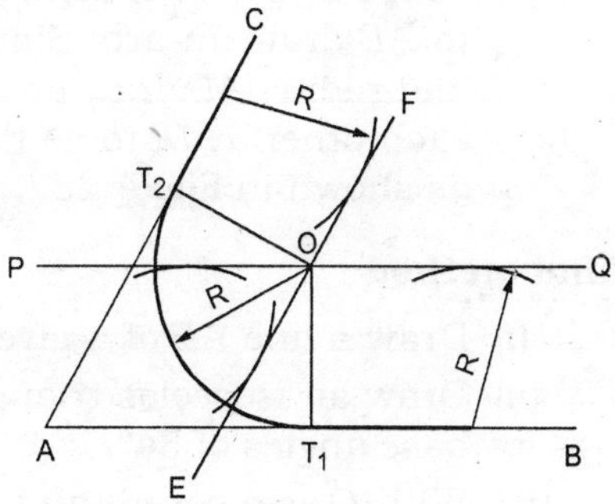

Fig. 4.26

4.8 CONSTRUCTION OF REGULAR PENTAGONS

Problem 7. Inscribe a pentagon in a circle of a given diameter.

Solution. (*i*) With centre *O*, draw a circle of a given diameter.

(*ii*) Draw diameters *AB* and *CD* perpendicular to each other.

(*iii*) Bisect *OB* and mark the point *N*. With centre *N* and radius *NC* draw an arc *CM*.

(*iv*) With centre *C* and radius *CM*, draw an arc cutting the circle in *S* and *R*.

(*v*) With centres *S* and *R* and the same radius, draw an arcs cutting the circle in *P* and *Q* respectively.

(*vi*) Now join the intersecting points to each other to obtained the required pentagon as shown in Fig. 4.27.

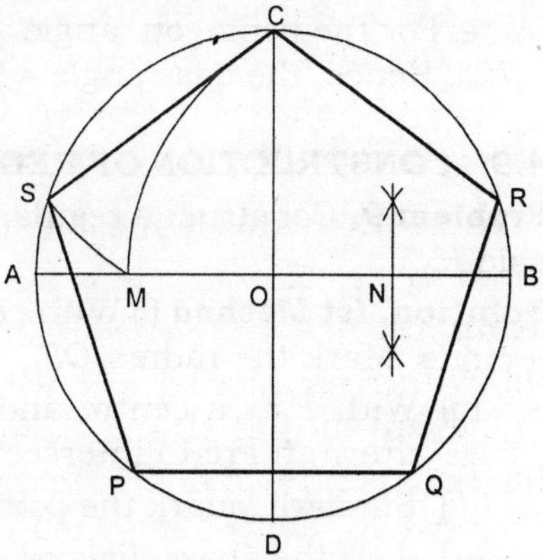

Fig. 4.27

Problem 8. Construct a regular pentagon, given the length of side *AB*.

Ist Method

Solution. (*i*) Draw a line *AB* of a given length.

(*ii*) Draw the circles with centres *A* and *B* with a radius equal to *AB*. The circles intersect each other at T_1 and T_2.

(*iii*) With centre T_1 and radius equal to *AB*, draw a circle intersecting two circles at *X* and *Y*. The circle also intersects perpendicular bisector of *AB* at *P*.

(*iv*) Joint *XP* and extend it to get a point *C* on the circle. Similarly, join *PY* and extend it at a point *E*.

(*v*) Join *AE*, *BC* with centre *E* and radius equal to *AB* draw an arc. Similarly, with centre *C* and radius *AB* draw another arc intersecting each other at *D*, to ge the required pentagon *ABCDE* as shown in Fig. 4.28.

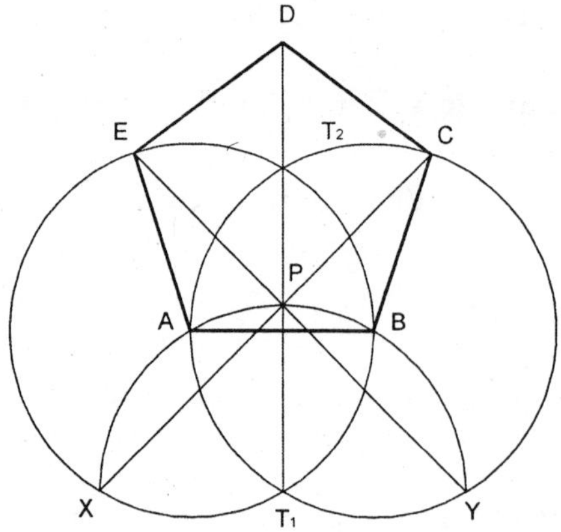

Fig. 4.28

IInd method

(*i*) Draw a line *AB* of a given length.

(*ii*) Draw an isosceles triangle *OAB* with *AB* as base and base angles of 54°.

(*iii*) With *O* as a centre and *OA* as a radius, draw a circle passing through *A* and *B*.

(*iv*) With *AB* as a radius, intersect the circle successively at the points *C*, *D* and *E*. Join *BC*, *CD*, *DE* and *EA* to get the required pentagon *ABCDE* as shown in Fig. 4.29.

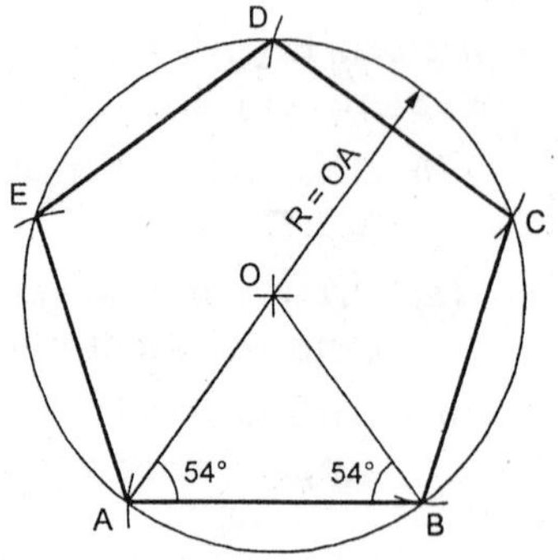

Fig. 4.29

[*Note:* For the pentagon, angle substanded at the centre of the isosceles triangle = 360°/5 = 72°. Hence, the base angle = (180° – 72°)/2 = 54°.

4.9 CONSTRUCTION OF REGULAR HEXAGON

Problem 9. Construct a regular hexagon, given length of one side *R*.

Solution. Ist Method (*i*) With centre *O* and the radius *R* draw a circle. Mark the radius *OF*.

(*ii*) With *F* as a centre and given side length as radius draw an arc to intersect the circle at *E*.

(*iii*) Similarly, mark the points *A*, *B*, *C* and *D* respectively.

(*iv*) Join the above division points in proper sequence, to obtained the required hexagon *ABCDEF* as shown in Fig. 4.30.

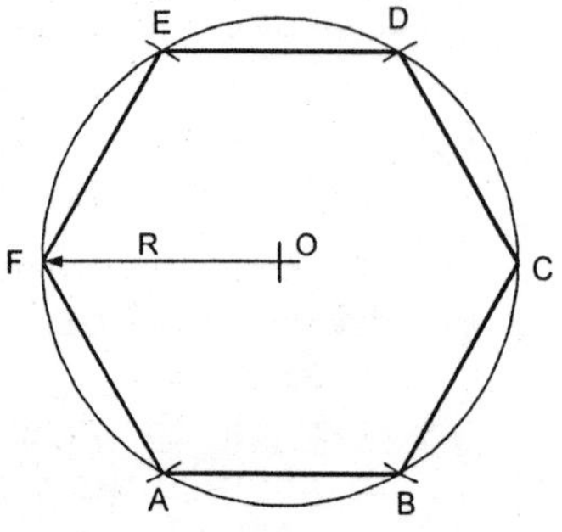

Fig. 4.30

IInd method

(*i*) Draw a line *AB* equal to the given length.

(*ii*) From *A*, draw a line A_1 and A_2 making 60° and 120° respectively with *AB* by help of mini drafter.

(*iii*) From *B*, draw a line B_3 and B_4 making 60° and 120° respectively with *AB* by the help of mini drafter.

(*iv*) From *O* the point of intersection of A_1 and B_3, draw a line parallel to *AB* and intersecting A_2 at *F* and B_4 at *C*.

(*v*) From *F*, draw a line parallel to *BC* and intersecting B_3 at *E*.

(*vi*) From *C*, draw a line parallel to *AF* and intersecting A_1 at *D*. Join the above division marks to obtain the required hexagon *ABCDEF* as shown in Fig. 4.31.

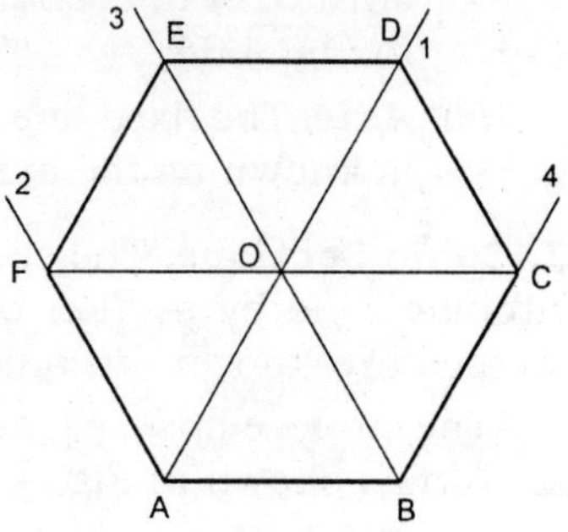

Fig. 4.31

4.10 CONSTRUCTION OF REGULAR OCTAGON

Problem 10. Describe a regular octagon about a given circle.

Ist method:

Solution: (*i*) With centre *O*, draw a given circle.

(*ii*) Draw the diameters *AB* and *CD* at right angles to each other.

(*iii*) Draw the diameters *EF* and *GH* inclined at an angle of 45° to *AB* or *CD*.

(*iv*) Draw eight tangents to the circle at the ends of the diameters *A, B, C, ... H* etc. respectively to intersect one another at the point 1, 2, 3 ... 8 etc. to complete the required octagon as shown in Fig. 4.32.

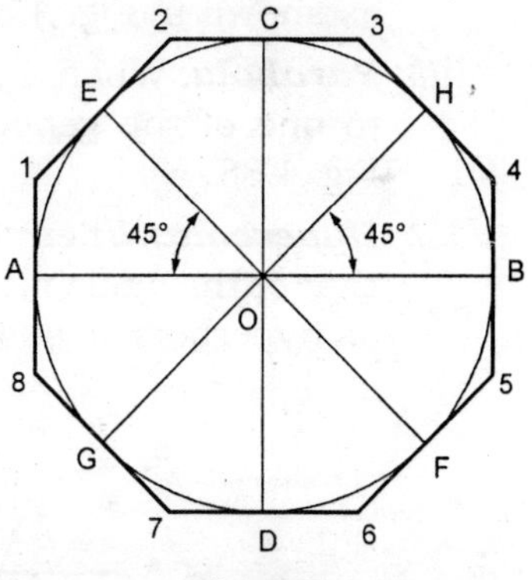

Fig. 4.32

IInd method

(*i*) Draw a line *AB* of a given length.

(*ii*) With centre *A*, draw a semi circle. Divide the semi circle into eight equal parts and mark 0, 1, 2, 3, 4, 5, 6, 7 and 8 respectively and join A_2.

(*iii*) Bisect *AB* and A_2 at C_1 and C_2. Draw lines through C_1 and C_2 to intersect at *O*.

(*iv*) Draw a circle with centre *O* and radius equal to *OA* or *OB* or *O*2.

(*v*) Mark the remaining six sides equal to *AB* to complete the required octagon as shown in Fig. 4.33.

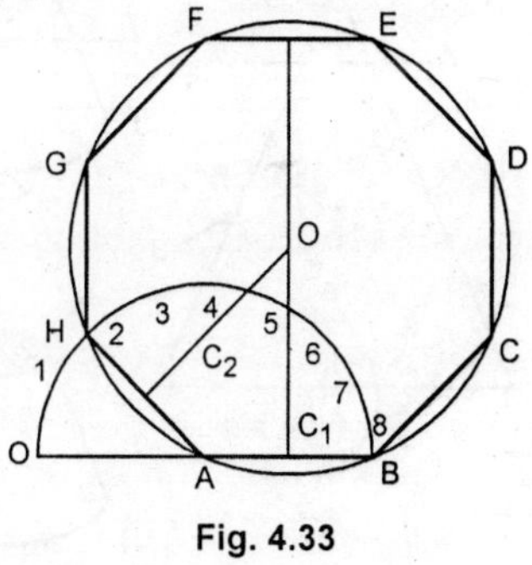

Fig. 4.33

4.11 CONIC SECTION

1. Cone: A cone is a surface generated by the rotation of a straight line whose one end is in contact with a fixed point while the other end is in contact with a closed curve, not lying in the plane of the curve as shown in Fig. 4.34.

(*i*) ***Vertex or Apex:*** The point of intersection of the axis and the generator is known as vertex or apex of the cone.

(*ii*) ***Generator:*** The revolving line which generates the surface of the cone is known as the generator as shown in Fig. 4.34.

(*iii*) ***Axis:*** The fixed line, about which the other line revolves, is known as the axis of a cone.

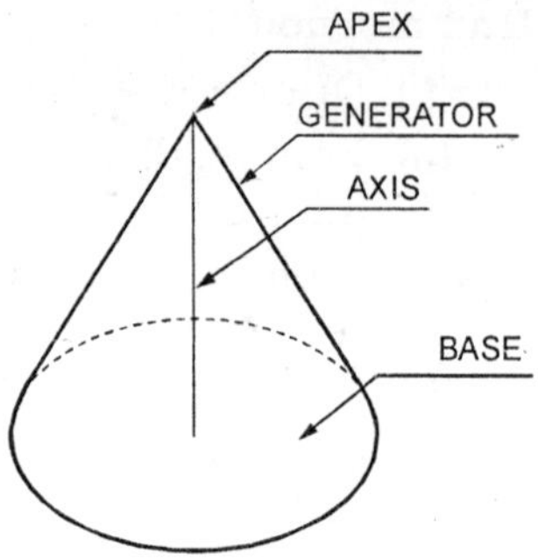

Fig. 4.34

2. Conic Sections: The sections obtained by cutting off a right circular cone by section planes at different angles relative to its axis are known as conic sections.

The circle, ellipse, parabola, hyperbola are examples of conic section as shown in Fig. 4.35.

(*i*) ***Circle:*** When a cutting plane *AA* is perpendicular to the axis and cuts all the generators, the section obtained is known as circle as shown in Fig. 4.36.

(*ii*) ***Ellipse:*** When a cutting plane *BB* is inclined to the axis of the cone and cuts all the generators on one side of the apex, the section obtained is known as an ellipse as shown in Fig. 4.37.

(*iii*) ***Parabola:*** When a cutting plane *CC* is inclined to the axis of the cone and parallel to one of the generators, the section obtained is known parabola as shown in Fig. 4.38.

(*iv*) ***Hyperbola:*** When the cutting plane *DD* makes a smaller angle with the axis then that of the angle made by the generator of the cone, the section obtained is known as hyperbola as shown in Fig. 4.39.

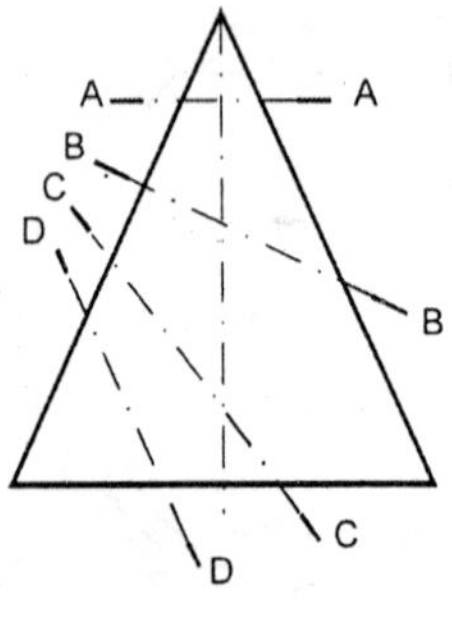

Fig. 4.35

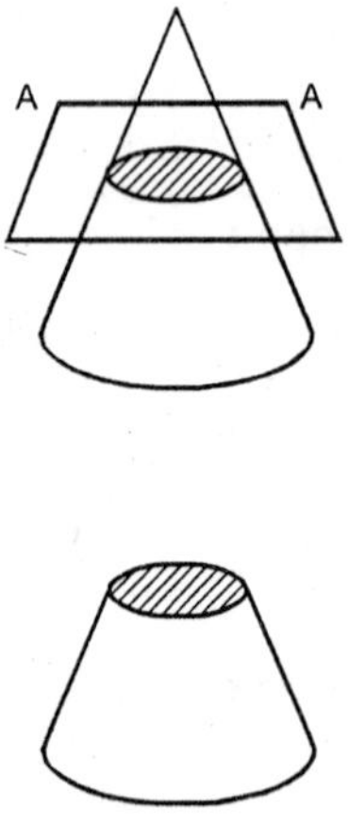

Circle

Fig. 4.36

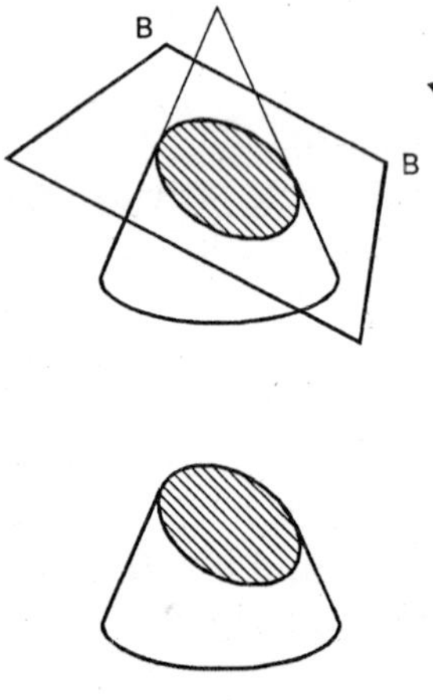

Ellipse

Fig. 4.37

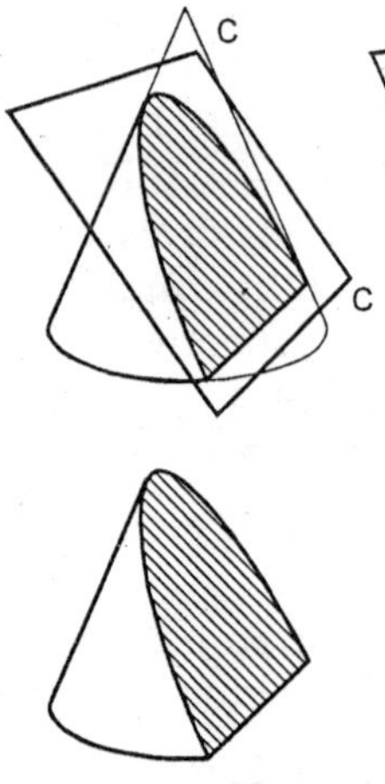

Parabola

Fig. 4.38

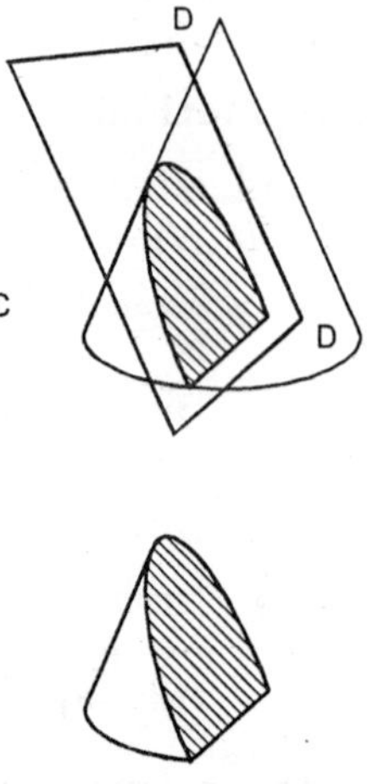

Hyperbola

Fig. 4.39

3. Eccentricity, Focus and Directrix

(*i*) ***Conic:*** The conic section is defined as locus of a point moving in a plane such that the ratio of its distance from a fixed point to a fixed straight line is always a constant as shown in Fig. 4.40. This ratio is called *eccentricity* (*e*).

(*ii*) ***Ellipse:*** Ellipse is the locus of a point moving in a plane such that the ratio of its distance from a point (F) to the fixed straight line (DD) is a constant as shown in Fig. 4.40. It is always < 1.

(*iii*) ***Parabola:*** It is the locus of a point moving in a plane such that the ratio of its distance from a fixed point (F) to the fixed straight line (DD) is a constant and is always = 1 (see Fig. 4.40).

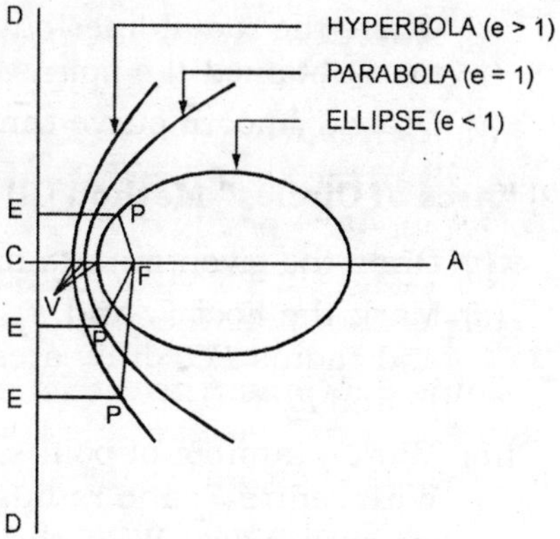

Fig. 4.40

(*iv*) ***Hyperbola:*** It is the locus of a point moving in a plane in such a way that the ratio of its distance from a fixed point (F) to the fixed straight line (DD) is constant and is > 1 (see Fig. 4.40).

(*v*) ***Focus (F):*** The fixed point is called the Focus.

(*vi*) ***Directrix (DD):*** The fixed line is called the Directrix.

(*vii*) ***Axis (CA):*** Axis is the line passing through focus and perpendicular to the directrix.

(*viii*) ***Vertex (V):*** Vertex is a point at which the conic cuts its axis.

(*ix*) ***Eccentricity:*** $e = \dfrac{\text{Distance of the moving point from the focus}}{\text{Distance of the moving point from the directrix}}$

4.12 ELLIPSE

Uses: Elliptical shape is used in the construction of arches, bridges, dams, elliptical gears of textile machines and printing presses, ends of cylindrical tanks, tops or bottoms of utensils, man-holes, glands, stuffing boxes, flanges of pipes, monuments etc.

Problem 11. To draw an ellipse, given major axis and minor axis.

Solution. (1) **"Cocentric circles" Method (I)**

(*i*) Draw the given minor axis *RS* and major axis *PQ*.

(*ii*) Draw two concentric circles with centre *O* using each axis as diameter.

(*iii*) Divide each circle into 12 equal parts by drawing 30° and 60° radial lines.

(*iv*) Where these radial lines cut the outer circle, draw vertical lines and

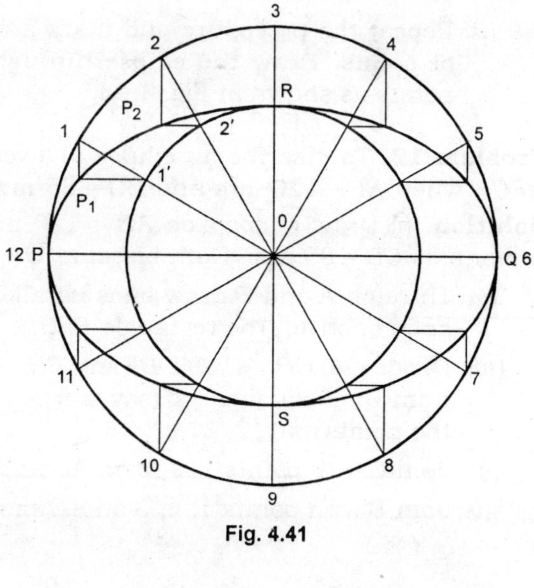

Fig. 4.41

where the radial lines cut the inner circle, draw horizontal lines. The intersection thus obtained the points P_1, P_2 etc. of the ellipse.

(*v*) Draw a smooth curve through these points as shown in Fig. 4.41.

(2) "Arcs of Circles" Method (II)

(*i*) Draw the given minor and major axis.

(*ii*) Mark the Foci F_1 and F_2. With centre *R* and radius *PO*, draw arcs cutting *PQ* at F_1 and F_2.

(*iii*) Mark a number of points 1, 2, 3 on F_1O. With centre F_2 and radius *Q*1, draw arcs on both sides. With the centre F_1 and radius *P*1, draw arcs intersecting on both sides at P_1 and P'_1.

(*iv*) Similarly, obtain other points and draw the required ellipse as shown in Fig. 4.42.

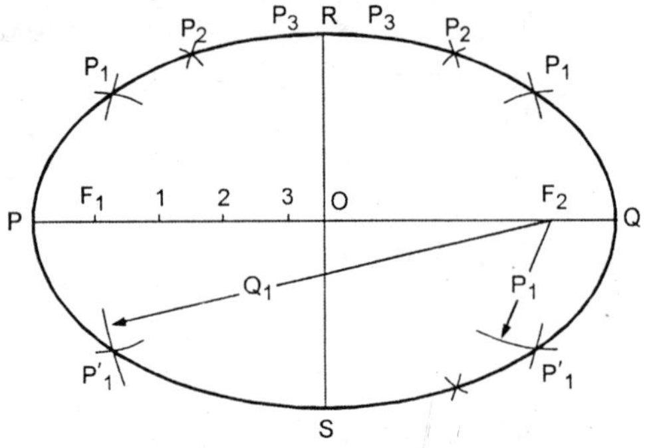

Fig. 4.42

(3) "Trammel" Method (III)

(*i*) Draw the given major and minor axis.

(*ii*) Mark off on the TRAMMEL. A trammel is a strip of a paper or card as shown in Fig. 4.43.

(*iii*) Lay the Trammel across the two axes. The point *R* always lies on the minor axis and point *Q* always lies on the major axis.

(*iv*) Move the trammel keeping *R* on minor axis and *Q* on major axis and mark a point in position of *P*.

(*v*) Repeat the procedure and mark a number of points. Draw the ellipse through these points as shown in Fig. 4.43.

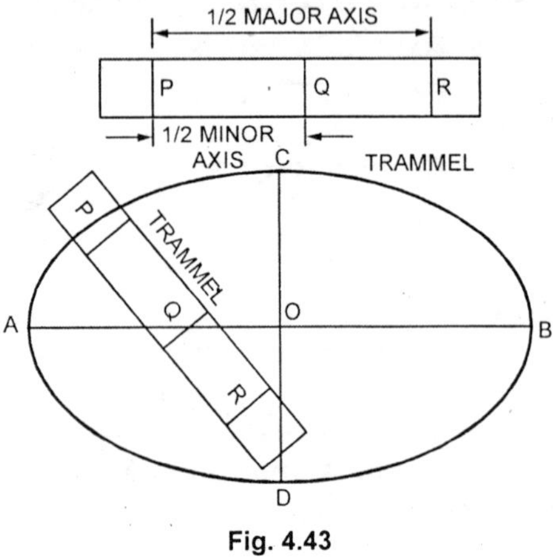

Fig. 4.43

Problem 12. To inscribe an ellipse is a rectangle *EFGH* when *EF* = 120 mm and *EG* = 85 mm.

Solution. (*i*) Draw major axis *AB* = 120 mm and minor axis *CD* = 85 mm. Both bisect at *O*.

(*ii*) Through *A* and *B* draw lines parallel to *CD* and construct the rectangle *EFGH*.

(*iii*) Divide *OA*, *OB*, *AE*, *AG*, *BF* and *BH*, into any number of equal parts, (say four) and name the points as 1, 2, 3.

(*iv*) Join *C* with points 1, 2, 3 on *AG* and *BH*.

(*v*) Join *D* with points 1, 2, 3 on *AE* and *BF*.

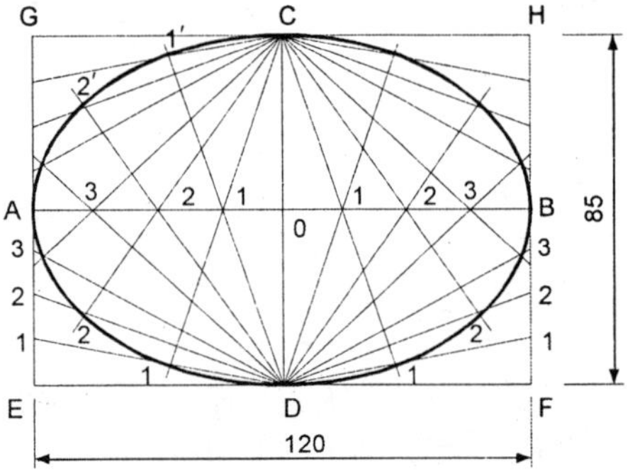

Fig. 4.44

(*vi*) Join *C* and *D* with points 1, 2, 3 on *OA* and *OB* and produce them to cross the lines from *C* and *D*, already drawn, in points 1′, 2′, 3.

(*vii*) Draw a smooth curve through these points as shown in Fig. 4.44.

4.13 PARABOLA

Parabola is used for suspension bridges, reflectors for parallel beams such as head lights of automobiles, solar concentrators, including machine tool structures, etc. Path of a thrown object missile and path of a jet of water issuing from vertical orifice are of parabolic shape.

Problem 13. To draw the parabola using focus and directrix.

Solution. See Fig. 4.45

1. Draw the directrix as a vertical line and the axis as a horizontal line.
2. Mark the focus *F* on the axis at a distance 40 mm from the directrix.
3. Mark the vertex *V* at the mid-point of *AF* such that $VF/AV = 1$ to get the parabola.
4. Draw a vertical line from *V* and mark *C* on it such that $VC = VF$, then draw a line from *A* passing through *C* for convenient length.
5. Draw a vertical line at any distance and mark *1* on the axis and *1′* on the inclined line *AC*.
6. Use the length *1 – 1′* as radius, focus *F* as centre, draw an arc to cut the line *1 – 1′* at M_1 and N_1.
7. Repeat this procedure by drawing vertical lines *2 – 2′*, *3 – 3′* etc. and get M_2, N_2, M_3, N_3 ... etc.

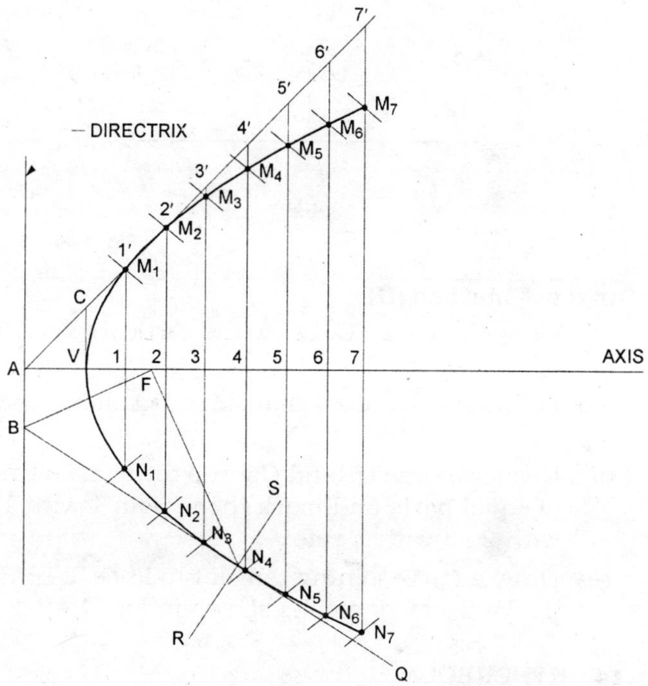

Fig. 4.45

8. Join these points by drawing a smooth curve to complete the parabola as shown in Fig. 4.45.

To draw tangent and normal to the parabola

1. Mark a point *P* on the parabola and join it with focus *F*. Then draw a line from *F* at 90° to the liner *FP* to get *B* on the directrix.
2. Draw a line from *B* passing through *P* which is the tangent to the parabola.
3. Draw another line through *P*, perpendicular to the tangent is a normal to the curve.

Problem 14. Draw a parabola given the base and the axis.

Solution. "Rectangle method" (I)

(*i*) Draw the base *PQ*. Draw the vertical axis *AB* at the mid-point *A* of *PQ*.

(*ii*) Construct a rectangle *PQRS*, as shown in Fig. 4.46(i).

(*iii*) Divide *PA* and *PS* into equal number of parts and mark 1, 2, 3 and 1′, 2′, 3′ so as to cut the vertical lines through 1, 2, 3 at P_1, P_2, P_3 respectively when 1′, 2′, 3′ are joined with *B*.

(*iv*) Draw the curve through points P_1, P_2 and P_3. Similarly, complete the other half of the parabola as shown in Fig. 4.46 (ii).

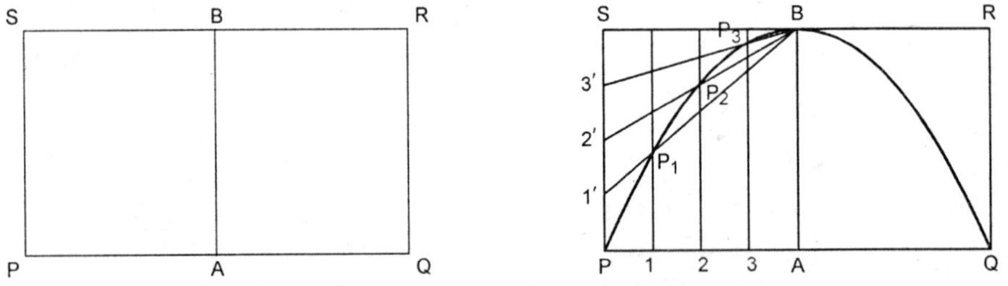

(i) (i)

Fig. 4.46

"Tangent" method (II)

(*i*) Draw the base *PQ*. Draw the vertical axis *AB* at the mid-point *A*.

(*ii*) Produce *AB* to *O* so that *AB* = *BO*. Join *OP* and *OQ*.

(*iii*) Divide the line *OP* and *OQ* into the same number of equal parts and mark them. Join 1 with 1′, 2 with 2′, 3 with 3′, etc.

(*iv*) Draw a curve joining tangent to lines 1 – 1′, 2 – 2′, 3 – 3′, 4 – 4′ etc. as shown in Fig. 4.47.

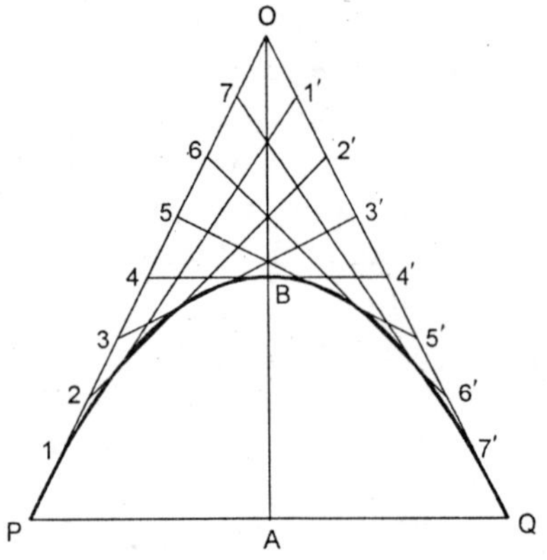

Fig. 4.47

4.14 HYPERBOLA

Hyperbola is used in the design of cooling towers, hydraulic channels, electronic transmitters and receivers like radar antenna, etc. *Rectangular hyperbola* is used to represent the Boyle's Law expansion curve or the Theoretical Indicator Diagram of an Engine.

Problem 15. The vertex of the hyperbola is 65 mm from its focus. Draw the curve if the eccentricity is 3/2. Draw also a tangent and normal at any point on the curve.

Solution. See Fig. 4.48.

We know that

$$\text{Eccentricity } e = \frac{\text{Distance of moving point from focus}}{\text{Distance of moving point from the directrix}}$$

i.e. $$e = \frac{VF}{AV}$$

Given that $(e) = \frac{3}{2}$ and $VF = 65$ mm

$$\therefore \quad AV = \frac{VF}{e} = \frac{2}{3} \times 65 = 43.3 \text{ mm}$$

To draw the hyperbola using focus and directrix

1. Draw the directrix as a vertical line and the axis as a horizontal line.
2. Mark the vertex V at a distance 43.3 mm from directrix and the focus F 65 mm from the vertex V.
3. Draw a vertical line from *V* and mark *C* on it such that *VC* = *VF*, then draw a line from *A* passing through *C* for convenient length.
4. Draw a vertical line at any convenient distance and mark 1 on the axis and 1′ on the inclined line *AC*.
5. Use the length 1 – 1′ as radius, focus *F* as centre, draw an arc to cut the line 1 – 1′.
6. Repeat this procedure by drawing vertical lines 2 – 2′, 3 – 3′ etc.
7. Join the points by drawing a smooth curve as shown in Fig. 4.48.

To draw tangent and normal to the hyperbola

1. Mark a point *P* on the curve and join focus *F* and *P*, then draw a line from *F* at 90° to the line *FP* to get *B* on the directrix.
2. Draw a line from *B* passing through *P* which is the tangent to the hyperbola.
3. Draw another line through *P*, perpendicular to the tangent and which is a normal to the curve.

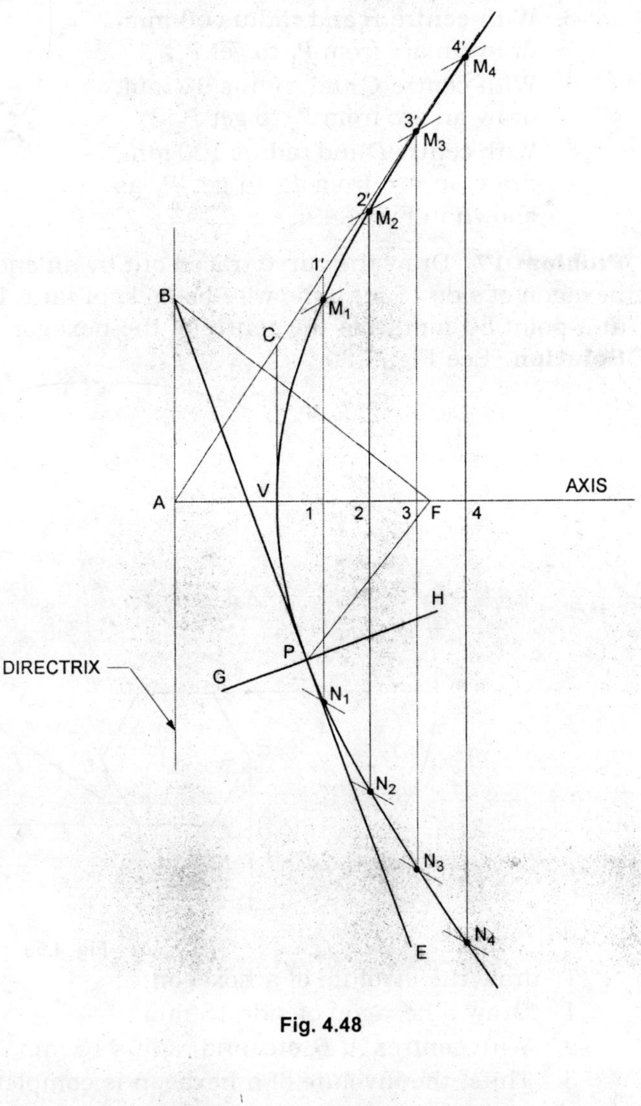

Fig. 4.48

4.15 INVOLUTE

An involute is a spiral curve traced out by a point on a cord or thread as it unwinds from the surface of a polygon or a circle. The involute of a circle is the basic curve of gear teeth profile.

Problem 16. Draw the involute of a square of side 30 mm.

Solution. See Fig. 4.49

To draw the involute of a square

1. Draw square *ABCD* of side 30 mm.
2. With centre *A* and radius 30 mm, draw an arc to get P_1.
3. With centre *B* and radius 60 mm, draw an arc from P_1 to get P_1.
4. With centre *C* and radius 90 mm, draw an arc from P_2 to get P_3.
5. With centre *D* and radius 120 mm, draw an arc from P_3 to get P_4 as shown in Fig. 4.49.

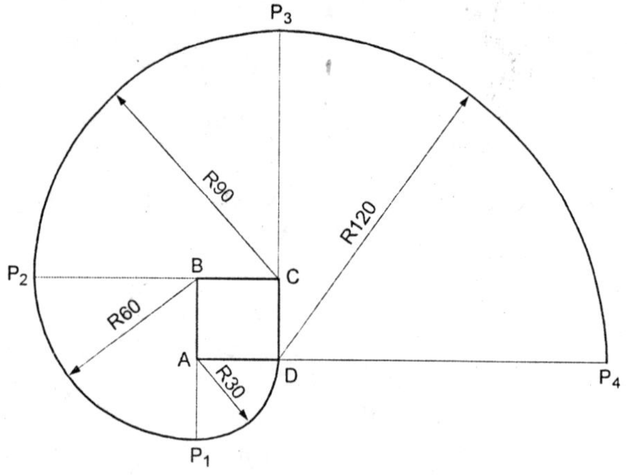

Fig. 4.49

Problem 17. Draw the curve traced out by an end of a thin wire unwound from a regular hexagon of side 15 mm, the wire being kept taut. Draw a tangent and normal to the curve at a point 80 mm from the centre of the hexagon.

Solution. See Fig. 4.50.

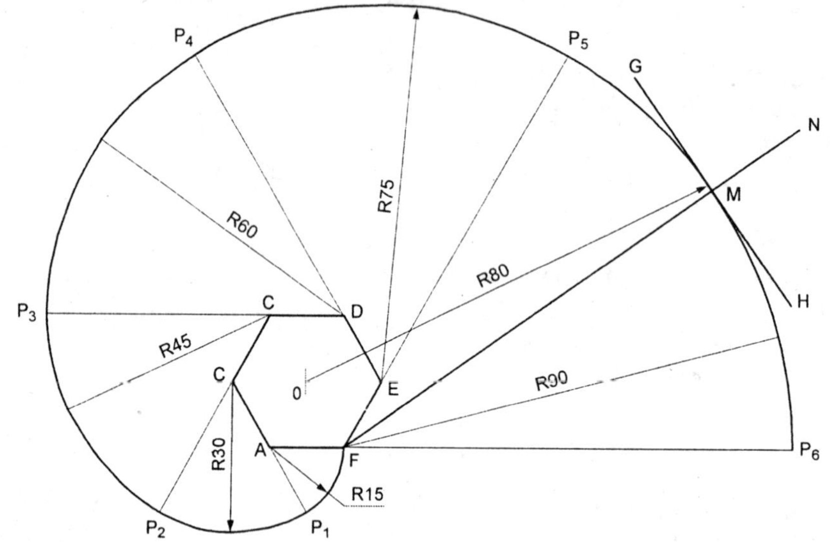

Fig. 4.50

To draw the involute of a hexagon.

1. Draw a hexagon of side 15 mm.
2. With centres *A*, *B*, etc. and radius 15 mm, 30 mm, etc., draw arcs to get P_1, P_2, etc.
3. Thus, the involute of a hexagon is completed as shown in Fig. 4.50.

To draw tangent and normal to the involute

1. Mark the point M on the curve at a distance 80 mm from the centre O of the hexagon. Note that the part of the involute $P_5 - P_6$ has the centre F.
2. From F, draw a line passing through M to get the normal to the curve FN.
3. Draw a line through M perpendicular to FN to get the tangent to the curve GH.

Problem 18. (Fig. 4.52) To draw an involute of a given circle. Draw normal and tangent at any point P on the involute.
Solution. See Fig. 4.51.

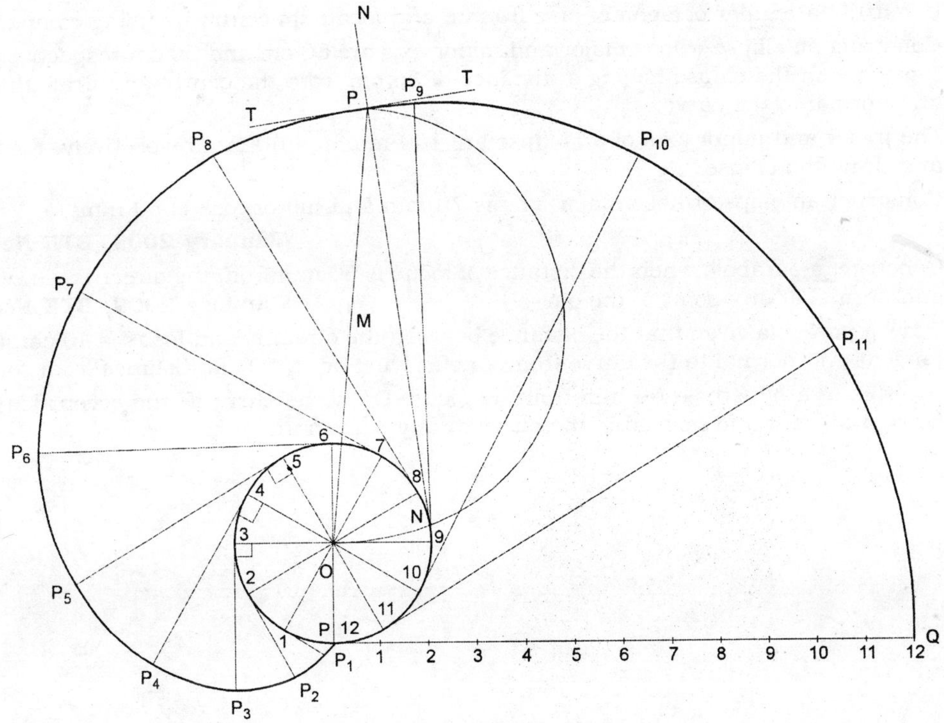

Fig. 4.51

1. Draw a circle of a given diameter and divide it into 12 equal parts. Draw a line PQ tangent to the circle at a point P.
2. Take PQ equal to circumference of the circle. Divide PQ into the 12 number of equal parts.
3. Draw tangents at point 1, 2, 3 etc.. Mark 1 $P_1 = P1'$, 2 $P_2 = P2'$, 3 $P_3 = P3'$ etc.
4. Draw a smooth curve through the points P_1, P_2, P_3 etc as shown in Fig. 4.51.

EXERCISE

1. What do you meant by conic section?
2. Draw a circle of dia 50 mm and divide it into 12 equal parts by using compass.
3. Draw an arc of radius 25 mm touching two straight lines at right angles to each other.
4. Draw a regular pentagon of 40 mm side with an side keeping horizontal and locate its centre.
5. Draw a pentagon of side 45 mm with one side vertical and mark its centre.
6. Construct a regular hexagon of side 30 mm when one side is vertical and locate its centre only use compass.
7. Construct a regular polygon having seven sides given the length of its side 35 mm. *Only use compass.*
8. Construct a regular octagon of side 30 mm and locate its centre by using compass only.
9. Construct an ellipse whose major and minor axis are 80 cm and 50 cm respectively. Locate a point *P* on the ellipse having a distance of 35 cm from the centre and draw the tangent and normal to the curve.
10. The major and minor axis of an ellipse are 100 mm and 60 mm respectively. Find the foci and draw the ellipse.
11. Construct an ellipse whose major axis is 70 mm and minor axis is 50 mm. **[January 2009, BTE New Delhi]**
12. Construct a parabola when the distance of focus is 50 mm from the directrix. Draw tangent and normal at any point of the curve. **[January 2009, BTE New Delhi]**
13. Draw a parabola given that the distance between the directrix and focus is 40 cm. Draw the tangent and normal to the curve from a point lying on it, 50 cm distance from the focus.
14. A vertex of a hyperbola 60 mm from its focus. Draw the curve if the eccentricity is 5/2. Draw a tangent and normal to the curve at any point on it.

❑❑❑

5

SCALES

5.1 INTRODUCTION

In most of the cases drawing of big object can not be draw in full size scale because the object may be too big. Similarly, the drawings of small object also cannot be prepared in full size. Hence it is necessary to draw them with suitable scale as per the drawing sheet. Therefore, scale may be defined as, "ratio of the linear dimension of an element of an object as represented in the original drawing to the real linear dimension of the same element of the object itself". In other words, the proportion by which a dimension is either reduced or increased in the drawing is known as scale. This scale is also known as draftsman scale.

5.2 SIZE OF SCALE

Scale may be represented by the following ways:

1. Full scale
2. Enlarge scale
3. Reducing scale.

   1. **Full scale:** A scale with the ratio of 1 : 1, then it is known as full scale.
   2. **Enlarge scale:** A scale where the ratio is larger than 1 : 1, then it is said to be larger as its ratio increases, watches, electronic devices etc.
   3. **Reducing scale:** A scale where the ratio is smaller than 1 : 1, then it is said to be smaller as its ratio decreases e.g. maps, building, structure etc.

The recommended scales for the use of technical drawings as per SP : 46 –1988 are specified in Table 5.1.

Table 5.1 Specified Recommended Scale

Category	*Recommended Scales*
Full scale	1 : 1
Enlarge scales	50 : 1 20 : 1 10 : 1 5 : 1 2 : 1
Reducing scales	1 : 2 1 : 5 1 : 10 1 : 20 1 : 50 1 : 100 1 : 500 1 : 1000 1 : 2000 1 : 5000 1 : 10000

5.3 UNITS OF MEASUREMENTS

Two international system of length measurement are to be used, which are as follows:

1. Metric system
2. English system.

1. **Metric System:** As per Indian Standard Institute the metric system are given below in Table 5.2

Table 5.2

10 millimetres	(mm)	= 1 centimetre	(cm)
10 centimetres	(cm)	= 1 decimetre	(dm)
10 decimetres	(dm)	= 1 metre	(m)
10 metres	(m)	= 1 decametre	(dam)
10 decametres	(dam)	= 1 hectometre	(hm)
10 hectometres	(hm)	= 1 kilometre	(km)

2. **English System:** According to British measures the English system are given below in a Table 5.3.

Table 5.3

12 inches	= 1 Foot
3 feet	= 1 Yard
5½ Yards	= 1 Pole
4 Poles	= 1 chain
10 chains	= 1 Furlong
8 furlongs	= 1 mile

5.4 REPRESENTATIVE FRACTION (R.F.)

The ratio of length of an object on the drawing to the actual length in the same units is known as reprersentative fraction. It is denoted by R.F.

$$\text{R.F.} = \frac{\text{Length of an object on the drawing}}{\text{Actual length of the object}}$$

For example:

1 cm long line on a drawing represents 50 metres length of an object.

$$\text{R.F} = \frac{1\text{ cm}}{50\text{ metres}} = \frac{1}{50 \times 100\text{ cm}} = \frac{1}{5000}$$

$$\text{R.F.} = \frac{1}{5000} \quad \text{or} \quad 1:5000$$

5.5 CLASSIFICATION OF SCALES

1. Plain scales
2. Diagonal scales
3. Comparative scales
4. Vernier scales
5. Chord scales
6. Isometric scale.

5.6 PLAIN SCALE

A plain scale is used to represent either two units or one unit and its fraction. A plain scale is simply a line which is divided into suitable number of equal parts, the first part of the scale is sub-divided into smaller parts.

The following informations are necessary for construction of a plain scale.

(*i*) Calculate the R.F, if not given

(*ii*) Calculate the length of the scale

Where length of the scale = R.F. × maximum length of the object.

Note: If maximum length is not given, then it may be assumed, 15 cm or 16 cm.

5.7 PROCEDURE FOR CONSTRUCTION OF PLAIN SCALE

(*i*) Find the R.F. if not given

(*ii*) Find the length of scale = R.F. × Maximum length of the object. It may be assumed.

(*iii*) Divide the calculated length of scale into equal number of parts.

(*iv*) The zero mark should be placed at the end of the first main division and this first unit is further sub-divided into smaller equal parts.

(*v*) Numbering is done from zero mark, the units are numbered to the right and sub-divisions to the left.

(*vi*) R.F. of the scale must be mentioned below the scale.

(*vii*) The width of scale is taken as 1 cm approximately.

(*viii*) All the dimensions of the scale must be in the same unit.

Problem 1. Construct a plain scale to show metres, decimeters when 1 centimetre represents 6 metres and long enough to measure upto 60 metres. Find the R.F. and mark on it a distance of 43 metres.

Solution:

(*i*)
$$\text{R.F.} = \frac{\text{Length of an object on the drawing}}{\text{Actual length of the object}}$$

$$= \frac{1\text{ cm}}{6\text{ m}} = \frac{1\text{ cm}}{6 \times 100\text{ cm}} = \frac{1}{600}$$

$$\text{R.F.} = \frac{1}{600} \quad \text{or} \quad 1:600$$

(*ii*) Length of scale = R.F. × maximum length to be measured

Maximum length to be measured = 60 m

$$\therefore \text{ Length of scale} = \text{L} = \frac{1}{600} \times 60\,m = \frac{1}{600} \times 60 \times 1\,cm = 10\text{ cm.}$$

(*iii*) Draw a horizontal line of 10 cm in length as shown in Fig. 5.1

(*iv*) Draw a rectangle of size 10 cm × 1 cm on the horizontal line.

(*v*) Total length to be measured is 60 metres. Therefore divide the rectangle into 6 numbers of equal parts, and each part represents 10 metres.

(*vi*) Mark zero at the end of the first main division.

(*vii*) From zero number 10, 20, 30, 40 and 50 are marked at the end of subsequent main parts towards the right as shown in Fig. 5.1.

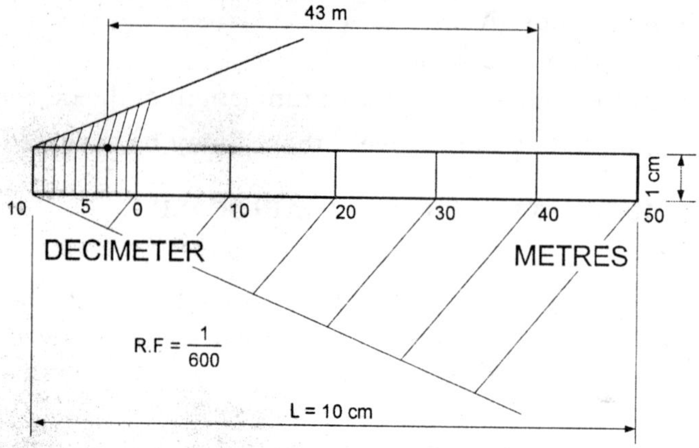

Fig. 5.1

(*viii*) Sub-divide the first main part into 10 sub-equal parts to represent metres (By using geometrical construction method).

(*ix*) Number the sub-divisions i.e., metres to the left of zero.

(*x*) Write the main unit and sub-unit (metres) below the scale. Also mention the R.F. below the scale.

(*xi*) Indicate on the scale a distance of 40 metres to the right side of zero and 3 decimetres to the left of zero.

Problem 2. Construct a plain scale of R.F. = 1 : 50,000 to show kilometres and hectometres and long enough to measure upto 9 kilometres. Measure a distance of 5 kilometers and 6 hectometres on the scale.

Solution. $\text{R.F.} = \dfrac{1}{50,000}$ (Given)

Length of scale = R.F × maximum length of be measured

$$\text{Length of scale} = \frac{1}{50000} \times 9 \text{ km}$$

$$= \frac{1}{50000} \times 9 \times 1000 \times 100 \text{ cm}$$

$$= 18 \text{ cm}$$

Draw a rectangle of 18 cm × 1 cm. Divide the rectangle into 9 equal parts, each part representing 1 km. Mark zero at the end of the first main part and mark 1, 2, 3, ... 8 at the end of subsequent main part towards right. Sub-divide the first part into 10 sub-divisions each representing 1 hectometre. Number the sub-division to the left of zero.

Indicate on the scale, the given distance i.e., 5 kilometres and 6 hectometres as shown in Fig. 5.2.

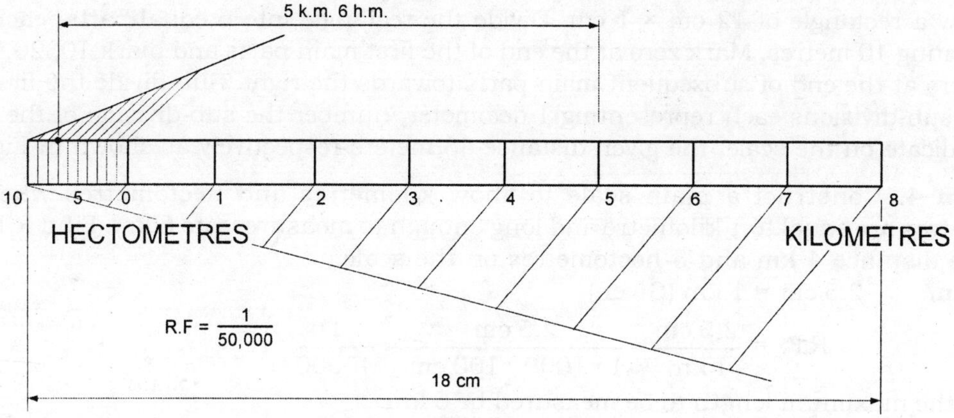

Fig. 5.2

Problem 3. Construct a plain scale to show metres when 1 cm represents 5 metres and long enough to measure upto 60 metres. Find the R.F. and mark on it a distance 47 metres on the scale.

Solution.

$$\text{R.F.} = \frac{\text{Length of an object on the drawing}}{\text{Actual length of the object}}$$

$$= \frac{1 \text{ cm}}{5 \text{ metre}} = \frac{1}{5 \times 100 \text{ cm}} = \frac{1}{500}$$

$$\text{R.F.} = \frac{1}{500} \quad \text{or} \quad 1:500$$

Length of scale = **R.F.** × maximum length to be measured.

Maximum length to be measure = 60.

Length of scale = **L** = $\frac{1}{500} \times 60 = \frac{1}{500} \times 60 \times 100 \text{ cm} = 12 \text{ cm}$

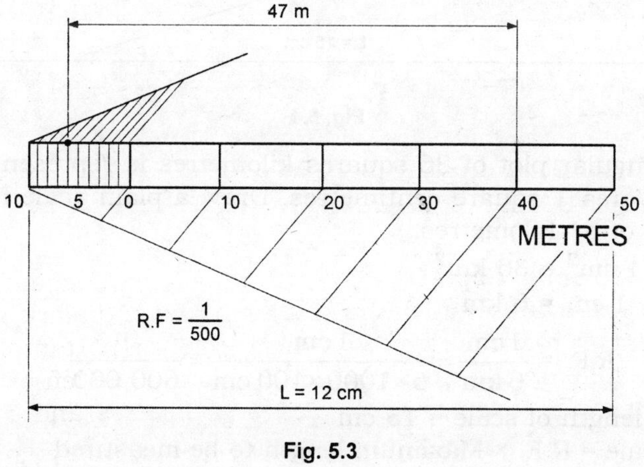

Fig. 5.3

Draw a rectangle of 12 cm × 1 cm. Divide the rectangle into 6 equal parts, each part representing 10 metres. Mark zero at the end of the first main parts and mark 10, 20, 30, ... 50 meters at the end of subsequent main parts towards the right. Sub-divide the first part into 10 sub-divisions each representing 1 decimeter, number the sub-division of the left of zero. Indicate on the scale, the given distance 43 meters respectively as shown in Fig. 5.3.

Problem 4. Construct a plain scale to show kilometres and hectometres when 2.5 centimetres are equal to 1 kilometre and long enough to measure upto 6 km. Find R.F. and indicate distance 4 km and 5 hectometres on the scale.

Solution. 2.5 cm = 1 km (Given)

$$\text{R.F.} = \frac{2.5 \text{ cm}}{1 \text{ km}} = \frac{2.5 \text{ cm}}{1 \times 1000 \times 100 \text{ cm}} = \frac{1}{40000}$$

Let the maximum length to be measured be 6 km.

Length of the scale = R.F. × Maximum length to be measured.

$$\text{Length of the scale} = L = \frac{1}{40000} \times 6 \times 1000 \times 100 = 15 \text{ cm.}$$

Draw a rectangle of size 15 cm × 1 cm as shown in Fig. 5.4. Divide the rectangle into 6 equal parts, each part representing 1 km. Mark zero, at the end of first mainpart. Then mark 1, 2, ..., 5 at the end of first main parts towards right. Sub-divide the first main parts into 10 equal parts and number them to the left of zero.

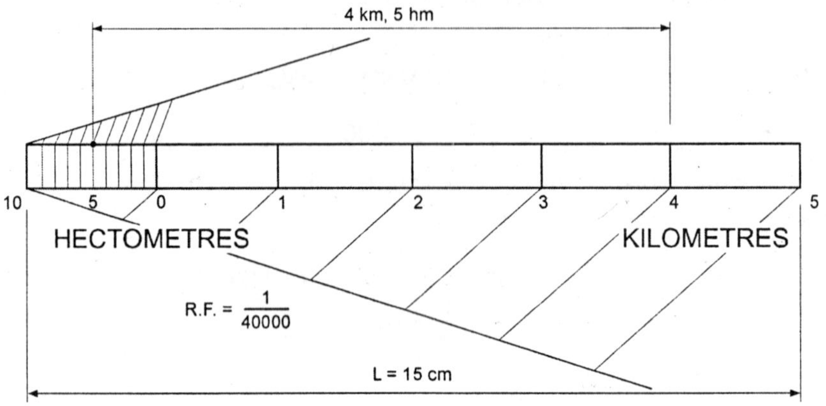

Fig. 5.4

Problem 5. A rectangular plot of 36 squares kilometres is represented on a map by a similar rectangle of area 1 square centimetres. Draw a plain scale to show kilometres. Measure a distance of 54 kilometres.

Solution. $1 \text{ cm}^2 = 36 \text{ km}^2$

$1 \text{ cm} = 6 \text{ km}$

$$\text{R.F.} = \frac{1 \text{ cm}}{6 \text{ km}} = \frac{1 \text{ cm}}{6 \times 1000 \times 100 \text{ cm}} = \frac{1}{600{,}000}$$

Let assume the length of scale = 15 cm

Length of the scale = R.F. × Maximum length to be measured

Length of the scale = L = $\frac{1}{600000}$ × Maximum length to be measured

$$15 = \frac{1}{600000}$$

or 15 × 600000 = maximum length to be measured

or maximum length to be measured = 90,000,00 cm = 90 km

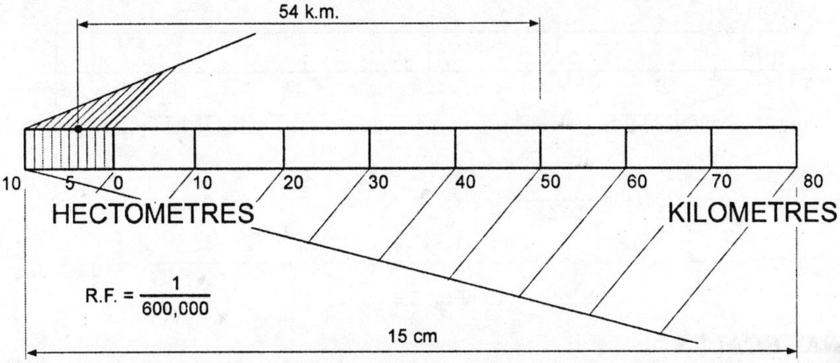

Fig. 5.5

Draw a rectangle of size 15 cm × 1 cm as shown in Fig. 5.5. Divide the rectangle into 9 equal parts, each part representing 10 km. Mark zero at the end of first main part. Then mark 10, 20, ..., 80 at the end of first main parts towards right. Subdivided the first-main parts into 10 equal parts and number then to the left of zero.

Problem 6. The distance between New Delhi and Aligarh is 132 kms. An express train covers the distance in 2 hours and 12 minutes. Construct a plain scale to measure time upto a single minute and mark a distance covered in 35 minutes. Take R.F. of the scale $\frac{1}{400,000}$.

Solution. R.F. = $\frac{1}{400,000}$ (Given)

where R.F. = $\frac{\text{Length of an object on the drawing}}{\text{Actual length of the object}}$

Let us assume true length of the scale is 15 cm.

$$\text{Actual length of the object} = \frac{\text{Length of an object on the drawing}}{\text{R.F.}}$$

$$= \frac{15}{1/400,000} = 15 \times 400,000 \text{ cm} = 60 \text{ km}$$

or Actual length of the object = 60 kms

$$\text{Average speed of the train} = \frac{132}{2.20} = 60 \text{ kms/hr.}$$

Thus, 60 kms are covered in 1 hour or 60 minutes.

Draw a rectangle of 15 × 1 cm, Divide the rectangle into 6 equal parts, each part representing 10 km in 10 minutes. Mark zero at the end of the first main part and mark

10, 20, 30 ... 50 at the end of subsequent main part, towards right sub-divide the first part into 10 sub-divisions each representing 1 km and 1 minute. Number the sub-division to the left of zero.

Indicate on scale, the distance covered in 35 minutes as shown in Fig. 5.6.

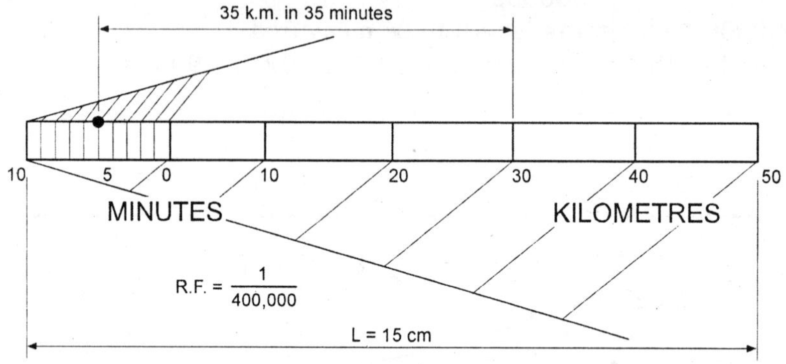

Fig. 5.6

5.8 DIAGONAL SCALES

A diagonal scales are used to represent three units such as metres, decimetres, centimetres or only one unit and its fraction upto second place of decimal points. In diagonal scale a line is divided into suitable number of equal parts, the first of which is sub-divided into smallest parts by diagonal.

Note: The procedure of construction of diagonal scale is same as in plain scale, the only difference is in construction of diagonal and width is taken as 50 mm approximately.

Small divisions of short line are obtained by the principles of diagonal division, as shown in Fig. 5.7.

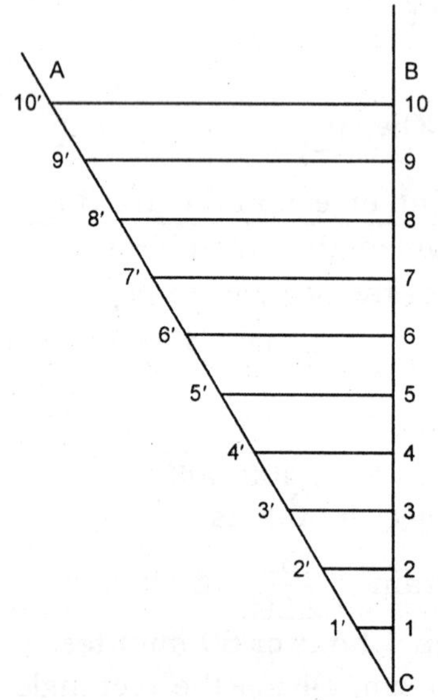

Fig. 5.7

To obtain division of a given line AB in multiples of $\frac{1}{10}$ its length e.g. 0.1 AB, 0.2 AB, 0.3 AB, 0.6 AB etc.

At B, draw a perpendicular BC to AB and step of 10 equal parts of any convenient length. Join AC, through these parts, point 1, 2, 3 etc. Draw lines 1, 1′, 2, 2′, 3, 3′ etc parallel to AB.

It is clear that triangle C11′, C22′, C33′, CBA etc. are all similar.

Similarly $C_5 = \frac{1}{2}$ CB, $55' = \frac{1}{2}$ AB = 0.5AB

Similarly C_4 = 0.4 CB, 44′ = 0.4 AB

Thus, each horizontal line becomes progressively shorter in length by $\frac{1}{10}$ AB.

Problem 7. Construct a diagonal scale of R.F. 1 : 500 to show metres and decimetres, and long enough to measure upto 70 metres. Measure a distance 53.4 metres on the scale.

Solution.

(*i*) R.F. = 1 : 500 (Given)

(*ii*) Length of the scale = L = R.F. × Maximum length to be measured

$$L = \frac{1}{500} \times 70 \times 100 \text{ cm} = 14 \text{ cm}$$

(*iii*) Draw a line AB of 14 cm length as shown in Fig. 5.8

(*iv*) Maximum length to be measured is 70 metres, therefore, divide the length of scale into 7 equal parts.

(*v*) Using geometrical construction, sub-divided the main parts into 10 equal sub-parts, each representing 1 decimetre.

(*vi*) Draw a line AC 2 cm long perpendicular to AB.

(*vii*) Divide AC into 10 equal parts and name the parts as 0, 1, 2, 3, ..., 10 from AC.

(*viii*) Draw horizontal lines from each part on AC to construct the diagonal.

(*ix*) Join C to the first sub-division from A on the main scale AB. Thus the first diagonal line is drawn.

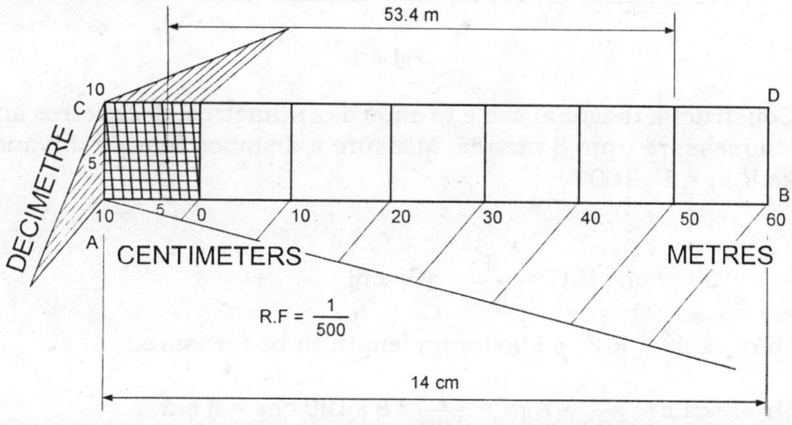

Fig. 5.8

(x) Similarly, draw the remaining diagonals parallel to the first diagonal into 10 equal parts.

(xi) Complete the scale and show 53.4 metres on the diagonal scale.

Problem 8. Construct a diagonal scale of R.F. = $\frac{1}{50,000}$ to show kilometres, hectometres, decametres, and long enough to measure upto 6 km. Measure a distance of 4 km, 6 hm, 4 dam on the scale.

Solution.

R.F. = 1/50000 or 1 : 50000 (Given)

Length of the scale = R.F. × Maximum length to be measured.

$$= \frac{1}{50000} \times 6 \text{ km}$$

$$= \frac{1}{50000} \times 6 \times 1000 \times 100 \text{ cm} = 12 \text{ cm}$$

Draw a rectangle of 12 × 2 cm as shown in Fig. 5.9. Divide the rectangle into 6 equal parts, each part representing 1 kilometre and follow the same method to draw the scale in problem 7.

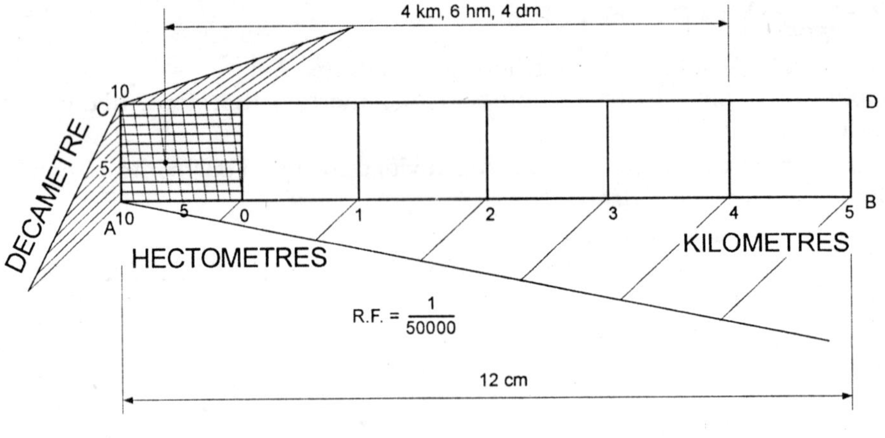

Fig. 5.9

Problem 9: Construct a diagonal scale to shown centimetres, decimetres and metres and long enough to measure upto 8 metres. Measure a distance 5 m , 6 dm and 3 cm on the scale and take R.F. = 1 : 100.

Solution.

R.F. = 1 : 100 or R.F. = $\frac{1}{100}$ (Given)

Length of scale = R.F. × Maximum length to be measured

Length of scale = $\frac{1}{100} \times 8 \text{ m} = \frac{1}{100} \times 8 \times 100 \text{ cm} = 8 \text{ cm}$

Draw a rectangle of 8 × 2 cm as shown in Fig. 5.10. Divide the rectangle into 8 equal parts, each part representing 1 meter and follows the same method to draw the scale as problem 7.

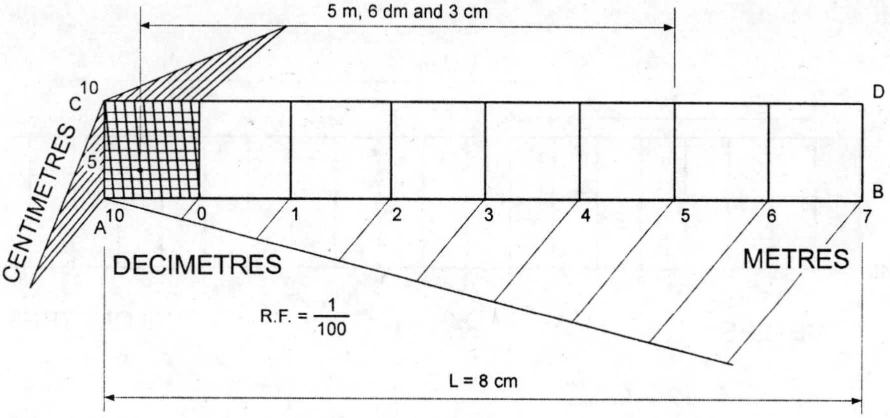

Fig. 5.10

Problem 10: On a road map a line 28 cm long represents a distance of 40 kilometres. Construct a diagonal scale for this representation to read upto 20 kilometres and hectometres. Indicate on a scale a length of 17 km and 7 km.

(December 2001, B.T.E. N. Delhi)

Solution: 28 cm = 40 km

$$1 \text{ cm} = \frac{28 \text{ cm}}{40 \text{ km}} = \frac{7 \text{ cm}}{10 \text{ km}} = \frac{1 \text{ cm}}{1.43 \text{ km}}$$

$$\text{R.F} = \frac{1 \text{ cm}}{1.43 \text{ km}} = \frac{1 \text{ cm}}{1.43 \times 1000 \times 100 \text{ cm}}$$

$$\text{R.F.} = \frac{1}{143000}$$

Now calculate the length of scale

= R.F. × Maximum length to be measured

$$= \frac{7}{10} \times 20 \text{ (Given)}$$

$$= \frac{7}{10 \times 1000 \times 100} \times 20 \times 1000 \times 100$$

= 14 cm

Draw a rectangle of 14 × 2 cm as shown in Fig. 5.11. Divide the rectangle into 20 equal parts, each part representing 1 kilometers and follows the same method to draw the scale as in problem 7.

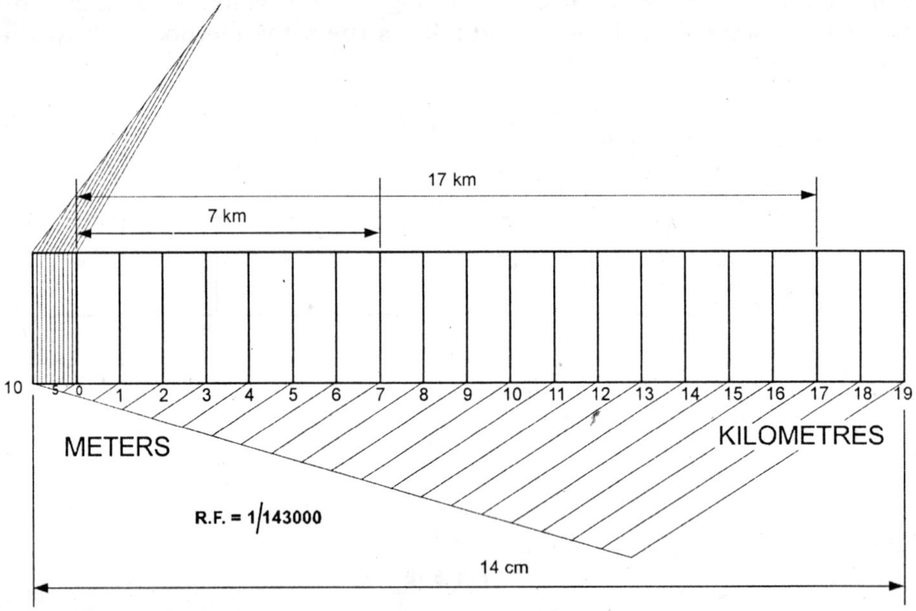

Fig. 5.11

Problem 11: The distance between to station is 240 km and its is represented on a map by a line 12 cm long. Find R.F. Draw a scale to measure 300 km. Show a distance of 267 km on the scale. **(December 2004, B.T.E. New Delhi)**

Solution: Calculate the R.F.

$$\text{R.F.} = \frac{\text{Length of an object on the drawing}}{\text{Actual length of the object}}$$

$$= \frac{12 \text{ cm}}{240 \text{ km}} = \frac{1 \text{ cm}}{20 \text{ km}}$$

$$= \frac{1}{20 \times 1000 \times 100} \text{ cm}$$

$$\text{R.F.} = \frac{1}{20{,}00{,}000}$$

In the above problem, maximum length to be measured is given 300 km. Therefore, calculate the length of the scale.

Length of the scale = R.F. × Maximum length to be measure.

$$= \frac{1}{2000000} \times 300 \times 1000 \times 100$$

$$= 15 \text{ cm}$$

Now draw a line AB of length 15 cm, and divide it into three equal parts, and also sub-divide the main part into 10 equal sub-parts, each part representing 1 hrs as shown in Fig. 5.12. Draw a line AC of suitable length which is perpendicular to AB and divide AC into 10 equal parts respectively. Then complete the scale and show 267 km on the scale as shown in Fig. 5.12

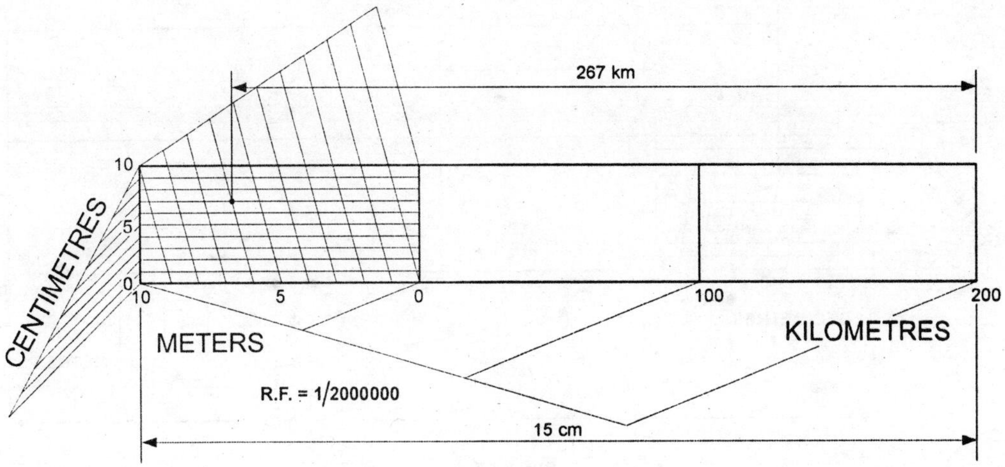

Fig. 5.12

Problem 12: A line of 20 cm long on a map represents a distance of 400 metres. Find the representative fraction of the map. Draw a diagonal scale so as to measure upto a single metre and long enough to measure a distance of 400 metres. Measure and mark distance of 356 metres and 108 metres on the scale. **(January 2009, B.T.E. New Delhi)**

Solution: Calculate the R.F.

$$\text{R.F.} = \frac{\text{Length of an object on the drawing}}{\text{Actual length of the object}}$$

$$20 \text{ cm} = 400 \text{ metres}$$

$$1 \text{ cm} = \frac{20 \text{ cm}}{400 \text{ metres}} = \frac{1 \text{ cm}}{20 \text{ metres}}$$

$$\text{R.F.} = \frac{1 \text{ cm}}{20 \text{ metres}} = \frac{1 \text{ cm}}{20 \times 100 \text{ cm}} = \frac{1}{2000}$$

$$\text{R.F.} = \frac{1}{2000}$$

Now calculate the length of scale

$$= \text{R.F.} \times \text{Maximum length to be measured}$$

$$= \frac{1}{2000} \times 400 \text{ metres (Given)}$$

$$= \frac{1}{2000} = 400 \times 100 = 20 \text{ cm.}$$

Draw a rectangle of 20 × 2 cm as shown in Fig. 5.13. Divide the rectangle into 4 equal parts, each part represent 100 metres and follow the same method to draw the scale as in problem 7.

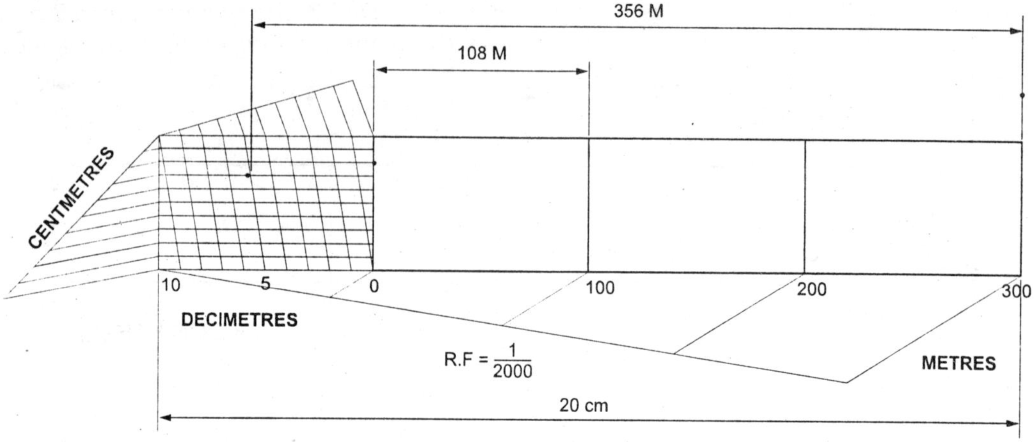

Fig. 5.13

Problem 13: Construct a diagonal scale to read metres, decimetres and centimetres for a R.F. of $\frac{1}{50}$ and long enough to measure upto 5 metres. Show on it a length of 2.34 metres, 3.67 metres and 4.44 metres. **(January 2009, B.T.E New Delhi)**

Solution:

$$\text{R.F.} = \frac{1}{50} \quad \text{(Given)}$$

Length of scale = R.F. × Maximum length to be measured.

$$= \frac{1}{50} \times 5 \text{ m} = \frac{1}{50} \times 5 \times 100 = 10 \text{ cm.}$$

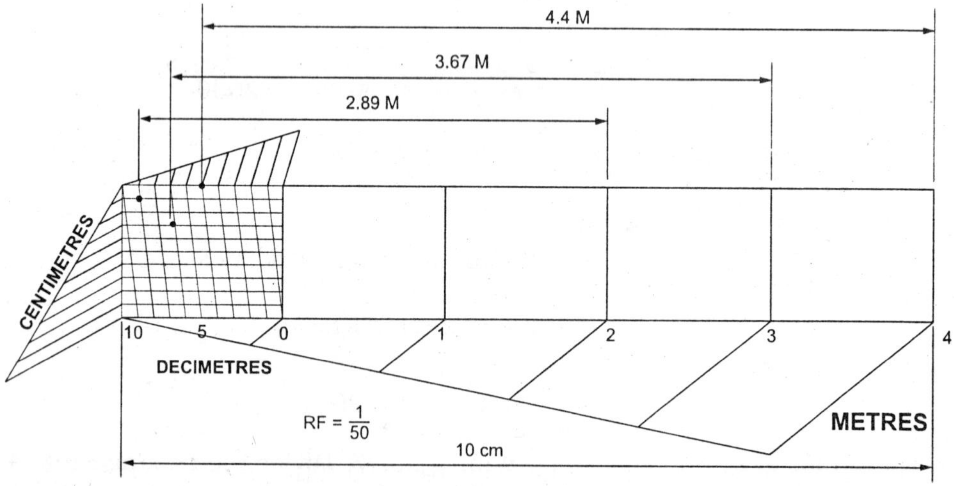

Fig. 5.14

Draw a rectangle of 10 × 2 cm as shown in Fig. 4.14. Divide the rectangle into 5 equal parts, each part representing 1 metre and follows the same method to draw the scale as in problem 7.

5.9 SCALE OF CHORDS

Scale of chords is used for measuring angles with great accuracy as shown in Fig. 5.15.

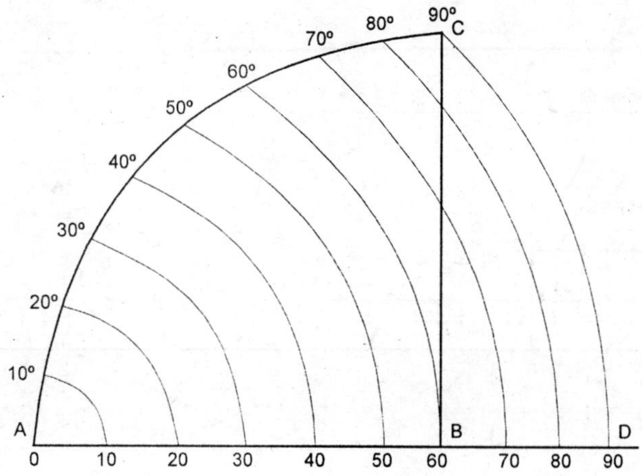

Fig. 5.15 Scale of Chords

5.10 VERNIER SCALE

A vernier scale is used to measure very small unit with great accuracy. Vernier scales are used in slide callipers and screw guage. It consists of a primary scale and a vernier, which slides on the primary scale. The fractional distance can be read from vernier scale as shown in Fig. 5.16.

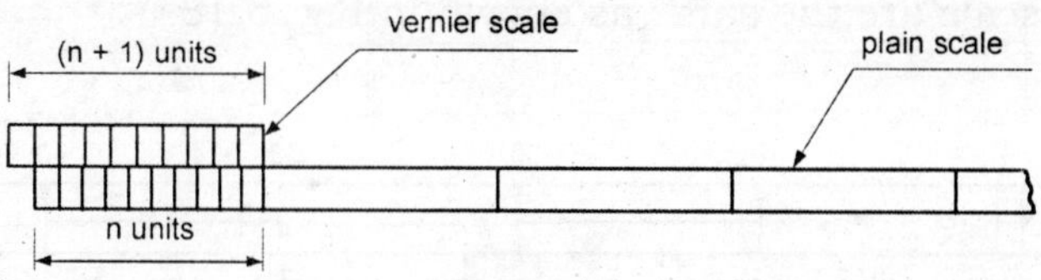

Fig. 5.16

Problem 14: Construct a vernier scale to read meters, decimeters and centimeters and long enough to measure up to 4 m. R.F. of the scale is 1/20. Mark on your scale a distance of 2.28 m. (Backward/Retrograde Vernier)

Solution: See Fig. 5.17

(i) Least Count = Smallest distance to be measured = 1 cm (given) = 0.01 m

(ii) L = R.F. × Maximum distance to be measured = (1/20) × 4 m = 20 cm

(iii) Draw a line of 20 cm length. Complete the rectangle of 20 cm × 1 cm. Divide this into 4 equal parts each representing 1 meter.

(iv) Sub-divide each part into 10 main scale divisions. Hence, 1 m.s.d. = 1 m/10 = 0.1 m = 1 dm.

(v) Take 11 division on main scale. Divide into 10 equal parts on the vernier scale. Hence 1 v.s.d. = 11 m.s.d/10 = 11 × 1 dm/10 = 0.11 m = 1.1 dm = 11 cm.

(vi) Mark 0, 55, 110 towards left from 0 on the vernier scale. The units of main divisions is meters, sub-divisions is decimeters and vernier divisions is centimeters.

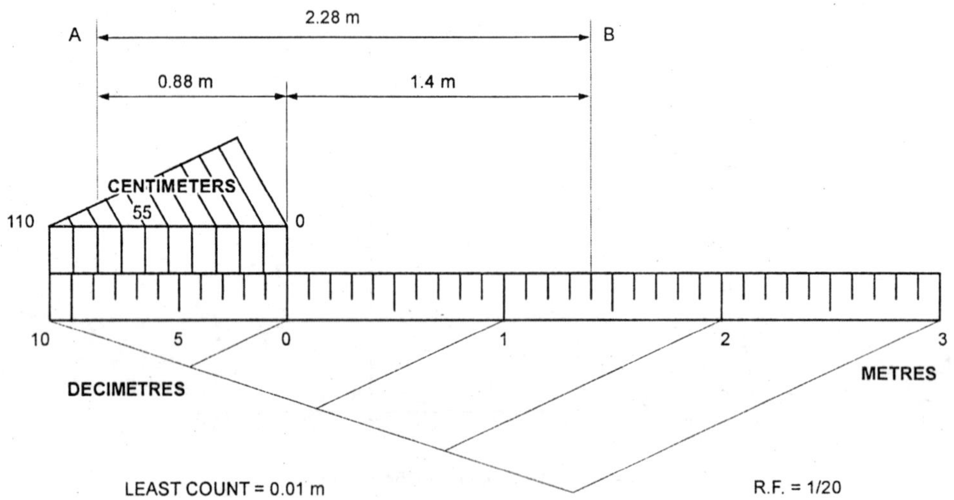

Fig. 5.17

5.11 COMPARATIVE SCALE

These scales are used to read different units of length. The comparative scales may either be plain or diagonal and may be constructed separately or one above the other. The R.F. of comparative scale are the same as shown in Fig. 5.18.

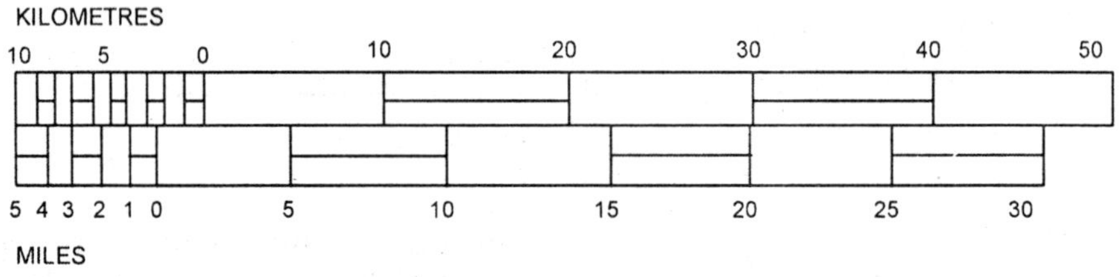

Fig. 5.18

5.12 ISOMETRIC SCALE

The isometric scale is used to measure the projected length. Isometric length are reduced upto 81.6% of their true length. Therefore, an isometric scale can be constructed which can measure the reduced length required for isometric projection as shown in Fig. 5.19.

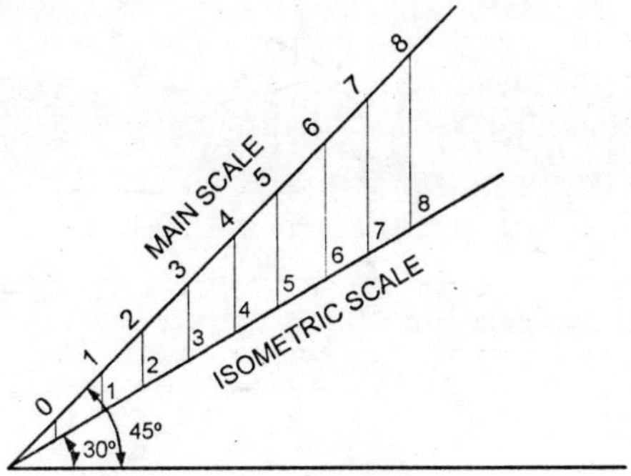

Fig. 5.19

EXERCISE

1. What do you mean by draftsman scale? Give the classification of scales?
2. What do you mean by plain scale?
3. What do you mean by R.F.?
4. Construct a plain scale of R.F. $\frac{1}{50000}$ to read kilometres and Hectometres, and long enough to measure a distance of 4 km and 7 hm on the scale.
5. Construct a scale of 1 : 1000 to show metres and long enough to measure upto 100 metres. Measure a distance of 63 m on the scale.
6. What is the difference between plain scale and diagonal scale.
7. Construct a diagonal scale to read km having spaces of 110 km and long enough to read upto 100 km. R.F. = $\frac{1}{4000000}$ Indicate a distance of 537 km on the scale.
8. Draw a vernier scale of metres when 1 cm represents 2.5 metres. Find the R.F. of this scale and shown a distance of 35.2 metres on this scale. **(January 2009, B.T.E. New Delhi)**

❑❑❑

IMPORTANT NOTES:

6

PROJECTION OF POINTS

6.1 THEORY OF PROJECTION

As we know engineering drawing is the graphic representation of real things. A young engineer should be able to read and write this language and must possess knowledge of its grammar and composition. Practically, the drawing of an object is made of different views of the object taken by the observer from different positions by means of projections.

If a straight line is drawn from the various points on the contour of an object to meet a plane, the figure obtained on the plane is called to projection of an object and object is said to be projected on the plane. In other words, we can say that, projecting the image of an object to the plane of projection is known as projection. Therefore, different views of an object are drawn by projection. A drawing of an object should consist of four imaginary things.

1. Object
2. Projector
3. Plane of projection
4. Observer's eye.

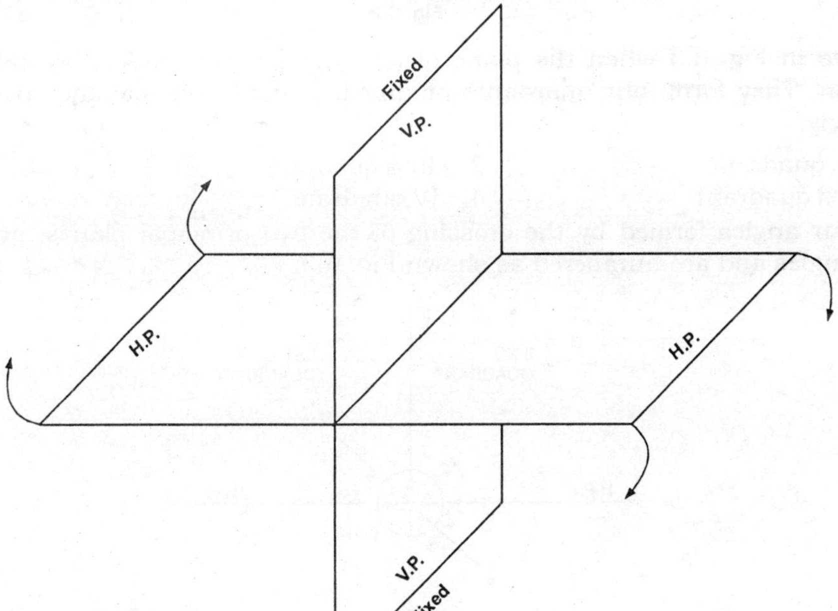

Fig. 6.1

In engineering drawing, two principal planes are used to get the projection of an object, the vertical plane denoted by (V.P.) and horizontal plane denoted by (H.P.) as shown in Fig. 6.1. They intersect each other at right angles called axis of the plane. The vertical plane of projection is always infront of the observer. The projection on vertical plane is known as front view or elevation. The other plane is the horizontal plane of projection is known as the (H.P.) The projection on the H.P. is called the top view or plan. The view obtained by viewing object form right side is called right side view or right end view. A plane perpendicular to both H.P. and V.P. is called profile plane (P.P).

The right side view is always on the right to the front view. If the object is viewed from left on profile plane then the view is known as left side view or left end view. Fig 6.2 shows projection by folding the top and right side planes in line with the front plane.

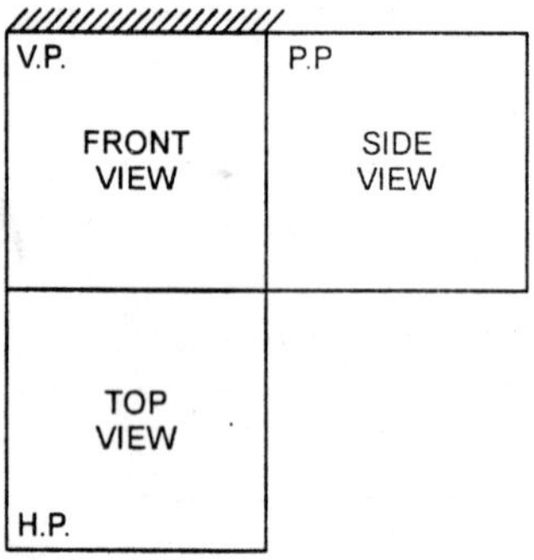

Fig. 6.2

Observe in Fig. 6.3 when the plane of projection are extended beyond the line of intersection. They form four quardants or dihedral angles on reference planes (V.P. & H.P.) namely:

1. Ist quadrant
2. IInd quadrant
3. IIIrd quadrant
4. IV quadrant.

The four angles formed by the crossing of the two principal planes, are called the dihedral angles and are numbered as shown Fig. 6.3.

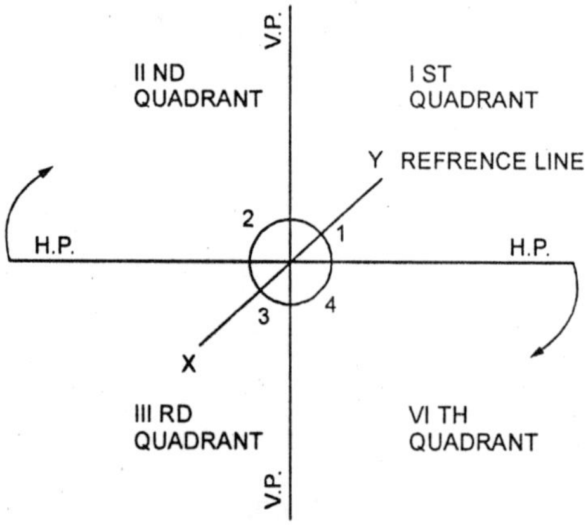

Fig. 6.3 Plane of Projection

Note: The standard practice of rotation of planes is to keep the V.P. fixed and horizontal plane is rotated in clockwise direction to bring it in vertical plane.

- The figure obtained in Ist quadrant is known as Ist angle projection.
- The figure obtained in IInd quadrant is known as IInd angle projection.
- The figure obtained in IIIrd quadrant is known as IIIrd angle projection.
- The figure obtained in IVth quadrant is known as IVth angle projection.

6.2 PROJECTION OF POINTS

A point is a dimension less entity that is represented by a single dot. The position of a point may be suited in any one of the quadrant to visualized the position of a point. The points are denoted by capital letters such as, *P*, *Q*, *R* etc. Their positions on horizontal plane by lower case letters *p*, *q*, *r* ... etc. and their position on vertical plane by p', q', r' ... etc. The student should carefully study the following rules relating to the projection of points.

6.3 POSITION OF POINTS IN VARIOUS QUADRANTS (Fig. 6.4)

(i) Ist quadrant Above H.P. and infront V.P.
(ii) IInd quadrant Above H.P. and behind V.P.
(iii) IIIrd quadrant Below H.P. and behind V.P.
(iv) IVth quadrant Below H.P. and infront V.P.

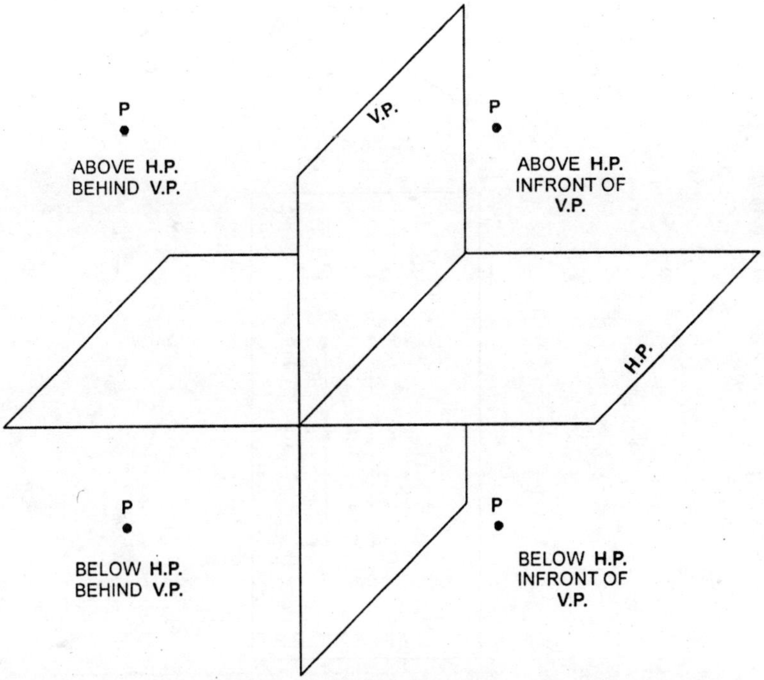

Fig. 6.4

6.4 WHEN POINT P IS IN THE IST QUADRANT

Let a point P is at a distance "*a*" above horizontal plane (H.P.) and "*b*" infront of the vertical plane (V.P.). Its front view *p′* will be above the axis XY at a distance "*a*" on the vertical plane and the top view p on horizontal plane at a distance "b", as shown in Fig. 6.5 (i). After getting projection on horizontal plane and vertical plane, horizontal plane is rotated by 90° in clockwise direction to bring it in line with the vertical plane as shown in Fig. 6.5 (ii).

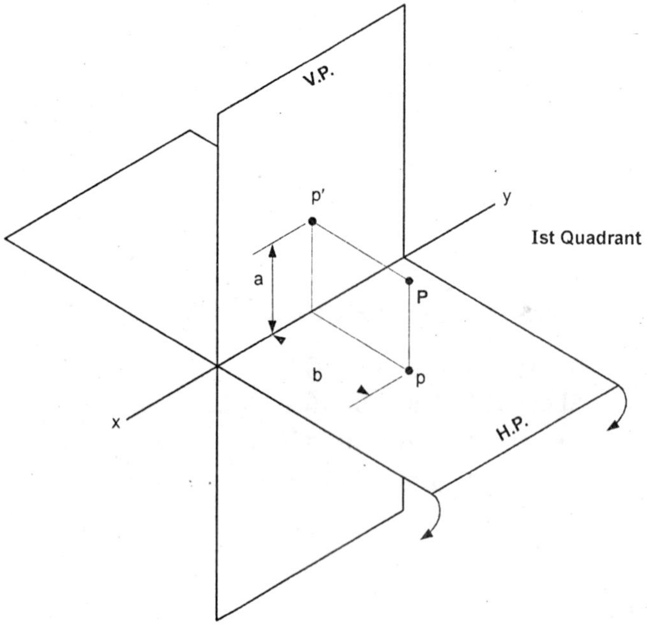

Fig. 6.5 (i)

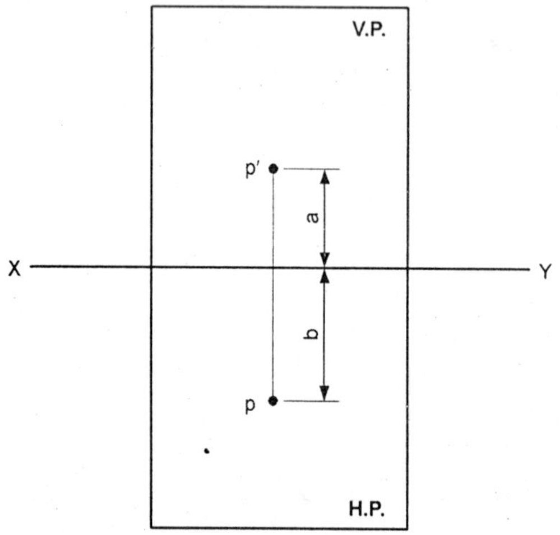

Fig. 6.5 (ii)

6.5 WHEN POINT P IS IN IInd QUADRANT

Let a point P is at a distance "*a*" above horizontal plane (H.P.) and "*b*" behind the vertical plane (V.P.). The projections *p* and *p'* are obtained by extending projectors on horizontal plane as well as on vertical plane as shown in Fig. 6.6 (i). After getting projection on both the planes, horizontal plane is rotated by 90° in the clockwise direction. In IInd quadrant front view *p'* at a distance "*a*" and top view p at a distance "*b*" are seen above the axis XY in a same line as shown in Fig. 6.6 (ii).

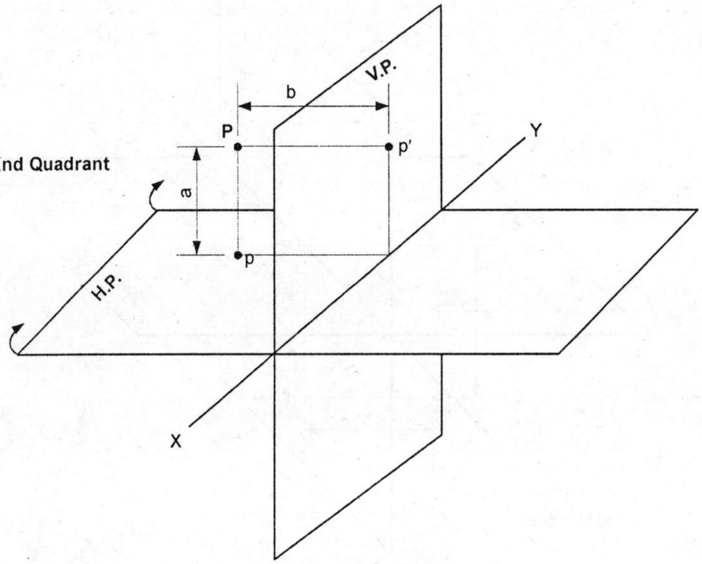

Fig. 6.6 (i)

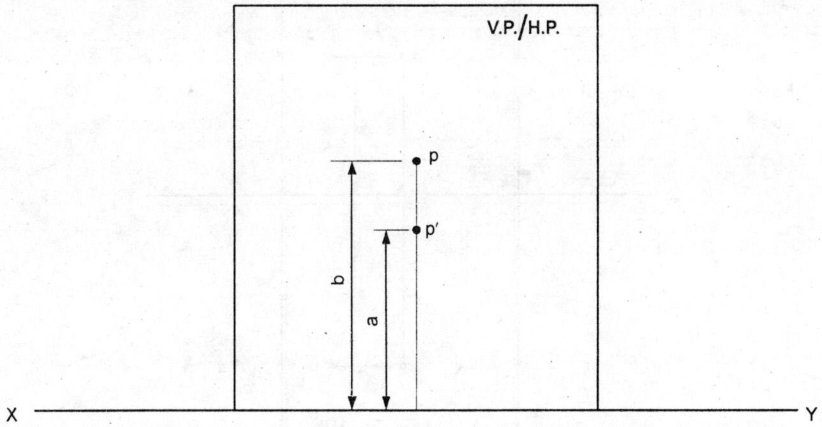

Fig. 6.6 (ii)

6.6 WHEN POINT P IS IN THE IIIRD QUADRANT

In IIIrd quadrant, the point *P* is below the horizontal plane and behind the vertical plane. Its front view *p′* is in the vertical plane (V.P.) and top view *p* is in the horizontal plane (H.P.) as shown in Fig. 6.7 (i)

After getting projection on horizontal plane and vertical plane, horizontal plane is rotated by 90° to bring it in line with the vertical plane as shown in Fig. 6.7 (ii).

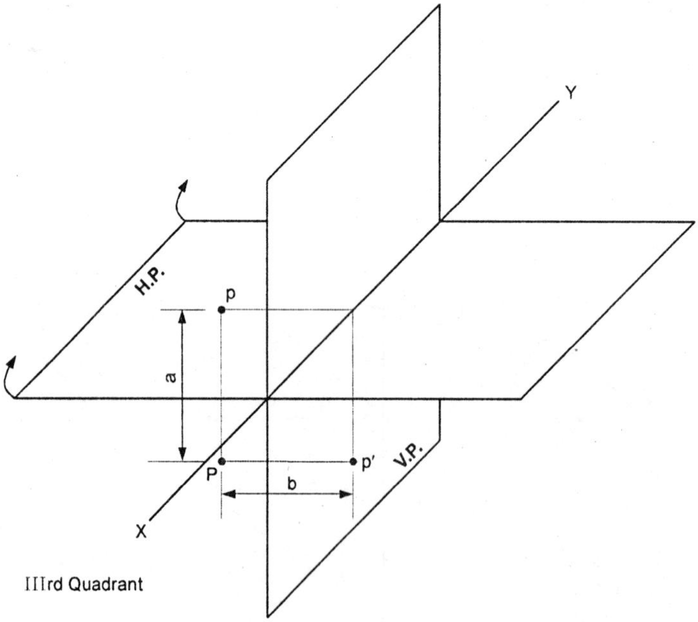

Fig. 6.7 (i)

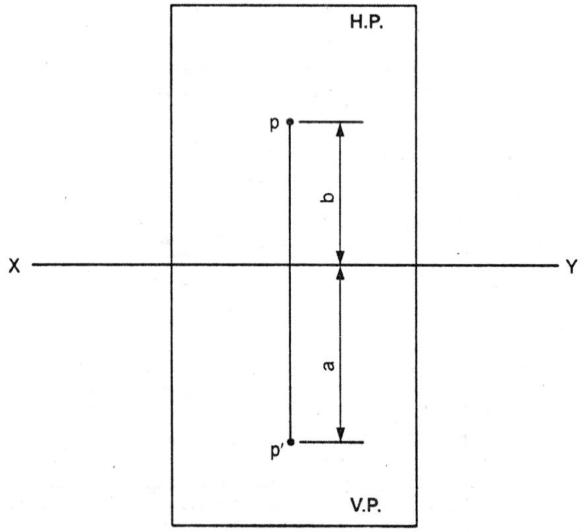

Fig. 6.7 (ii)

6.7 WHEN POINT P IS IN THE IVTH QUADRANT

Let the point *P* is below the horizontal plane and infront of the vertical plane. The projections *p* and *p'* are obtained by extending projectors on horizontal plane (H.P.) and vertical plane as shown in Fig. 6.8 (i). The horizontal plane is rotated in clockwise direction to bring it with the vertical plane as shown in Fig. 6.8 (ii).

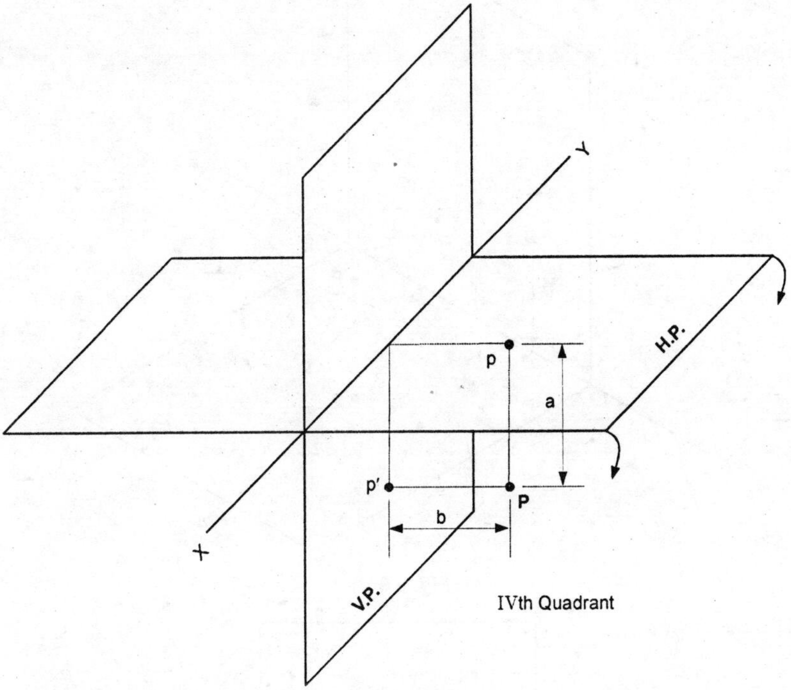

Fig. 6.8 (i)

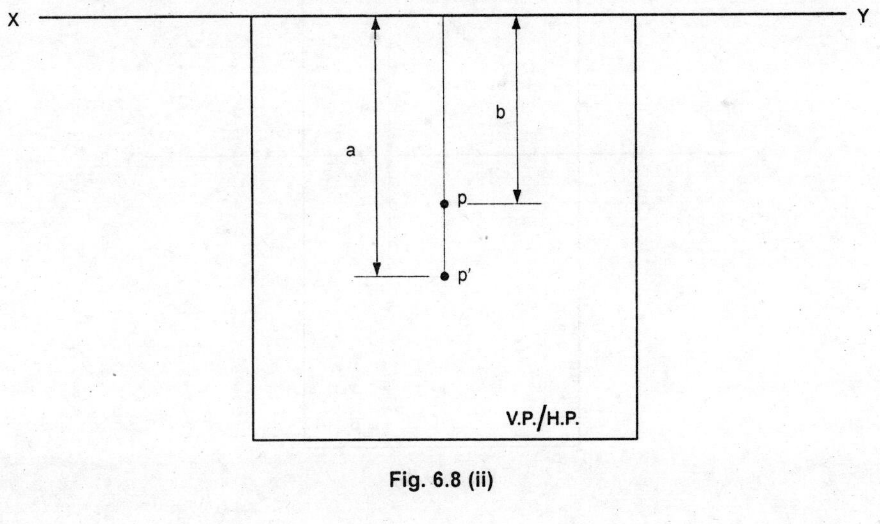

Fig. 6.8 (ii)

Problem 1. Draw the projection of a point P, 20 mm infront of the vertical plane and 15 mm above the horizontal plane.

Solution. See Fig. 6.9 (i & ii).

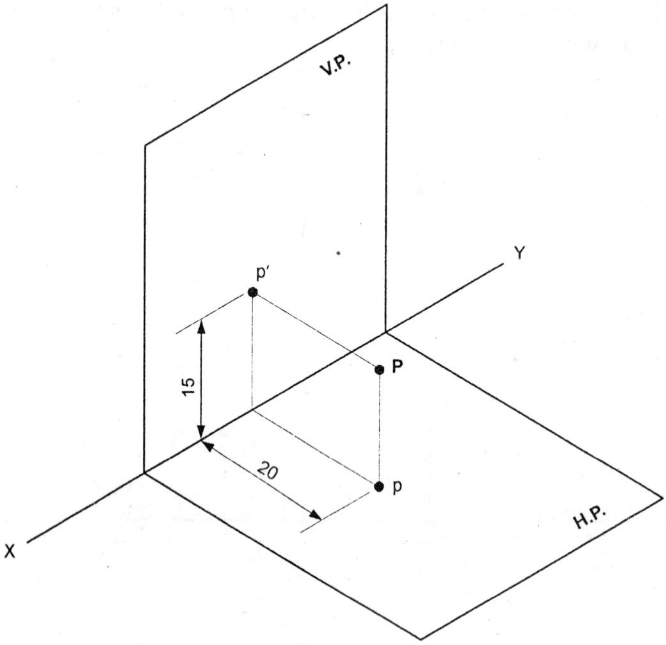

Fig. 6.9 (i)

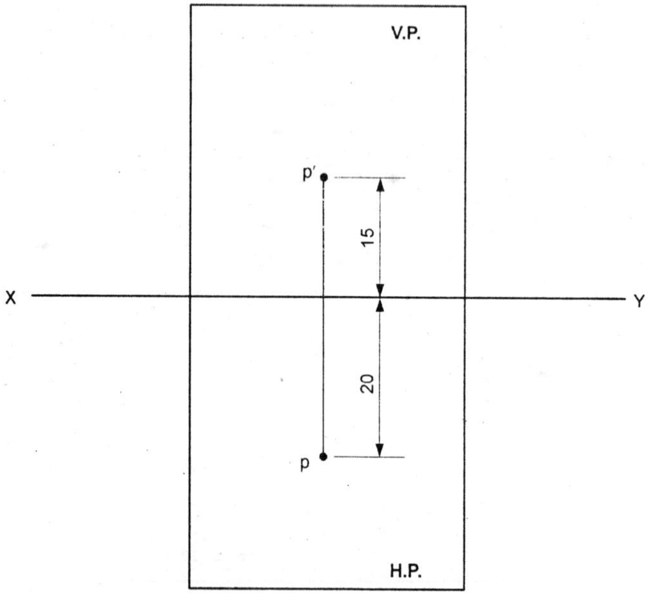

Fig. 6.9 (ii)

Problem 2. Draw the projection of a point P when its is 12 mm above the horizontal plane and 15 mm infront of the vertical plane.
Solution. See Fig. 6.10 (i & ii).

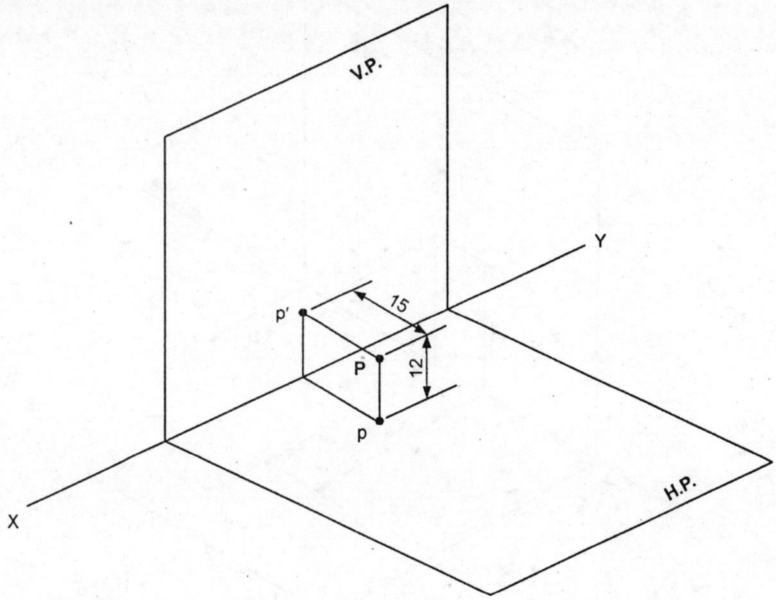

Fig. 6.10 (i)

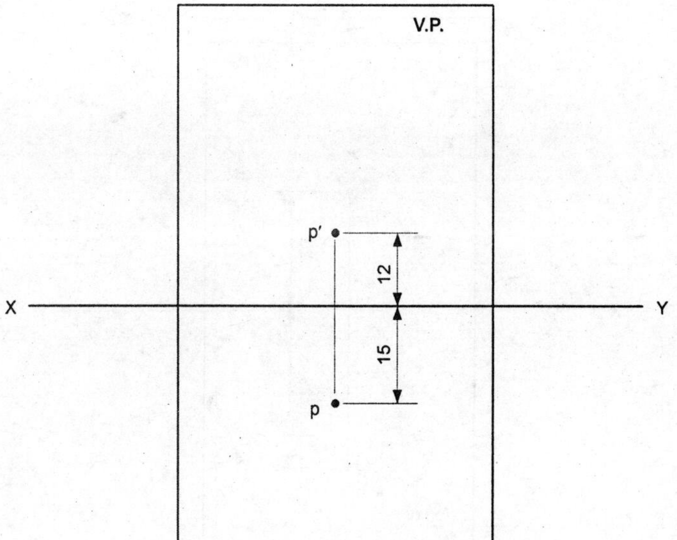

Fig. 6.10 (ii)

Problem 3. A point Q is 20 mm above H.P. and 25 mm infront of V.P. Draw its projection.
Solution. See Fig. 6.11 (i & ii).

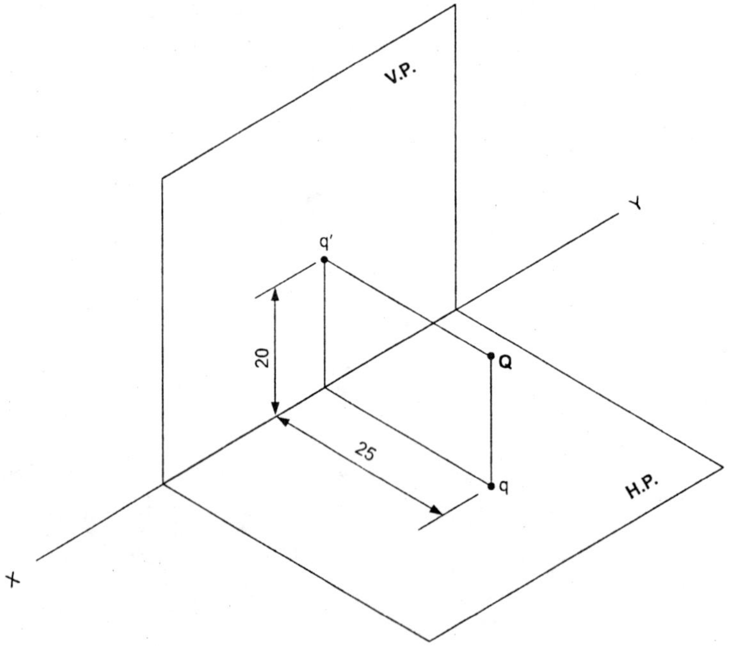

Fig. 6.11 (i)

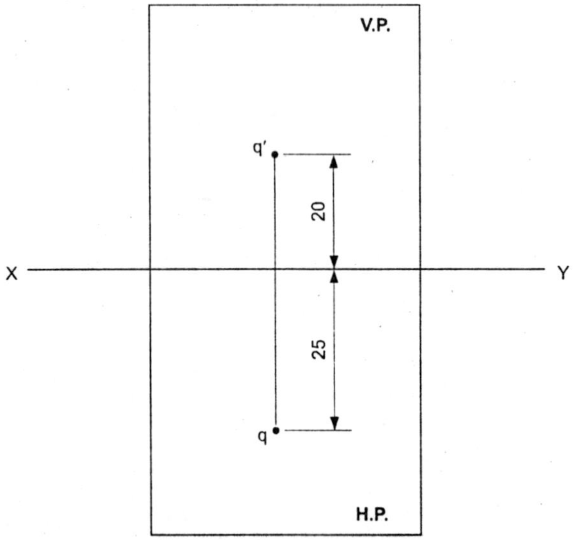

Fig. 6.11 (ii)

Problem 4. A point R is 20 mm infront of V.P. and 45 mm above the H.P. Draw the front view and top view of the point.

Solution. See Fig. 6.12 (i & ii).

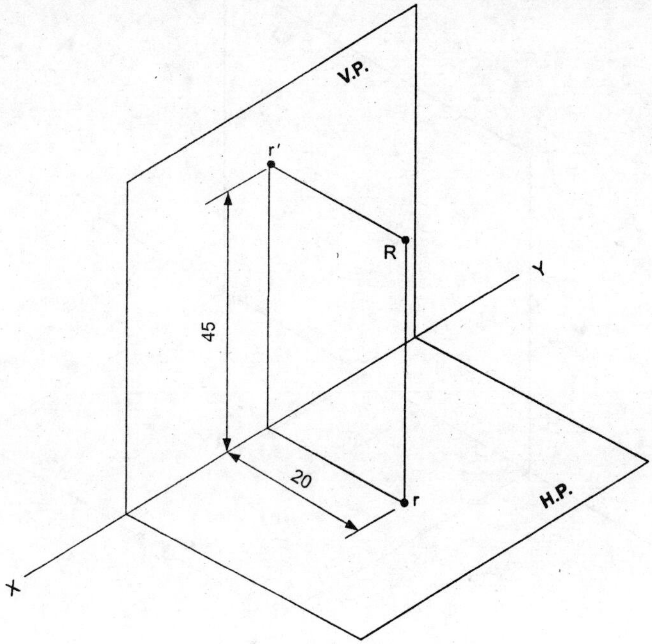

Fig. 6.12 (i)

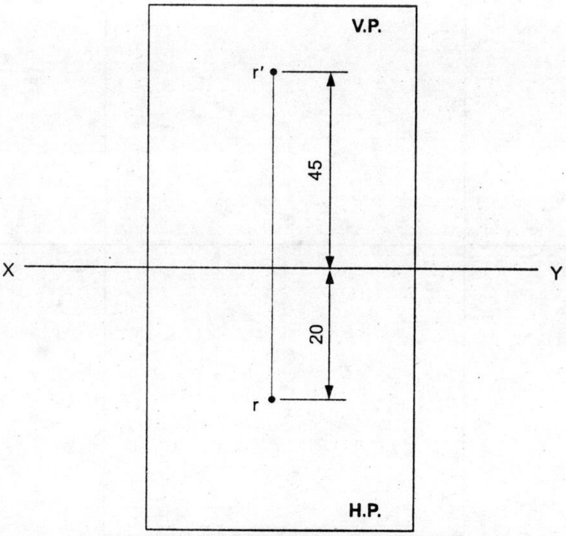

Fig. 6.12 (ii)

Problem 5. Draw the front view and top view of a point Q which is touching H.P. and 20 mm from V.P.

Solution. See Fig. 6.13 (i & ii).

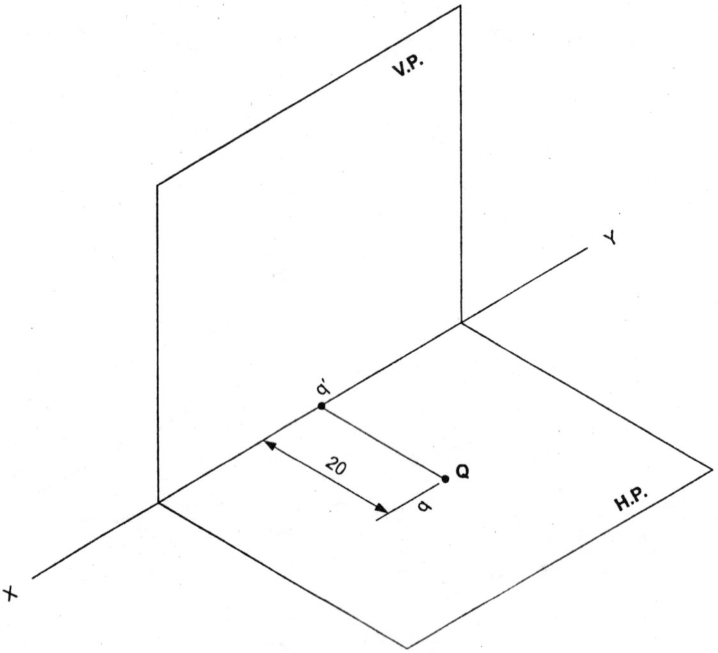

Fig. 6.13 (i)

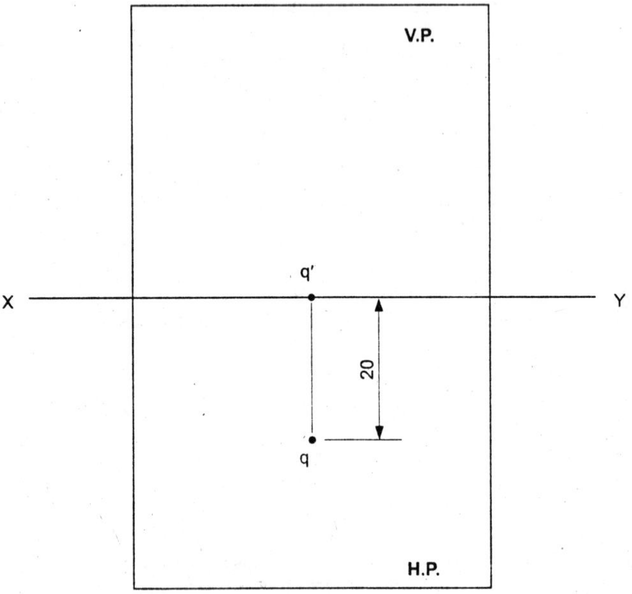

Fig. 6.13 (ii)

Problem 6. A point P is 30 mm behind the vertical plane and 25 mm above the horizontal plane. Draw its projection.

Solution. See Fig. 6.14 (i & ii).

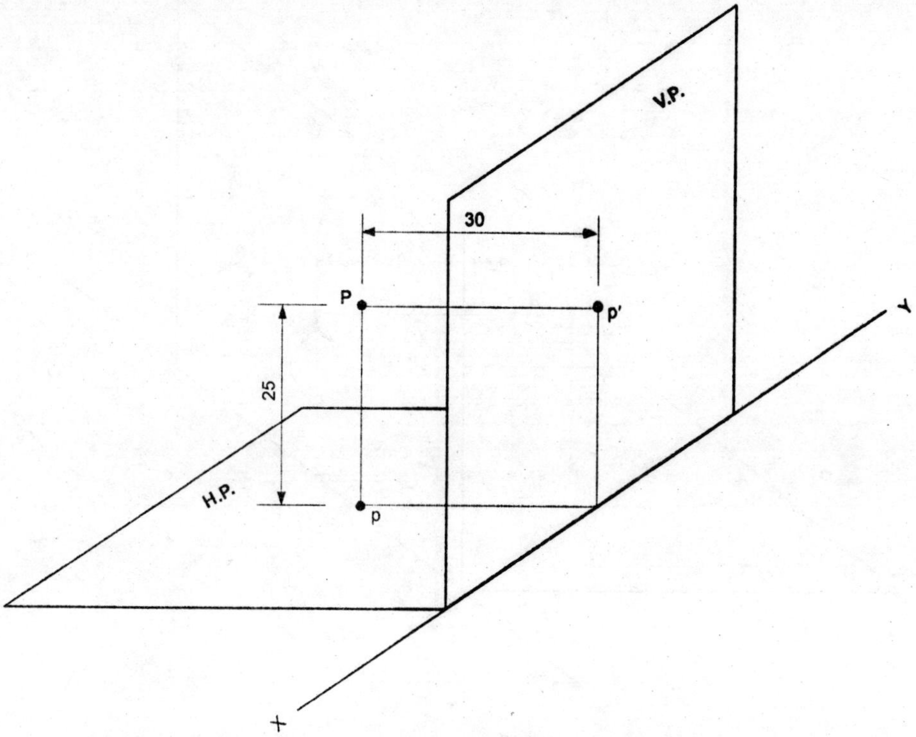

Fig. 6.14 (i)

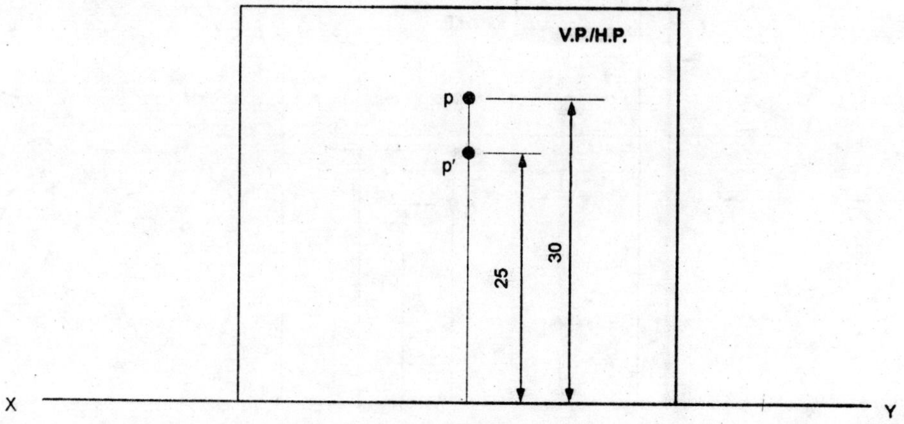

Fig. 6.14 (ii)

Problem 7. Draw the projection of a point R, 30 mm behind the V.P. and 20 mm above the H.P.

Solution. See Fig. 6.15 (i & ii).

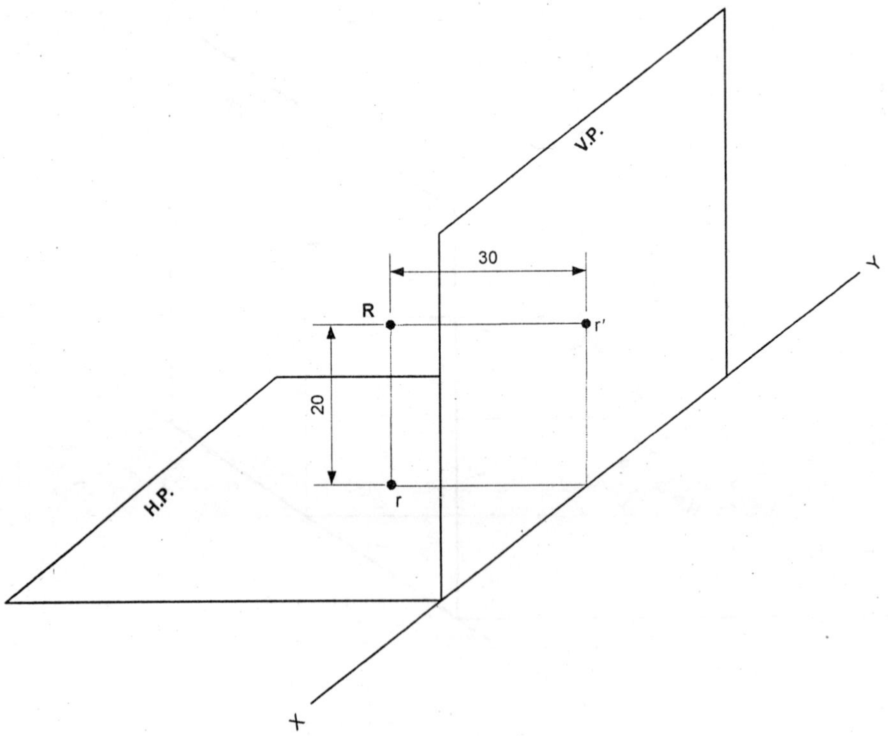

Fig. 6.15 (i)

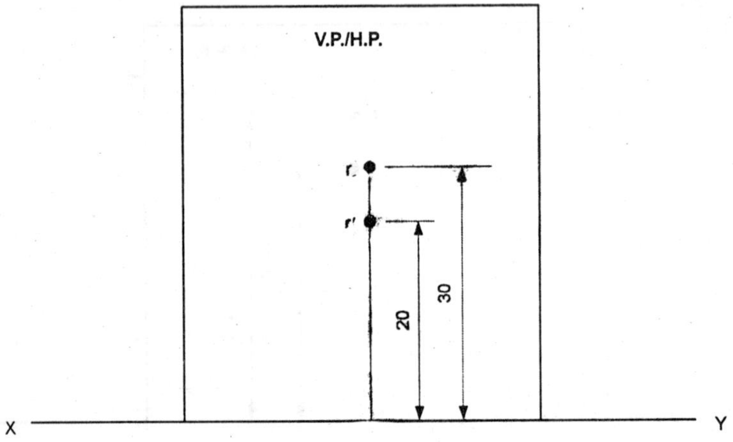

Fig. 6.15 (ii)

Problem 8. A point Q is 30 mm behind the V.P. and 20 mm below the H.P. Draw its projection.

Solution. See Fig. 6.16 (i & ii).

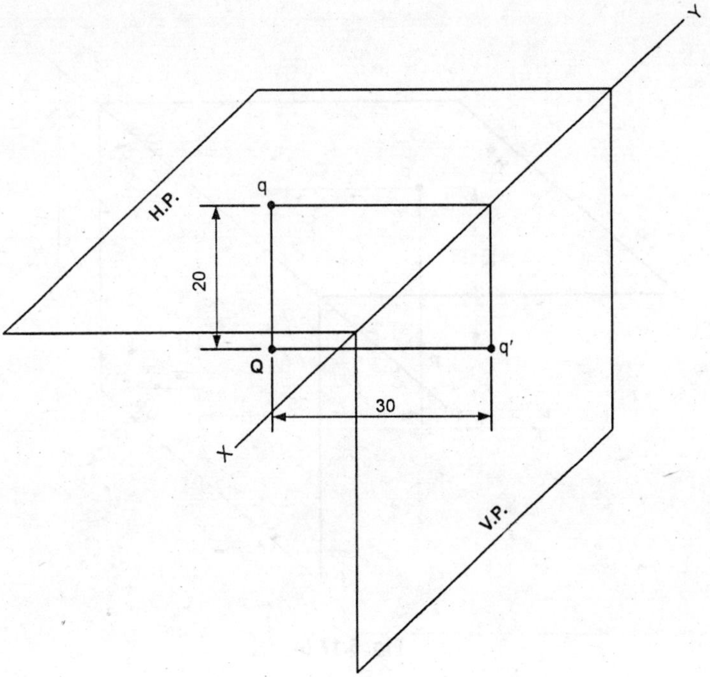

Fig. 6.16 (i)

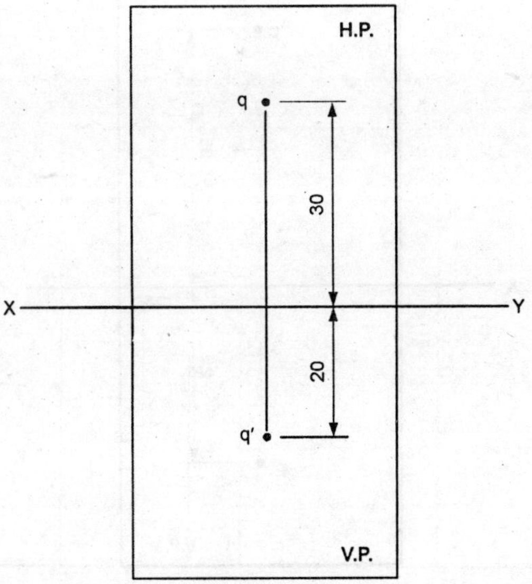

Fig. 6.16 (ii)

Problem 9. A point P is 25 mm below the horizontal plane and 35 mm behind the vertical plane. Draw its projection.

Solution. See Fig. 6.17 (i & ii).

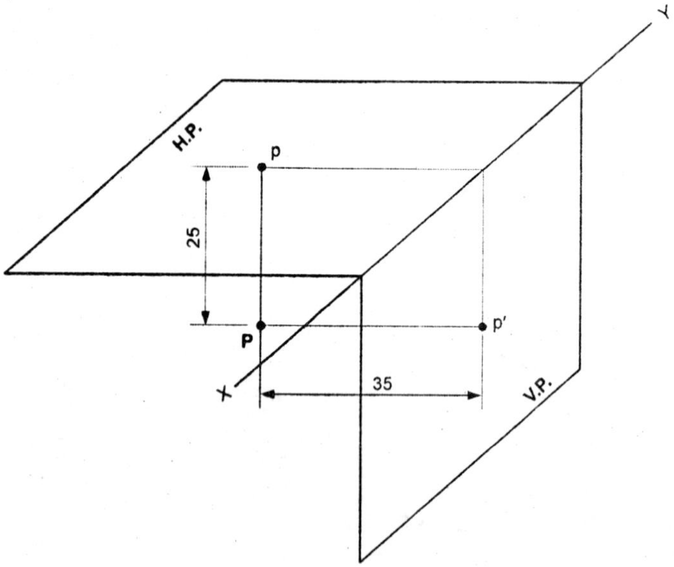

Fig. 6.17 (i)

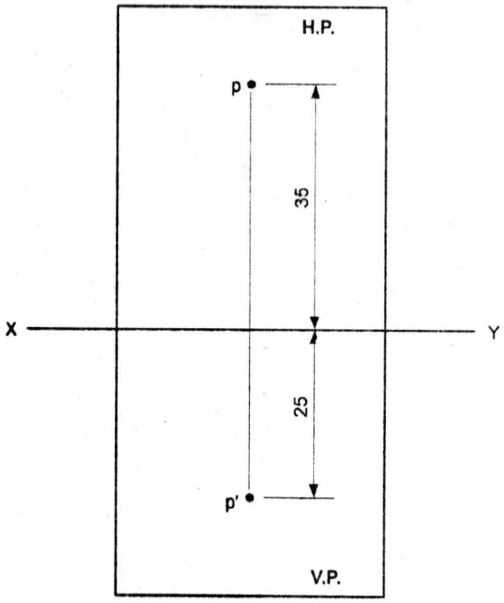

Fig. 6.17 (ii)

Problem 10. A point P is 20 mm below H.P. and lies in third quadrant. Its shortest distance from XY is 40 mm. Draw its top view and front view.

Solution. See Fig. 6.18 (i & ii).

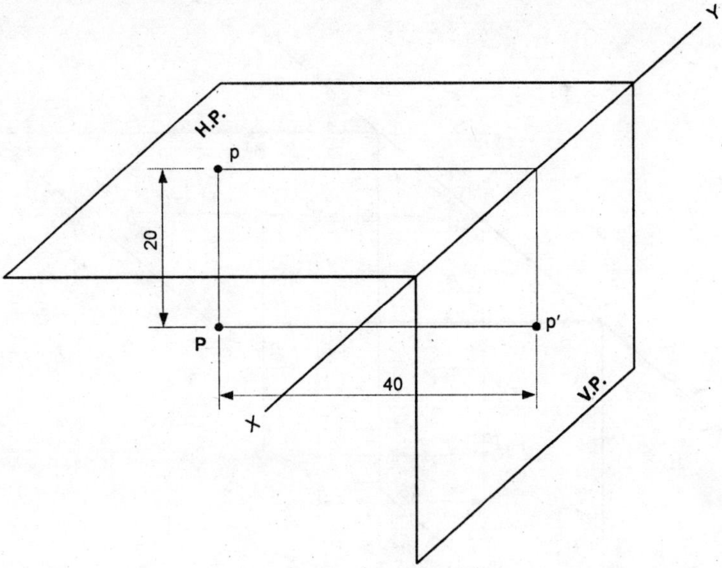

Fig. 6.18 (i)

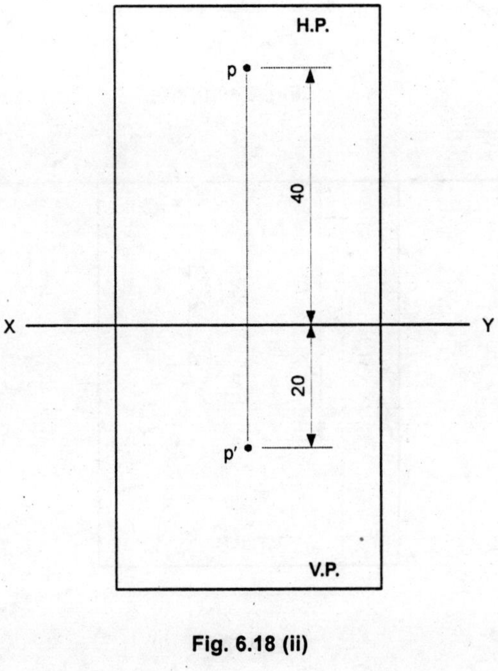

Fig. 6.18 (ii)

Problem 11. A point P is 35 mm below the H.P. and 25 mm infront of the V.P. Draw its projection.

Solution. See Fig. 6.19 (i & ii).

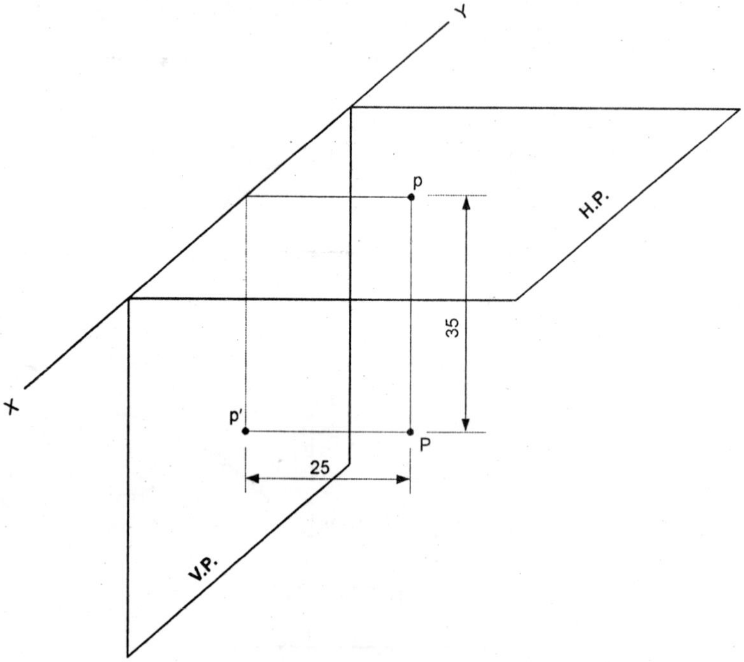

Fig. 6.19 (i)

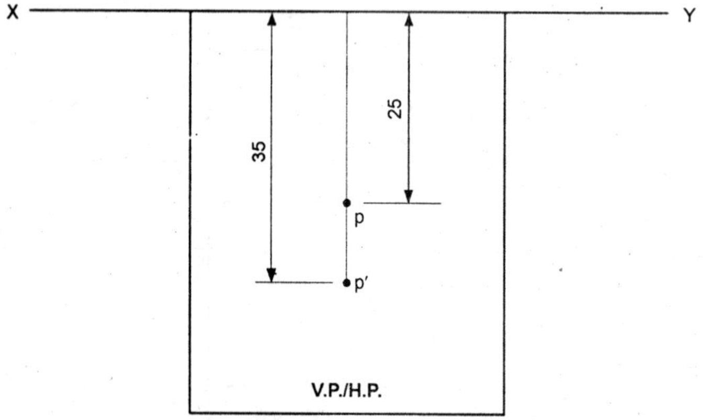

Fig. 6.19 (ii)

Problem 12. A point P is 20 mm above the H.P. and 30 mm infront of the V.P. Another point Q is 30 mm below the H.P. and 50 mm behind the V.P. Draw the projections of these points taking the distance between the ends projectors as 70 mm.

Solution. See Fig. 6.20.

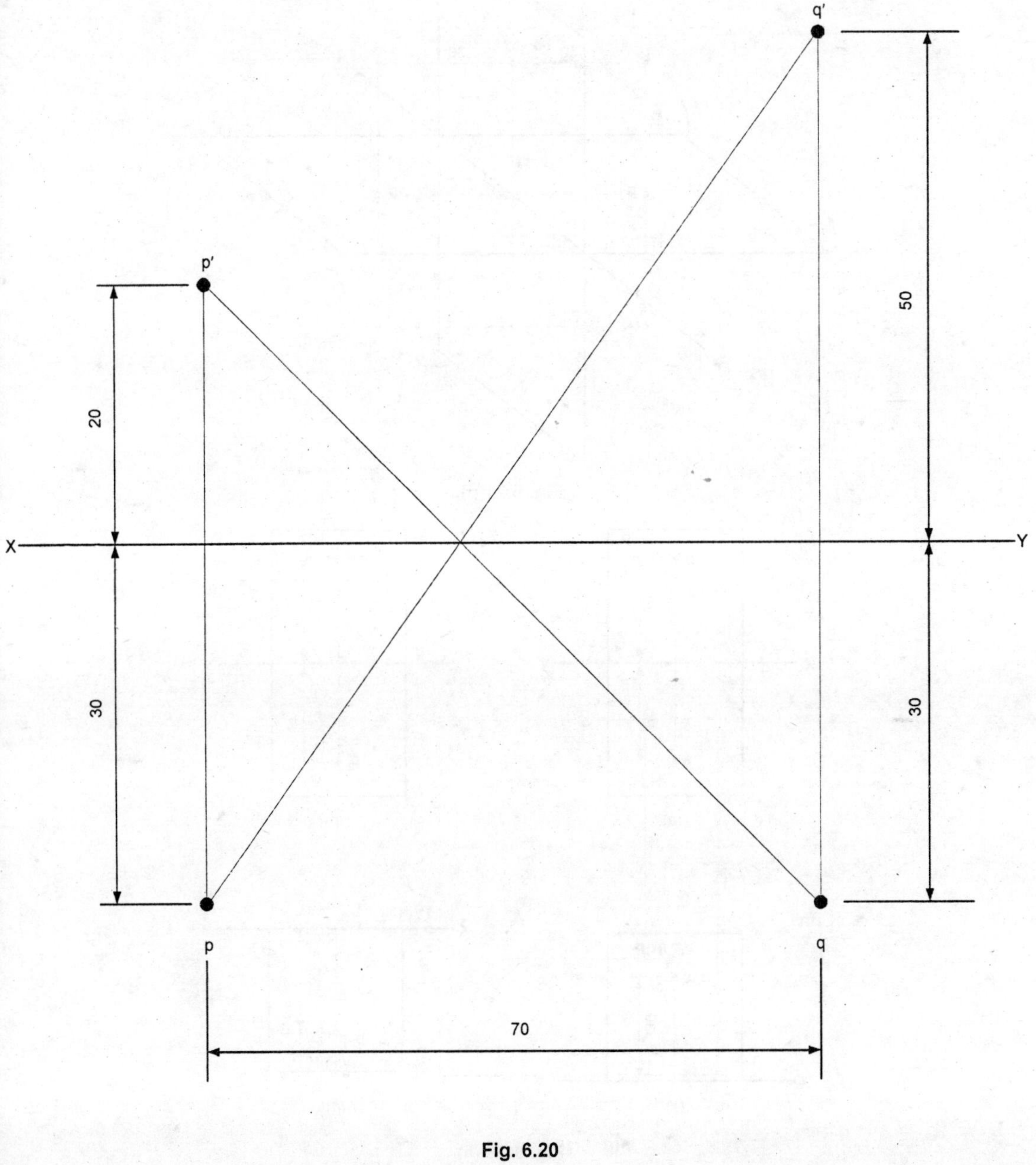

Fig. 6.20

Problem 13. A point P is 30 from both the reference planes. Draw its projections in all possible positions.

Solution. See Fig. 6.21 (i & ii).

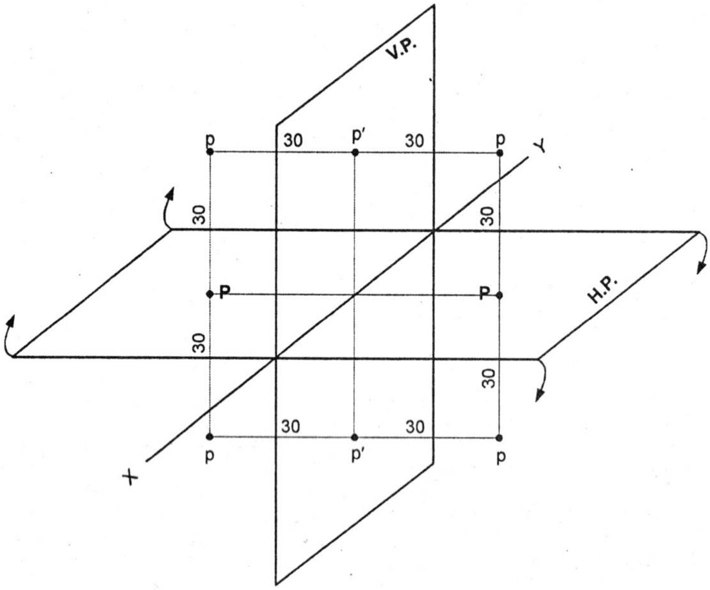

Fig. 6.21 (i)

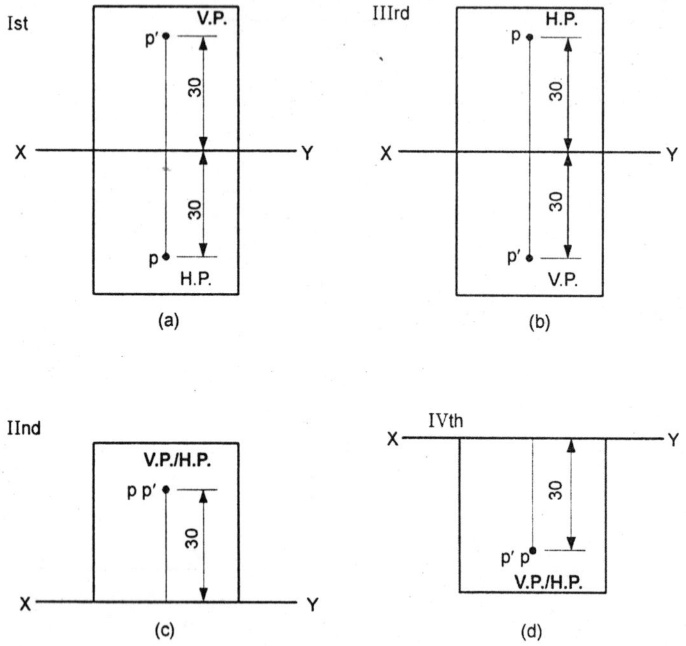

Fig. 6.21 (ii)

EXERCISE

1. How you define the terms point ?
2. Name the two principal planes of projection.
3. Draw the projections of a point Q when it is
   (a) 15 mm above the H.P. and 25 mm in front of the V.P.
   (b) 30 mm above the H.P. and 15 mm infront of the V.P.
   (c) 25 mm above the H.P. and 15 mm behind the V.P.
   (d) 35 mm below the H.P. and 20 mm behind the V.P.
   (e) 30 mm below the H.P. and 30 mm behind the V.P.
   (f) in the V.P. and 25 mm above the H.P.
   (g) in the H.P. and 25 mm behind the V.P.
4. State the position of the following points with respect to the planes of projections, as shown in Fig. 6.22.

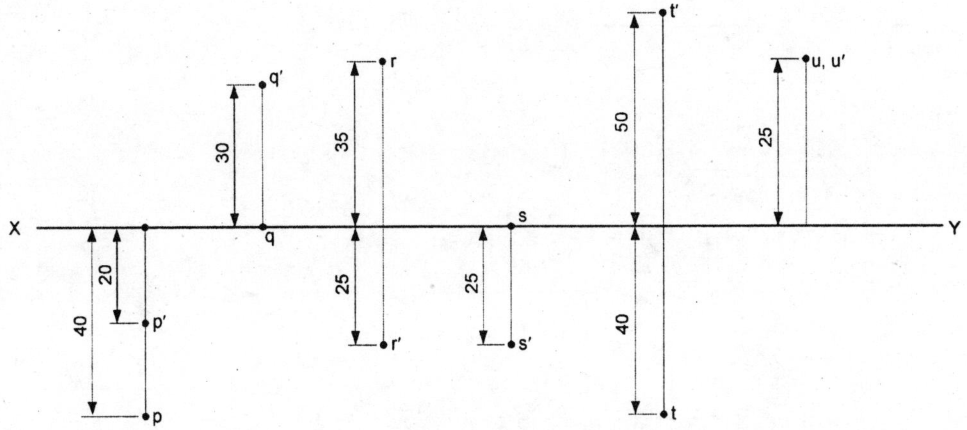

Fig. 6.22

5. A point P is in H.P. and 25 mm in front of V.P. Another point Q is also in H.P. and behind V.P. The distance between their end projectors is 50 mm. Draw its projections when the line joining their planes makes as angle of 45° with reference line.

❑❑❑

IMPORTANT NOTES:

7

PROJECTION OF LINES

7.1 INTRODUCTION

A straight line is the shortest distance between the two given points. It has a length without a thickness. The projections of a straight line are obtained by joining the two end points. A line may project either in true length (TL), for shortened depending on its relationship to the principal plane on which the view is projected as shown in Fig. 7.1.

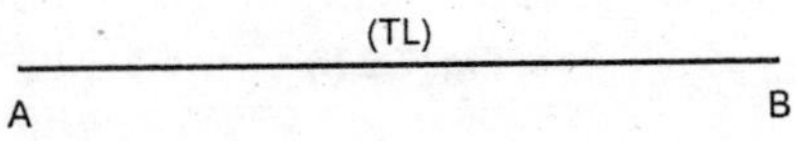

Fig. 7.1

7.2 POSITION OF STRAIGHT LINES

The projection of a straight line in different positions are as follows:

1. Line parallel to one or both the plane, (H.P & V.P)
2. Line contained by one or both the plane, (H.P. & V.P)
3. Line perpendicular to both the plane, (H.P. & V.P.)
4. Line inclined to one reference plane and parallel to the other.
5. Line inclined to both the plane, (H.P. & V.P.).

In first angle projection, a line is assumed to be placed in first quadrant. The projection of the straight line in the above positions are discussed in this chapter.

7.3 LINE PARALLEL TO ONE OR BOTH THE PLANE (H.P. & V.P.)

Case I: **Line parallel to the vertical plane (V.P.)** consider a line PQ, which is inclined to the horizontal plane and parallel to the vertical plane as shown in Fig. 7.2(i). Its front view p', q', equal to its true length (TL). The top view projected onto horizontal plane is also a line and will be in reduced length as shown in Fig. 7.2 (ii).

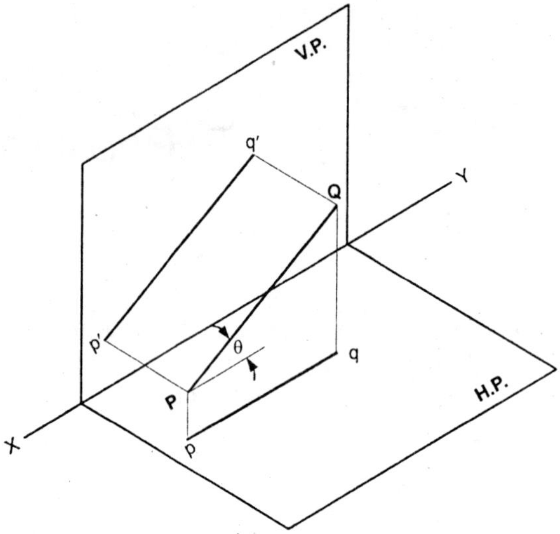

Fig. 7.2 (i)

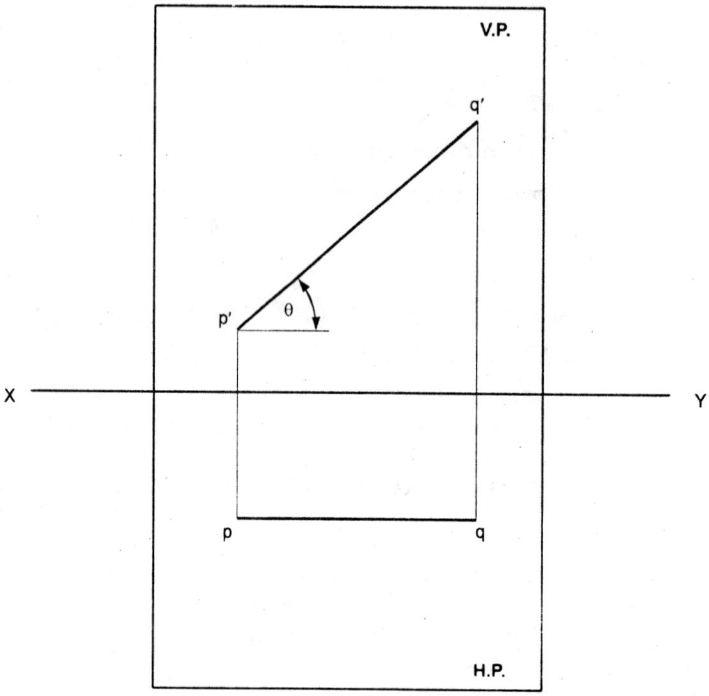

Fig. 7.2 (ii)

***Case II:* Line parallel to the horizontal plane (H.P.)** Consider a line PQ which is inclined to vertical plane and parallel to the horizontal plane as shown in Fig. 7.3 (i). Its top view *p*, *q* is projected onto the horizontal plane which is inclined at an angle of θ to the vertical plane, will be equal to its true length (TL). The front view projected onto vertical plane is also a line and will be in reduced length as shown in Fig. 7.3 (ii).

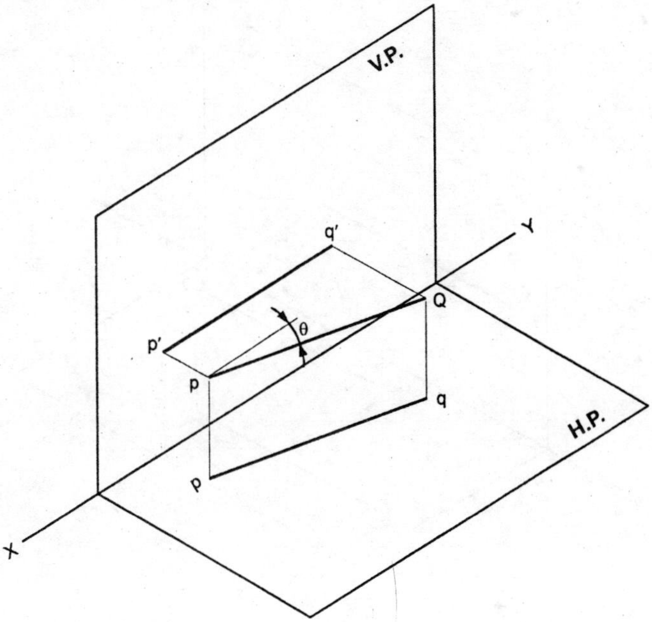

Fig. 7.3 (i)

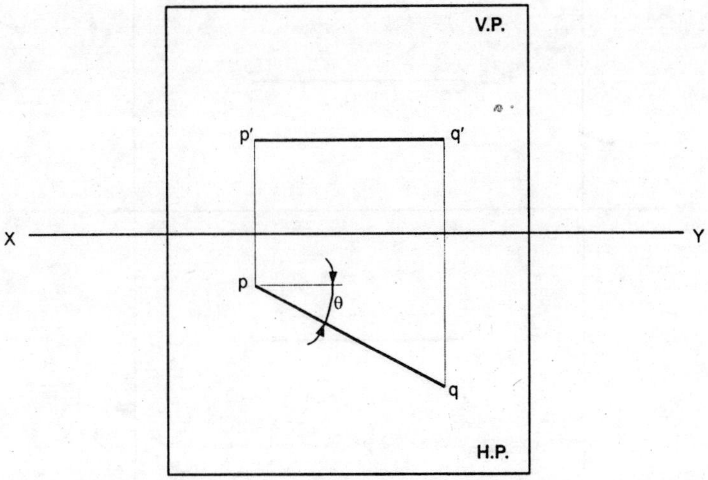

Fig. 7.3 (ii)

Case III: **Line parallel to horizontal plane and vertical plane (H.P. & V.P.):** Consider a line PQ which is parallel to both the reference planes as shown in Fig. 7.4 (i). Its front view is projected onto vertical plane which is a line having true length. Its top view is also in true length and parallel to reference line XY which is projected onto horizontal plane as shown in Fig. 7.4 (ii).

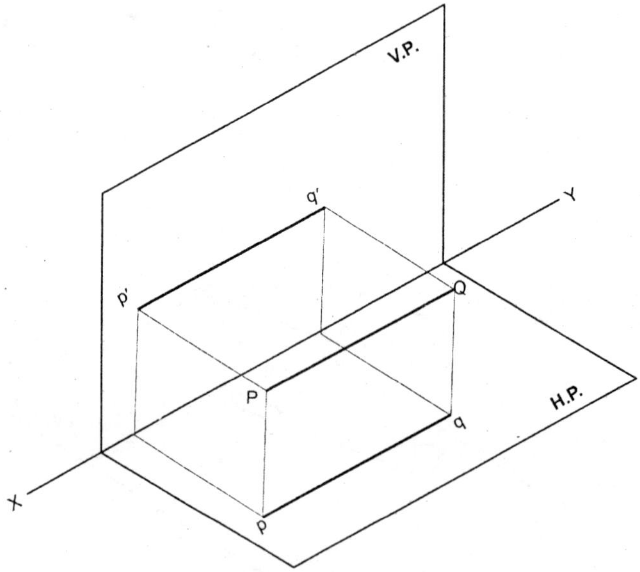

Fig. 7.4 (i)

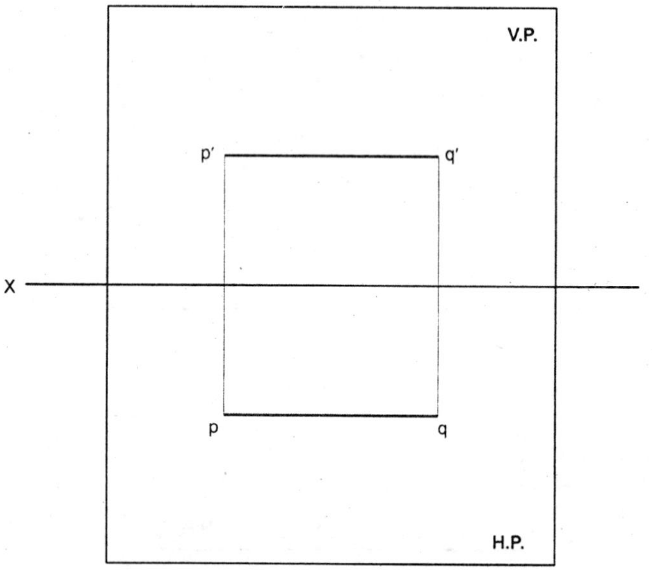

Fig. 7.4 (ii)

7.4 LINE CONTAINED BY ONE OR BOTH THE PLANE (H.P. & V.P.)

***Case I:* Line contained by horizontal plane (H.P.):** Consider a line PQ contained by horizontal plane as shown in Fig. 7.5 (i). Its top view is projected onto horizontal plane which is a line having true length (TL). The front view is projected onto the reference line XY. Since the line is inclined to vertical plane, the front view will be in reduced length as shown in Fig. 7.5 (ii).

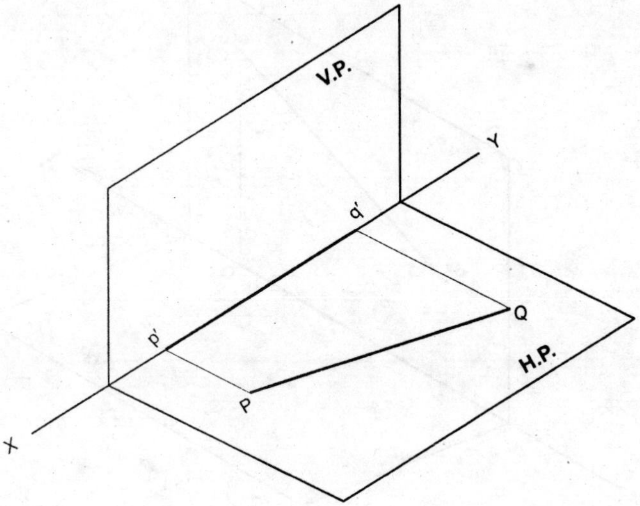

Fig. 7.5 (i)

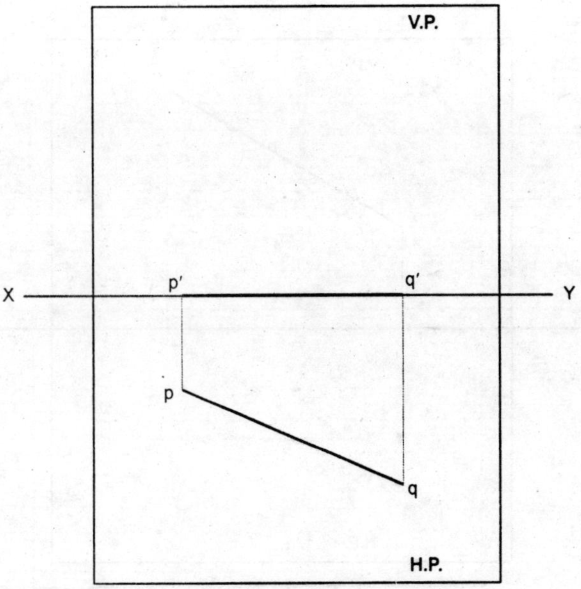

Fig. 7.5 (ii)

***Case II:* Line contained by vertical plane (V.P.)** Consider a line PQ contained by vertical plane as shown in Fig. 7.6 (i). Its front view is projected onto vertical plane which is a line having true length (TL). The top view is projected onto the reference line XY. Since the line is inclined to horizontal plane, the top view will be of reduced length as shown in Fig. 7.6 (ii).

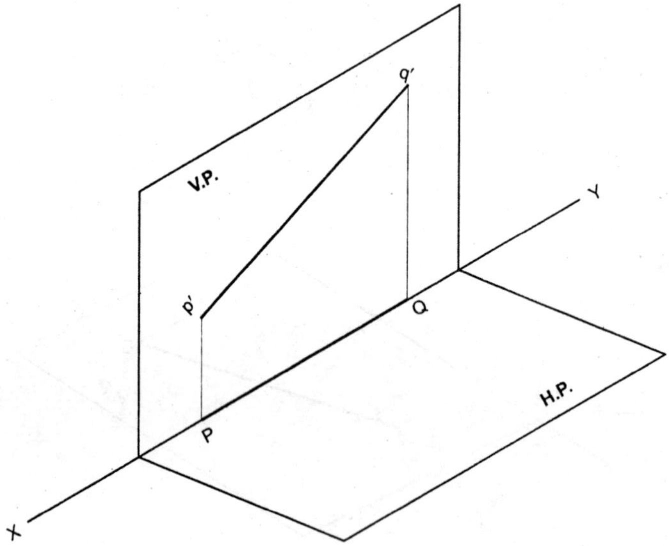

Fig. 7.6 (i)

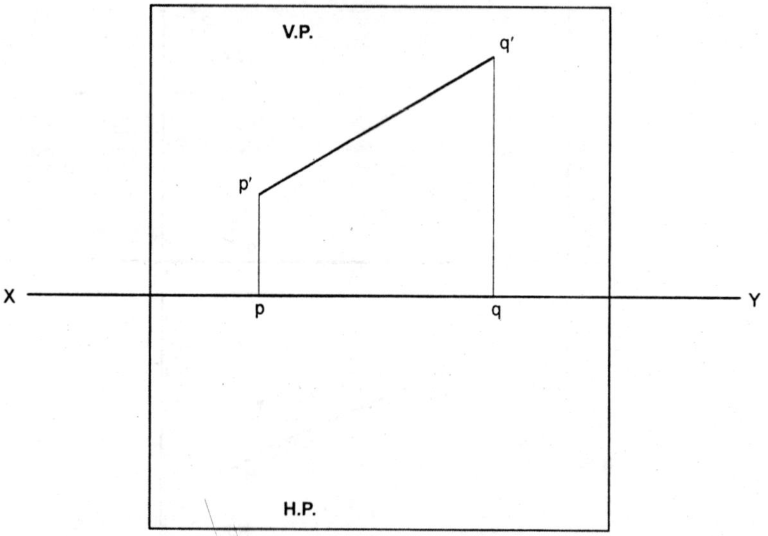

Fig. 7.6 (ii)

Case III: **Line contained by horizontal plane and vertical plane (H.P. & V.P.):** Consider a line PQ contained by both the planes as shown in Fig. 7.7 (i). Its front view and top view are projected onto the reference line XY which is a line having true length as shown in Fig. 7.7 (ii).

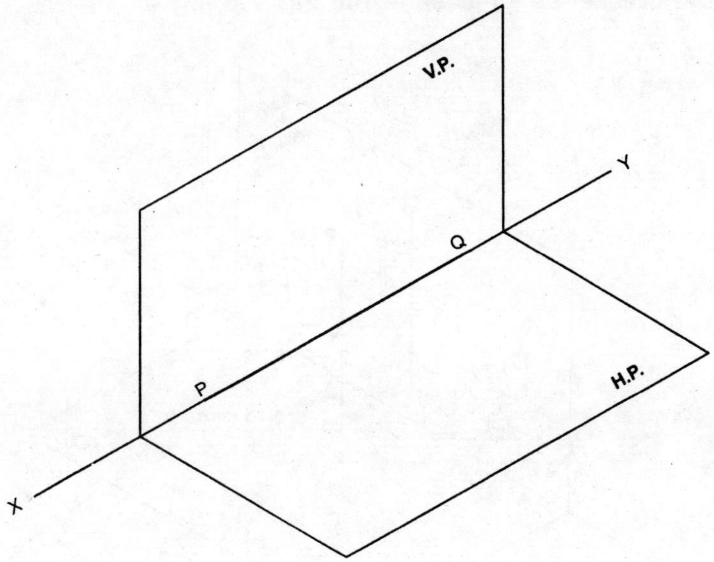

Fig. 7.7 (i)

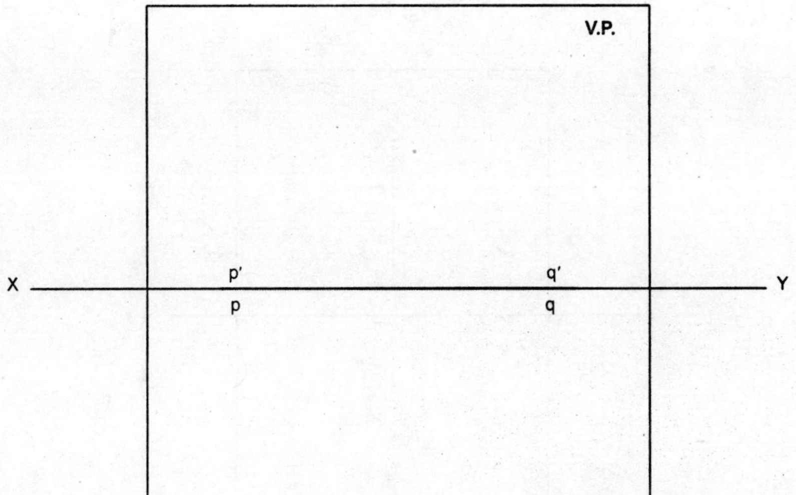

Fig. 7.7 (ii)

7.5 LINE PERPENDICULAR TO BOTH THE PLANE (H.P. & V.P.)

***Case I:* Line perpendicular to horizontal plane (H.P.):** Consider a line PQ kept perpendicular to horizontal plane and parallel to vertical plane as shown in Fig. 7.8(i). Its front view is projected onto vertical plane which is a line having true (TL). The top view is projected onto horizontal plane which is a point. The invisible point Q in the top view, is represented within bracket as (q) as shown in Fig. 7.8 (ii).

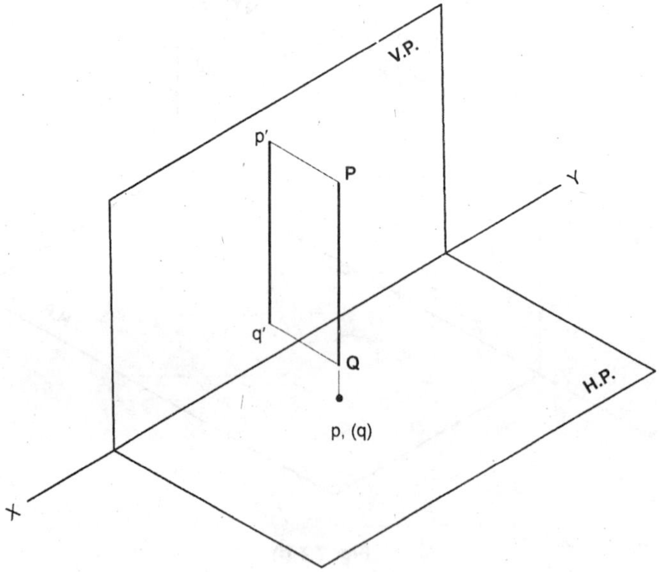

Fig. 7.8 (i)

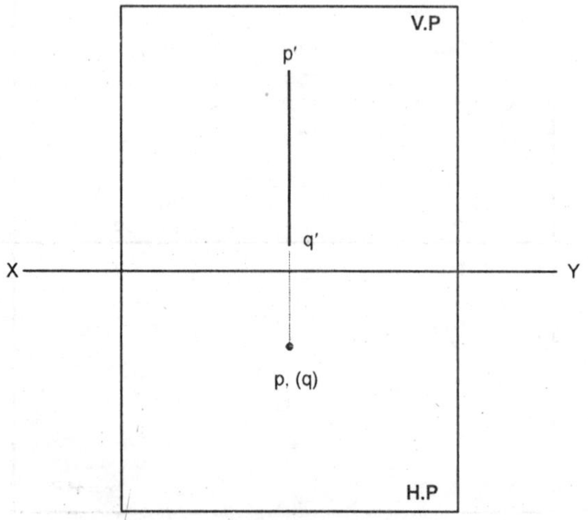

Fig. 7.8 (ii)

***Case II:* Line perpendicular to vertical plane (V.P.):** Consider a line PQ perpendicular to vertical plane and parallel to horizontal plane as shown in Fig. 7.9 (i). Its top view is projected onto horizontal plane which is a line having true length (TL). The front view is projected onto vertical plane which is a point. The invisible point *P* in the front view is represented within bracket as (p′) as shown in Fig. 7.9 (ii)

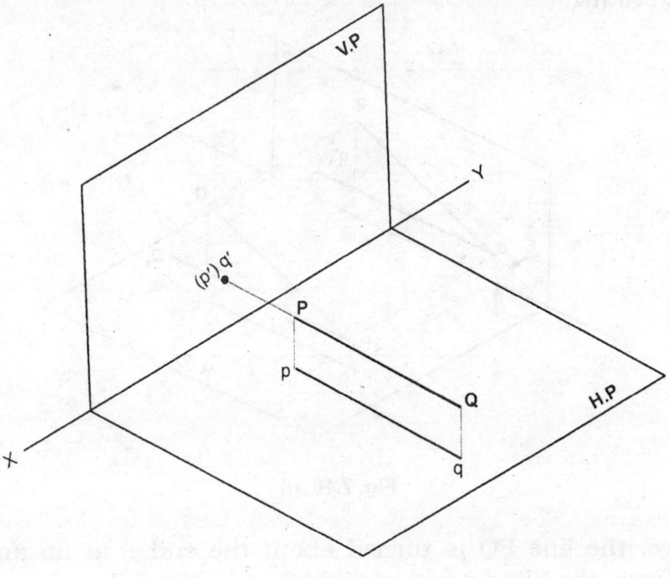

Fig. 7.9 (i)

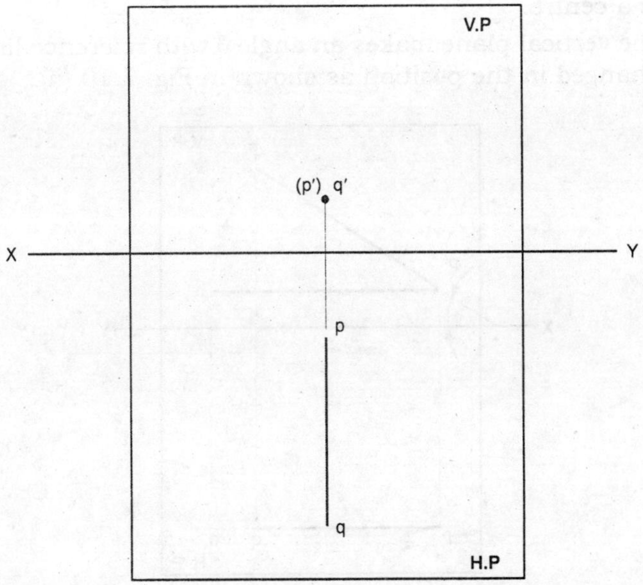

Fig. 7.9 (ii)

7.6 LINE INCLINED TO ONE REFERENCE PLANE AND PARALLEL TO THE OTHER

***Case I:* Line inclined to HP and parallel to the (V.P.):** The projection of a line PQ is drawn in two stages. In first stage, the line PQ is parallel to horizontal plane and vertical plane. Its front view *p′ q′* is projected onto the vertical plane and the top view *pq,* is projected onto the horizontal plane. Both pq_1 and $p'\ q_1'$ will be parallel to reference XY. as shown in Fig. 7.10 (i).

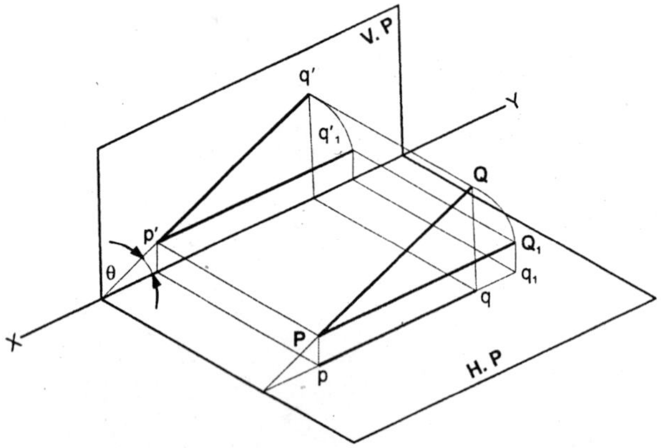

Fig. 7.10 (i)

In second stage, the line PQ is turned about the end *P* at an angle of θ with the horizontal plane. Thus, the tilted position of the line is PQ while remaining parallel to the vertical plane. The point *q′*, on the vertical plane will be moved along an arc to *q′*. The arc is drawn with *p′* as a centre.

Front view on the vertical plane makes an angle θ with reference line XY. The position of the top view is changed in the position as shown in Fig. 7.10 (ii).

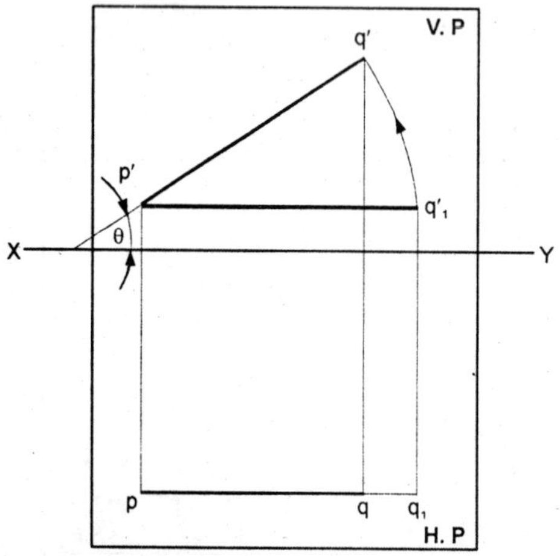

Fig. 7.10 (ii)

***Case II:* Line inclined to V.P. and parallel to the H.P.:** The projection of a line PQ is also drawn in two stages which are discussed below:

In first stage, the line PQ_1 is parallel to both the reference planes. Its front view $P'q'_1$ is projected onto the vertical plane and the top view *pq*, is projected onto the horizontal plane. Both $p'q'_1$ and pq_1 are parallel to reference line XY. In second stage, the line PQ_1 is turned about the end *P* at an angle of θ with the vertical plane. So, the tilted position of the line is PQ while remaining parallel to the horizontal plane. The point *q* will move along an arc to *q*′. The arc is described with centre *p* and radius *pq*. Top view *pq* onto the horizontal plane makes an angle θ with reference line XY. The position of the front view is changed in position as shown in Fig. 7.11 (i & ii).

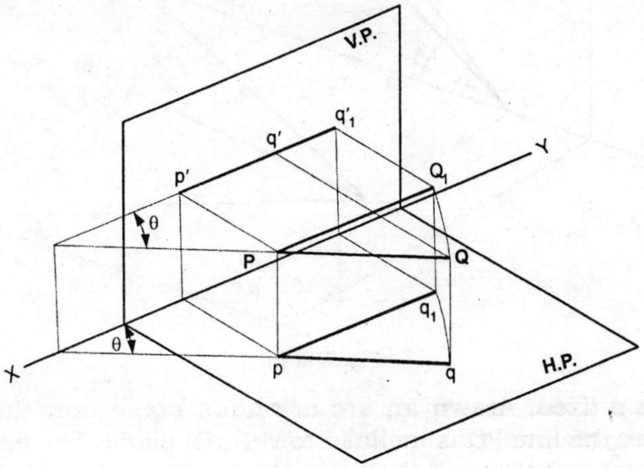

Fig. 7.11 (i)

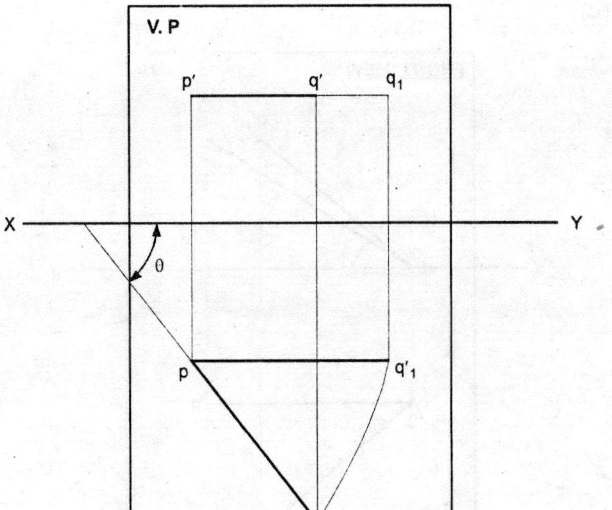

Fig. 7.11 (ii)

7.7 LINE INCLINED TO BOTH H.P. & V.P.

Case I: Consider a line PQ which is kept inclined to horizontal plane at an angle of θ and parallel to vertical plane as shown in Fig. 7.12 (i). Its front view *p'q'* is inclined at an angle θ to the reference line XY and top view *pq* is parallel to the reference line.

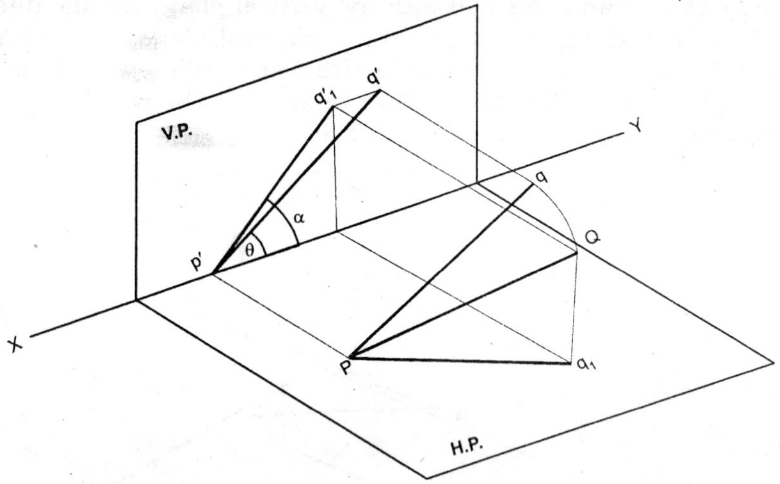

Fig. 7.12 (i)

Keeping the end *p* fixed, drawn an arc of radius *pq* so that the end *q* moves to a position q_1. Therefore, the line PQ is inclined to vertical plane. The line pq_1 is the new top view. Draw a horizontal line through the point q'_1 will lie on it through projector q_1. Thus the line $p'q'_1$ is the new front view and inclined at an angle α to the reference line XY as shown in Fig. 7.12 (ii).

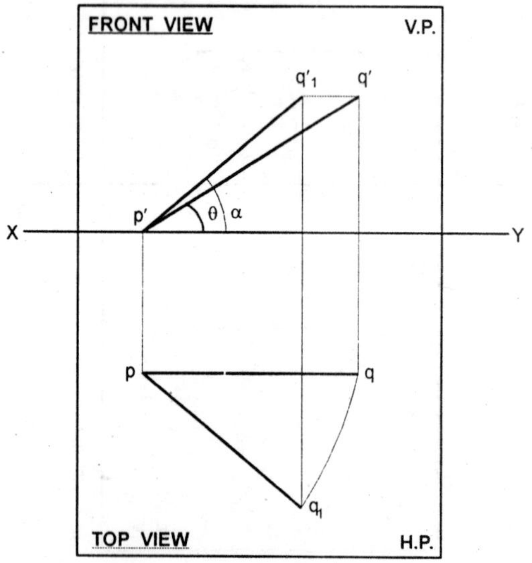

Fig. 7.12 (ii)

Case II: Consider a line PQ which is kept inclined to vertical plane at an angle θ and parallel to horizontal plane as shown in Fig. 7.13 (i). Its front view p' q' is parallel to the reference line XY and the top view pq is inclined at an angle θ to the reference line. Keeping the end p' fixed, drawn an arc of radius p' q' so that the end q' moves to q_1. Therefore, the line PQ is inclined to horizontal plane.

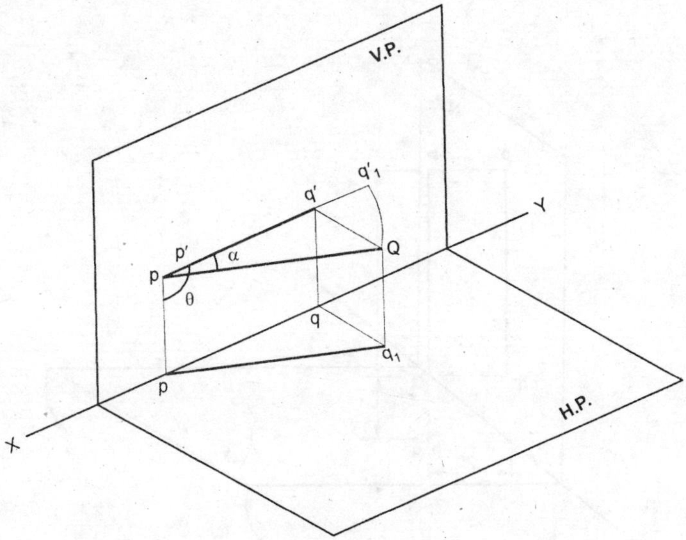

Fig. 7.13 (i)

The point q_1' will lie on the projector through q_1. The line pq_1 is the new top view where as p' q'_1 is the new front view. The new top view is inclined at angle α to the reference line XY as shown in Fig. 7.13 (ii).

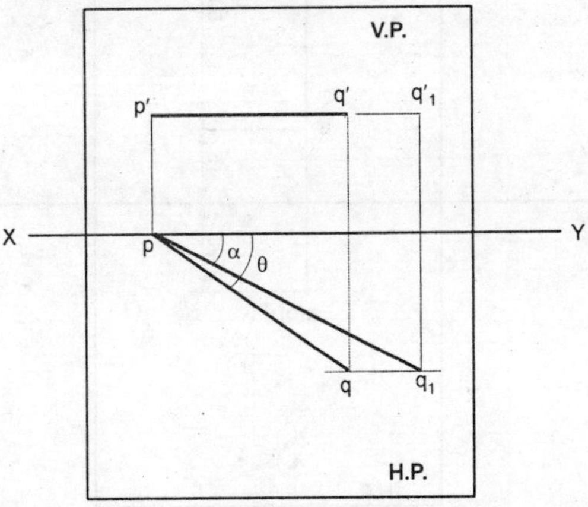

Fig. 7.13 (ii)

Problem 1. A line PQ, 50 mm in length is perpendicular to the horizontal plane and 20 mm infront of the vertical plane. End *Q* is a 15 mm above the H.P. Draw its projection.

Solution. The projection obtained are drawn with reference line XY as shown in Fig. 7.14 (i). Draw the front view *p'q'* is a line having true length of 50 mm. Top view is a point, the end *p* is visible and *q* is invisible. Its front view *p'q'* is 15 mm above the reference line XY and top view *p*(*q*) 20 mm below reference line XY as shown in Fig. 7.14 (ii).

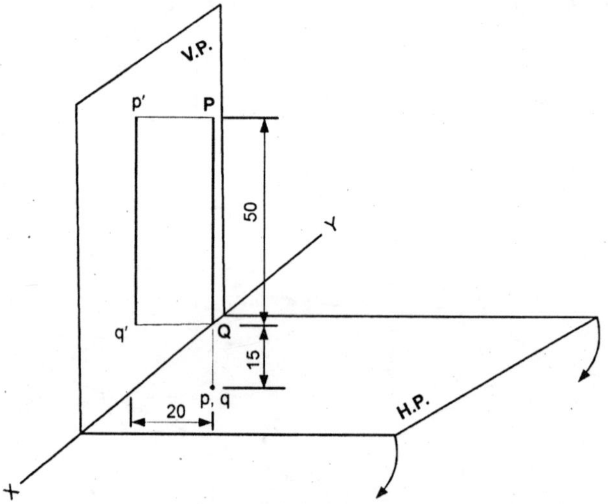

Fig. 7.14 (i)

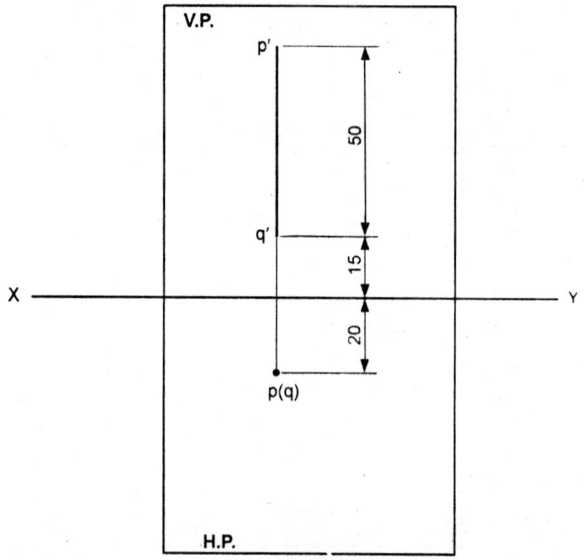

Fig. 7.14 (ii)

Problem 2. A line PQ is 50 mm long has its end *P* 25 mm above H.P and 30 mm in front of V.P. The line is perpendicular to V.P. and parallel to H.P. Draw its projection.

Solution. The projections obtained are drawn with reference line XY as shown in Fig. 7.15 (i). Draw the top view *pq* is a line having true length. Its top view *pq* is 30 mm below the XY line and the front view (*p*′) *q*′ is 25 mm above the reference line. The front view is a point, the end *q*′ is visible and *p*′ is invisible. The invisible end *p*′ is enclosed in ( ) as shown in Fig. 7.15 (ii).

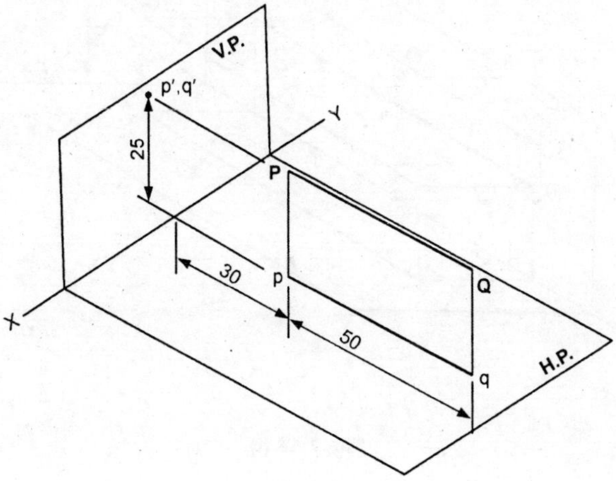

Fig. 7.15 (i)

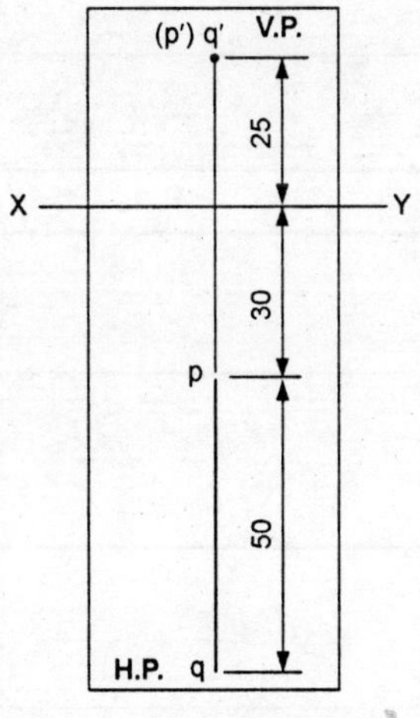

Fig. 7.15 (ii)

Problem 3. Draw the projection of a line PQ 70 mm long parallel to both the reference planes and laying 20 mm above H.P. and 25 mm in front of V.P.

Solution. The projections obtained are drawn with reference line XY as shown in Fig. 7.16 (i).

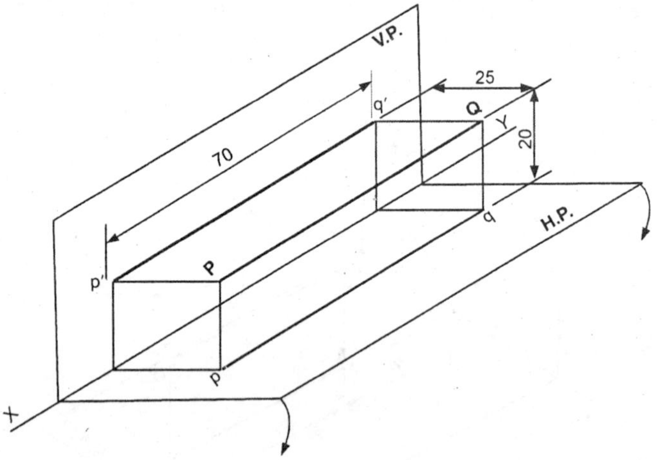

Fig. 7.16 (i)

The front view *p'q'* and top view *p*, *q* are lines having true length and also parallel to XY line. It front view *p'* is 20 mm above reference line and top view *p* is 25 mm below reference line as shown in Fig. 7.16 (ii).

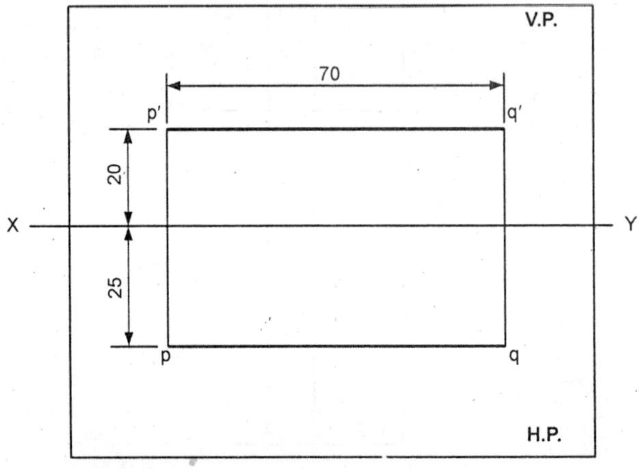

Fig. 7.16 (ii)

Problem 4. Line PQ is parallel to V.P. and inclined at an angle of 30° to H.P. and measures 50 mm in top view. Its end *P* is 15 mm above the H.P. and 20 mm in front of the V.P Draw its projection.

Solution. The projections obtained are drawn with reference to the XY line as shown in Fig. 7.17 (i). The front view *p′q′* is a line inclined at an angle of 30° to reference line having true length. Top view *pq* is parallel to reference line and smaller then true length. Its front view *p′* is 15 mm above reference line and top view *p* is 20 mm below the reference line as shown in Fig. 7.17 (ii).

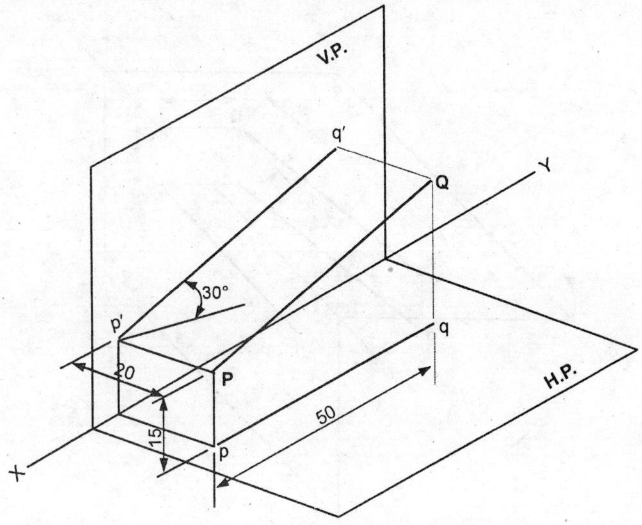

Fig. 7.17 (i)

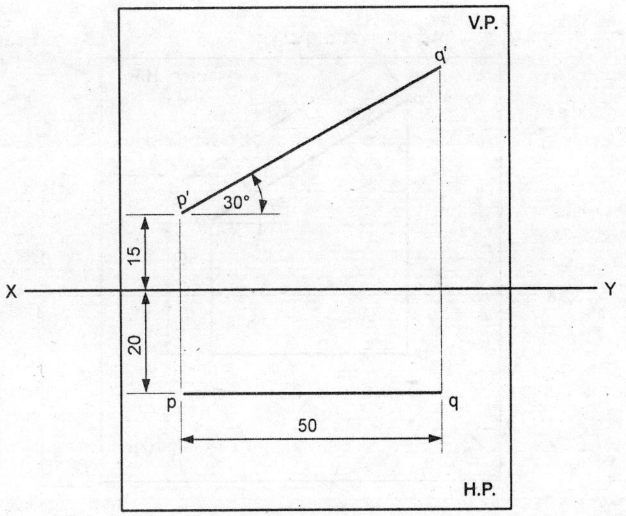

Fig. 7.17 (ii)

Problem 5. Draw the front view and top view of a line PQ 60 mm long, inclined to V.P. at an angle of 30° towards left and parallel to H.P. The end *Q* is 20 mm from H.P. and 15 mm from V.P.

Solution. The projections obtained are drawn with reference to the XY line as shown in Fig. 7.18 (i). The top view *pq* is a line inclined at an angle of 30° to XY from *q* and having a length of 60 mm. Front view *p'q'* is parallel to XY and smaller than true length. Its front view *p'q'* is 15 mm below the reference line and top view *q* is 20 mm above the reference line as shown in Fig. 7.18 (ii).

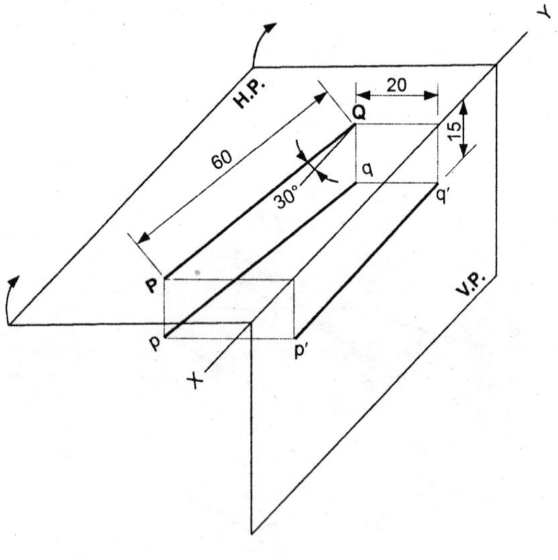

Fig. 7.18 (i)

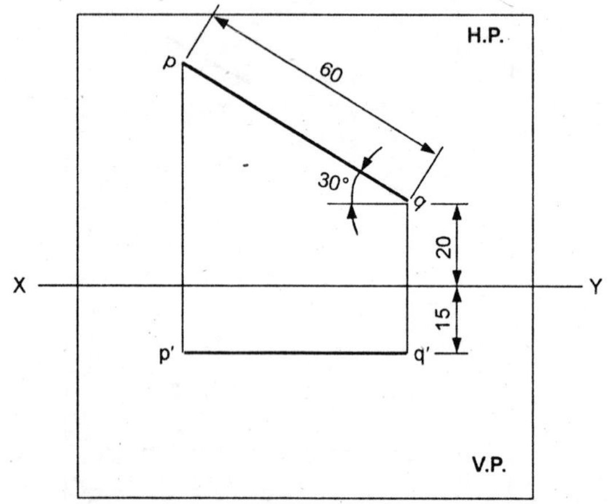

Fig. 7.18 (ii)

Problem 6. The front view of a 60 mm long line PQ measures 45 mm. The line is parallel to the H.P. and 20 mm above the H.P. with one of its ends in the V.P. Draw the projections of the line and determine its inclination with the V.P.

Solution. The projections obtained are drawn with reference to the XY lines as shown in Fig. 7.19 (i). The front view *p'q'* is a line parallel to XY line and equal to 45 mm. Top view *pq* is inclined to XY line is 60 mm long, having true length. Its end *p'* is 20 mm above reference line as shown in Fig. 7.19 (ii).

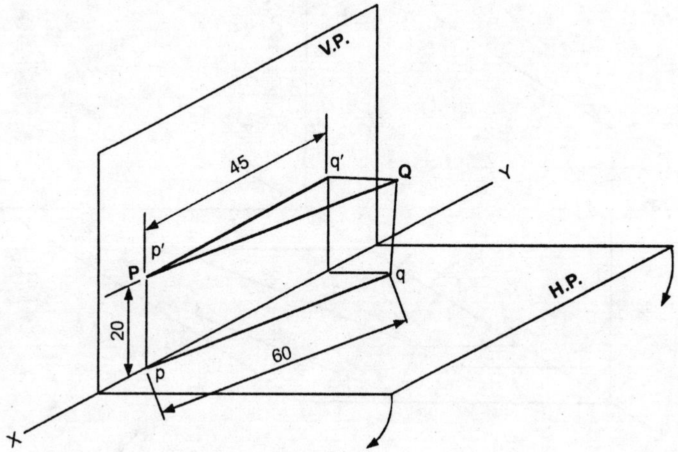

Fig. 7.19 (i)

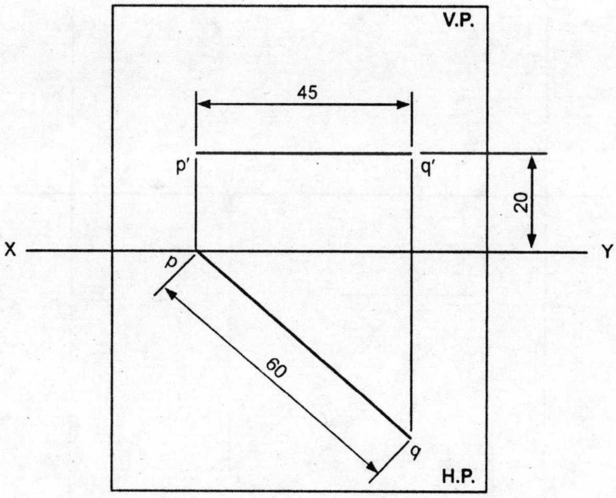

Fig. 7.19 (ii)

Problem 7. A line PQ is 50 mm long, is in the H.P. and makes an angle of 45° with the V.P. Its end *P* is 20 mm in front of the V.P. Draw its projection.

Solution. The projection obtained are drawn with reference to the XY lines as shown in Fig. 7.20 (i). The front view *p′q′* is a line parallel to the XY line smaller then true length. Its top *pq* is a line inclined at an angle of 45° to the reference line having true length. Its end *P* is 20 mm below the reference line as shown in Fig. 7.20 (ii).

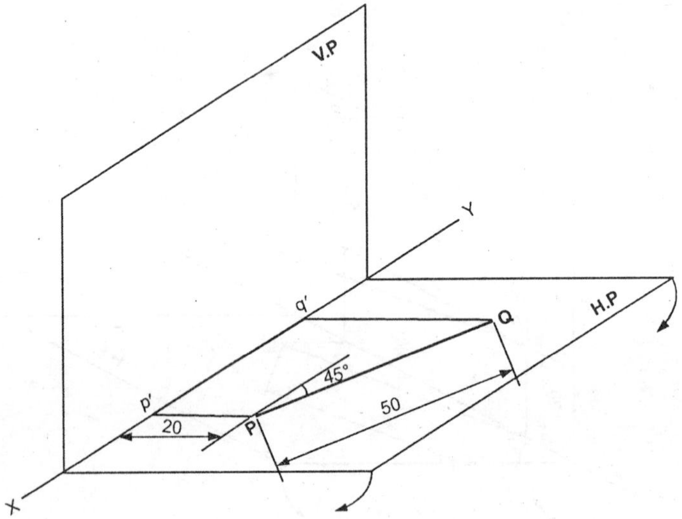

Fig. 7.20 (i)

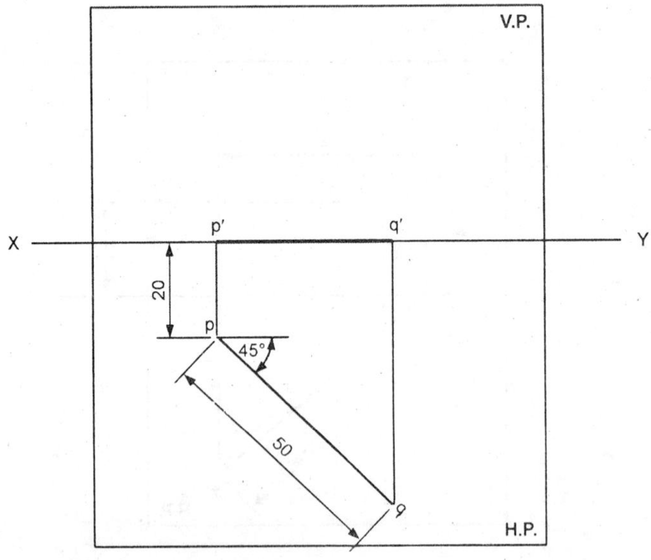

Fig. 7.20 (ii)

Problem 8. Draw the projection of a 70 mm long line PQ. Its end *p* is 20 mm above H.P. and 15 mm in front of the V.P. The line is parallel to V.P. and inclined to H.P. at 30°.

Solution. The projections obtained are drawn with reference line XY as shown in Fig. 7.21 (i). The front view *p′q′* is a line inclined at an angle of 30° to the reference line having true length of 70 mm and top view *pq* is parallel to XY line is smaller in length. Its front view *p′* is 20 mm above XY line and top view *p* is 15 mm below XY line as shown in Fig. 7.21 (ii).

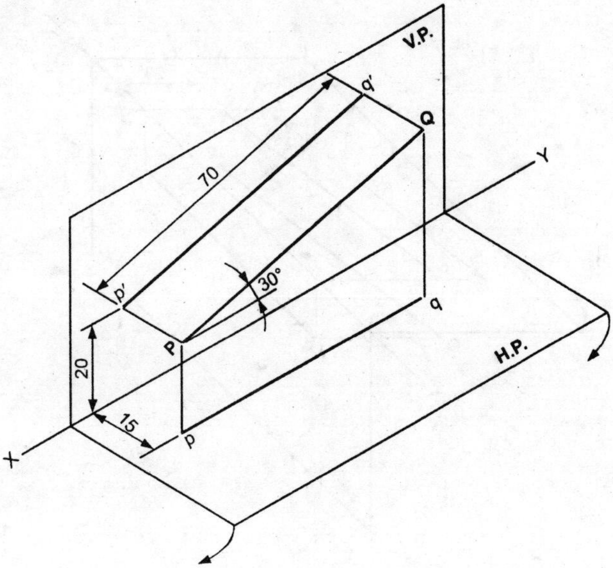

Fig. 7.21 (i)

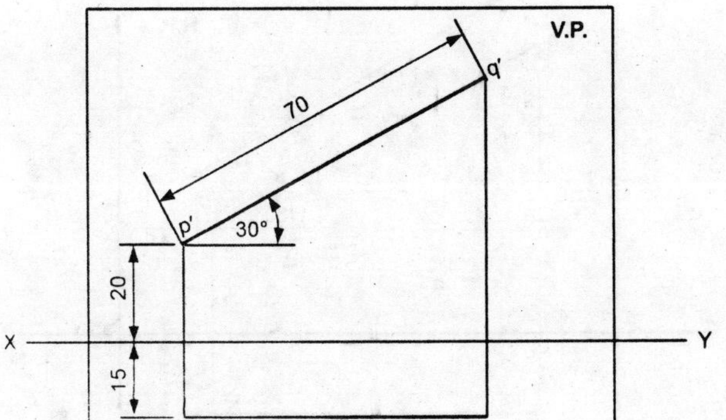

Fig. 7.21 (ii)

Problem 9. Draw projection of a 70 mm long line PQ. Its end *p* is 15 mm below H.P. and 20 mm behind V.P. The line is parallel to H.P. and inclined to V.P. at an angle of 30°.

Solution. The projections obtained are drawn with reference line XY as shown in Fig. 7.22 (i). The top view *pq* is a line inclined at an angle of 30° to reference line having true length. Front view *p'q'* is parallel to reference line and smaller than true length is in third quadrant. Its top view *p* is 20 mm above reference line XY and front view *p'* is 15 mm below reference line as shown in Fig. 7.22 (ii).

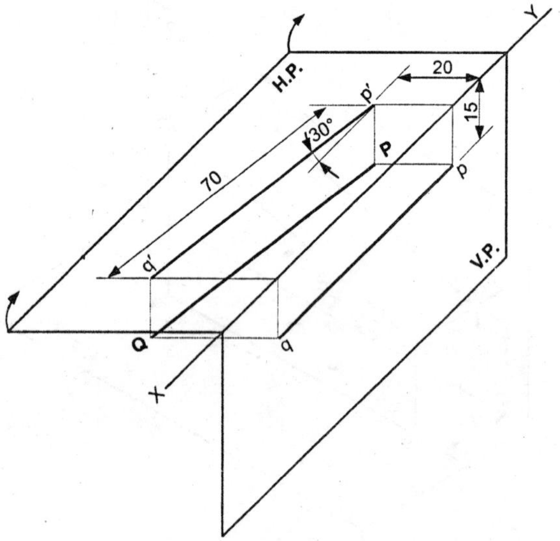

Fig. 7.22 (i)

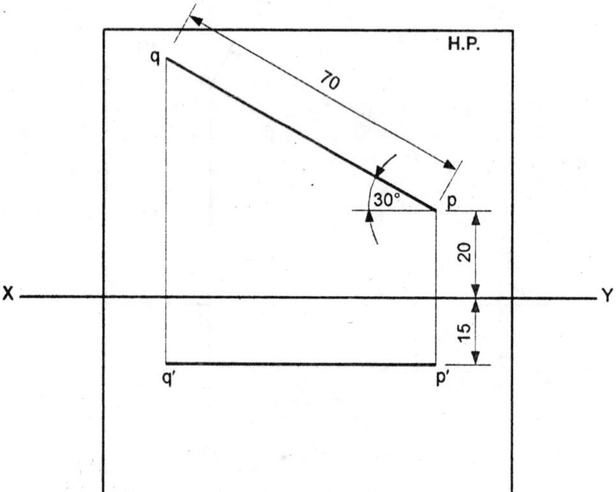

Fig. 7.22 (ii)

Problem 10. Draw the front view and top view of a line PQ 60 mm long, inclined to H.P. at 45° towards right and parallel to V.P. The end *P* is 20 mm from H.P. and 15 mm from V.P. (Used Ist angle projection).

Solution. The projections obtained are drawn with reference to the XY line as shown in Fig. 7.23 (i). The top view *pq* is a line inclined at an angle of 45° to reference line of 60 mm (true length). The front view *p'q'* is parallel to reference line and smaller then true length.

Its front view *p'* is 20 mm above reference line and top view *p* is 15 mm below reference line as shown in Fig. 7.23 (ii)

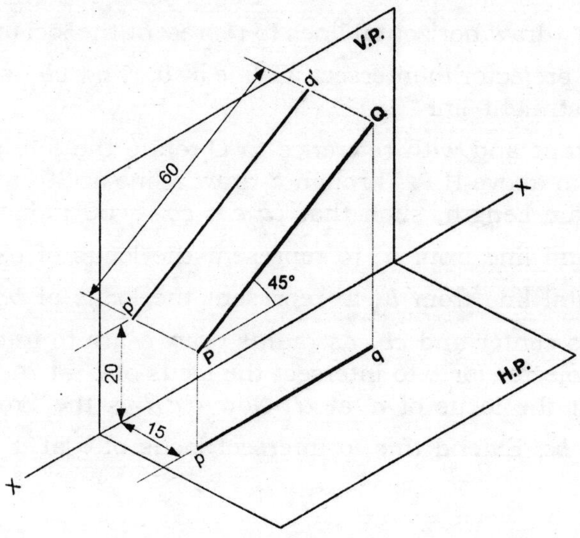

Fig. 7.23 (i)

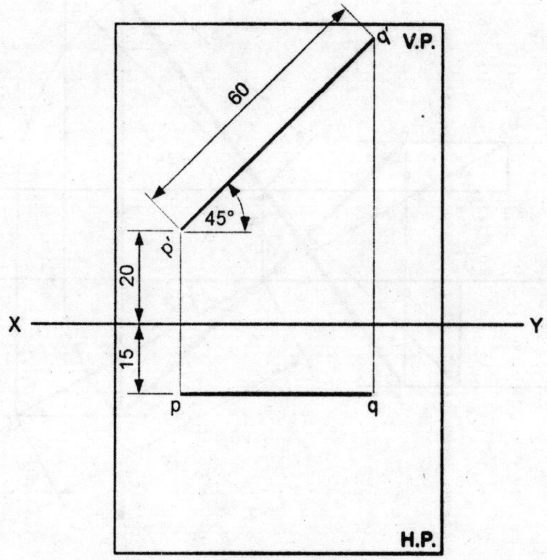

Fig. 7.23 (ii)

Problem 11. A line AB 120 mm long is inclined at 45° to H.P. and 30° to the V.P. Its mid point C is in V.P. and 20 mm above H.P. The end A is in the 3rd quadrant and B is in the Ist- quadrant. Draw the projections of the line AB. **(Jan 2009, B.T.E. New Delhi)**

Solution. See Fig. 7.24

(i) Projections of mid-point C in the VP Mark c' 20 mm above XY and c on XY.

(ii) Keeping θ constant and with reference to C rotate AB to lie on V.P. Through c' draw a line at 45° to XY. Mark $a'_1c'b'_1$ = 120 mm = T.L. such that $a'_1c' = c'b'_1$ = 60 mm.

(iii) Through b'_1 & a'_1 draw horizontal lines to represent the loci of b' & a' respectively.

(iv) From b'_1 draw a projector to intersect XY line at b_1. Now cb_1 is the Top View length for half of the straight line.

(v) Keeping ϕ constant and with reference to C rotate the line parallel to H.P. Now the line is 20 mm above H.P. Through c' draw a line at 30° to XY and mark a_2cb_2 = 120 mm = True Length, such that $a_2c = cb_2$ = 60 mm.

(vi) Draw a horizontal line from a_2 to represent the locus of a.

(vii) Draw a horizontal line from b_2 to represent the locus of b.

(viii) Front View: c as center and cb_1 as radius draw a arc to intersect the locus of b at b. Draw a projector for b to intersect the locus of b' at b'. Join $b'c'$ and extend this to intersect the locus of a' at a'. Now $a'c'b'$ is the Front View.

(ix) Top View: Join bc. Extend this to intersect locus of a at a. Now abc is the Top View.

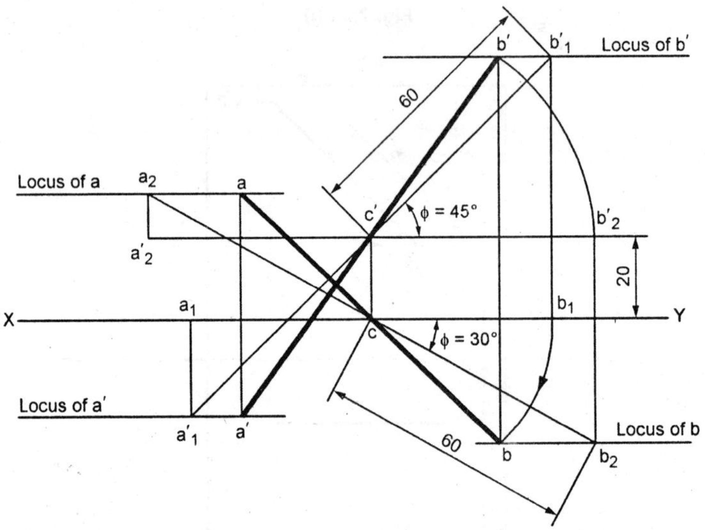

Fig. 7.24

EXERCISE

1. Define the terms straight lines.
2. A line PQ has its end *P* 20 mm above H.P. and 25 mm infront of V.P. The other end Q is 45 above H.P. and 40 mm infront of V.P. The distance between end projectors is 60 mm. Draw its projector. Also find (TL), true inclinations of line with H.P. & V.P.
3. The length of the top view of a straight line parallel to H.P. and inclined at an angle of 30° to the V.P. is 60 mm. one end A of the straight line is 20 mm above the H.P. and 15 mm infront of the V.P. Draw its projector.
4. A line PQ has one of its end 60 mm above H.P. and 20 mm infront of V.P. The other end is 15 mm above H.P. and 45 mm infront of V.P. The front view of the line is 70 mm long. Draw the projections of line.
5. A straight line PQ has point P 40 mm above H.P. and 30 mm in front of V.P. The front view and top view of the straight line measure 90 mm and 80 mm respectively. Draw the projections if the front view of the line make 45° with XY. Find out the length of the line and its inclination with H.P. and V.P.
6. The end P of a line PQ 100 mm long is 15 mm in front of V.P. and 25 mm above H.P. The end Q is 30 mm in front of V.P. and 40 mm above H.P. Draw the projections trace and find inclinations of the line with the H.P. and V.P.
7. The view from the front of a line PQ 160 mm measures 140 mm and its view from above measures 120 mm. The mid-point of the line PQ is 70 mm from both the planes. Draw the projections of the line PQ.
8. The length of the plan of a straight line PQ is 50 mm and the length of elevation is 70 mm. The plan PQ is inclined at 30° to XY line. Draw the projections of the line, assuming point P to be situated on H.P. and 20 mm infront of V.P. Also find the true length and true inclinations with H.P. & V.P.
9. A line PQ is 60 mm long makes an angle of 30° with the V.P. and lies in a plane perpendicular to both H.P. and V.P. Its end P is in the H.P. and Q is in the V.P. Draw the projections and show its traces.
10. A line PQ 70 mm long has its and P in both H.P. and V.P. the line is kept inclined at 45° to H.P. and 30° to V.P. Draw its projections.

❑❑❑

IMPORTANT NOTES:

8

PROJECTION OF PLANE

8.1 INTRODUCTION

A plane has only two dimensions, i.e. length and breadth with negligible thickness. A plane has no boundary and it extends to infinity in all direction. A plane may be of any shape such as, square rectangle, circle, pentagon, hexagon etc.

8.2 TYPES OF PLANES

There are two types of planes:

(1) Perpendicular planes

(2) Oblique planes.

8.3 PERPENDICULAR PLANES

The planes which are perpendicular to any one of the reference plane, i.e. H.P. and V.P. are known as perpendicular planes. These planes can be divided into the following sub-types:

(i) Plane perpendicular to H.P. and parallel to V.P.

(ii) Plane perpendicular to V.P. and parallel to H.P.

(iii) Plane perpendicular to both H.P. and V.P.

(iv) Plane perpendicular to H.P. and inclined to V.P.

(v) Plane perpendicular to V.P. and inclined to H.P.

8.4 OBLIQUE PLANES

The planes which are inclined to both the reference plane are known as oblique planes.

8.5 TRACES OF PLANE

The trace of plane is a line of intersection or meeting of the plane surface with the reference plane are known as traces of plane.

8.6 TYPES OF TRACES

There are two types of traces:

(i) Horizontal trace

(ii) Vertical trace.

(i) Horizontal trace: The intersection line of the plane surface with the horizontal plane is known as horizontal trace (H.T.). Fig. 8.1 shows the horizontal trace.

(ii) Vertical Trace: The intersection lines of the plane surface with the vertical plane is known as vertical trace (V.T.). Fig. 8.2 shows the vertical trace.

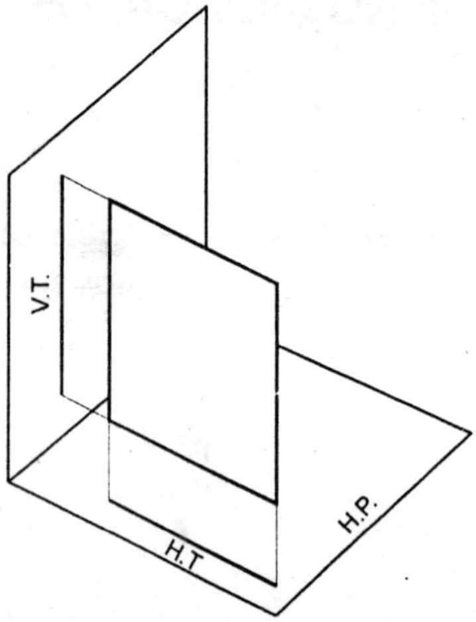

Fig. 8.1

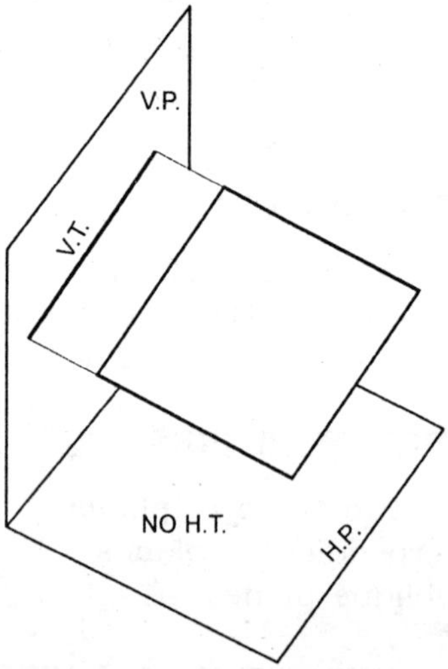

Fig. 8.2

8.7 REPRESENTATION OF PERPENDICULAR PLANES

The following are the possible positions of the perpendicular planes with their traces.

(i) Plane perpendicular to H.P. and Parallel to V.P.: Consider a square plane ABCD having its surface perpendicular to H.P. and parallel to V.P. as shown in Fig. 8.3.

The front view is projected on V.P. is *a*′, *b*′, *c*′, *d*′ having true shape and top view is projected on H.P., is line *a*, *b*. The projections and traces obtained are drawn with the reference line as shown in Fig. 8.4.

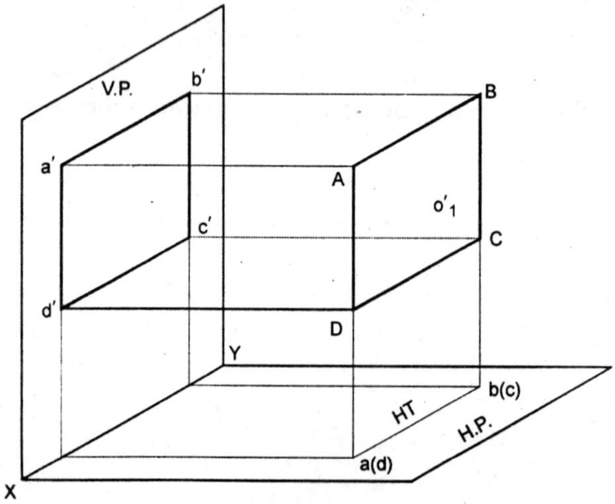

Fig. 8.3

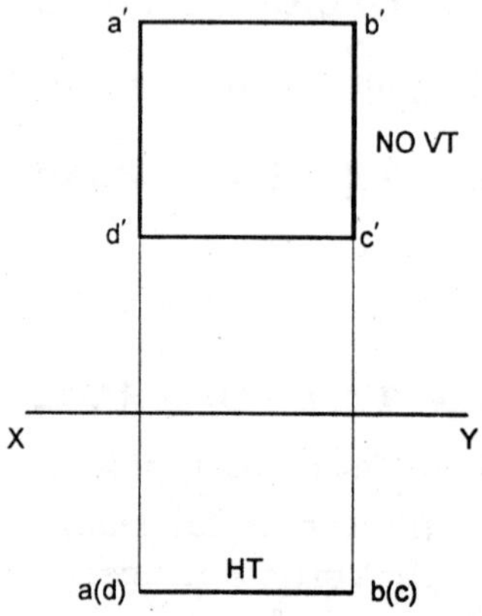

Fig. 8.4

(ii) Plane perpendicular to V.P. and parallel to H.P.: Consider as square plane ABCD with its surface perpendicular to V.P. and parallel to H.P. as shown in Fig. 8.5

The top view is projected one H.P. is abcd having true shape and front view is projected on V.P. is a line *a'b'*. The projections and trace obtained are drawn with the reference line as shown in Fig. 8.6.

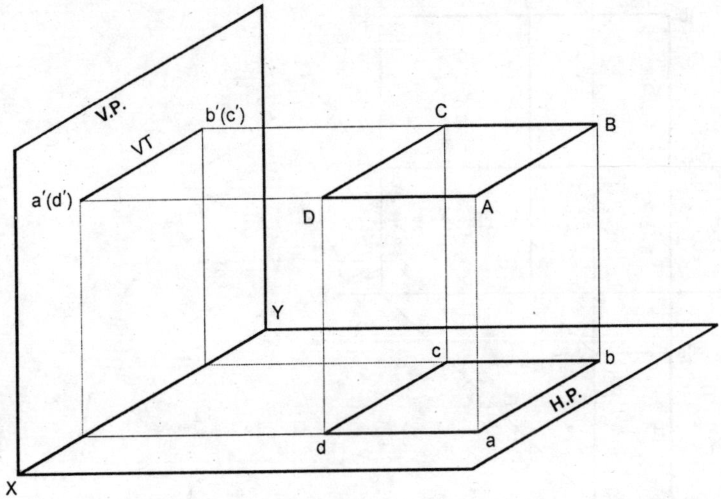

Fig. 8.5

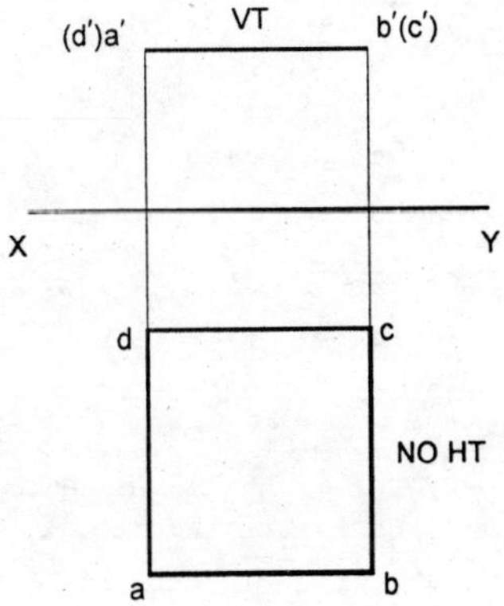

Fig. 8.6

(iii) Plane perpendicular to both H.P. and V.P: Consider a square plane ABCD having its surface perpendicular to both H.P. and V.P. as shown in Fig. 8.7.

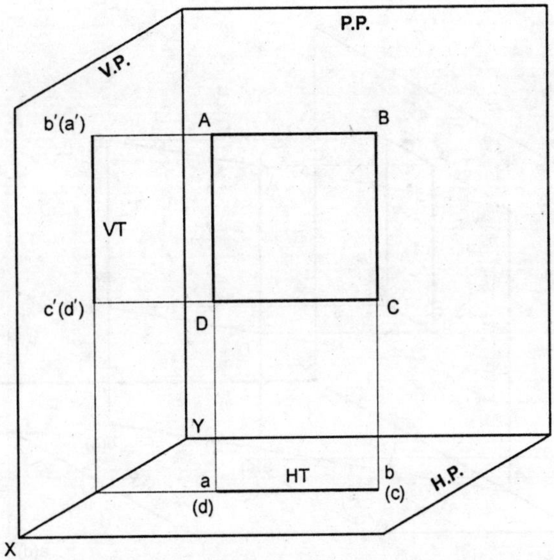

Fig. 8.7

The projection of plane on V.P. is *b′c′* and on H.P. is ab respectively. Both the views are lines perpendicular to the reference line. The front view *b′c′* and top view ab coincides with V.T and H.T. The projections and trace obtained are drawn with the reference line as shown in Fig. 8.8.

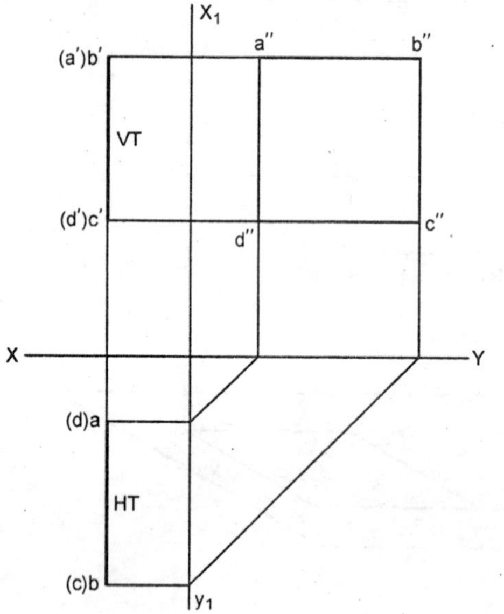

Fig. 8.8

(iv) Plane perpendicular to H.P. and inclined to V.P.: Consider a square plane ABCD perpendicular to H.P. and inclined to V.P. at an angle ϕ as shown in Fig. 8.9

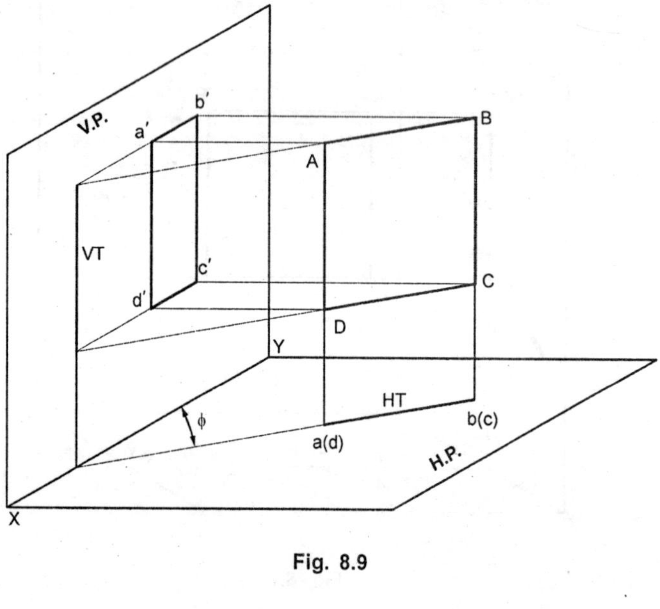

Fig. 8.9

The front view *a'b'c'd'* is projected on V.P. is smaller than the true shape. The top view is projected on H.P., is a line ab inclined at an angle of ϕ to the reference line.

Its V.T. is perpendicular to the reference line whereas its H.T. is inclined at the same angle ϕ to the reference line when produced.

The projections and traces obtained are drawn with the reference line as shown in Fig. 8.10

(v) Plane perpendicular to V.P. and inclined to H.P.: Consider a square ABCD perpendicular to V.P. and inclined to H.P. at an angle ϕ as shown in Fig. 8.11.

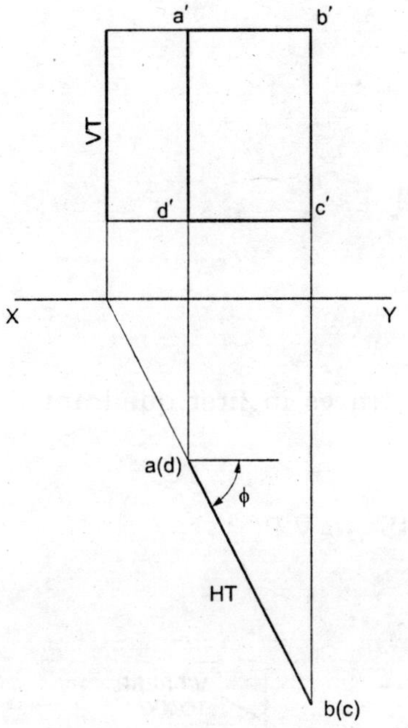

Fig. 8.10

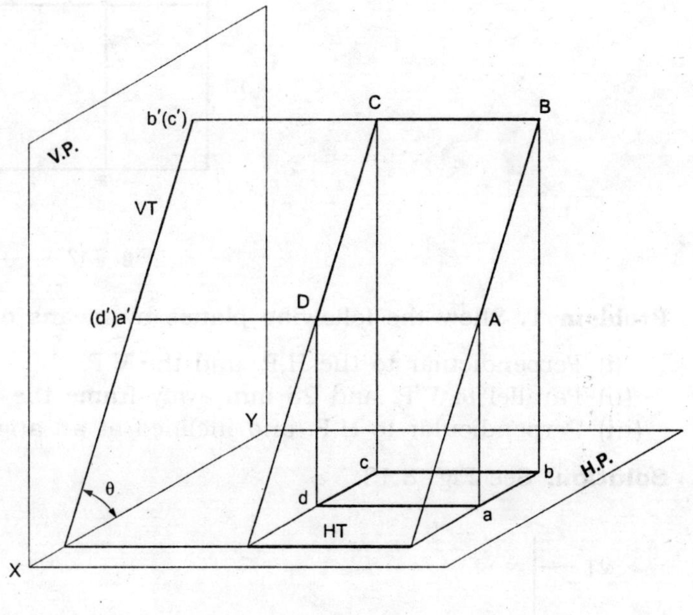

Fig. 8.11

The top view *abcd* is projected on H.P. smaller than the true shape. The front view is projected on V.P. is a line a'b' inclined at an angle θ to the reference line. Its H.T. is perpendicular to the reference line whereas its V.T. is inclined at the same angle θ to the reference line when produced. The projections and traced obtained are drawn with the reference line as shown in Fig. 8.12.

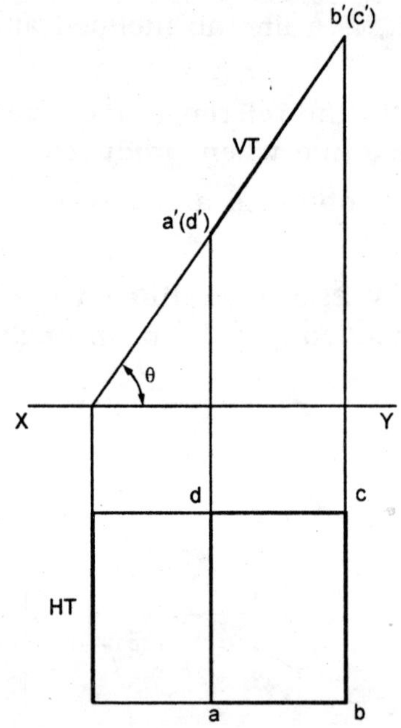

Fig. 8.12

Problem 1. Show the following planes by means of their traces in first quadrant.

(i) Perpendicular to the H.P. and the V.P.

(ii) Parallel to V.P. and 25 mm away frame the V.P.

(iii) Perpendicular to H.P. and inclined at an angle of 45° to V.P.

Solution: See Fig. 8.13

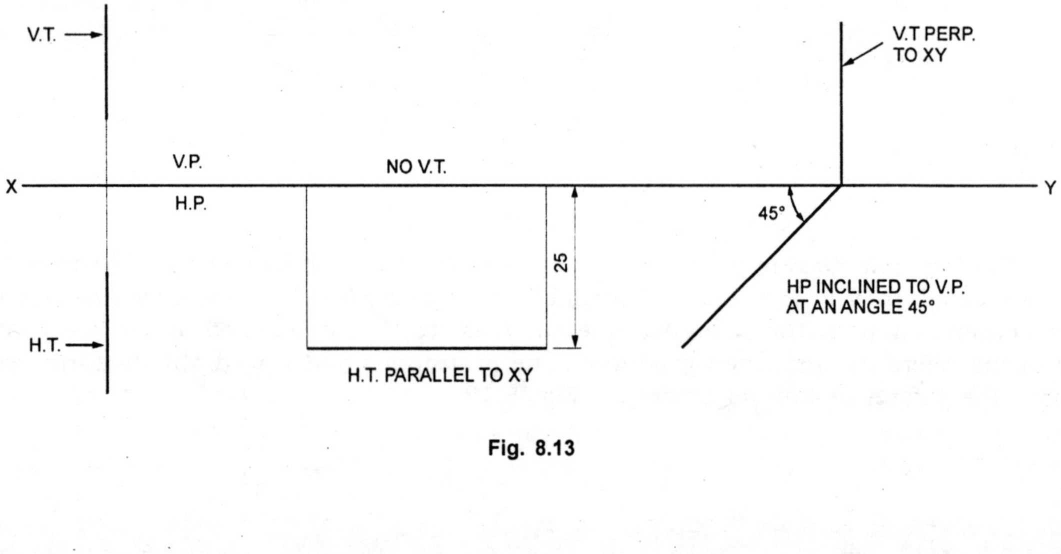

Fig. 8.13

Problem 2. A square plane of side 40 mm has its surface parallel to V.P. and perpendicular to H.P. Draw its projections when one of the sides is inclined at an angle of 30° to H.P.

Solution: See Fig. 8.14

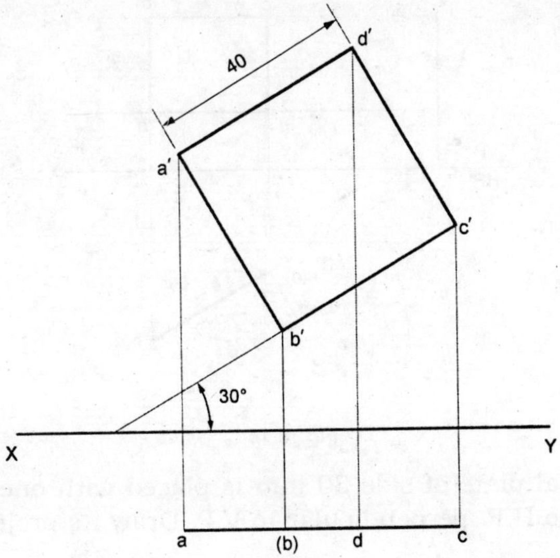

Fig. 8.14

Problem 3. A square plane of side 40 mm is parallel to H.P. and perpendicular to V.P. Draw its projections and find its traces.

Solution: See Fig. 8.15

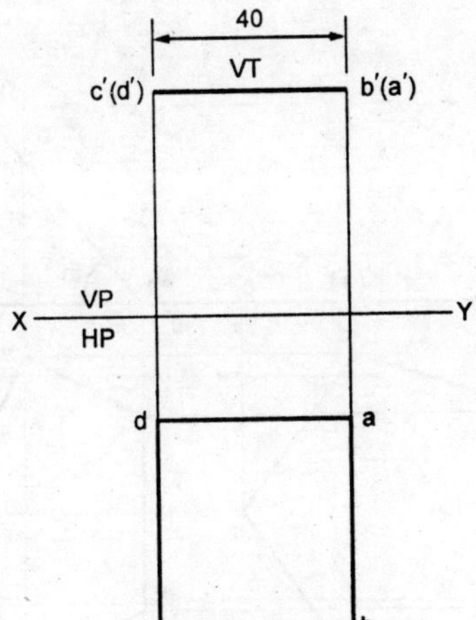

Fig. 8.15

Problem 4. A rectangular plane of side 30 mm × 40 mm is perpendicular to H.P. and inclined at an angle of 30° to V.P. Draw its projections are obtain the traces.

Solution: See Fig. 8.16.

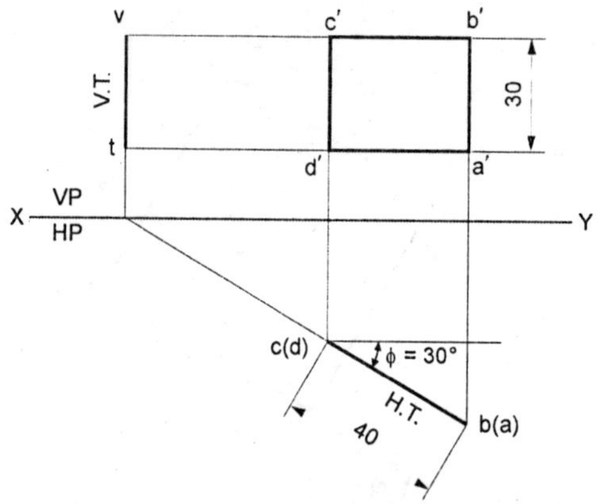

Fig. 8.16

Problem 5. A pentagonal plate of side 30 mm is placed with one side on H.P. and the surface inclined at 45° to H.P. perpendicular to V.P. Draw its projections and obtain the traces.

Solution: See Fig. 8.17.

When a plane is placed with its surface inclined 45° to H.P. and perpendicular to V.P. Draw the top view which will have the true shape. Project the front view which will be a line parallel to reference line. Now, reproduce the front view tilted to the given angle 45° to H.P. and project the top view of the plane which will be smaller than the true shape.

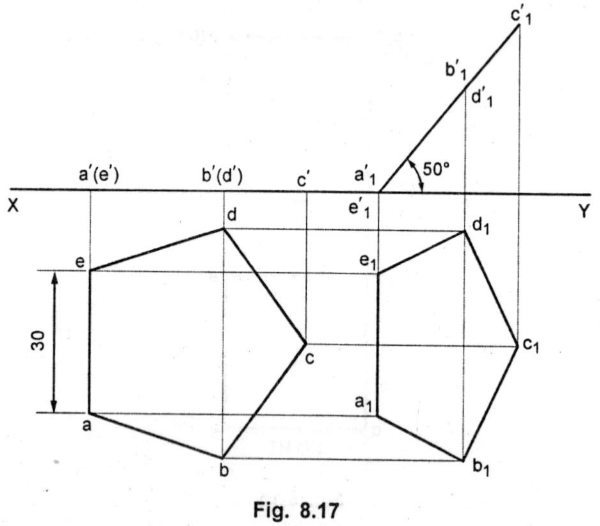

Fig. 8.17

Problem 6. A circulat plate of diameter 40 mm is resting on H.P. on a point on the circumfernece with its surface incluied at an angle of 45° to H.P. and perpendicular to V.P. Draw its projections and find its traces.

Solution: See Fig. 8.18.

(i) Assume that the plate has its surface parallel to H.P. and perpendicular to V.P. Draw the top view.

(ii) Project and get the front view which is a line on reference line.

(iii) Divide the circle into twelve equal parts and project them to the front view.

(iv) Tilt and reproduce the front view to the given angle of 45° with reference line, in such a way that the end *a'* is on reference line.

(v) Draw horizontal lines from *abc* etc. and vertical lines from a_1', b_1', c_1' etc. to get the required top view.

(vi) Join a_1, b_1, c_1 etc. by drawing a smooth curve to get the top view of the circle as an ellipse as shown in Fig. 8.18.

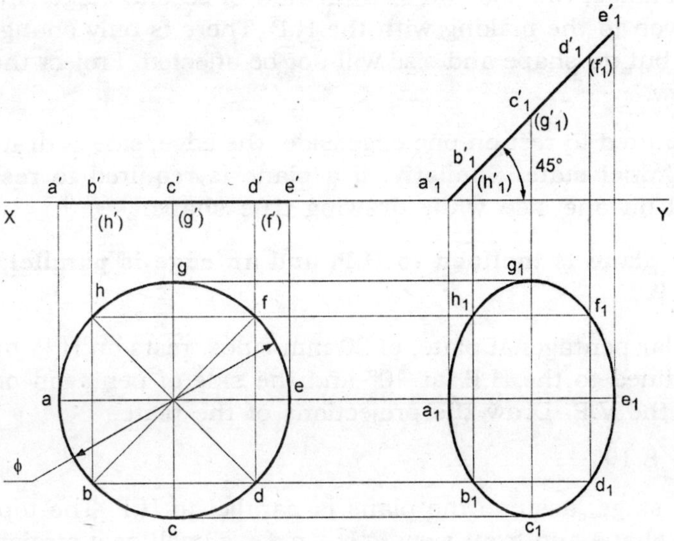

Fig. 8.18

8.8 OBLIQUE PLANES

When a plane is inclined to both the principal planes, projections of such planes are drawn in three stages:

Case 1 When the plane is inclined to H.P. and an edge is parallel to the H.P. and inclined to the V.P.

(i) In the initial stage, the plane is assumed parallel to one principal plane and its projections (top view and front view) are drawn. If the plane is assumed parallel to H.P., the top view will be true shape and front view will be a straight line.

(ii) In the second stage, the front view is tilted so as to make the required angle with the principal plane (H.P. in the present case). Project top view from the straightline front view in second stage. The top view will be smaller in size.

(iii) In the third stage, the position of top view of second stage is tilted at an angle which is given to be making with the V.P. There is only change in the position of top view but its shape and size will not be affected. Project the final front view and top view.

Case 2 When the plane is inclined to V.P. and an edge is parallel to the V.P. and inclined to the H.P.

(i) In the initial stage, the plane is assumed parallel to the V.P. and its projections are drawn.

(ii) In the second stage, the top view is tilted so as to make the required angle with the principal plane V.P. The top view will be a straight line and front view will be smaller in size.

(iii) In the third stage, the position of front view of second stage is tilted at an angle which is given to the making with the H.P. There is only change in the position of top view but its shape and size will not be affected. Project the final front view and top view.

If a plane is required to rest on one edge/side, the edge/side is drawn perpendicular to *XY* line in the initial state. Similarly, if a plane is required to rest on corner, the corner is arranged on one side while drawing true shape.

Case I When the plane is inclined to H.P. and an edge is parallel to the H.P. and inclined to the V.P.

Problem 7. A regular pentagonal plate, of 20 mm sides, rests on H.P. on one of its sides such that it is inclined to the H.P. at 40° and the side of pentagon on which it rests, inclined at 45° to the V.P. Draw the projections of the plate.

Solution: See Fig. 8.19.

(i) In the first stage, assume the plane is parallel to H.P. The top view *abcde* will be the true shape and front view ($a'b' - e'c' - d'$) will be a straight line. Note that one side of pentagon *ab* is perpendicular to V.P.

(ii) In the second stage the front view ($a'b' - e'c' - d'$) is tilted at 40° with *XY*. Draw projectors vertically downward front view and horizontally from first stage top view, intersection of two gives points a_1, b_1, c_1 d_1 and e_1 a_1 b_1 c_1 d_1 e is top view in IInd stage and smaller in size.

(*iii*) In the IIIrd stage, the position of top view is tilted at 45° to *XY* line. The side a_2b_2 is inclined at 45°. Automatically all the sides will be inclined at 45°. Complete the final front view by projecting vertically upward from the top view and horizontally front view ($a'b' - e'c' - d$) as shown.

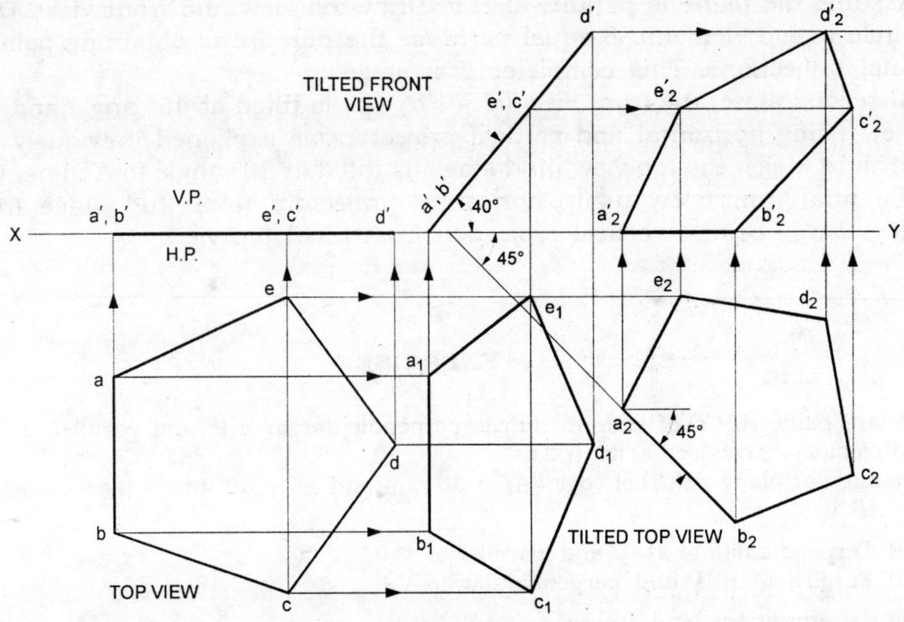

Fig. 8.19

Problem 8. A circular disc of 36 mm diameter resting in the H.P. on its rim and inclined at 45° to the H.P. Draw its projections when diameter (BD) is inclined to V.P. at 30°.
Solution: See Fig. 8.20.

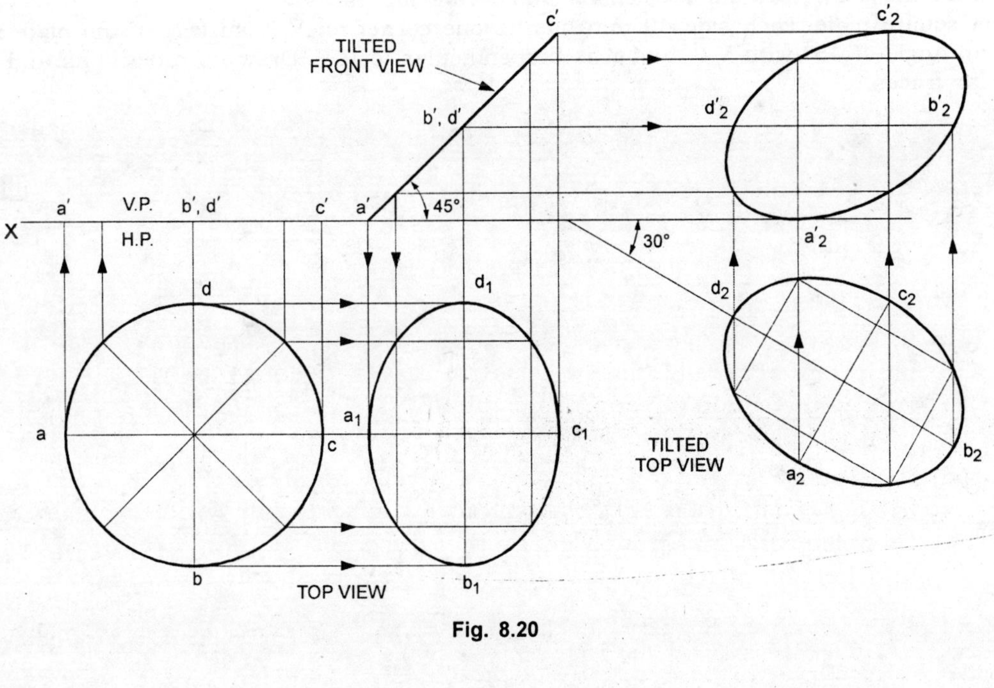

Fig. 8.20

(i) Assume the plane is parallel to H.P. Draw top view and front view. Divide the circle in top view into 8 equal parts for the purpose of obtaining points in the final projections. This completes first stage.

(ii) In second state, the front view ($a' - b'd' - c'$) is tilted at 45° angle and draw top view using horizontal and vertical projectors as explained previously.

(iii) In third stage, the top view (IInd stage) is tilted at 30° angle to *XY* line. Complete the final front view using horizontal projectors from IInd stage front view ($a' - b'd' - c'$) and vertical projection from tilted top view.

EXERCISE

1. A square plane *ABCD* of side 45 mm is perpendicular to H.P. and parallel to V.P. Draw its projections and locate its traces.
2. A rectangular plane *ABCD* of edges *AB* = 30 mm and *BC* = 40 mm is placed such that the edge *AB* is:

   (i) Perpendicular to H.P. and parallel to V.P.

   (ii) Parallel to H.P. and perpendicular to V.P.

   Draw its projections and traces.
3. A square *ABCD* of 40 mm side has its end 10 mm above H.P. and 20 mm infront of V.P. All the sides of the square are equally inclined to H.P. and parallel to V.P. Draw its projections and locate its traces.
4. A regular hexagonal plate of 30 mm side, is resting on one of its sides/edges in H.P. making an angle of 45° to H.P. and perpendicular to V.P. Its corner nearest to V.P. is 20 mm away from the V.P. Draw its projections and locate its traces.
5. A square plate, each side 40 mm has its one corner on V.P. surface of the plate makes an angle of 45° with V.P. and it is perpendicular to H.P. Draw its projections and locate its traces.

❑❑❑

9

Projection of Solids

9.1 INTRODUCTION

A solid is a three dimensional object, which has three dimensions i.e., length, breadth and thickness. It is bounded by planes or curved surfaces. The simplest method of representing the solid is drawing of at least two orthographic views—one is front view showing length and thickness (height) and the other view is known as top view, showing length and breadth of solid object. Sometime, additional view such as side view may be drawn for complete description of the object for clarity.

9.2 TYPES OF SOLIDS

Solids may be broadly divided into two groups:

1. Polyhedra
2. Solids of revolution.

9.3 POLYHEDRA

A polyhedron is defined as, a solid which is bounded by plane surfaces or faces. The boundary lines of the faces of a solid are called edges. It may be regular or irregular. The polyhedra are of the following types:

1. Regular polyhedra
2. Prisms
3. Pyramids.

(1) Regular Polyhedra: In a regular polyhedron all the faces are of the same shape and size and shape. The common types of regular polyhedron are given below:

(*i*) Tetrahedron

(*ii*) Cube or Hexahedron

(*iii*) Octahedron

(*iv*) Dodecahedron.

***(i)* Tetrahedron:** A tetrahedron is bounded by four equal, equilateral triangular faces as shown in Fig. 9.1. It has four faces, six equal edges and four vertices.

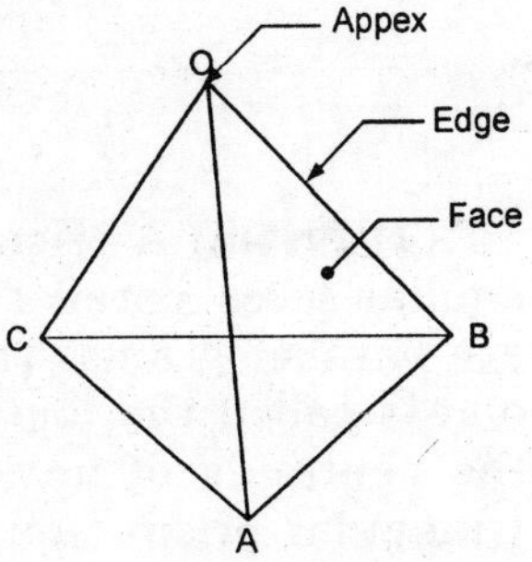

Fig. 9.1

***(ii)* Cube or Hexahedron:** A cube or hexahedron is bounded by six equal square faces as shown in Fig. 9.2. The diagonal of a face of a cube is called the facial diagonal. The line joining the opposite end of two parallel facial diagonals, is called the cube diagonal. It has six faces, twelve edges and eight vertices.

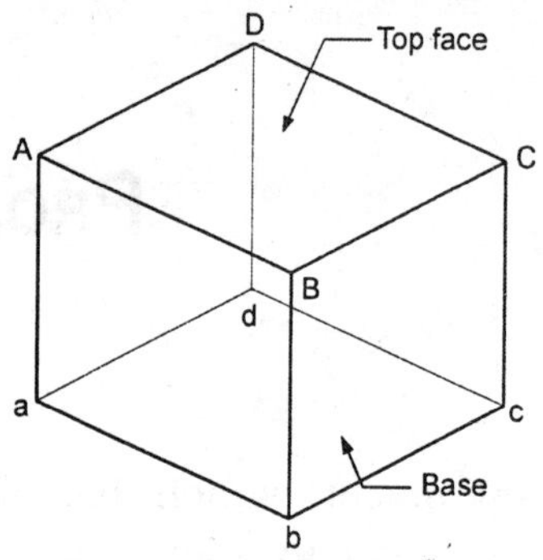

Fig. 9.2

(*iii*) Octahedron: An octahedron is bounded by eight equal equilateral triangles as shown in Fig. 9.3. It has twelve edges and six vertices.

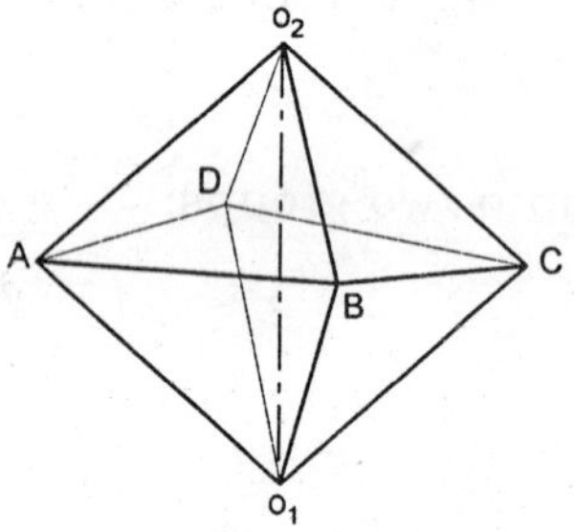

Fig. 9.3

(*iv*) Dodecahedron: A dodecahedron is bounded twelve equal faces, each one being a regular pentagon as shown in Fig. 9.4. It has thirty equal edges and twenty vertices.

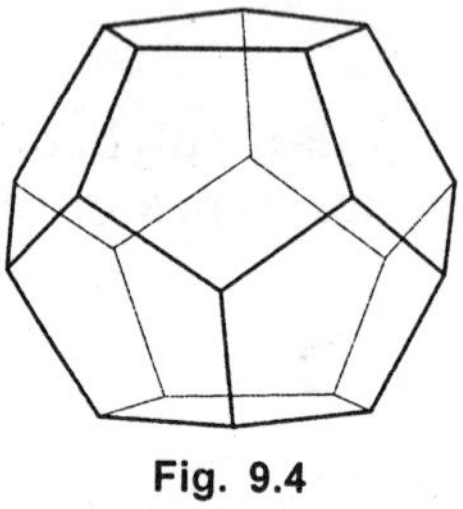

Fig. 9.4

(2) Prism: A prism is a solid contained by plain surfaces, having two equal and similar faces parallel to each other which, are called the ends and the other faces are parallelograms. The lower end of a prism is called the bottom face and the upper one is called the top face. The axis of a prism is the imaginary straight line joining the centroids of its ends. A prism is named after the shape of its ends, such as triangular prism, square prism, rectangular prism, pentagonal prism and hexagonal prism etc. as shown in Fig. 9.5.

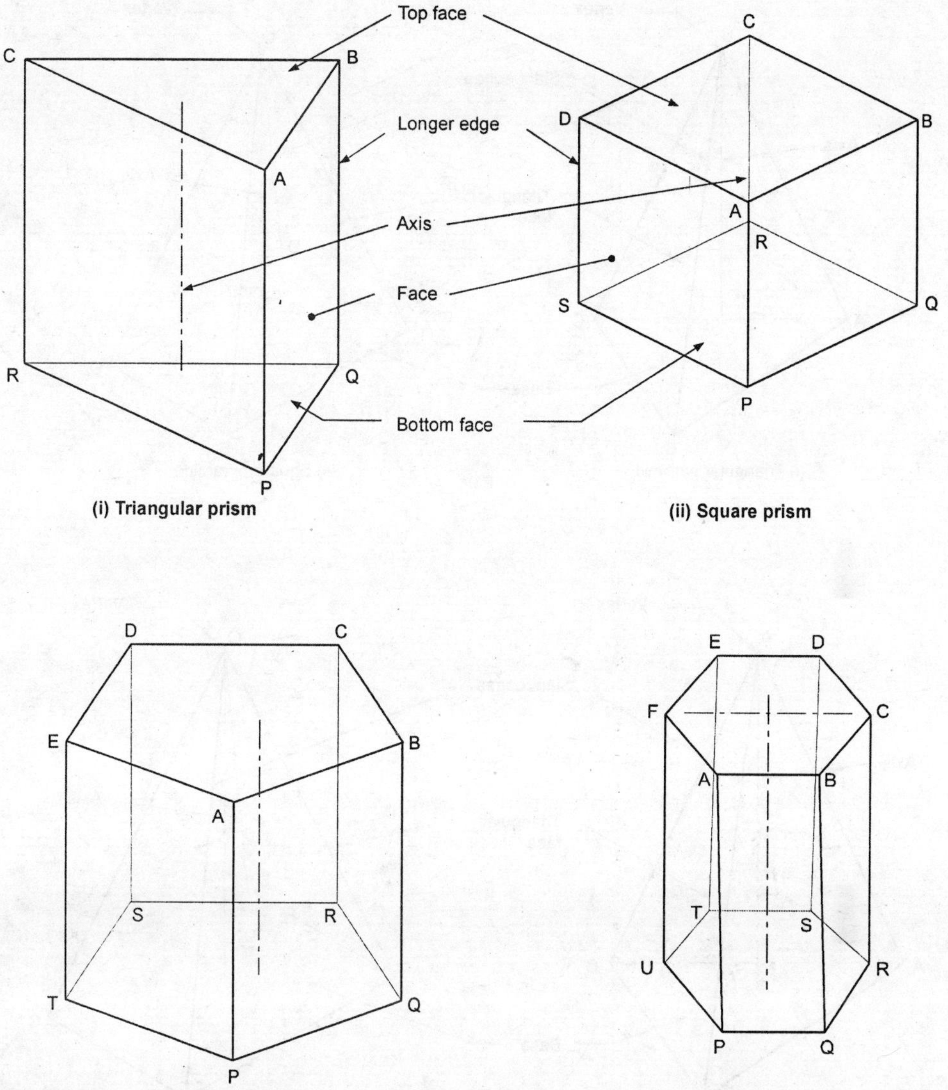

(i) Triangular prism (ii) Square prism

(iii) Pentagonal prism (iv) Hexagonal prism

Fig. 9.5

(3) Pyramids: A pyramid is a solid, contained by plane figures, having a base and a number of triangular faces meeting at a point, called the apex or vertex. A pyramid is named after the shape of its base such as, triangular pyramid, square pyramid, rectangular pyramid, pentagonal pyramid and hexagonal pyramid etc., as shown in Fig. 9.6.

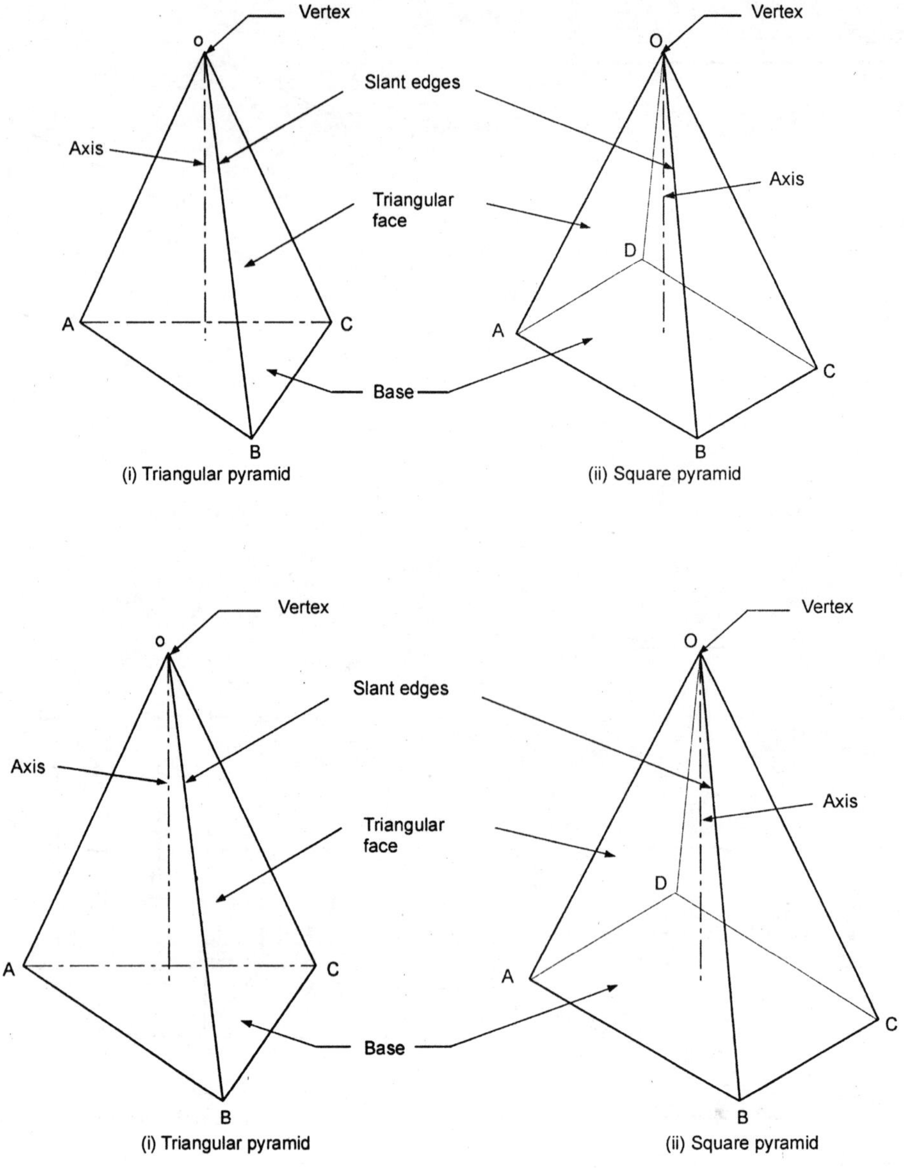

Fig. 9.6

9.4 SOLIDS OF REVOLUTION

If a plane is rotated about one of its edges, which is kept fixed, a solid is obtained. Such a solid will be symmetrical about its axes is called solid of revolution. These are as follows:

(*i*) Cone

(*ii*) Cylinder

(*iii*) Sphere.

(*i*) Cone: A cone is a solid, obtained by the revolution of a right angled triangle, about one of its perpendicular sides which remains fixed.

It has a circular base and an apex or vertex. The line joining the centre of the base with the apex is called axis as shown in Fig. 9.7(i).

(*ii*) Cylinder: A cylinder is a solid, obtained by the revolution of a rectangle about one of its sides which remains fixed. It has two circular faces. The lower end of a cylinder is called the bottom face and the upper one is called the top face as shown in Fig. 9.7(ii).

The axis of the cylinder is the side about which the rectangle revolves i.e., the line joining the centres of the ends of the cylinder is its axis.

(*iii*) Sphere: A sphere is a solid, obtained by the revolution of a semi-circular solid about its diameter, which remains fixed. The mid-point of the diameter is the centre of sphere as shown in Fig. 9.7(iii).

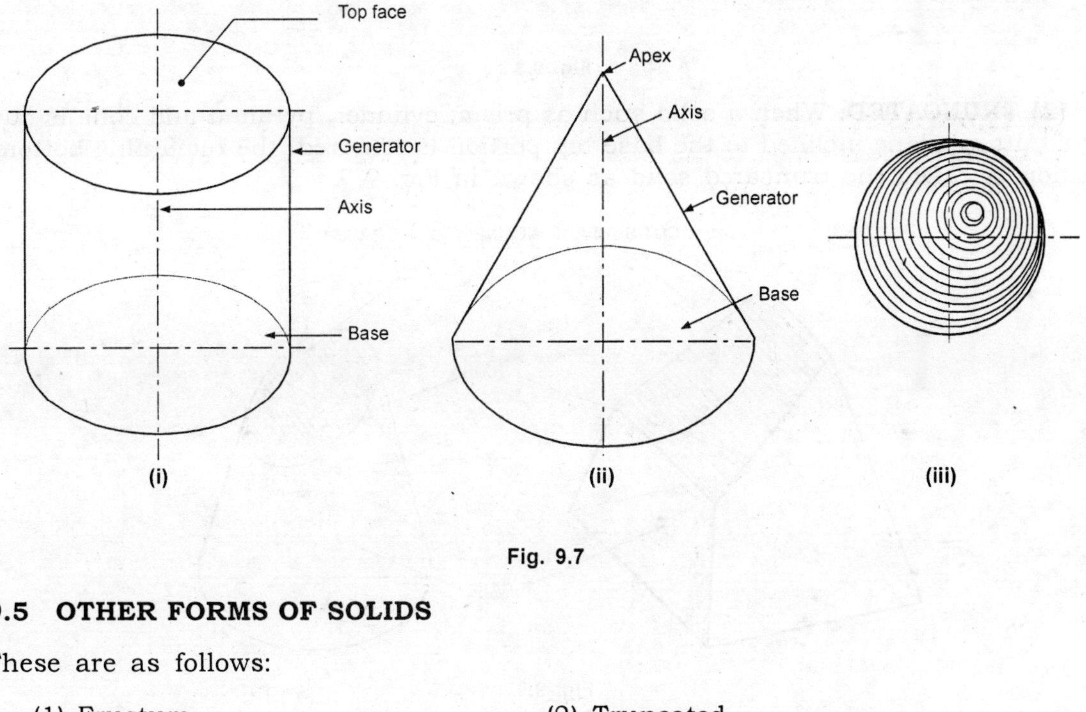

Fig. 9.7

9.5 OTHER FORMS OF SOLIDS

These are as follows:

(1) Frustum (2) Truncated.

(1) FRUSTUM: When a solid is cut by a cutting plane parallel to the base, after removing the top portion is called the frustum. For example, if a cone pyramid is cut by a plane parallel to its base and the top portion is removed, the remaining bottom portion is called the frustum of a cone pyramid as shown in Fig. 9.8 (i) and (ii) shows frustum of a square pyramid.

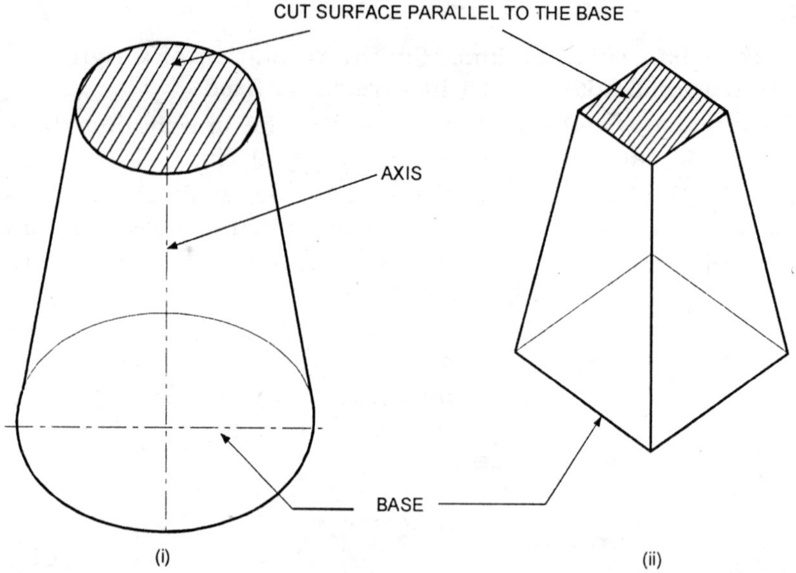

Fig. 9.8

(2) TRUNCATED: When a solid such as prism, cylinder, pyramid and cone is cut by a cutting plane inclined to the base top portion is removed, the remaining bottom portion is called the truncated solid as shown in Fig. 9.9.

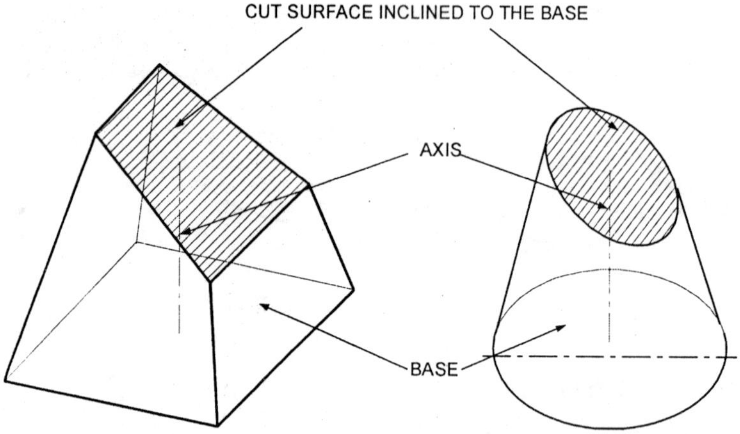

Fig. 9.9

9.6 POSITION OF SOLID

A solid is positioned with reference to the planes of projections by refering to inclination its axis to planes of projection which are horizontal and vertical.

(*i*) Axis perpendicular to H.P and parallel to V.P.
(*ii*) Axis perpendicular to V.P and parallel to H.P.
(*iii*) Axis parallel to both H.P and V.P.
(*iv*) Axis inclined to H.P and parallel to V.P.
(*v*) Axis inclined to V.P and parallel to H.P.
(*vi*) Axis inclined to both H.P and V.P.

9.7 SIMPLE POSITION OF A SOLID

A solid is said to be in simple position if its base is resting on H.P. i.e., when its axis is perpendicular to H.P and parallel to V.P.

1. Use Ist angle projection, when the base of a solid is resting on H.P. plane.
2. When the axis is perpendicular to H.P, the top view shows the true shape and size of the base.
3. When the axis is perpendicular to V.P, the front view shows the true shape and size of the base.
4. When the axis is parallel to both H.P and V.P, the side view shows the true shape and size of the base.
5. When a solid is mentioned without any specific type, it is always considered as regular solid.

Problem 1. A cube of 50 mm edges is resting with one of its square face on H.P. such that one of its vertical face is parallel to and 20 mm in front of V.P. Draw the top view and front view of the square as shown in Fig. 9.10 (i). (Using Ist angle projection.)

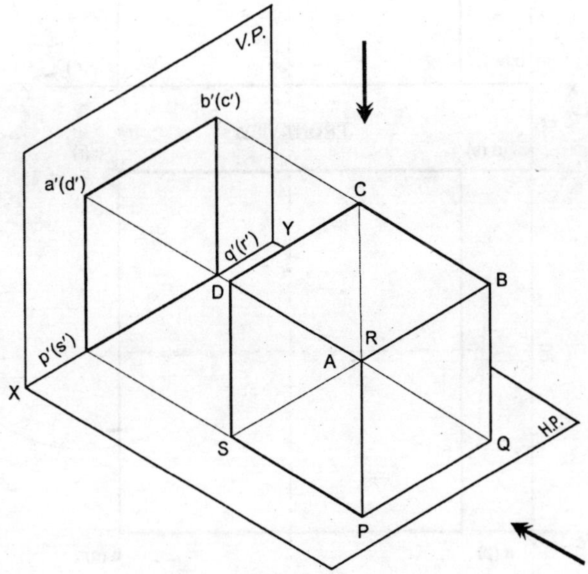

Fig. 9.10 (i)

Solution:

1. A cube of 50 mm with a horizontal face ABCD is parallel to H.P, and an edge CD of a vertical face is parallel to and 20 mm in front of V.P. as shown in Fig. 9.10 (i). Therefore, draw the top view *abcd*, a square of 50 mm side with its edge cd parallel to and 20 mm below the reference line XY.
2. Bottom face PQRS is hidden by the top face ABCD. Therefore, in the top view mark the bottom faces as (*p*), (*q*), (*r*) (*s*) such that *p* and *a* coincide, *q* and *b* coincide etc. Thus, complete the top view.
3. Draw the projectors from the top view.
4. See the cube from the front portion. Bottom face PQRS is on H.P. Draw the front view of the bottom face as *p*′, *q*′, *r*′, *s*′ on the XY-axis.
5. Height 50 mm is seen in front view. Draw a horizontal line 50 mm on the XY-axis to cut the projectors draw from *a, b, c* and *d* at *a*′, *b*′, *c*′ and *d*′ respectively.
6. Now complete the front view of a cube as shown in Fig. 9.10 (ii).

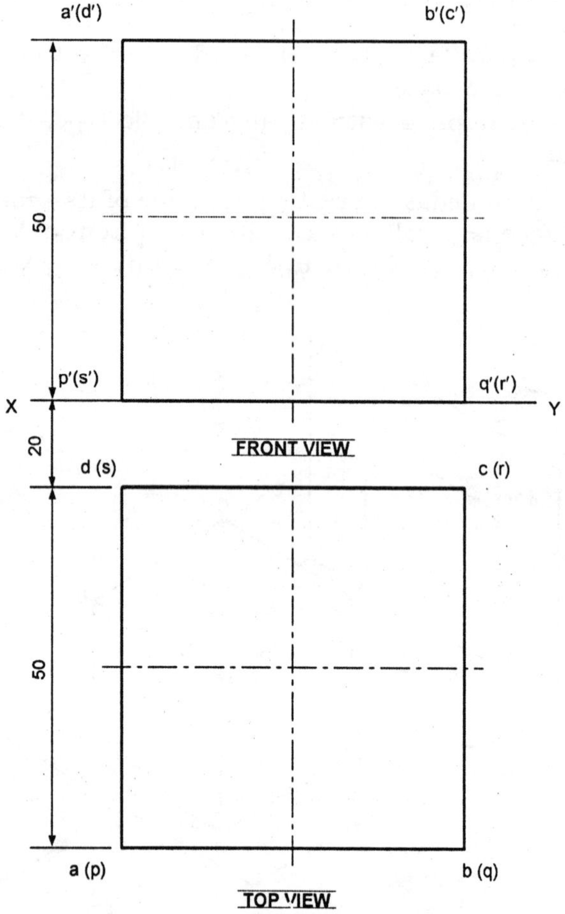

Fig. 9.10 (ii)

Problem 2. Draw a top and front view of a cube of 40 mm edges, is at 20 mm from H.P, and 10 mm from V.P. with its top face parallel to H.P and front face parallel to V.P as shown in Fig. 9.11 (i).

Solution. See in Fig. 9.11 (ii).

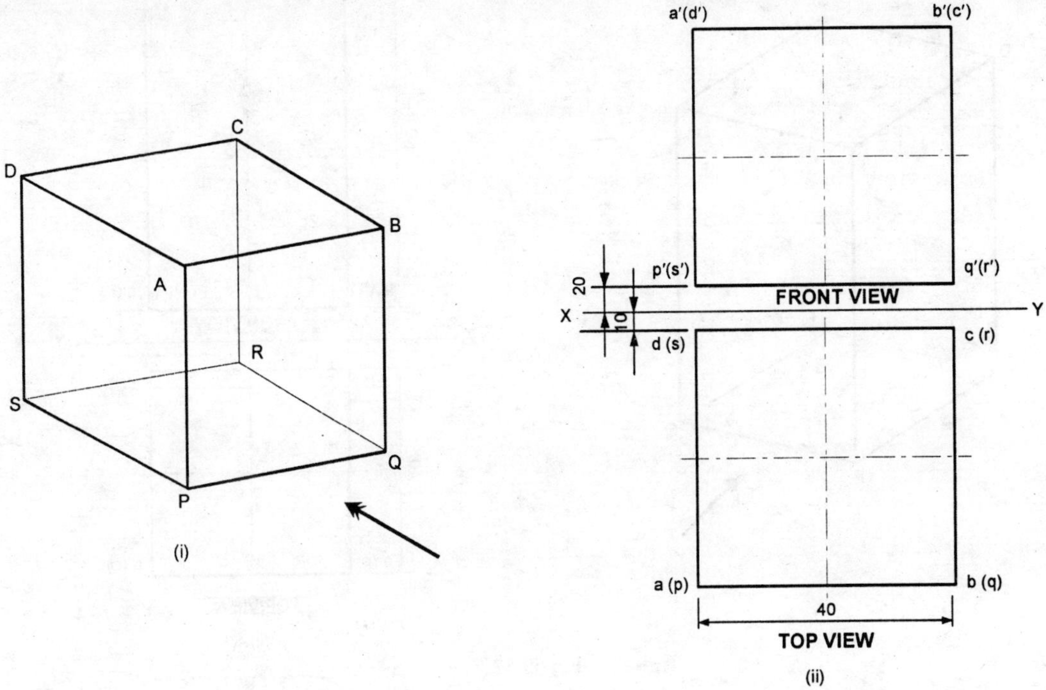

Fig. 9.11

Problem 3. Project the top view and front view of a square prism of 40 mm side and 60 mm height, having its axis vertical and its face infront of and parallel to the V.P. as shown in Fig. 9.12 (i).

Solution. A pictorial view of a square prism is shown in Fig. 9.12 (i) where ABCD is the top face, PQRS is the base and four rectangular faces are bounded by the vertical edges AP, BQ, CR and DS.

1. Prism rests with its base on H.P. Hence the top face ABCD is parallel to H.P. Also edges BC is perpendicular to V.P. Therefore, draw the top view abcd, as a square of side 40 mm with edge *bc* perpendicular to XY.
2. The base PQRS is hidden by ABCD. Therefore, in the top view mark the four corners of the base as (*p*), (*q*), (*r*), (*s*) i.e. (*p*) and *a* coincide, (*q*) and *b* coincide etc.
3. Draw projector from the top view.
4. Look at the prism from the front. The base PQRS is above XY-axis and marks in front view *p*′, *q*′, *r*′, *s*′.

5. Height 60 mm is seen in the front view. Hence, draw a horizontal line 60 mm above *p'*, *r'*, to cut the projectors draw from *a*, *b*, *c*, *d* at *a'*, *b'*, *c'* and *d'* respectively.
6. Now complete front view of a square prism as shown in Fig. 9.12 (ii).

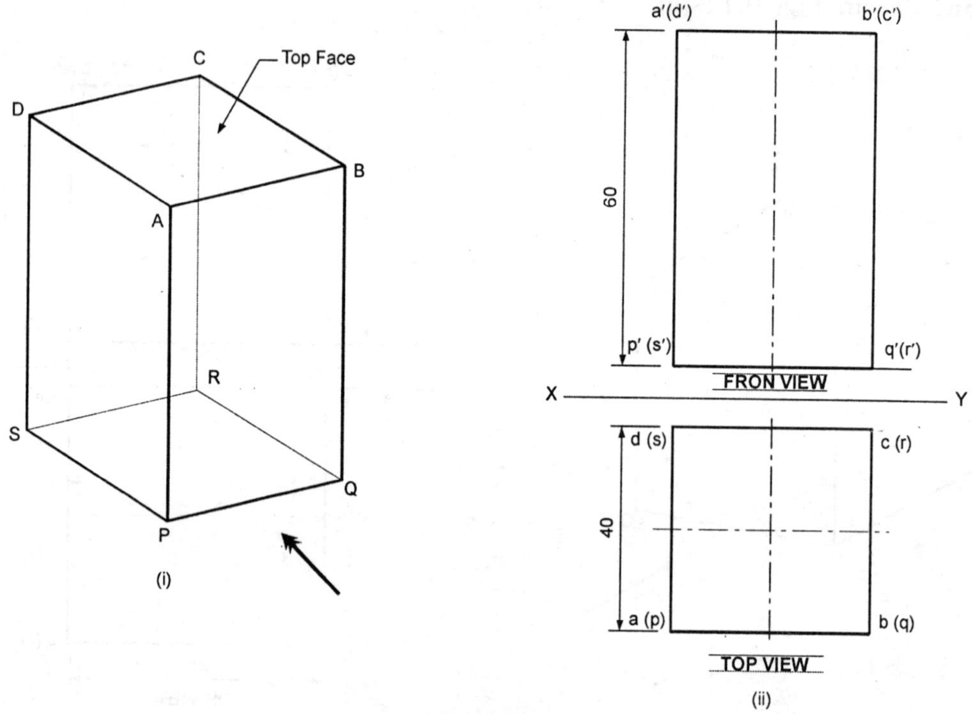

Fig. 9.12

Problem 4: A triangular prism, side of base 30 mm and height 50 mm, is resting on its base on the H.P. One side of the base is parallel to V.P and its opposite corner is nearer to V.P as shown in Fig. 9.13 (i). Draw its projections.

Solution: 1. Look at the pictorial view. Since the prism rests with its base on H.P; as shown in Fig. 9.13 (i).

2. Look at the prism from top. Edge AB is parallel to V.P.
3. Draw the top view of Δabc, which is an equilateral triangle of 30 mm side below XY-axis, having side *ab* parallel to XY and corner *c* nearer to XY.
4. Base PQR is hidden by the top face ABC. So in the top view mark (*p*), (*q*), (*r*) i.e. (*p*) and a coincide, (*q*) and *b* coincide etc.
5. Draw the projectors from top view.
6. Look from the front, base PQR is on H.P. so mark *p'*, *q'*, *r'* on XY as shown in Fig. 9.13 (ii).
7. Height 50 mm is seen in the front view. Draw a horizontal line at a height of 50 mm long above reference line. It cuts the projectors from *a*, *b* and *c* at *a'*, *b'*, *c'* respectively.
8. Now complete the front view of a square prism as shown in Fig. 9.13 (ii).

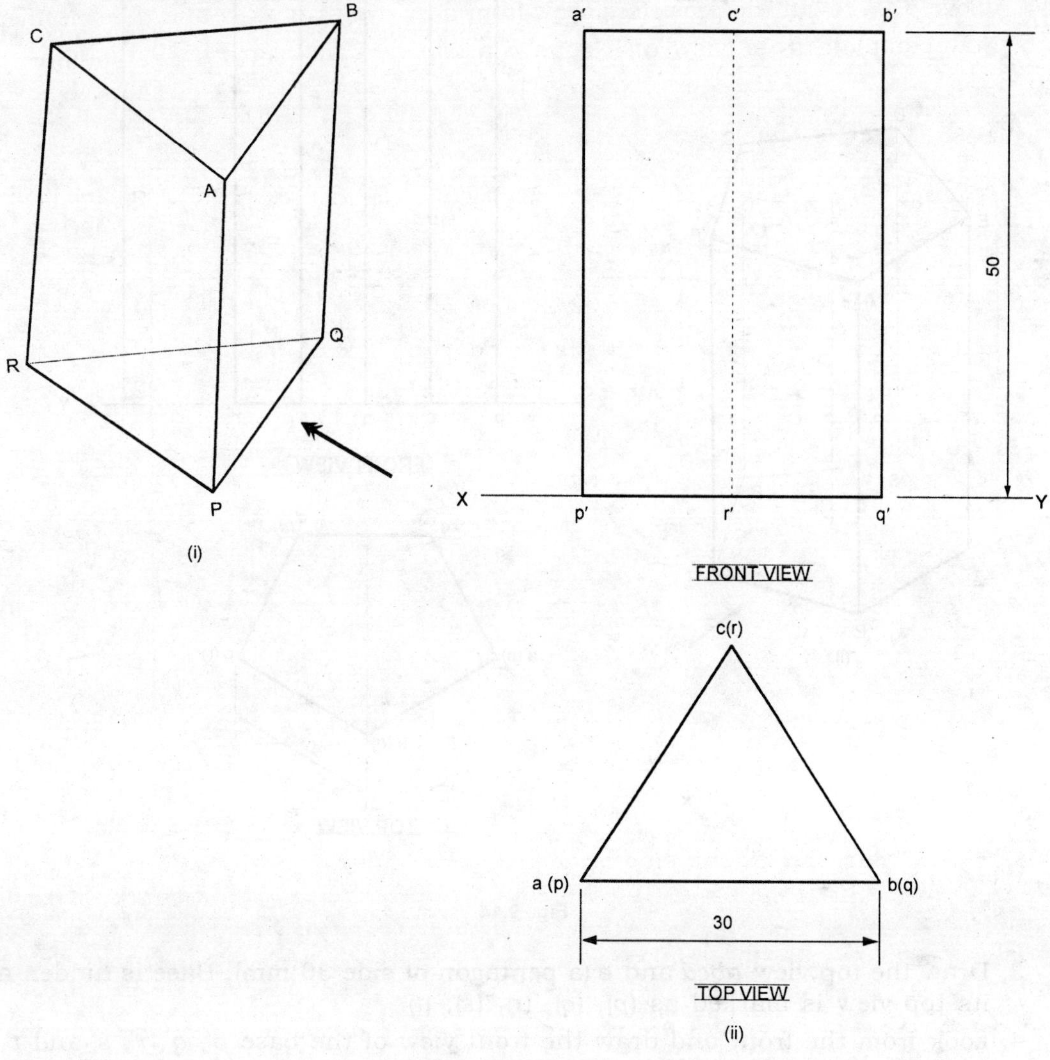

Fig. 9.13

Problem 5: Draw the projections of a pentagonal prism of base side 30 mm and axis length 70 mm resting on H.P. One of its base with a side of base parallel to V.P. as shown in Fig. 9.14 (i).

Solution. 1. Look at the pictorial view. ABCDE is the top face and PQRST is base. Since the prism rests with its base on H.P. The view gives true size of the end face as shown in Fig. 9.14 (i).

2. Look the prism from the top. The face ABCDE is parallel to H.P. its base is a pentagon with a side DE (ST) parallel to XY.

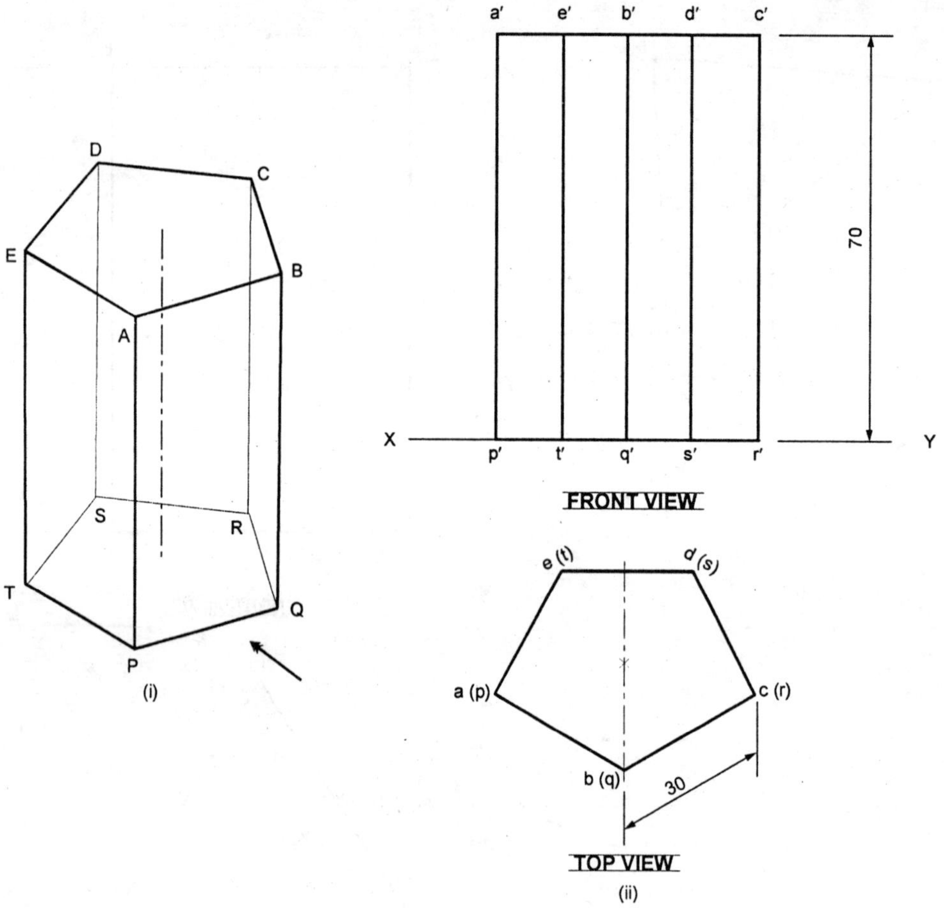

Fig. 9.14

3. Draw the top view *abcd* and *e* (a pentagon of side 30 mm). Base is hidden and its top view is marked as (*p*), (*q*), (*r*), (*s*), (*t*).
4. Look from the front and draw the front view of the base *p*', *q*', *r*', *s*' and *t*' on XY line.
5. Height 70 mm is seen in the front view. Draw the horizontal line on XY and mark the front view of the top face as *a*', *b*', *c*', *d*', *e*'.
6. Now complete front view of a pentagonal prism as shown in Fig. 9.14 (ii).

Problem 6: A hexagonal prism, of 30 mm side and 60 mm height, is at 15 mm from H.P and 10 mm from V.P with its hexagonal ends parallel to H.P. and two of its rectangular faces parallel to V.P. Draw its projection as shown in Fig. 9.15 (i).

Solution: 1. Draw a hexagonal prism *abcdef* with *ed* parallel to V.P. and 10 mm below the XY line to represent the top view.

2. The base is hidden. Therefore, mark its top view as (*p*), (*q*) (*r*) (*s*) (*t*) (*u*) i.e. (*p*) and a coincide etc.
3. From the point *a*, *b*, *c*, *d*, *e* and *f* draw the projectors to XY and produce them 15 mm above XY, to get the front view.
4. Height 60 mm is seen in the front view. Draw a horizontal line of 60 mm, above XY and mark the front view of the top face as *a'*, *b'*, *c' d'*, *e'* and *f'*.
5. Now complete front view of a hexagonal prism as shown in Fig. 9.15 (ii).

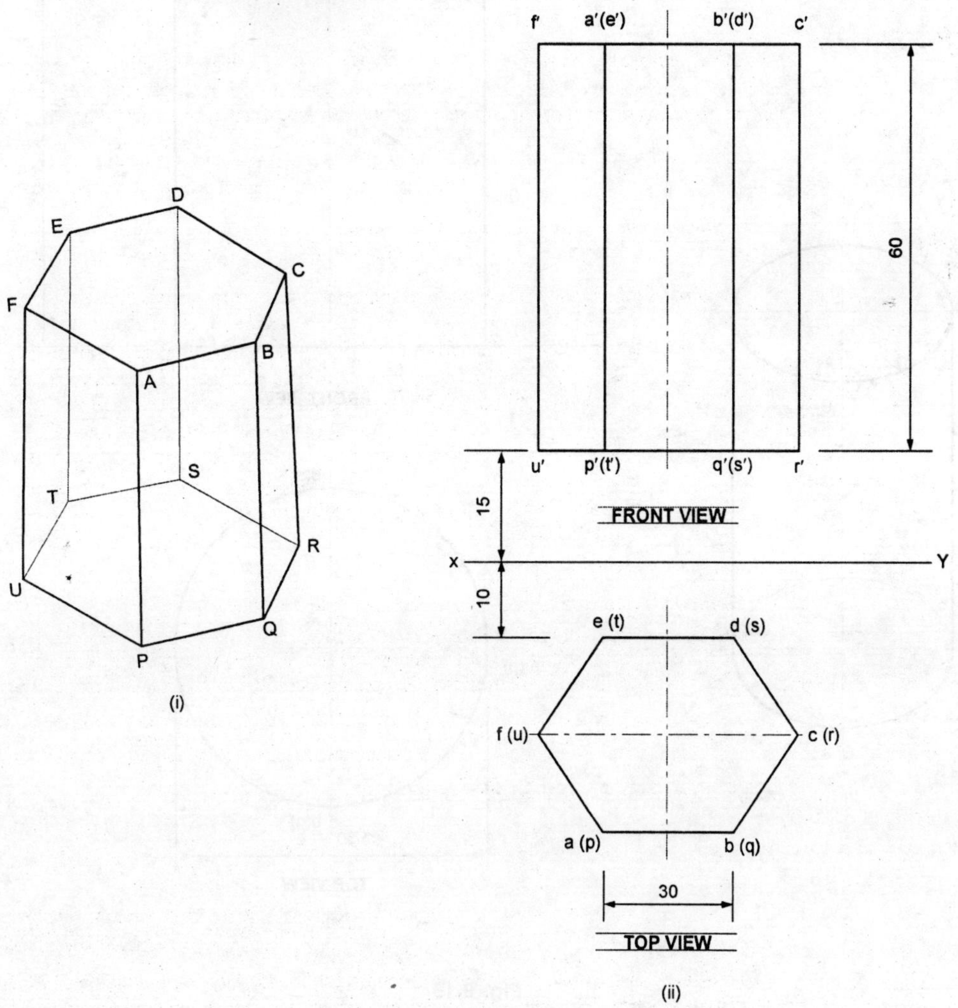

Fig. 9.15

Problem 7: A cylinder, base 30 mm in diameter and axis 60 mm long is resting on the H.P. Draw its projection as shown in Fig. 9.16 (i).

Solution: See in Fig. 9.16.

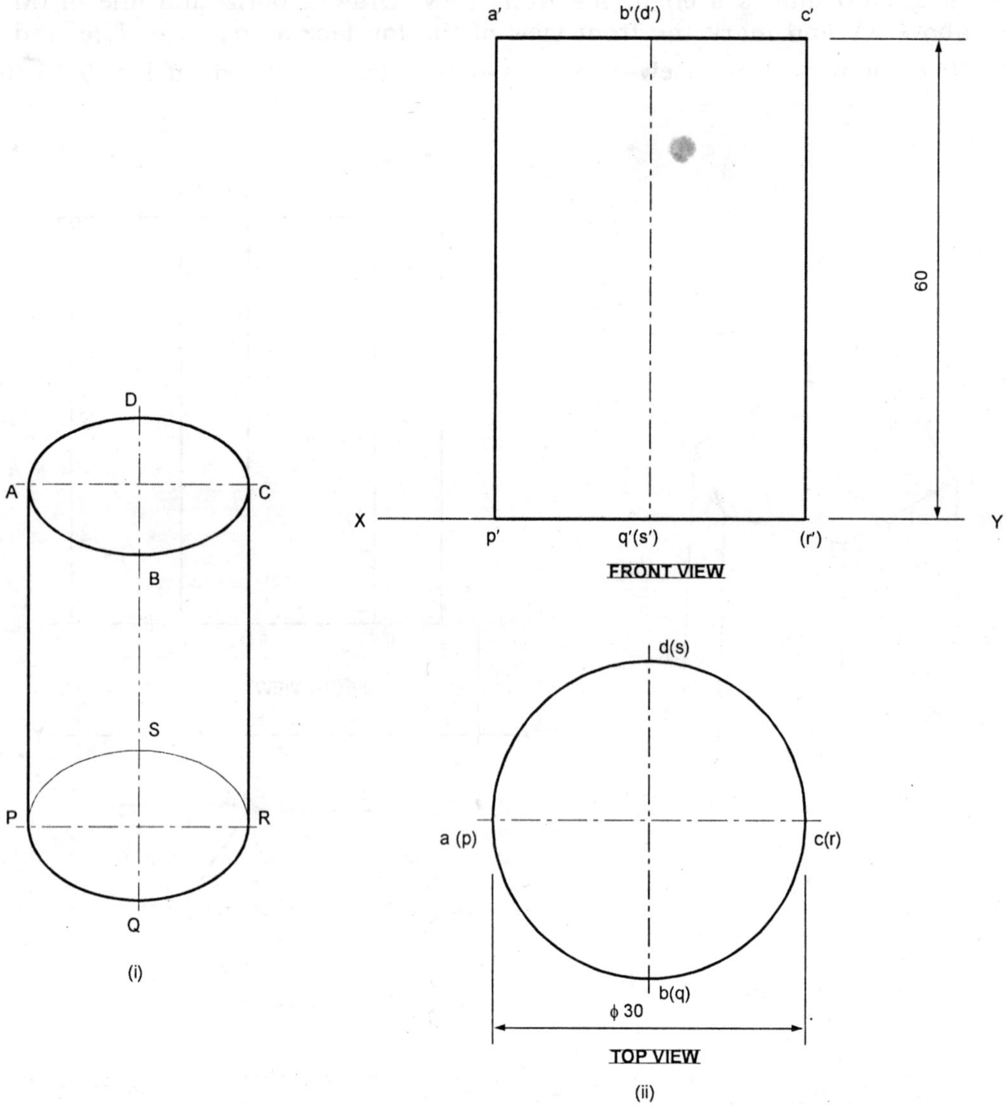

Fig. 9.16

Problem 8. Draw the projections of a square pyramid, side of base 40 mm and axis is 60 mm long. The pyramid is 15 mm above H.P and 20 mm in front of V.P, with its axis vertical and two sides of its base parallel to V.P. as shown in Fig. 9.17 (i).

Solution: See in Fig. 9.17 (ii).

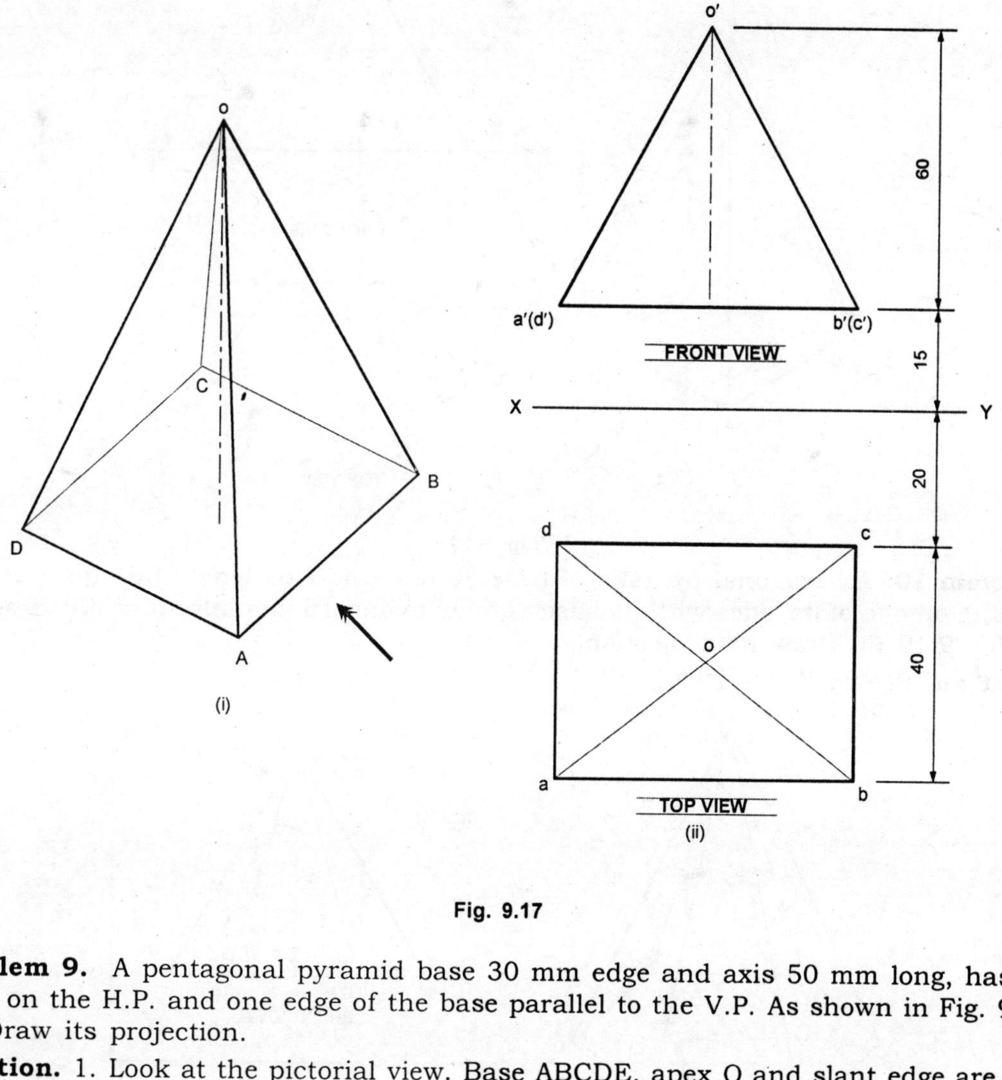

Fig. 9.17

Problem 9. A pentagonal pyramid base 30 mm edge and axis 50 mm long, has its base on the H.P. and one edge of the base parallel to the V.P. As shown in Fig. 9.18 (i). Draw its projection.

Solution. 1. Look at the pictorial view. Base ABCDE, apex O and slant edge are OA, OB ... etc.

2. Draw the pentagon prism *abcde* of side 30 mm with *ab* parallel to XY.
3. Draw the perpendicular bisectors of any two sides of the pentagon to intersect at *o*, the top view of the apex and join *oa*, *ob*, etc.
4. Mark *a'*, *b'*, *c'*, *d'*, *e'* the front view of the base on XY. Mark *o'* front view of the apex 50 mm above XY. Join *o'*, *e'* etc. to represent front view of the slant edge.
5. Now complete the top view and front view of a pentagonal pyramid as shown in Fig. 9.18 (ii).

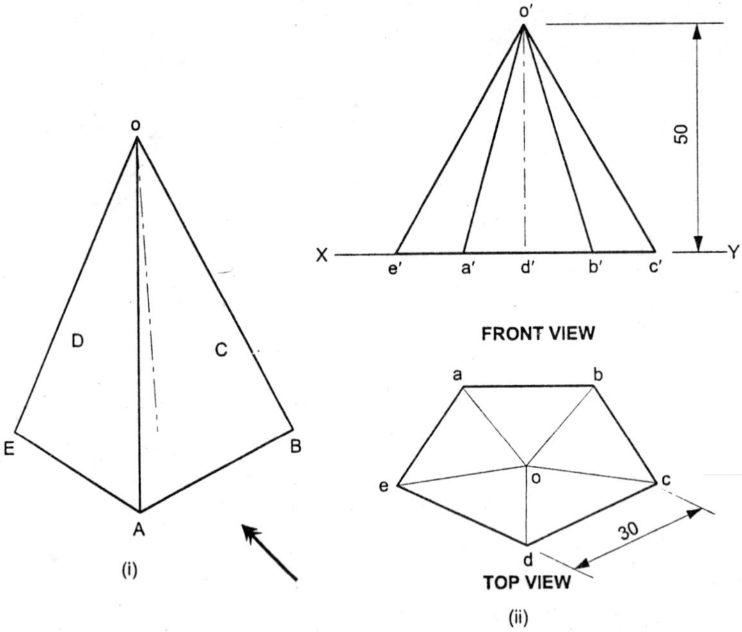

Fig. 9.18

Problem 10. A hexagonal pyramid of base 30 mm and axis length 60 mm is resting on H.P. on one of its sides with its base parallel to and 15 mm infront of V.P as shown in Fig. 9.19 (i). Draw its projection.

Solution. See in Fig. 9.19 (ii).

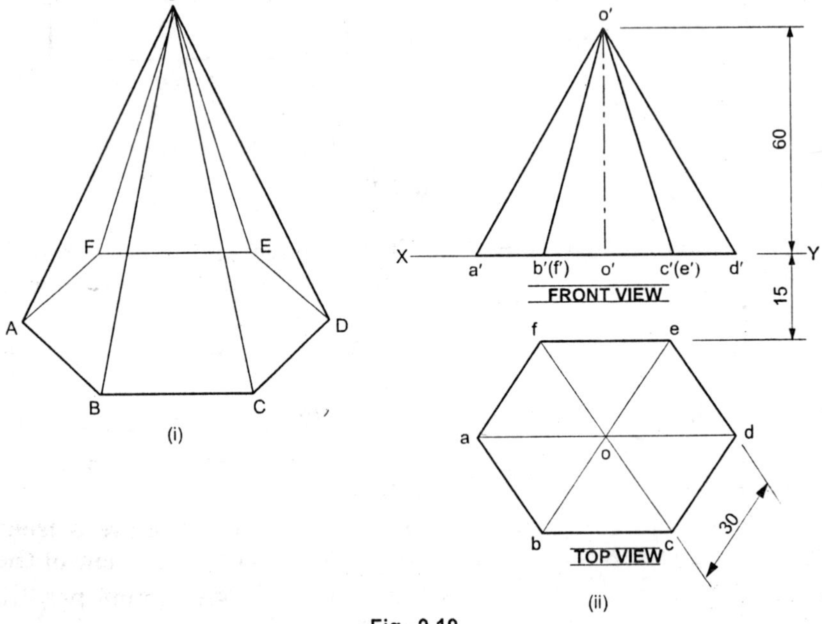

Fig. 9.19

Problem 11. A cone, base 30 mm diameter, axis 50 mm long, when resting with its base on H.P as shown in Fig. 9.20 (i). Draw its projection.

Solution. See in Fig. 9.20 (ii).

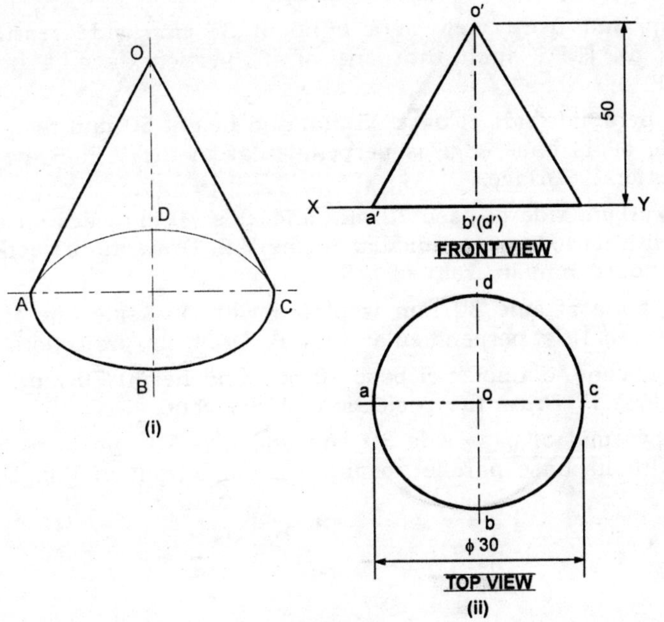

Fig. 9.20

Problem 12. A right regular square pyramid is resting on the H.P. with its axis perpendicular to H.P. and parallel to V.P. the side of base is 15 mm and height 30 mm. One of its base is parallel to V.P. and 15 mm infront of it. Draw the projections of the pyramid in H.P. and V.P. **(January 2009, B.T.E. New Delhi)**

Solution. See in Fig. 9.21.

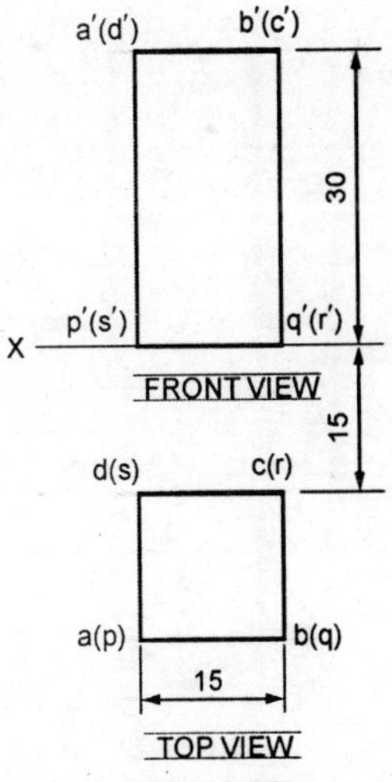

Fig. 9.21

EXERCISE

1. What do you understand by projection of solid?
2. Name the various type of regular polyhedra.
3. Draw the top and front view of a cube of 35 mm side resting with one of its square faces on H.P., such that one of its vertical face is parallel and 15 mm infront of V.P.
4. A pentagonal pyramid side of base 25 mm and height 50 mm rests on its base on H.P. such that one of its base edge is perpendicular to the V.P. Draw its projections and develop its Lateral Surface.
5. A pentagonal prism, side of base 30 mm and axis 70 mm, lies on one of its triangular face in H.P. with its axis perpendicular to the V.P. Draw its projections of one end face of the prism be 10 mm in front of V.P.
6. A pentagonal plate of side 30 mm is placed with one side one H.P. and the surface inclined at 50° to H.P. perpendicular to V.P. Draw its projection.
7. A right circular cone, diameter of base 40 mm and height 70 mm, lies on H.P. and its axis parallel to V.P. Draw the projection of the cone.
8. A hexagonal pyramid of base side 30 mm and axis 70 mm is resting on H.P. on one of its sides with its base parallel to and 15 mm infront of V.P. Draw its projections.

❑❑❑

10

SECTION OF SOLIDS

10.1 INTRODUCTION

Section views, commonly known as sections are used to show the interior details of an object that are too complicated to be shown clearly by regular views using hidden lines.

The main aim of sectioning is to show the interior details of complicated machine parts. In order to achieve this, the object is supposed to be cut by a plane and the material lying between the observer and the section plane is removed, to bring out the interior details of the object clearly. The exposed surface of the solid is known as the section and the cutting plane as section plane.

The sections are generally shown by hatching, i.e. by drawing thin parallel lines inclined to the main outline or axis of the views, usually at an angle of 45°. The gap between two hatching lines is 2 mm.

10.2 TERMINOLOGY

(i) Section: The surface obtained by cutting the object by the section plane is known as section.

(ii) Section views: The projection of the section of an object with its remaining position is known as sectional view. The cut portion shown on H.P is known as sectional top view and that on V.P as sectional front view.

(iii) Section plane: The section planes are assumed to be transparent and increased according to the object shape and size. It should be perpendicular to one of the reference plane and either parallel or inclined or perpendicular to the other.

(iv) True section: The projection of the section obtained on a plane parallel to the section plane, which is same as the section exposed by the section plane is known as true section as shown in Fig. 10.1.

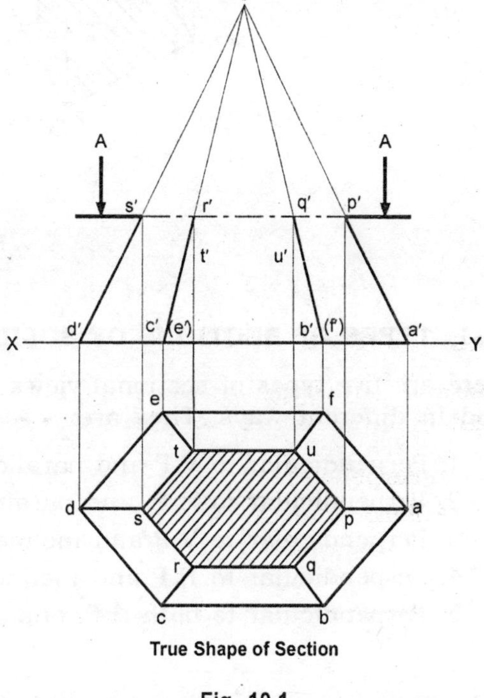

True Shape of Section

Fig. 10.1

(v) Apparent section: The projection of a section on the principal plane to which the section plane is perpendicular is a straight line coinciding with the face of the section plane on it whereas its projection on the principal plane to which it is inclined is apparent section as shown in Fig. 10.2.

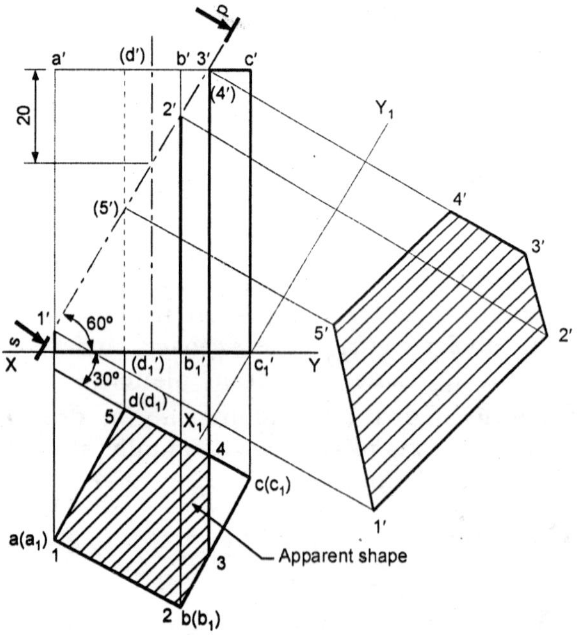

Fig. 10.2

10.3 TYPES OF SECTIONS OF SOLIDS

There are five types of sectional views of solid which are obtained after cutting the solid in different ways. They are:

1. Perpendicular to V.P and parallel to H.P.
2. Perpendicular to H.P. and parallel to V.P.
3. Perpendicular to V.P and inclined to H.P.
4. Perpendicular to H.P and inclined to V.P.
5. Perpendicular to both H.P. and V.P.

10.4 SECTION PLANE PERPENDICULAR TO V.P AND PARALLEL TO H.P

Problem 1. A square prism, side of base 40 mm and height 60 mm, rests with its base on H.P. i.e. two of its rectangular faces are parallel to V.P. is sectioned by a horizontal plane which passes through it is 20 mm below its top face as shown in Fig. 10.3 (i). Draw its front view and sectional top view.

Solution: See in Fig. 10.3 (ii).

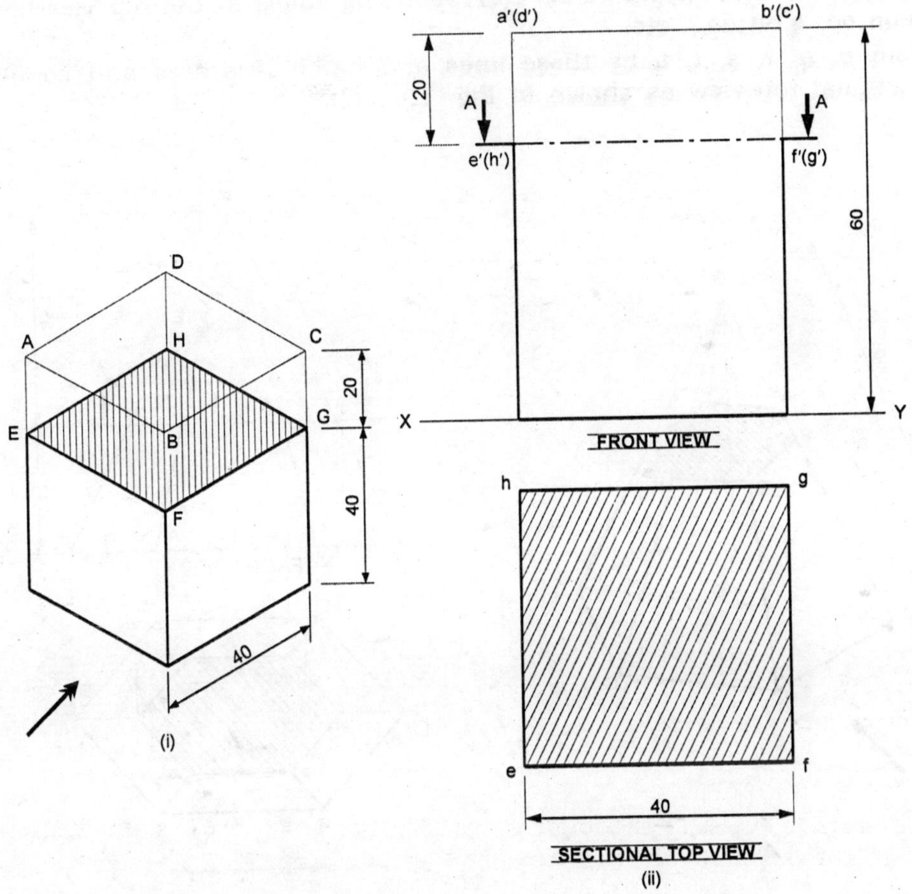

Fig. 10.3

Problem 2. A hexagonal pyramid, side of base 30 mm and height 60 mm, with its axis vertical and two sides of its base parallel to V.P. is cut by a horizontal plane which passes through its axis, 35 mm below its vertex as shown in Fig. 10.4 (i). Draw, sectional top view and front view.

Solution. 1. Draw the section plane to XY and passing through the axis at 35 mm below the vertex *o'*.

2. Name the points *p'*, *q'*, *r'*, *s'* etc where the section plane cuts the visible edges *o'a'*, *o'b'* and *o'c'* respectively.
3. Show the remaining part of the pyramid *a'*, *b'*, *c'*, (*d'*), (*e'*), *f'*.
4. Project the section points on corresponding edges in the top view i.e., mark *p* on *oa*, *q* on *ob*... etc.
5. Join *p*, *q*, *r*, *s*, *t*, *u* by these lines and hatch this area and complete the sectional top view as shown in Fig. 10.4 (ii).

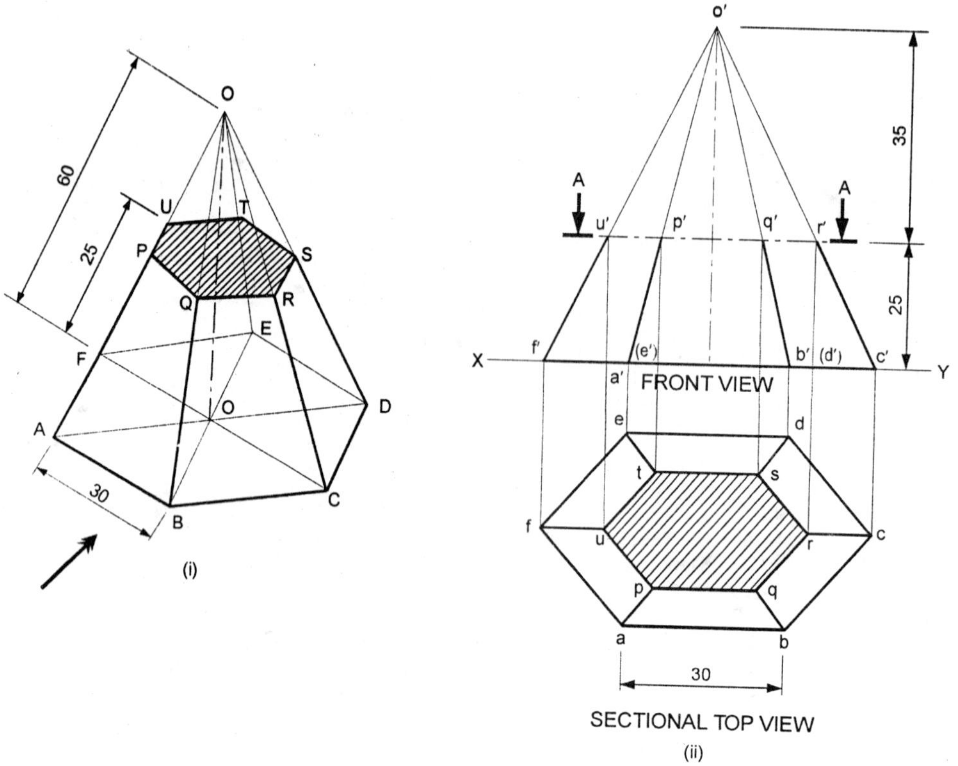

Fig. 10.4

Problem 3. A cone of 40 mm diameter and 60 mm height with its axis vertical is cut by a horizontal plane, 30 mm below its vertex as shown in Fig. 10.5 (i). Draw its front view and sectional top view.

Solution. 1. Fig. 10.5 (i) shows the pictorial view of a cone cut and the upper portion removed. The sectional top view is observed in the direction A.

2. Draw the section plane XY passing through the axis at 30 mm below the vertex *o'*.
3. Name the points *p'*, *q'*, *r'*, *s'* where the section plane cuts the visible edges *o'a'* and *o'c'* respectively.
4. Show the remaining parts of the cone *a'*, *b'*, *c'*, *d'*.
5. Project the section point on corresponding edges in top view i.e., mark *p*, *q*, *r*, *s*.
6. Draw the circle and hatch this area and complete the sectional top view as shown in Fig. 10.5 (ii).

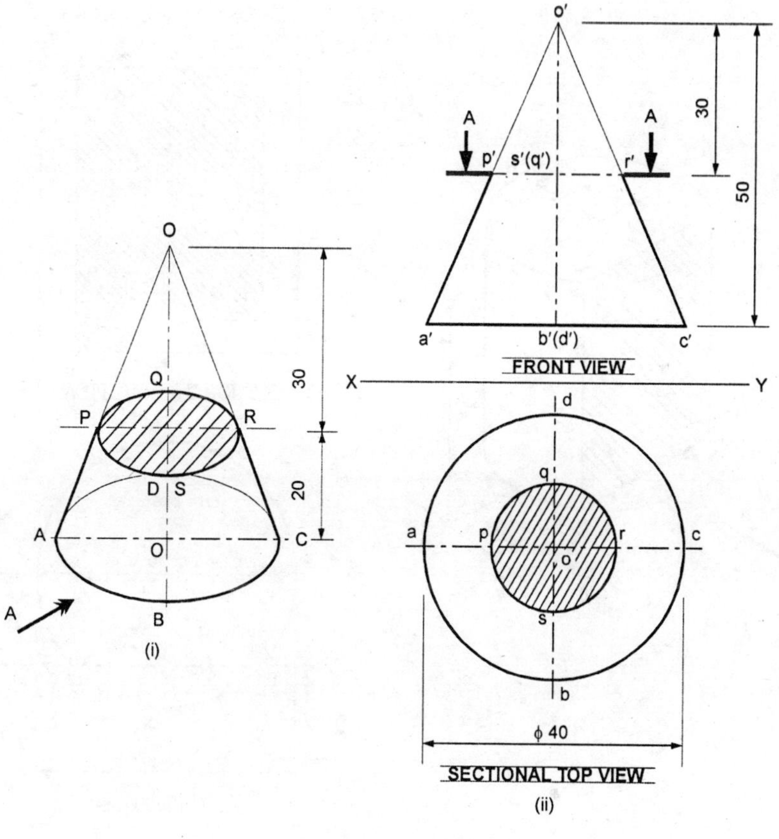

Fig. 10.5

10.5 SECTION PLANE PERPENDICULAR TO H.P. AND PARALLEL TO V.P.

Problem 4. A cylinder of 40 mm diameter and 60 mm height stands vertically on H.P. and is cut by a section plane perpendicular to H.P; parallel to V.P at a distance of 12 mm from the axis. Draw its top and sectional front view.

Solution. 1. Fig. 10.6 (i) shows the cylinder actually cut by the vertical plane. The portion removed is shown by section line.

2. Draw the top view of the cylinder and draw the cutting plane line *e* and *f* parallel to XY, 12 mm from the axis and section is viewed in the direction A-A.
3. Draw the front view of the cylinder and draw projectors from *e* and *f* intersecting the top and bottom faces of the front view in *e'*, *h'* and *f'*, *g'* respectively.
4. Hatching the rectangle *e'*, *f'*, *g'* and *h'* to complete the sectional front view as shown in Fig. 10.6 (ii).

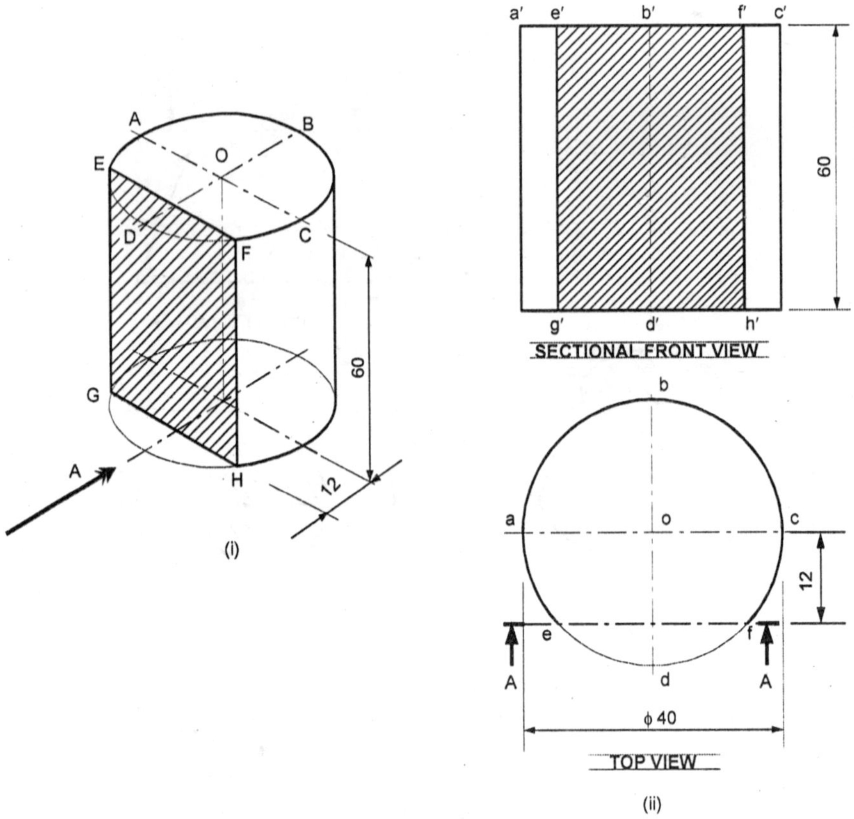

Fig. 10.6

Problem 5. An equilateral triangular prism, side of triangle is 35 mm rests on horizontal plane. The height of the prism is 60 mm, with its axis vertical and back rectangular face parallel to V.P. is cut by a vertical plane, parallel to the V.P 20 mm, behind the edge infront as shown in Fig. 10.7 (i). Draw its top and sectional front viwe.

Solution. See in Fig. 10.7 (ii).

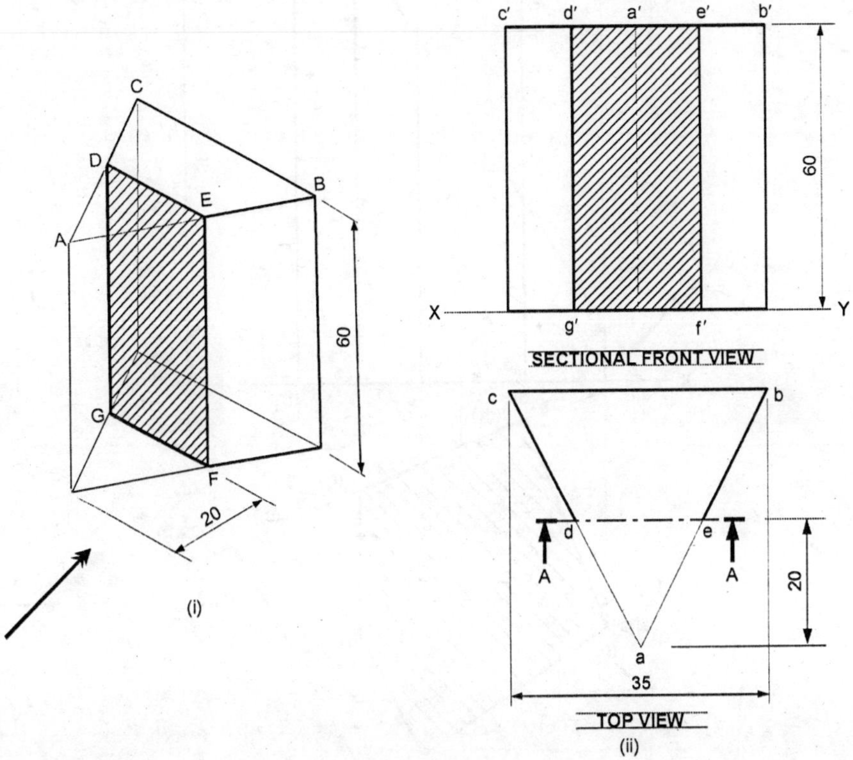

Fig. 10.7

10.6 PERPENDICULAR TO V.P. AND INCLINED TO H.P.

Problem 6. A square prism, side of base 35 mm and height 60 mm rests with its base on H.P and one of its rectangular faces is inclined at 30° to V.P. A section plane perpendicular to V.P. and inclined at 60° to H.P. cuts the axis of the prism at a point 20 mm from its top end. Draw the sectional top view.

Solution. 1. *a*, *b*, *c*, *d* is the top view of the prism a', c', c_1', a_1' the front view.

2. Draw section plane at 60° to XY and passing through a point on the axis 20 mm from its top end. Name the section points p', r', q' s' and t' in front view.

2. Project the section points on the corresponding edges in the top view and draw the cut surface. Then complete the sectional top view as shown in Fig. 10.8.

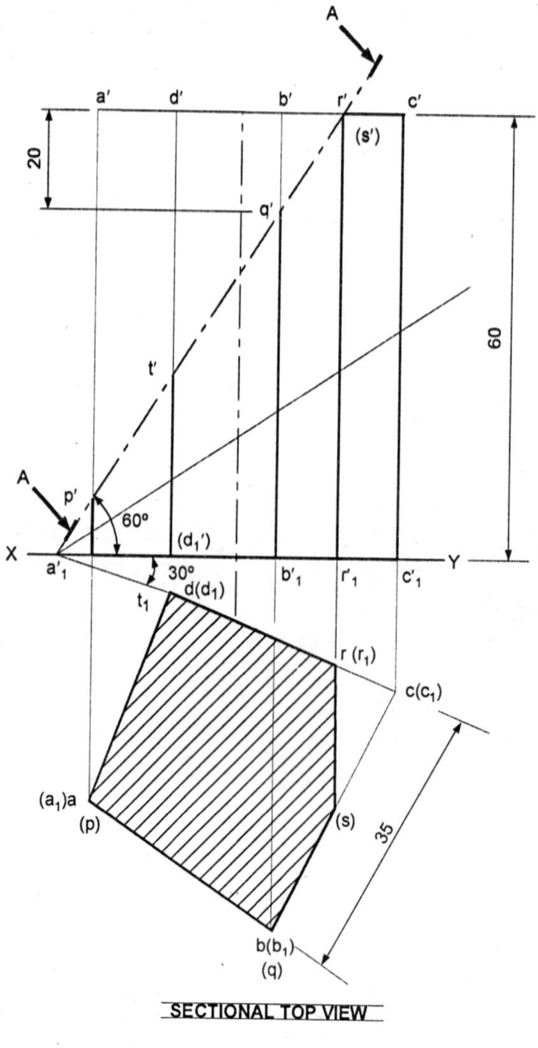

Fig. 10.8

Problem 7. A pentagonal pyramid, side of base 35 mm and height 60 mm, rests with its base on H.P. and an edge of its base is parallel to V.P. A section plane perpendicular to V.P. and inclined at 45° to H.P. passes through the axis at a point 40 mm above the base. Draw the sectional top view.

Solution. See in Fig. 10.9.

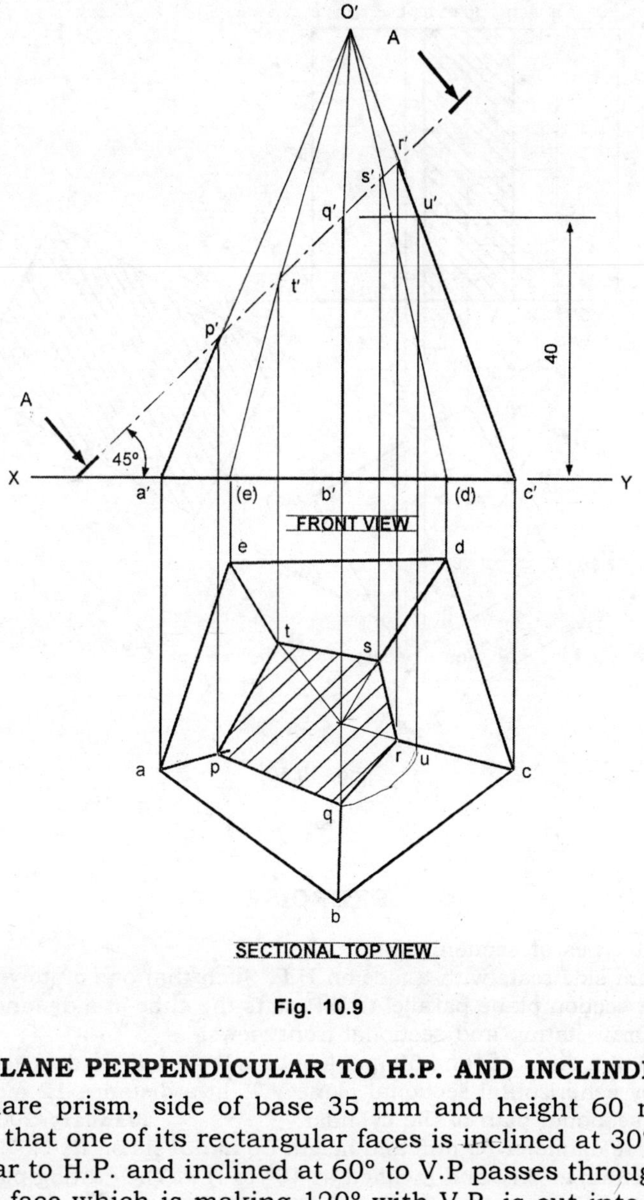

Fig. 10.9

10.7 SECTION PLANE PERPENDICULAR TO H.P. AND INCLINDED TO V.P.

Problem 8. A square prism, side of base 35 mm and height 60 mm rests with its base on H.P. such that one of its rectangular faces is inclined at 30° to V.P. A section plane perpendicular to H.P. and inclined at 60° to V.P passes through the prism such that a rectangular face which is making 120° with V.P. is cut into two halves. Draw the top view, sectional front view and true shape of section.

Solution.

1. Draw the projections of the prism for the given position.
2. Draw section plane inclined at 60° to XY such that it passes through the mid-point of the edge in the top view.
3. Draw the sectional front view and true shape of the section of the square prism as shown in Fig. 10.10.

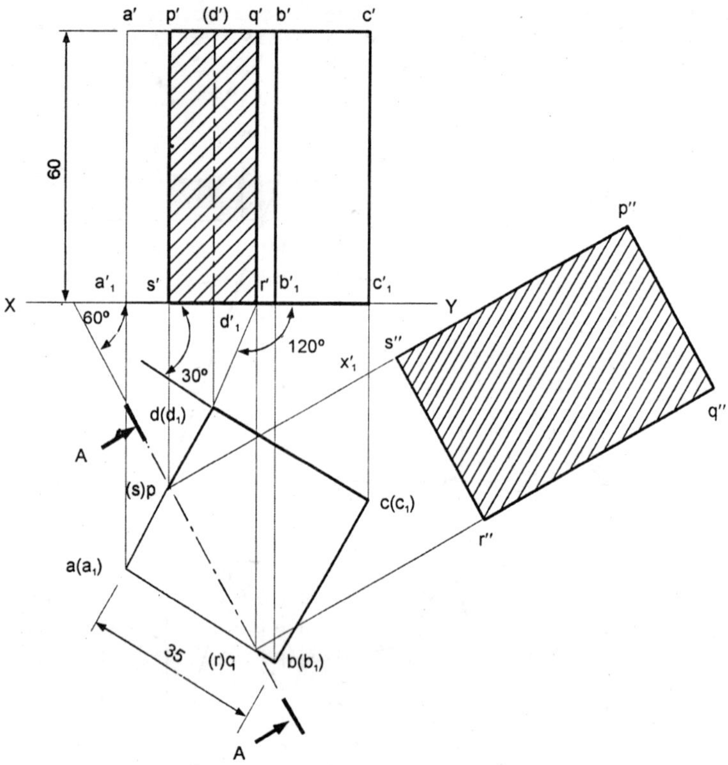

Fig. 10.10

EXERCISE

1. Define different types of section planes.
2. A cube of 55 mm side rests with a face on H.P. Such that one of its vertical face is inclined at 30° to V.P. A section plane parallel to V.P. cuts the cube at a distance of 12 mm from the vertical edge. Draw its top and sectional front views.
3. A cylinder of 30 mm diameter and 60 mm length is lying with its axis at an angle of 45° to the V.P. It is cut by a horizontal sectional plane V.T. at a distance 12 mm infront of the axis. Draw the true sectional plan of the cylinder. **(January 2009, B.T.E. New Delhi)**
4. A cylinder of base diameter 50 mm and height 60 mm rests on its base on H.P. It is cut by a plane perpendicular to V.P. and inclined at 45° to H.P. The cutting plane meets the axis at a distance 15 mm from top to the base. Draw the sectional top view and true shape of section.
5. A right circular cone diameter of base 60 mm and height 80 mm, has its base in the H.P. and it is cut by an inclined plane cutting the axis at an angle of 45° at a point 30 mm below the vertex.

   Draw the top view, front view and find the true shape of section.

□□□

11

INTERSECTION OF SOLID

11.1 INTRODUCTION

Intersection occurs frequently in the design world. Therefore, a deep knowledge is must for designers and engineers.

The intersecting surfaces may be two plane surfaces or two curved surfaces of solids. The lateral surface of every solid taken a whole is a curved surface. This surface may be made of only curved surface as in case of cylinders, cones etc. or of plane surface as in case of prisms, pyramids etc. In the former case the problem is said to be "intersection of surfaces" and in the latter case, it is known as interpenetration of solids.

When one solid penetrates the other, it is known as interpenetration of solids.

In both the above cases the surfaces of the solids come in contact with another, the former is known as "the curve of intersection of surfaces" and the later "the curve of interpenetration".

It may be curved, straight or combination of curved and straight lines that occurs when geometrical surfaces such as cylinders, cones, prisms etc. intersect each other. In many engineering components such as different shapes of containers; tanks, machine casting, boiler shells, pipe joints etc, interpenetration of one part into another part may appear, hence the knowledge in intersection of their surface is required in order to fabricate those parts. The methods presented in this chapter are reorganized procedure for finding the more complicated lines of intersecting created by intersection of geometrical surface.

11.2 CLASSIFICATION OF INTERSECTING SURFACES

The intersecting surfaces are classified as follows:

1. Intersection of two plane surfaces.
2. Intersection of two curved surfaces.
3. Intersection between a plane surface and a curved surface.

1. Intersection of two plane surfaces: When two solids bounded by plane surfaces such as prism and pyramid, penetrate each other we get straight lines as their lines of intersections.

2. Intersection of two curved surfaces: When two solids, bounded by curved surfaces, such as cone and cylinder, intersect each other, the line of intersection is a tortuous curve.

3. Intersection between a plane surface and a curved surface: When two solids, one bounded by plane surface and other by curved surface, such as prism and cylinder, penetrate each other, the line of intersection is a curve.

11.3 METHODS OF DETERMINING THE LINE OF INTERSECTION

There are two methods of determining the line of intersection between surfaces of two interpenetrating solids.

(*i*) Line method (*ii*) Cutting plane method.

(*i*) Line method: The process consists of drawing a number of lines on one surface and locating the points at which these lines intersect with the surface of the other solid. The points obtained lie on the line of intersection which may be either straight or curved.

(*ii*) Cutting plane method: This method is generally used to determine the line of intersection. The two solids, are assumed to be cut by a series of cutting planes which are so selected as to cut the surface of one of the solids in straight lines and that of the other in straight lines or circles.

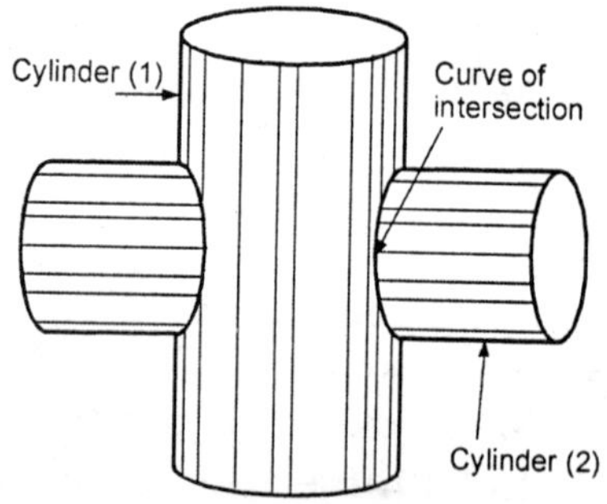

(i) Interpenetration of two cylinders

Fig. 11.1

Problem 1: A cylinder of 50 mm diameter and axis 70 mm long stands with its base on H.P. It is completely penetrated by a horizontal cylinder of 40 mm diameter and axis 80 mm long such that their axis bisect each other at right angles. The axis of the penetrating cylinder is parallel to V.P as shown in Fig. 11.1 (i). Draw the projections showing curves of intersection.

Solution. See Fig. 11.1(ii).

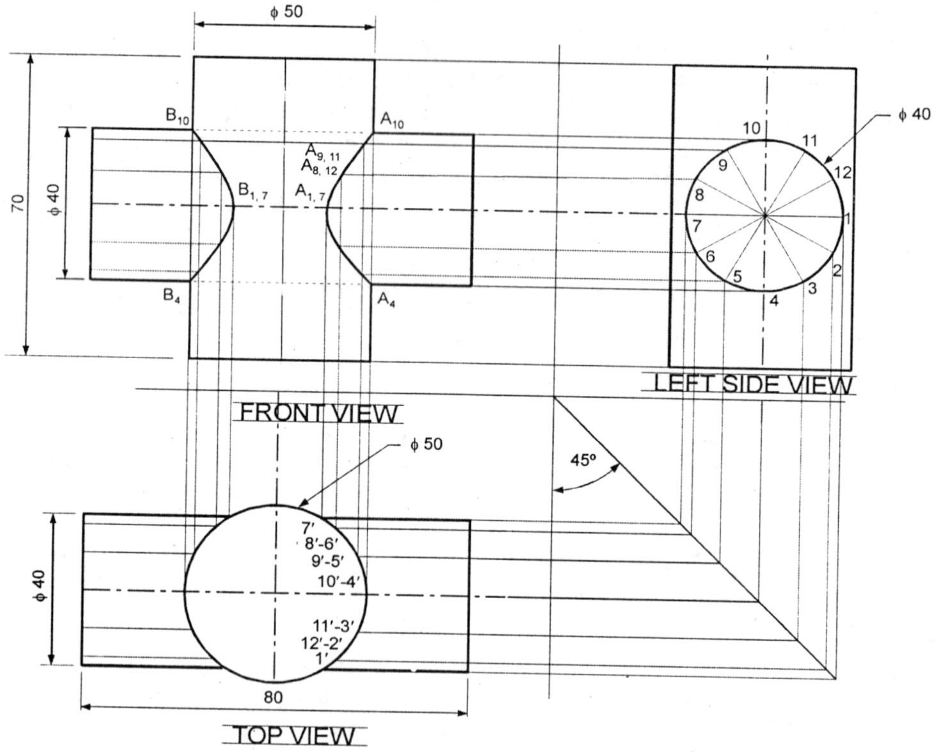

Fig. 11.1 (ii)

Method Ist

Line Method

1. Draw the top, front and left side views of the vertical cylinder.
2. Draw the left side view of the horizontal cylinder as a circle of diameter 40 mm such that its centre is at the mid-point of the axis of the vertical cylinder. Divide the circle into 12 equal parts and mark point 1, 2, 3, ... etc.
3. Project these points on circle in the top view as 1′, 2′, 3′ ... etc.
4. Transfer these points 1′, 2′, 3′ ... from top view to front view by projectors so as to cut the corresponding points projected from the left side view.
5. Join all the intersecting points and draw a smooth curve as shown in Fig. 11.1(ii)

Method IInd

Cutting Plane Method

Assume a series of horizontal section planes, passing through the generators of the horizontal cylinder to cut both the cylinders. For all the horizontal section planes, the sectional top view of the vertical cylinder will always be circle of 50 mm diameter. The cutting planes passing through the lines 2-12 as shown in Fig. 11.2. Points at which circle and rectangles intersect each other, will lie on the curve of intersection. P_2, P_{12} are two such points at which the sides of the rectangle cut the circle. Other cutting plane may be 3-11, 4-10, 5-9 etc. and corresponding intersecting points are p_3 and p_{11}, p_4 and p_{10}, p_5 and p_9 etc. Join all the intersecting points and draw a smooth curve. Another intersecting curve on right side may be completed similarly.

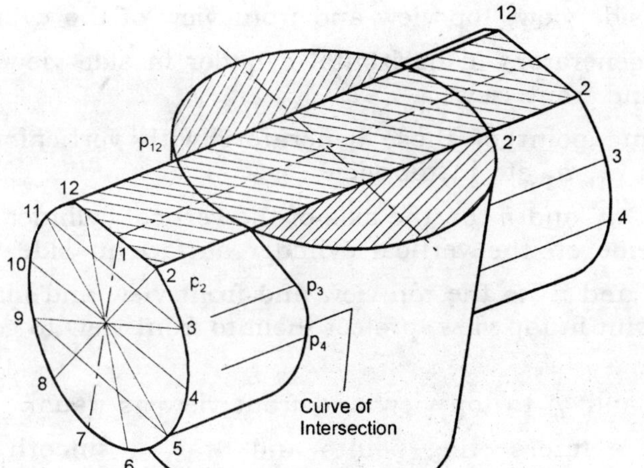

Fig. 11.2

Problem 2. A vertical cylinder of base diameter 50 mm is penetrated by a horizontal cylinder of 60 mm diameter and the axis of which is 10 mm infront of the vertical cylinder axis as shown in Fig. 11.3 (i). Draw the projections showing the curves of intersection when the axis of the horizontal cylinder is parallel to V.P.

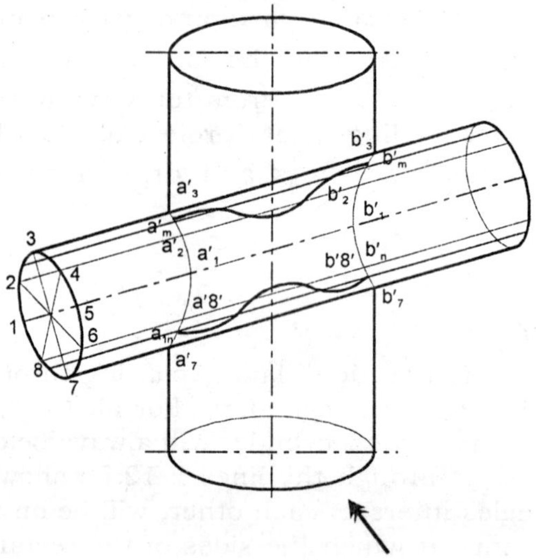

Fig. 11.3(i)

Solution: See Fig. 11.3(ii).

1. Draw the side view, top view and front view of the cylinders.
2. Mark the generators in horizontal cylinder in side view and project them to top view and front view.
3. The piercing point of these generators with vertical cylinder surface are marked as a_1, a_2 etc in top view.
4. Mark point m'' and n'' on the axis of the vertical cylinder and P'' and q'' as the right extreme on the vertical cylinder surface in side view.
5. Project m'' and n'' to the top view and front view and mark a_m and a_n as the piercing point in top view, project them to front view to get a'_m and a'_n in front view.
6. Project p'' and q'' to top view and front view as usual.
7. Join all the intersecting points and draw a smooth curve as shown in Fig. 11.3 (ii).

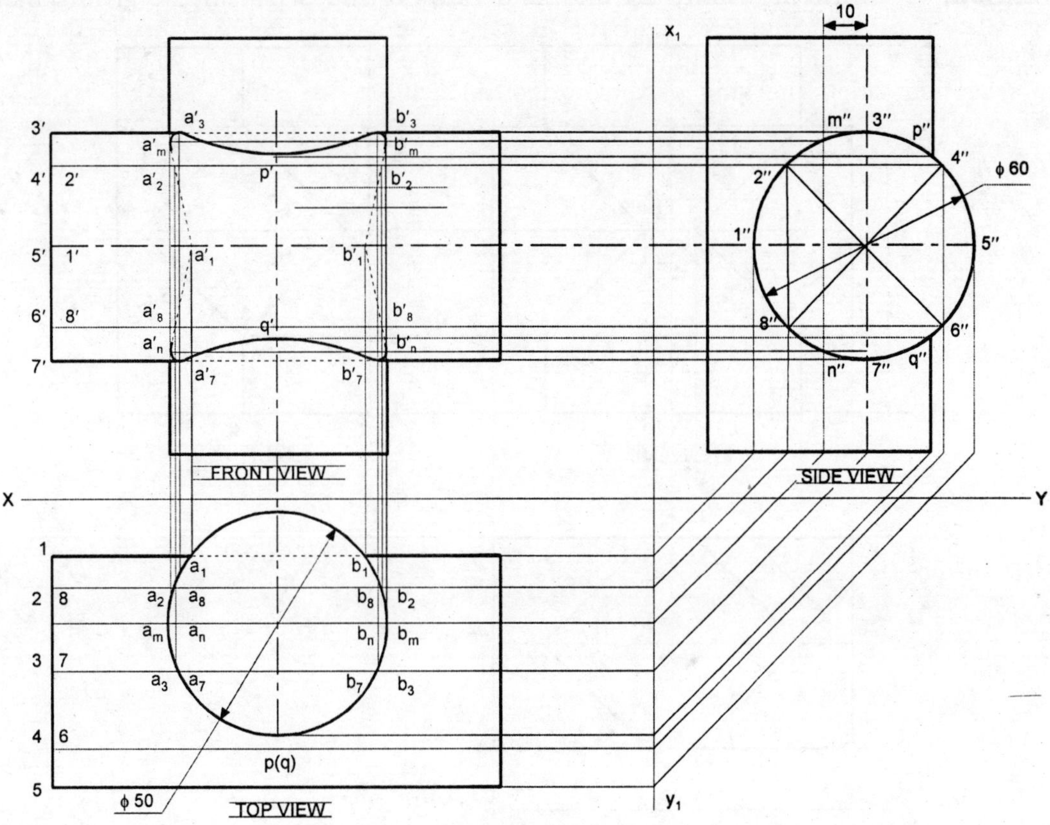

Fig. 11.3 (ii)

Problem 3: A square prism, base 40 mm side 80 mm long is resting vertically on the H.P. It is completely penetrated by a horizontal square prism, base 50 mm side 80 mm long so that their axis intersect each other at right angles. The faces of the two prisms, are equally inclined to the V.P as shown in Fig. 11.4 (i). Draw the projection of the solids showing the lines of intersection.

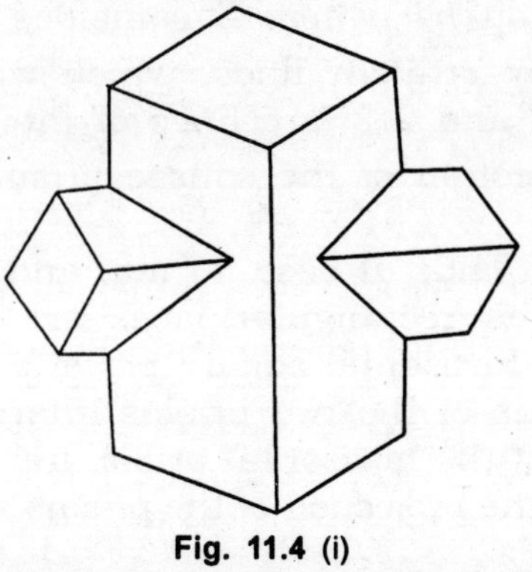

Fig. 11.4 (i)

Solution. 1. Draw the front, top and side views of the prism in the given position.

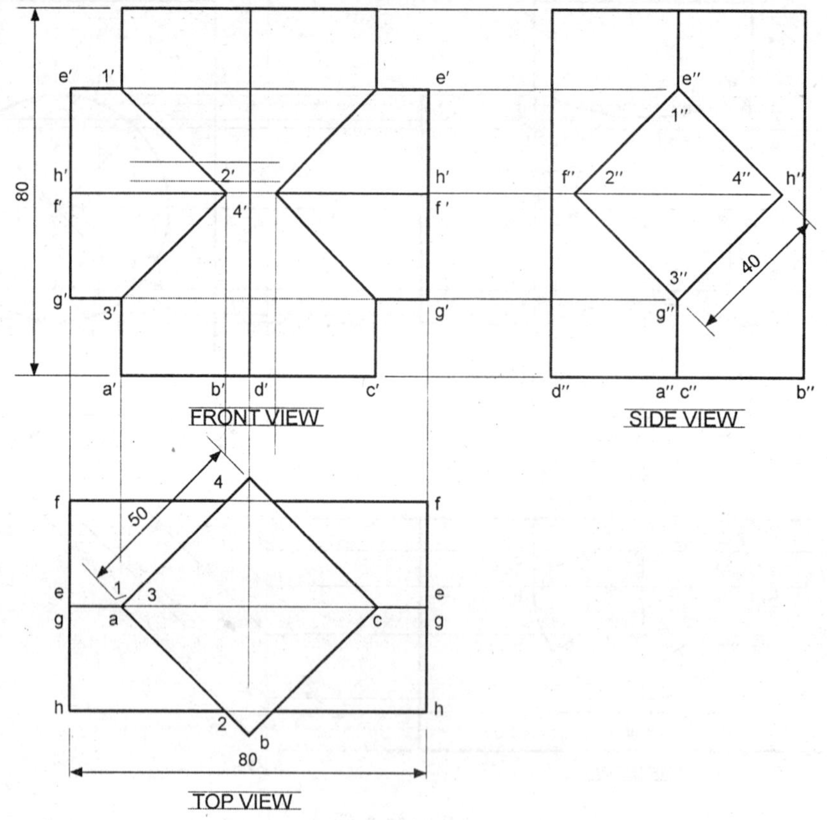

Fig. 11.4 (ii)

2. The faces of the vertical prism are seen as lines in the top. Hence locate the points of intersection in the top view as shown in Fig. 11.4 (ii) e.g. line $h - h$ intersects the line *ab* at 2.
3. Project all these points in front view on the corresponding lines such as point 2 is projected to 2′ on *h′h′* where 2′ coincides with 4′.
4. Join these points by straight lines, which will be the line of intersection. Thus, the lines 1′2′ and 2′3′ are lines of intersection.
5. Complete the intersection of the square prism as shown in Fig. 11.4 (ii).

Problem 4: A square prism, side of base 50 mm and height 70 mm stands with its base on H.P and two of its rectangular faces are equally inclined to V.P. It is completely penetrated by a horizontal square prism side of base 35 mm and axis 70 mm long, such that the axis of the two prisms intersect each other at right angle. The two rectangular faces of the horizontal prism are equally inclined to H.P. and its axis is parallel to V.P. Draw the projection of the prisms showing the lines of intersection.

Solution: See Fig. 11.5.

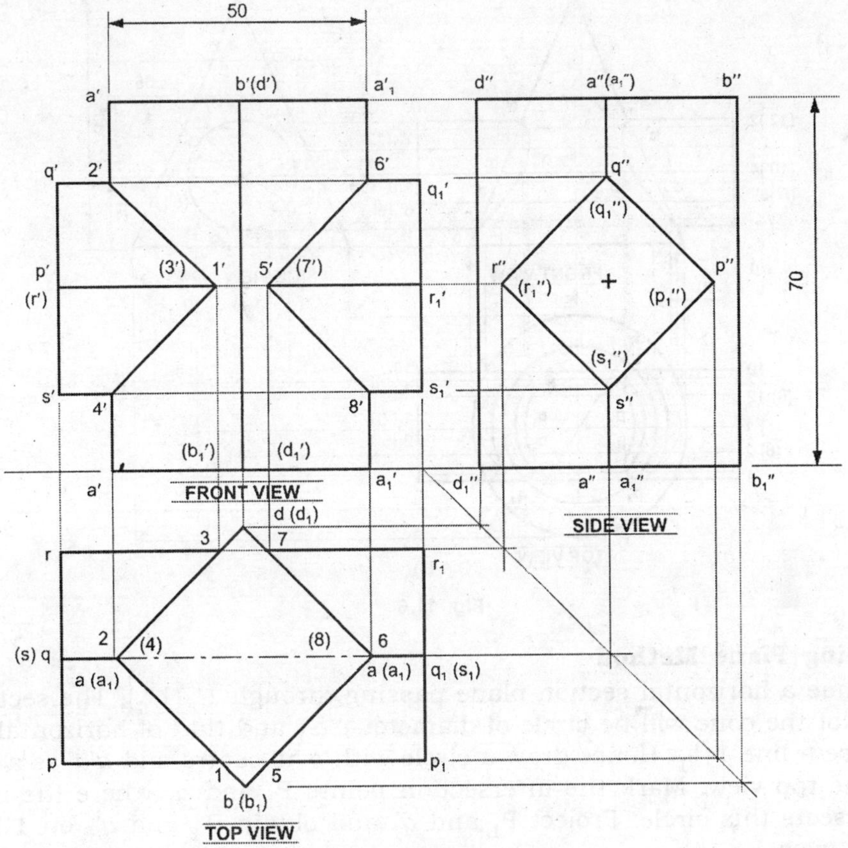

Fig. 11.5

Problem 5. A cone of base 50 mm diameter and axis 80 mm long rests with its base on H.P. It is completely penetrated by a horizontal cylinder of 35 mm diameter such that both the axis intersect each other at right angles. The axes of the cylinder is parallel to V.P. and 20 mm above the base of the cone as shown in Fig. 11.6 (i). Draw the projections of the solid.

Solution: 1. Draw the top view, front view and side view of given cone.

2. On the axis of the cone in the side view mark o'' at 20 mm above the base of the cone to represent the axis of the horizontal cylinder. With o'' as centre and 35 mm as diameter draw a circle to represent the cylinder. Project the corresponding front and top views of the cylinder and name the generators as shown in Fig. 11.6 (ii).

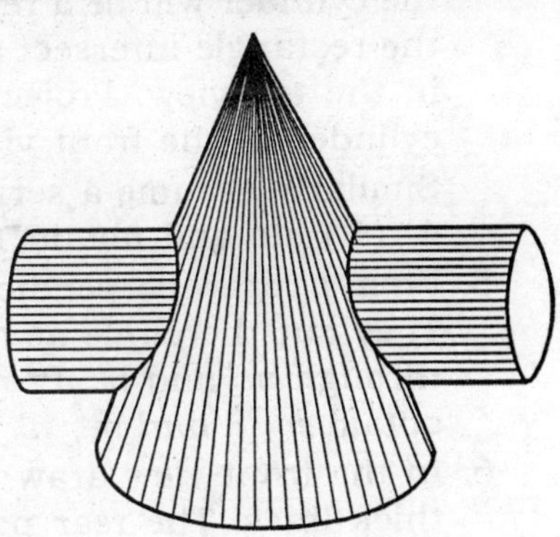

(I)

Fig. 11.6

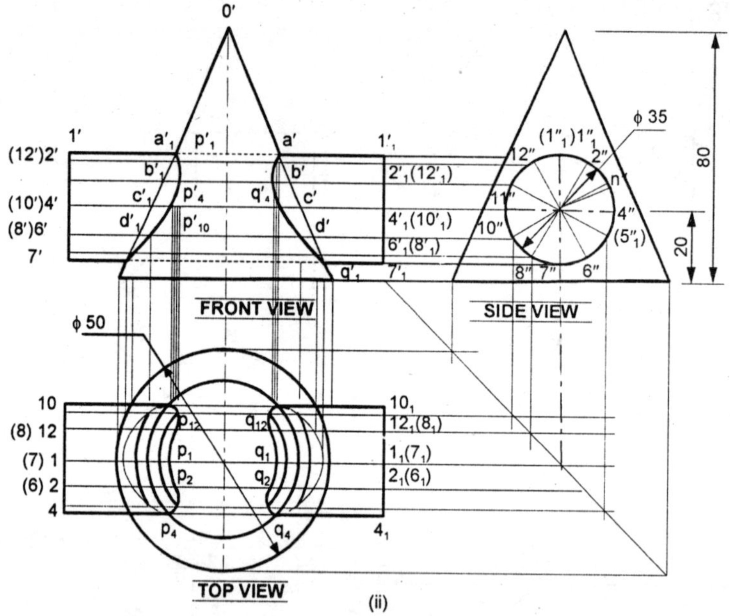

Fig. 11.6

Cutting Plane Method

3. Assume a horizontal section plane passing through 1″ ($1''_1$). The sectional top view of the cone will be circle of diameter $a'a'_1$ and that of horizontal cylinder will be a line $1\text{-}1_1$. Hence draw a circle with o as centre and $a'a'$ as a diameter in the top view. Mark the intersection points P_1 and q_1 where the line $1\text{–}1_1$, intersects this circle. Project P_1 and q_1 and obtain P'_1 and q'_1 on $1'1'_1$ in the front view.
4. Assume the horizontal section plane passing through 2″ ($2''_1$) and 12″ ($12''_1$). The sectional top view of the cone will be a circle of diameter $b'b'_1$ and that of the cylinder will be a rectangle of length $2\text{-}2_1$, and breadth 2–12. The circle and the rectangle intersect at 4 intersection points. Mark them as $P_2 q_2$ q_{12} and p_{12} in the top view. Project these points on the corresponding generators of the cylinder in the front view and obtain P'_2, q'_2 (q'_{12}) and (P'_{12}) respectively. Similarly assume a series of horizontal section planes passing through 3″ (3′), 4″ (4′) etc and obtain the intersection points in top and front views.
5. From o'' draw perpendiculars to the end generators of the cone in the side view. They cut the circle at m'' and n'' . Assume a horizontal section plane passing through m'' and n''. Project these critical points to the top and front views and obtain *m, n and m′, n′*.
6. In the front view draw the curve passing through P'_1, P'_2, P'_3, n', P'_4 ... P_7' as thick lines. The rear portion of the intersection curve coincide with the front position. Hence it is not shown as dotted line in this view.
7. In the top view join n, P_2, P_1, P_{12} and m to represent the visible portion of the curve. The hidden portion is shown dotted as shown in Fig. 11.6 (ii).

Problem 6. A cone base 50 mm diameter axis 80 mm long, is resting on its base on the H.P. It is completely penetrated by a cylinder of 40 mm dia, 90 mm long, the axis of which is parallel to both the reference planes and intersects the axis of the cone. Draw the projections of the solids showing the curves of intersection. Using the cutting plane method.

Solution. 1. Draw the front view, top view and side view of the solids in the given position.

2. Divide the circle in side view into 12 equal parts. Project these division points in the front view and top view.
3. In Fig. 11.7, assume a horizontal cutting plane passing through points 2 and 12. The section of the cylinder is a rectangle of width 2–12 while that of the cone is a circle of diameter *ee*. These two sections intersect at point P_2 and P_{12}.
4. Mark the points a_1 and b_1, in the side view. Project these points in the front view a' and b' and in the top view a and b on the corresponding lines.

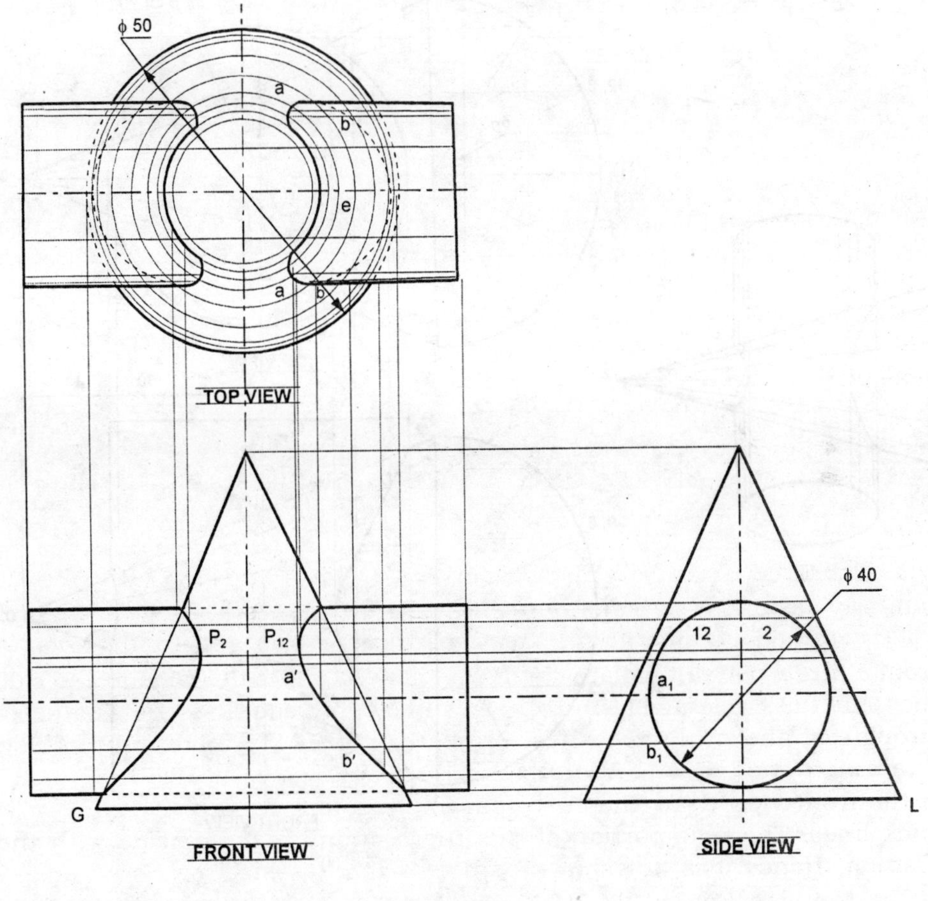

Fig. 11.7

5. Similarly, obtain other points in the front view and top view, and draw the required curves through them. In the front view the back curve will coincide with the front curve and obtain the similar curves on the left hand side of the axis of the cone as shown in Fig. 11.7.

Problem 7: A cone penetrates a cylinder at right angle. The horizontal cone of base 60 mm diameter, axis 90 mm is penetrates by the vertical cylinder 50 mm diameter as shown in Fig. 11.8 (i). Draw the projections showing curves of intersection when the vertex of cone reaches 60 mm byond the axis of the cylinder.

Solution: 1. Draw the front view and top view in the given position.

2. Draw the semi circle in the front view and top view and divide it in 12 equal parts.

3. Project the point 1, 2, 3 etc. on the base of cone and join with the vertex point *o'* and *o* in the front view and top view respectively.

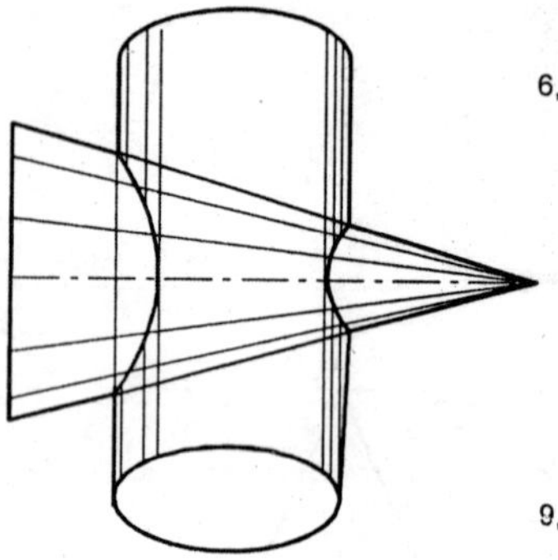

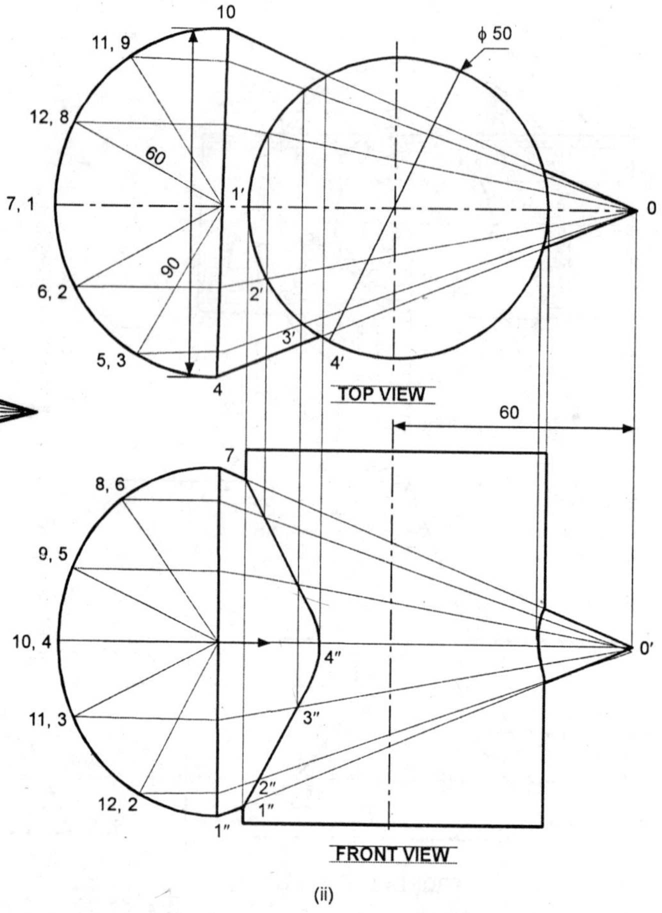

Fig. 11.8

4. Locate the points of intersection of generators and circle in top view. These points are 1′, 2′, 3′ etc.
5. Transfer these points 1′, 2′, 3′ etc from top view to front view by projector so as to cut the corresponding points projected from the half circle at 1″, 2″, 3″ etc and draw similar points on the other side.
6. Join all the intersecting points and draw the smooth cone as shown in Fig. 11.8 (ii).

Problem 8. A vertical hexagonal duct, side 30 mm and height 80 mm is intersected by a square branch duct 32 mm side at a distance 15 mm above the base whose axis in inclined at an angle 60° to V.P. All the faces of the square branch duct are equally inclined to the V.P. Draw the projections of the ducts showing lines of intersection.

Solution:

1. Draw the top view and front view of hexagonal duct in the given position.
2. Draw the centre line of the branch square duct at a distance 15 mm from the base at an angle of 60° to V.P.

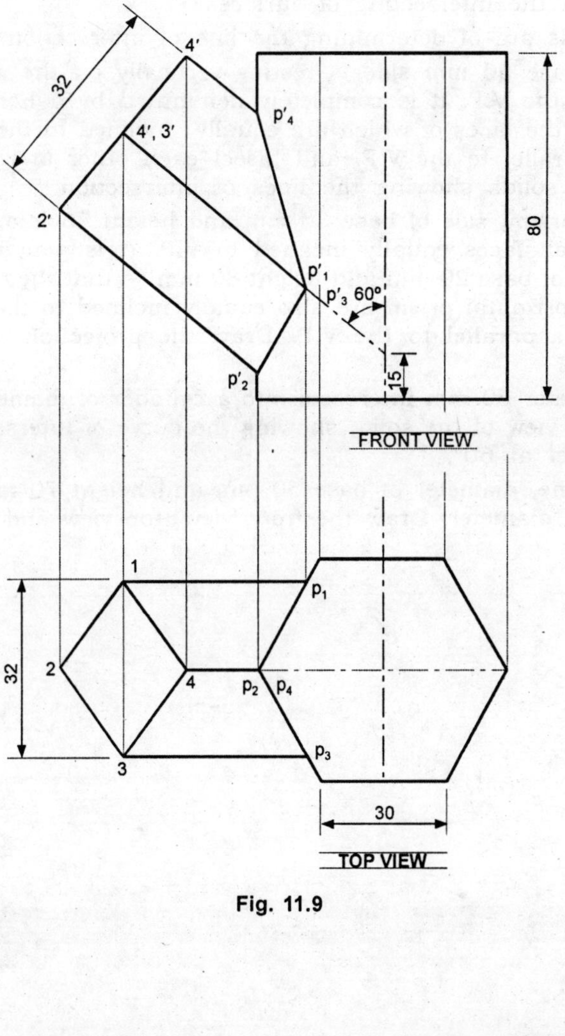

Fig. 11.9

3. Draw the line 2′ – 4′ at right angle to the centre line.
4. Project the points 1′, 2′, 3′, 4′ from the front view and top view as points 1, 2, 3, 4 respectively.
5. Locate the points of intersection in top view. Points P_1 and P_3 are obtained when the edge of vertical duct intersects lines through points 1 and 3 respectively. Similarly locate the point P_2 and P_4.
6. Project the point P_1, P_2, P_3, P_4 in the front view to find exact corresponding position where point P'_3 coincides with P'_1.
7. Draw lines joining $P'_4P'_1$ and P'_1 P_2'. These lines represent lines of intersection as shown in Fig 11.9.

EXERCISE

1. Define the terms intersection of solid.

2. How you classified the intersecting of surfaces?

3. How many methods are of determining the line of intersection?

4. A square prism, base 50 mm side is resting vertically on the ground, having a face inclined at 30° to the V.P. It is completely penetrated by a horizontal square prism, base 35 mm side, the faces of which are equally inclined to the V.P. The axes of the two prisms are parallel to the V.P. and bisect each other at right angles. Draw the projections of the solids showing the lines of intersection.

5. A vertical square prism, side of base 30 mm and height 75 mm, is resting on ground on its base with all faces equally inclined to V.P. It is penetrated by a horizontal square prism, side of base 20 mm and height 80 mm so that their axes are 5 mm apart. The faces of the horizontal prism are also equally inclined to the V.P. and the axis of horizontal prism is parallel to the V.P. Draw the projection and show the line of intersection.

6. A cylinder of diameter 50 mm intersects into a cylinder of diameter 80 mm. Draw the front view and top view of the solid, showing the curve of intersection when their axis intersect each other at 60°.

7. A right circular cone, diameter of base 50 mm and height 70 mm is penetrated by a cylinder of 25 mm diameter. Draw the front view, top view and curve of intersection.

❑❑❑

12

DEVELOPMENT OF SURFACES

12.1 INTRODUCTION

In engineering practice, the study of development of surfaces finds wide practical application in industries, such as packing, shiping, air-conditioning, fabrication etc.

Development of surfaces means unrolling of surface into a single plane. Development is defined as "A layout of the complete surface of an object". For examples, cans, funnels, cake pans, furnace, pipe, elbow, duct, chimneys, hoppers, boxes, buckets and process vessels etc., are made from sheet metal that is cut so that when folded, formed or rolled, it takes the shape of an object.

In industrial drawing, the development must be shown to furnish the necessary information for making a pattern to facilitate the cutting of required shape from sheet metal. Many manufactured items can be made by rolling, folding or pressing. These operations require the use of development views. In this chapter, we will deal with the study of development, engineering applications, principle and various method for developing objects in engineering field.

12.2 SHEET METAL DEVELOPMENT

We have learned the method of finding the true size of a plane surface by projecting its normal views. Surface development drawing is also known as pattern drawing. The layout, when made on heavy cardboard, thin metal or wood is used as a pattern for tracing out the development shape on flat material. Such patterns are commonly used in sheet metal shop.

When making a development drawing of an object which will be constructed from thin metal such as a tin can, the drafter must be concerned not only with the developed surface, but also with joining of the edges of these surfaces and with exposed edges. Allowance must be made for the additional material necessary for such seams and edges as shown in Fig. 12.1.

The surface of cones and cylinders may be unrolled on a plane. The development of a right cylinder is a rectangle having a width equal to the height of the cylinder and a length equal to the circumference (πd) as shown in Fig. 12.2. The development of a right circular cone is a sector of a circle having a radius equal to the true length of slant height and an arc length equal to the circumference of the base as shown in Fig. 12.3.

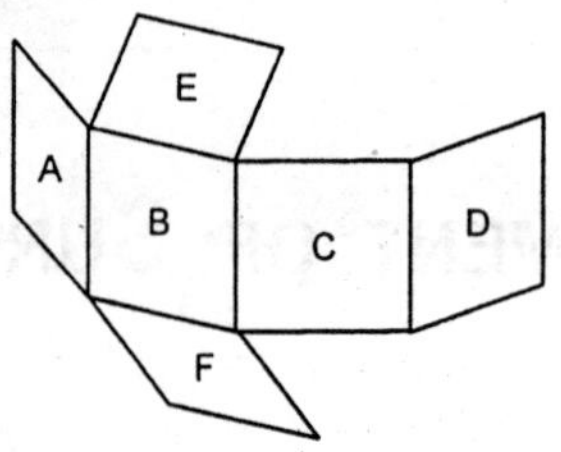

(i) Thin Lines

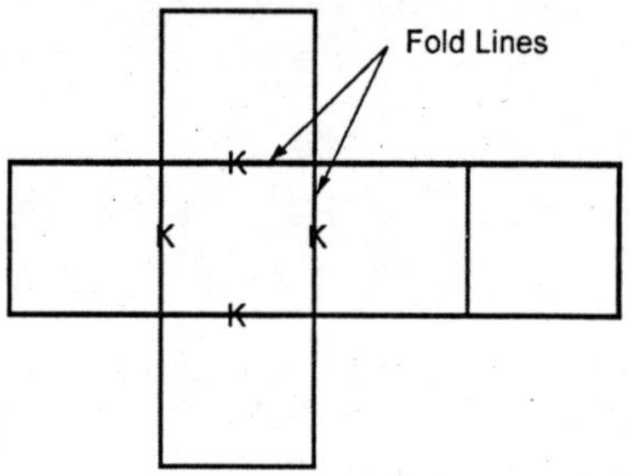

(ii) Thin Lines Marked With K

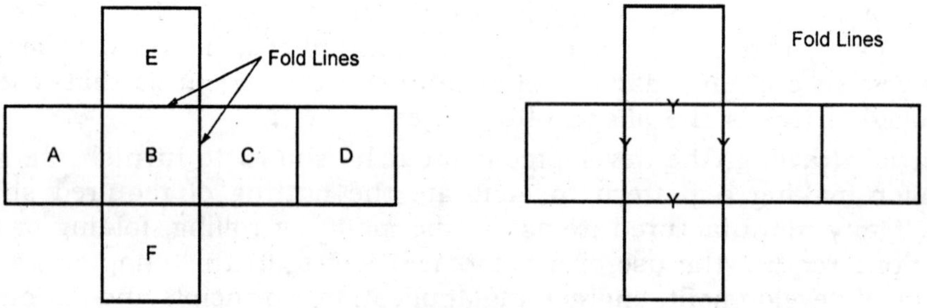

(iii) Thin Lines Marked With Y

Fig. 12.1

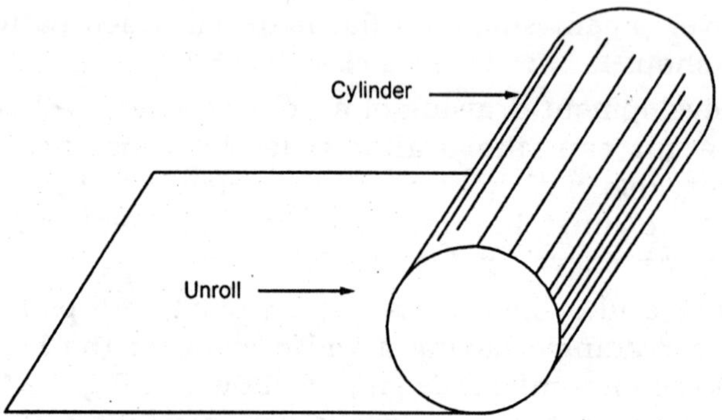

Fig. 12.2 (i)

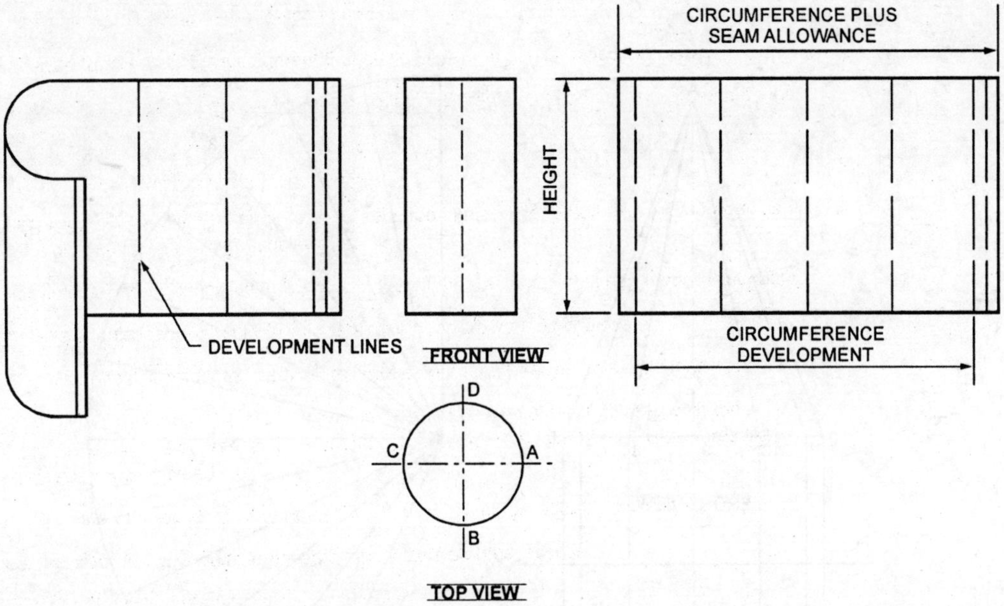

(ii)

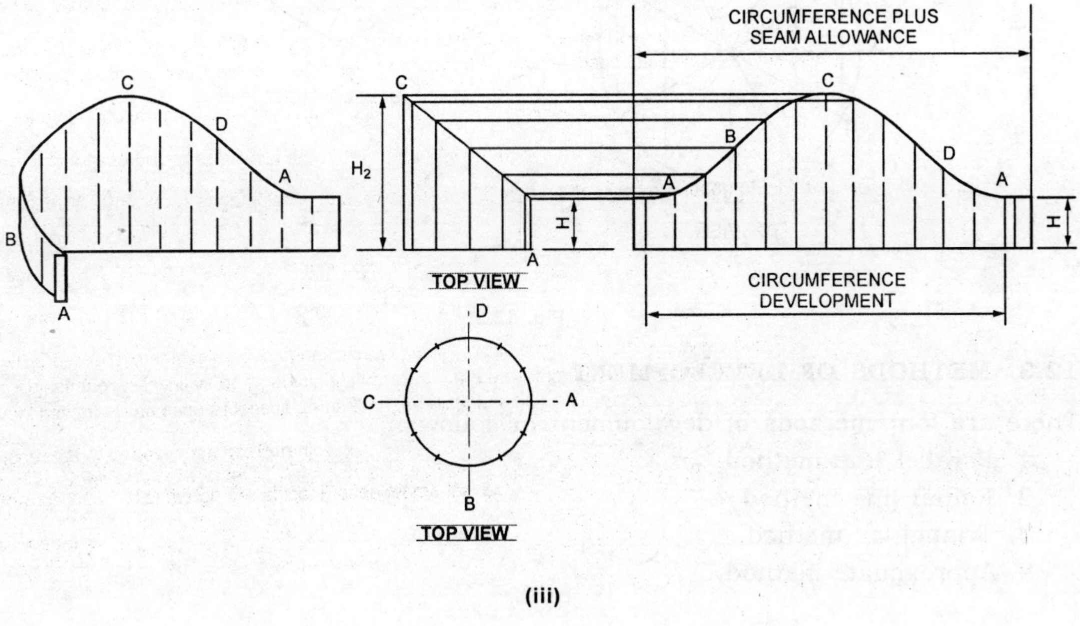

(iii)

Fig. 12.2

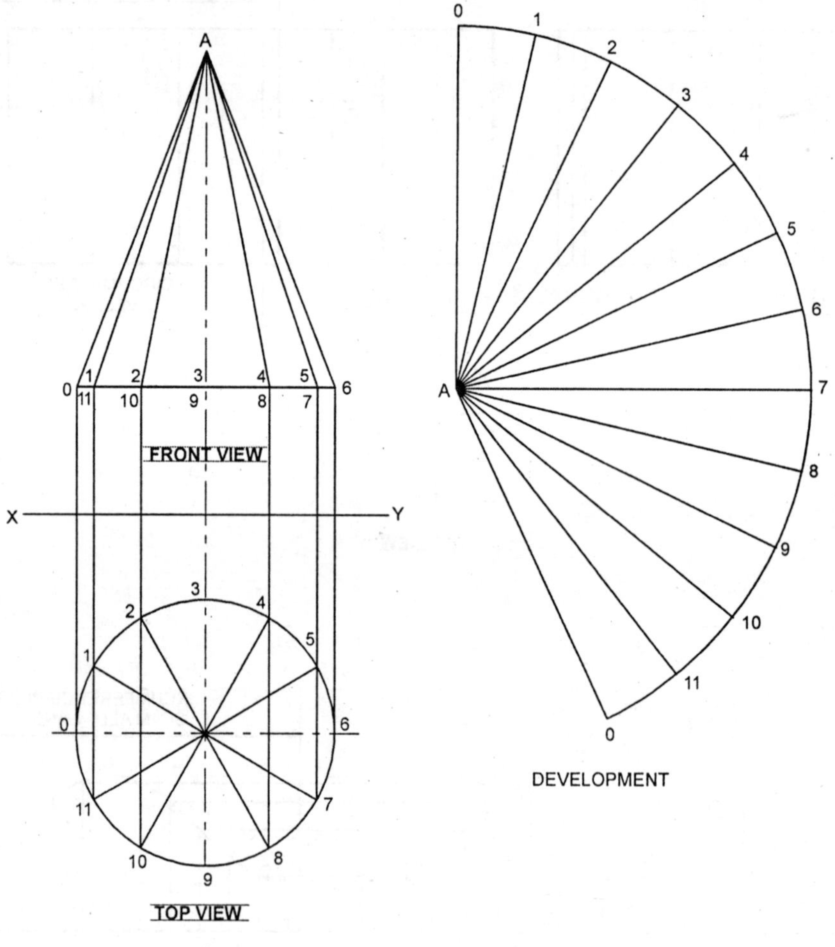

Fig. 12.3

12.3 METHODS OF DEVELOPMENT

There are four methods of development as follows:

1. Parallel line method
2. Radial line method
3. Triangular method
4. Approximate method.

1. Parallel Line Method: This method of development is used for development of surfaces of prism and cylinder. In this method all the lines or edge/generators of lateral surfaces are parallel to each others.

2. Radial Line Method: This method of development is used for development of surfaces of pyramids and cone. In this method, the true length of the slant edge or the generator is used as radius.

3. Triangular Method: This method is used to draw the development of transition pieces and non-uniform connecting surfaces. In this method, we divide the surface into a number of triangles and transfer them into the development.

4. Approximate Method: This method is used to develop the objects of warped and double-curved surfaces like sphere, paraboloid, hyperboloid and helicoid.

Note: Generally the lateral surface of solids are developed and the end or bases are omitted from the development. They can easily be added whenever required.

12.4 DEVELOPMENT OF A RIGHT CYLINDER

When a right cylinder is rolled and onto a plane, the top and bottom of the lateral surface develop into straight lines. The width of the development is equal to the height of the cylinder, and the length of the development is equal to the circumference of the cylinder ($\pi \times D$) plus the seam allowance as shown in Fig. 12.2 (*a* & *b*). Fig. 12.3 shows the development of cylinder with the top truncated at a given angle.

In rolling the cylinder on a tangent plane, the base or right section, being perpendicular to the axis, will develop into a straight line. For convenience in drawing, divide the top view of the cylinder into eight or twelve equal number of parts. Project these points onto the front view. The stretch out line is also divided into the same number of equal parts and draw the perpendicular through each division points. Then transfer the true lengths of each elements which is projected to its respective representation on the development. The development is completed by joining the points. An irregular curve is used to connect the points of intersection as shown in Fig. 12.3.

Problem 1: To develop a right cylinder of base diameter 50 mm and height 100 mm.

Solution:

1. Draw the front view and top view of a cylinder.
2. Draw a strech out line 1-1 equal to πD = 157.14 mm in line with front view. This is equal to the circumference of the cylinder.
3. Draw the perpendiculars from point 1, 1 to cut the horizontal line projecting from front view at a A, A.
4. Complete the development as shown in Fig. 12.4. In this the top and bottom bases are omitted.

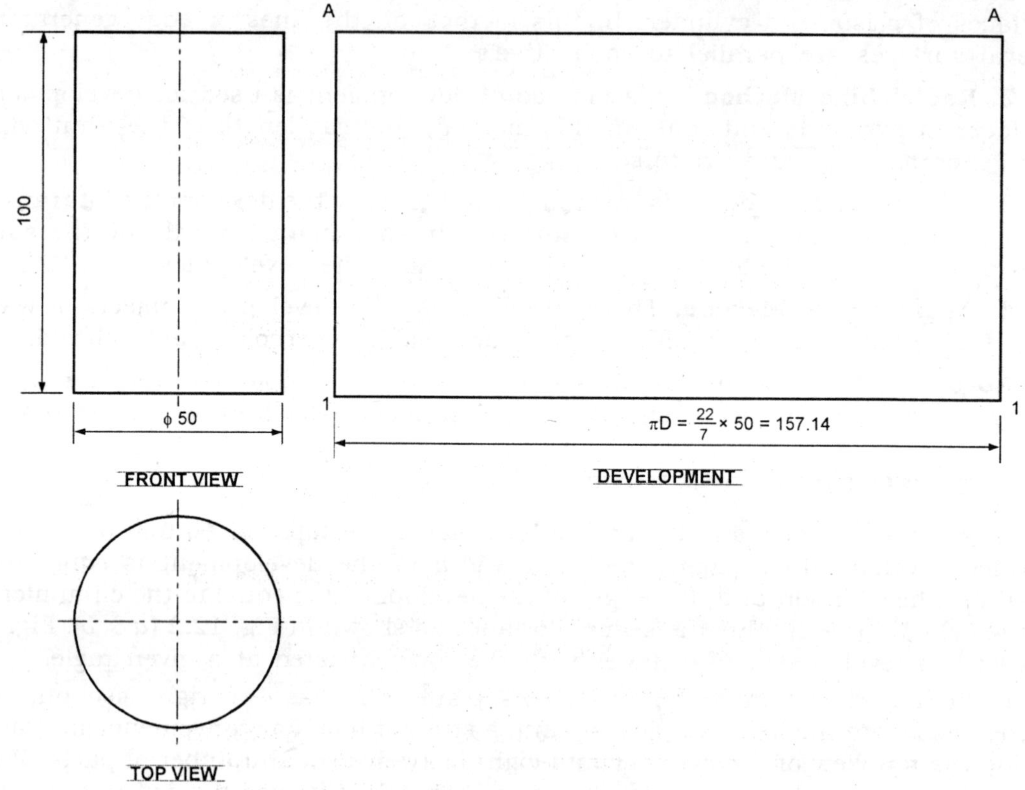

Fig. 12.4

Problem 2: A right cylinder of 35 mm diameter and height 60 mm, is cut by a section plane inclined at 30° to H.P and passes 25 mm above the base along the axis. Draw the development of the lower portion of the cylinder.

Solution:

1. Draw the top view and front view of the cylinder and show it on the line X-Y for the section plane. The section plane cuts the generators at points 1′, 2′, 3′, 4′, 5′ etc.
2. Divide the base circle into 12 equal parts, 1, 2, 3 ... etc.
3. Project these points to the front view 1′, 2′, 3′, 4′, 5′ etc.
4. Draw a line 1-1 equal to the circumference of the circle, i.e. πD with the front view.
5. Divide the line 1-1 into twelve equal parts and number them as 1, 2, 3, 4, 5 etc.
6. Erect perpendicular through each division points 1, 2, 3, 4, 5 etc.
7. Draw a horizontal line through the top of the cylinder at the point 1′, 2′, 3′, 4′, 5′ etc so as to cut corresponding perpendiculars from the point 1, 2, 3, 4, 5 etc at *a*, *b*, *c*, *d*, *e* etc.
8. Connect these points with smooth curve, with the help of irregular curve as shown in Fig. 12.5.

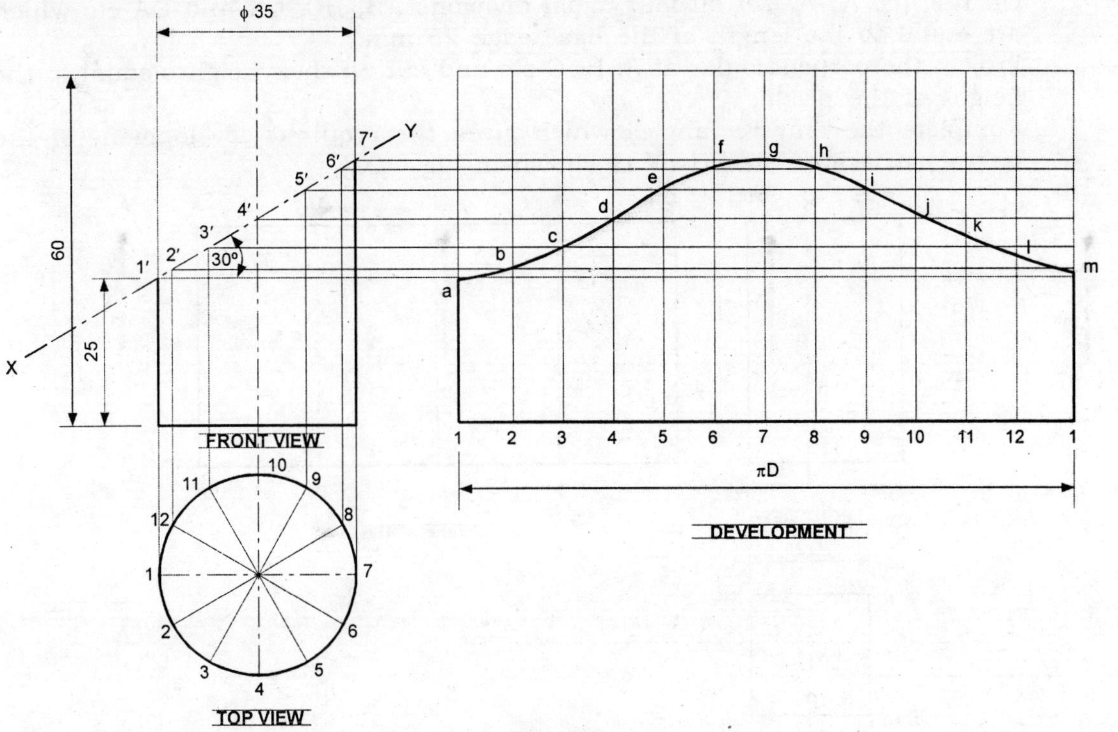

Fig. 12.5

12.5 DEVELOPMENT OF A RIGHT PRISM

The development of the surface of right prism is shown in Fig. 12.6. It consists of a number of rectangular faces in contact. One side of the rectangular face being equal to the length of the base edge and the other equal to the height of the prism.

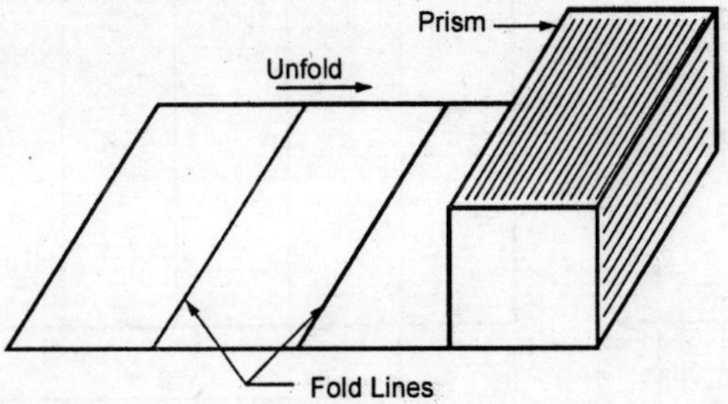

Fig. 12.6

Problem 3: Draw the development of the lateral surface of a right square prism of edge of base 25 mm and axis 50 mm long.

Solution:

1. Draw the top view and front view of a square prism and name the corners.
2. Develop the lateral surface of the prism consisting of four equal rectangles of size 50 mm × 25 mm respectively in square.

3. On the line A_1–A_1 set off four equal divisions AB, BC, CD and DA etc which are equal to the length of the base edge 25 mm.
4. Project the perpendicular at A, B, C etc and cut off their heights equal to the height of the prism.
5. Complete the four rectangles which gives the required development of the lateral surface of the prism as shown in Fig. 12.7.

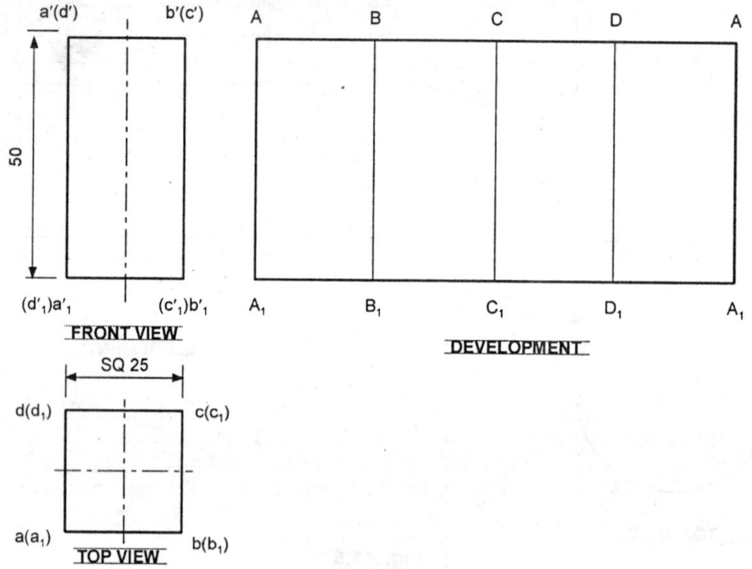

Fig. 12.7

Problem 4: Develop the lateral surface of a right regular hexagonal prism of 25 mm base edge and 60 mm height.

Solution: See in Fig. 12.8.

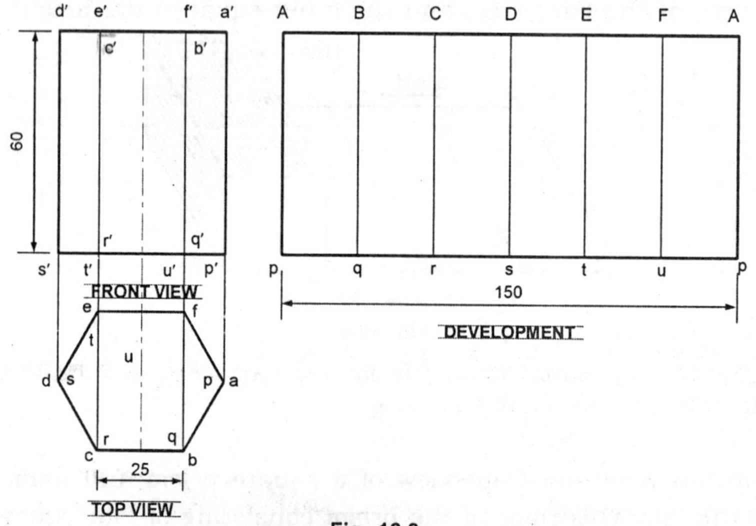

Fig. 12.8

Problem 5: A hexagonal prism of base side 25 mm and axis length 50 mm is resting on H.P on its base with two of its vertical faces perpendicular to V.P. It is cut by a plane inclined at 45° to H.P. and perpendicular to V.P. and meets the axis of prism at a distance 10 mm from the top end. Draw the development of the lateral surface of the prism.

Solution:

1. Draw the top view and front view of a hexagonal prism for the given position.
2. Draw the section plane in front view inclined at an angle of 45° to XY passing through a point at a distance 10 mm from its top end and mark the section points.
3. Draw two stretch-out line A-A and P-P each equal to the perimeter of the base (150 mm) of prism.
4. Divide A-A into six equal parts and draw six equal rectangles to represent the development of the lateral surface of the prism.
5. From the section point, draw a horizontal line and mark 1 on AP, similarly obtain the other point 2, 3, ... 6 in the development.
6. Join 1-2, 2-3, 3-4, 4-5 and ... 6-1 as straight lines and darken the development of the truncated prism as shown in Fig. 12.9.

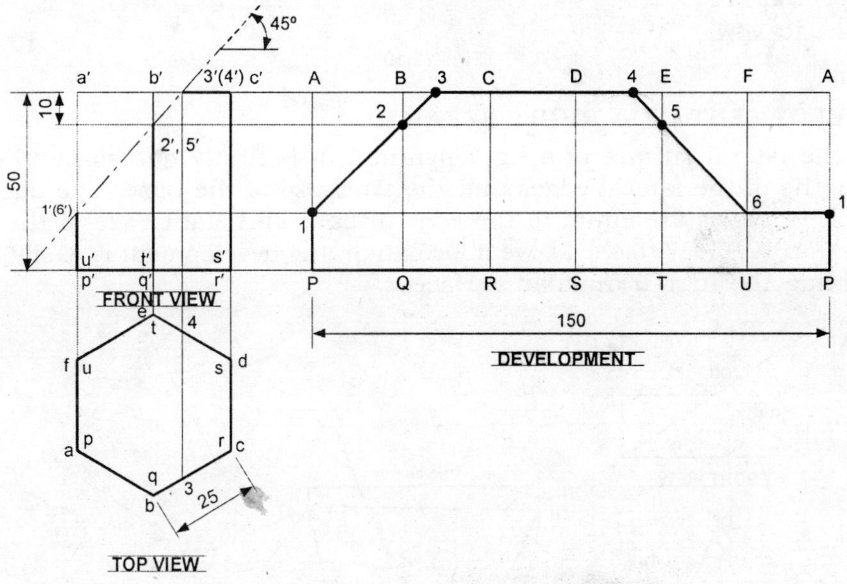

Fig. 12.9

Problem 6: A pentagonal prism of 25 mm base edges and 60 mm long, is resting on its base with an edge of base at 45° to V.P. The prism is cut by a section plane V.T inclined at 30° to H.P and passing through a point 25 mm from the base along its axis. Draw the development of the lateral surface of the truncated prism.

Solution: See Fig. 12.10.

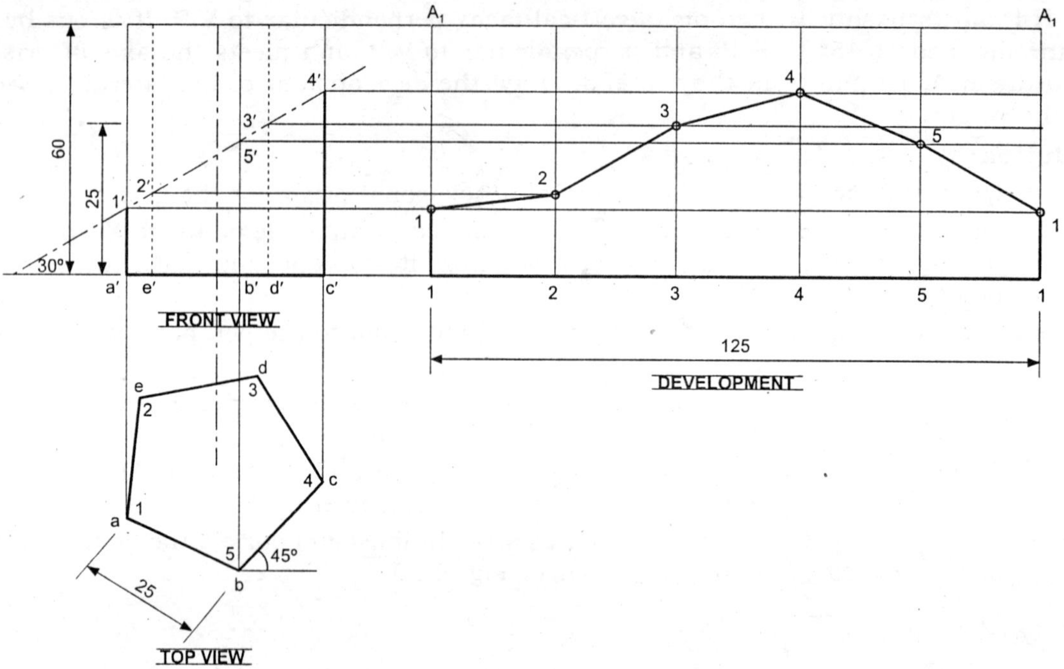

Fig. 12.10

12.6 DEVELOPMENT OF A RIGHT PYRAMID

To develop the lateral surface of a right pyramid, it is firstly necessary to determine the true lengths of the lateral edges and the true size of the base. The base and the sides of each triangles are equal to the edge of base and slant edge of the pyramids as shown in Fig. 12.11. With the above information, the development is easily completed by constructing the four triangular surfaces.

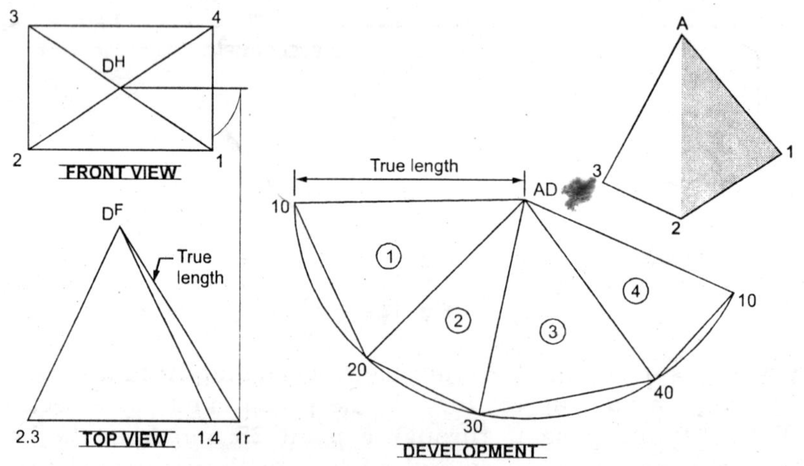

Fig. 12.11

Problem 7: Draw the development of the lateral surface of a square pyramid. Side of base 30 mm and height 60 mm, resting with its base on H.P. and an edge of the base parallel to vertical plane.

Solution:

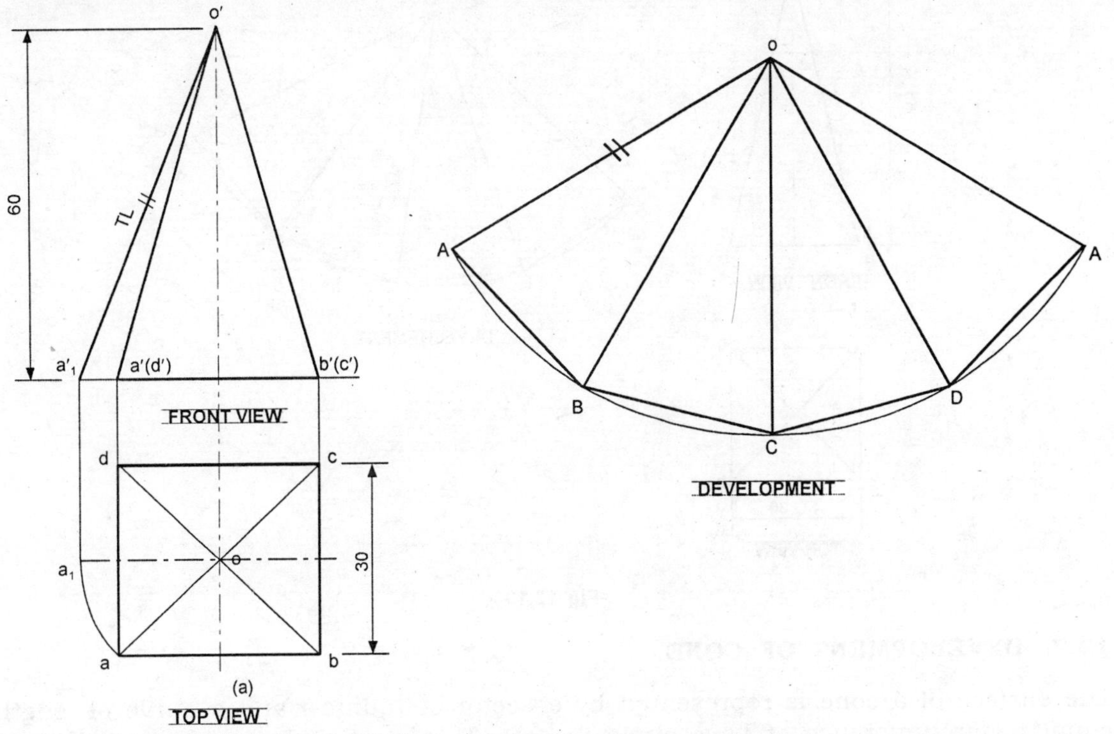

Fig. 12.12

1. Draw the top view and front view of the square pyramid.
2. To draw its development true length of the slant edge is required.

   Rule: If the top view of a slant edge of a pyramid is parallel to XY, then the front view of that edge will give its true length and vice-versa. Hence, in both the views, the projections of none of the slant edges is parallel to XY. Hence its true length cannot be measured directly either from the top view or front view.

   Therefore, to obtain the true length of a slant edge (say OA) make *oa* parallel to XY : i.e. with *o* as centre and *oa* as radius draw an arc to cut the horizontal from *o* at *a*. Now *o'a'*, will be the true length of the slant edge OA.
3. With *o* as centre and $o'a'_1$ as radius draw an arc, this arc step off the divisions AB, BC and DA.
4. Complete the triangles OAB, OBC, OCD and ODA which gives the development of lateral surface of a pyramid as shown in Fig. 12.12.

Problem 8: Draw the development of a square pyramid base 30 mm and height 65 mm.

[B.TE New Delhi, January 2009]

Solution: See Fig. 12.13.

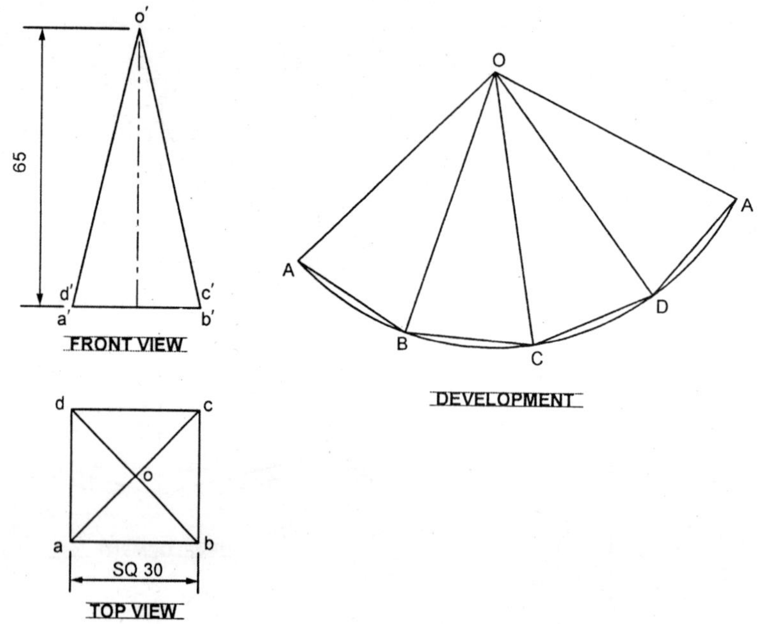

Fig 12.13

12.7 DEVELOPMENT OF CONE

The surface of a cone is represented by a sector of radius r and a curve of length equal to circumference of base circle i.e. πD. The base circle can be attached as usual to complete the development. A cone has a circle at its one end and the other end called the vertex is connected to circle through curved surface. The development of the lateral surface of a cone is obtained by unrolling it. It open out the lateral surface of the cone in a single plane, then the sector angle, equal to θ is calculated as follows:

Let

L = Slant height

D = diameter of cone

θ = sector angle.

Therefore

$$\theta = \frac{\pi D}{L}$$

$$\text{Sector angle } \theta = 180° \times \frac{\text{base diameter}}{\text{slant height}} = \frac{D}{L} \times 180°$$

Problem 9: A cone of base 50 mm and height 65 mm rests with its base on H.P. Draw its development.

Solution:

1. Draw top view and front view of a cone.
2. Divide the circle into twelve equal parts and project then in front view as 1′, 2′, 3′ etc.
3. Join these points 1′, 2′, 3′. with vertex 0.
4. Measure the slant height L from the front view. Take any point O' as centre and radius equal to L. Draw an angle θ = 180° D/L.
5. Divide the arc by divider or angle θ in twelve equal parts 01, 02, 03 etc to get the required development of the lateral surfaces of the curve as shown in Fig. 12.14.

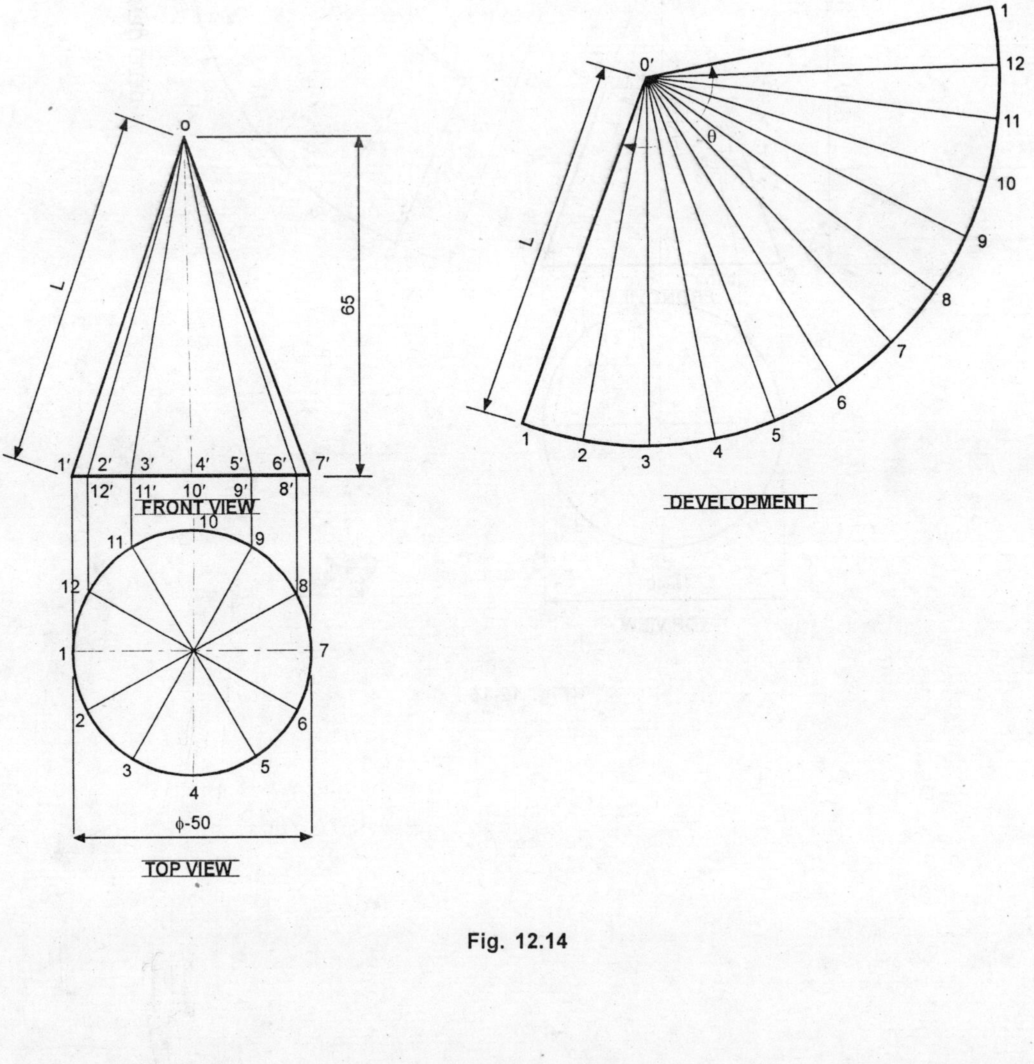

Fig. 12.14

Problem 10: A cone of base 40 mm diameter and height 60 mm rests with its base on H.P. A section plane perpendicular to V.P. and inclined at 30° to H.P. bisects the axis of the cone. Draw the development of the lateral surface of the truncated cone.

Solution: See Fig. 12.15.

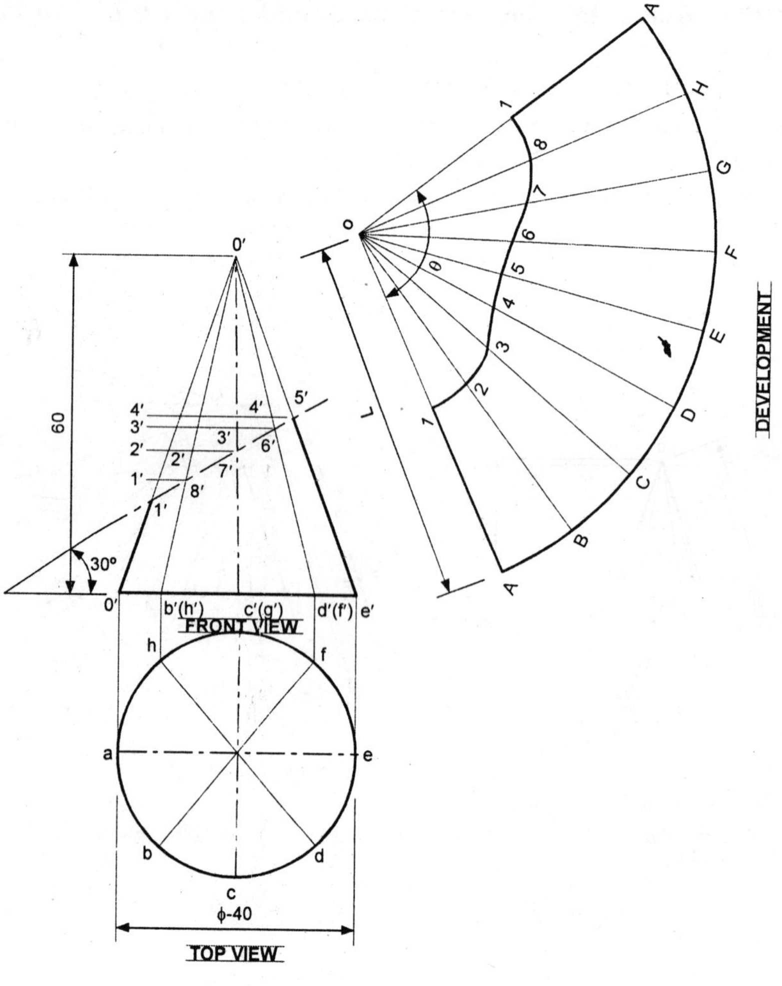

Fig. 12.15

EXERCISE

1. Define the terms development.
2. Define different methods of development.
3. Draw the development of the lateral surface of right square prism of edge of base 40 mm and axis 70 mm long.
4. A frustum of a square pyramid has its top 15 mm, bottom 30 mm and height 30 mm. It is resting on ground with two sides of bottom parallel to V.P. Draw its development.
5. A cube of 40 mm edge stands on one of its face on H.P. with a vertical face making 45° to V.P. A horizontal hole of 25 mm diameter is drilled centrally through the cube i.e. the hole passes through the opposite vertical edges of the cube. Obtain the development of the lateral surface of the cube with the hole.
6. Draw the development of a cylinder whose diameter is 35 mm and height 65 mm.
7. Draw the development of a hexagonal prism of base 25 mm and axis 65 mm long, rest, with its base on H.P. such that one of its rectangular face is parallel to V.P. It is cut by a plane perpendicular to V.P., inclined at 30° to H.P. and passing through the right corner of the top face of the prism.
8. A cone of diameter 50 mm and height 70 mm rests an H.P. on its base. It is cut by a section plane inclined at 30° to the base at a distance 40 mm from the H.P. Draw the development of the truncated cone.
9. A right regular triangular pyramid side of base 40 mm and axis 65 mm long is lying on H.P. on one of its triangular slant faces such that the axis is parallel to the V.P. A vertical cutting plane, parallel to the V.P. cuts the pyramid and is at a distance of 10 mm from the axis. Draw its sectional front view, top view and develop its lateral surface. **[BTE, New Delhi, January 2009]**

❑❑❑

IMPORTANT NOTES:

13

Orthographic Projection

13.1 INTRODUCTION

In technical drawings, the engineer or draftsmen is always concerned with the task of describing the shape of a solid on a sheet of paper, in order to represent the exact size of an object. It is possible by converting the three-dimensional object into two-dimensional projection which is known as orthographic projection. This chapter deals with only orthographic projection to represent some essential projection fundamentals employed in engineering drawing.

13.2 PROJECTION

If straight lines are drawn from various points on the contour of an object to meet a plane, the figure obtained on the plane is called the projection of an object and object is said to be projected on the plane.

Definition: Projection is defined as the image produced by mapping a geometric representation of an object on a plane of projection. Different views of an object are drawn by taking projections on orthogonal planes. A drawing of an object should consist of four things viz.:

1. Object
2. Projector
3. Plane of projection
4. Observer's eye.

13.3 METHODS OF PROJECTION

The following methods of projection are commonly used in engineering practice.

1. Orthographic projection.
2. Isometric projections.
3. Oblique projections.
4. Perspective projections.

Isometric projections, oblique projections and perspective projections are known as pictorial views.

13.4 ORTHOGRAPHIC PROJECTION

The engineers must represent the part which appears as three-dimensional with dimensions such as width, height and depth to the eye on the plane of the drawing. Different views of an object are systematically arranged on the drawing to convey the necessary information such as front view, top view, side view etc. This type of drawing is called an *orthographic projection.* The word orthographic is derived from Greek words, orthos, means "right angle" and graphikus means drawing lines. Basically it is the method of representing an object in two or more views on planes at right angle to each other by extending perpendiculars from the object to the planes. Let's take an object and imagine that it is placed within the planes of projection which are transparent as shown in Fig. 13.1.

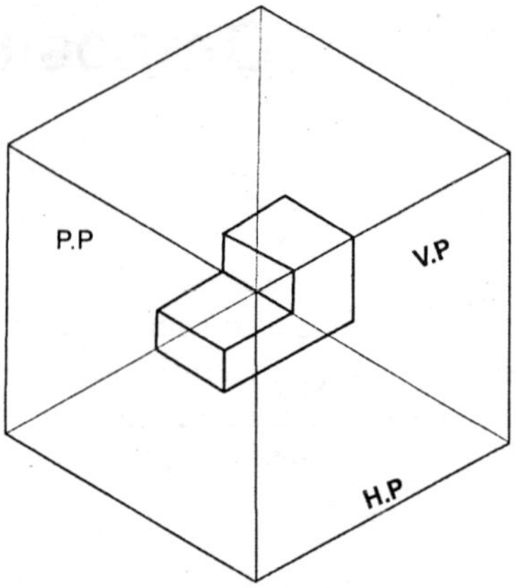

PLANES OF PROJECTION

Fig. 13.1

Imagine that the views of the object are projected to the front, top and side of the transparent planes. Two different principal planes are used to get the projections of an object—the vertical plane (V.P.) and horizontal plane (H.P.) These planes intersect each other at right angles and the line of intersection is called axis of the planes. The projection on the vertical plane is called *elevation* or *front view* and the projection on horizontal plane is called *plan* or *top view.* The plane perpendicular to both horizontal and vertical is called profile plane (P.P.). The projection on profile plane is called side view as shown in Fig. 13.2. The principles of orthographic projection can be applied in four different angles; first; second, third and fourth angle projection. This does not make any thing clear. Dihedral is not clarified. Crossing of the principal plane means nothing.

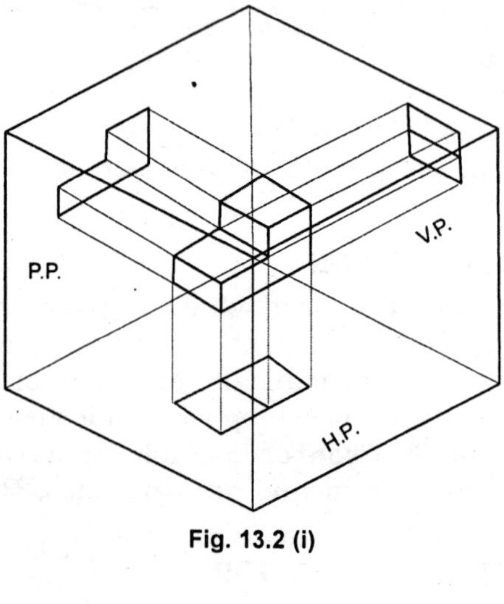

Fig. 13.2 (i)

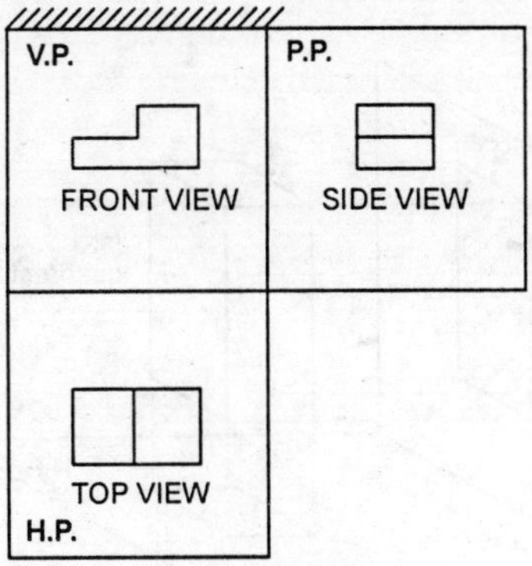

Fig. 13.2 (ii)

Rotation of Planes: The standard practice of rotation of planes is to keep the V.P fixed and horizontal plane is rotated in clockwise direction to bring it in vertical plane.

13.5 TYPES OF ORTHOGRAPHIC PROJECTION

The following two types of orthographic projections are used in engineering drawings.

1. First angle projection.
2. Third angle projection.

13.6 FIRST ANGLE PROJECTION

In first angle projection, the object is assumed to be positioned in first quadrant as shown in Fig. 13.3. The object is placed between the observer and the plane of projection with top view being below the front view, because when horizontal plane is rotated in clockwise direction by an angle of 90°, it will become vertical. The relative positions of top view and front view are shown in Fig. 13.3. Remember that, in first angle projection, the right side view goes to the left and left side view goes the right of front view.

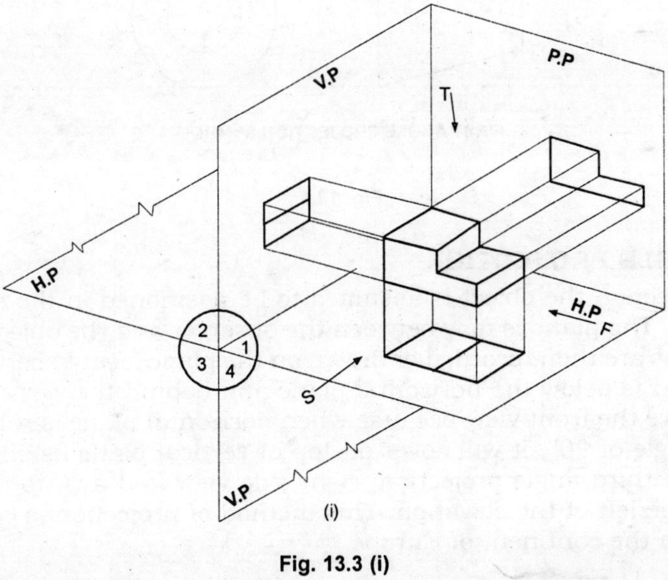

Fig. 13.3 (i)

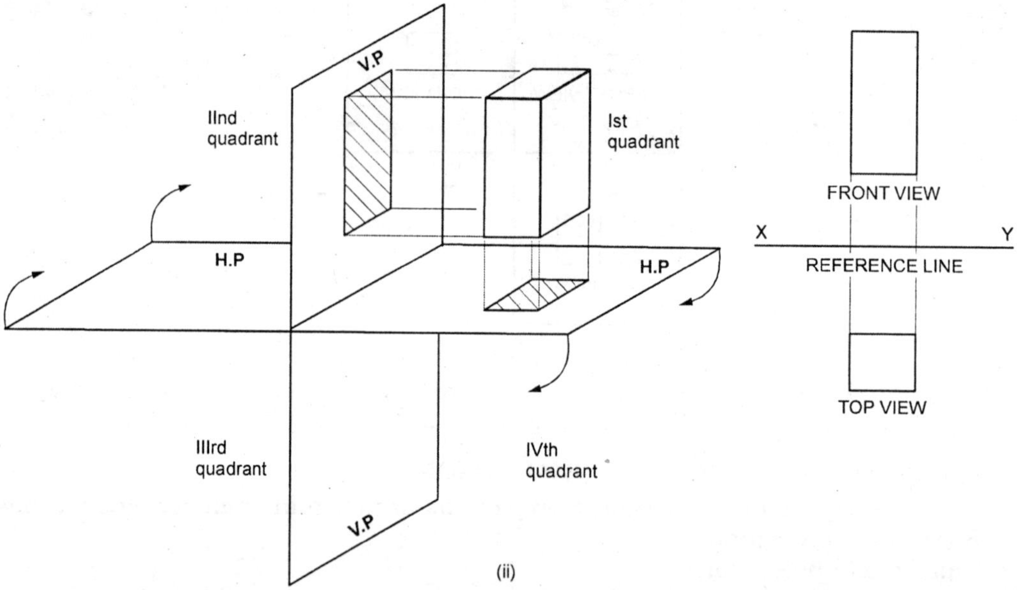

(ii)

Fig. 13.3

This method of projection is recommended by the "Bureau of Indian Standards" from 1991. The first angle projection symbol is shown in Fig. 13.4.

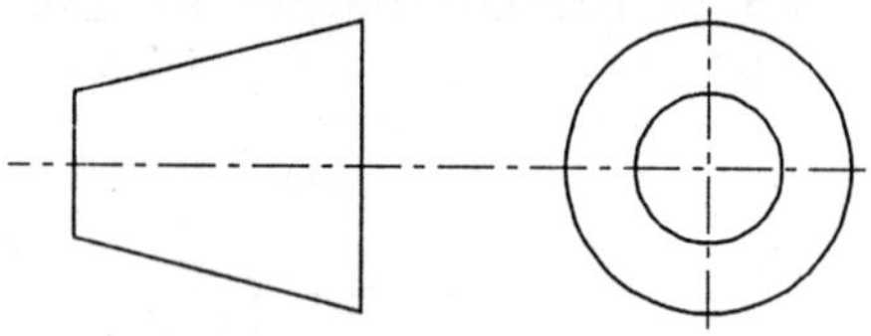

FIRST ANGLE PROJECTION SYMBOL

Fig. 13.4

13.7 THIRD ANGLE PROJECTION

In third angle projection the object is assumed to be positioned in the third quadrant as shown in Fig. 13.5. The plane is now between the observer and the object. The views seen from these positions are then recorded or drawn on the plane located between the observer and the object, that is below the horizontal plane and behind the vertical plane. The top view is always above the front view because when horizontal plane is rotated in clockwise direction by an angle of 90°, it will cover on top of vertical plane as shown in Fig. 13.5. Remember that, in third-angle projection, right side view is drawn to right and left side view is drawn to the left of the elevation. This method of projection is commonly used in U.S.A. as well as in the continent of Europe.

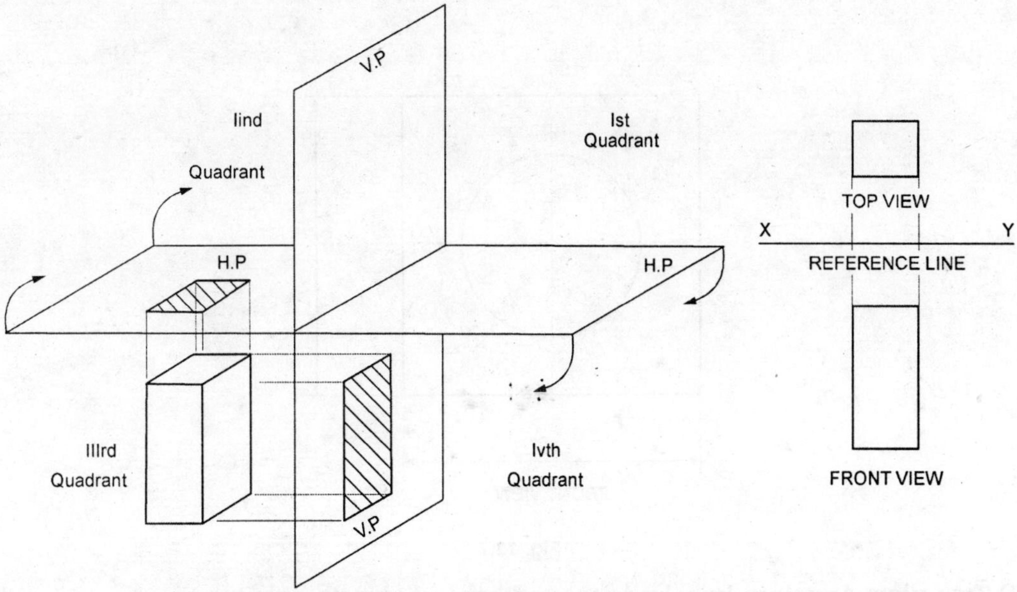

Fig. 13.5

The third angle projection symbol is shown in Fig. 13.6.

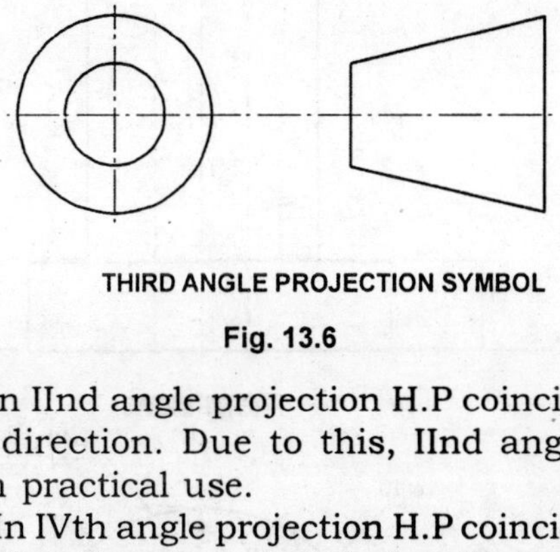

THIRD ANGLE PROJECTION SYMBOL

Fig. 13.6

IInd angle projection: In IInd angle projection H.P coincide with VP, when horizontal plane rotates in clockwise direction. Due to this, IInd angle projections overlap each other. Therefore, it is not in practical use.

IV th angle projection: In IVth angle projection H.P coincide with V.P, when horizontal plane rotates in clockwise direction. Due to this fourth angle projections overlap each other. Therefore, it is not in practical use.

13.8 SELECTION OF VIEWS

The selection of views to represent the object is very important in engineering drawing. The requirement of different views are as follows:

1. One view drawing.
2. Two view drawing.
3. Three view drawing.
4. Six view drawing.

(1) One view drawing: In one view drawing only one view is required to describe certain objects completely as shown in Fig. 13.7.

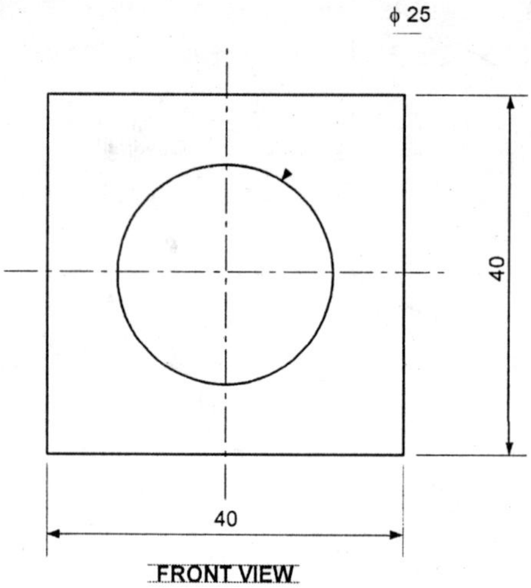

Fig. 13.7

(2) Two view drawing: In cylindrical and conical objects only two views are required for complete description as shown in Fig. 13.8.

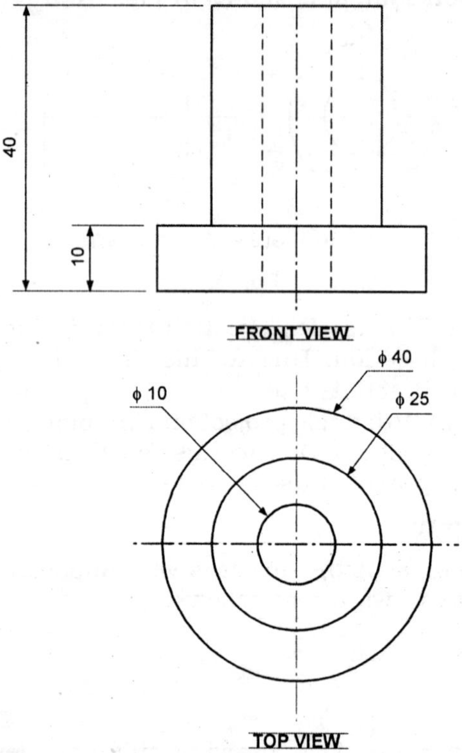

Fig. 13.8

(3) Three view drawing: The object which can be described completely with the help of three views except irregular shape of an object as shown in Fig. 13.9. These three views are:

1. Front view 2. Side view 3. Top view

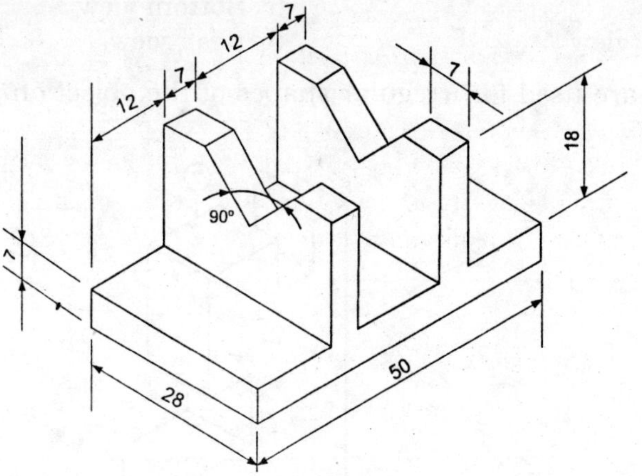

(i)

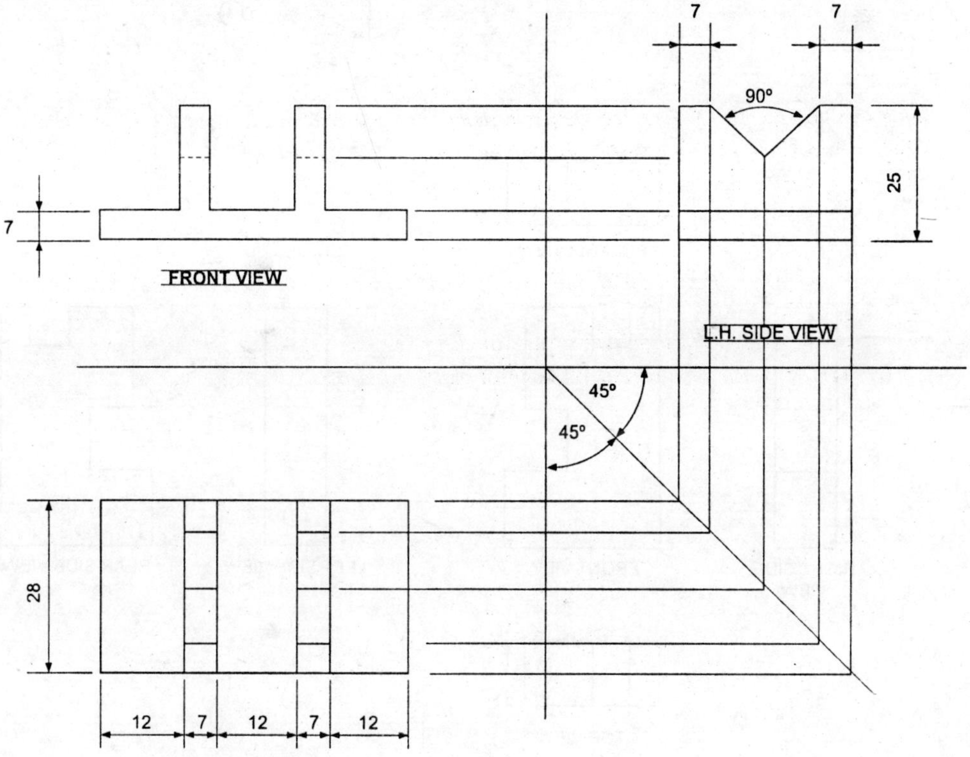

(ii)

Fig. 13.9

(4) Six view drawing: Maximum six views are used to show the detailed information of all the six sides of an object as shown in Fig. 13.10. These views are:

1. Front view
2. Top view
3. Left side view
4. Right side view
5. Bottom view
6. Rear view.

These views are used for irregular shapes of the object on various faces as shown in Fig 13.10.

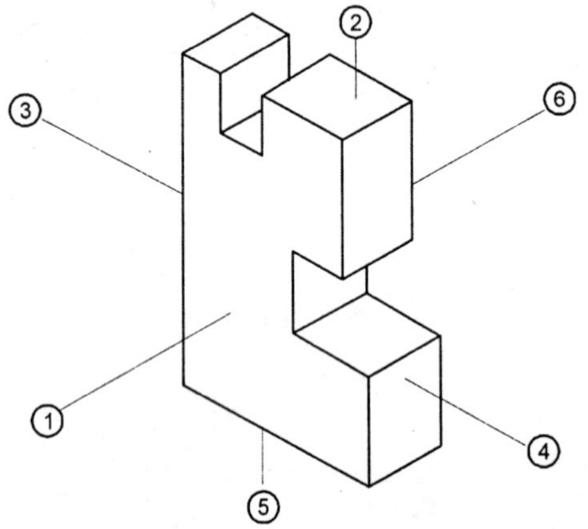

(i)

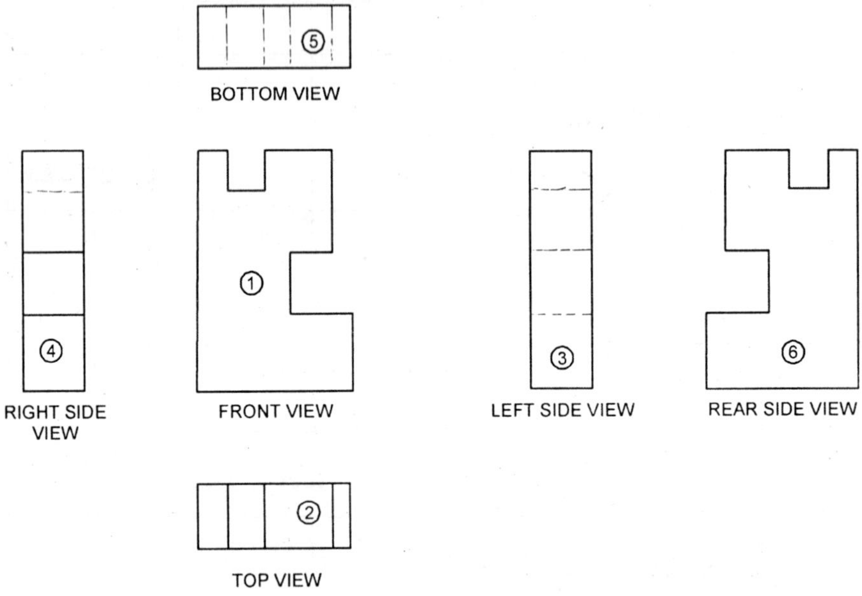

(ii)

Fig. 13.10

13.9 SPACING OF VIEWS

In technical drawings, spacing of views is very important factor before draw any object on the drawing sheet. It should be divided into suitable number of rectangles, if more than one view is required as shown in Fig. 13.11 (i and ii)
where A ≥ B and C ≥ D

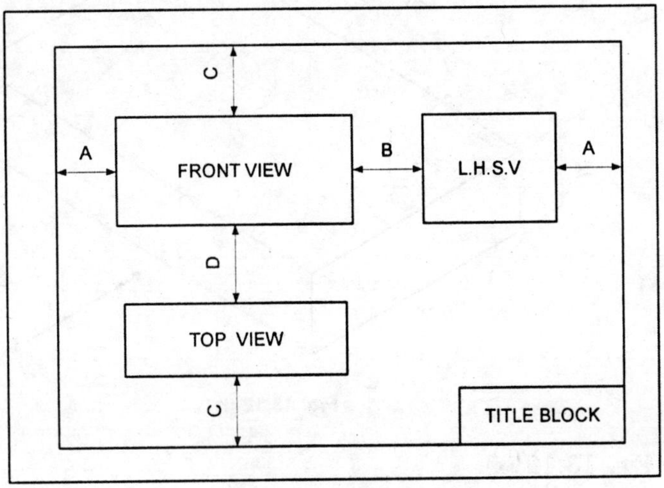

IST ANGLE PROJECTION

(i)

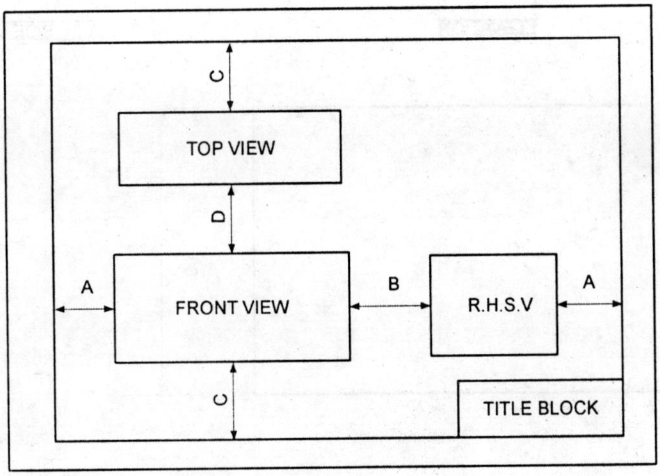

THIRD ANGLE PROJECTION

(ii)

Fig. 13.11

Problem 1. Fig. 13.12 (i) shows an isometric view of a block. Draw the following view: (Use Ist angle projection).

1. Elevation 2. Plan 3. L.H.S view.

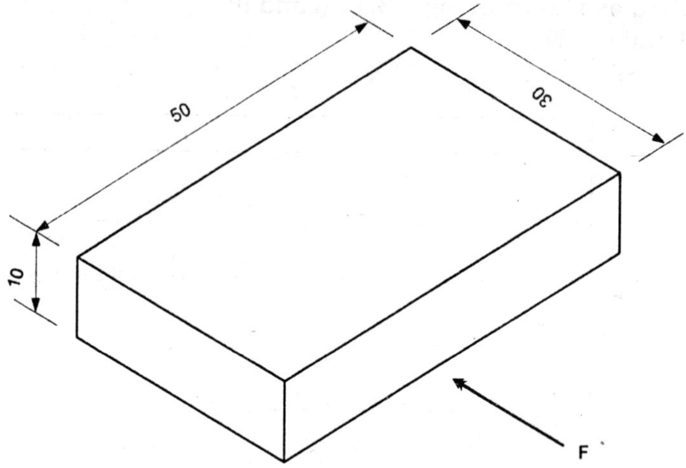

Fig. 13.12 (i)

Solution. See Fig. 13.12 (ii).

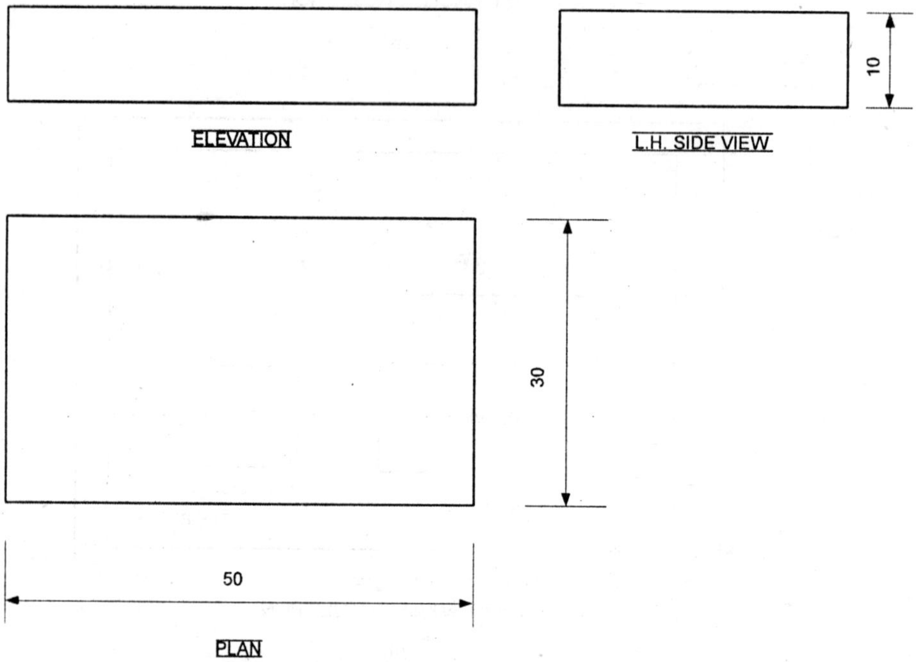

Fig. 13.12 (ii)

Problem 2. Fig. 13.13 (i) shows an isometric view of an object. Draw the following views: (Used Ist angle projection).

1. Front view 2. R.H.S view 3. Top view.

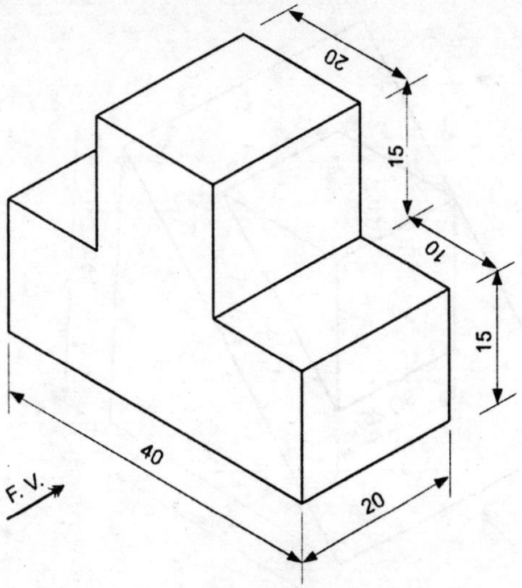

Fig. 13.13 (i)

Solution. See Fig. 13.13 (ii).

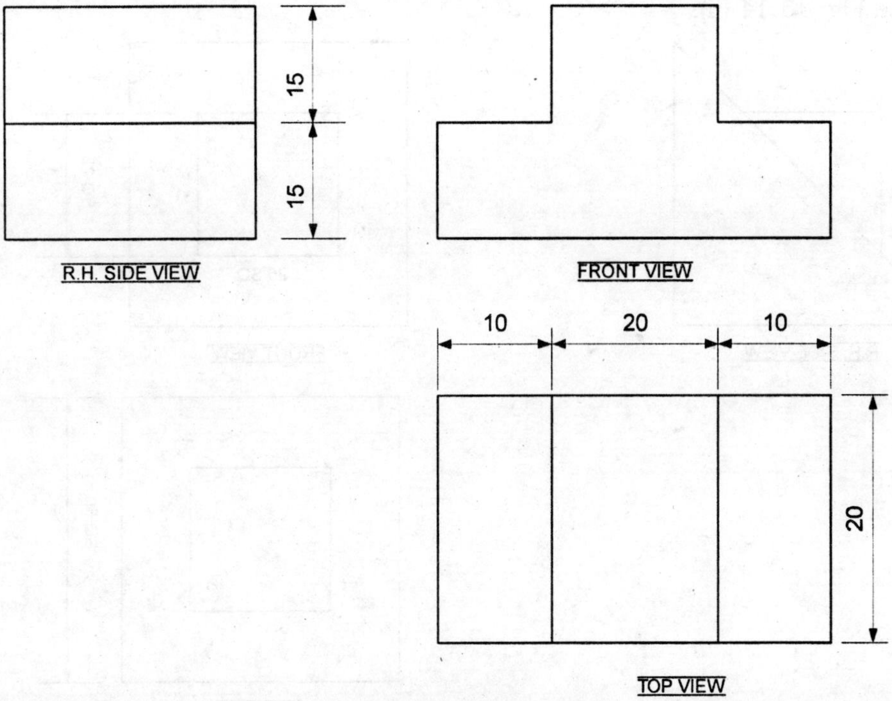

Fig. 13.13 (ii)

Problem 3. Fig. 13.14 (i) shows the isometric view of an object. Draw to scale full size of the following views: (Use Ist angle projection method).

1. Front view 2. Top view 3. R.H.S view.

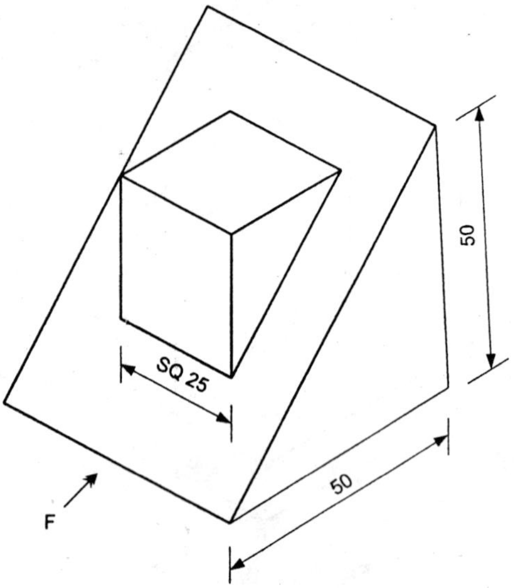

Fig. 13.14 (i)

Solution. See Fig. 13.14 (ii).

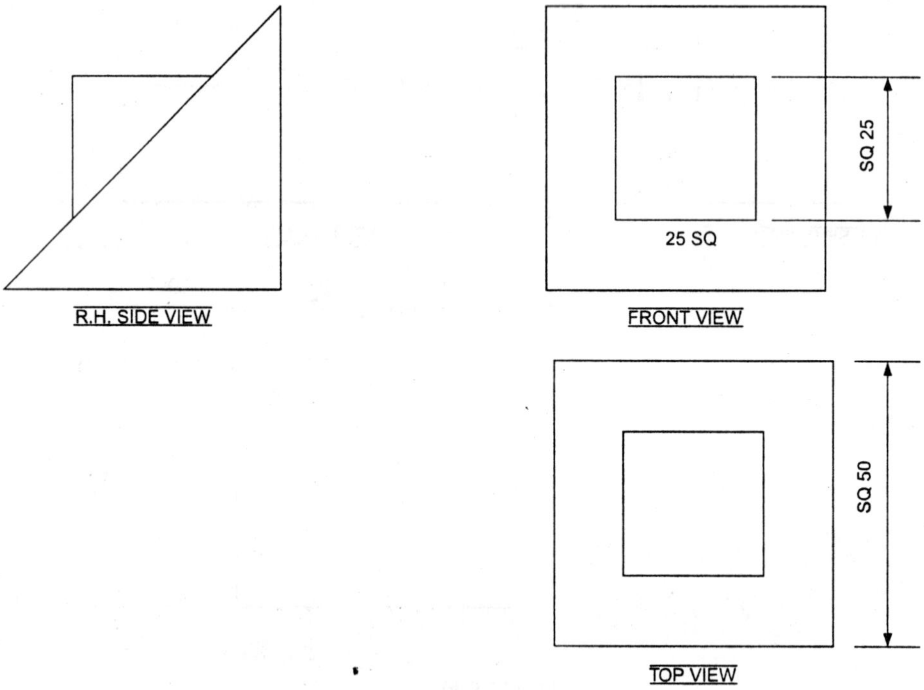

Fig. 13.14 (ii)

Problem 4. Fig. 13.15 (i) shows an object. Draw the following view: (Use Ist angle projection).

1. Front view 2. Top view 3. Side view.

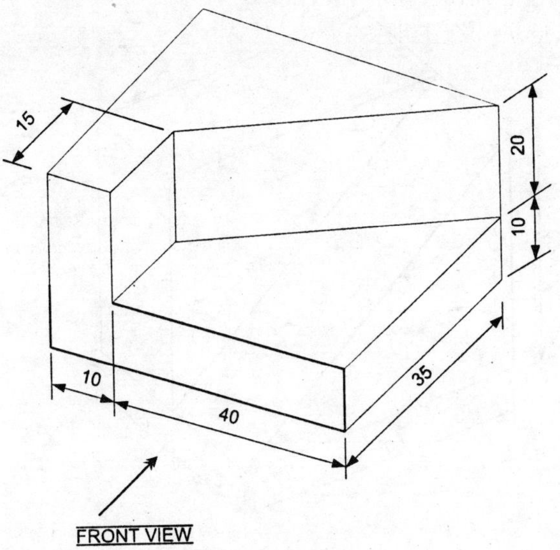

Fig. 13.15 (i)

Solution. See Fig. 13.15 (ii).

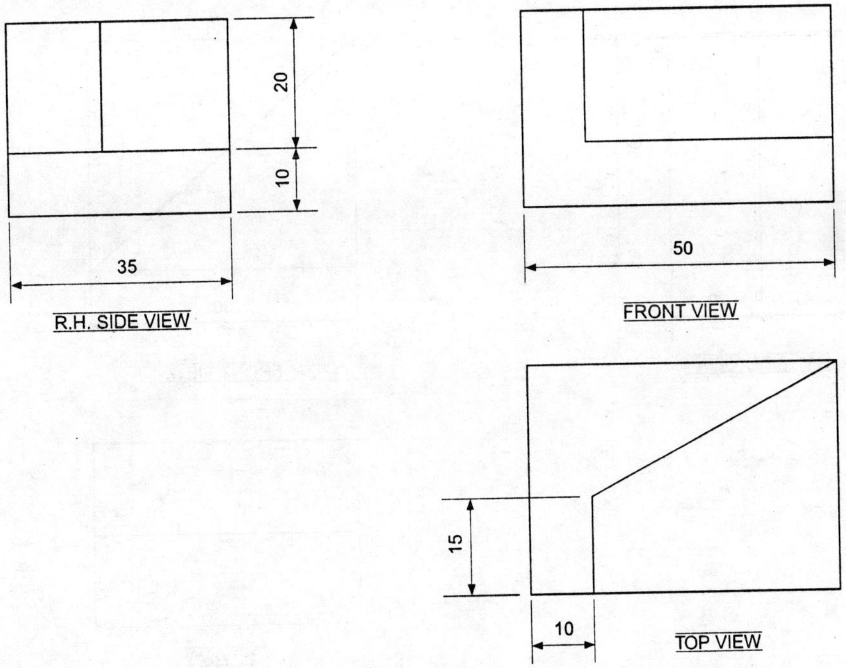

Fig. 13.15 (ii)

Problem 5. Fig. 13.16 (i) shows an isometric block of an object. Draw the following views:
1. Front view 2. Top view 3. R.H.S view.

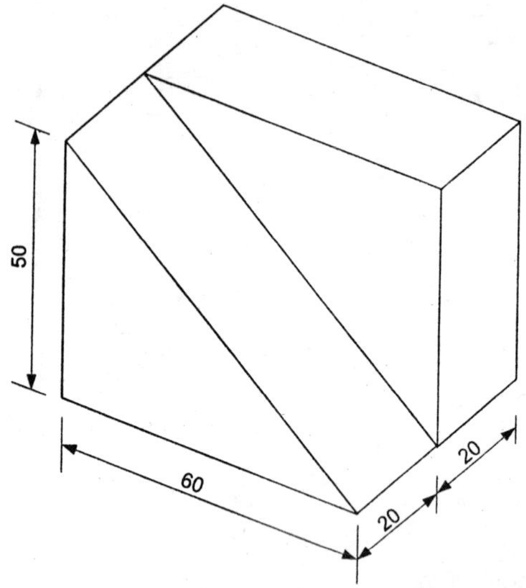

Fig. 13.16 (i)

Solution. See Fig. 13.16 (ii).

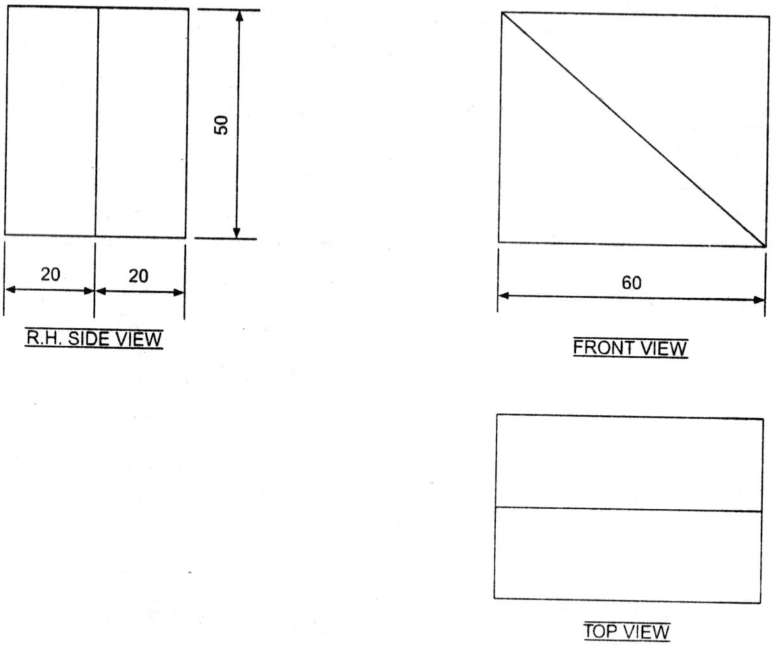

Fig. 13.16 (ii)

Problem 6. Fig. 13.17 (i) shows a square turncated prism. Draw the following views.
1. Front view 2. Top view 3. R.H.S view.

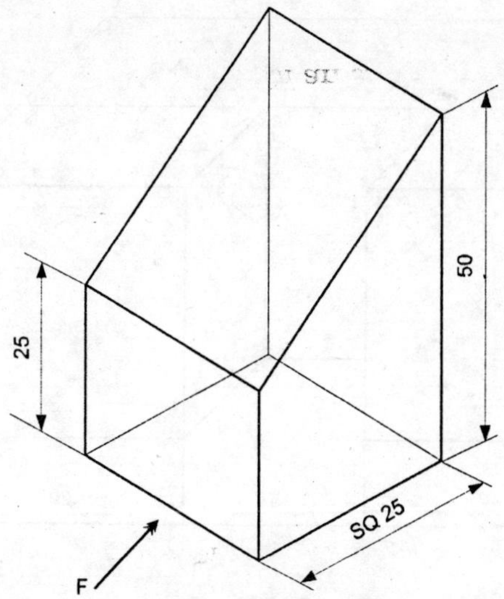

Fig. 13.17 (i)

Solution. See Fig. 13.17 (ii).

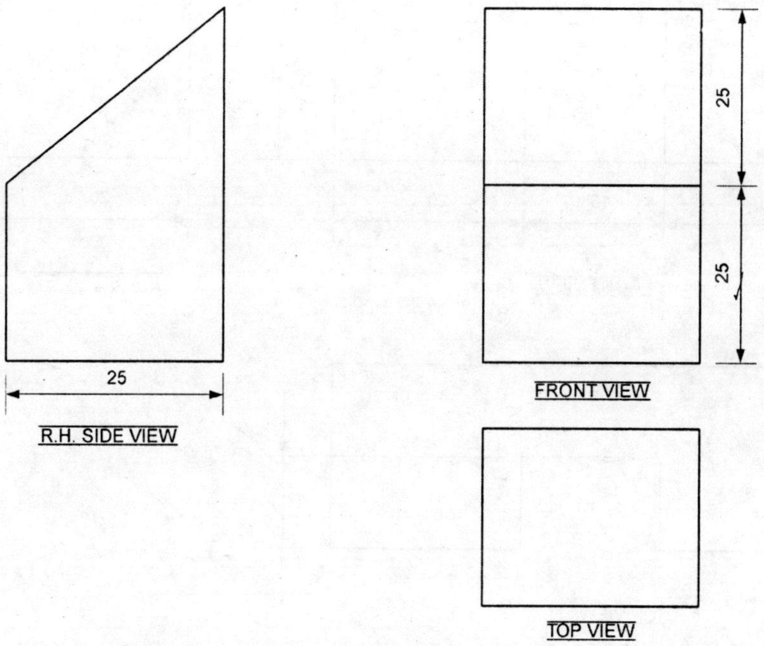

Fig. 13.17 (ii)

Problem 7. Fig. 13.18 (i) shows the pictorial view of a block. Draw the following views:
1. Front view 2. Top view 3. L.H.S view.

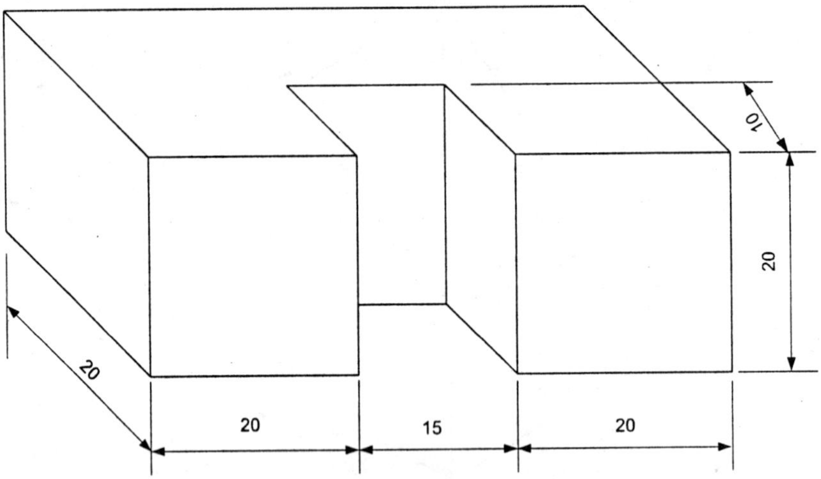

Fig. 13.18 (i)

Solution. See Fig. 13.18 (ii).

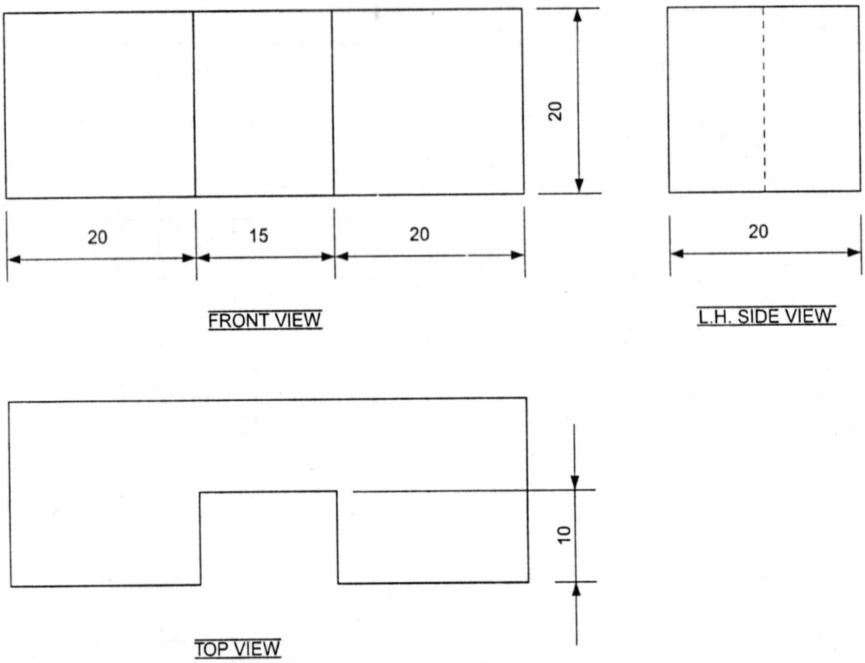

Fig. 13.18 (ii)

roblem 8. Fig. 13.19 (i) shows a semi-sphere of an object. Draw the following views.
1. Elevation 2. Plan.

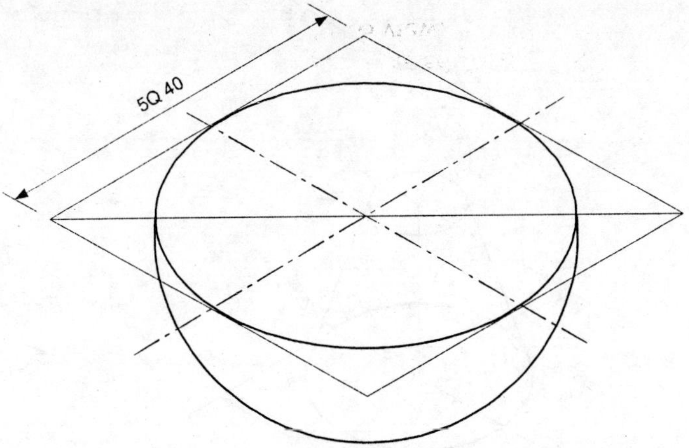

Fig. 13.19 (i)

olution. See Fig. 13.19 (ii).

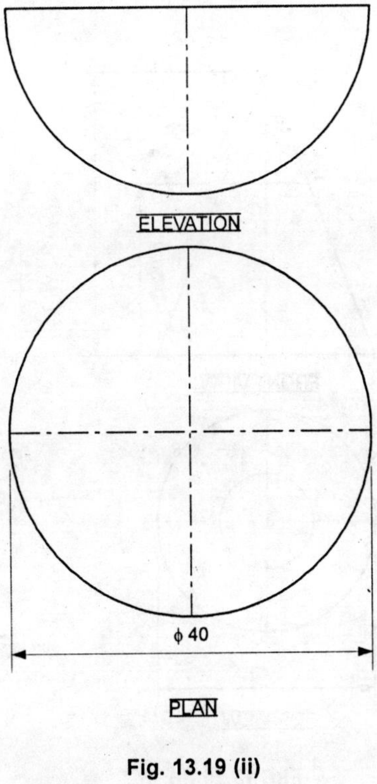

Fig. 13.19 (ii)

Problem 9. Fig. 13.20 (i) shows a frustumed cone. Draw the following views:
1. Front view 2. Top view.

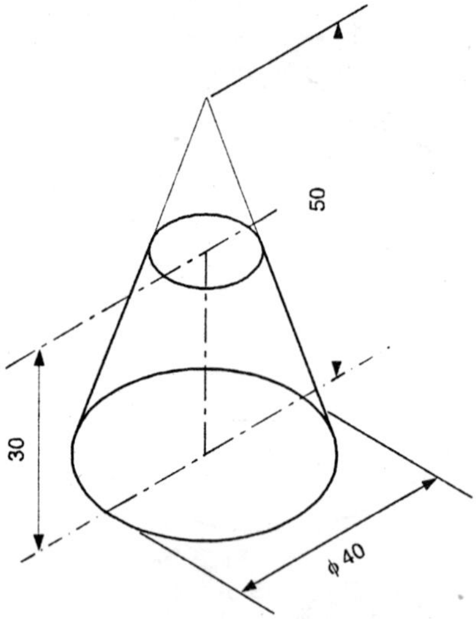

Fig. 13.20 (i)

Solution. See Fig. 13.20 (ii).

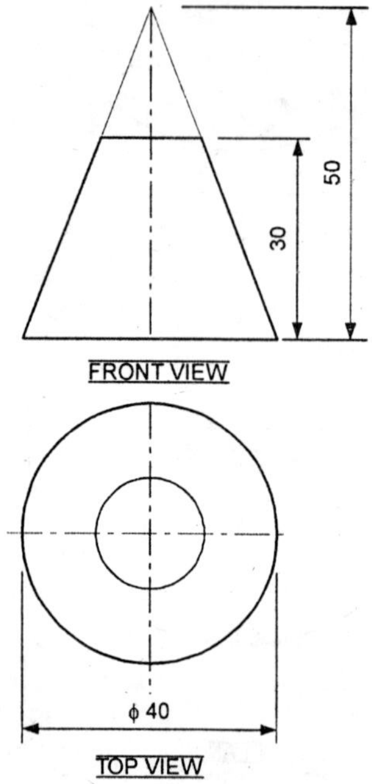

Fig. 13.20 (ii)

Problem 10. Fig. 13.21 (i) shows the isometric view of an object. Draw the following views.
1. Front view 2. Top view 3. Right side view.

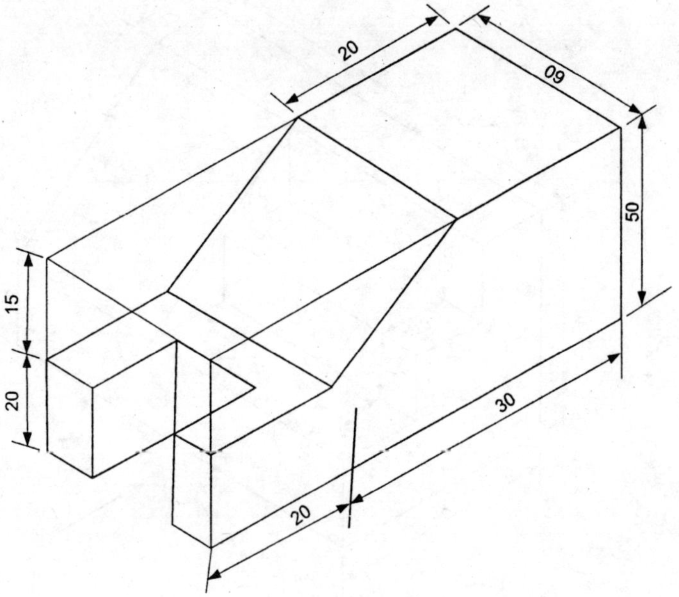

Fig. 13.21 (i)

Solution. See Fig. 13.21 (ii).

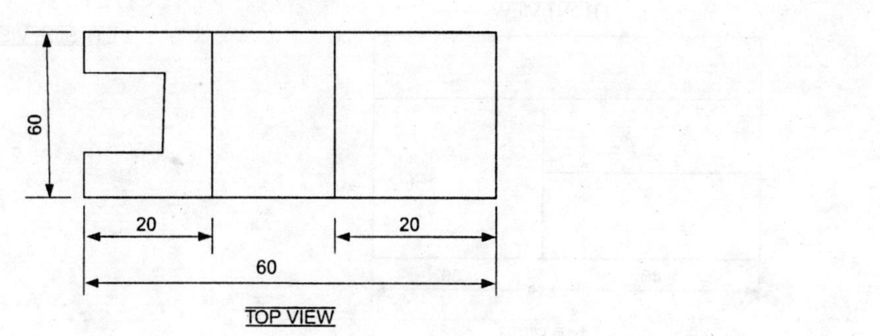

Fig. 13.21 (ii)

Problem 11. Fig. 13.22 (i) shows an isometric block of an object. Draw the following view

1. Front view 2. Top view 3. L.H.S view.

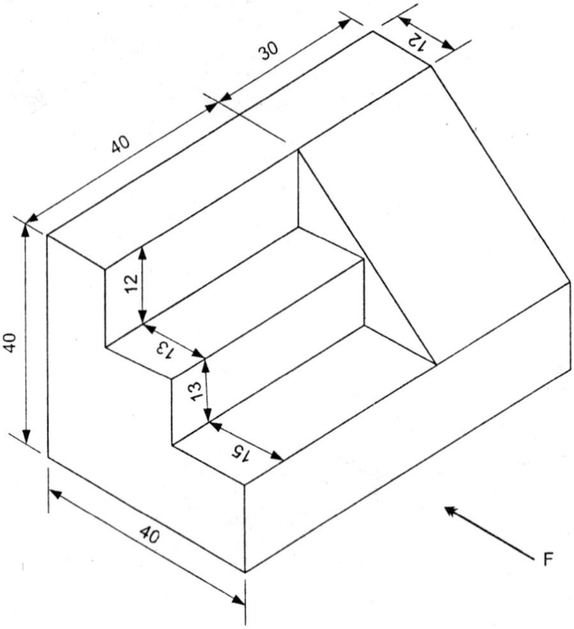

Fig. 13.22 (i)

Solution. See Fig. 13.22 (ii).

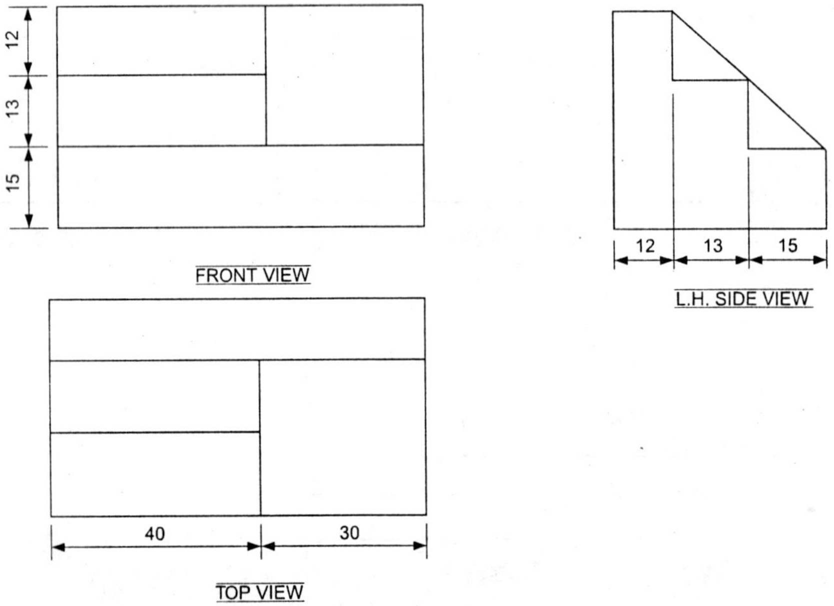

Fig. 13.22 (ii)

Problem 12. Fig. 13.23 (i) shows a pictorial view of an object. Draw the following views:
1. Front view 2. Top view 3. L.H.S view.

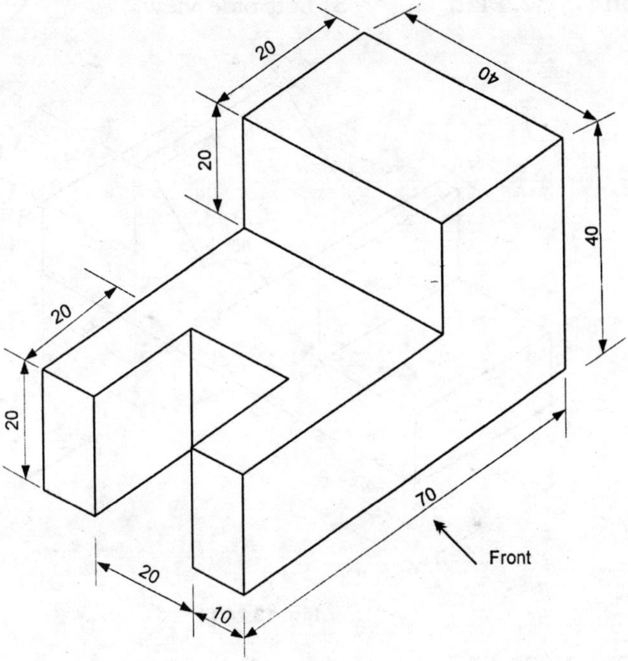

Fig. 13.23 (i)

Solution. See Fig. 13.23 (ii).

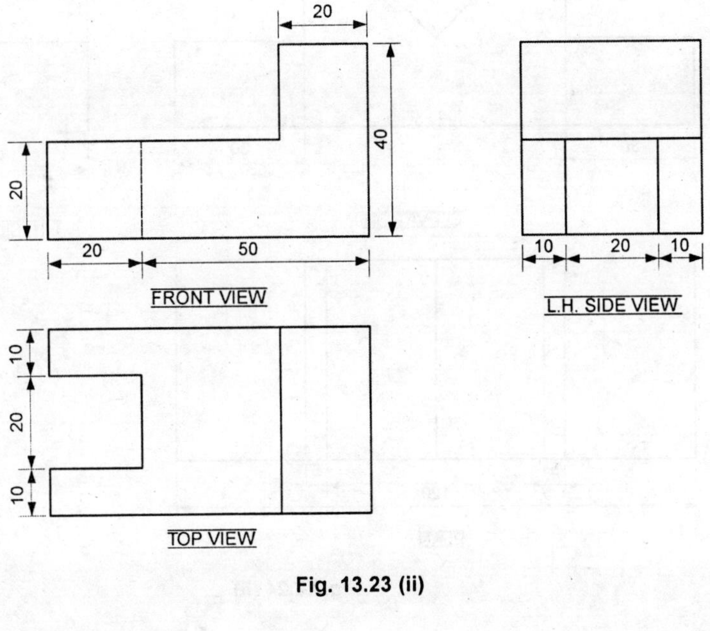

Fig. 13.23 (ii)

Problem 13. Fig. 13.24 (i) shows an Isometric view of a block. Draw the following views: (Use Ist angle projection).

1. Elevation 2. Plan 3. Left side view.

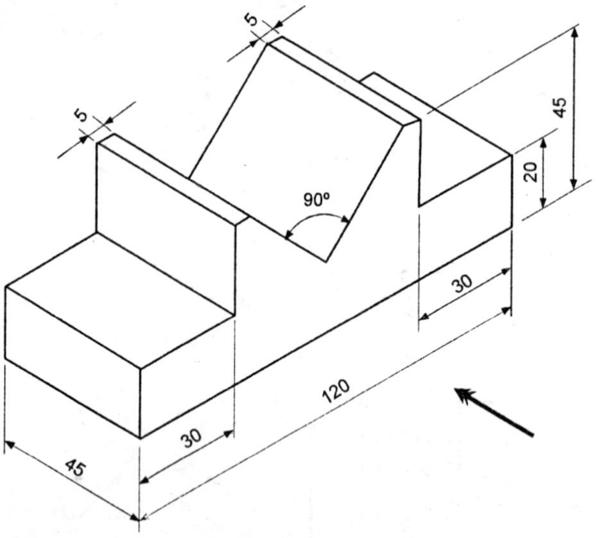

Fig. 13.24 (i)

Solution. See Fig. 13.24 (ii).

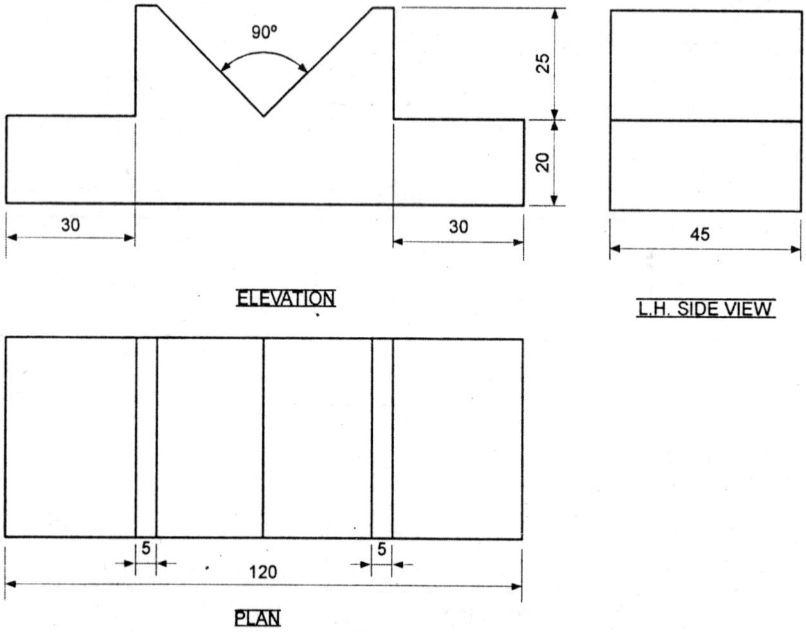

Fig. 13.24 (ii)

Problem 14. Fig. 13.25 (i) shows the pictorial view of a block. Draw the following views: (Use Ist angle projection).

1. Front view 2. Top view 3. Side view.

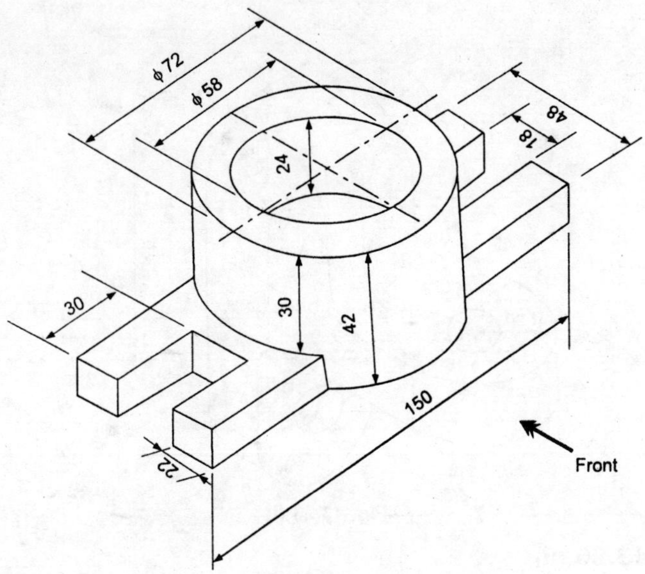

Fig. 13.25 (i)

Solution: See Fig 13.25(ii).

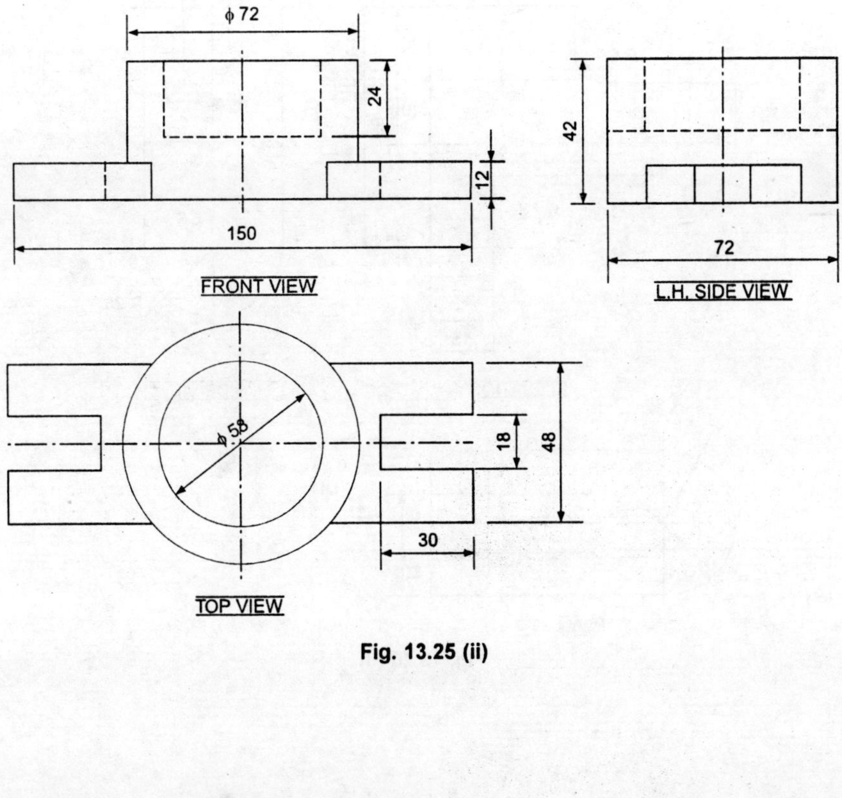

Fig. 13.25 (ii)

Problem 15. Fig. 13.26 show (i) an isometric view of a block. Draw the following of views: (Use Ist angle projection).

1. Elevation 2. Plan 3. Side view.

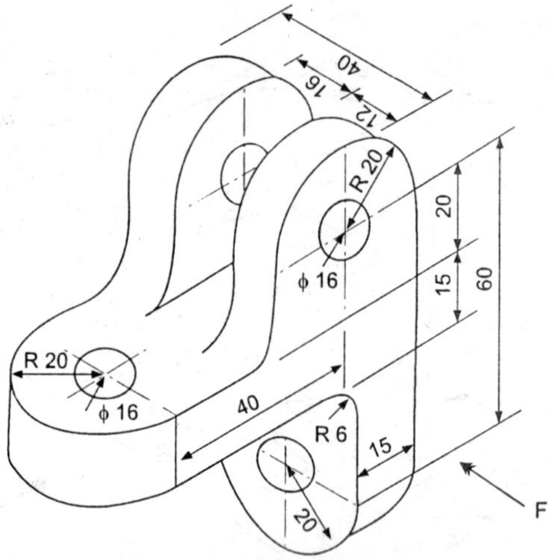

Fig. 13.26 (i)

Solution. See Fig. 13.26 (ii).

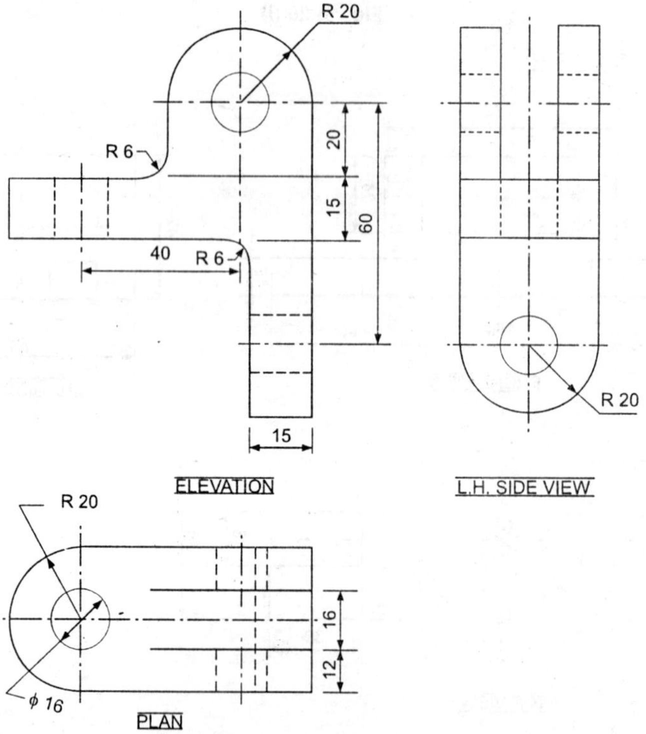

Fig. 13.26 (ii)

Problem 16. Fig. 13.27 (i) shows the pictorial view of an object. Draw the following views:
1. Front view 2. Top view 3. Side view.

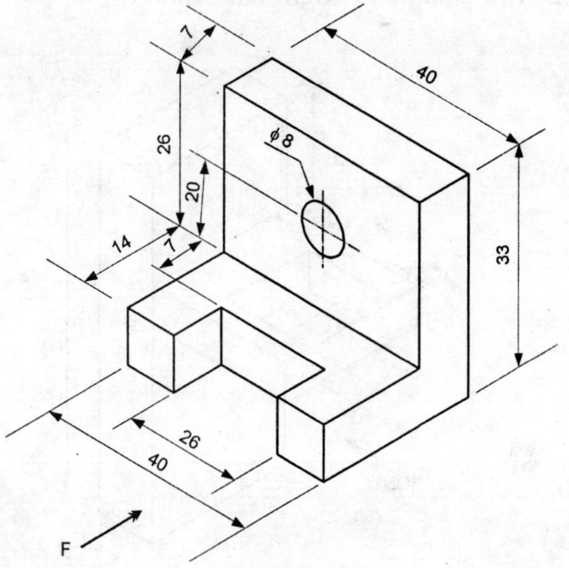

Fig. 13.27 (i)

Solution. See Fig. 13.27 (ii).

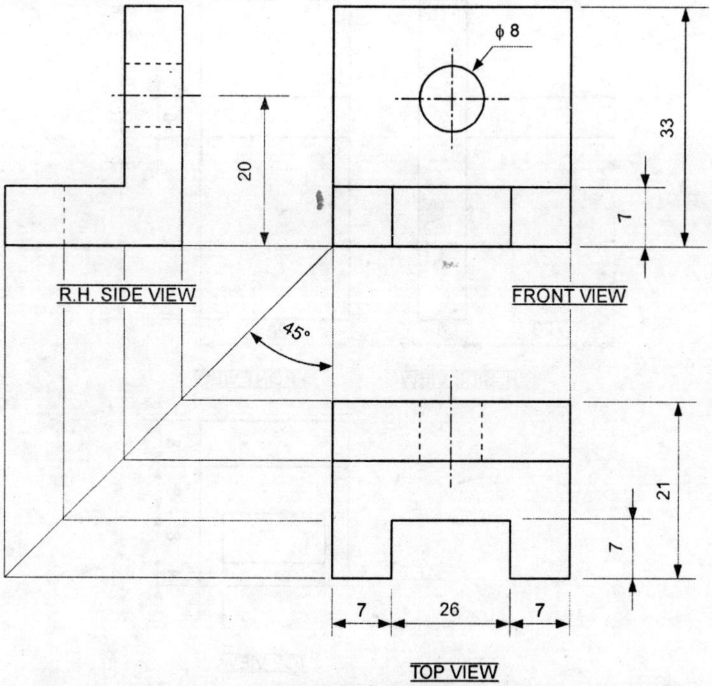

Fig. 13.27 (ii)

Problem 17. Fig. 13.28 (i) shows a tee bracket. Draw the following views: (Use 1st angle projection).

1. Front view 2. Top view 3. Right side view.

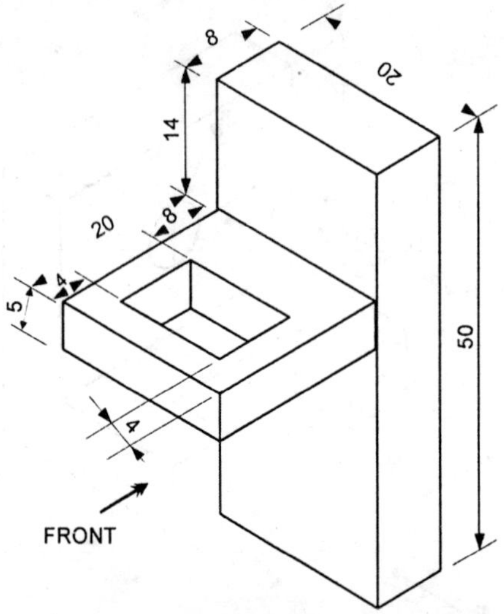

Fig. 13.28 (i)

Solution. See Fig. 13.28 (ii).

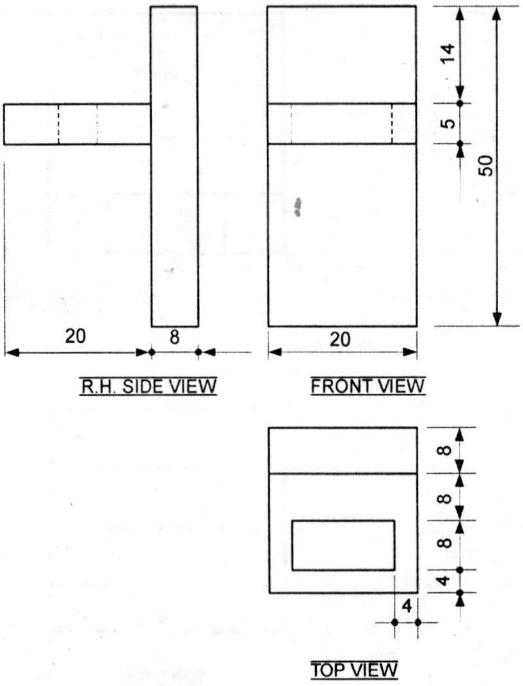

Fig. 13.28 (ii)

Problem 18. Fig. 13.29 (i) shows an object. Draw the following views: (Use 3rd angle projection method):

1. Front view 2. Top view 3. Right side view.

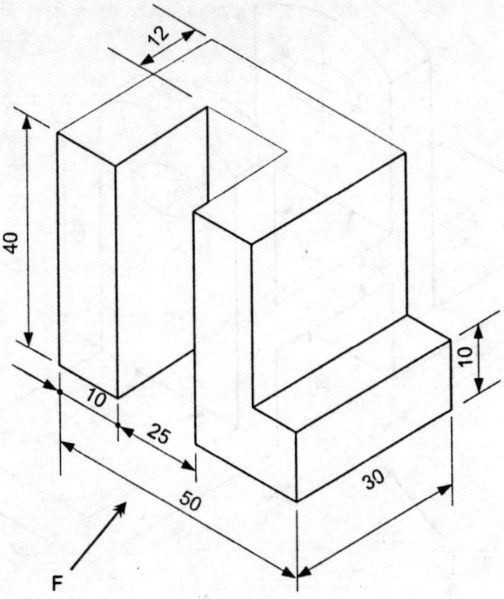

Fig. 13.29 (i)

Solution. See Fig. 13.29 (ii).

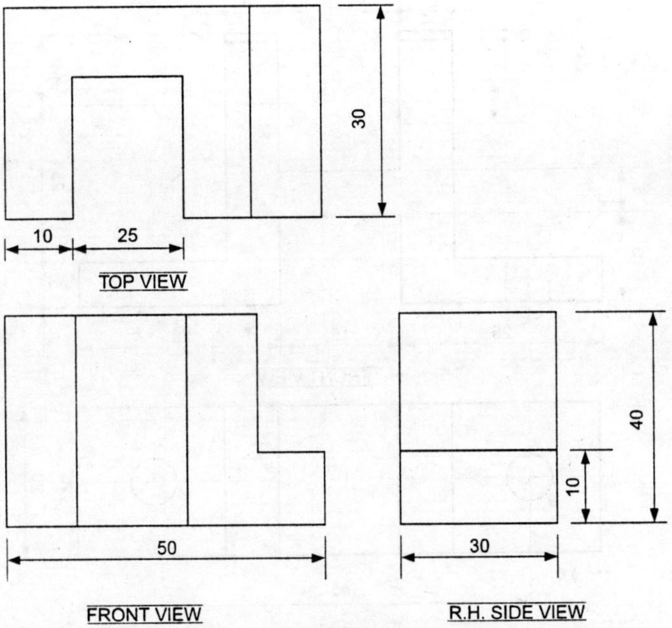

Fig. 13.29 (ii)

Problem 19. Fig. 13.30 (i) shows the isometric view of an object. Draw to scale full size in the following view:

1. Front view 2. Top view.

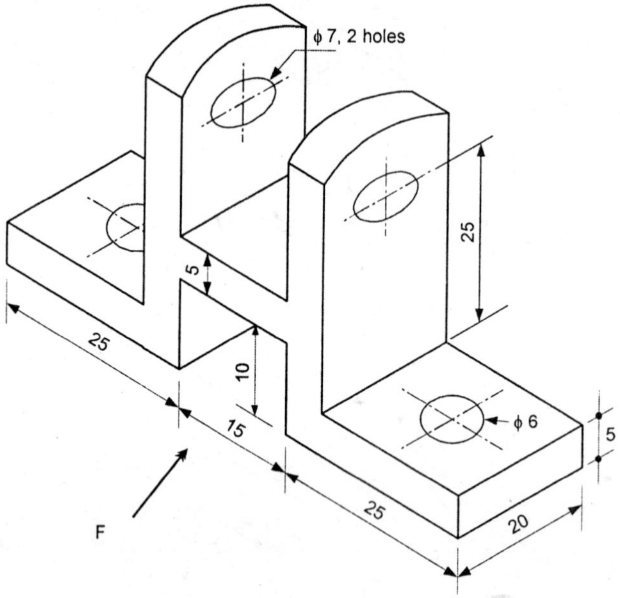

Fig. 13.30 (i)

Solution. See Fig. 13.30 (ii).

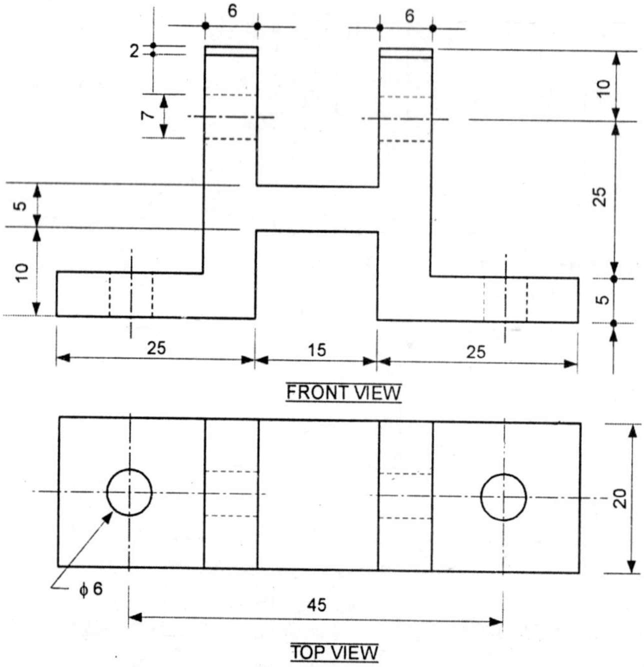

Fig. 13.30 (ii)

Problem 20. Fig. 13.31 (i) shows the pictorial view of a machine block. Draw the following views to a suitable scale of a giving dimensions.

1. Front elevation in the direction of arrow
2. Side view from left side
3. Top View.

(B.T.E. New Delhi, 2004)

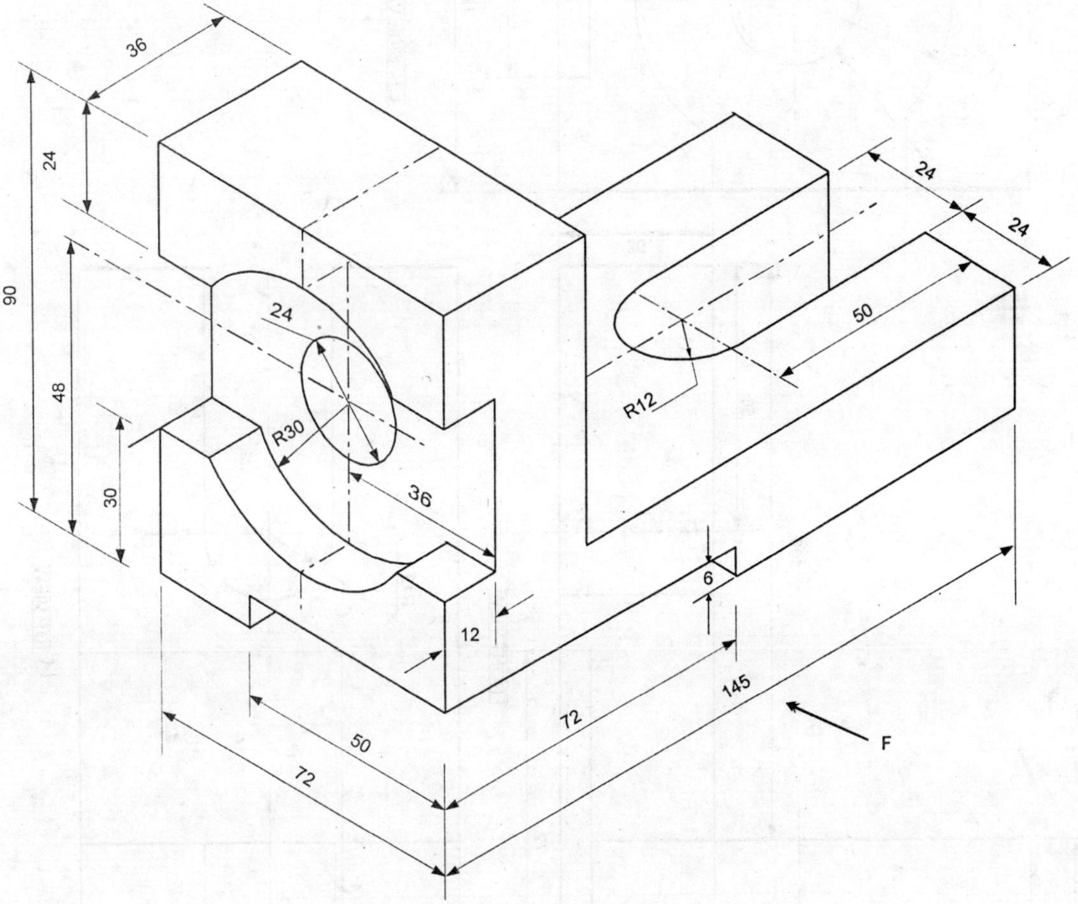

Fig. 13.31 (i)

Solution. See Fig. 13.31 (ii).

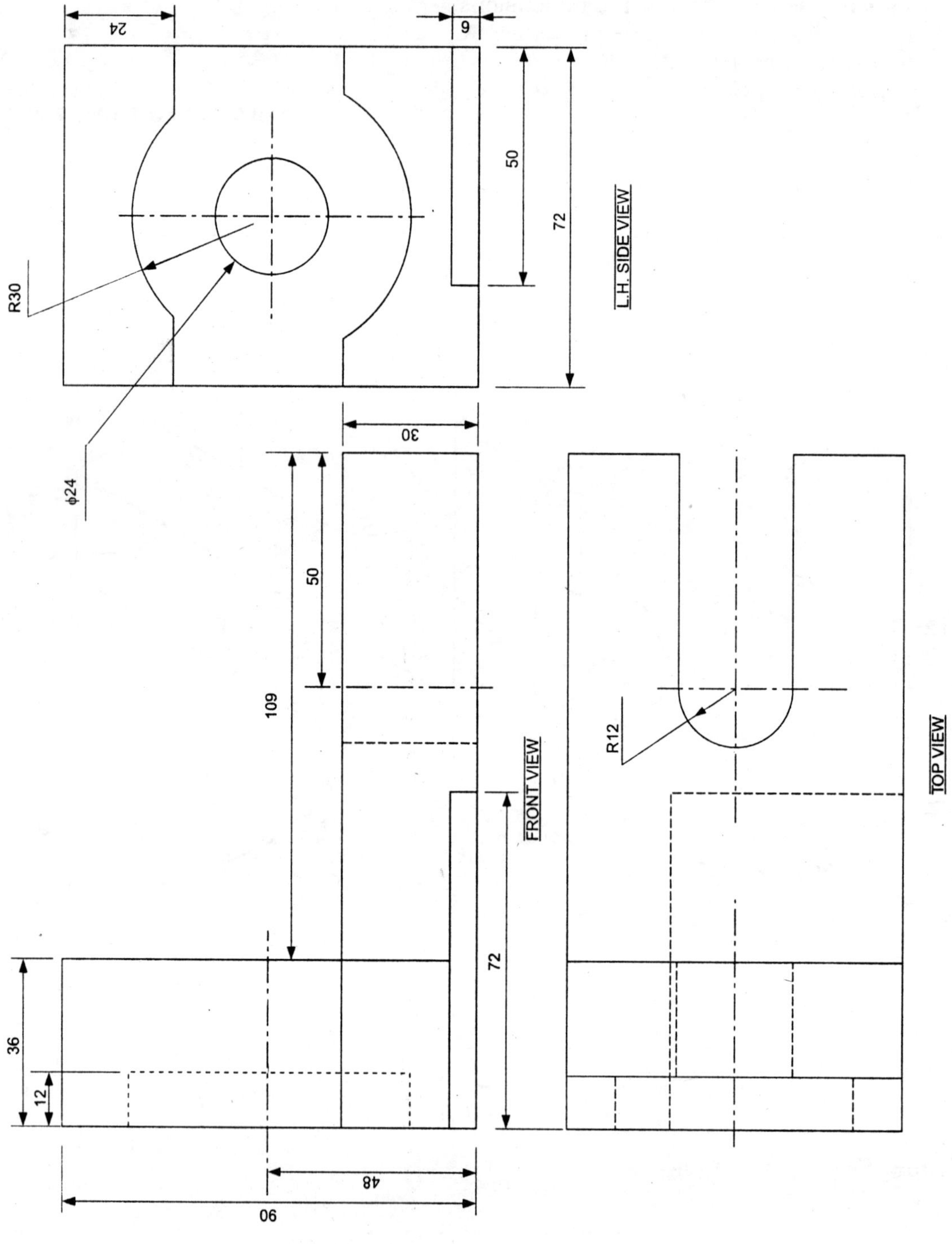
L.H. SIDE VIEW
FRONT VIEW
TOP VIEW
24
6
50
72
R30
ϕ24
30
109
50
72
36
12
48
90
R12

Fig. 13.31 (ii)

Problem 21. Fig. 13.32 (i) shows the pictorial view of an object. Draw the following views in scale full size:

1. Front view through – A
2. Top view
3. Right side view.

(B.T.E. New Delhi, Dec. 2004)

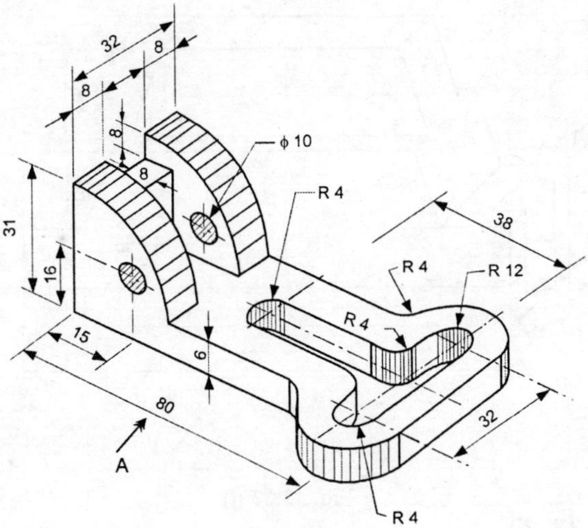

Fig. 13.32 (i)

Solution. See Fig. 13.32 (ii).

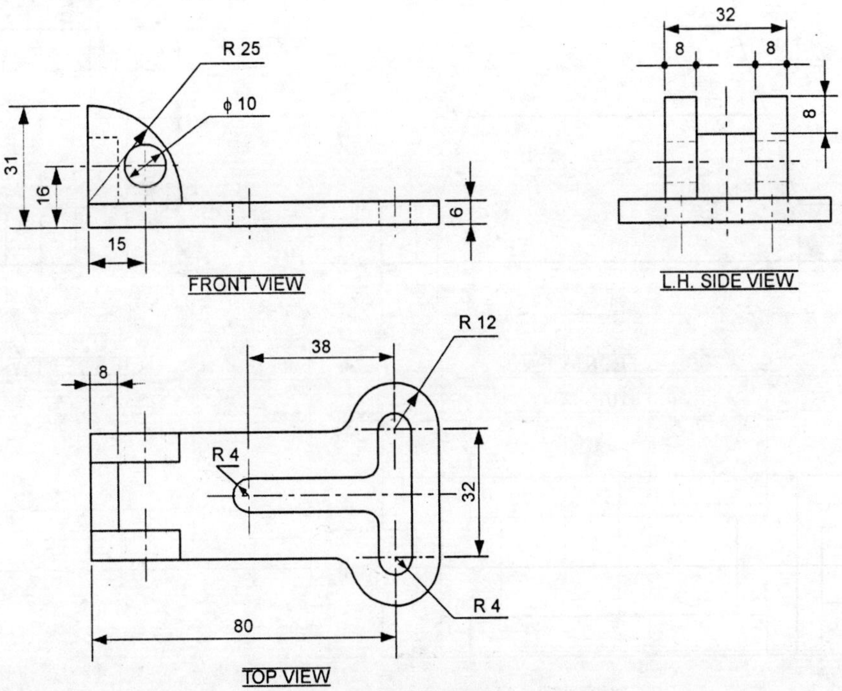

Fig. 13.32 (ii)

Problem 22. Fig. 13.33 (i) shows the pictorial view of an object. Draw to scale full size in following view:

1. Front view looking in the direction of draw – X
2. Left side view
3. Top view.

(B.T.E. New Delhi, Dec. 2003)

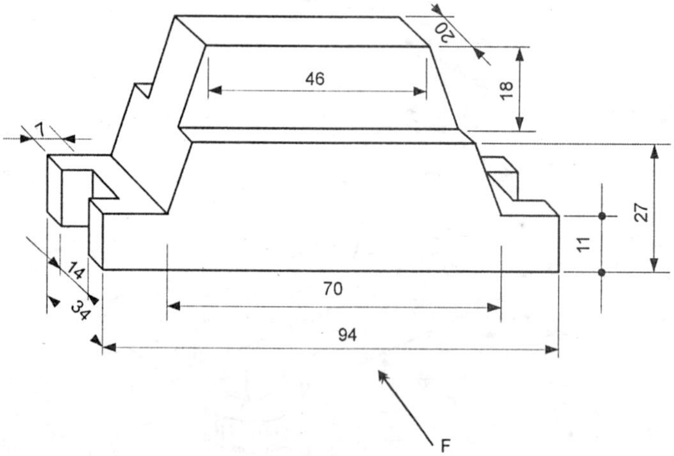

Fig. 13.33 (i)

Solution. See Fig. 13.33 (ii).

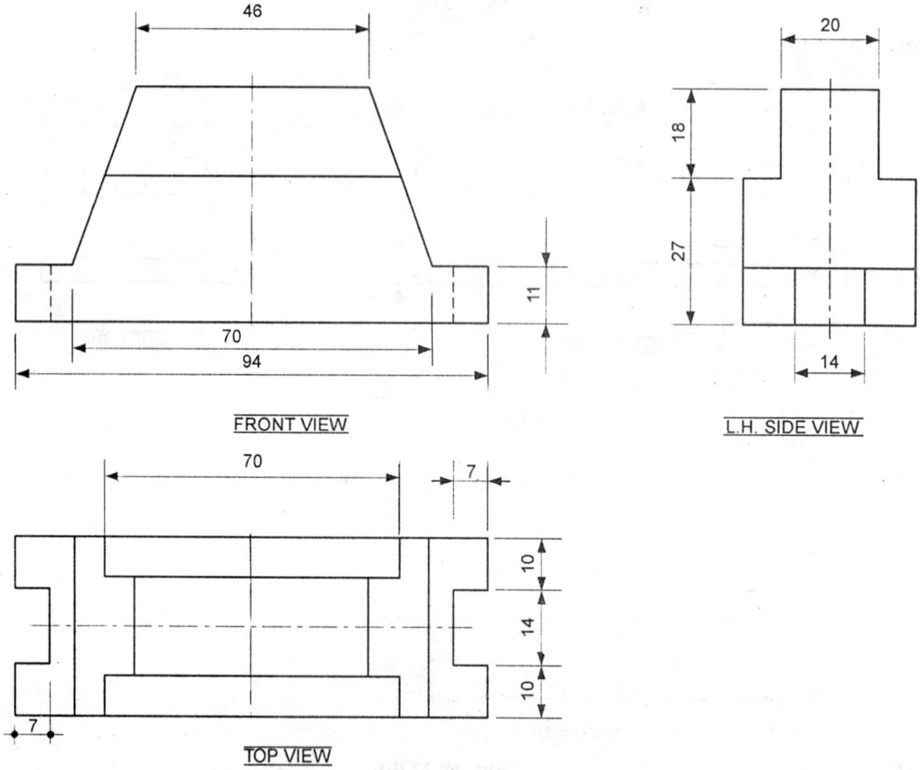

Fig. 13.33 (ii)

Problem 23. Fig. 13.34 (i) shows the pictorial view of an object. Draw the following views:

1. Front view 2. Top view 3. Left side view. **(B.T.E. New Delhi, Dec. 2007)**

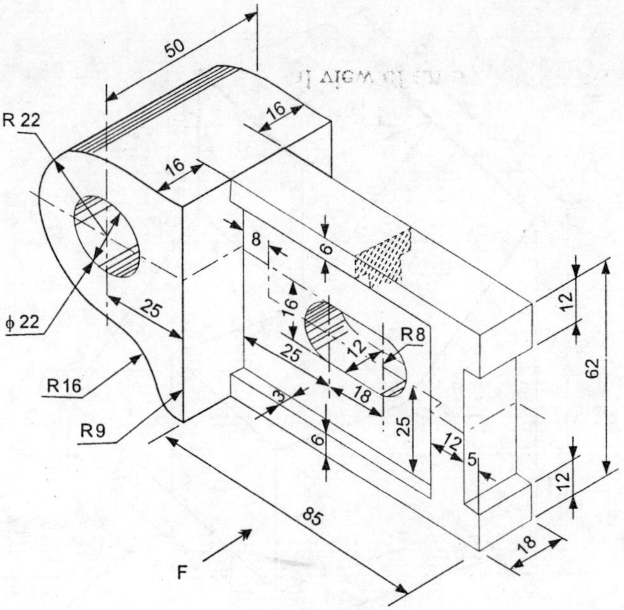

Fig. 13.34 (i)

Solution. See Fig. 13.34 (ii).

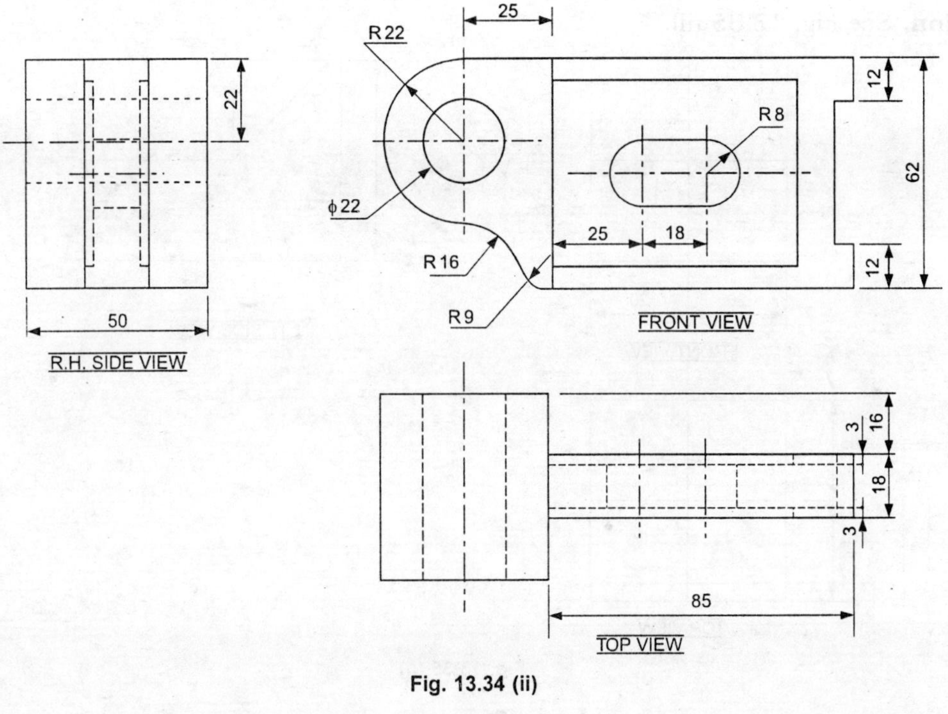

Fig. 13.34 (ii)

Problem 24. Fig. 13.35 (i) shows the pictorial view of an object. Draw the following views:
1. Front view 2. Left hand side 3. Top view.

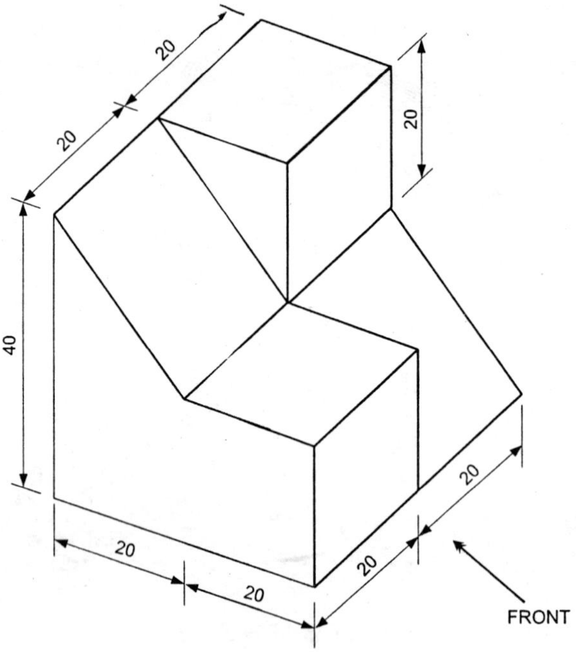

Fig. 13.35 (i)

Solution. See Fig. 13.35 (ii).

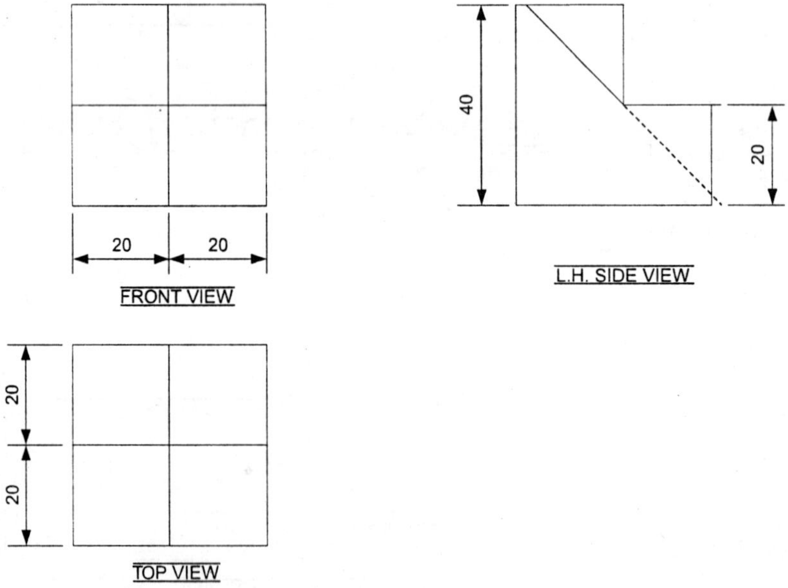

Fig. 13.35 (ii)

Problem 25. Fig. 13.36 (i) shows an object. Draw the following views:

1. Front view 2. Right hand side view 3. Top view.

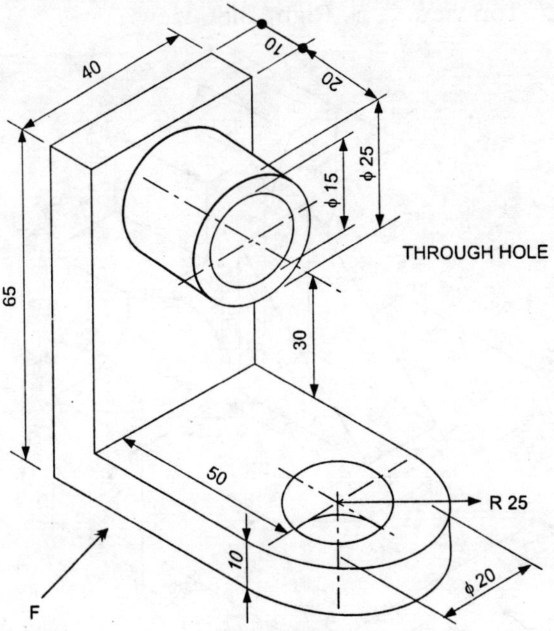

Fig. 13.36 (i)

Solution. See Fig. 13.36 (ii).

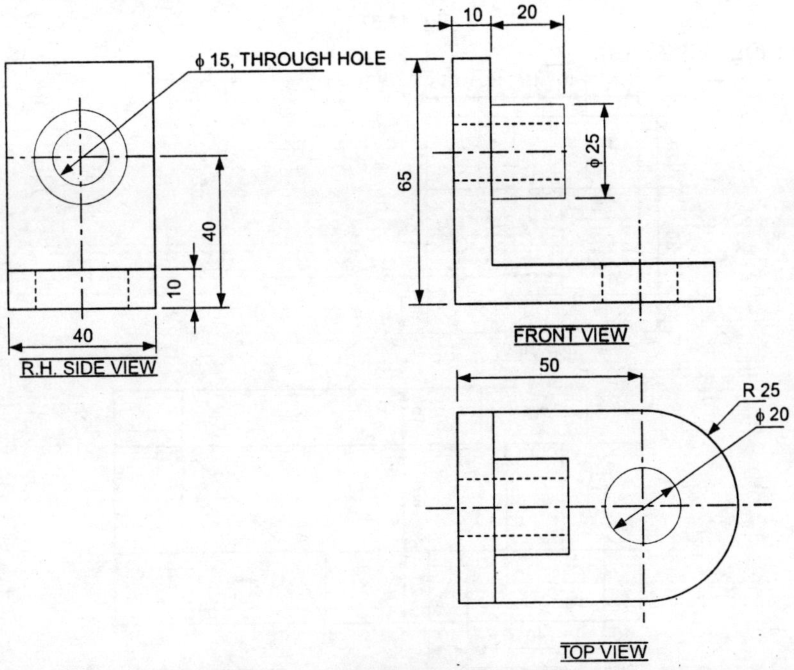

Fig. 13.36 (ii)

Problem 26. Figure 13.37 (i) shows an object. Draw the following views: (Use IIIrd angle projection).

1. Front view 2. Top view 3. Right Side view.

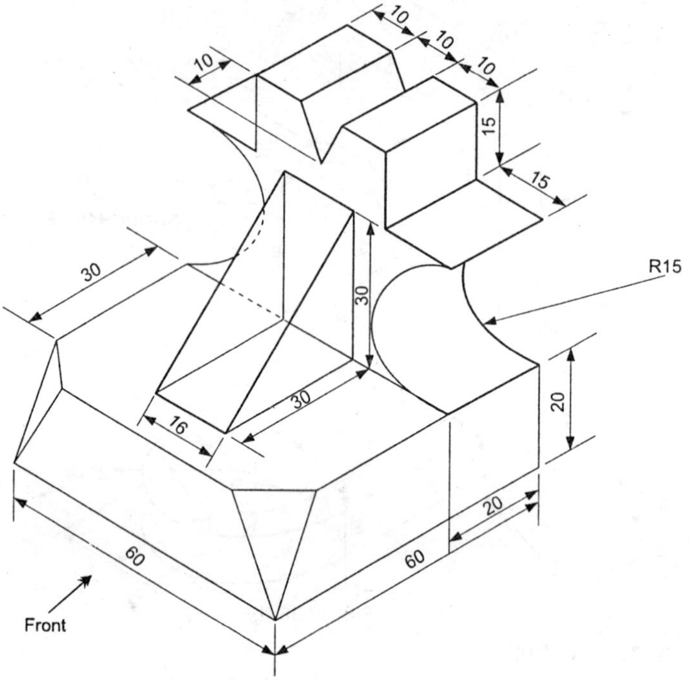

Fig. 13.37 (i)

Solution. See Fig. 13.37 (ii).

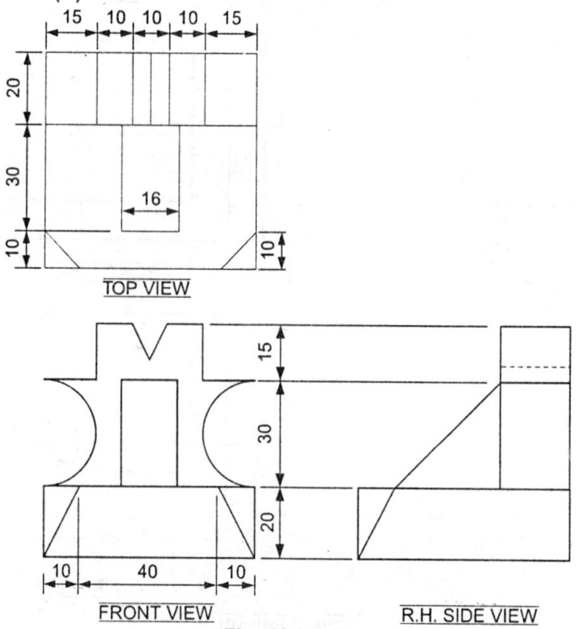

Fig. 13.37 (ii)

EXERCISE

1. What do you mean by orthographic projection plane of projection?

2. Write short notes on:
- Reference planes
- Reference line
- Projector
- Front view.

3. What do you mean by four dihedral angles?

4. What is the difference between Ist angle projection and third angle projection?

5. Define the terms:
- Elevation
- Plan
- Side view.

6. For the isometric view shown in Fig. 13.38, draw the following views in scale FULL SIZE:

(*a*) Front view looking in the direction of arrow shown

(*b*) Top view

(*c*) Left side view. **(B.T.E. New Delhi, January 2009)**

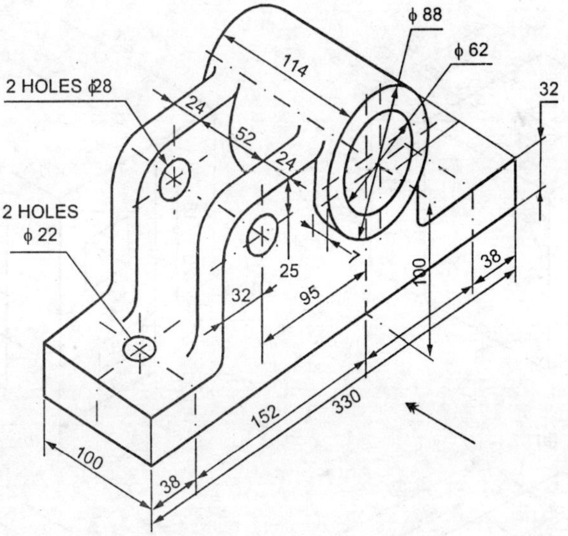

Fig. 13.38

7. An 'ISOMETRIC' view of Bevel is given in Fig. 13.39.

Draw to full size the following orthographic views, in First Angle projection, looking from 'Arrow A'

(*a*) Front view

(*b*) Top view. **(B.T.E., New Delhi, January 2009)**

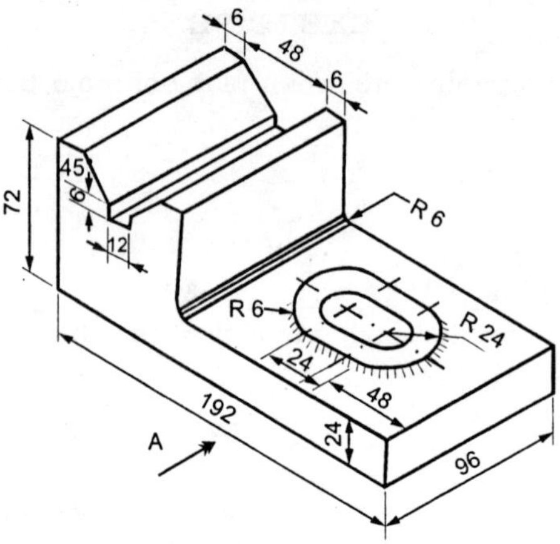

Fig. 13.39

8. The pictorial view of different types of objects are shown in Fig. 13.40 (*a* to *z*). Draw the elevation, plan and side view. Using first angle projection.

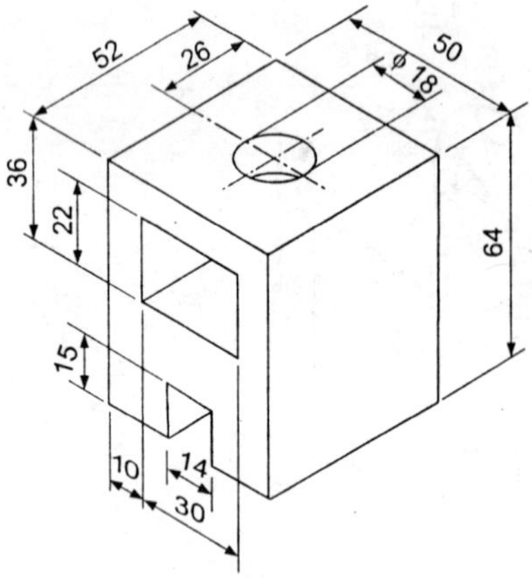

(a)

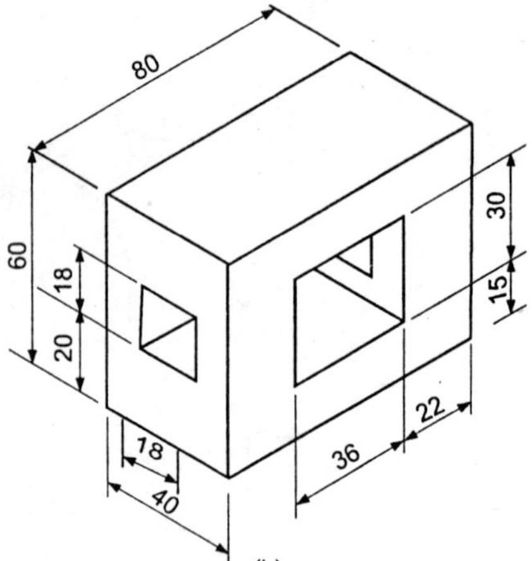

(b)

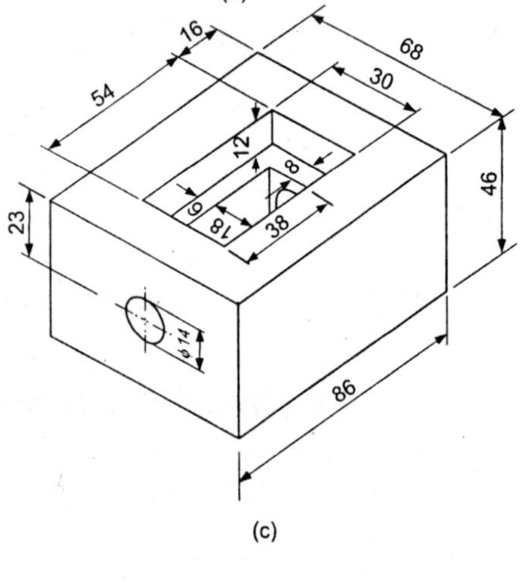

(c)

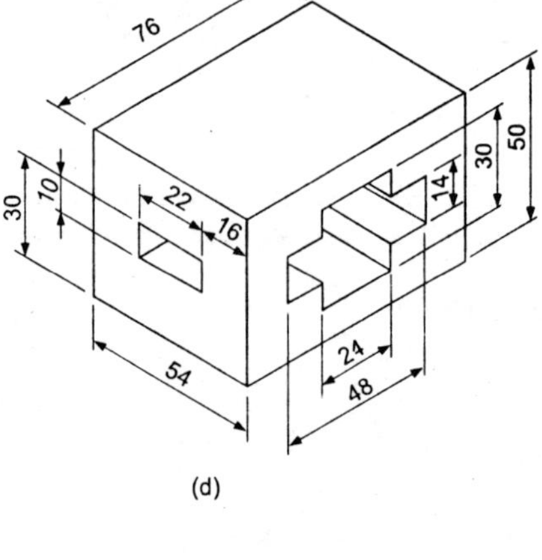

(d)

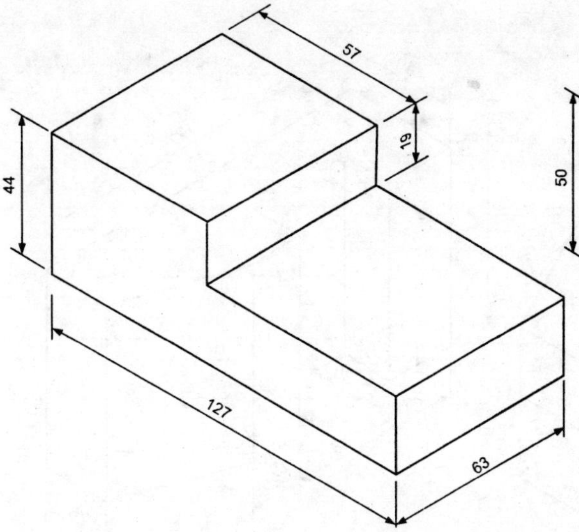
57
19
44
127
63

(e)

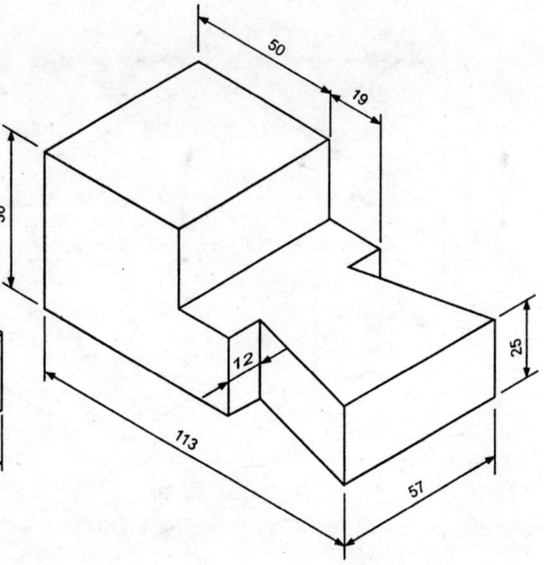
50
19
50
12
25
113
57

(f)

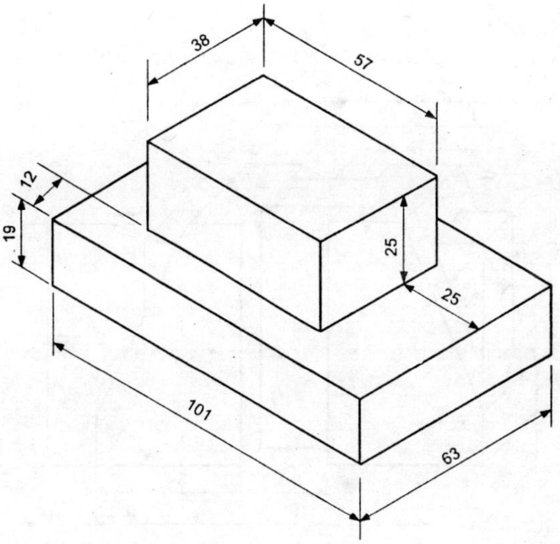
38
57
12
19
25
25
101
63

(g)

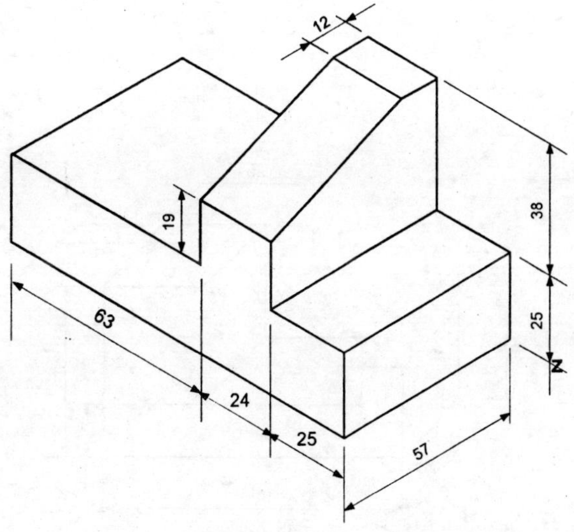
12
19
38
25
63
24
25
57

(h)

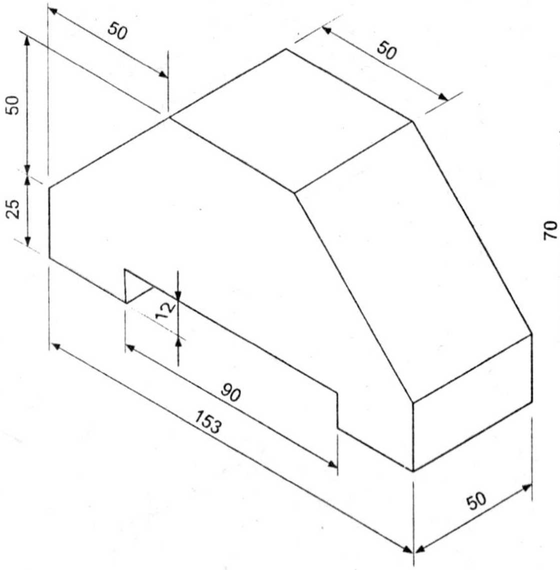
50
50
50
25
12
90
153
50

(i)

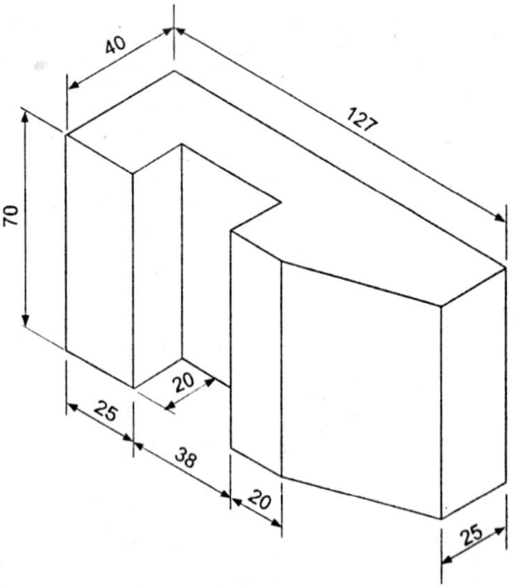
40
127
70
20
25
38
20
25

(j)

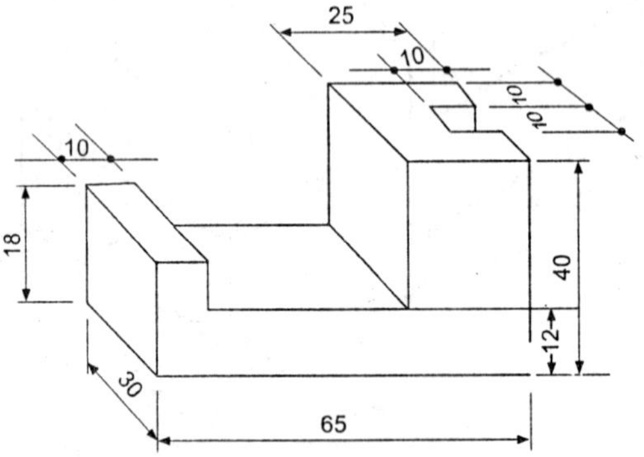
25
10
10
10
10
18
40
12
30
65

(k)

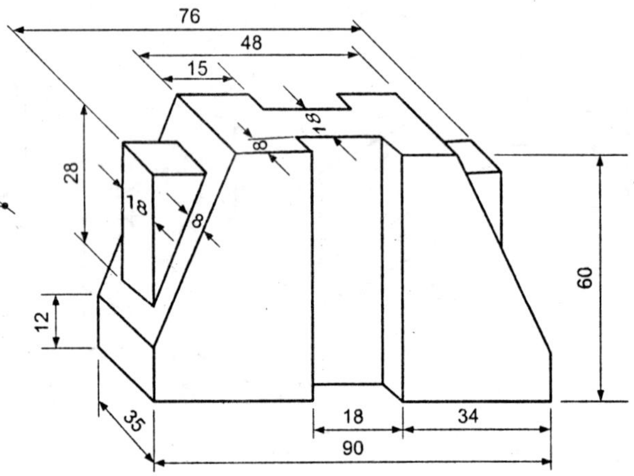
76
48
15
18
8
28
18
8
12
60
35
18
34
90

(l)

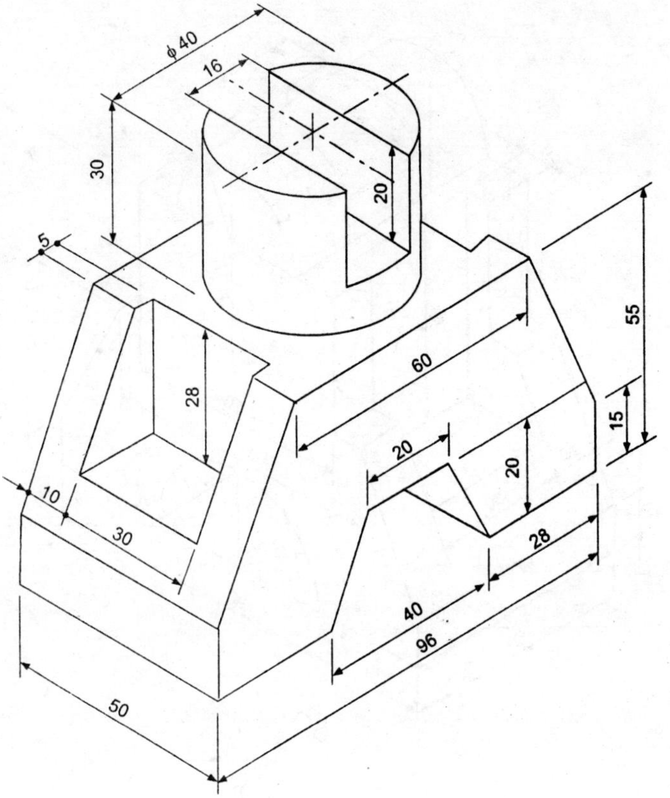
φ40
16
30
20
5
55
28
60
15
20
20
10
30
28
40
96
50

(m)

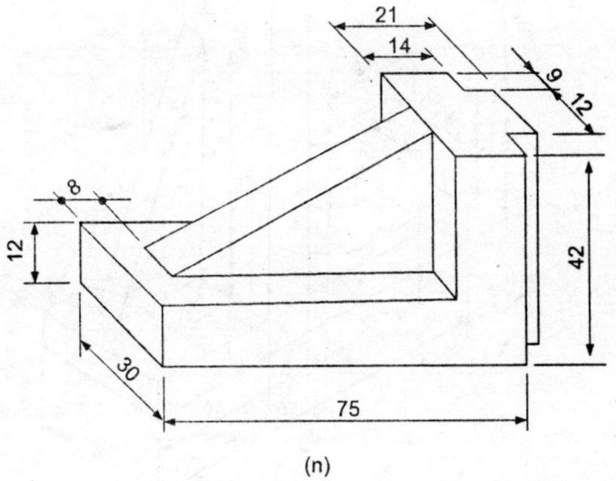
21
14
9
12
8
12
42
30
75

(n)

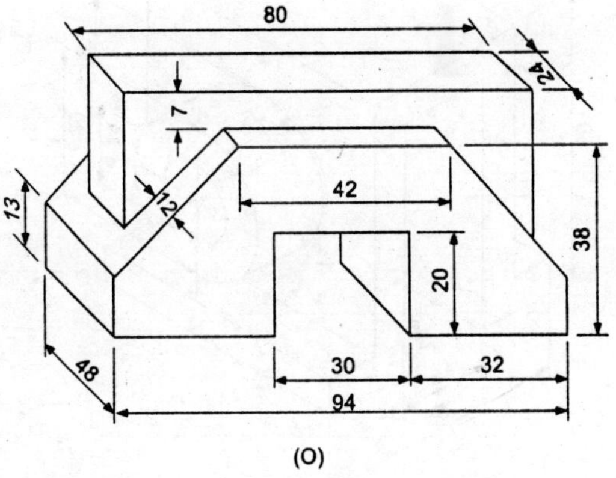
80
24
7
13
12
42
38
20
48
30
32
94

(O)

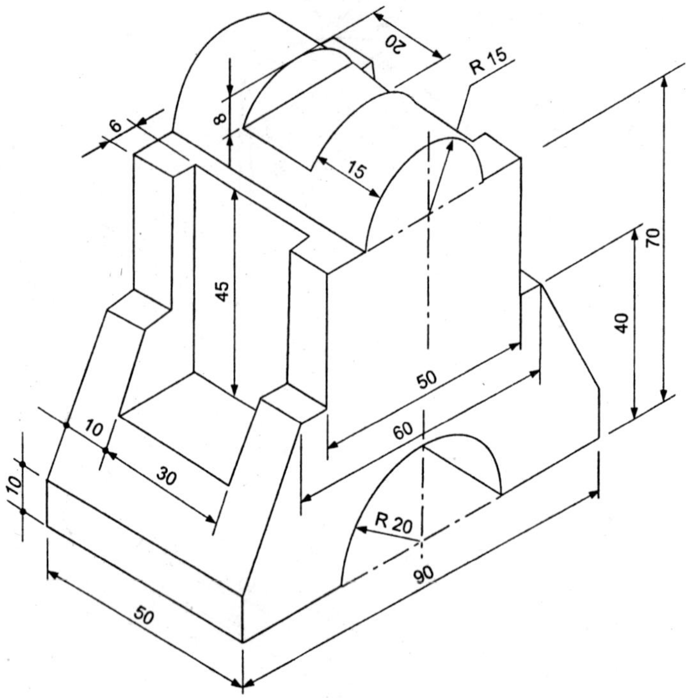
20
R 15
8
6
15
45
70
40
50
60
10
30
10
R 20
90
50

(p)

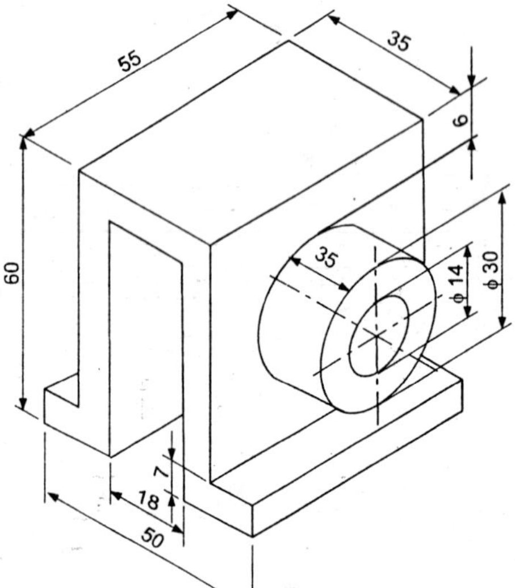
55
35
6
35
φ 14
φ 30
60
7
18
50

(q)

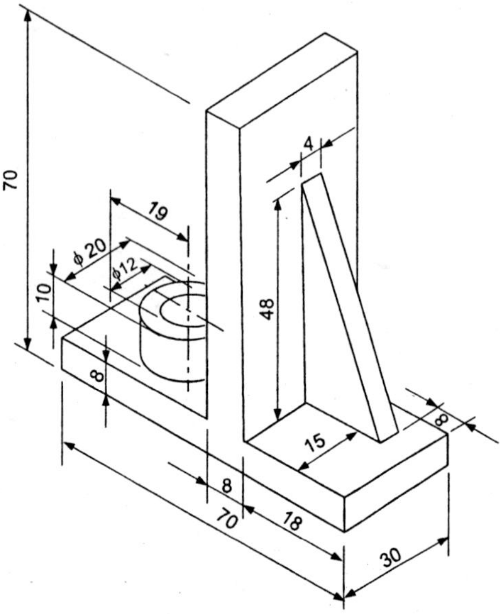
70
4
19
φ 20
φ12
10
48
8
8
15
8
70
18
30

(r)

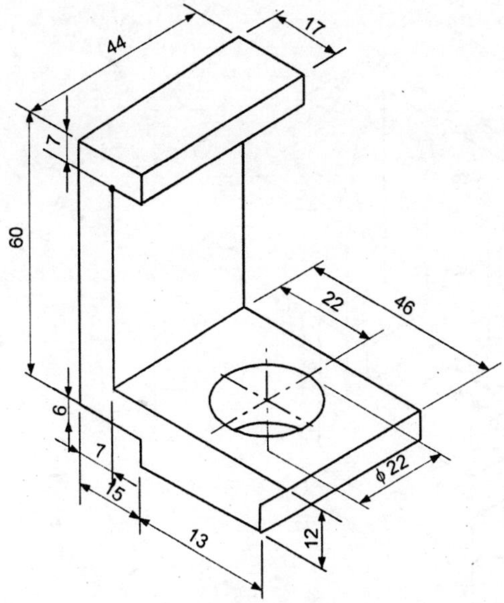
44
17
7
60
22
46
6
7
15
13
φ22
12

(s)

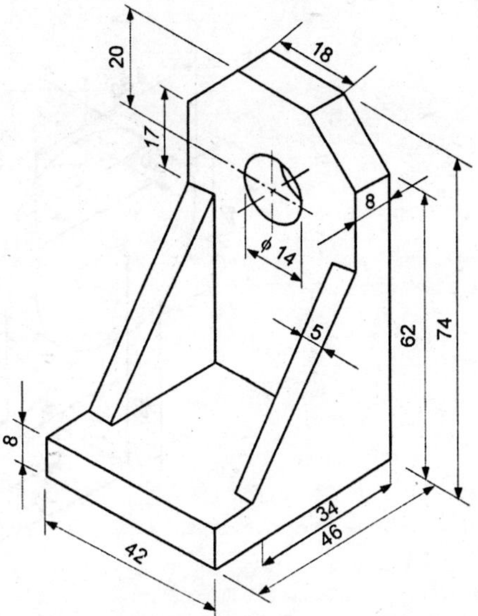
20
18
17
8
φ 14
5
62
74
8
42
34
46

(t)

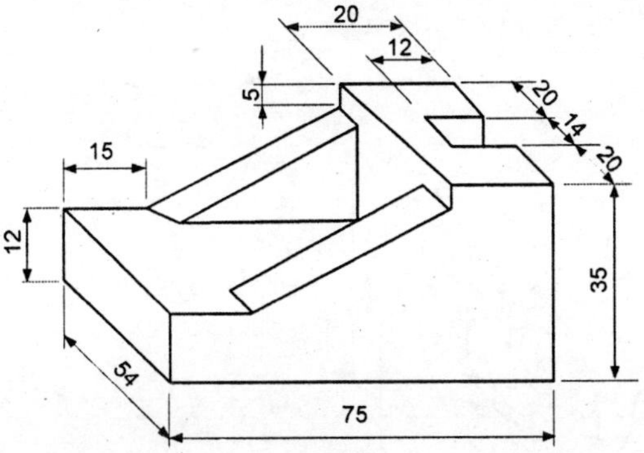
20
12
5
20
14
20
15
12
35
54
75

(u)

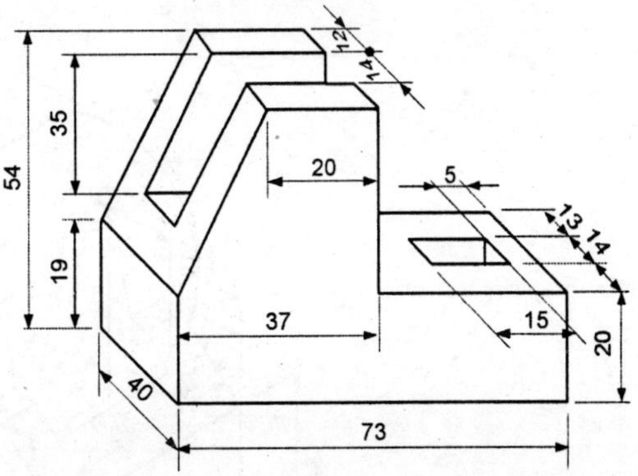
12
14
54
35
20
5
13
14
19
37
15
20
40
73

(v)

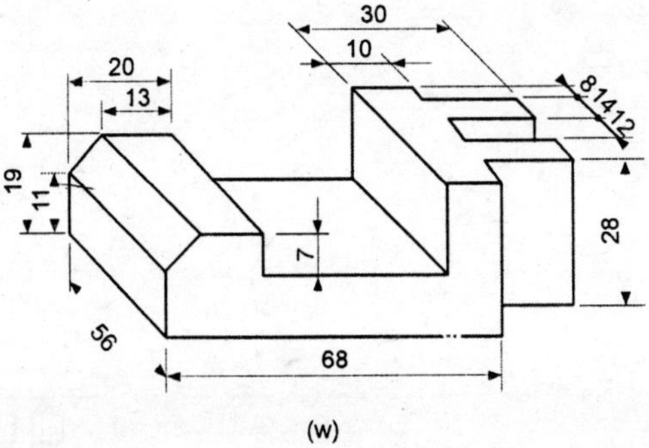
30
10
20
13
8
14
12
19
11
7
28
56
68

(w)

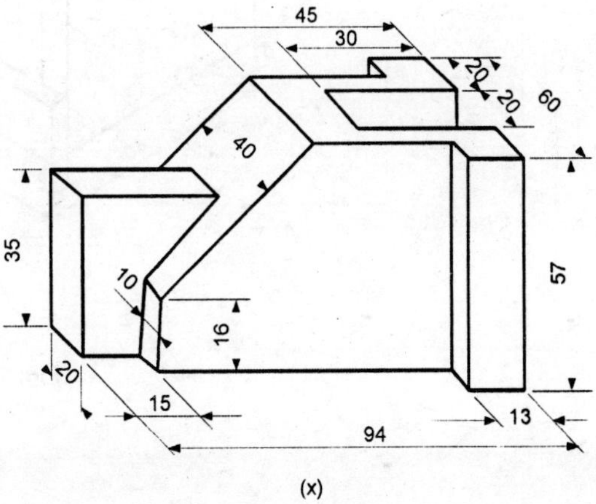
45
30
20
20
60
40
35
57
10
16
20
15
13
94

(x)

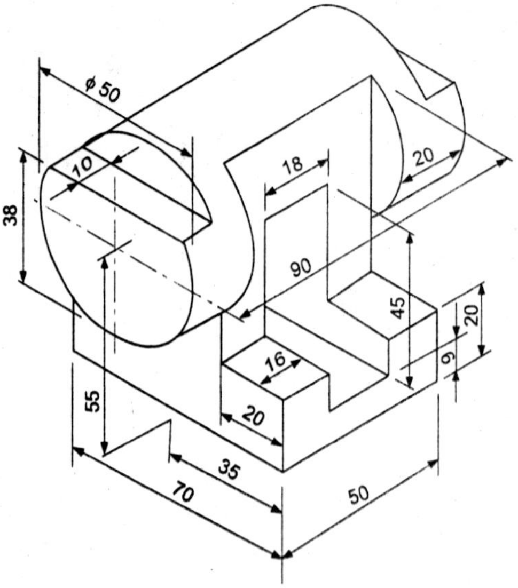
φ 50
10
38
18
20
90
45
20
9
16
55
20
35
70
50

(y)

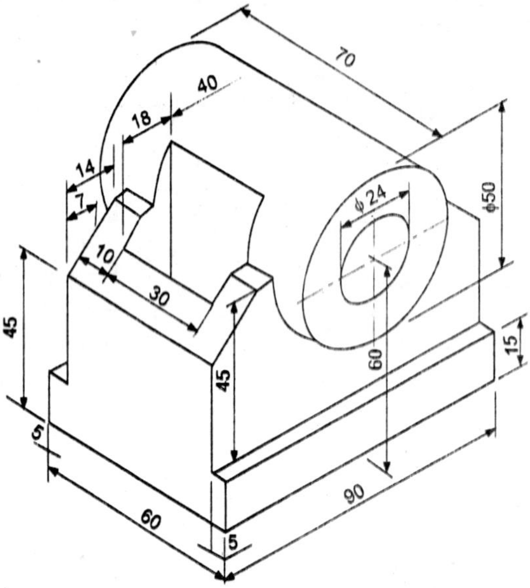
70
40
18
14
7
10
30
φ 24
φ50
45
45
60
15
5
60
90
5

(z)

Fig. 13.40

❑❑❑

14

ISOMETRIC PROJECTION

14.1 INTRODUCTION

In engineering drawing, orthographic projection of a solid is best for showing the details of an object when a solid is resting in its simple position, the front view or top view taken separately, gives an incomplete idea of the object. Even, sometimes an experienced engineer gets puzzled when studying the orthographic projection of complicated parts. To avoid this confusion, a pictorial projection is the best method to show the object in one view only. Basically, pictorial projection represents three dimensional shape of an object and represents real things in one view only, which indicates length, breadth and height of the object. Therefore, the object is easily visualized from a pictorial projection than from its orthographic projection. In other words, orthographic projection requires thorough knowledge of the principles of projection and only the experienced person should read these drawing. But the pictorial projection can be easily understood by the beginners.

There are three different types into which pictorial drawing may be divided. They are:

1. Oblique projection (Fig. 14.1(i))
2. Perspective projection (Fig. 14.1(ii))
3. Axonometric projection.

In this chapter you will learn about only the axonometric projections only which are commonly used in industries.

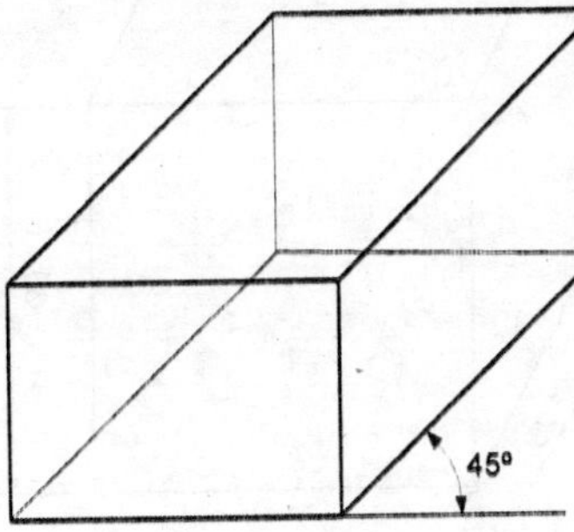

(i) OBLIQUE PROJECTION

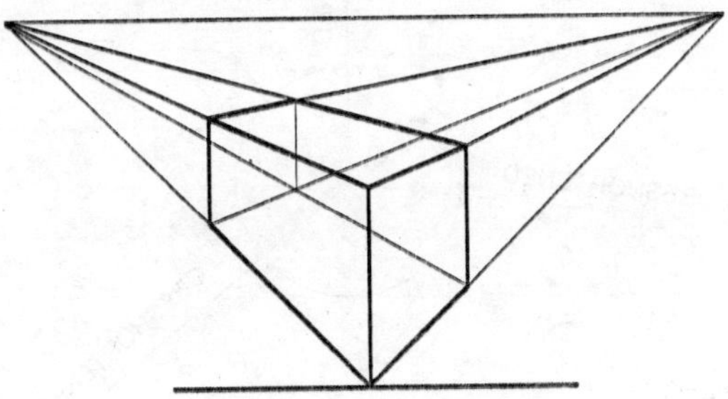

(II) PERSPECTIVE PROJECTION

Fig. 14.1

14.2 AXONOMETRIC PROJECTION

The word 'axonometric projection means measuring along axis in which "axon" means axis while metreo means measuring. Axonometric projections are commonly used to draw mechanical parts of an object for the clear picture of an object which are visualized from the orthographic projection. In this projection the object can be drawn at different angles and having the different length of edges.

Axonometric projections are classified as follows:

Axonometric Projection

- Diametric
- Trimetric
- Isometric
  - Isometric projection
  - Isometric view

(1) Diametric Projection: In diametric projection, only two faces are making equal angles, while the third angle is different one with the projection of plane as shown in Fig. 14.2 (i).

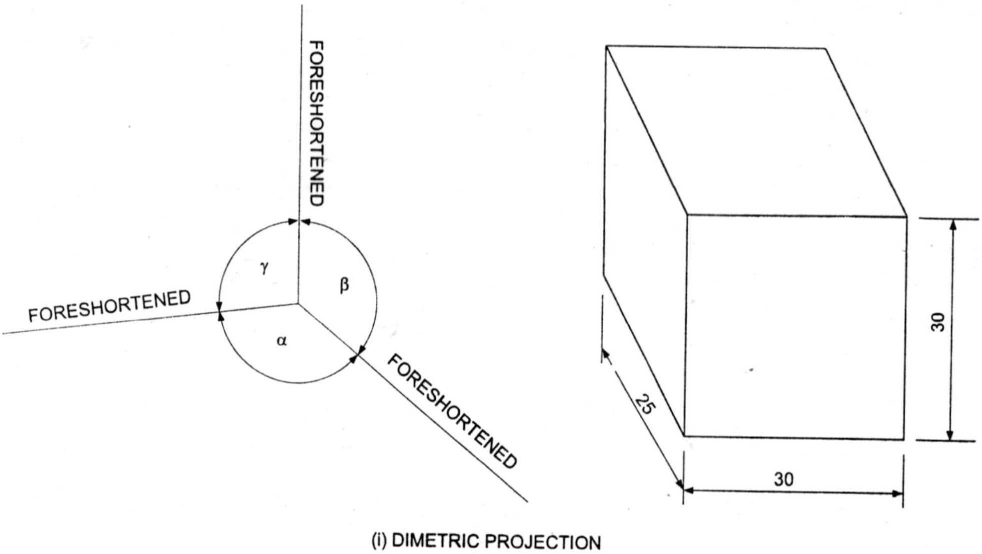

(i) DIMETRIC PROJECTION

Fig. 14.2

(2) Trimetric Projection: In trimetric projection, all the three faces are making different angles with the plane of projection as shown in Fig. 14.2 (ii).

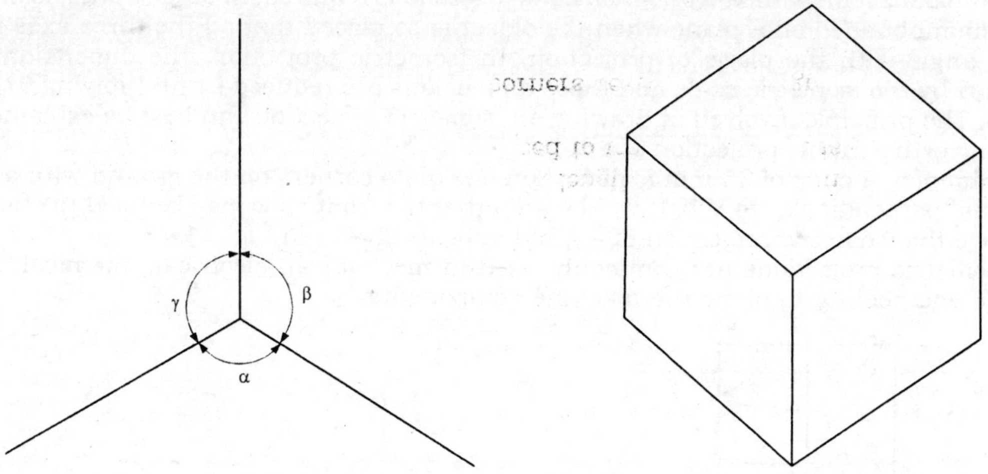

(ii) TRIMETRIC PROJECTION

Fig. 14.2

(3) Isometric Projection: In isometric Bojection, all the three faces are making equal angles with the plane of projection as shown in Fig. 14.3. It is a type of pictorial projection which is taken from the Greek word. ISO means equal METRON means measure. So, isometric means equal measure. Isometric projections are further divided into two types:

1. Isometric projection
2. Isometric view.

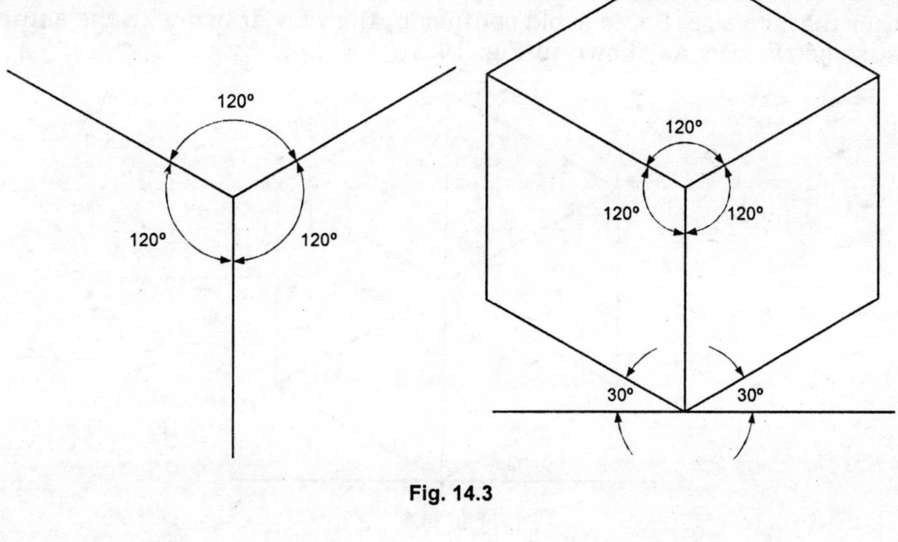

Fig. 14.3

14.3 ISOMETRIC PROJECTION

The isometric projection is the most common pictorial representation used in industries where visualization of the three dimensions of a solid is required. In other words, isometric projection obtained on a plane when the object is so placed that all the three axes make equal angle with the plane of projection. In isometric projection, the dimensions are reduced by the isometric scale and these dimensions are reduced by multiplying 9/11 or 0.816. The principle involved in drawing an isometric projection can best be explained by drawing orthographic projection of a cube.

Example: A cube of 35 mm is placed on one of its corners on the ground with a solid diagonal perpendicular to V.P. It will be seen that the front view may be used to obtained will give the isometric projection of a given cube as shown in Fig. 14.4.

Isometric projections are commonly used in mechanical, electrical, chemical, automobile engineering to show the machine components.

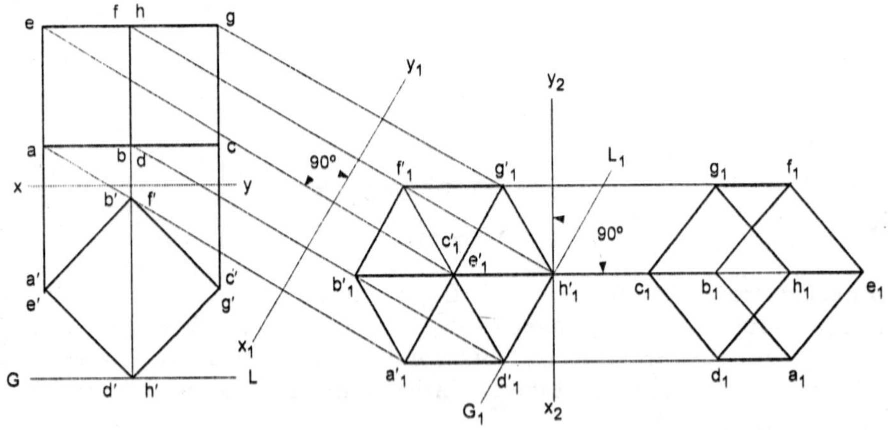

Fig. 14.4

14.4 ISOMETRIC VIEW

The measurements of the size of an object are taken with the actual scale without reducing dimension by isometric scale. In isometric view, we are interested in the shape of an object rather than its size. So, to avoid confusion, the view drawn with the actual scale is known as isometric view as shown in Fig. 14.5.

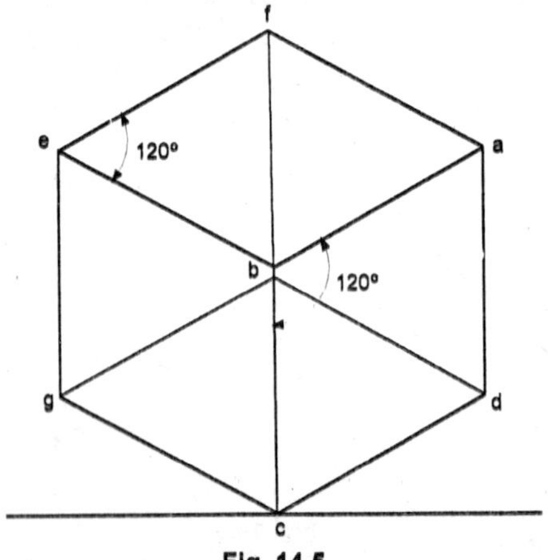

Fig. 14.5

14.5 ISOMETRIC SCALE

Isometric scale is used to measure the projected length of an object. In other words the proportion by which the actual length is reduced to isometric length is called isometric scale.

Let us consider a cube with one of its corners resting on the ground as shown in Fig. 14.6.

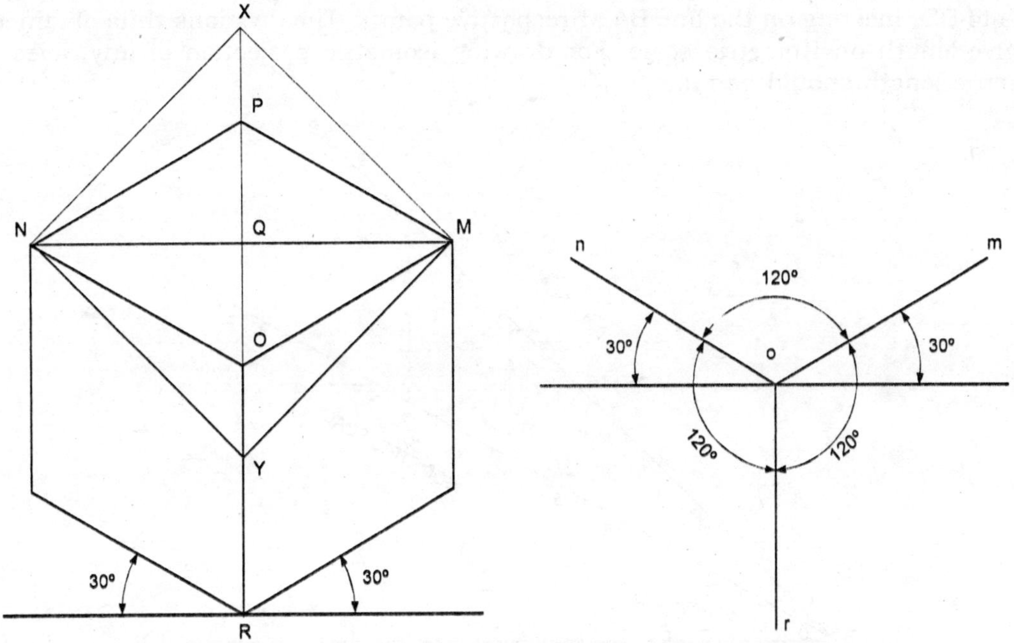

Fig. 14.6

The rhombus MONP represents the isometric projection of the top square face of the cube, in which MN is the length of the diagonal. The rhombus shows isometric projection of the square face (NYMX) of cube where MN is true length of the diagonal of square.

Let

$\angle MNP = 30°$

and $\angle MNX = 45°$

In triangle NQP, $\dfrac{NP}{NQ} = \dfrac{NP}{NP \cos 30°} = \dfrac{2}{\sqrt{3}}$

In triangle NQX, $\dfrac{NX}{NQ} = \dfrac{NX}{NX \cos 45°} = \dfrac{\sqrt{2}}{1}$

$$\therefore \quad \frac{NP}{NX} = \frac{2}{\sqrt{3}} \times \frac{1}{\sqrt{2}} = \frac{\sqrt{2}}{\sqrt{3}}$$

$$\frac{\text{Isometric length}}{\text{True length}} = \frac{\sqrt{2}}{\sqrt{3}} = 0.816 = \frac{9}{11} \text{ approx.}$$

Therefore, isometric lengths are 0.816 or 81.6% of the true length as stated earlier.

14.6 CONSTRUCTION OF ISOMETRIC SCALE

Isometric scale is define as the proportion by which the actual or true length is reduced to isometric distance.

Isometric scale is used to measure the projected length of an object. Draw a horizontal line BD of any length. From B, draw a line BA making an angle of 30° and a line BP making an angle of 45° with BD as shown in Fig. 14.7. On the line BP mark the points 0, 1, 2, 3 etc. to represent true lengths. From each division point, draw a vertical or 90° angle to BD, meeting on the line BA at respective points. The divisions thus obtained on BA give length on isometric scale. For drawing isometric projection of any object the isometric length should be taken.

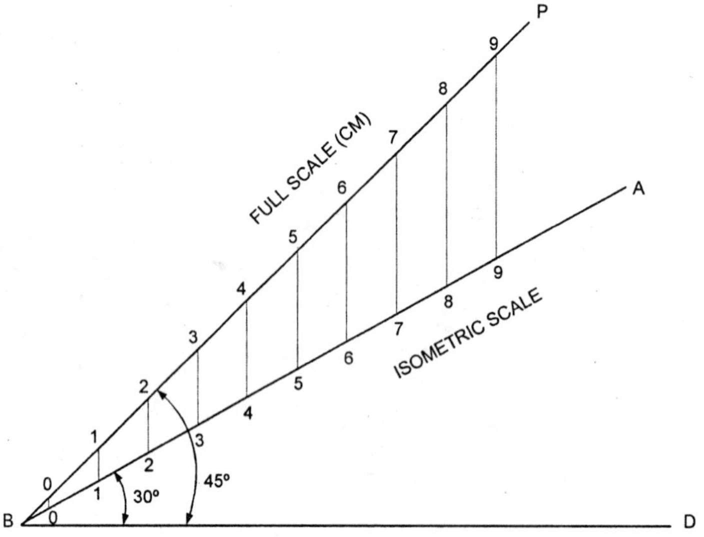

Fig. 14.7

14.7 METHODS OF MAKING AN ISOMETRIC PROJECTION OR VIEW

There are two methods can be used for making an isometric projection or view, if an object contains a number of non-isometric line, are as follows:

1. Box method 2. Off-set method.

14.8 BOX METHOD

The isometric projection of solid, such as cube, square and rectangular prism are drawn directly when their edges are parallel to the three isometric axis as shown in Fig. 14.8.

Step by step construction of box method is given below:

1. Draw a horizontal line *pq* and take a point *b* on the line *pq*. Through *b* draw the three isometric axes *ba*, *be* and *bc* with the help of minidrafter or set square, where *bc* is perpendicular to *pq* line.

   $\angle ebq = \angle abp = 30°$

2. Mark *ba*, *be* and *bc* the length, breadth and height of the object along the axis *ba*, *be* and *bc* respectively.
3. Through *a*, draw a line *ad* parallel to *bc* and through *c*, draw a line *cd* parallel to *ba* and intersect each other at a point *d*. Now through point *e* draw a line *ef* parallel to *bc* and through *c*, draw a line *cf* parallel to *be*, which intersect each other at a point *f*.

Similarly, through *d* draw a line *dg* parallel to *be* and through *f* draw a line *fg* parallel to *ba*, intersect at *g*. Now complete the rectangular block.

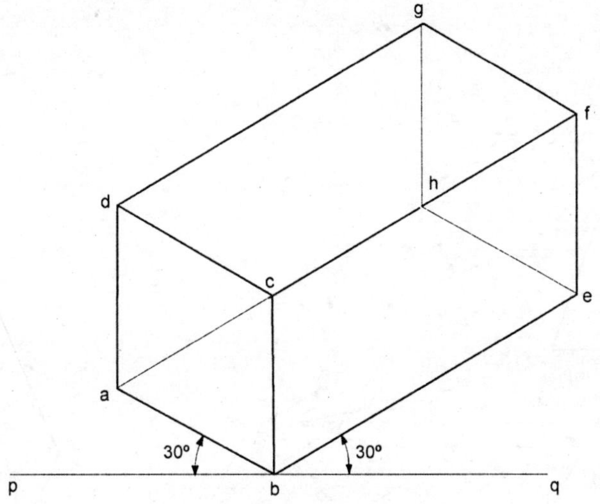

BOX METHOD

Fig. 14.8

14.9 OFF-SET METHOD

This method is used to draw isometric projection of the object which has neither non-isometric lines nor their ends lie in isometric plane. The isometric projection of pyramids and cones are generally drawn by co-ordinates or off-set method.

Step by step construction of off-set method is given below:

1. Draw the top and front view of the hexagonal pyramid.
2. Enclose the hexagon in a rectangle *pqrs* in the top view.
3. Draw the isometric view of the base of the pyramid in the parallelogram PQRS.
4. FC is an isometric line on which O_1 lies. Hence mark O_1 on the isometric line FC such that $FO_1 = y$.
5. From O_1 draw a vertical line and mark the apex O.
6. Join O with all the corners of the base of pyramid and complete the isometric view as shown in Fig. 14.9.

14.10 SOME IMPORTANT TERMS

The following are some important terms used in isometric projection or view as shown in Fig. 14.5.

(*i*) **Isometric axes:** The lines *ba*, *be* and *bc* meeting at a point *b* and making an angle of 120° with each other are known as isometric axes.

(*ii*) **Isometric lines:** The lines parallel to the isometric axes are known as isometric lines.

(*iii*) **Non-isometric lines:** The lines which are not parallel to isometric axes are known as non-isometric lines e.g. line *ae*.

(*iv*) **Isometric planes:** The planes representing the faces of the cube as well as other planes parallel to these planes are known as isometric planes.

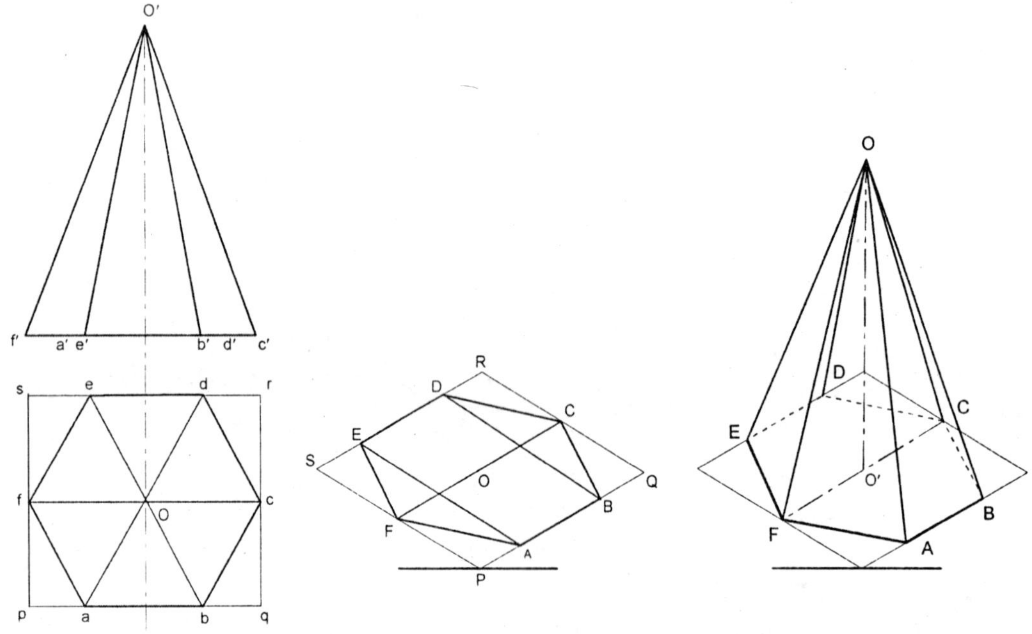

Fig. 14.9

14.11 ISOMETRIC PROJECTION OF A CIRCLE

In isometric projection or view of a circle is seen like an egg shape or like an ellipse. It may be drawn by enclosing it in a square and locating number of points on it by off set-method. Four centre method is commonly used to draw an isometric projection or view of a circle.

Step by step procedure to draw a four centre method is given below:

1. Draw the circle of given data
   (i) Close this circle by a square MNOP
   (ii) Now transfer MNOP in isometric
2. Mark the mid-points of the sides of rhombus such as A, B, C, and D.
3. Join M with B and C, which are the mid points of a rhombus. Similarly join O with the point A and D respectively.

4. With M as centre and MC as radius draw an arc CB, similarly with O as centre and OA as radius draw an arc AD. The line MC and OD intersect at a_1 with a_1 as centre and a_1D as radius draw an arc DC.

   Similarly, with a_2 (intersection of OA and MB) as a centre and a_2B as radius draw an arc BA.

   Now the enclosing curve ABCD is the required isometric projection or view of the given circle, as shown in Fig. 14.10.

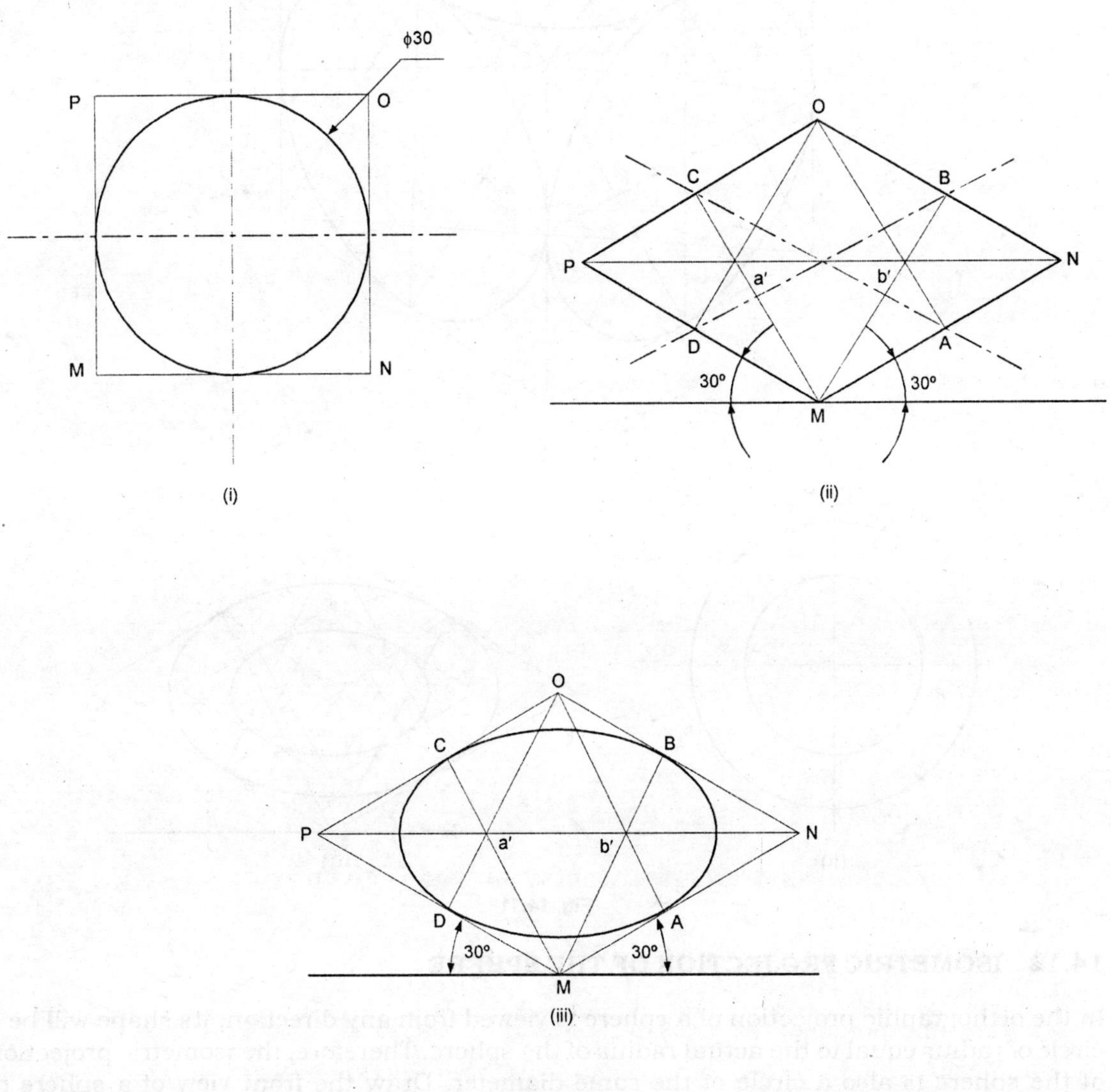

Fig. 14.10

Note: On different angles the isometric projection is shown in Fig. 14.11.

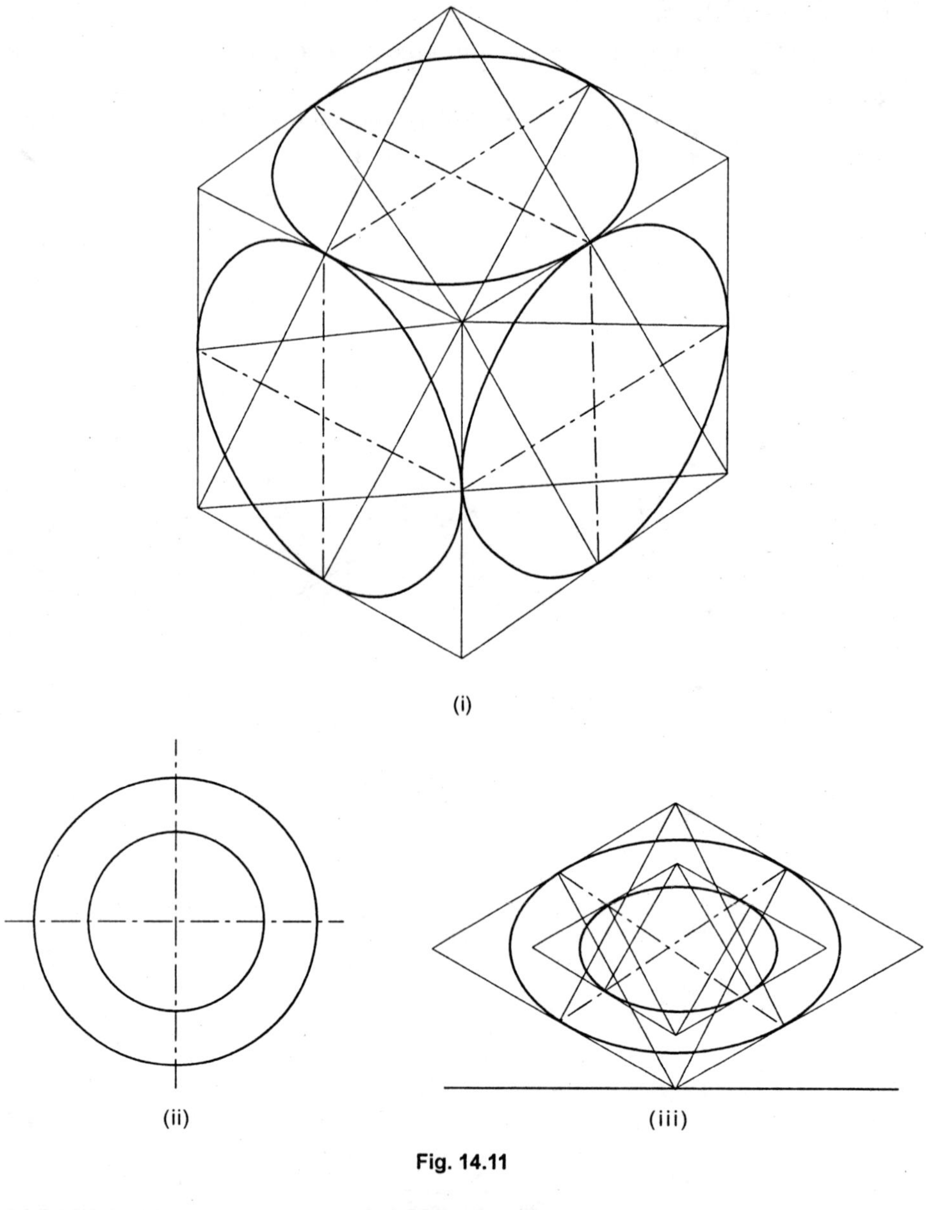

Fig. 14.11

14.12 ISOMETRIC PROJECTION OF THE SPHERE

In the orthographic projection of a sphere is viewed from any direction, its shape will be a circle of radius equal to the actual radius of the sphere. Therefore, the isometric projection of the sphere is also a circle of the same diameter. Draw the front view of a sphere of diameter D_1 by using true lengths and enclose it in a square as shown in Fig. 14.12.

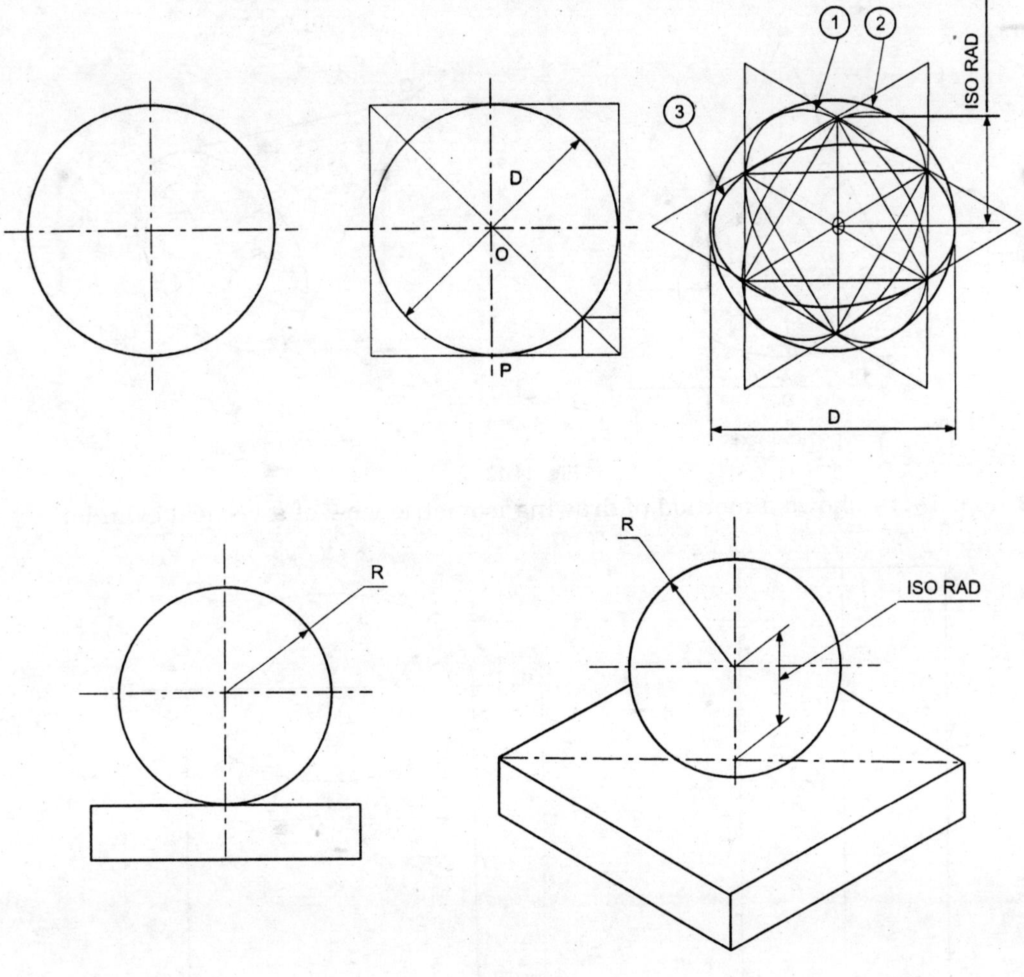

Fig. 14.12

Assume a vertical section through the centre of the sphere, which, will be a circle of diameter D_1. The isometric projection of this circle is shown in Fig. 14.12 by ellipse 1 and 2 drawn in two different vertical positions around the same centre O.

The length of the major axes in each case is equal to given diameter and its distance from the point of contact, to the centre point O is equal to the isometric radius of the sphere.

The ellipse 3 is the isometric projection of the circle assuming the section to be horizontal through the centre of the sphere. In this also, the length of the major axis is equal to the diameter D_1, of the sphere.

Thus, draw a smooth curve touching the outer most points on the ellipses which will be a circle of radius R_1 with centre O. It is the required isometric projection of the sphere.

14.13 DRAWING ISOMETRIC VIEWS OF SOME IMPROTANT OBJECTS

1. Fig. 14.13 shows a method of drawing isometric view of a cone.

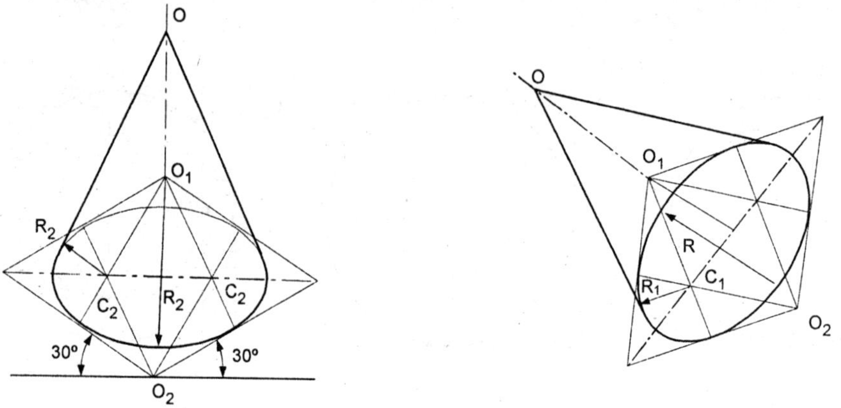

VERTICAL AXIS HORIZONTAL AXIS

Fig. 14.13

2. Fig. 14.14 shows a method of drawing isometric view of a vertical cylinder.

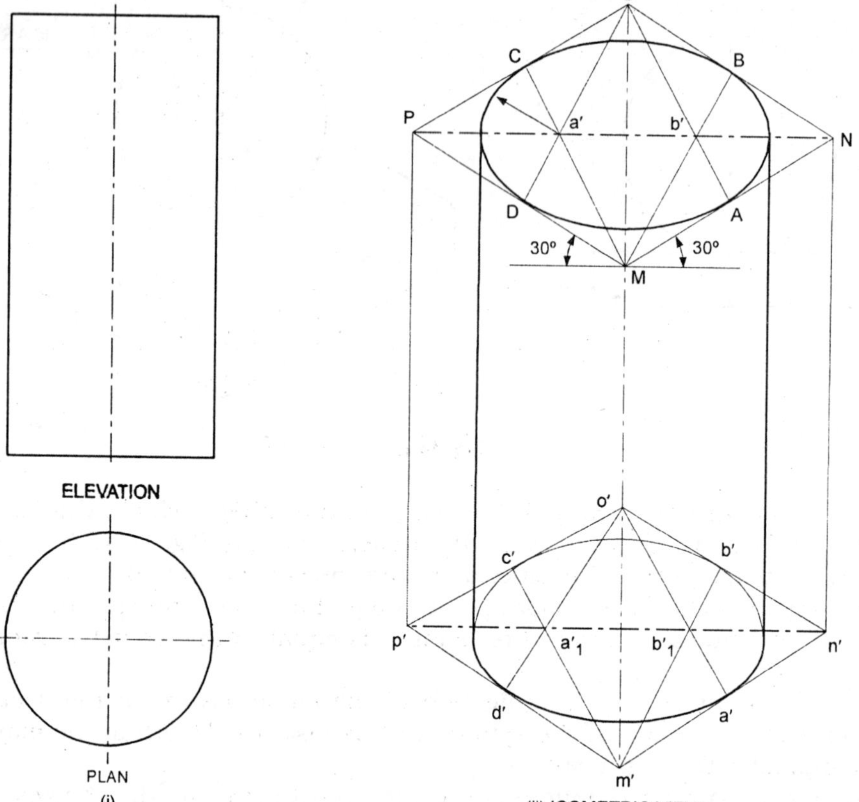

ELEVATION

PLAN

(i)

(ii) ISOMETRIC VIEW

Fig. 14.14

3. Fig. 14.15 shows a method of drawing isometric view of cylinder when its axis is horizontal.

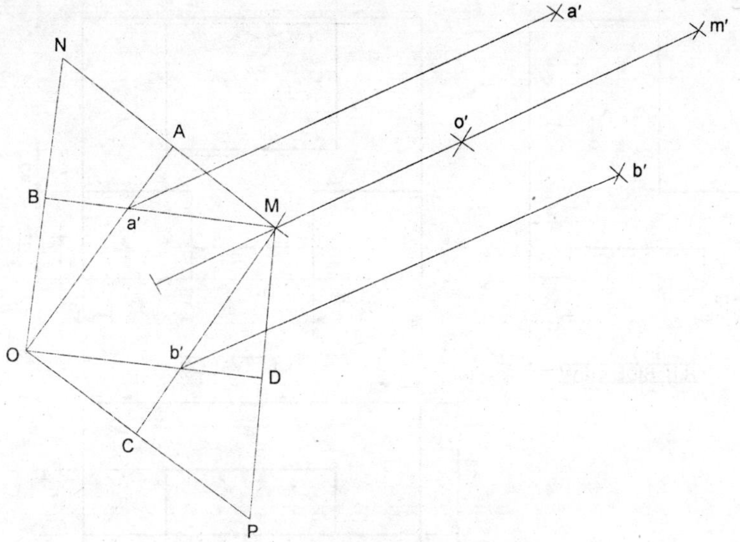

Fig. 14.15

4. Fig. 14.16 shows isometric view of a cylindrical object.

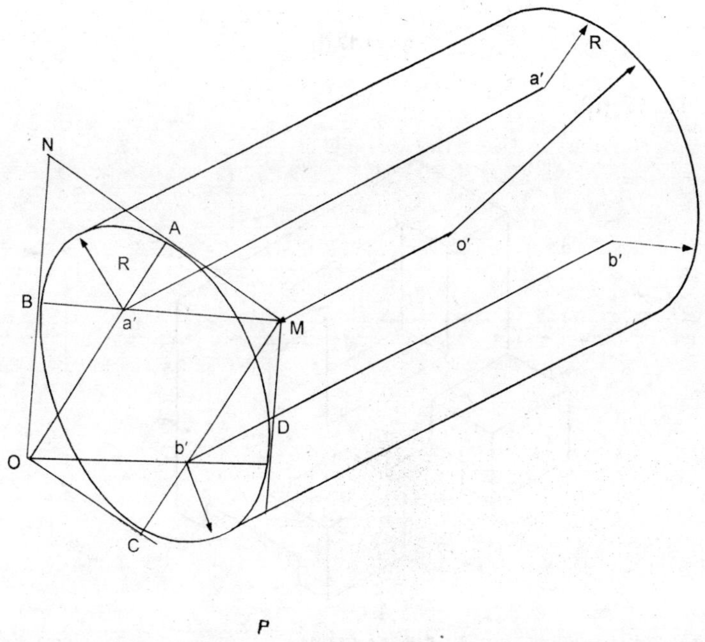

Fig. 14.16

Problem 1. Fig 14.17 (i) shows three views of an object. Draw its isometric view.

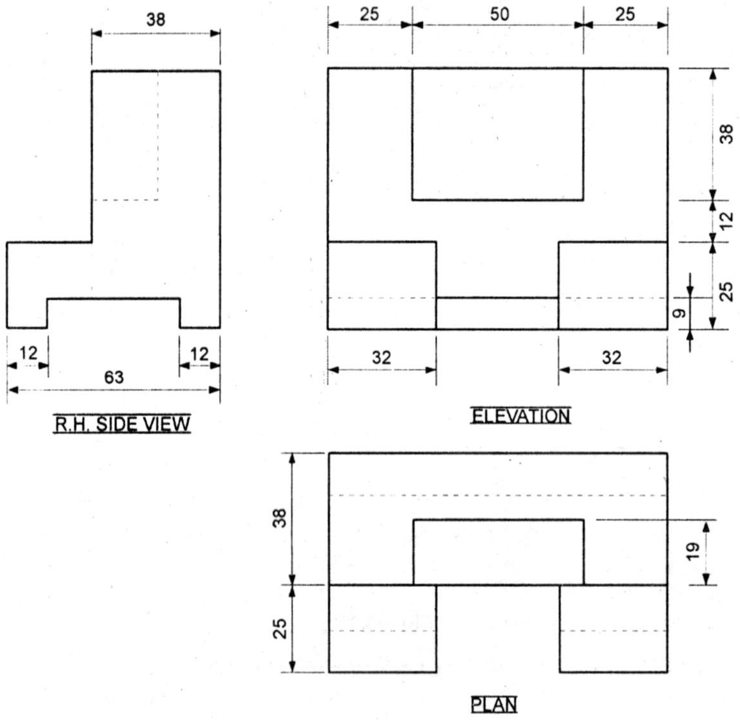

Fig. 14.17 (i)

Solution. See Fig. 14.17 (ii).

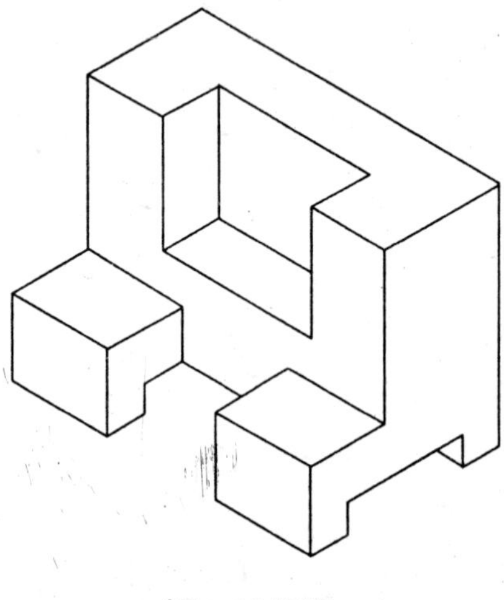

Fig. 14.17 (ii)

Problem 2. Fig. 14.18 (i) shows orthographic views of an object. Draw its isometric view. Use full scale. All dimentions are in mm.

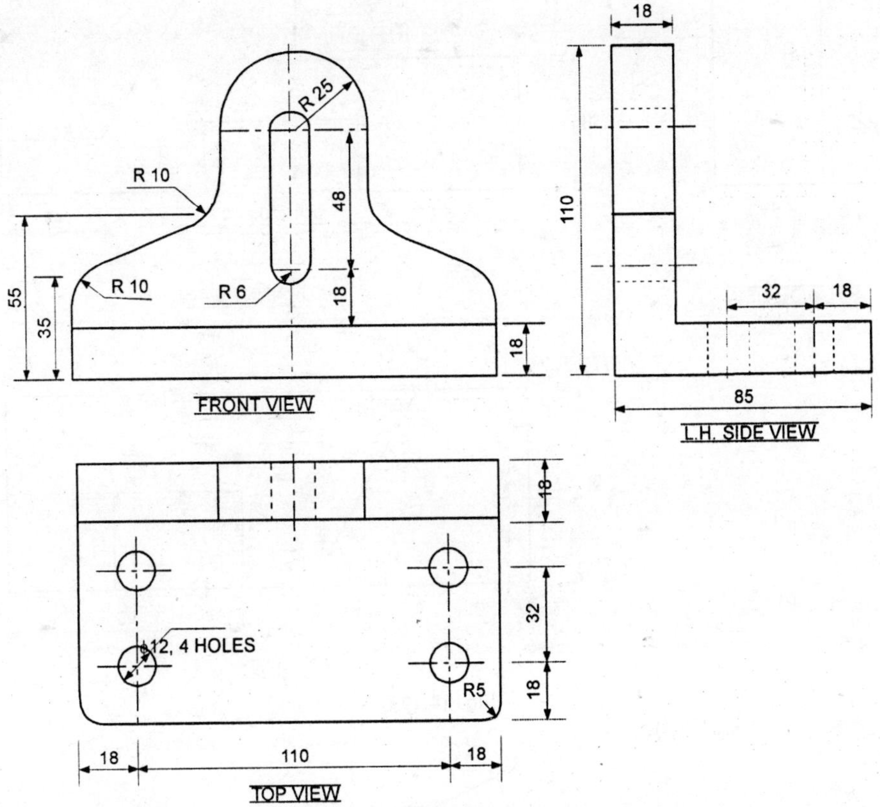

14.18(i)

Solution. See Fig. 14.18 (ii).

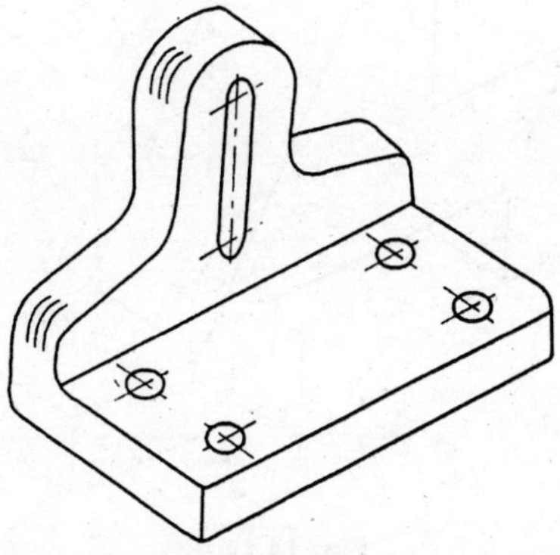

Fig. 14.18(ii)

Problem 3. Fig. 14.19 (i) shows three views of an object. Draw its isometric view.

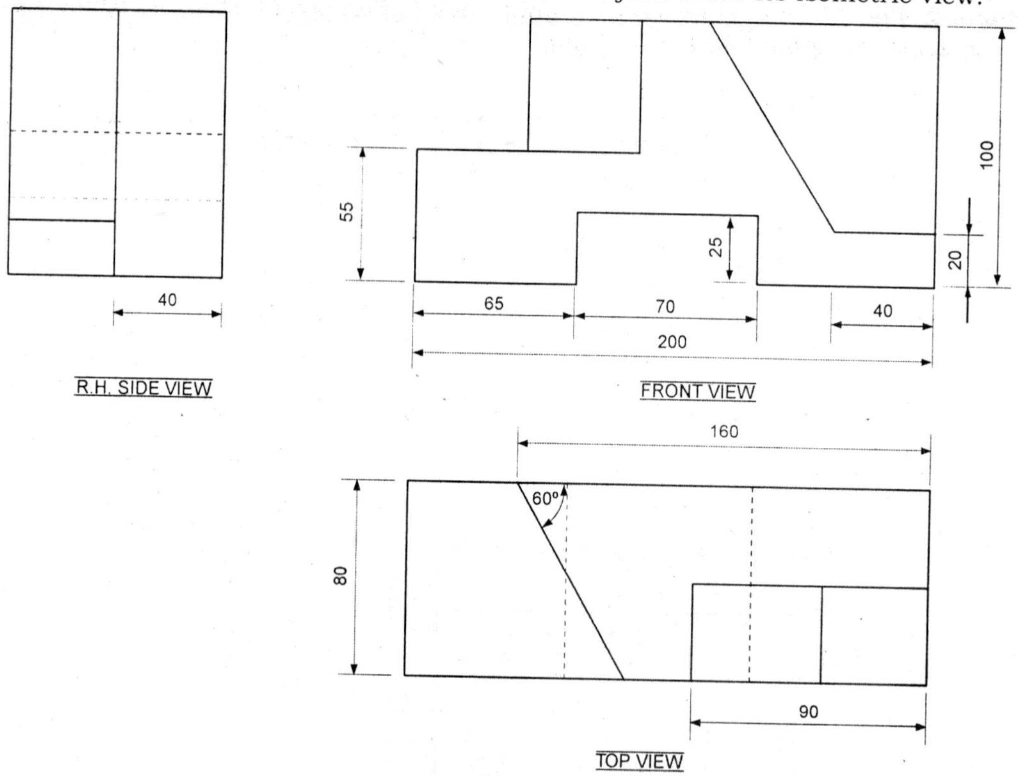

Fig. 14.19 (i)

Solution. See Fig. 14.19 (ii).

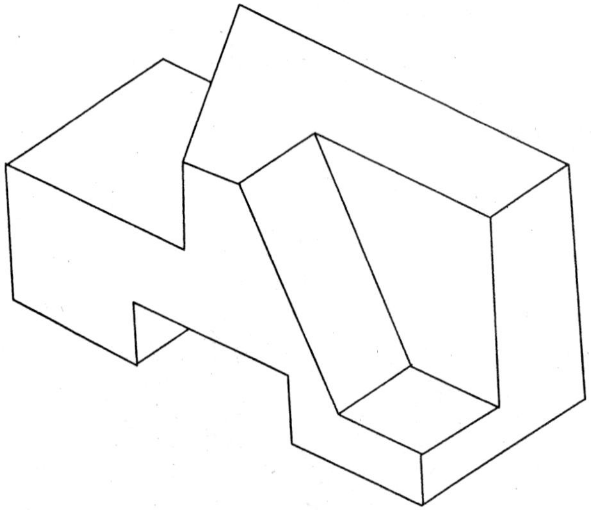

Fig. 14.19 (ii)

Problem 4. Fig. 14.20 (i) shows three views of an object. Draw its isometric view.

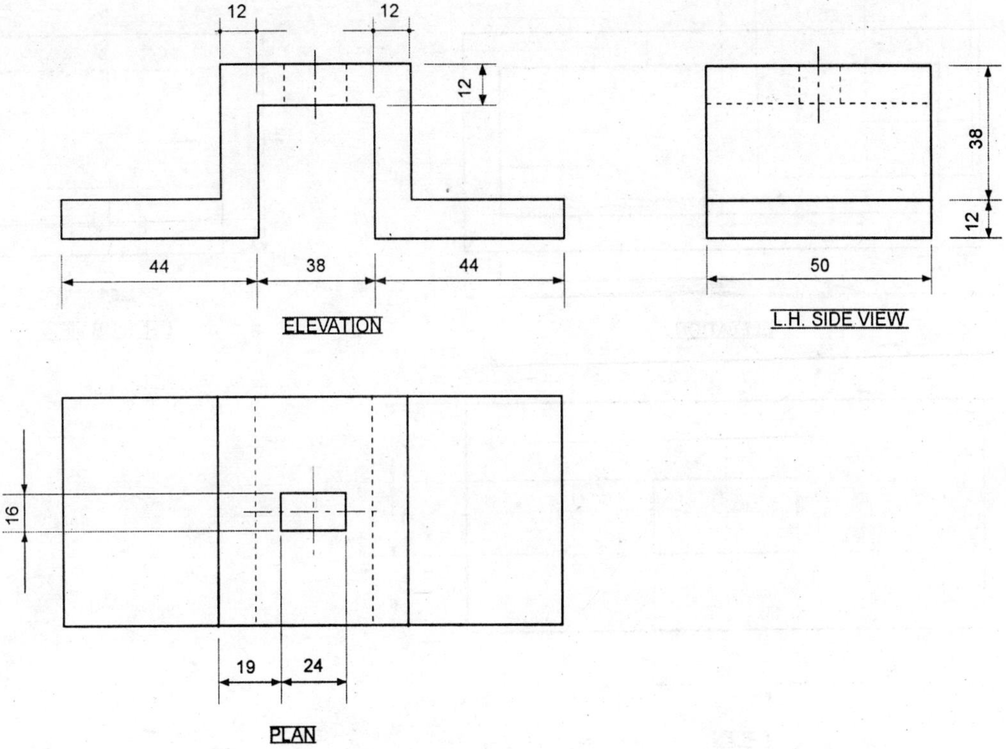

Fig. 14.20 (i)

Solution. See Fig. 14.20 (ii).

Fig. 14.20 (ii)

Problem 5. Fig. 14.21 (i) shows three views of an object. Draw its isometric view.

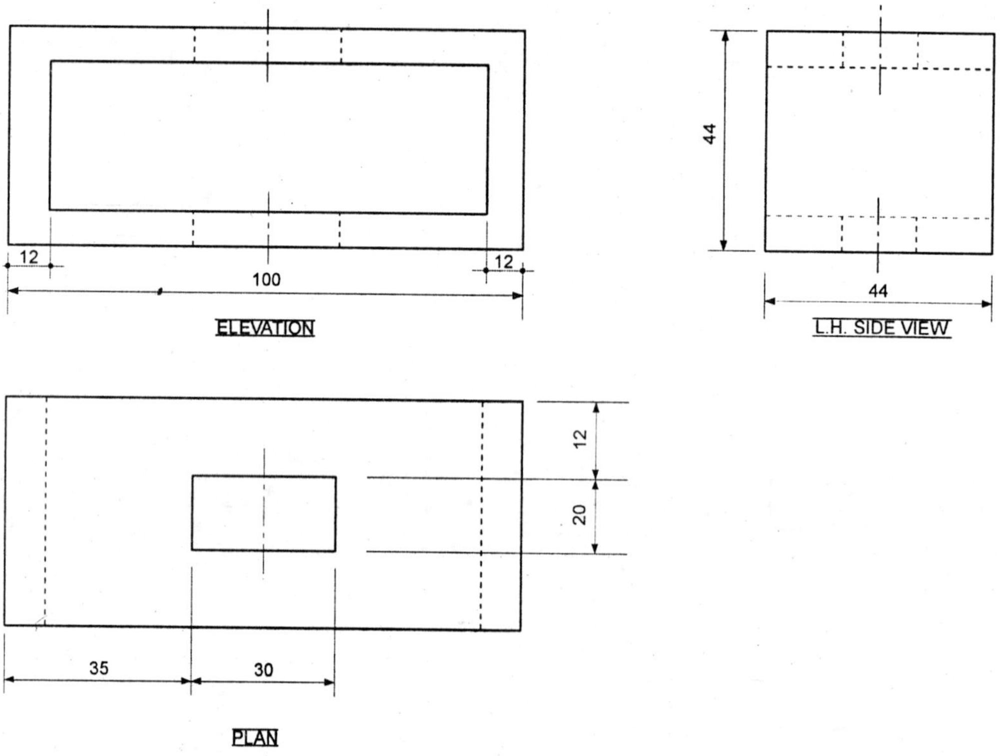

Fig. 14.21 (i)

Solution. See Fig. 14.21 (ii).

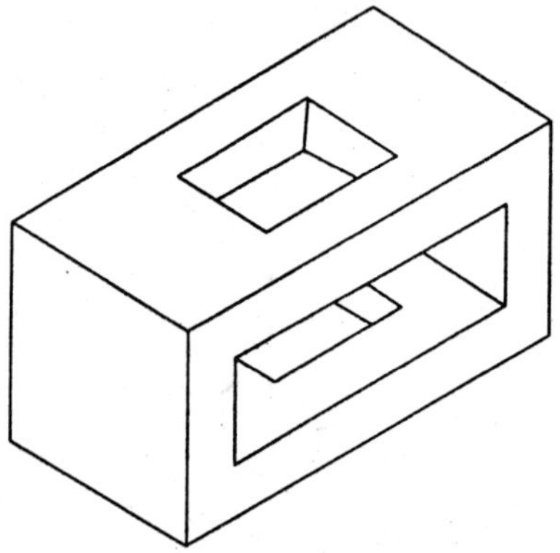

Fig. 14.21 (ii)

Problem 6. Fig 14.22 (i) shows the orthographic views of an object. Draw its isometric view.

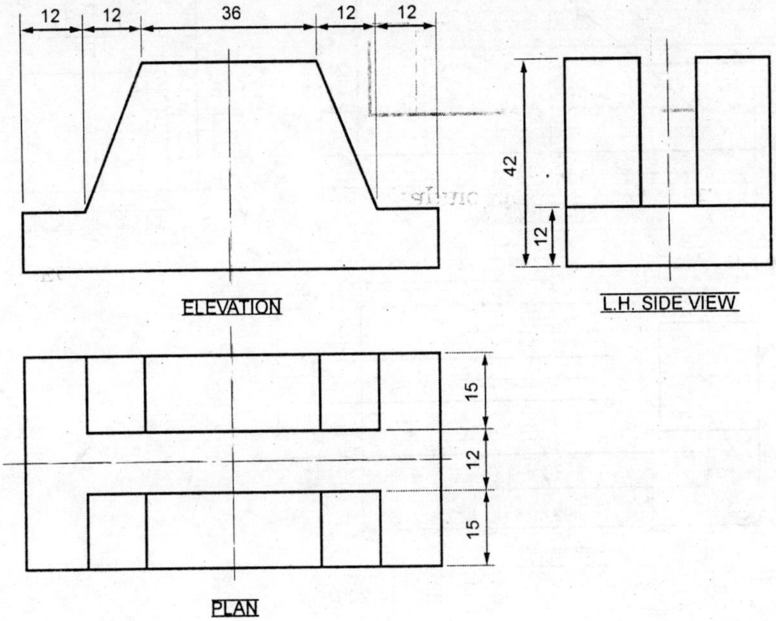

Fig. 14.22 (i)

Solution: See Fig. 14.22 (ii).

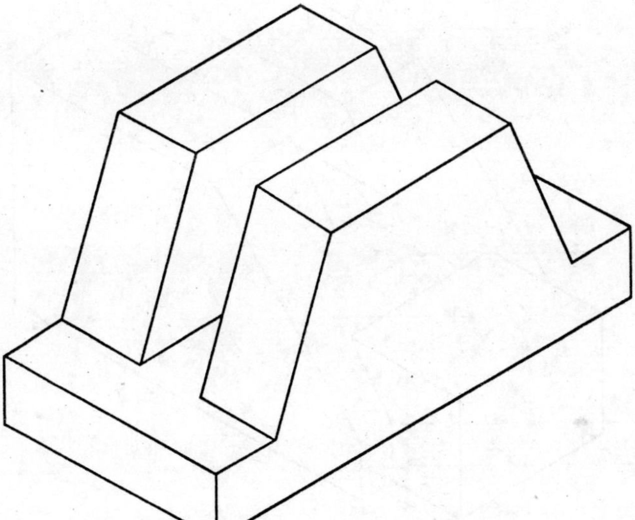

Fig. 14.22 (ii)

Problem 7. Fig 14.23 (i) shows the three views of an object. Draw isometric view.

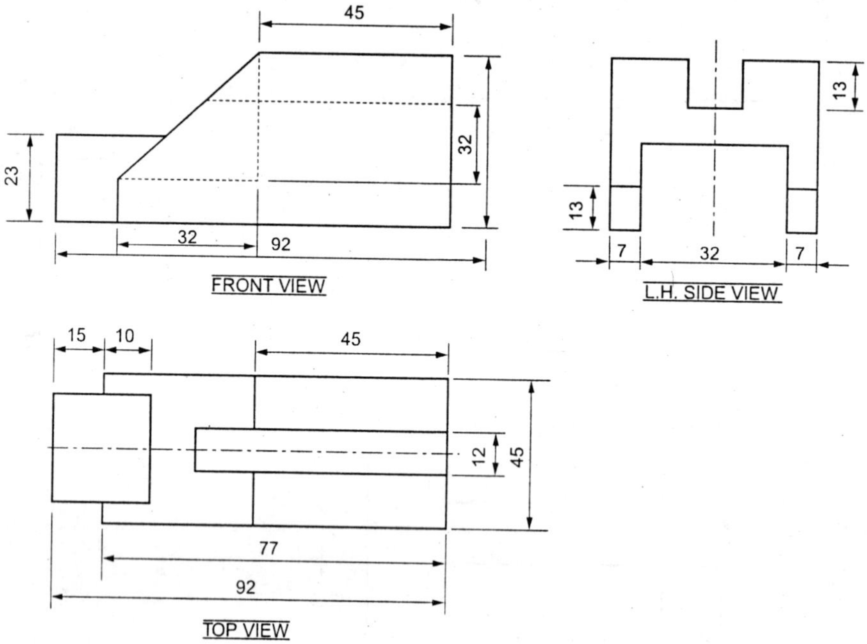

Fig. 14.22 (i)

Solution: See Fig. 14.23 (ii).

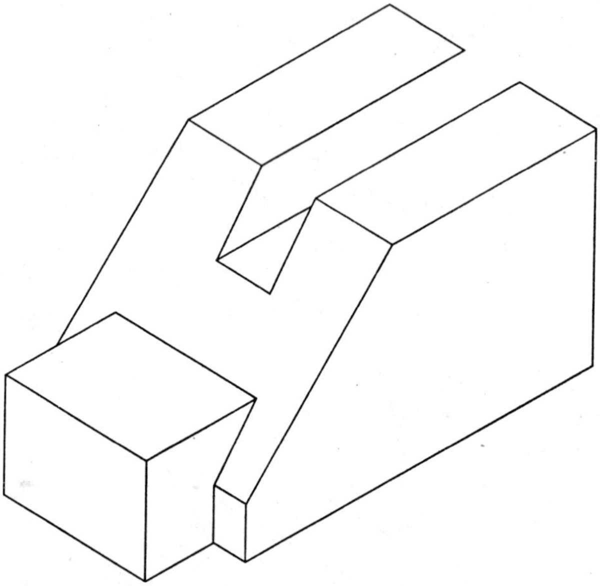

Fig. 14.23 (ii)

Problem 8. Fig 14.24 (i) shows the orthographic view of an object. Draw its isometric view.

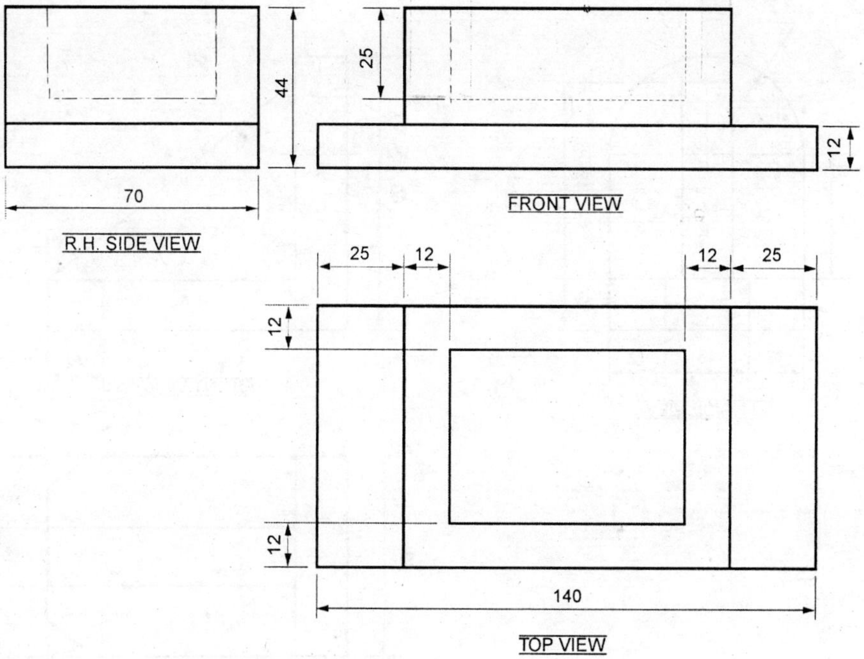

Fig. 14.24 (i)

Solution: See Fig. 14.24 (ii).

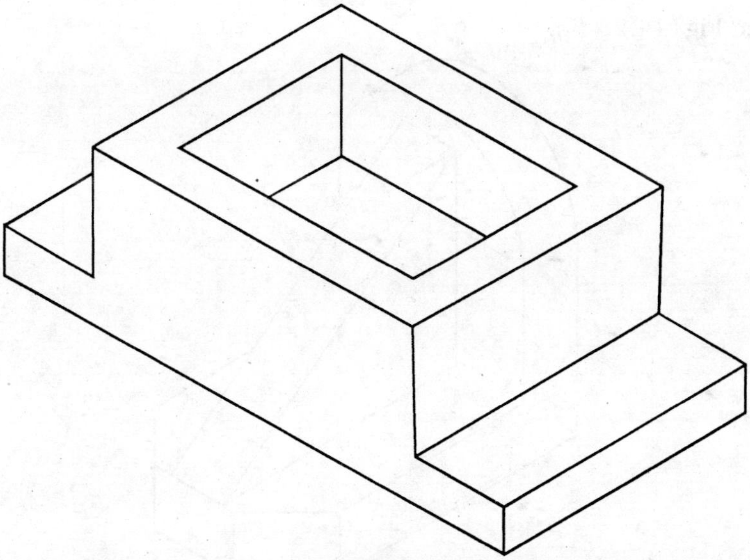

Fig. 14.24 (ii)

Problem 9. Draw the isometric view of an object whose three views are shown in Fig. 14.25 (i).

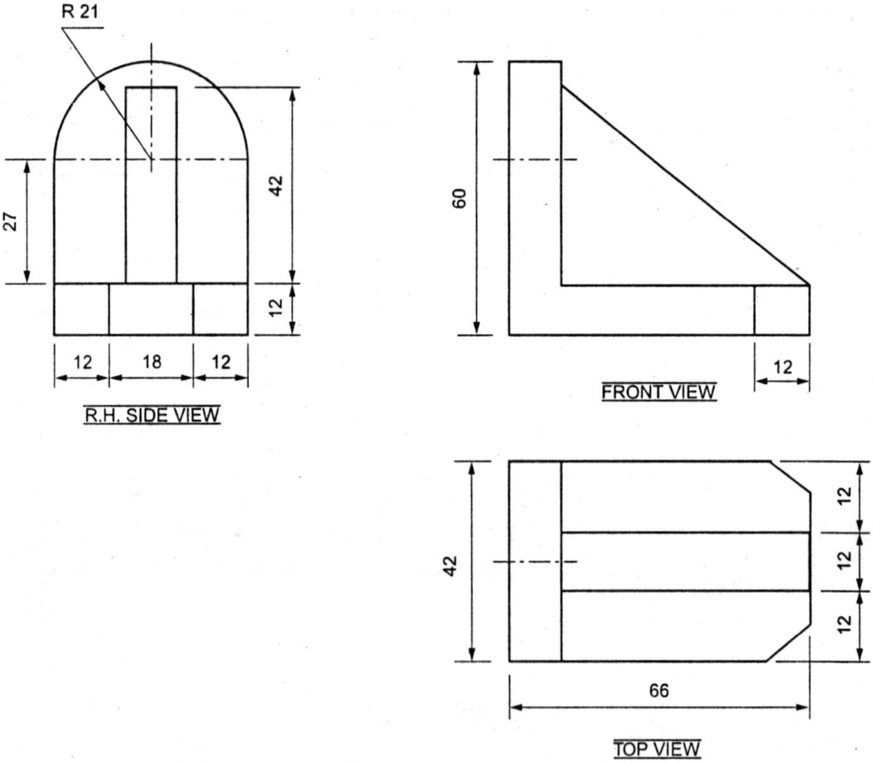

Fig. 14.25

Solution: See Fig. 14.25 (ii).

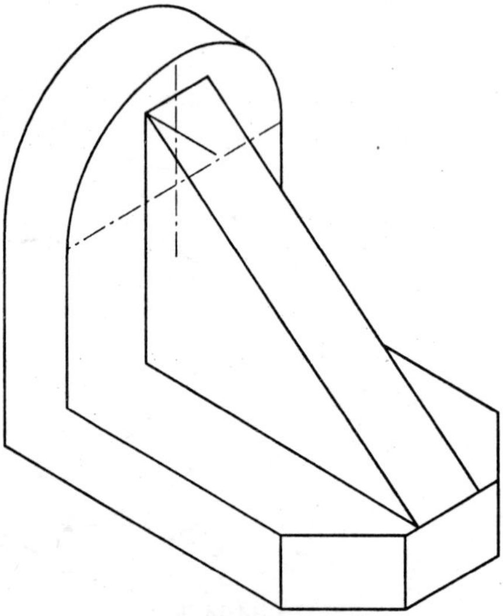

Fig. 14.25 (ii)

Problem 10. Draw the isometric view of an object whose views are shown in Fig. 14.26 (i).

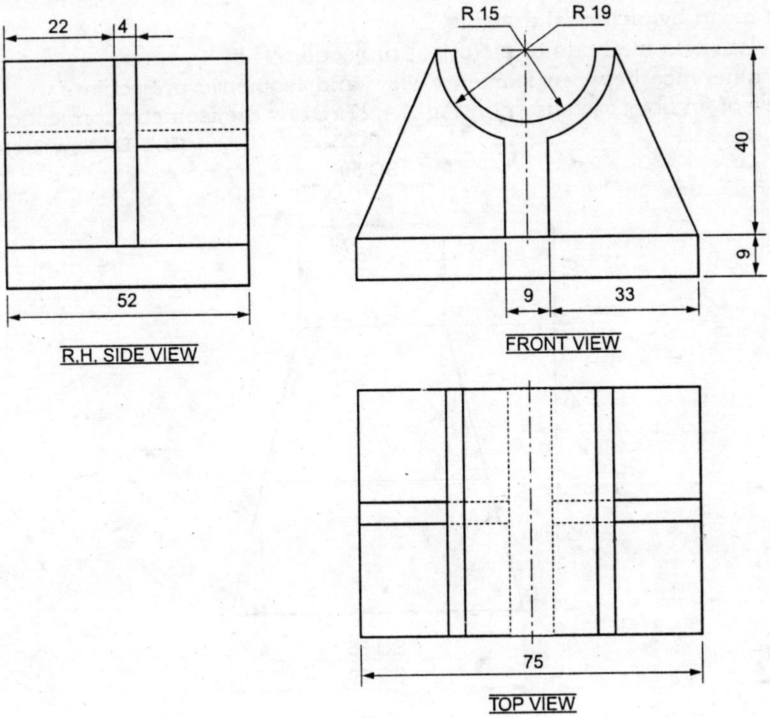

Fig. 14.26 (i)

Solution: See Fig. 14.26 (ii).

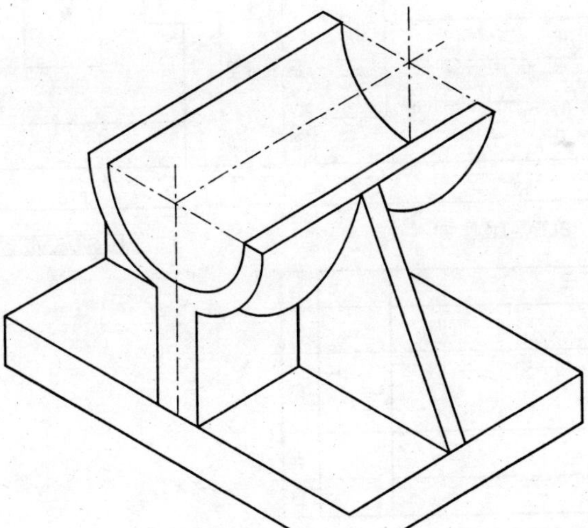

Fig. 14.26 (ii)

EXERCISE

1. What do you mean by pictorical drawing?
2. What are the various methods of pictorical projection?
3. What is the difference between Isometric view and Isometric projection?
4. The front view of an object is shown in Fig. 14.27. Draw the isometric projection of the object.

(B.T.E. New Delhi, Jan. 2009)

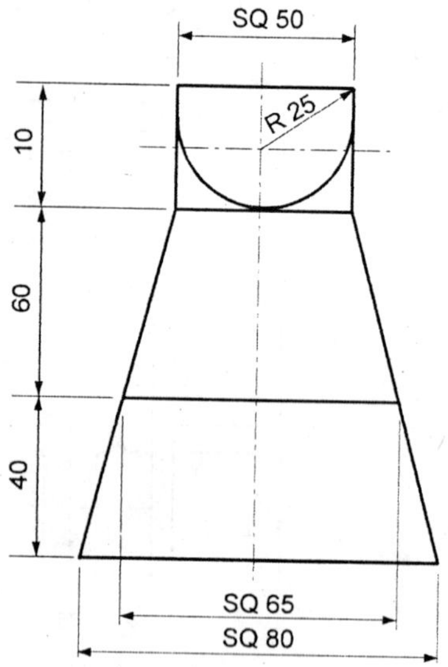

Fig. 14.27

5. Fig. 14.28 (*i–xviii*) shows three views of an object, draw its isometric view.

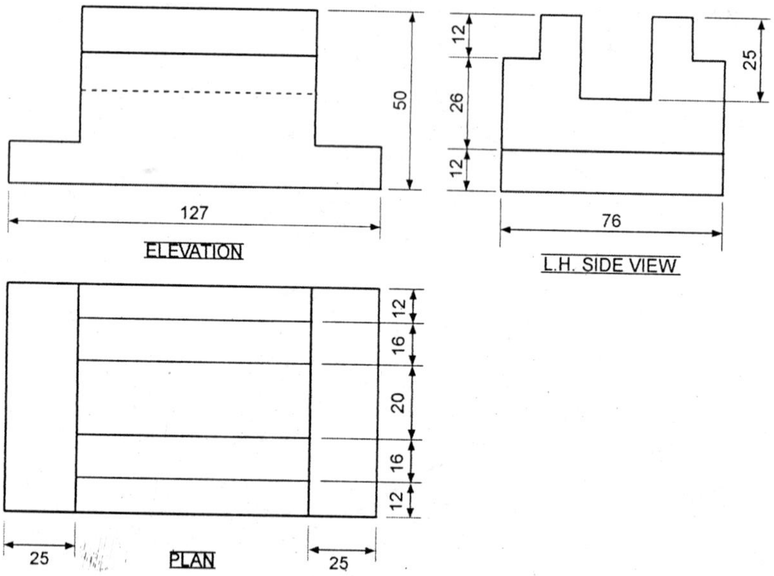

Fig. 14.28 (i)

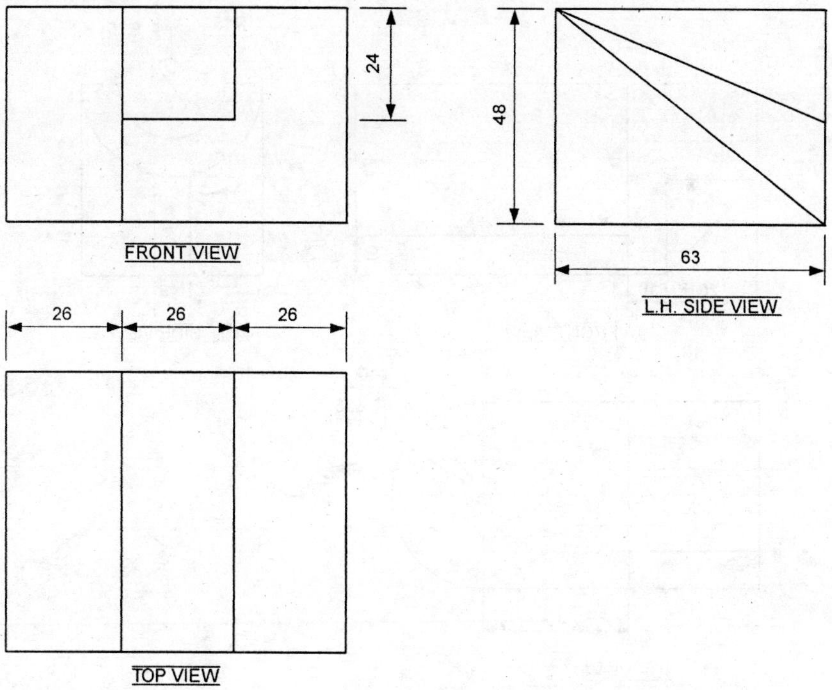

Fig. 14.28 (ii)

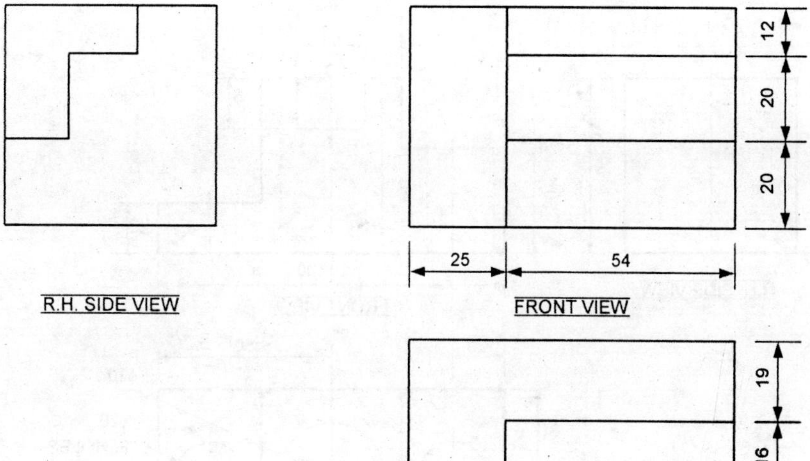

Fig. 14.28 (iii)

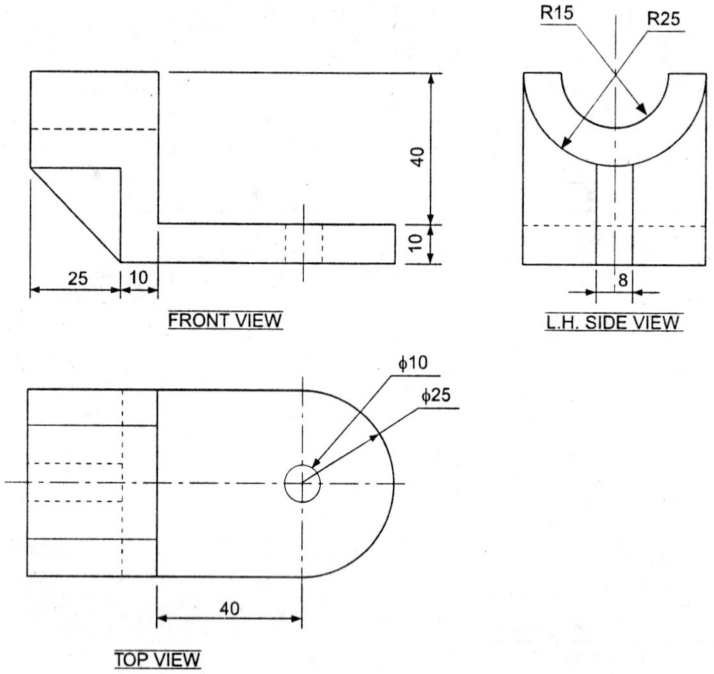

Fig. 14.28 (iv)

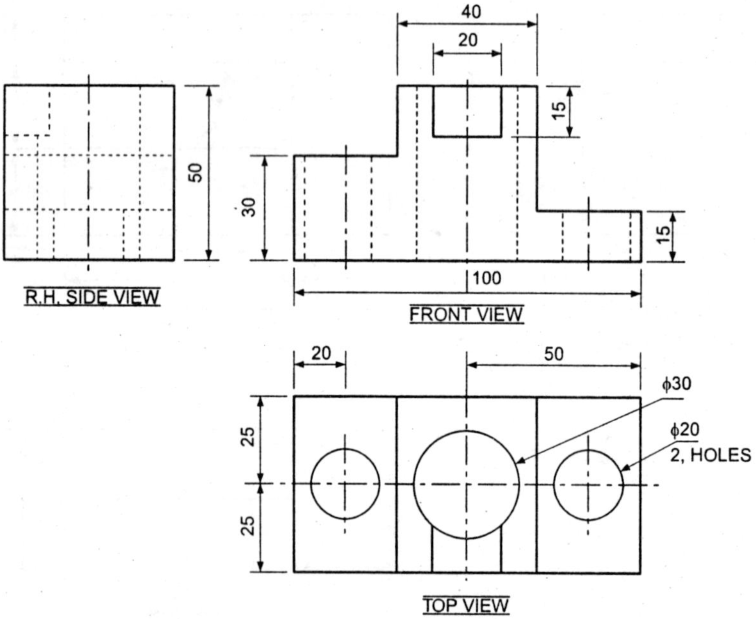

Fig. 14.28 (v)

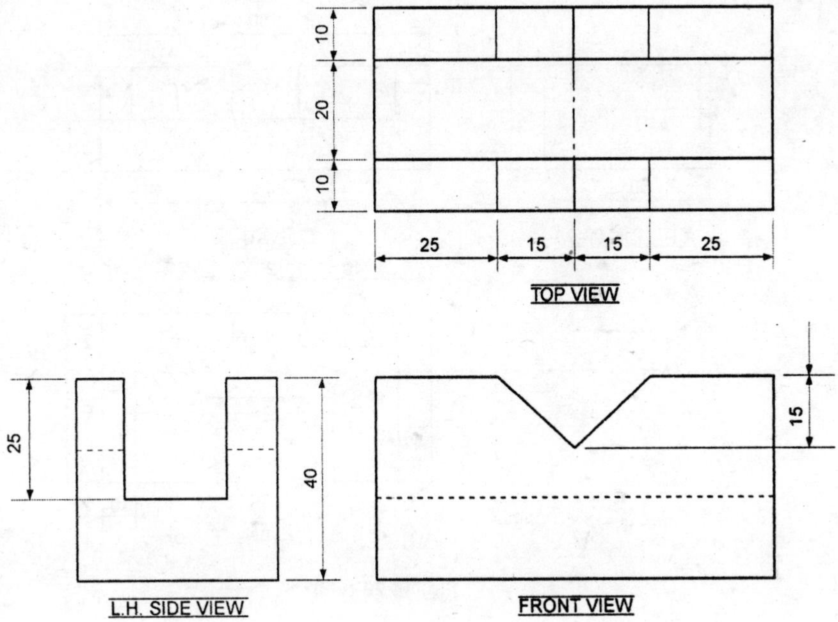

Fig. 14.28 (vi)

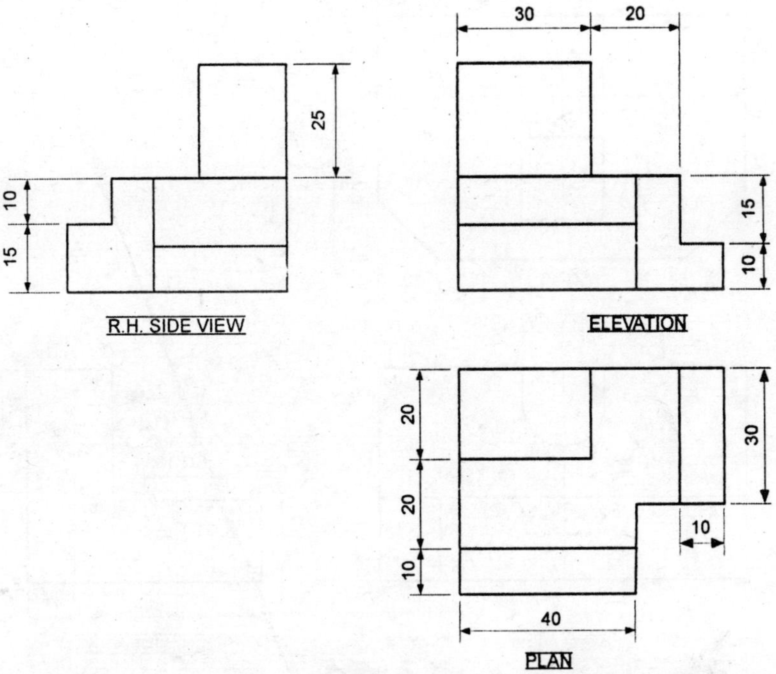

Fig. 14.28 (vii)

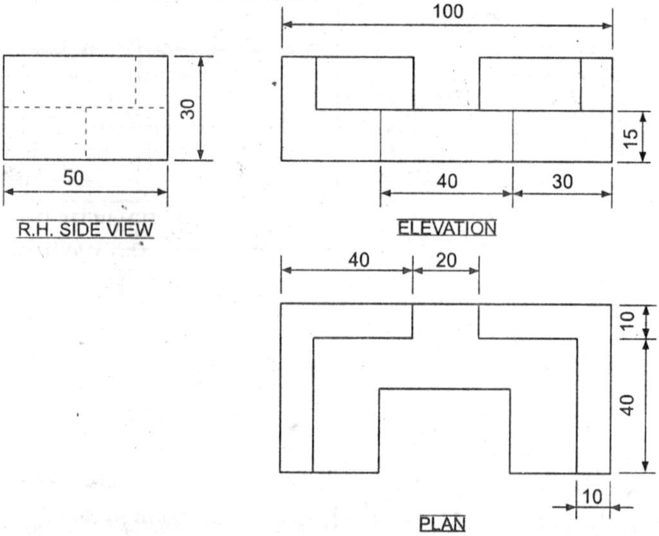

Fig. 14.28 (viii)

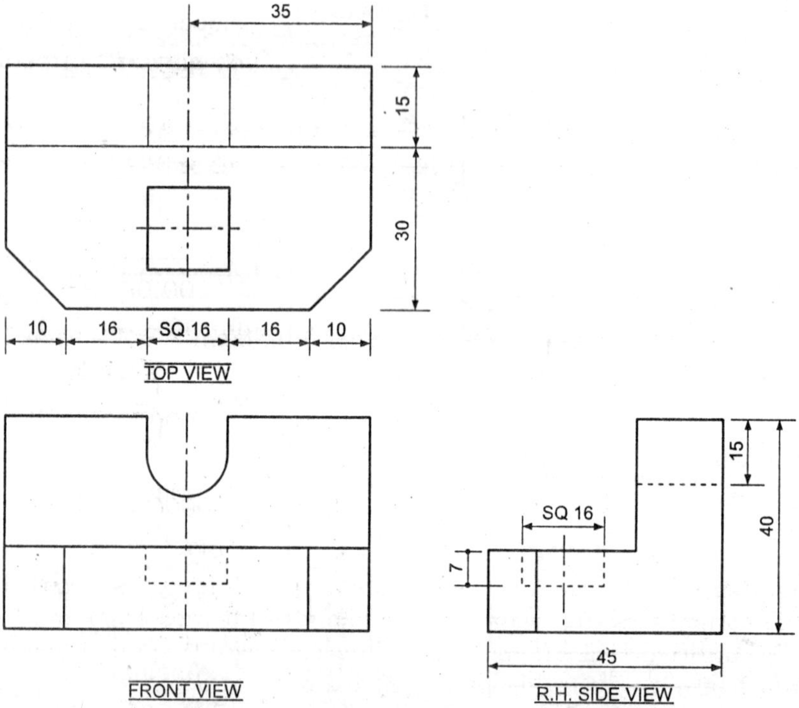

Fig. 14.28 (ix)

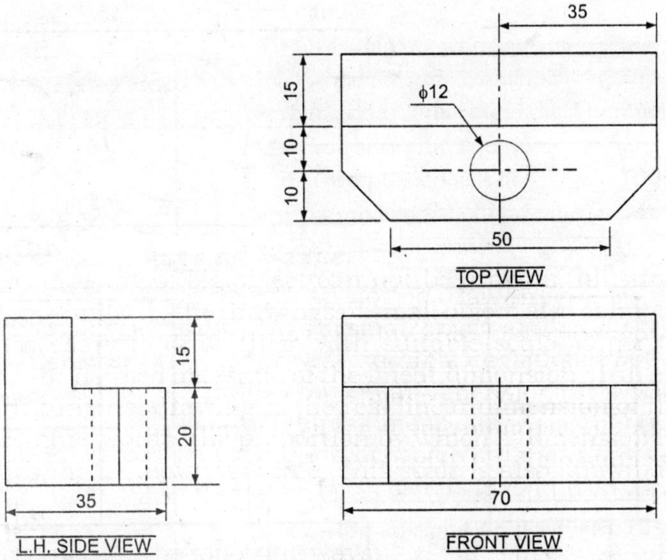

Fig. 14.28 (x)

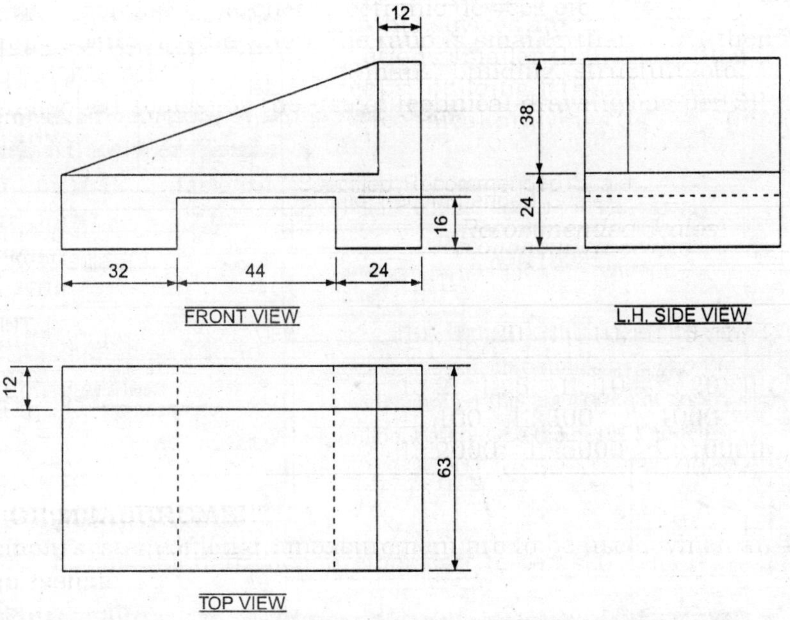

Fig. 14.28 (xi)

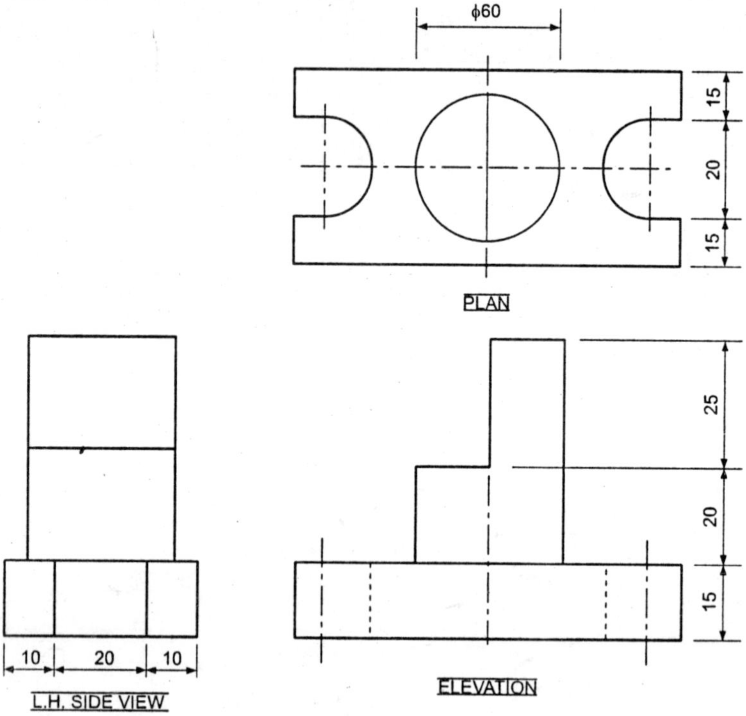

Fig. 14.28 (xii)

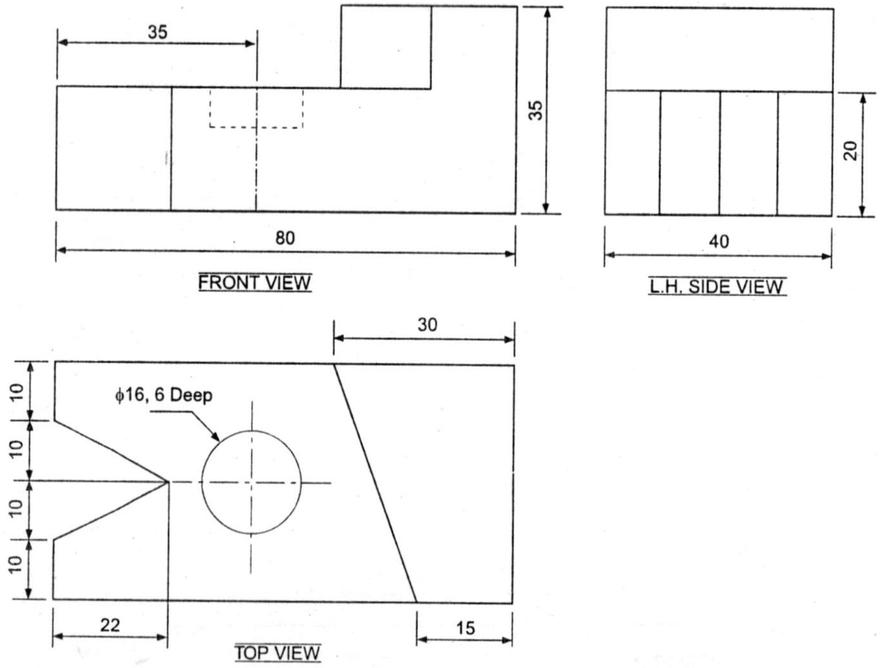

Fig. 14.28 (xiii)

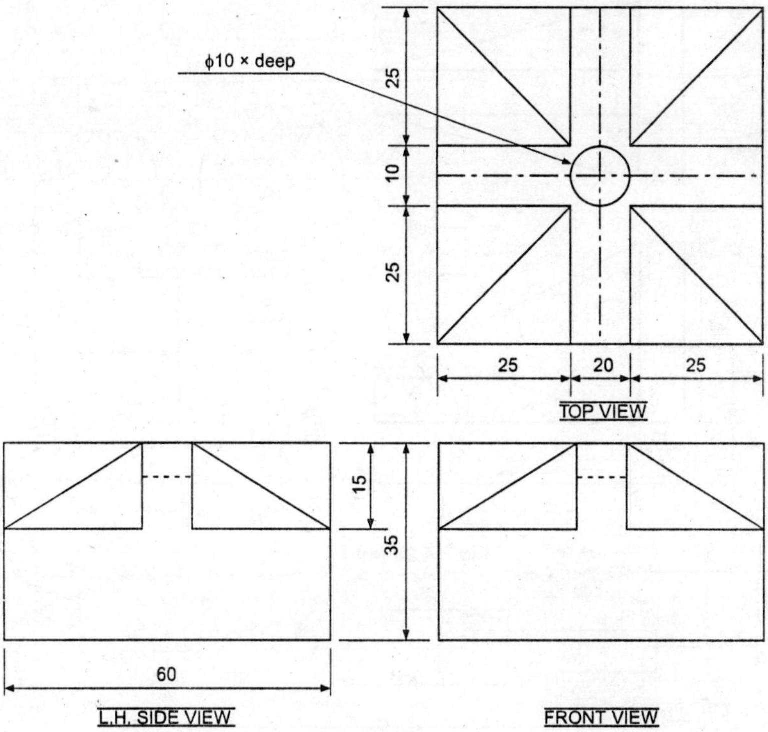

Fig. 14.28 (xiv)

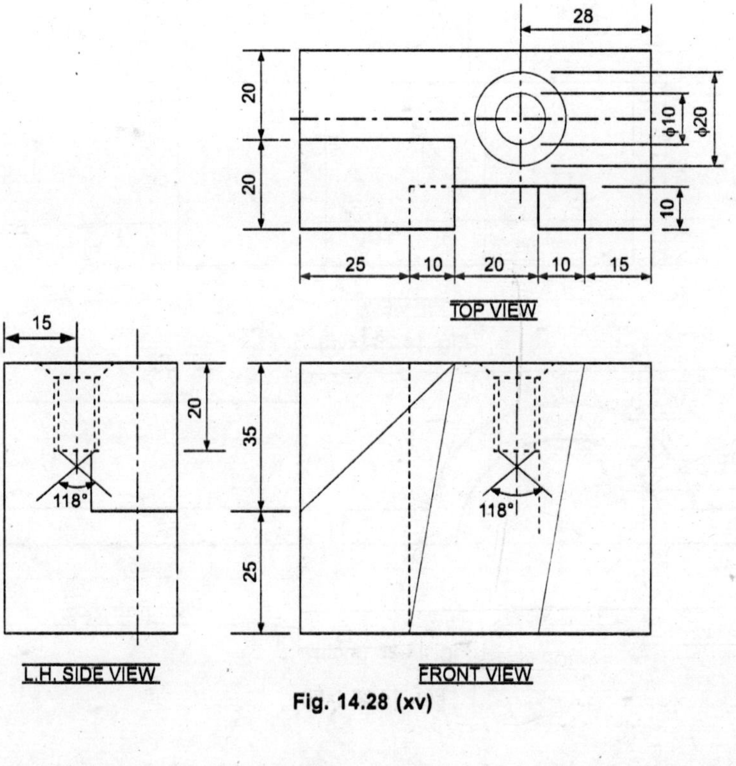

Fig. 14.28 (xv)

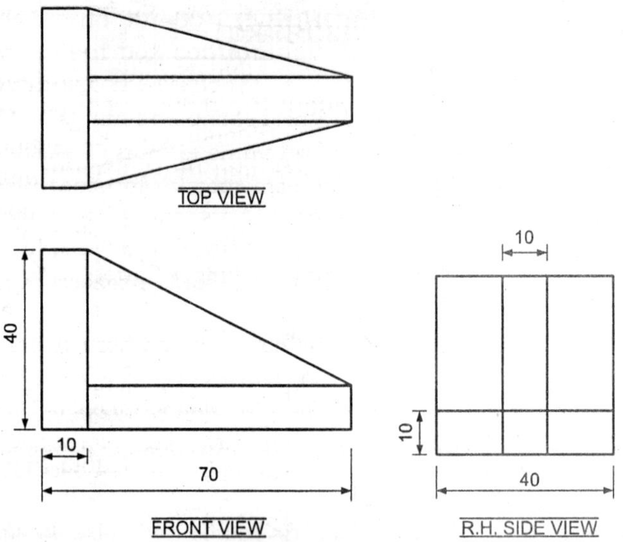

Fig. 14.28 (xvi)

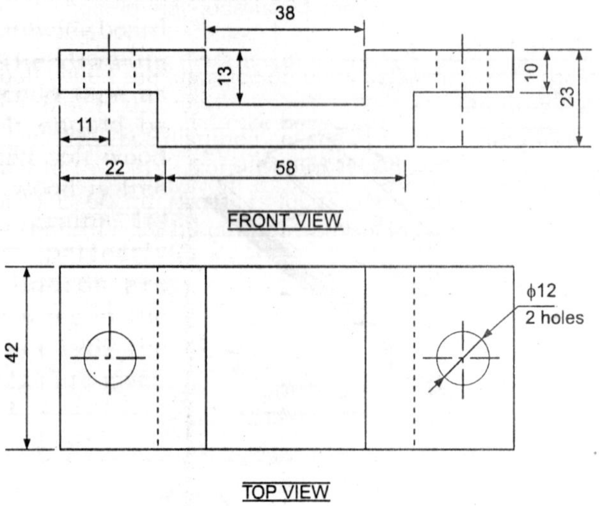

Fig. 14.28 (xvii)

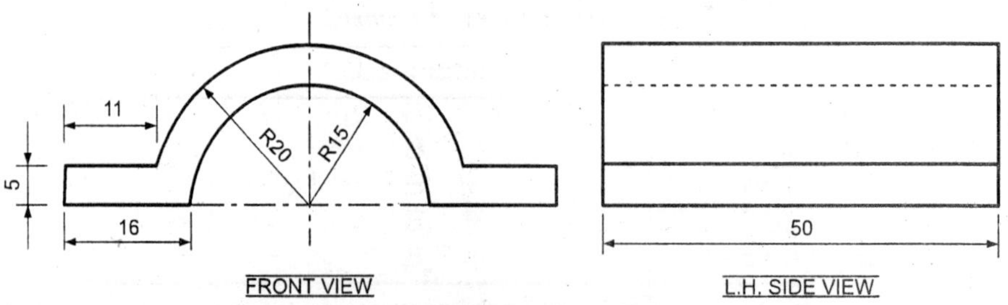

Fig. 14.28 (xviii)

15

Conversion of Isometric View into Orthographic View

15.1 INTRODUCTION

Orthographic view is best to show the details of interior construction, while isometric view represents real things by one view only. In engineering drawing, the conversion of isometric view into orthographic view is very important for engineers to get a grasp over the subject. For this purpose, a sound knowledge of principle of projection and some imagination is necessary for drawing orthographic view from the isometric view.

An isometric view should be drawn according to the principles of isometric view, which shows the object as it appear to the observer from one direction only. It does not represent its real shape of its surface. Hidden parts also are not shown by dotted lines. All these have to be imagined. Generally the direction from which the object is to be viewed is indicated by means of arrows. If there is no arrow, the direction for front view may be decided which gives the most prominent view of the object.

The following points should be remembered when converting isometric view into orthographic views:

1. Any two of the three overall dimensions (viz length, breadth and height) should be seen as points.
2. A hidden part of a symmetrical object should be assumed to be similar to the corresponding visible parts.
3. All the holes, grooves etc. should be assumed to be drilled or cut right through.
4. Suitable radii should be assumed for small curves of fillets etc.
5. An object in its isometric view may sometimes be shown with a portion cut and removed to clarify its interior details while preparing its orthographic view, such object should be assumed as a whole.

15.2 PROCEDURE FOR PREPARING ORTHOGRAPHIC VIEW

Before preparing a drawing of an object following rules of conversion should be remembered:

Step I. Take half empirical drawing sheet and draw the border line and title block.

Step II. The scale of drawing is decided from the size of the object and number of views required to draw and select the suitable scale so as to accommodate the required view of an object.

Step III. Draw the different rectangles of the view, keeping suitable space between them.

Step IV. Mark centres for circles in the view. If there is any cylinder or hole seen as rectangles, draw only one centre line, but if the circle is visible, draw more than one centre lines intersecting each other at right angles.

Step V. (*i*) Draw circle of required diameter in the front view and in the top view.

(*ii*) Draw the other straight lines in the front view and project them in the side view as well as in top view.

(*iii*) Rub the faint line (if required) after completion of required view of an object.

Step VI. Give the dimensions, the scale and print the title along with the other required particulars such as notes.

(*i*) First draw extension line.

(*ii*) Draw dimension lines and insert the dimension of an object as per rule.

Step VII. Check the drawing sheet carefully and see that it should be completed in all respects, as shown in Fig. 15.1

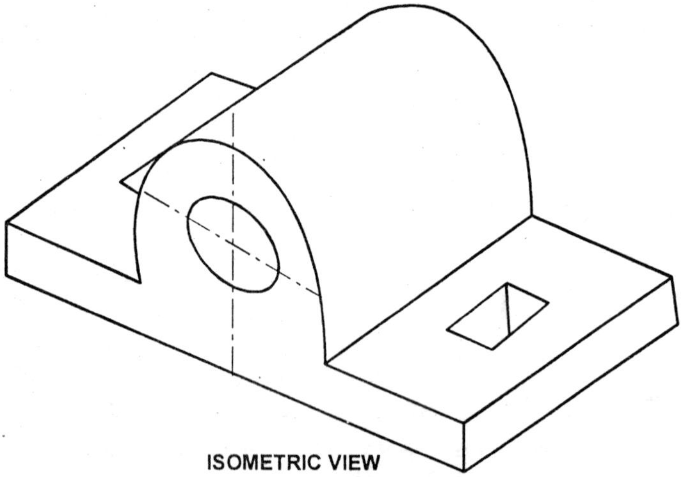

Fig. 15.1 (i)

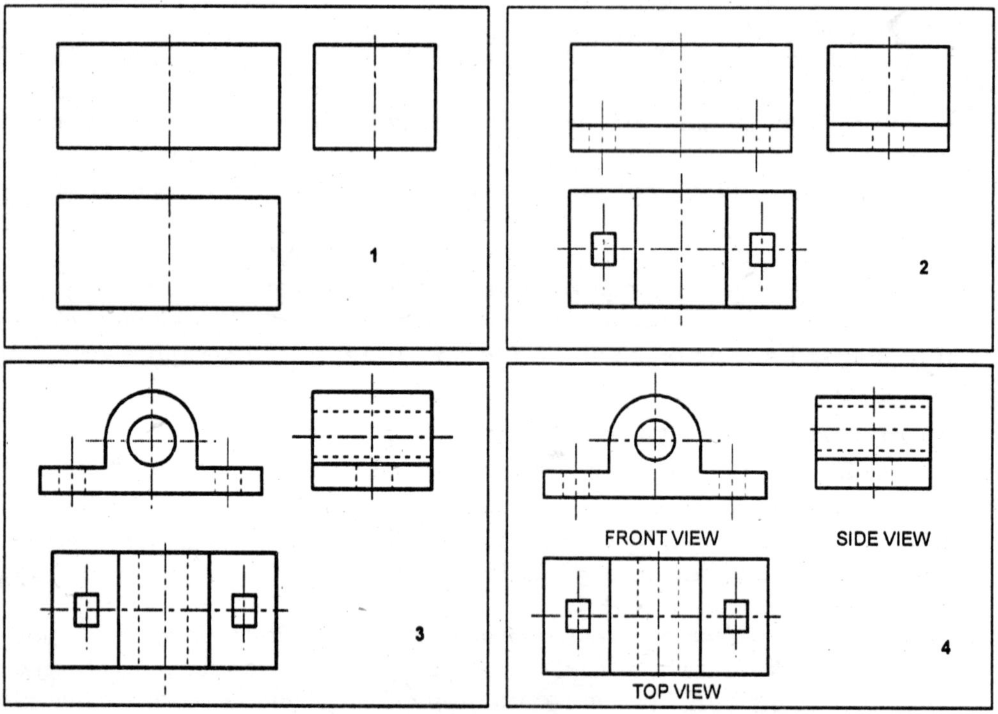

Fig. 15.1 (ii)

Problem 1. Draw the following views of an object shown pictorically in Fig. 15.2 (*i*): (1) Front view (2), Top view (3) Side view.

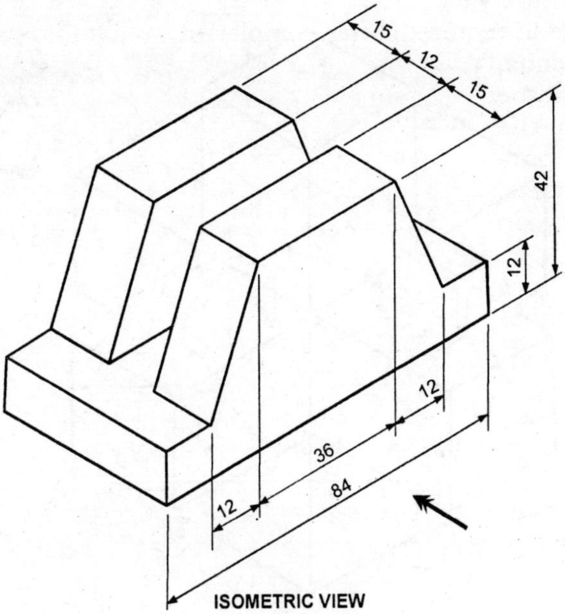

Fig. 15.2 (i)

Solution. See Fig. 15.2 (*ii*).

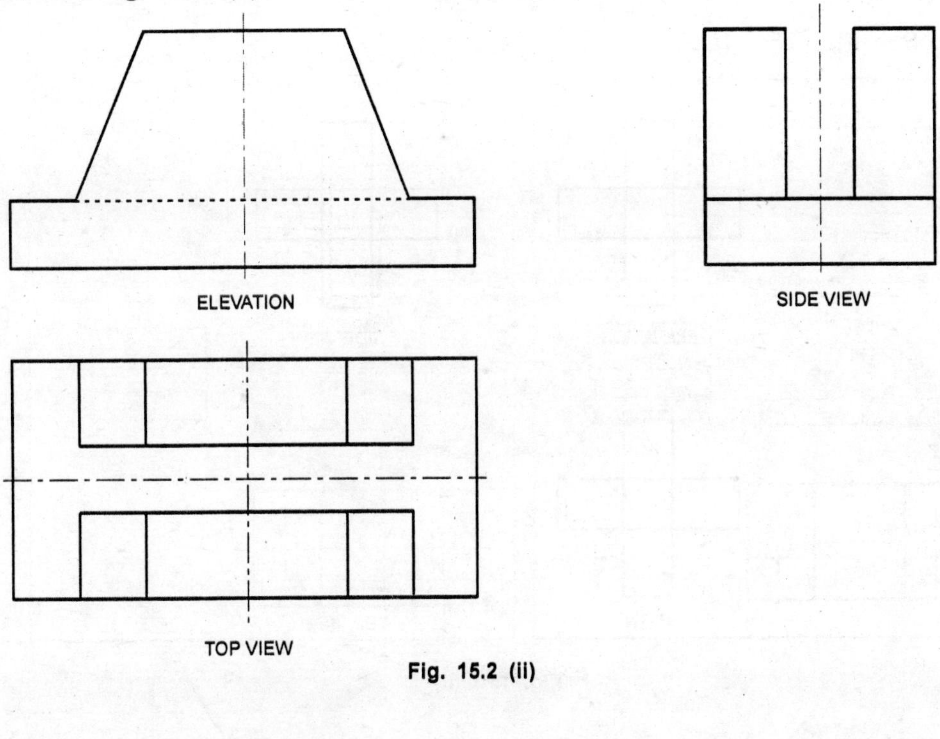

Fig. 15.2 (ii)

Problem 2. Draw the following views of the block shown pictorically in Fig. 15.3 (*i*): (1) Elevation (2), Plan (3) Side view.

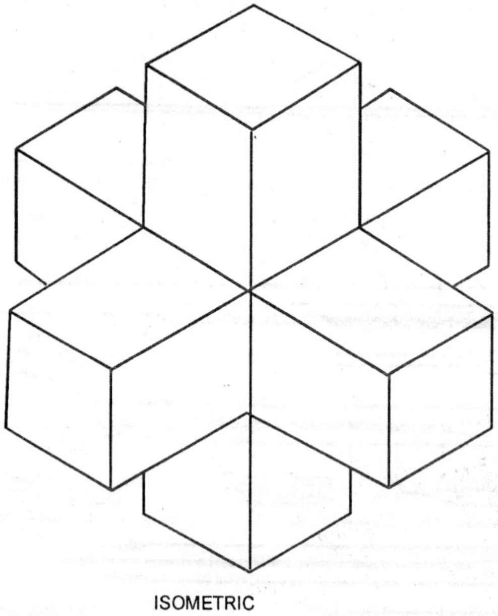

Fig. 15.3 (i)

Solution. See Fig. 15.3 (*ii*).

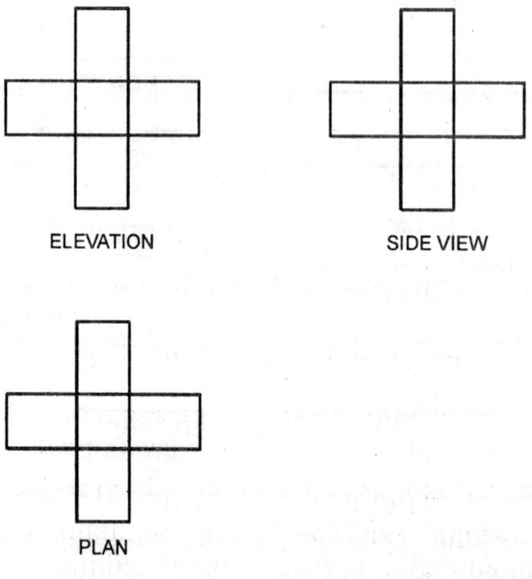

Fig. 15.3 (ii)

Problem 3. Fig. 15.4 (*i*) shows the isometric view of an object. Draw (1) Front view (2) Top view, and (3) Side view.

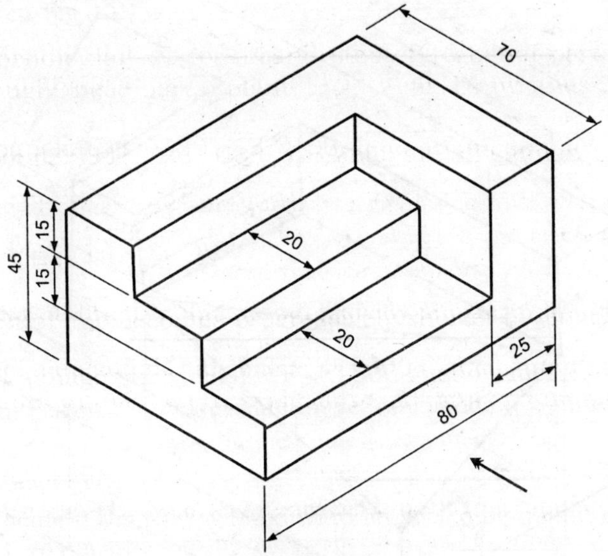

ISOMETRIC VIEW

Fig. 15.4 (i)

Solution. See Fig. 15.4 (*ii*).

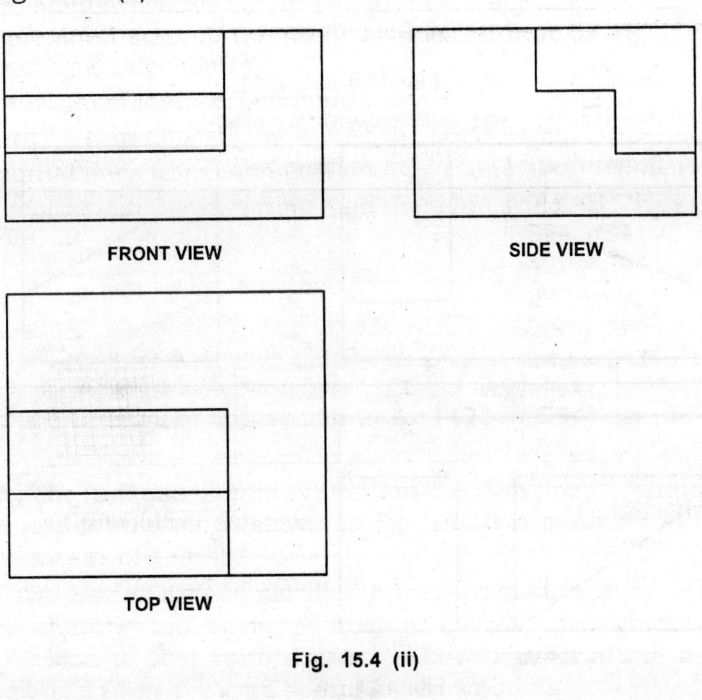

Fig. 15.4 (ii)

Problem 4. Draw the front view, top view and side view of an object as shown in Fig. 15.5 (*i*).

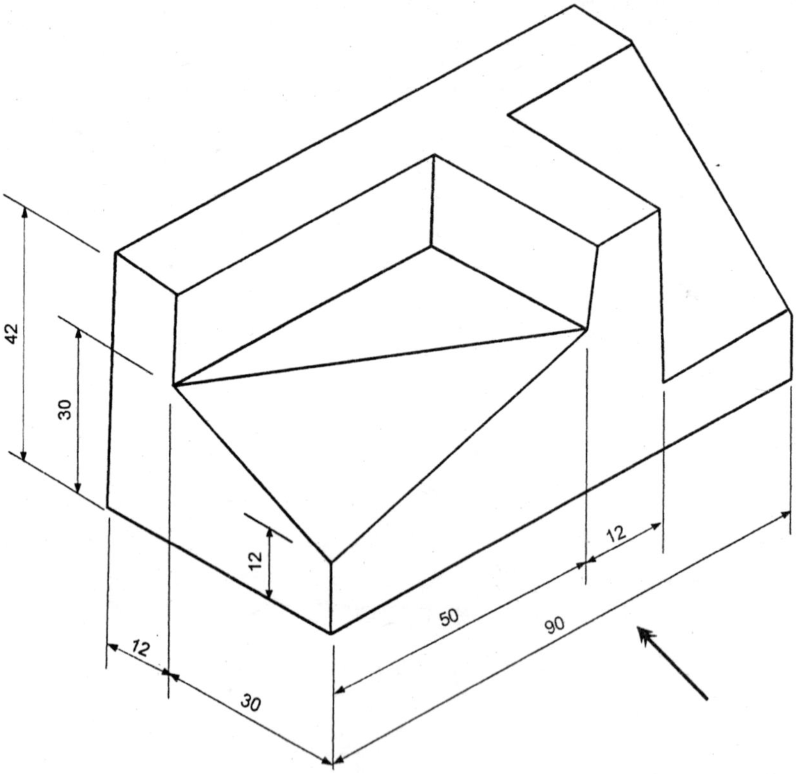

Fig. 15.5 (i)

Solution. See Fig. 15.5 (*ii*).

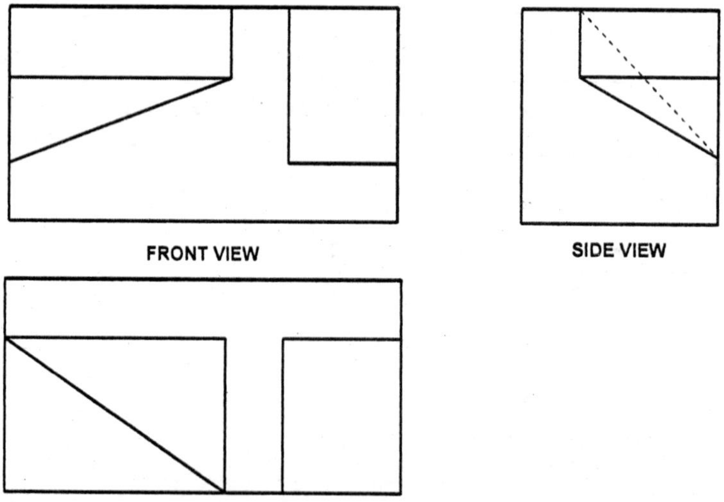

Fig. 15.5 (ii)

Problem 5. Fig. 15.6 (i) shows the isometric view of an object. Draw (1) Front view (2) Top view (3) Side view.

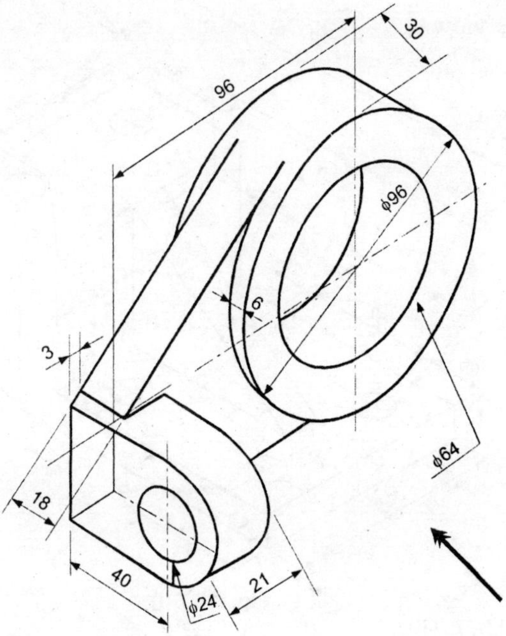

Fig. 15.6 (i)

Solution. See Fig. 15.6 (*ii*).

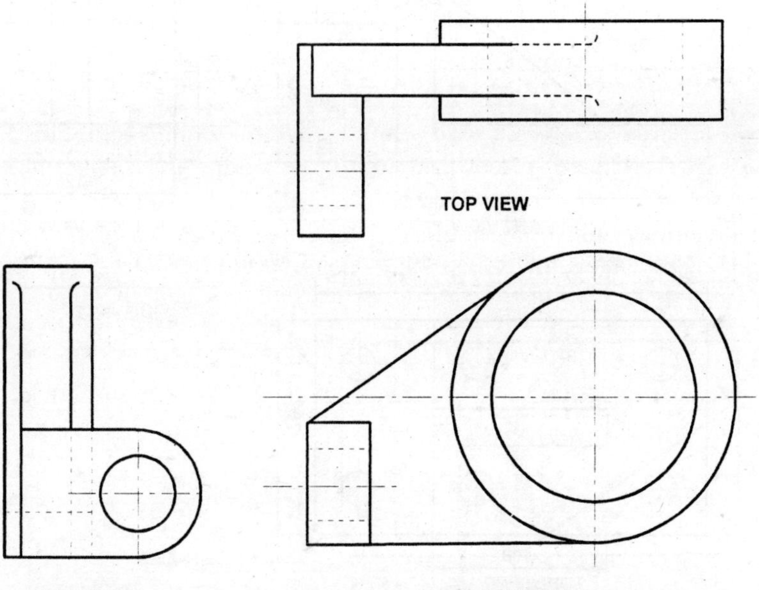

Fig. 15.6 (ii)

Problem 6. Figure 15.7 (i) is shows the isometric view of an object. Draw

(1) Front view
(2) Top view
(3) Left hand side view.

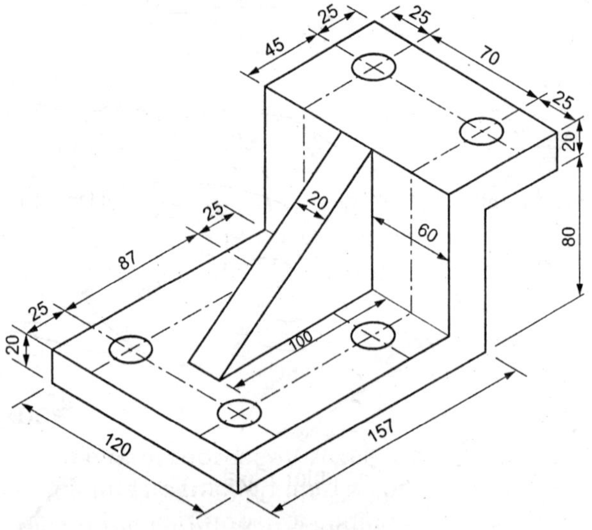

Fig. 15.7 (i)

Solution. See Fig. 15.7 (ii).

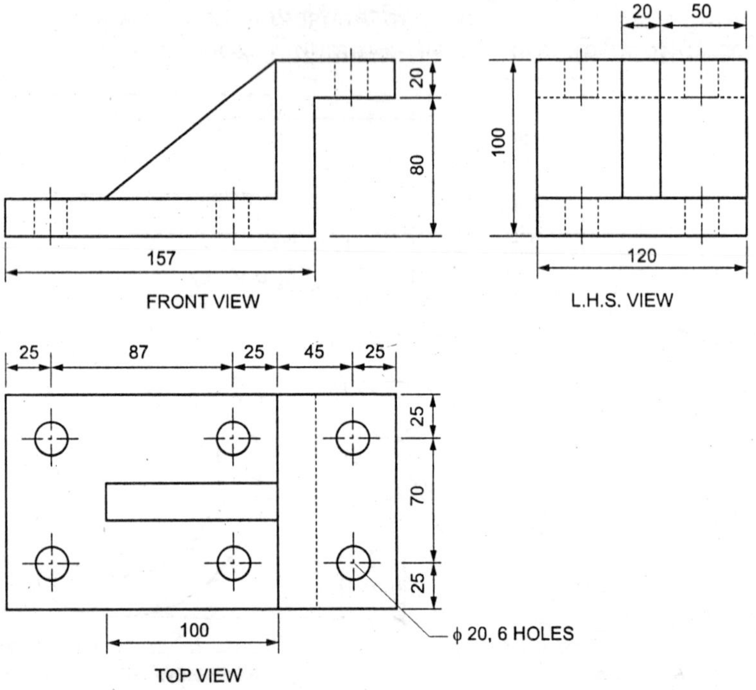

Fig. 15.7 (ii)

EXERCISE

1. Fig. 15.8 (1 to 33) shows isometric views of different objects. Draw orthographic views of each object such as, [Use Ist angle projection].

(*i*) Front-view (*ii*) Top view, and

(*iii*) Side view.

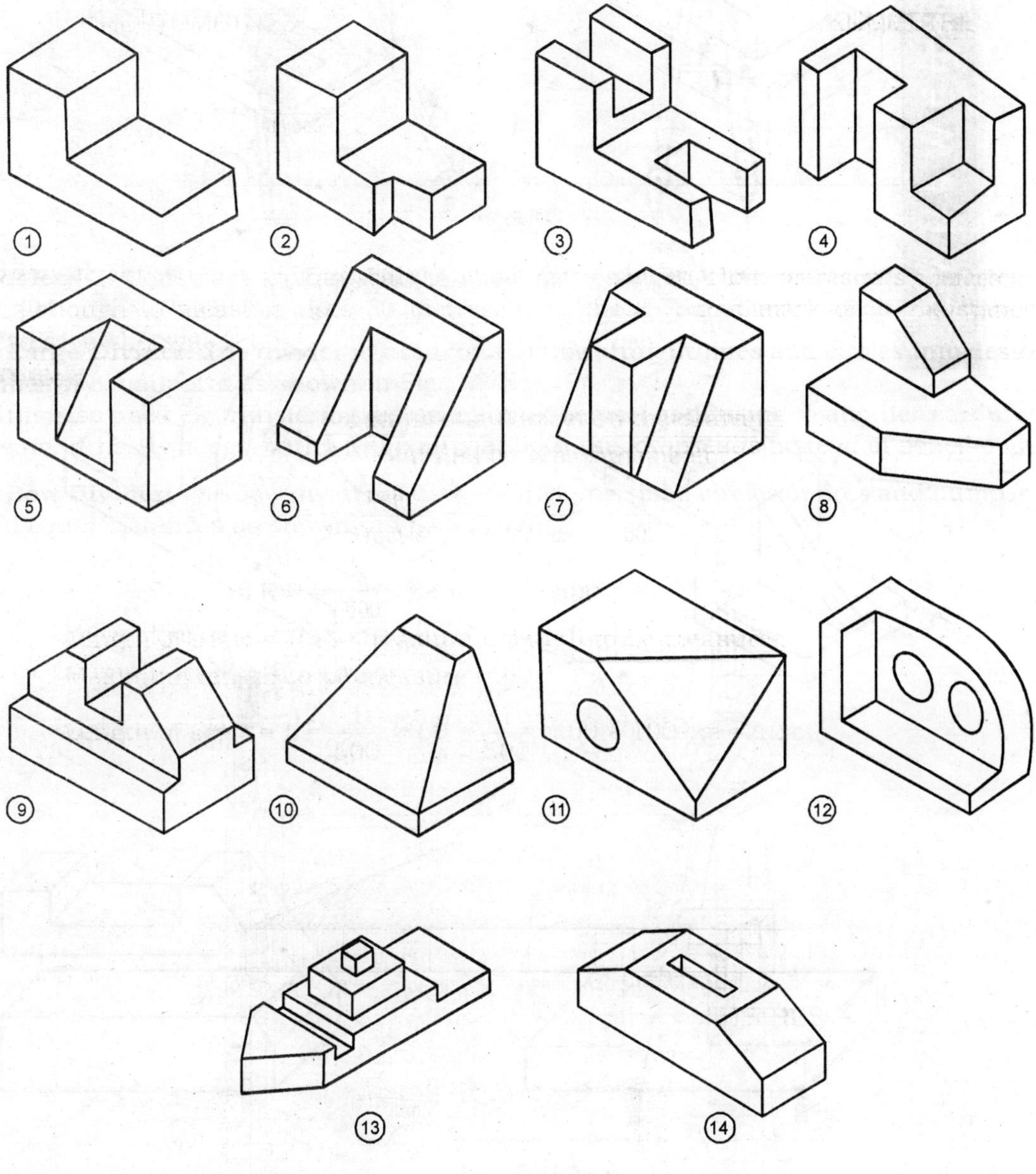

Fig. 15.8 Contd.

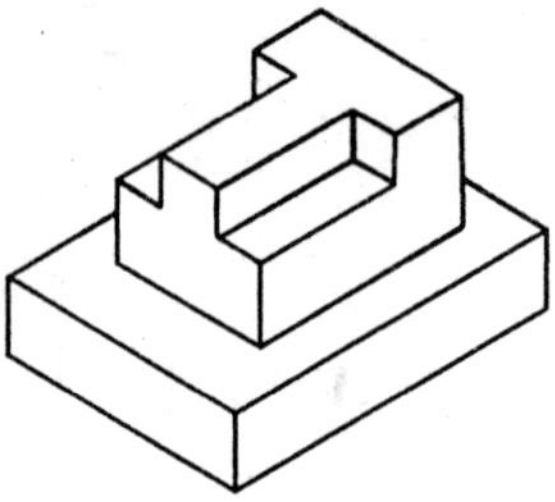

15

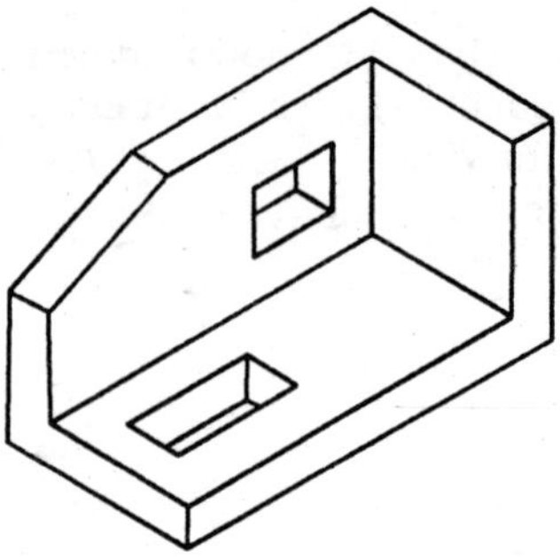

16

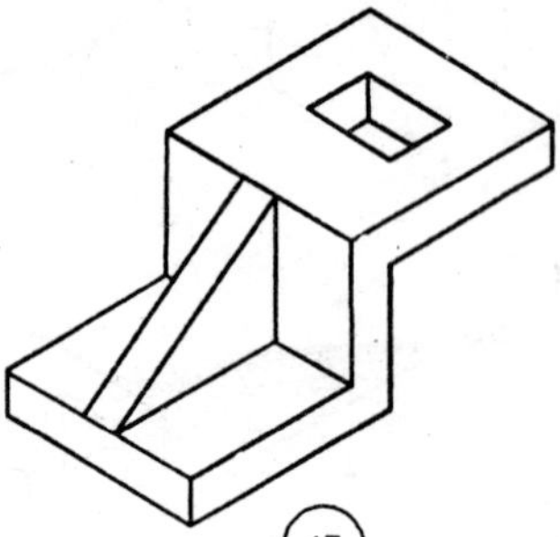

17

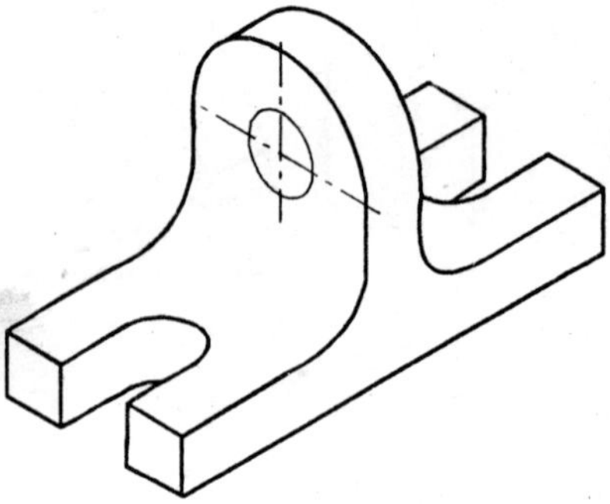

18

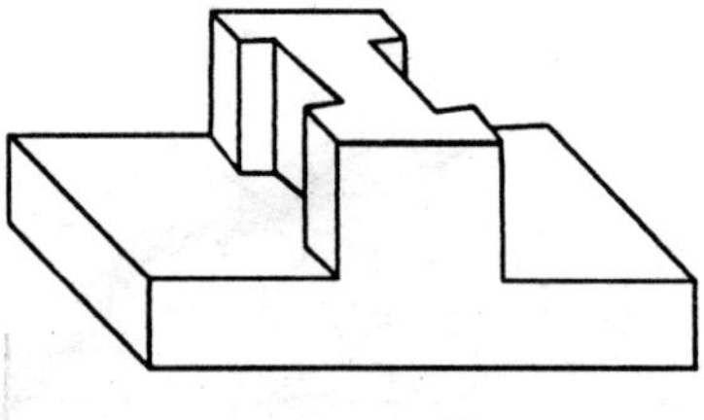

19

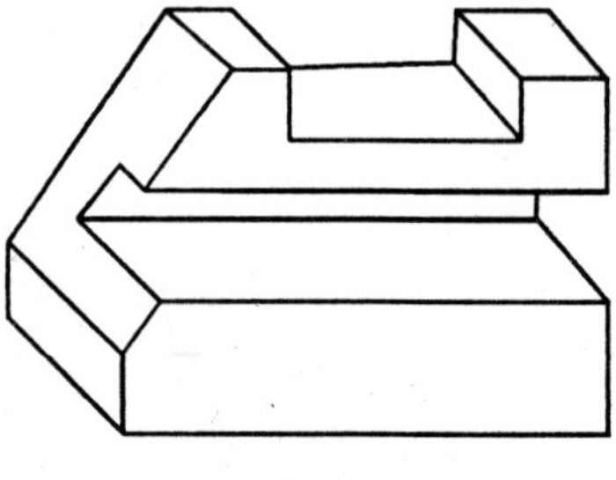

20

Fig. 15.8 Contd.

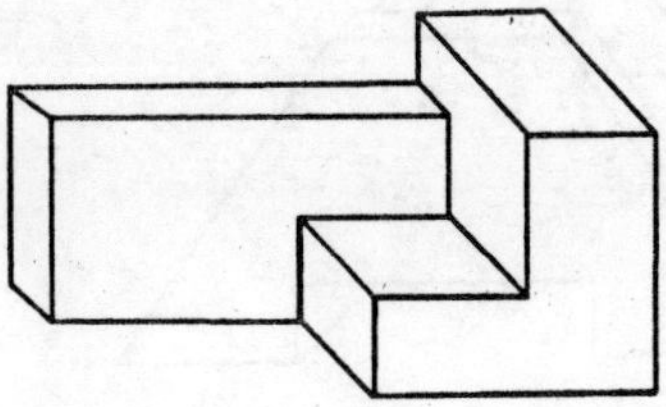

(21)

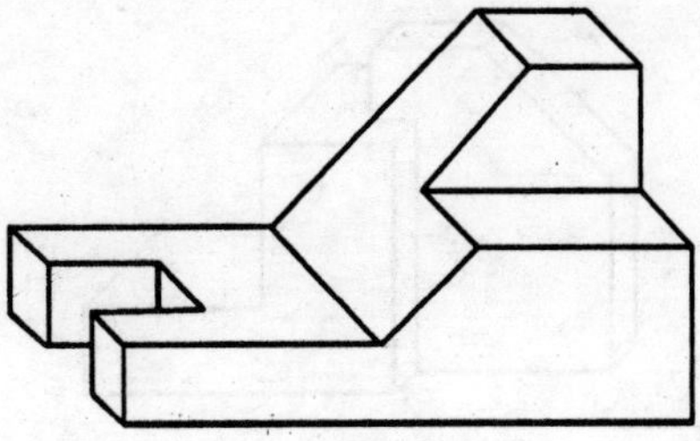

(22)

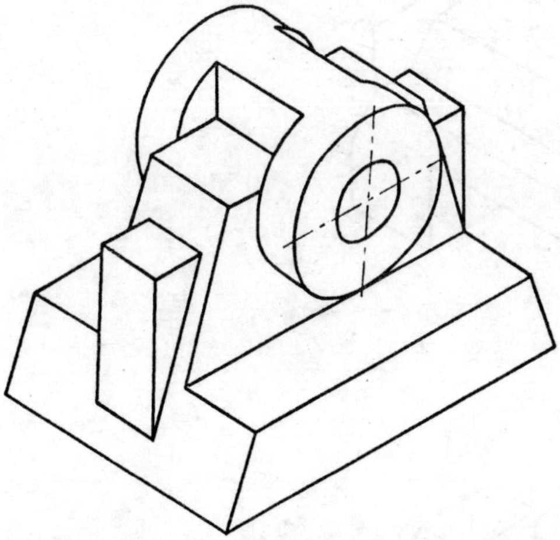

(23)

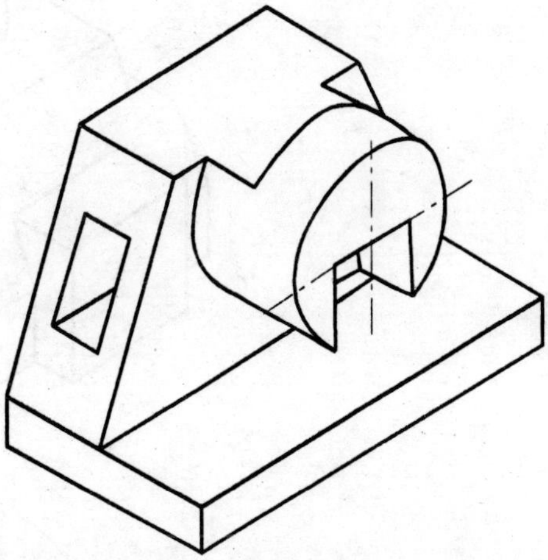

(24)

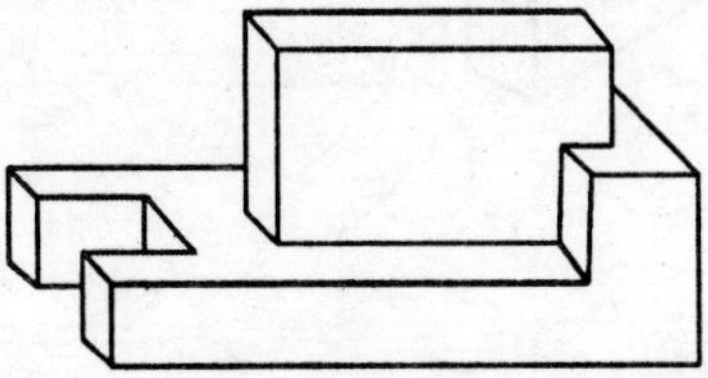

(25)

(26)

Fig. 15.8 Contd.

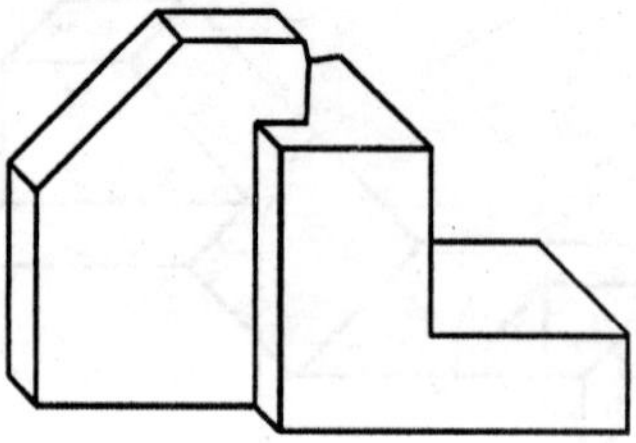

(27)

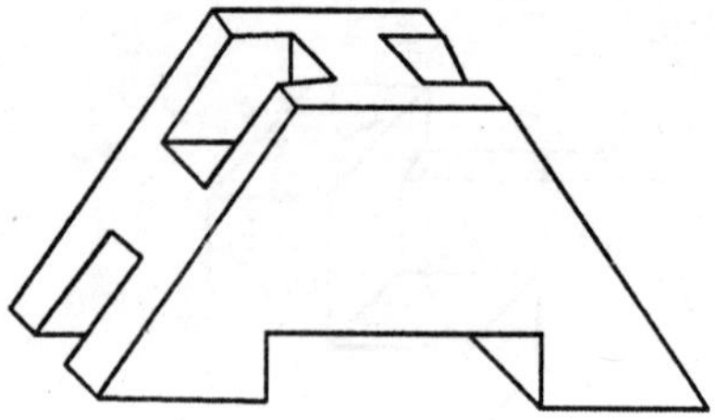

(28)

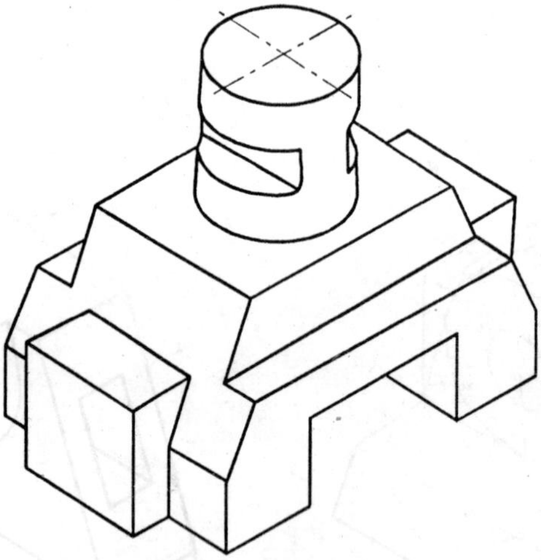

(29)

(30)

Fig. 15.8 Contd.

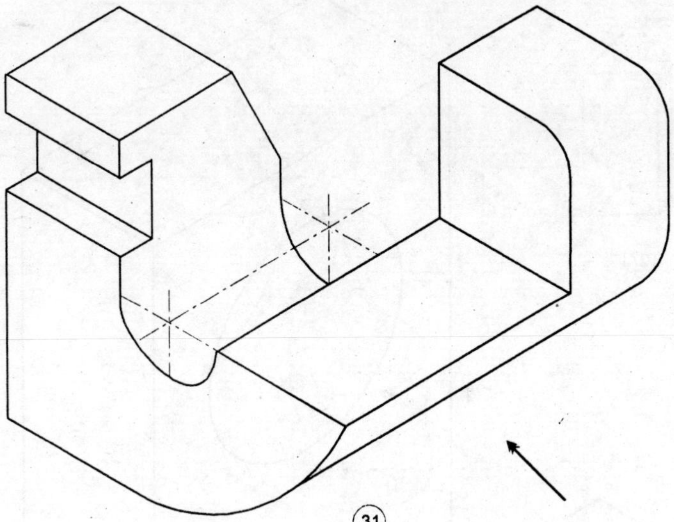

(31)

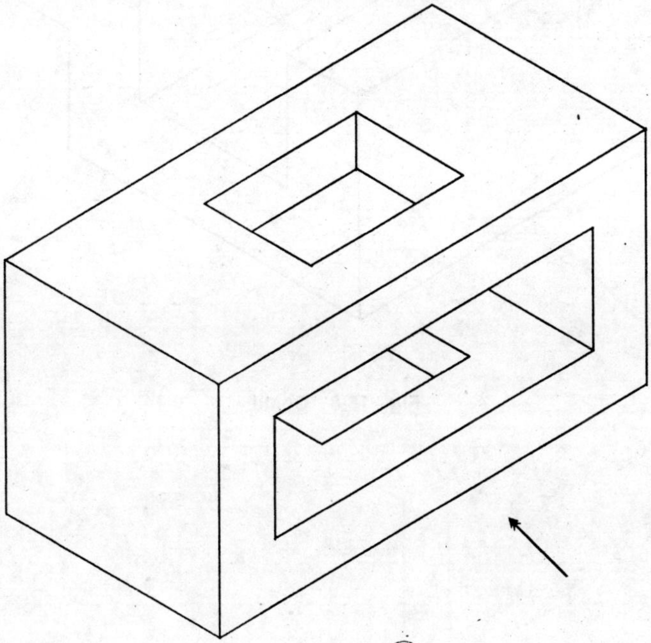

(32)

Fig. 15.8 Contd.

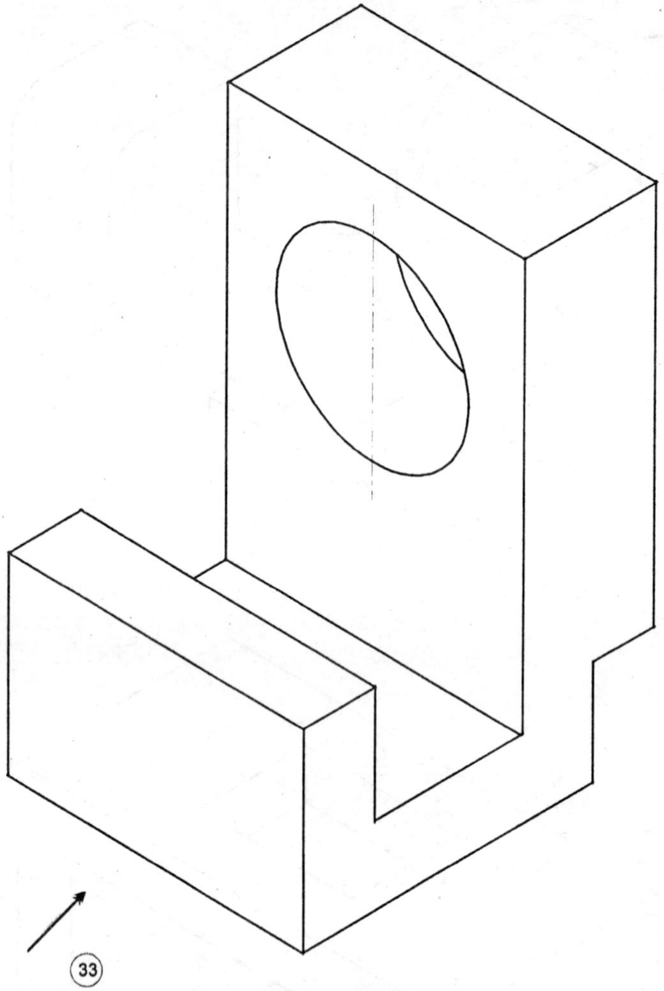

Fig. 15.8 Contd.

❑❑❑

16

SECTIONAL VIEWS

16.1 INTRODUCTION

In orthographic projection, the interior details of an object, which are not visible to observer from outside are shown by hidden lines. But some of the machine parts have the complicated interior details and they do not give the clear idea about the internal shape of an object. Too many hidden lines also confuse the observer. To avoid these confusions, the views are made in section and it is imagined that the object is being cut through or sectioned by a plane. The part of the object between the cutting plane and the observer is assumed to be removed and the remaining view of the object then obtained is called the sectional view. Therefore, section is define as, the view obtained after cutting the object in order to show the inner details by an imaginary cutting plane is called a sectional view. The imaginary plane is called a cutting plane or section plane. The cutting plane is taken parallel to the plane on which the view is projected and the section view is drawn by removing the nearer portion of the object. The sectional view of the object is represented by the thin lines, and these lines are known as sectional lines or hatching lines. These hatching lines are drawn parallel to each other at an angle of 45° to the out lines of the object as shown in Fig. 16.1.

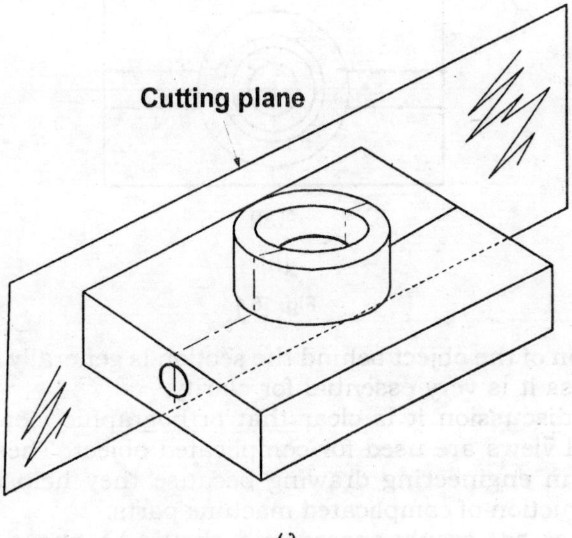

(*i*)

Fig. 16.1

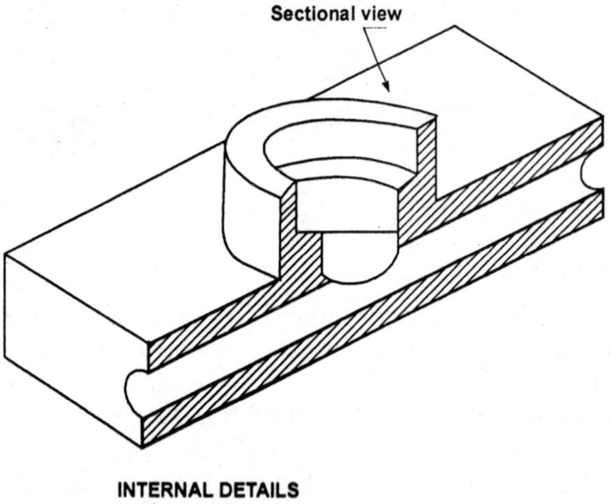

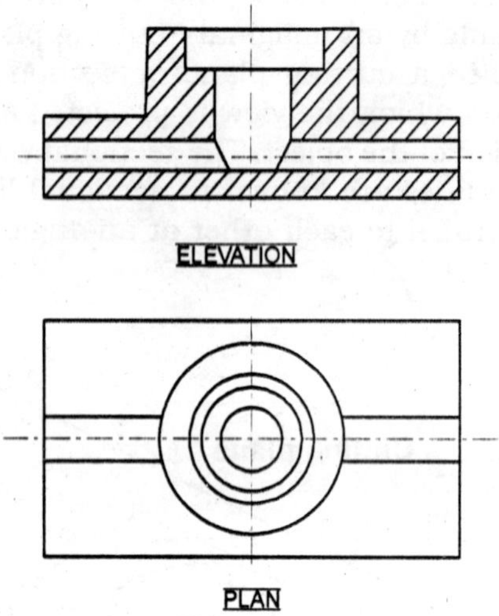

(ii)

Fig. 16.1

The hidden portion of the object behind the section is generally omitted and not shown by hidden lines unless it is very essential for clarity.

From the above discussion it is clear that orthographic views are used for simple objects and sectional views are used for complicated object. These sectional views play very important role in engineering drawing because they help in manufacturing and explaining the construction of complicated machine parts.

These section lines are evenly spaced and should be about 2 mm to 3 mm apart depending upon the size of drawing. For some assembly drawings, the sectional lines are used to indicate the difference in material as shown in Fig. 16.2.

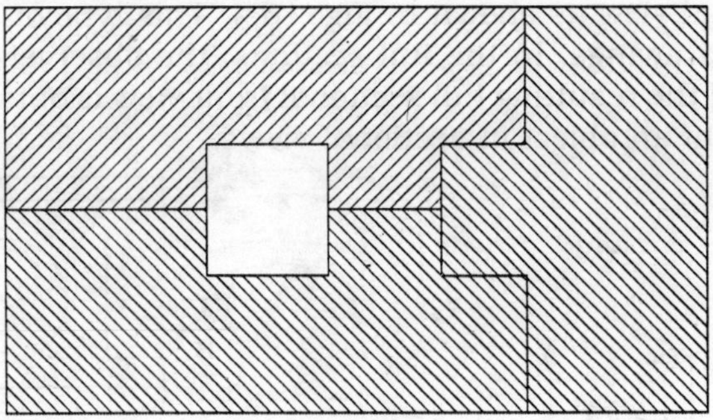

Fig. 16.2

16.2 CUTTING PLANE LINES

Cutting plane lines are used to indicate the location of sectional planes for sectional views and viewing position for removed partial views. It is represented by a long thick dashes and a short dashes alternatively spaced as shown in Fig. 16.3. The arrows are used to indicate the direction in which the cut surface is viewed and the lines show the edge of cutting plane.

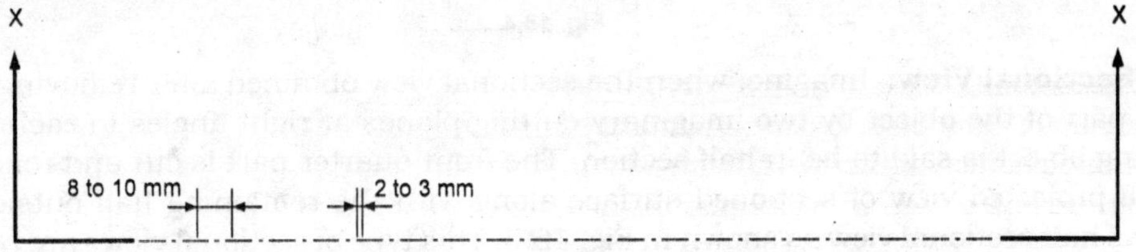

Fig. 16.3

16.3 RULES OF SECTIONING

The following are some of the important rules of sectioning:

1. Nuts, bolts, screws, keys, cotter, rods, ribs, spokes and handles are not sectioned.
2. Section lines are drawn, at an angle of 45° to the major outline of the object.
3. All the lines must be uniformly spaced and the distance between two section lines normally varies from 2 mm to 3 mm.
4. The parts which are actually cut by cutting plane are hatched.
5. Hatching of different components is done on opposite direction.
6. Hidden lines are not used in sectioned area unless they are needed for clarity.
7. The arrows at each end of the cutting plane lines indicate the direction of viewing.
8. The position of the cutting plane are shown on final drawing.
9. Section lines should be drawn by H or 2H pencil.

16.4 TYPES OF SECTIONAL VIEWS

There are different types of sectional views which are commonly used in engineering drawing. The following are the important types of sectional views:

1. Full Sectional View: Imagine when the sectional view obtained after removing the front half part of the object through its centre line by an imaginary cutting plane, the remaining object is said to be in full section. The projected view of the full sectioned surface along with the remaining half part to show clearly interior shape of the object is known as full sectional view as shown in Fig. 16.4. This type of section is used for both detail and assembly drawings. In the full sections, the observer views the object in the direction of arrow and the resulting full sectional front view is obtained. It is not necessary to draw all the views of an object in sectional views.

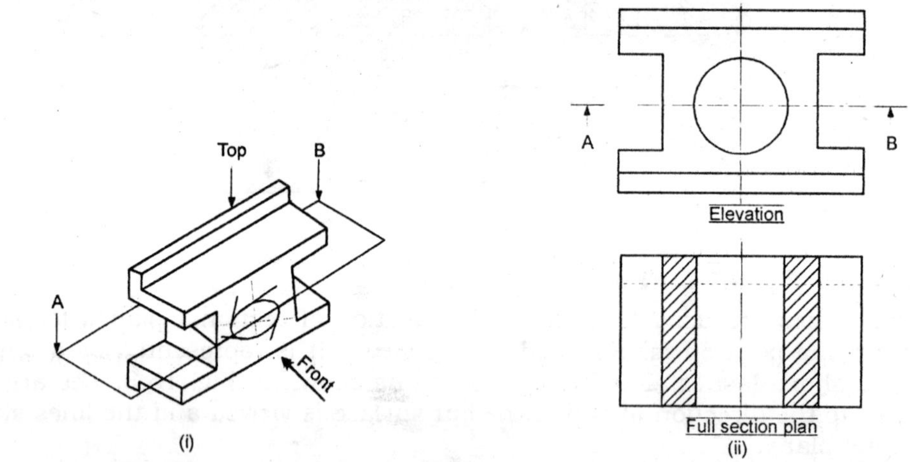

Fig. 16.4

2. Half Sectional View: Imagine, when the sectional view obtained after removing the front quarter part of the object by two imaginary cutting planes at right angles to each other the remaining object is said to be in half section. The front quarter part is cut and removed and then the projected view of sectioned surface along with the remaining half outside part is known as half sectional view as shown in Fig. 16.5. This type of sectional views are best suited for assembly drawings where both internal and external construction are to be shown in one view and where only overall and centre to centre dimensions are depicted.

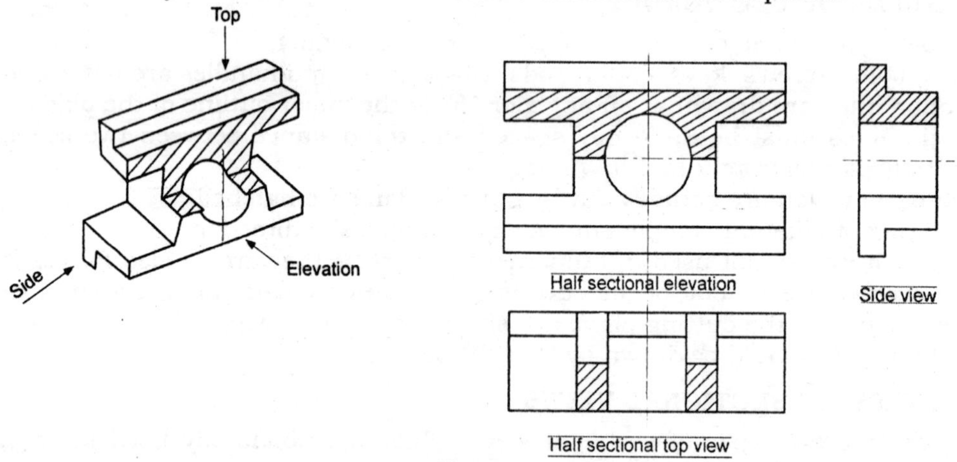

Fig. 16.5

3. Partial or Broken out Section. A partial section is used where a particular hidden detail of the object is required to show, only the partial section of that object. Such a partial section is drawn by free hand short break line as shown in Fig. 16.6.

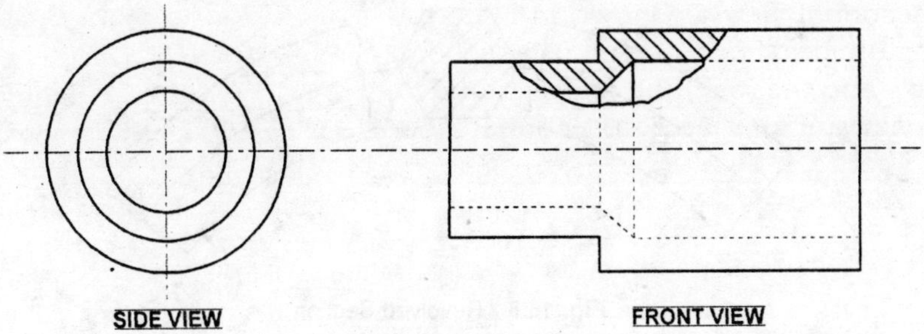

BROKEN-OUT SECTION

Fig. 16.6

4. Offset Section: An offset section is used when the irregular object is cut by an offset plane (two or more planes) to show the maximum details, as shown in Fig. 16.7.

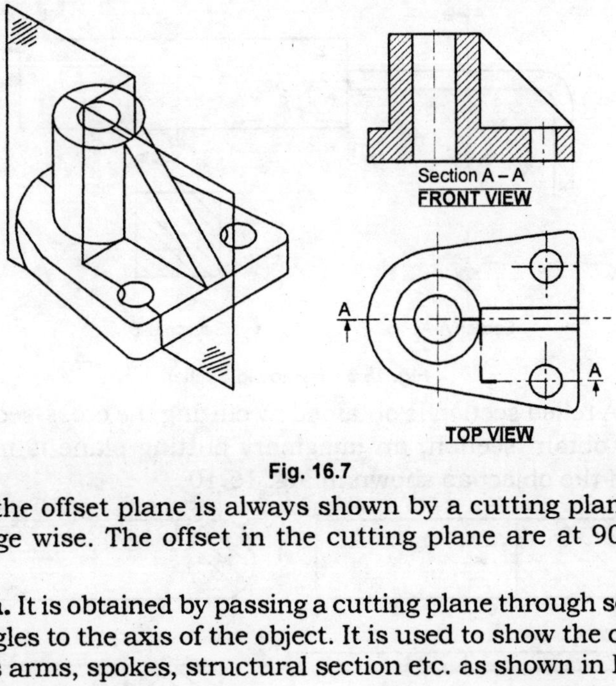

Fig. 16.7

The position of the offset plane is always shown by a cutting plane line in the view in which it is seen edge wise. The offset in the cutting plane are at 90° and also note the direction of arrows.

5. Revolved section. It is obtained by passing a cutting plane through some part of structure machine at right angles to the axis of the object. It is used to show the cross-sectional shape of the object such as arms, spokes, structural section etc. as shown in Fig. 16.8.

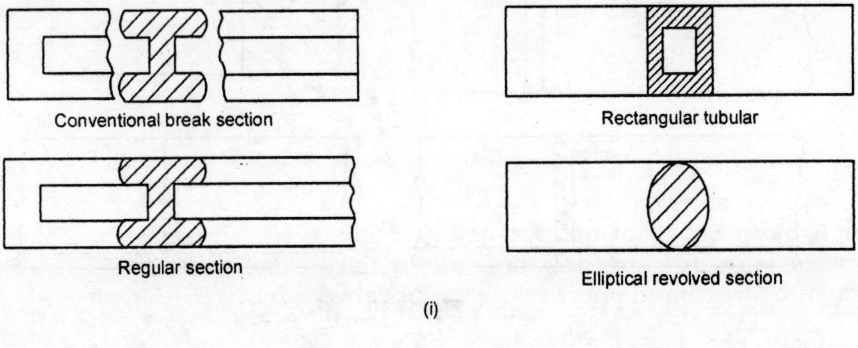

(i)

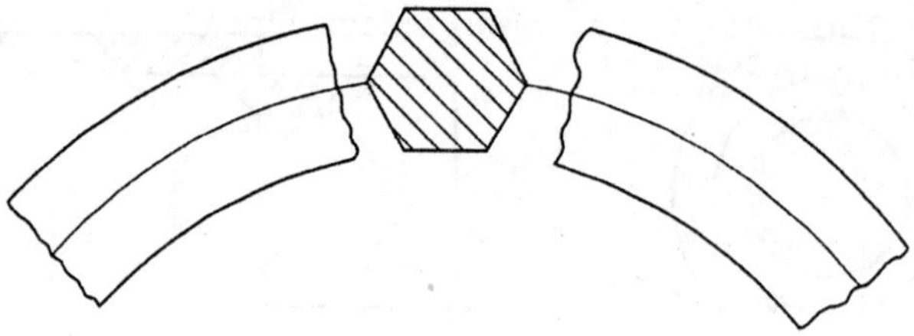
(ii)

Fig. 16.8 Revolved Section

6. Removed section. Removed section is obtained by passing a cutting plane through some part of structure machine at right angles to the axis of the object. The removed section is drawn separately outside the view, generally around the extension of the cutting plane as shown in Fig. 16.9. It is obtained in the same manner as the revolved section. Frequently the removed section is drawn to an enlarged scale, for clarification and easier dimensioning.

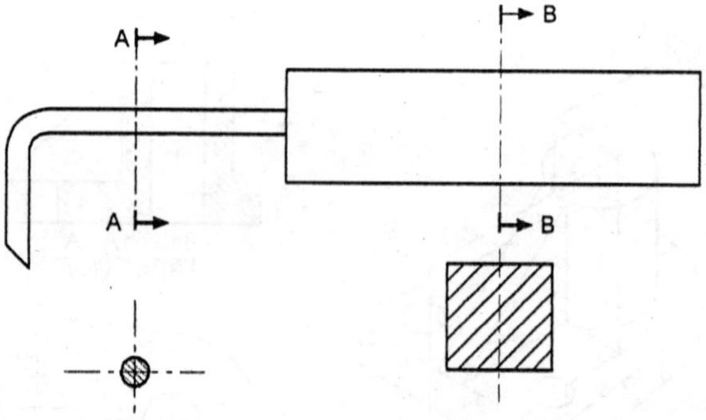

Fig. 16.9 Removed Section

7. Rolled Section. A rolled section is obtained by cutting the cross-section of a bar, channel and angles etc. To obtain section, an imaginary cutting plane is made to pass at right angles to the axis of the object as shown in Fig. 16.10.

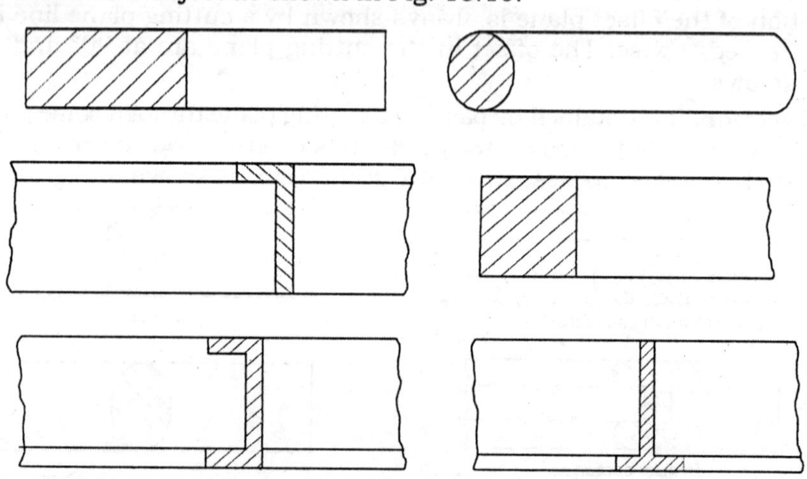

Fig. 16.10

Problem 1. Fig 16.11 shows cut view of an object. Draw
(*i*) Sectional front view
(*ii*) Half sectional side view
(*iii*) Top view. (Use Ist angle projection)

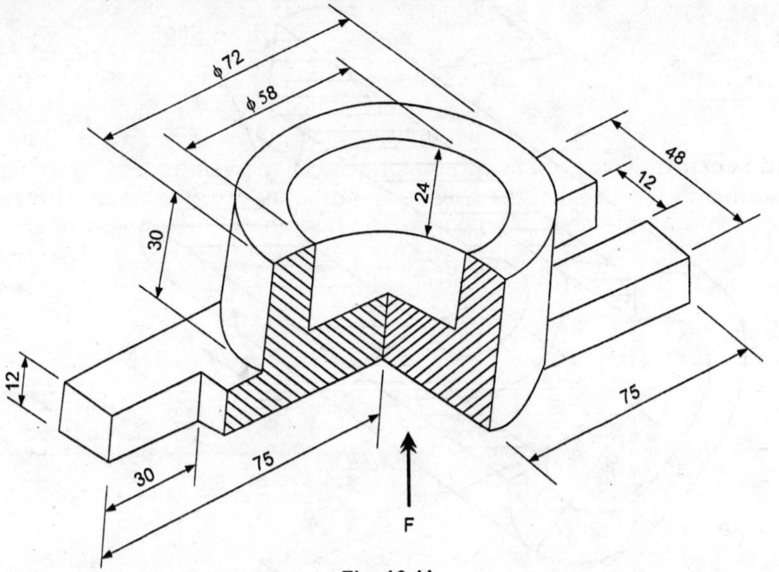

Fig. 16.11

Solution. See Fig. 16.12.

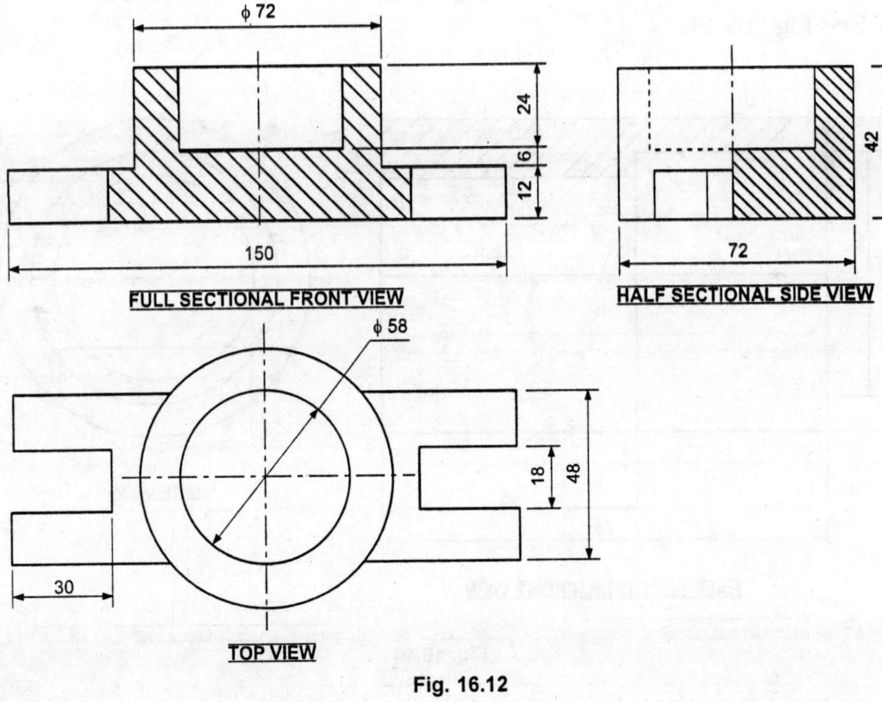

Fig. 16.12

Problem 2. Fig. 16.13 shows cut view of an object. Draw

(*a*) Falf sectional front view.

(*b*) Side view.

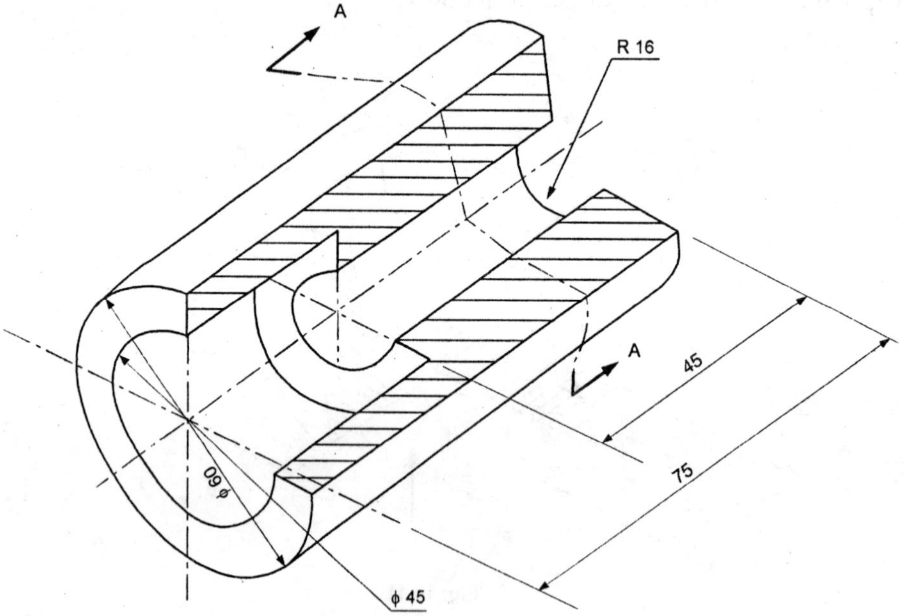

Fig. 16.13

Solution. See Fig. 16.14.

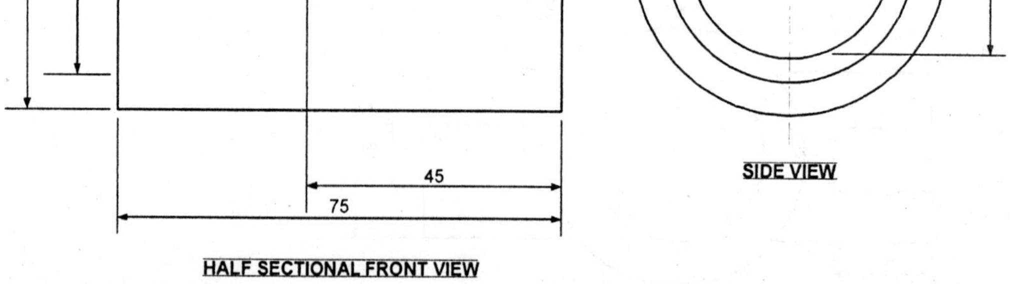

Fig. 16.14

Problem 3. Fig. 16.15 shows an object. Draw
(*i*) Full sectional elevation
(*ii*) Full sectional side view
(*iii*) Plan.

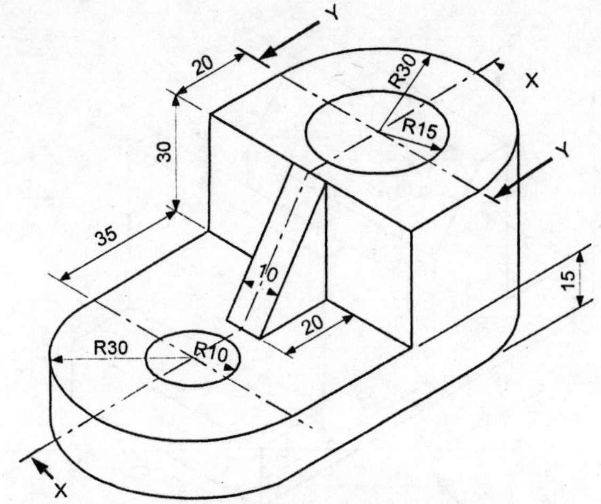

Fig. 16.15

Solution. See Fig. 16.16.

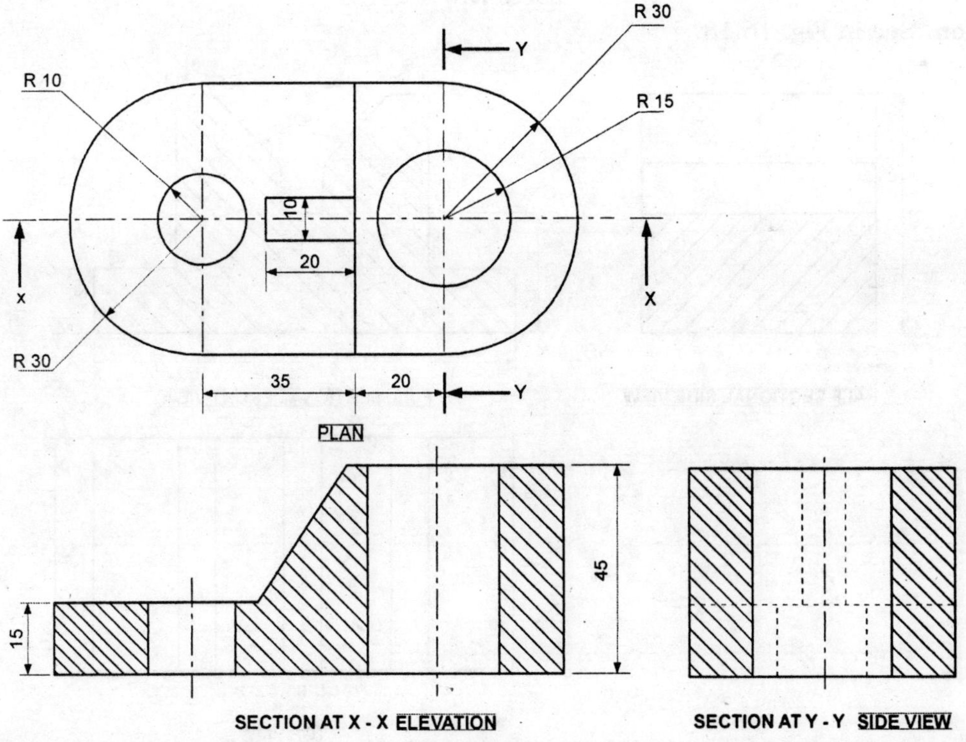

Fig. 16.16

Problem 4. Fig. 16.17 shows an object. Draw

(*i*) Sectional front view

(*ii*) Half-sectional side view

(*iii*) Top view. (Use Ist angle projection)

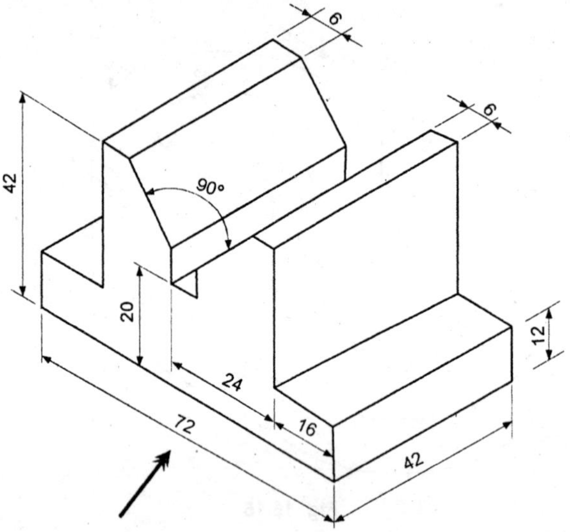

Fig. 16.17

Solution. See in Fig. 16.18.

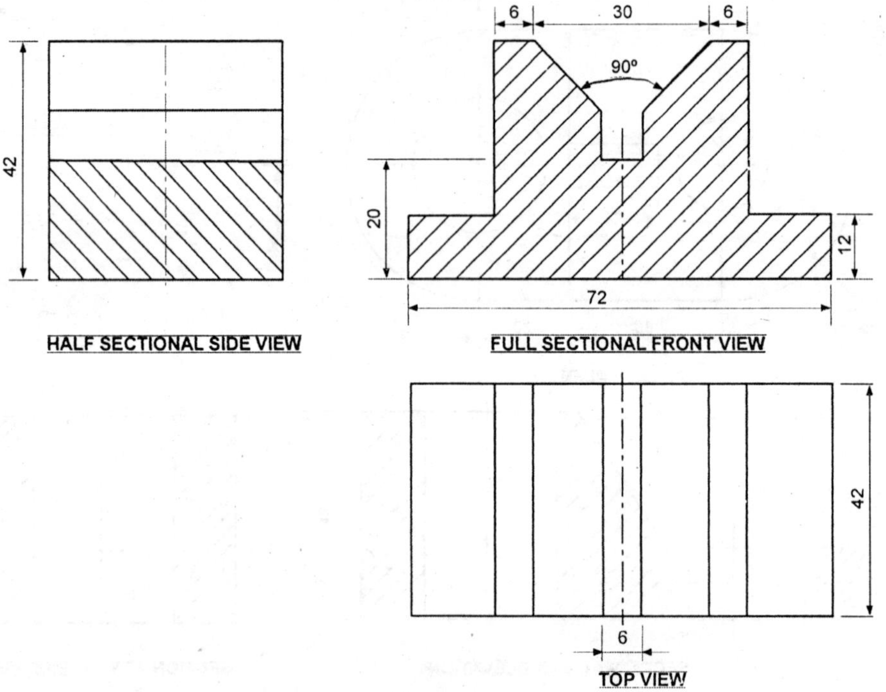

Fig. 16.18

Problem 5. Draw the full sectional front view, top view and side view of the object as shown in Fig. 16.19.

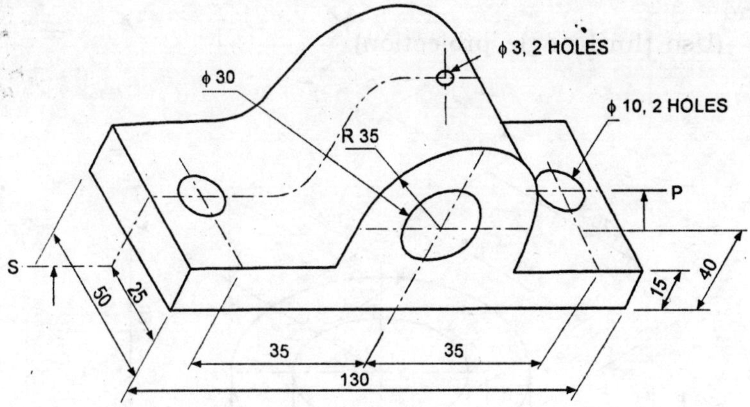

Fig. 16.19

Solution. See Fig. 16.20.

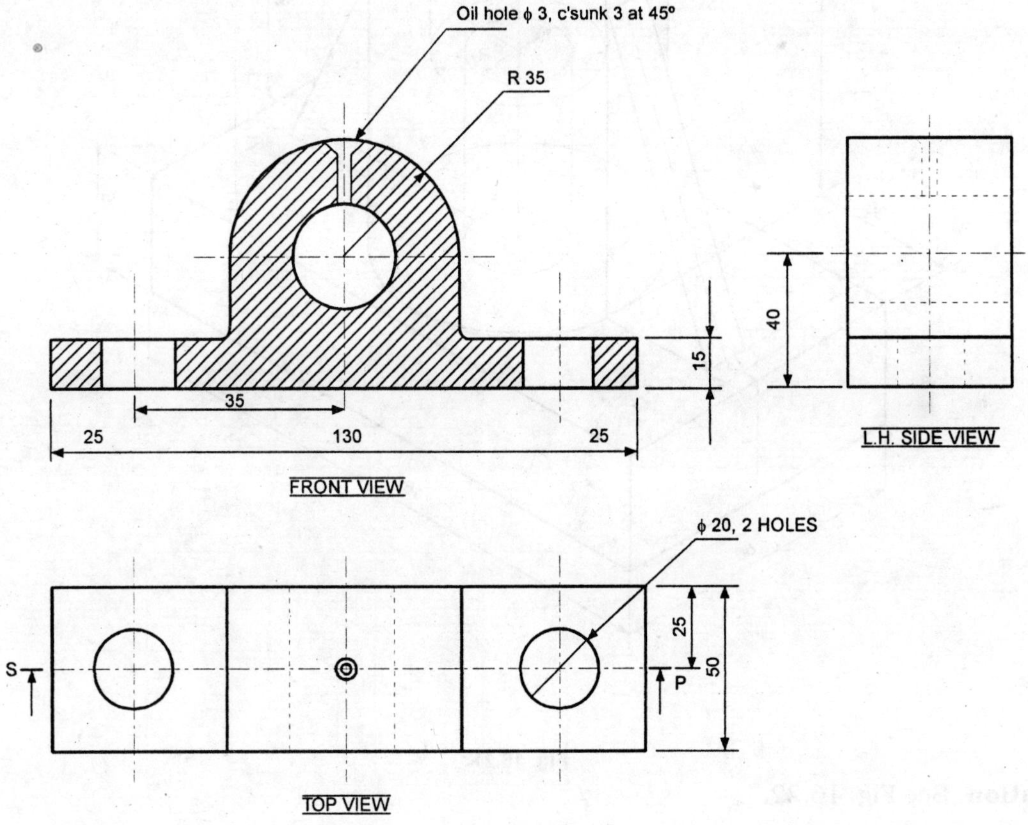

Fig. 16.20

Problem 6. Fig. 16.21 shows an isometric object. Draw

1. Full sectional front view
2. Top view and
3. Side view. (Use third angle projection)

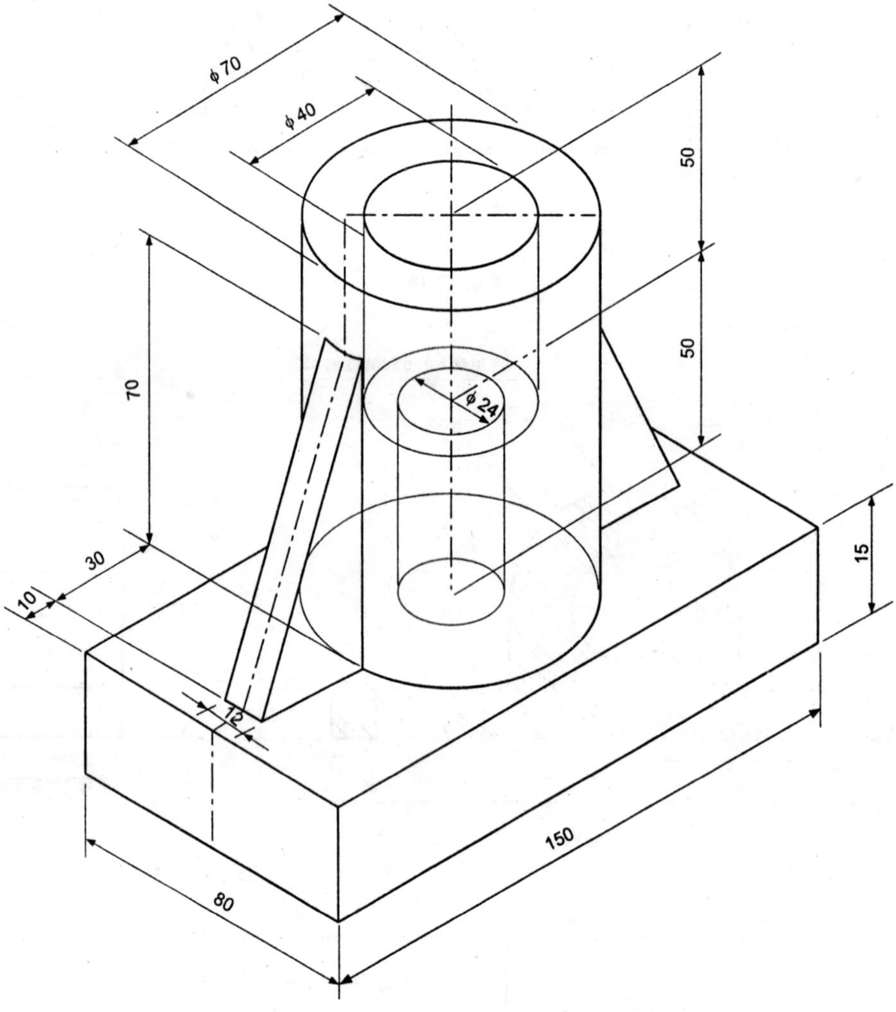

Fig. 16.21

Solution. See Fig. 16.22.

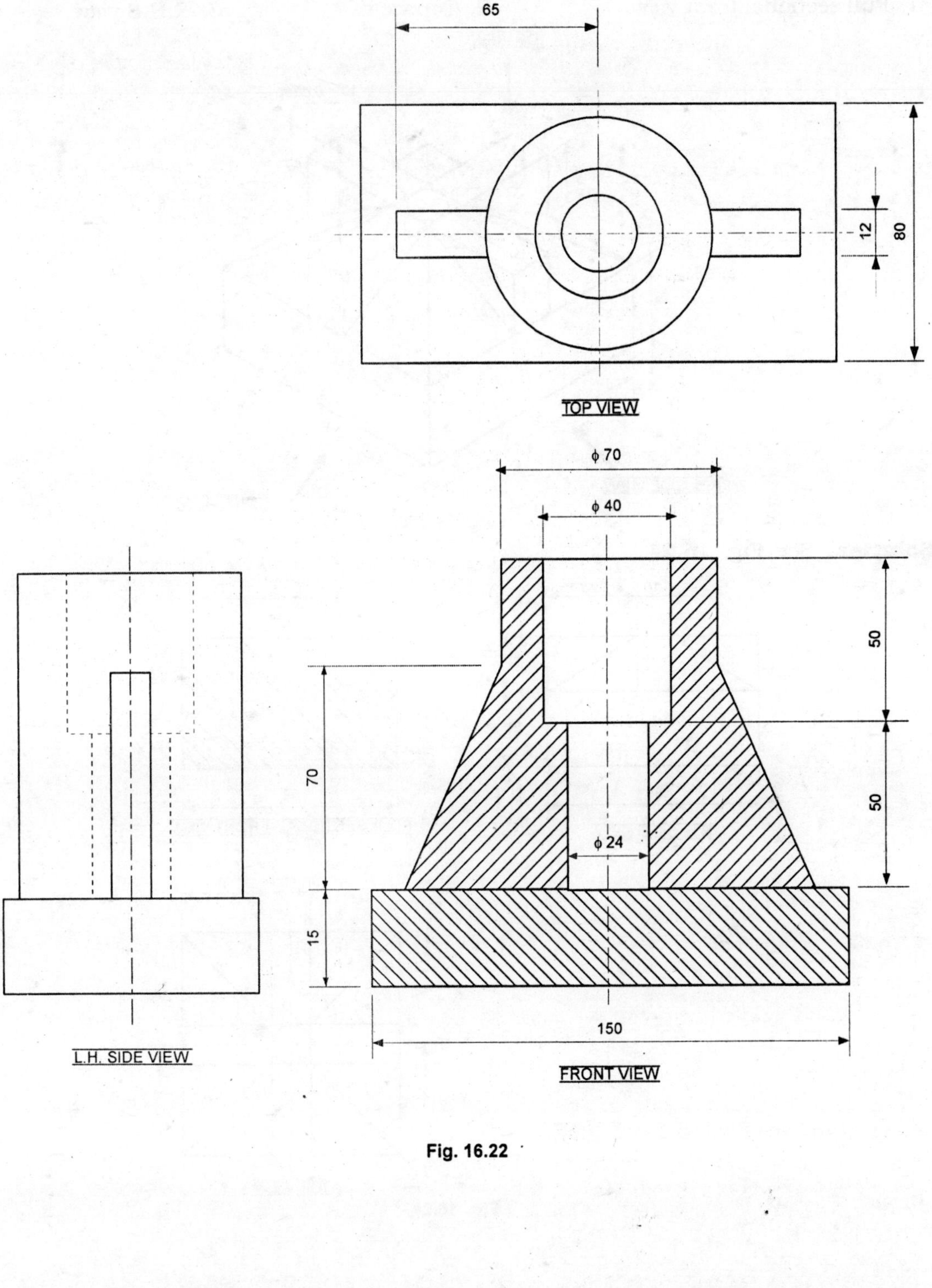
65
12
80
TOP VIEW
ϕ 70
ϕ 40
50
50
70
ϕ 24
15
150
L.H. SIDE VIEW
FRONT VIEW

Fig. 16.22

Problem 7. Fig. 16.23 shows the pictorial view of an object Draw to scale full size the following views:

1. Full sectional front view.
2. Top view
3. R.H.S view.

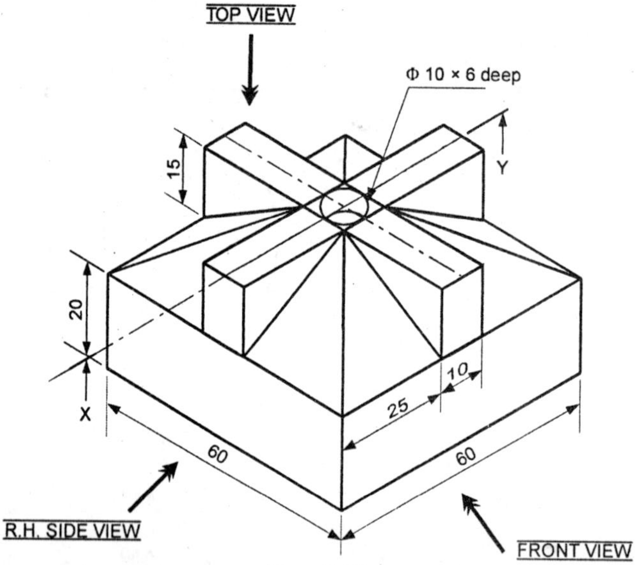

Fig. 16.23

Solution. See Fig. 16.24.

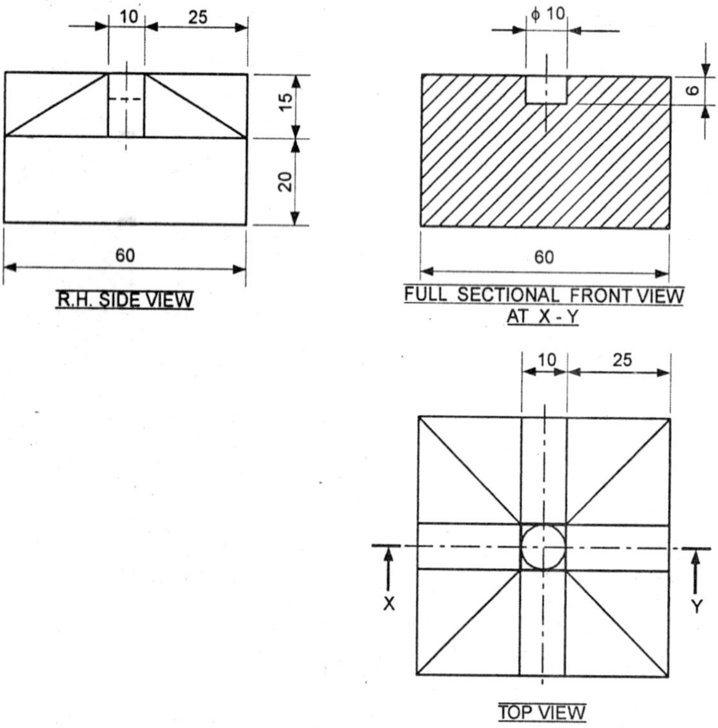

Fig. 16.24

Problem 8. Fig. 16.25 shows an isometric view of an object. Draw

1. Full sectional front view
2. Top view
3. L.H.S view.

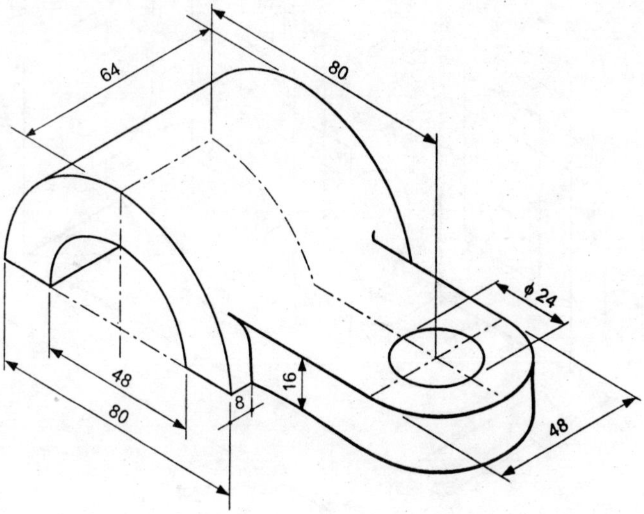

Fig. 16.25

Solution. See Fig. 16.26.

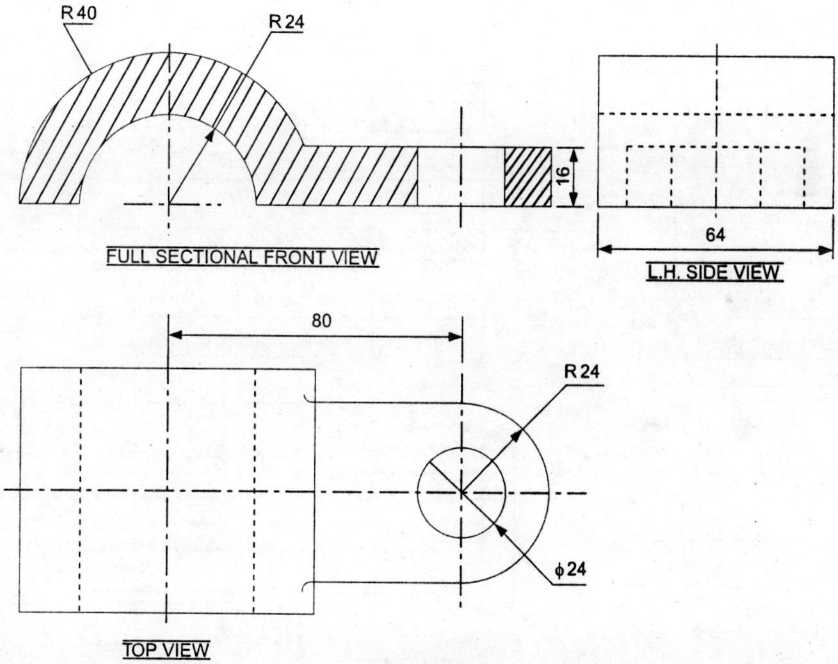

Fig. 16.26

Problem 9. Draw the full sectional front, top view and R.H.S view of an object as shown in Fig. 16.27.

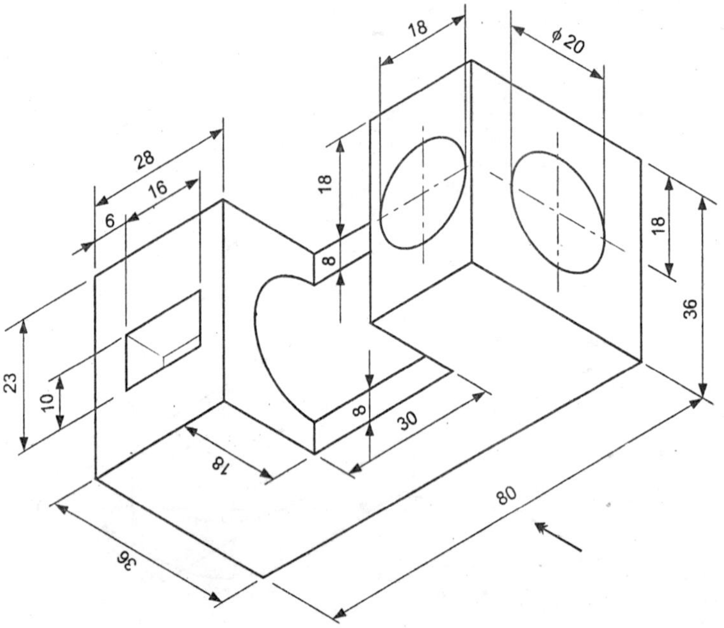

Fig. 16.27

Solution. See Fig. 16.28.

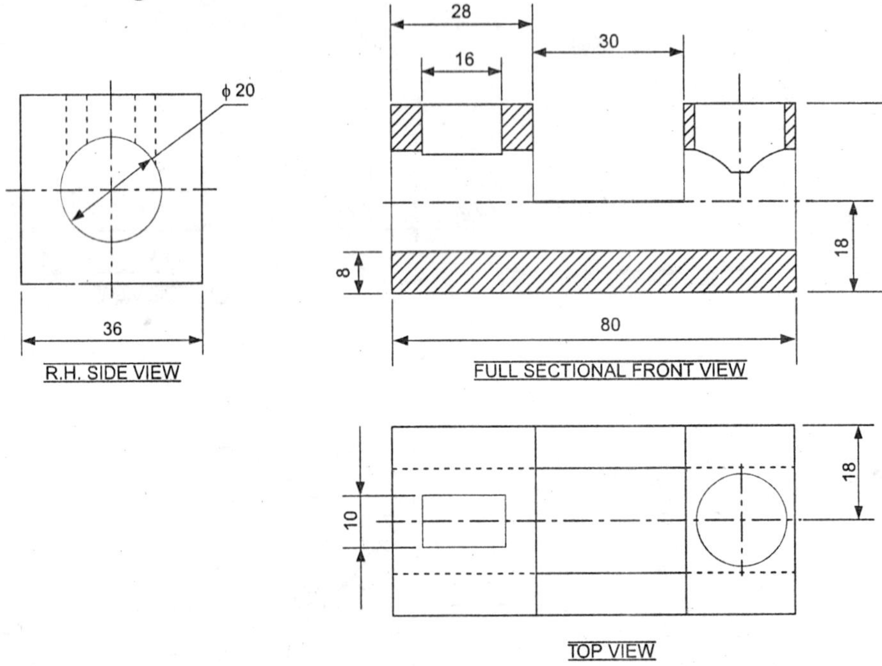

Fig. 16.27

Problem 10. Fig. 16.29 shows an pictorial view of an object. Draw

1. Front view
2. Top view
3. Full sectional L.H. side view.

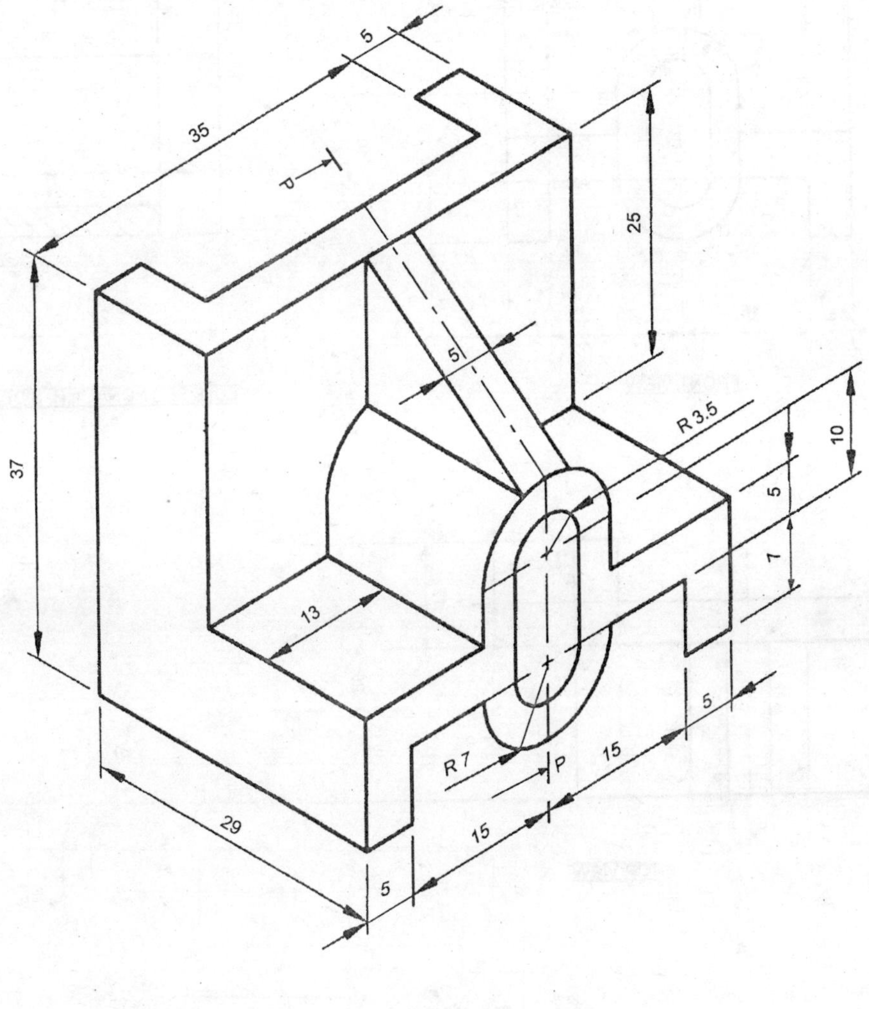

Fig. 16.29

Solution. See Fig. 16.30.

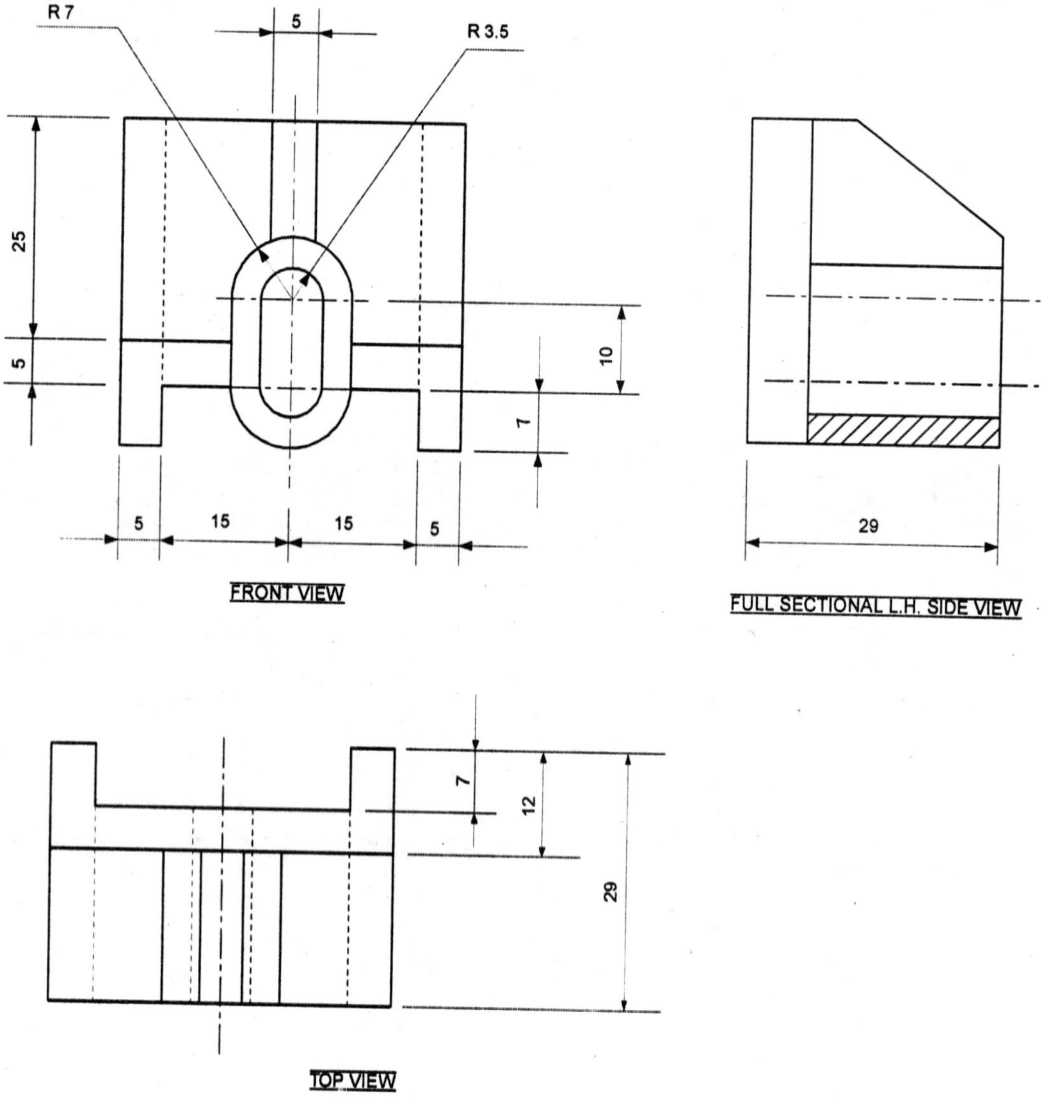

Fig. 16.30

Problem 11. Fig. 16.31 shows the pictorial view of a machine block. Draw the following views to a suitable scale.

(i) Sectional front view at B – B
(ii) Top view
(iii) Left side view. **(B.T.E. New Delhi, December 2005)**

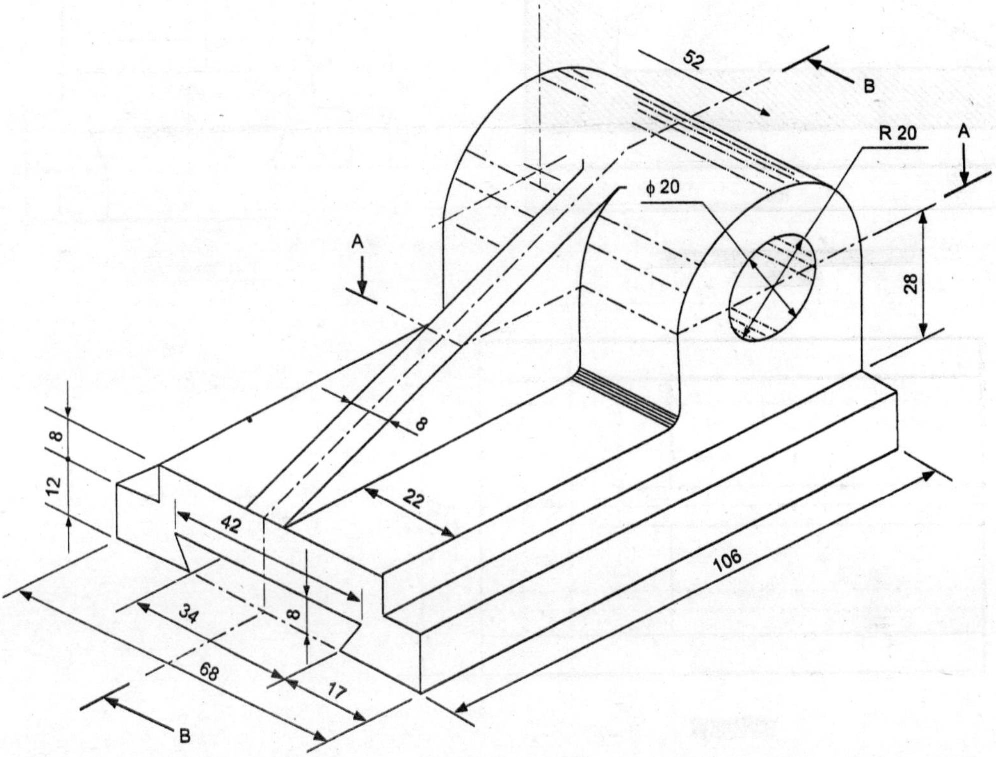

Fig. 16.31

Solution. See Fig. 16.32.

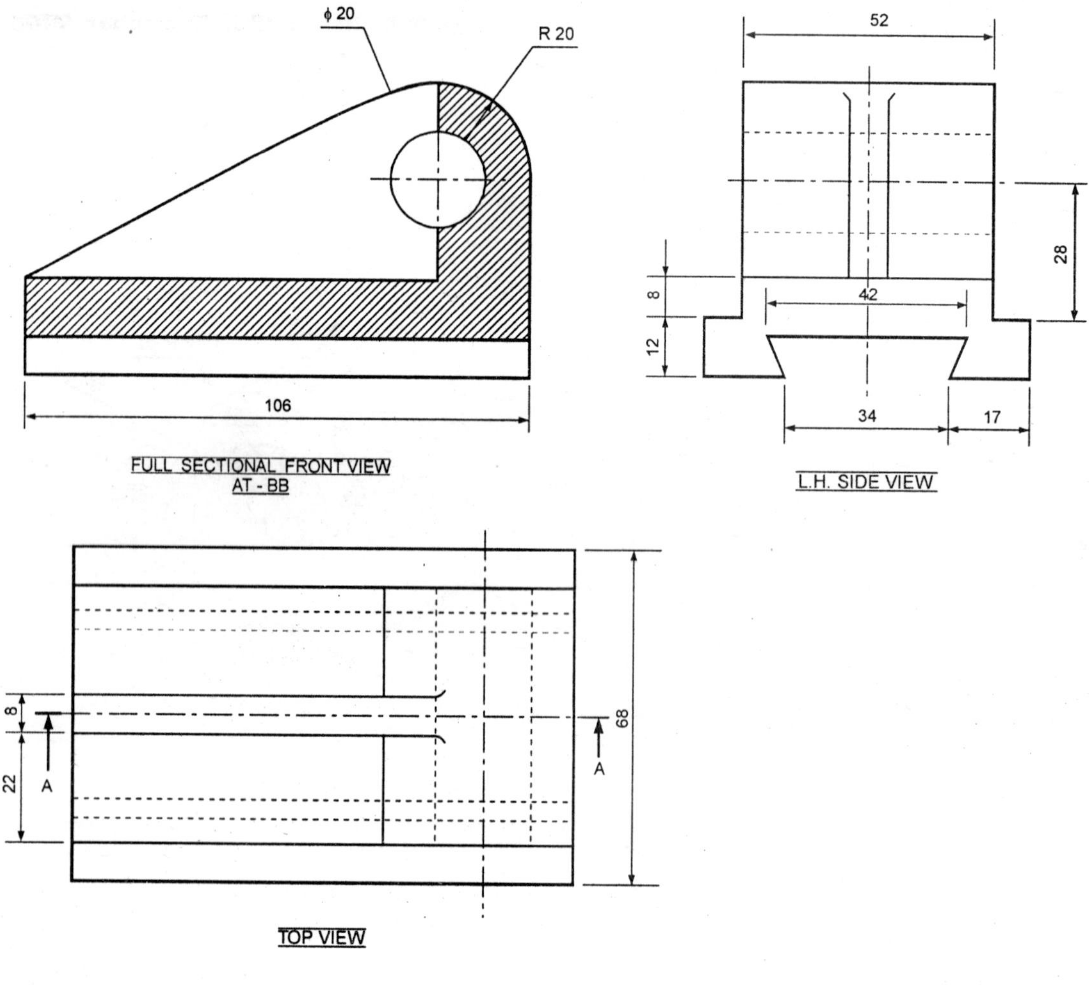

Fig. 16.32

Problem 12. Fig. 16.33 shows the isometric view of a model. Draw to scale full size the following views:

(i) Front view looking in the direction of arrow – X
(ii) Sectional side view at – YY
(iii) Top view. **(B.T.E. New Delhi, December 2003)**

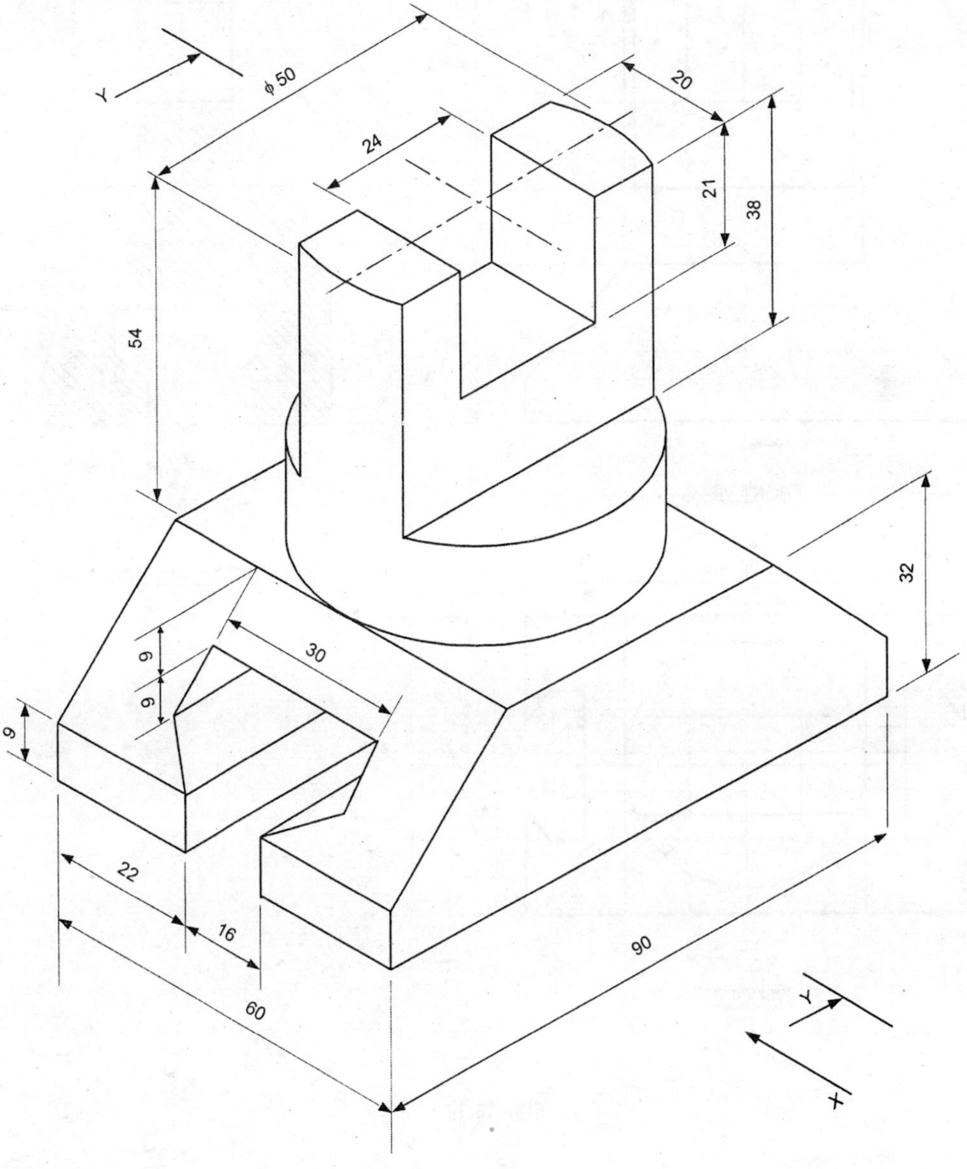

Fig. 16.33

Solution. See Fig. 16.34.

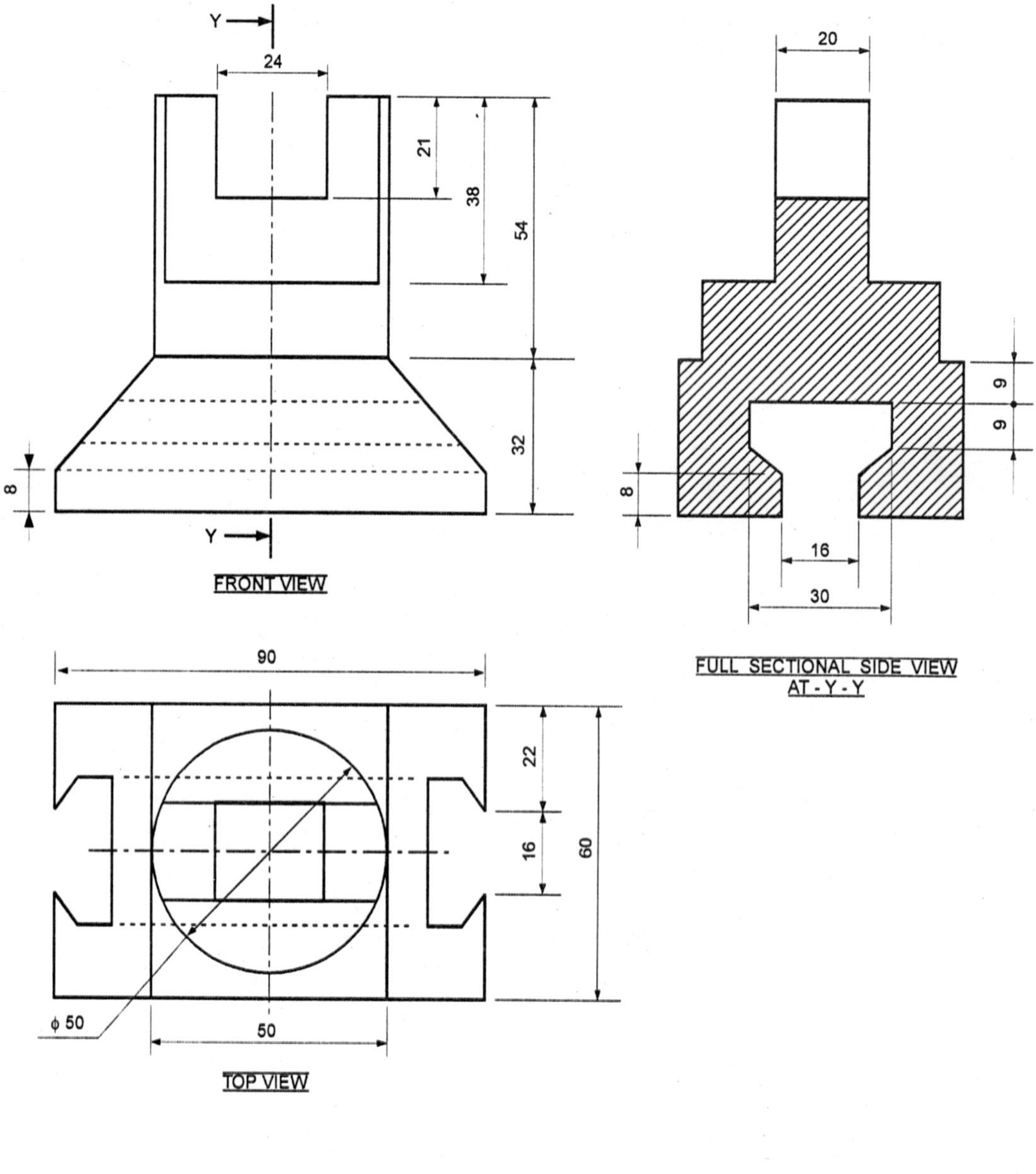

Fig. 16.34

Problem 13. Fig. 16.35 shows pictorial view of an object. Draw the following views in scale full size:

(a) Front view through–A.A

(b) Top view through–B

(c) Left side view through–C.

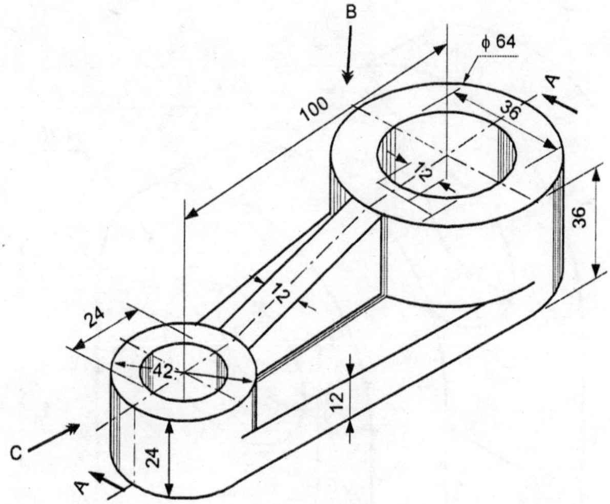

Fig. 16.35

Solution. See Fig. 16.36.

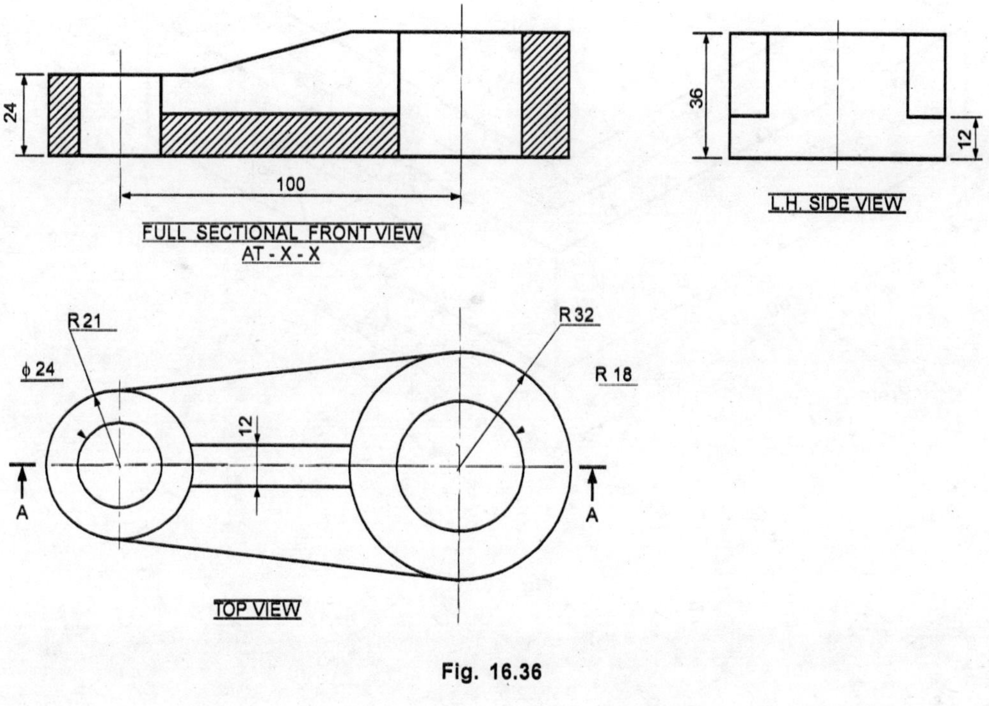

Fig. 16.36

Problem 14. Fig. 16.37 shows an isometric block of an object. Draw

1. Front view
2. Top view
3. Side view.

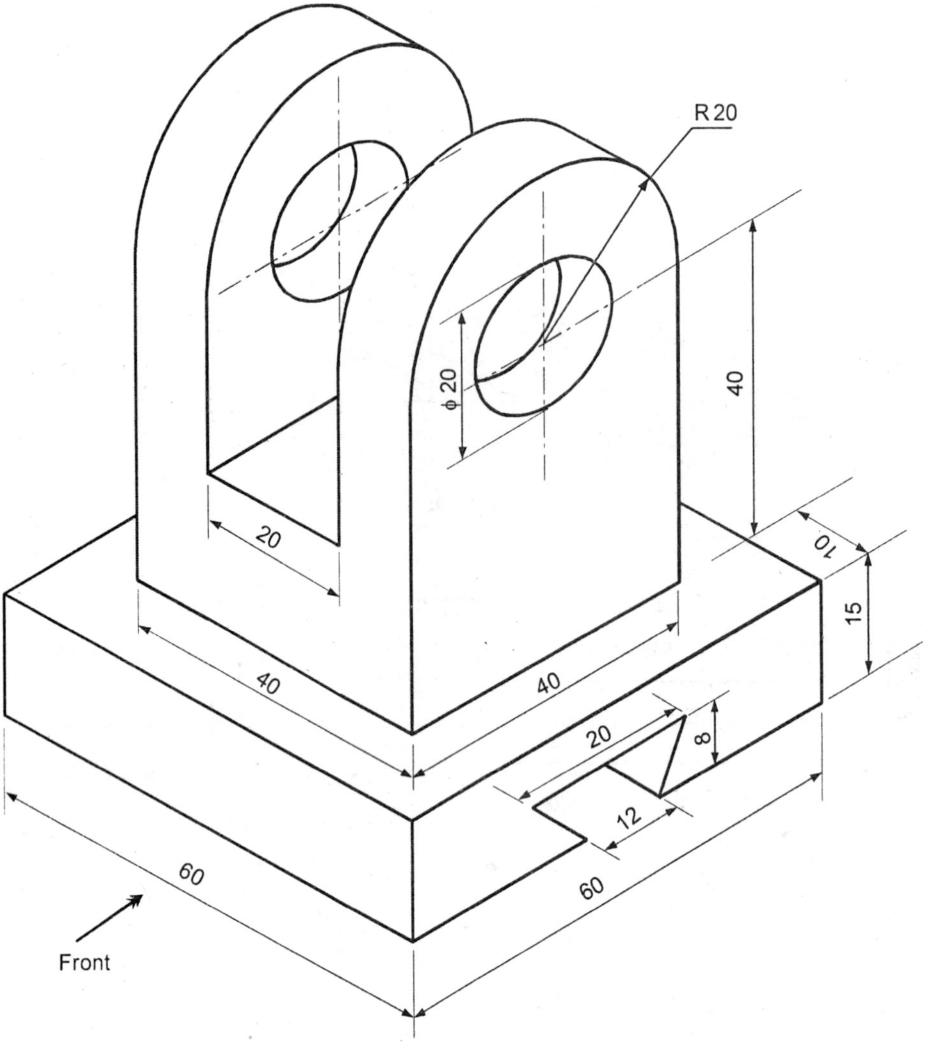

Fig. 16.37

Solution. See Fig. 16.38.

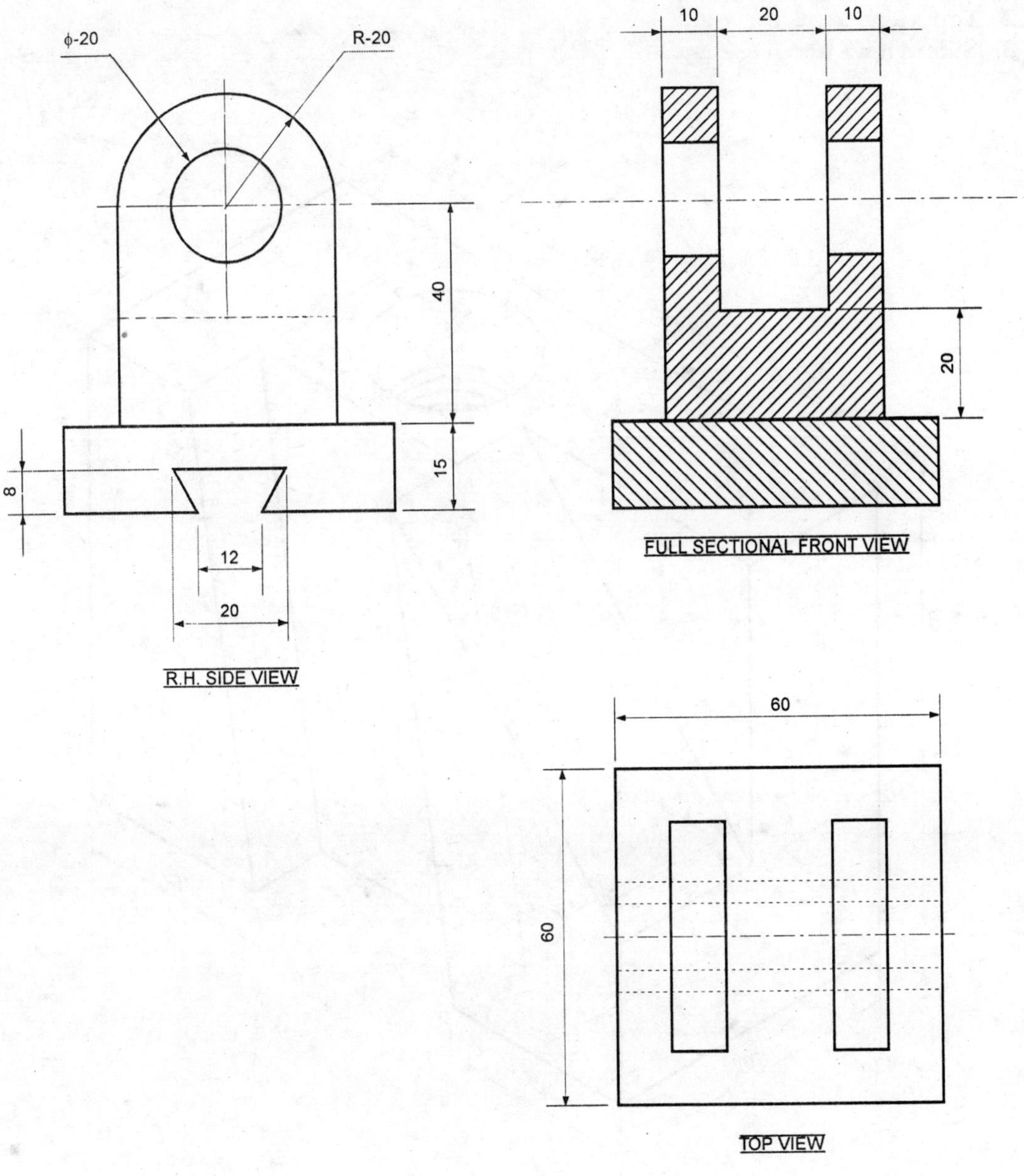

Fig. 16.38

Problem 15. Fig. 16.39 shows an isometric view of an object. Draw the following views:

1. Front view (full section)
2. Top view
3. Side view.

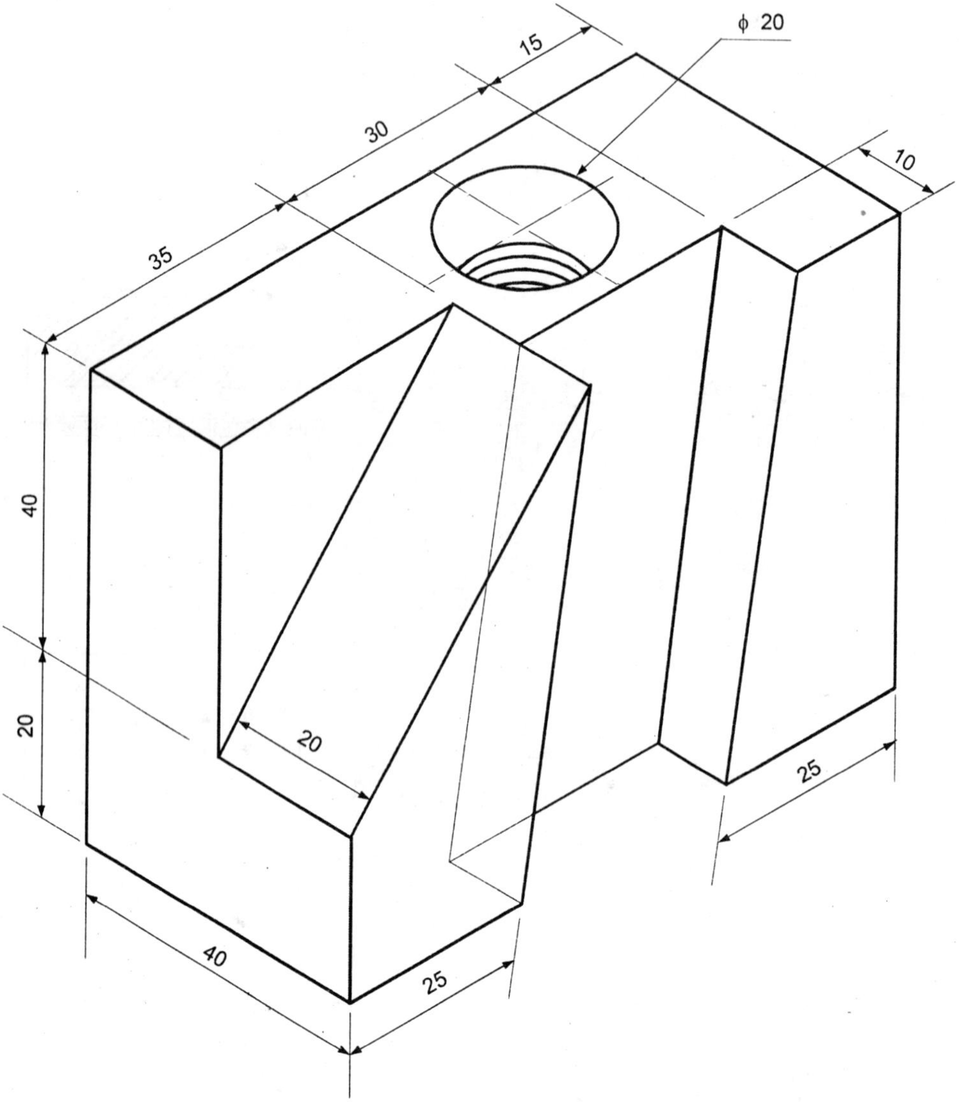

Fig. 16.39

Solution. See Fig. 16.40.

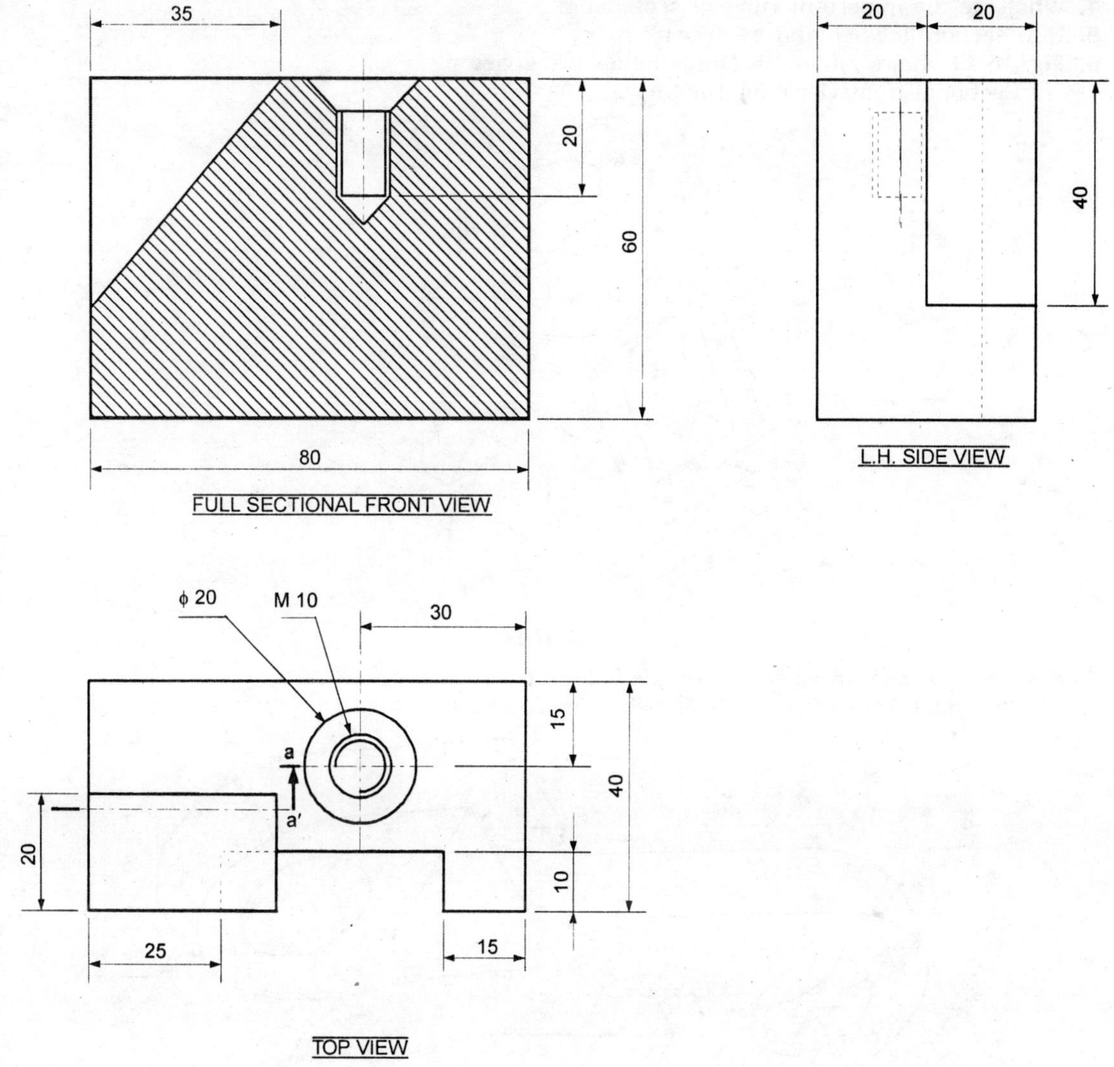

Fig. 16.40

EXERCISE

1. What is the necessity of sectional views?
2. What is a cutting plane?
3. What are the different types of section?
4. What are the important rules of sectioning?
5. How section lines should be drawn?
6. Fig. 16.41 shows an object. Draw the following views:
   (*i*) Sectional front view (*ii*) Top view.

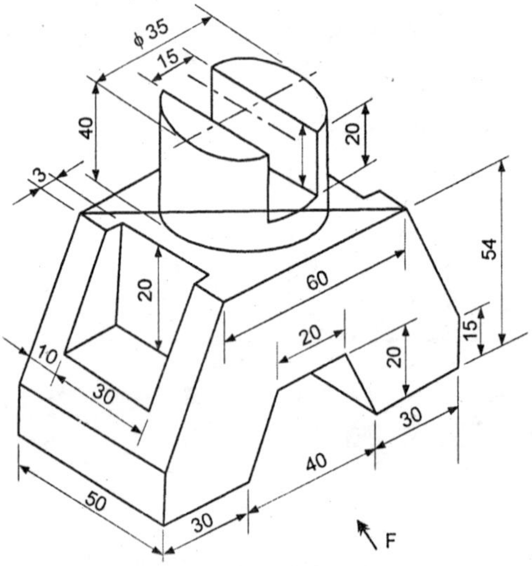

Fig. 16.41

7. Fig. 16.42 shows an object. Draw the following views:
   (*i*) Sectional front view (*ii*) Side view (*iii*) Top view.

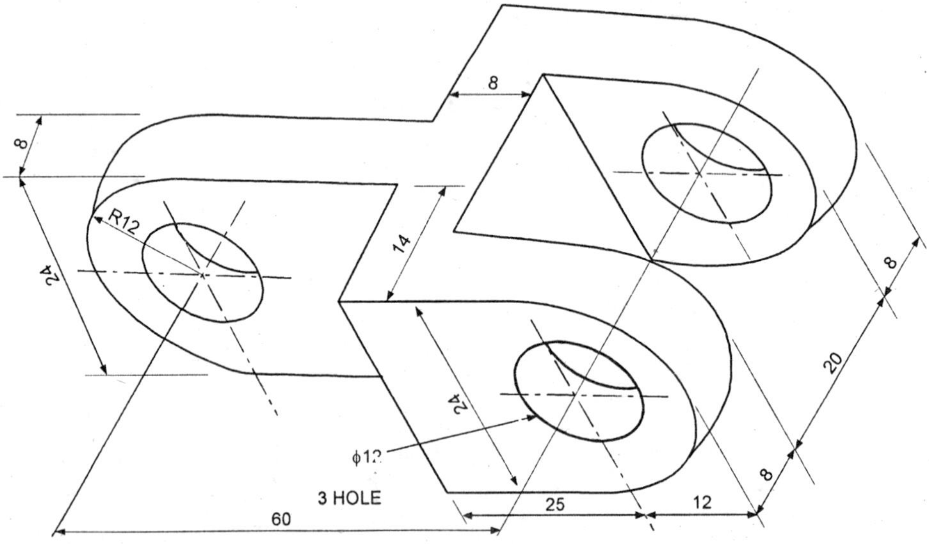

Fig. 16.42

8. Draw the full sectional elevation and Top view of the object shown in Fig. 16.43.

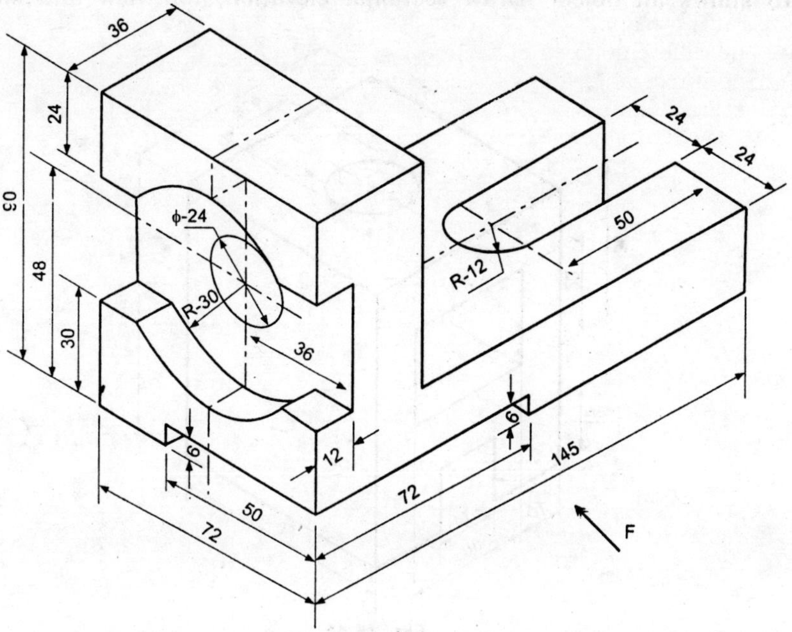

Fig. 16.43

9. Draw the full sectional elevation, plane and side view of the object shown in Fig. 16.44.

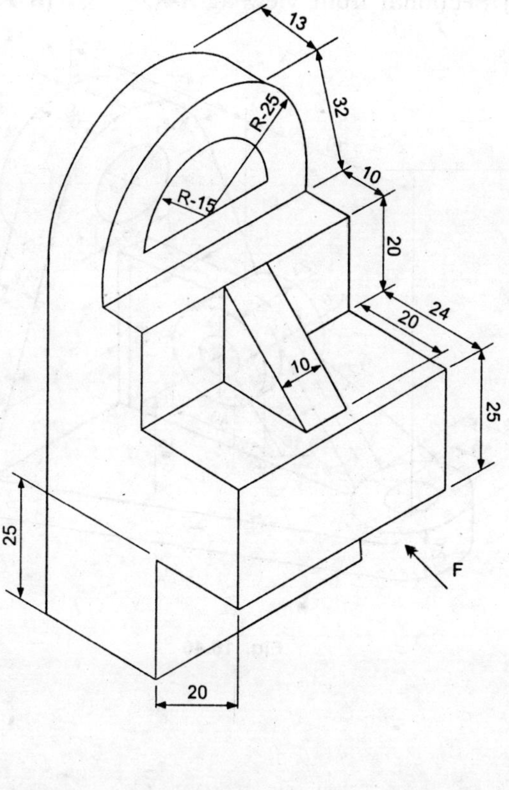

Fig. 16.44

10. Fig. 16.45 shows an object. Draw sectional elevation, top view and side view in full scale.

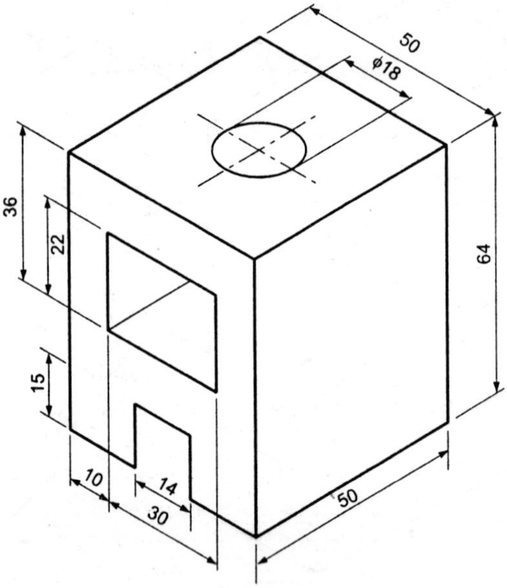

Fig. 16.45

11. For the pictorial view shown in Fig. 16.46, draw to full scale, the following views:
(*a*) Top view (*b*) Sectional front view at *A-A*. **(B.T.E. New Delhi, Jan. 2009)**

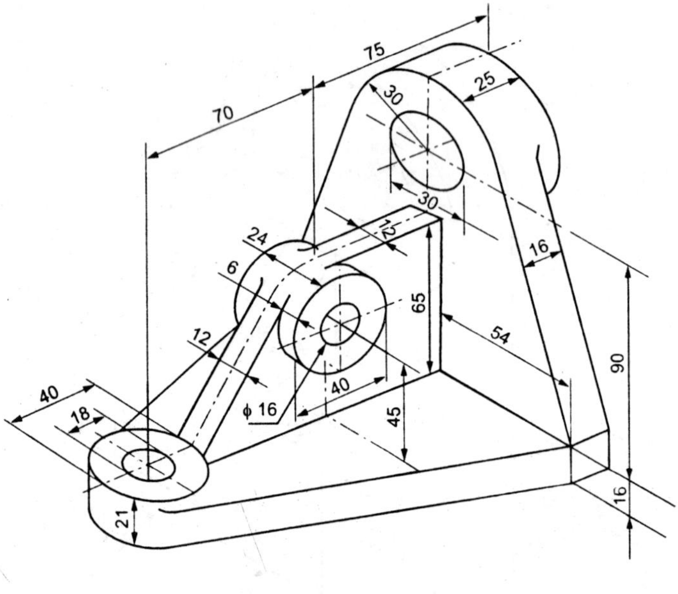

Fig. 16.46

17

MISSING LINES, MISSING VIEWS AND IDENTIFICATION OF SURFACES

17.1 MISSING LINES

Sometimes the three views of an object are given. In one or more ways some projection lines may be found missing, in that case, these missing lines are drawn by comparing the projection of the other views. Therefore, it is define as the lines which are added in the given orthographic view in order to complete the drawing of an object are known as missing lines.

At this stage we can take the help of isometric sketch. Try to get a combined picture of the object in the mind and add missing lines on the drawing. Simple problems are easy visualize and there is no need of drawing isometric view. Following procedure can be adopted in order to identify missing lines of various object:

Step I: Draw the given orthographic views of the object with missing lines.

Step II: Draw the given orthographic views, firstly visualize an object and prepare rough pictorial view.

Step III: Now from this rough pictorial view draw the orthographic view and compare it with the given orthographic view.

Step IV: Read carefully each line in each view and draw the required missing lines on the given orthographic view.

Problem 1. Fig. 17.1 shows an incomplete orthographic projection of an object. Draw the missing lines and complete the orthographic projection.

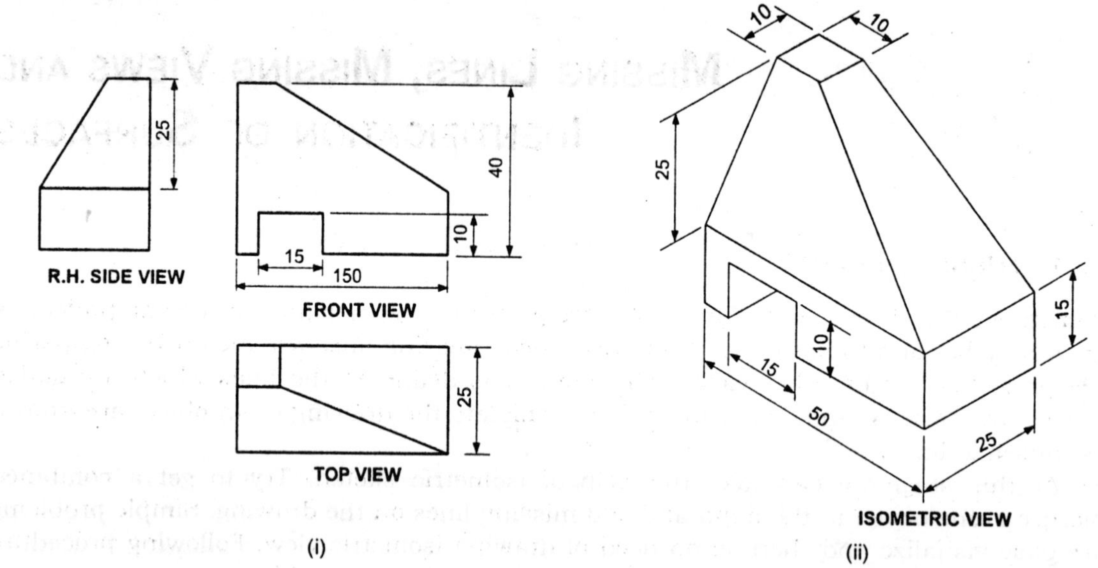

Fig. 17.1

Solution. See Fig. 17.2.

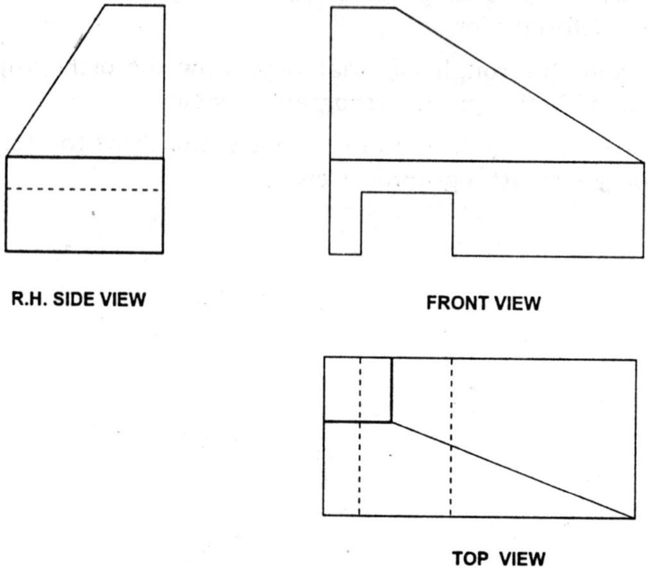

Fig. 17.2

Problem 2. Fig 17.3 shows an incomplete orthographic projections of an object. Draw the missing line and complete the orthographic projection.

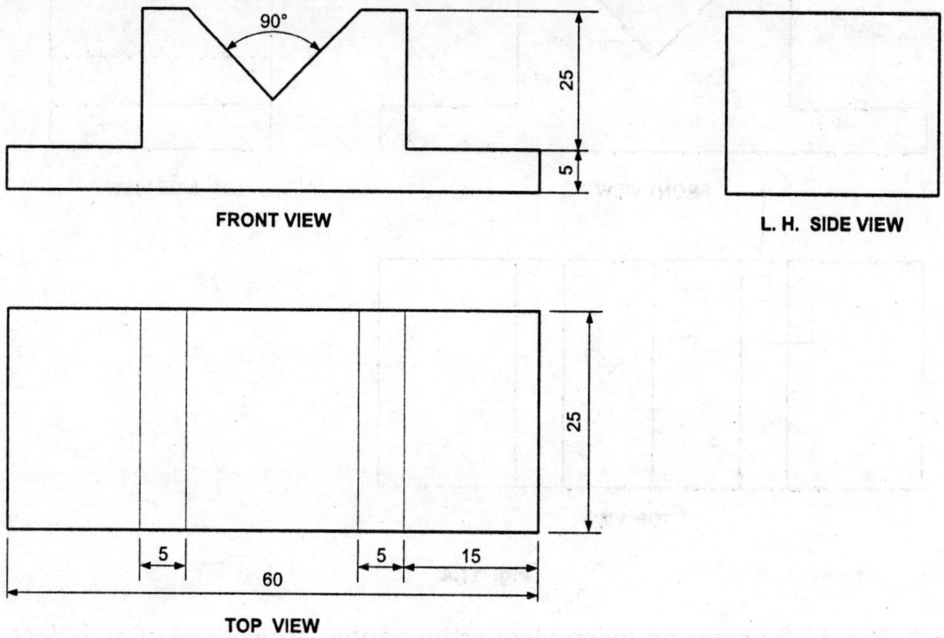

(i)

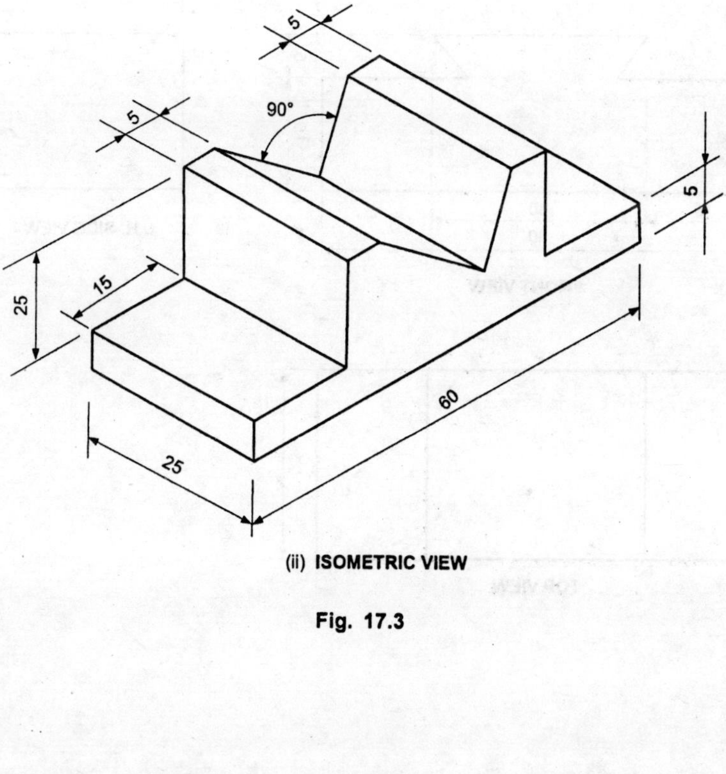

(ii) ISOMETRIC VIEW

Fig. 17.3

Solution. See Fig. 17.4.

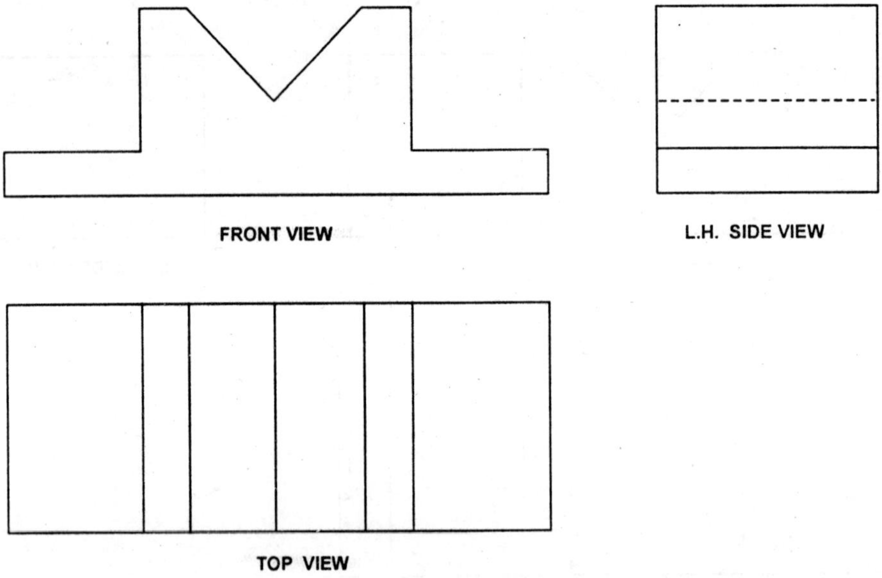

Fig. 17.4

Problem 3. Fig. 17.5 shows an incomplete orthographic projections of an object. Draw the missing lines and complete the orthographic projection.

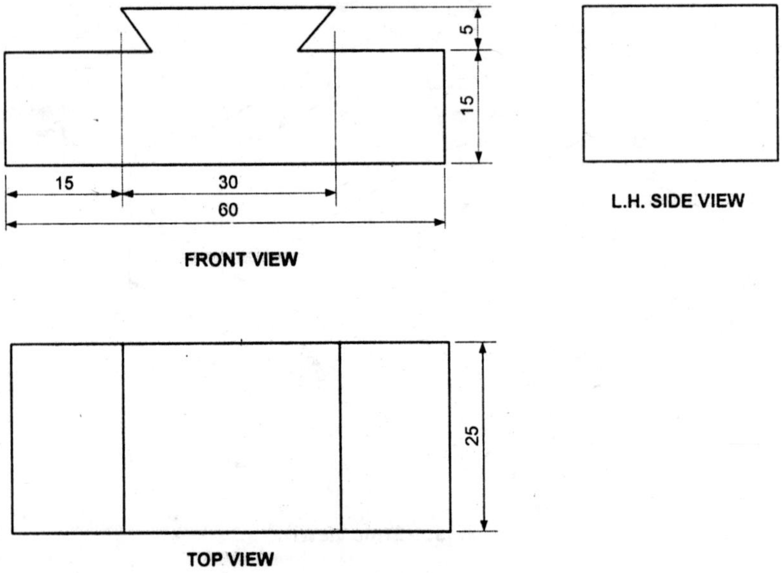

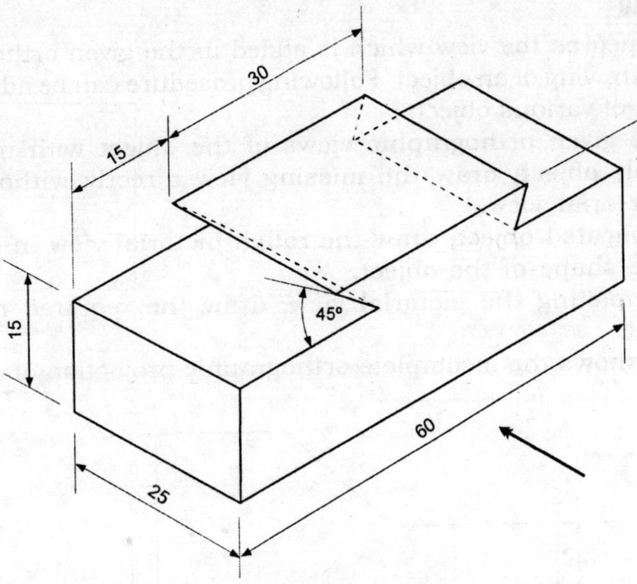

(ii) ISOMETRIC VIEW

Fig. 17.5

Solution. See Fig. 17.6.

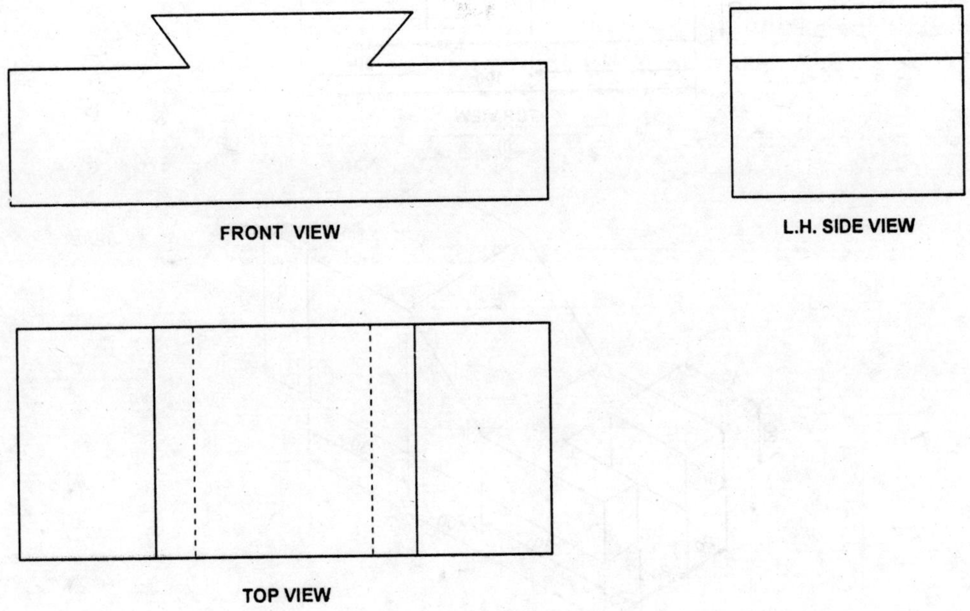

Fig. 17.6

17.2 MISSING VIEW

A missing view is defined as the view which is added in the given orthographic view in order to complete the drawing of an object. Following procedure can be adopted in order to identify missing views of various objects:

Step I. Draw the given orthographic views of the object with missing view.

Step II. For simple object, draw the missing view directly without drawing the rough pictorial view.

Step III. For complicated object, draw the rough pictorial view in order to understand the shape of the object.

Step IV. After completing the pictorial view, draw the required missing view of the object.

Problem 4. Fig. 17.7 shows the incomplete orthographic projection of an object. Draw the missing view.

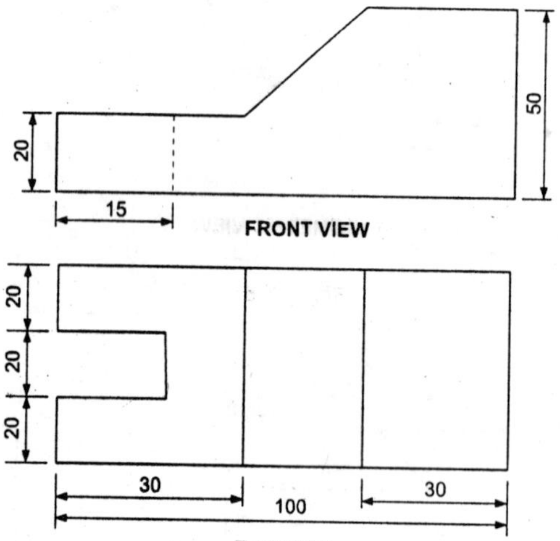

(i)

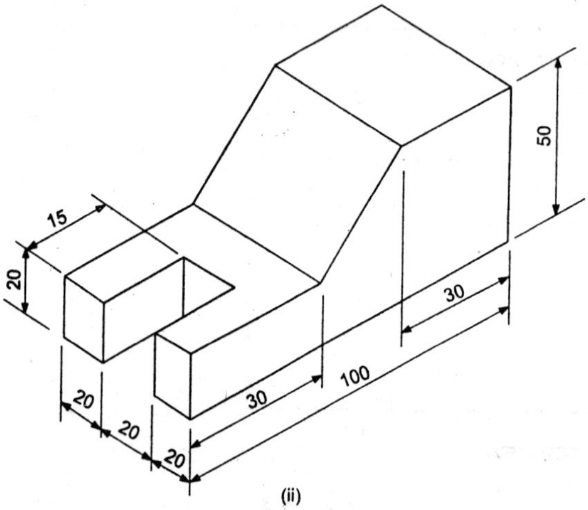

(ii)

Fig. 17.7

Solution. See Fig. 17.8.

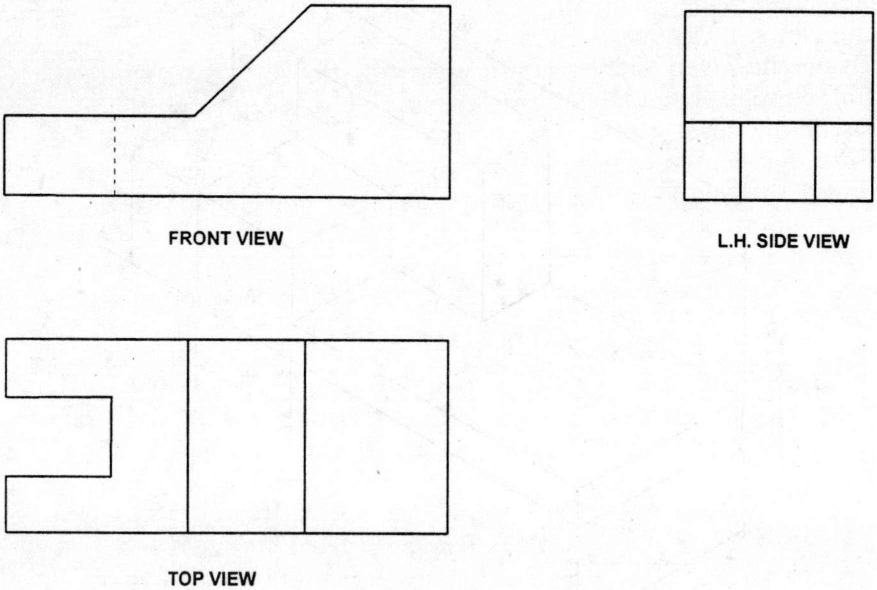

Fig. 17.8

Problem 5. Fig. 17.9 shows the incomplete orthographic projections of an object. Draw the missing view.

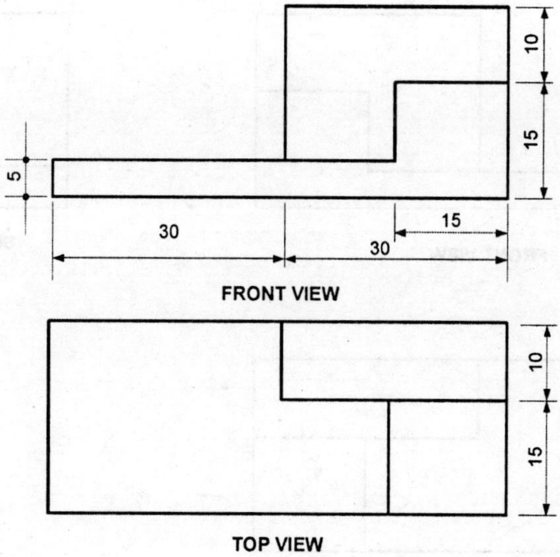

(i)

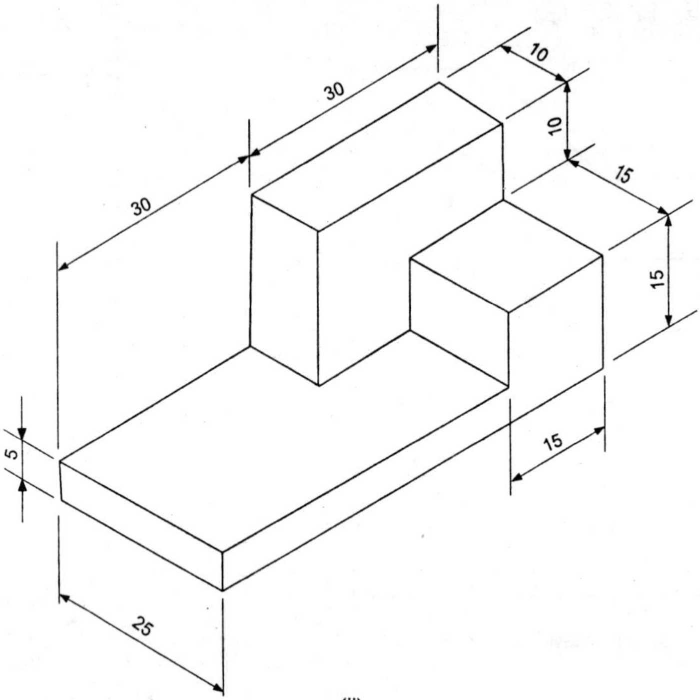

(ii)

Fig. 17.9

Solution. See Fig. 17.10.

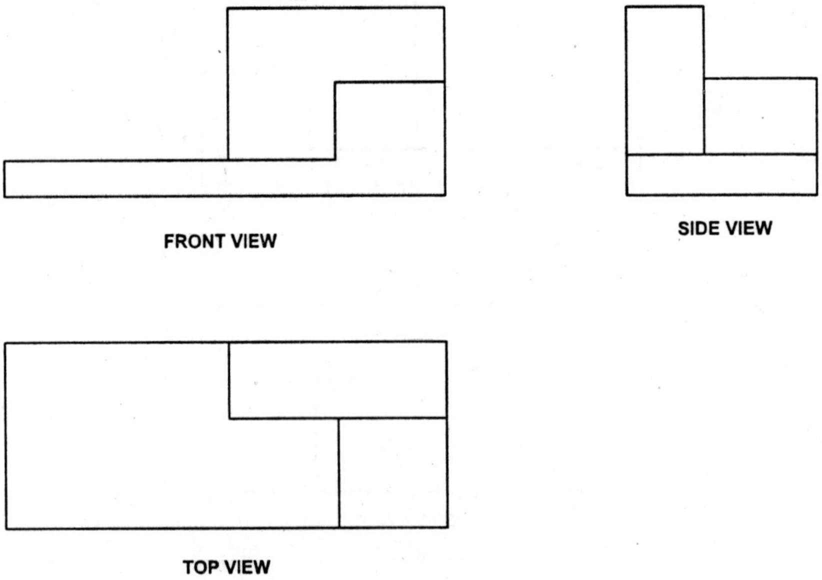

Fig. 17.10

Problem 6. Two orthographic views of a block are shown in Fig. 17.11.

(*i*) Redraw the given views.
(*ii*) Add the missing view.
(*ii*) Draw its isometric view. **(B.T.E. New Delhi, Jan. 2009)**

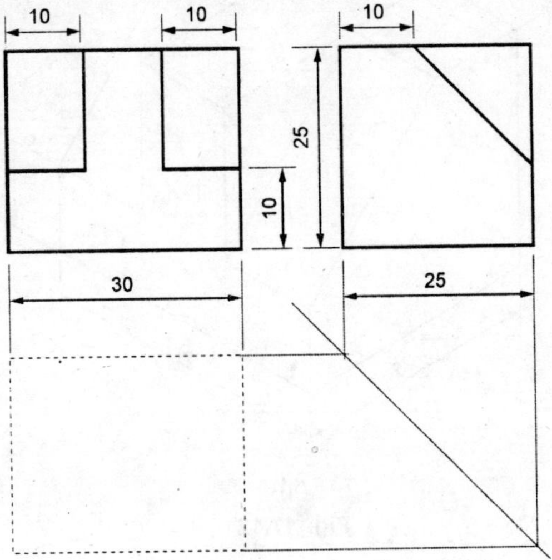

Fig. 17.11

Solution. See Fig. 17.12.

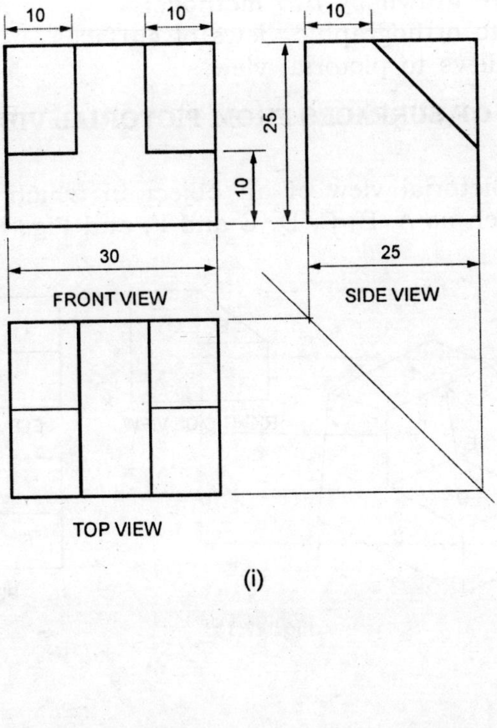

(i)

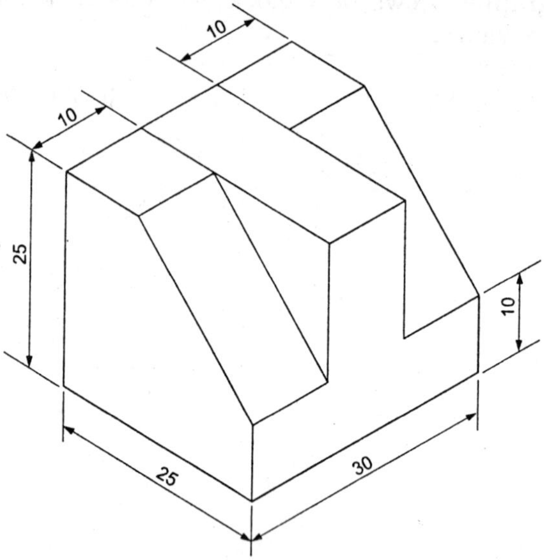

(ii)

Fig. 17.12

17.3 IDENTIFICATION OF SURFACES

The art of developing the surfaces of an object from a pictorial view to orthographic views such as plan, elevation and side view and vice versa is known as the identification of surfaces.

This identification are drawn by two methods:

1. From pictorial view to orthographic views of surfaces.
2. From orthographic views to pictorial view.

17.4 IDENTIFICATION OF SURFACES FROM PICTORIAL VIEW TO ORTHOGRAPHIC VIEWS

Fig. 17.13 shows the pictorial view of an object in which different surfaces are marked by alphabets such as A, B, C, D, E and F, and Fig. 17.14 Shows the orthographic projection.

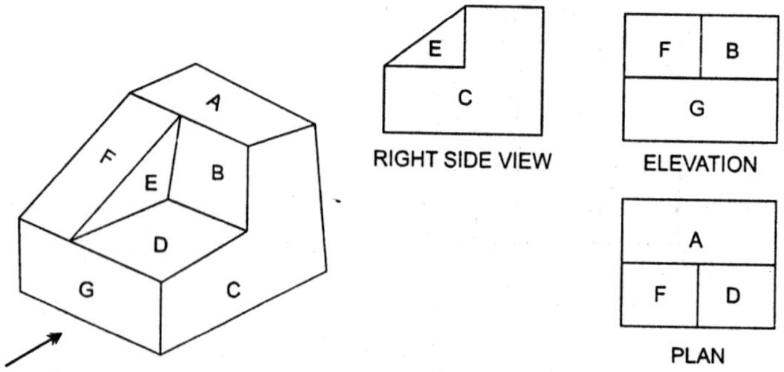

Fig. 17.13

Problem 7. Fig. 17.14 shows the pictorial view of an object in which the various surfaces are marked by different alphabets. Identify and mark the various surfaces from the pictorial view to orthographic views.

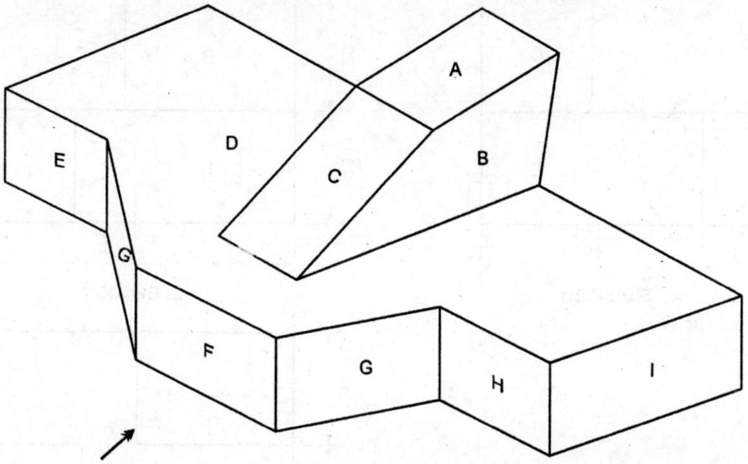

Fig. 17.14

Solution. See Fig. 17.15.

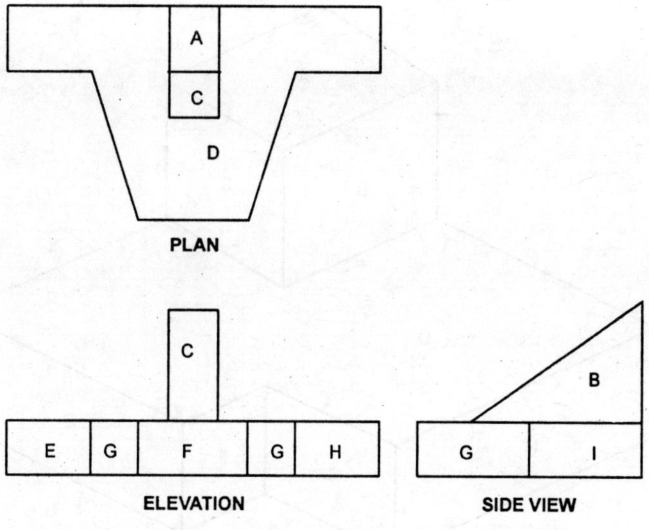

Fig. 17.15

Problem 8. Fig. 17.16 shows the orthographic projection of an object in which different surfaces are marked by alphabets such as A, B, C, D, E, F, G and H. Draw its isometric view.

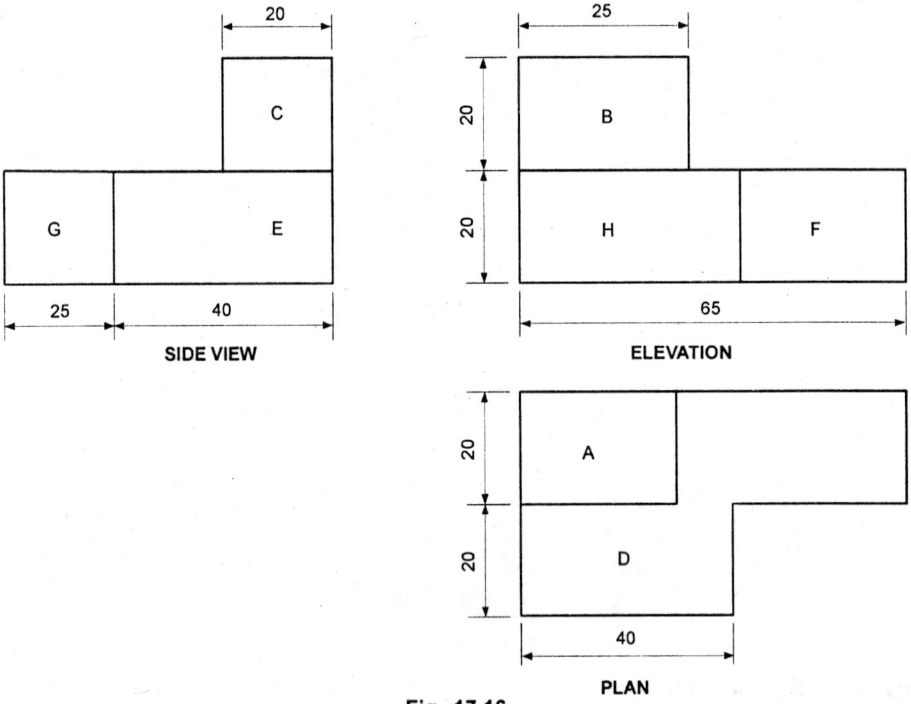

Fig. 17.16

Solution. See Fig. 17.17.

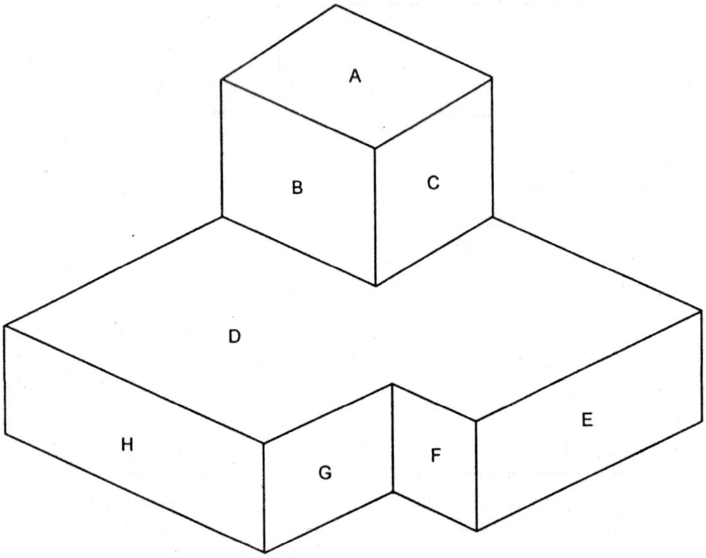

Fig. 17.17

Problem 9. Fig. 17.18 shows the pictorial view of an object in which the various surfaces are marked by different alphabets. Identify and mark the various surfaces from the pictorial view to orthographic views.

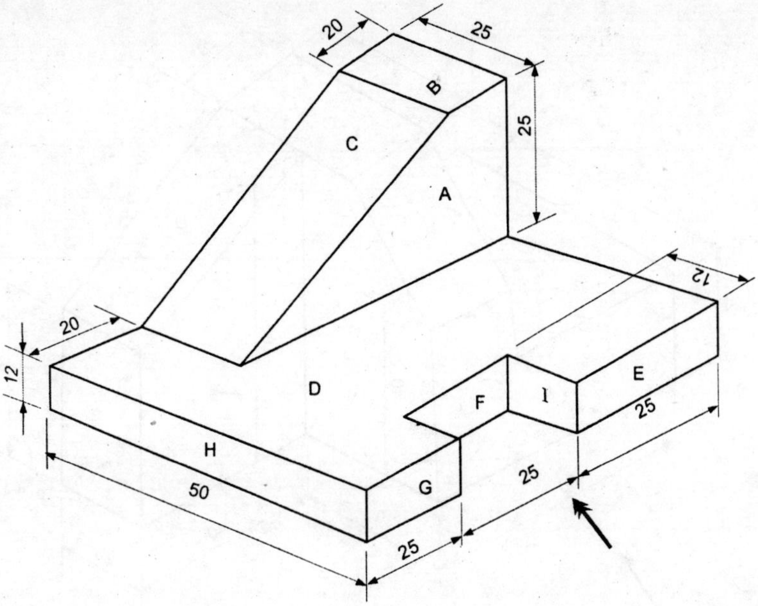

Fig. 17.18

Solution. See Fig. 17.19.

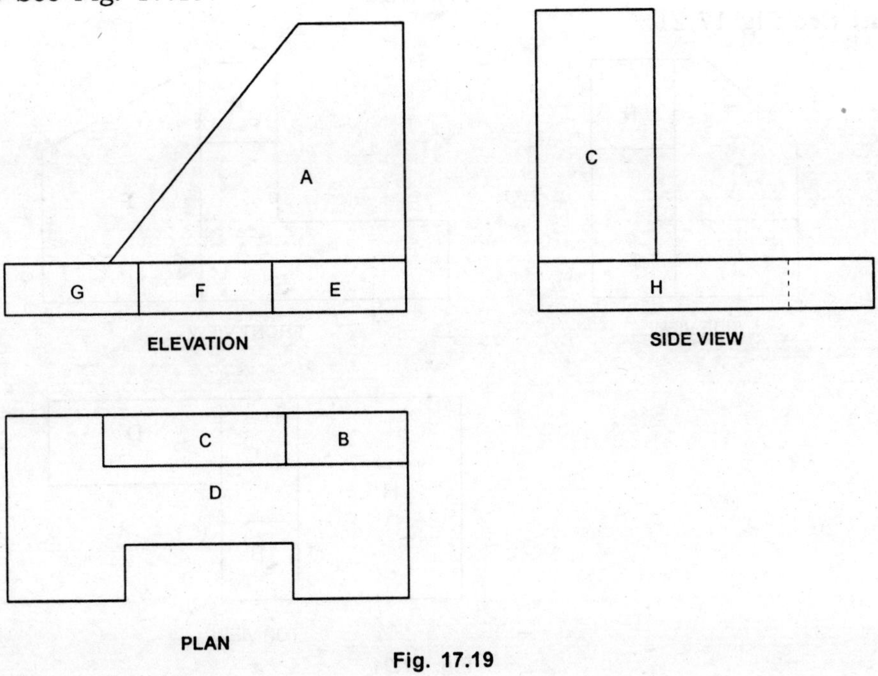

Fig. 17.19

Problem 10. Fig. 17.20 Shows the pictorial view of an object in which the various surfaces are marked by different alphabets. Identify and mark the various surfaces from the pictorial view to orthographic views.

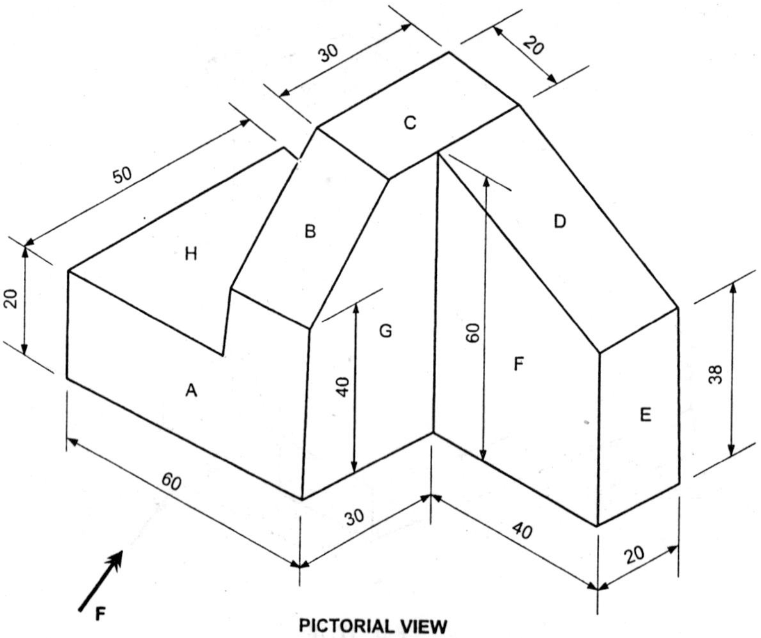

PICTORIAL VIEW

Fig. 17.20

Solution. See Fig 17.21.

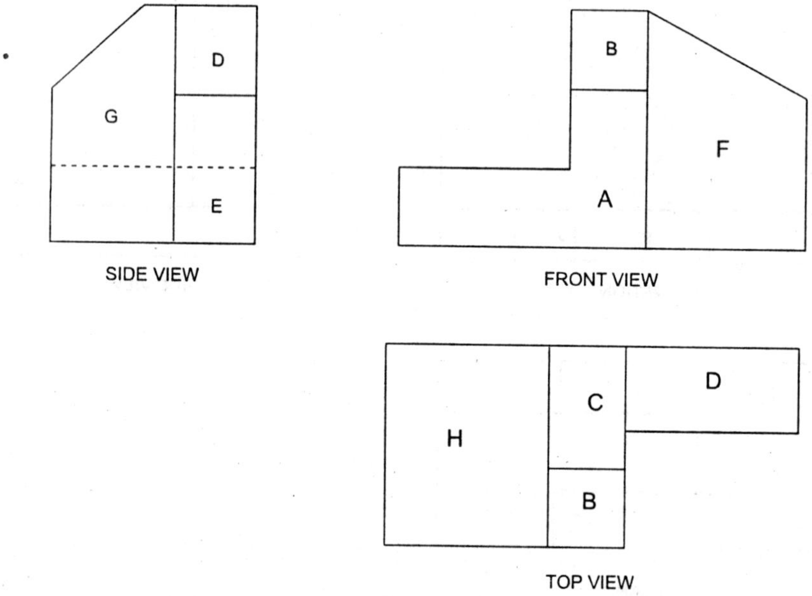

Fig. 17.21

Problem 11. Fig. 17.22 shows the orthographic projection of an object in which different surfaces are marked by alphabets such as A, B, C and D. Draw its isometric view.

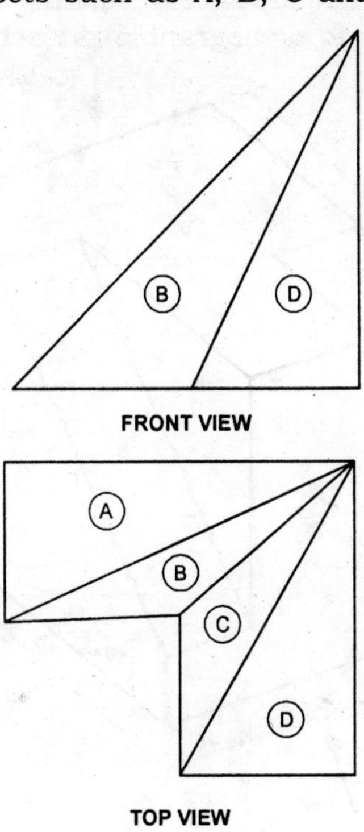

Fig. 17.22

Solution. See Fig. 17.23.

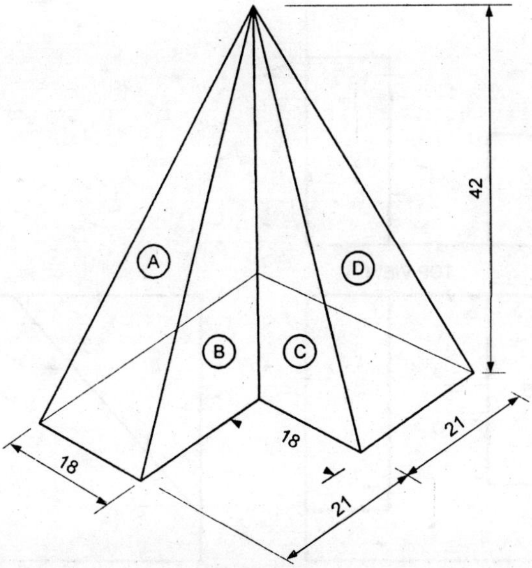

Fig. 17.23

Problem 12. Fig. 17.24 shows the isometric projection of an object in which various surfaces are marked by different alphabets. Identify and mark the various surfaces from the isometric projection to orthographic projection in IIIrd angle projection.

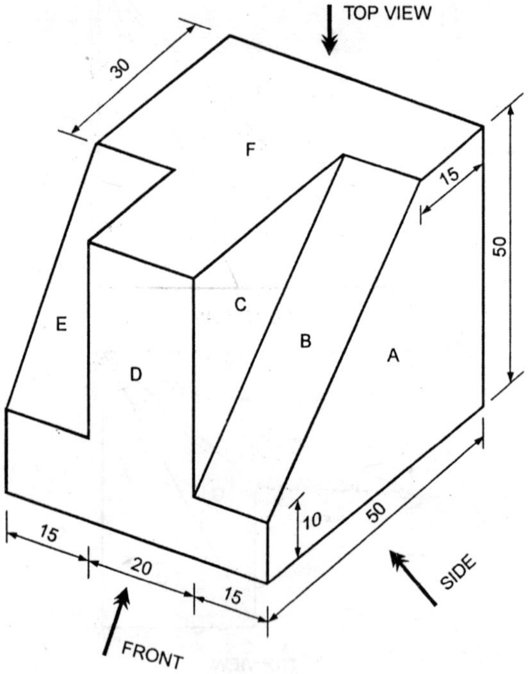

Fig. 17.24

Solution. See Fig. 17.25.

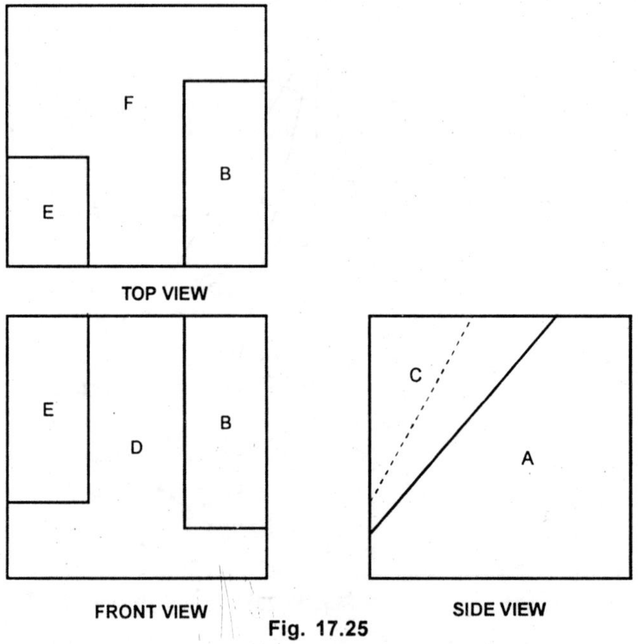

Fig. 17.25

Problem 13. Fig. 17.26 shows the pictoral view of an object in which various surfaces are marked by different alphabets. Identify and mark the various surfaces from the figure to orthographic projection.

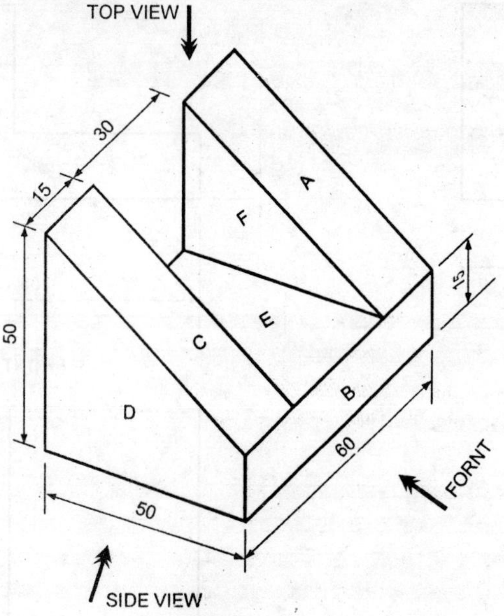

Fig. 17.26

Solution. See Fig. 17.27.

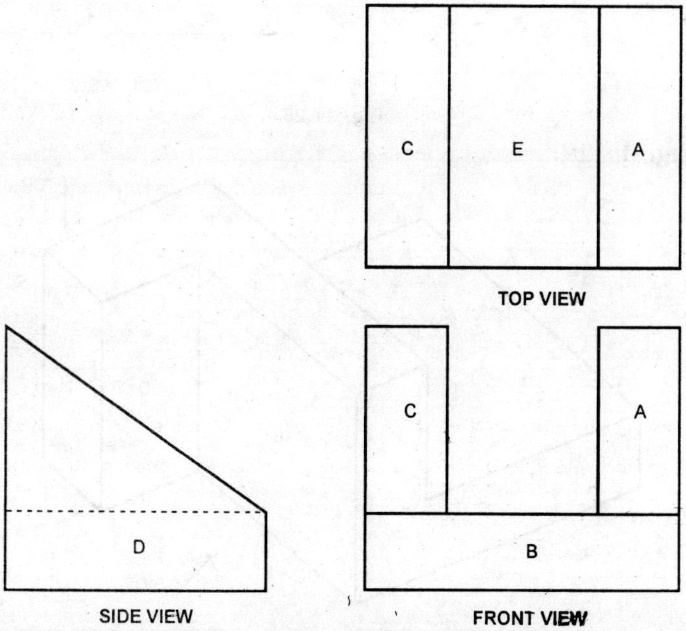

Fig. 17.27

Problem 14. Fig. 17.28 shows the orthographic projection of an object in which different surfaces are marked by alphabets such as *A*, *B*, *C*, *D*, *E* and *F*. Draw its isometric view.

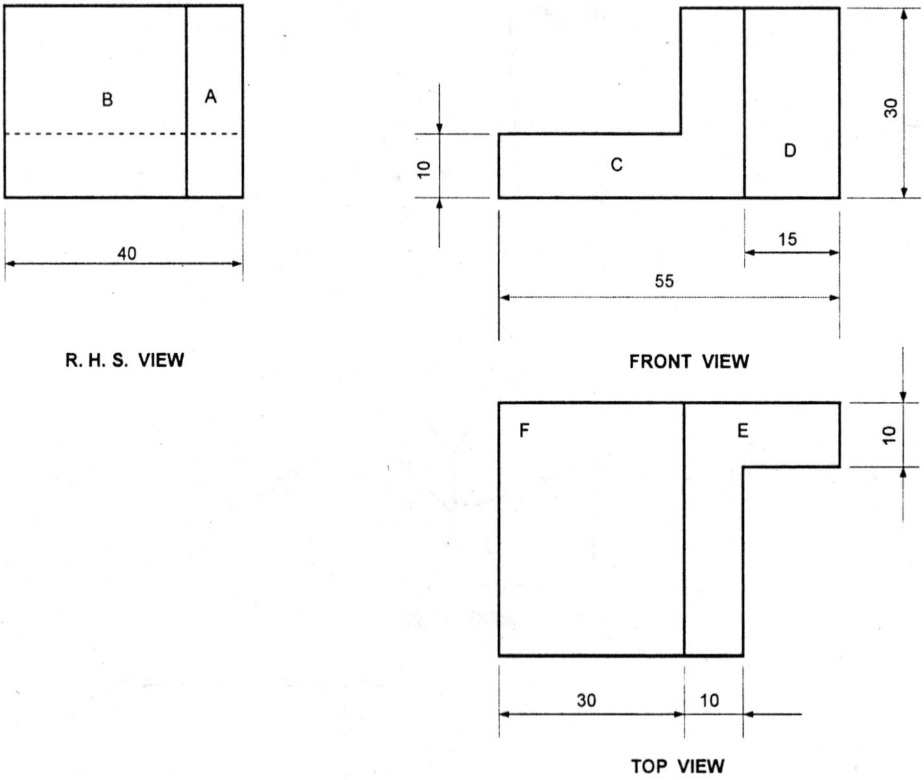

Fig. 17.28

Solution. See Fig. 17.29.

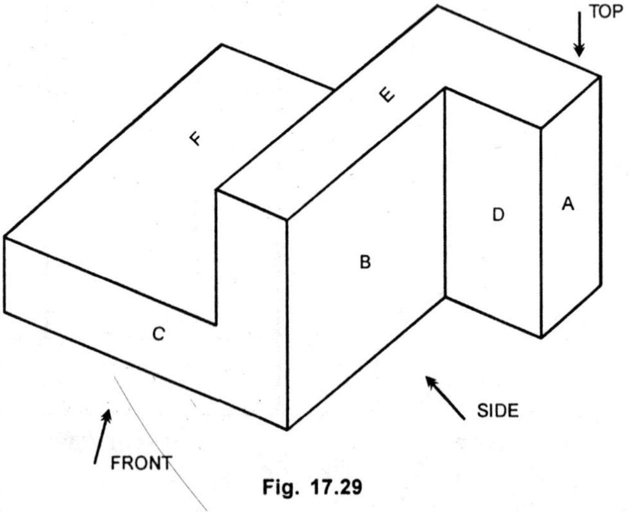

Fig. 17.29

Problem 15. Fig. 17.30 shows the orthographic projection of an object in which various surfaces are marked by *A*, *B*, *C*, *D* and *E*. Draw its isometric view.

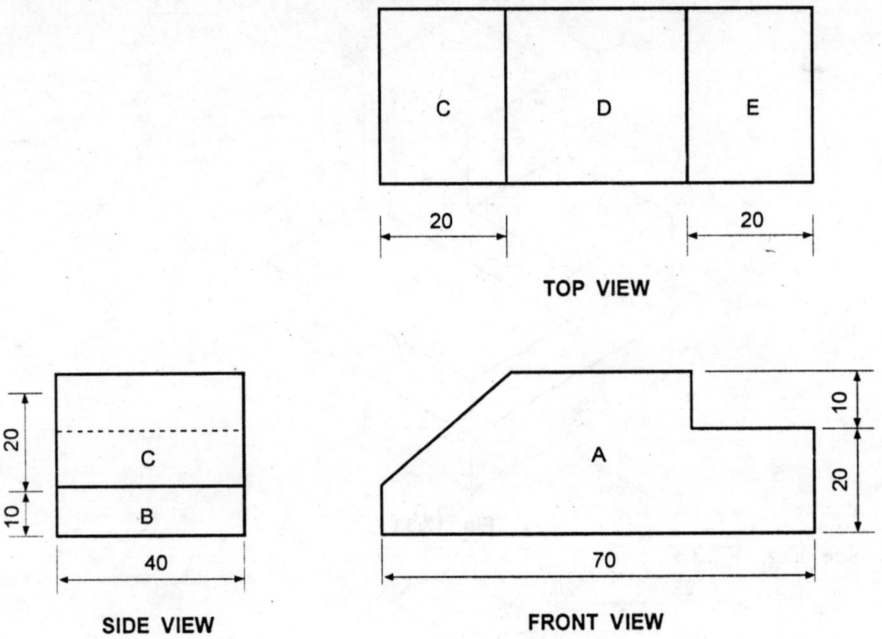

Fig. 17.30

Solution. See Fig. 17.31.

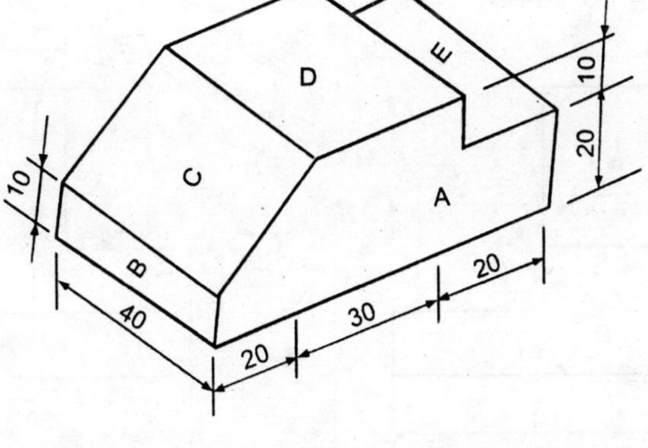

Fig. 17.31

Problem 16. Fig. 17.32 shows an isometric view of an object in which various surfaces are marked by *A, B, C, D, E, F* and *G*. Draw its orthographic projection of an object in IIIrd angle projection.

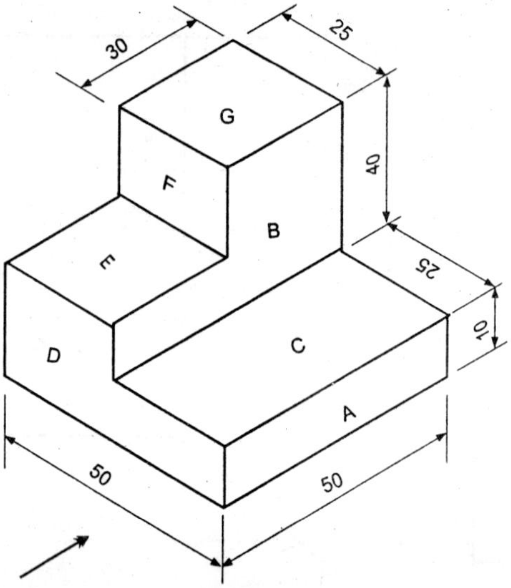

Fig. 17.32

Solution. See Fig. 17.33.

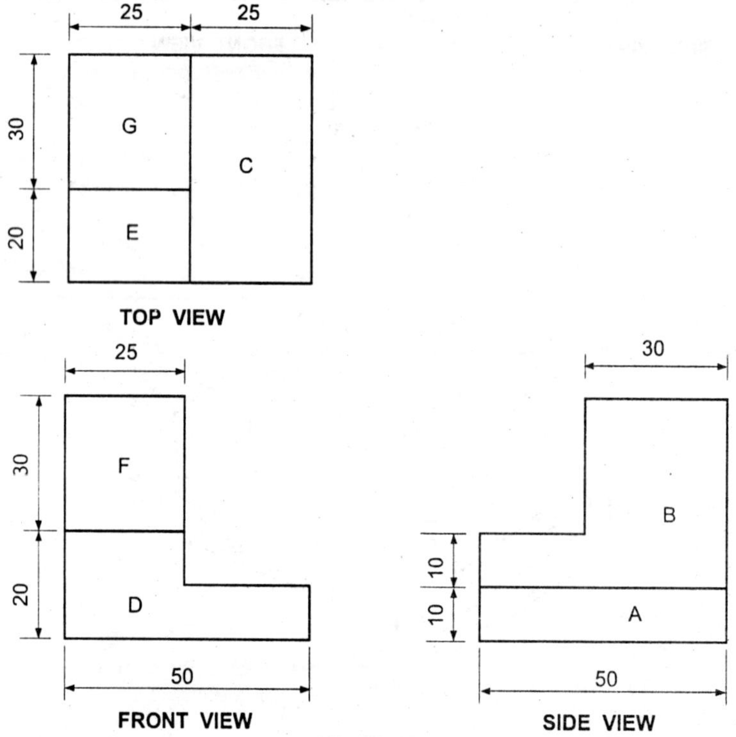

Fig. 17.33

EXERCISE

1. What do you mean by missing lines?

2. What is the need of missing lines and missing views in the drawing?

3. Two views of an object is given in Fig. 17.34. Draw the missing top view and also draw the isometric view of the object. **(B.T.E. New Delhi, Jan. 2009)**

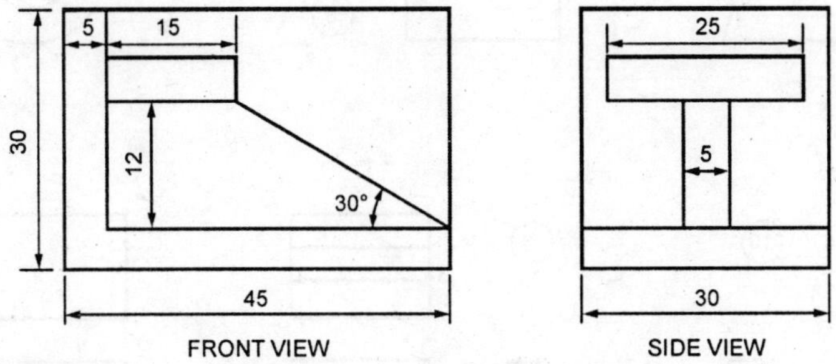

Fig. 17.34

4. Fig. 17.35 (1 to 30) shows the incomplete orthographic projection of an object. Draw the missing line and complete the orthographic projection.

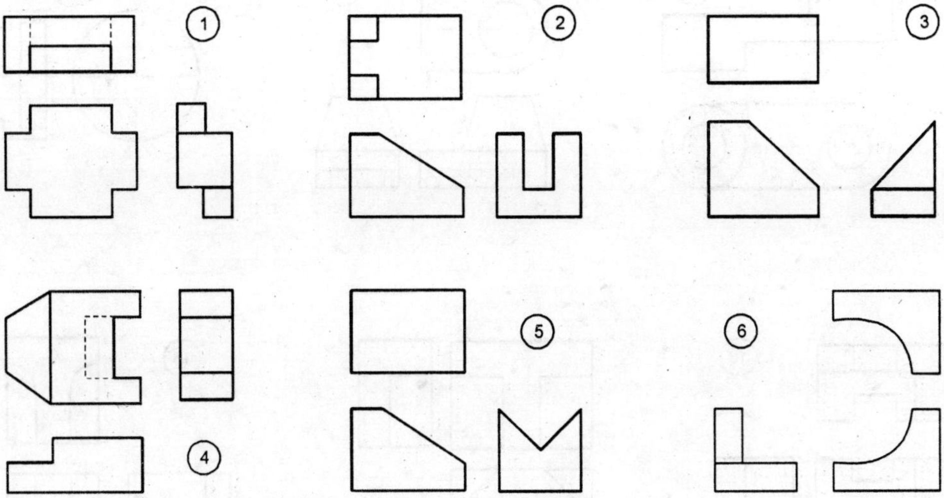

Fig. 17.35 Contd...

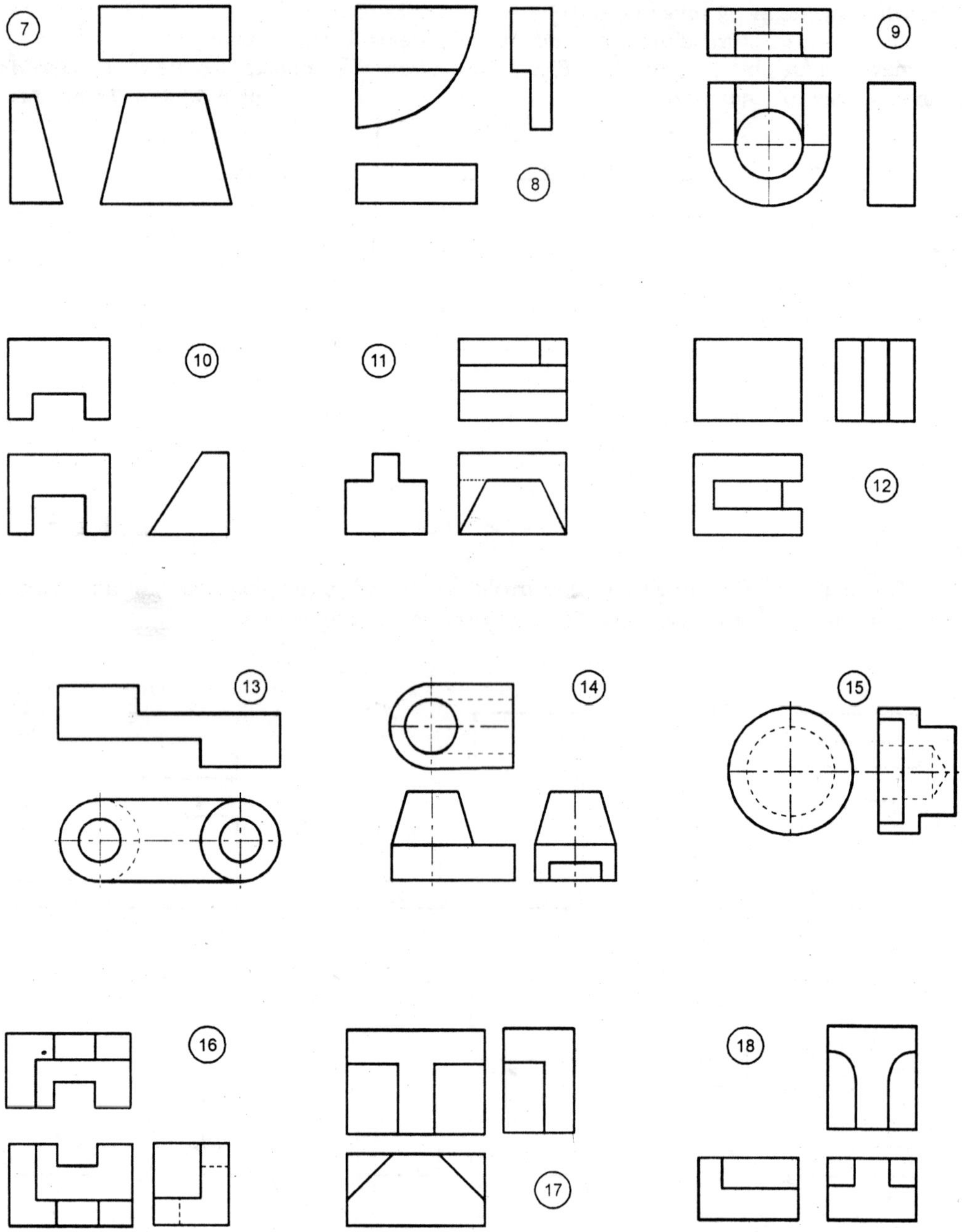

Fig. 17.35 Contd...

Fig. 17.35

5. Fig. 17.36 (1 to 22) show the incomplete orthographic projection of an object. Draw the missing view of an object and complete the orthographic projection.

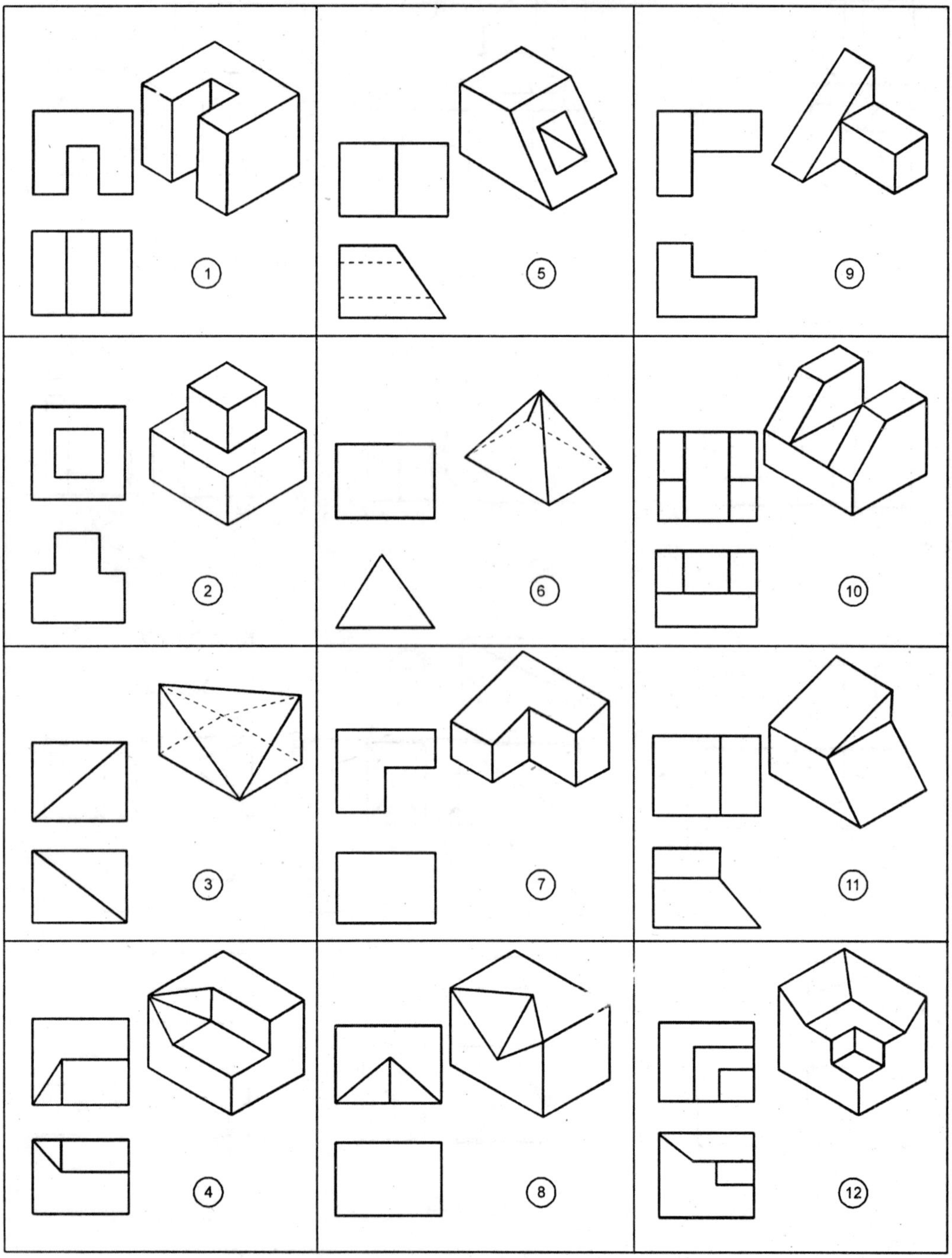

Fig. 17.36 Contd...

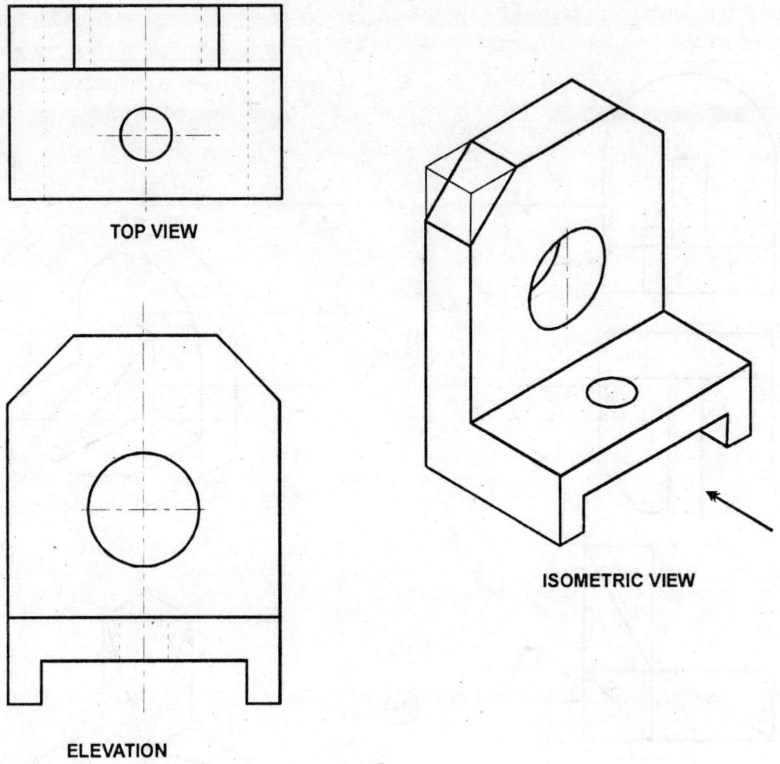

(13)

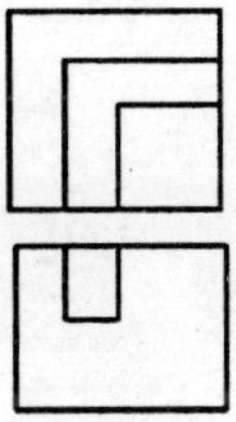

(14)

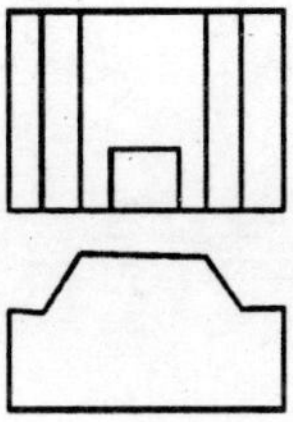

(15)

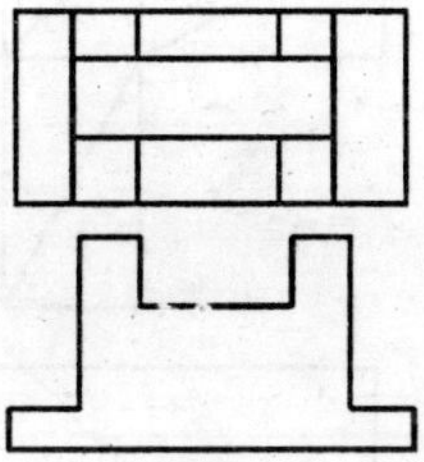

(16)

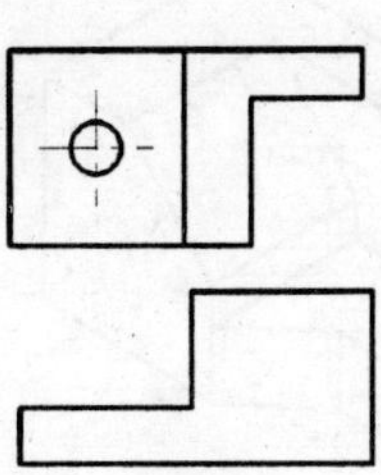

(17)

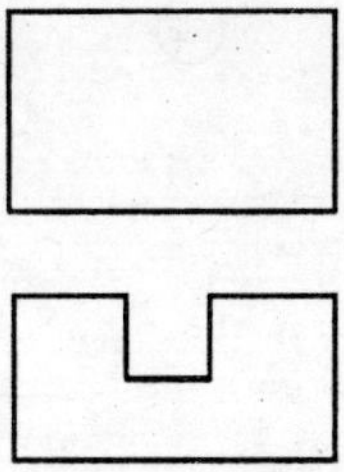

(18)

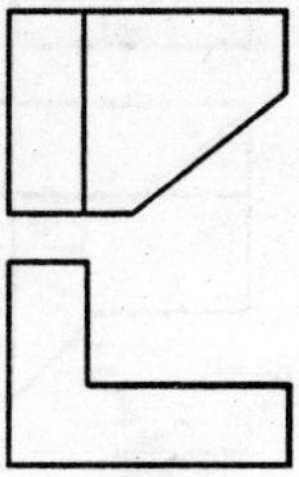

(19)

Fig. 17.36 Contd...

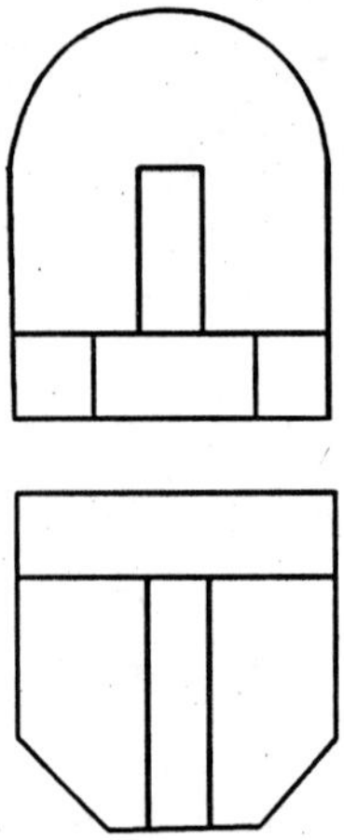

(20)

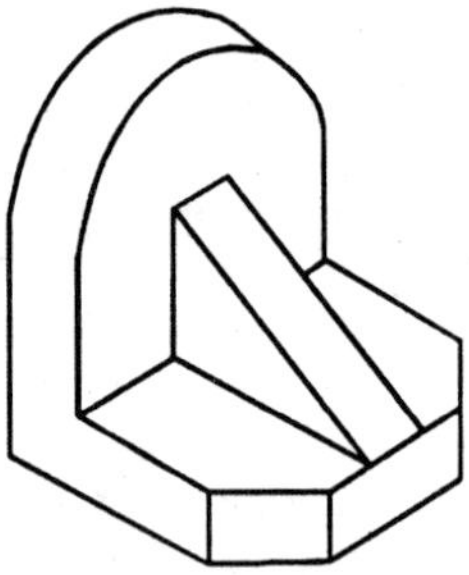

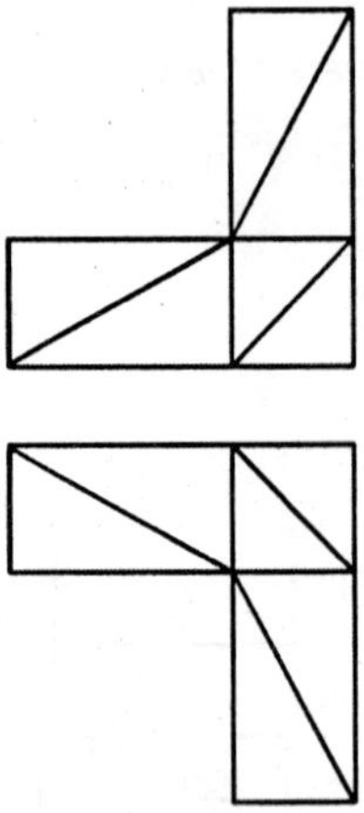

(21)

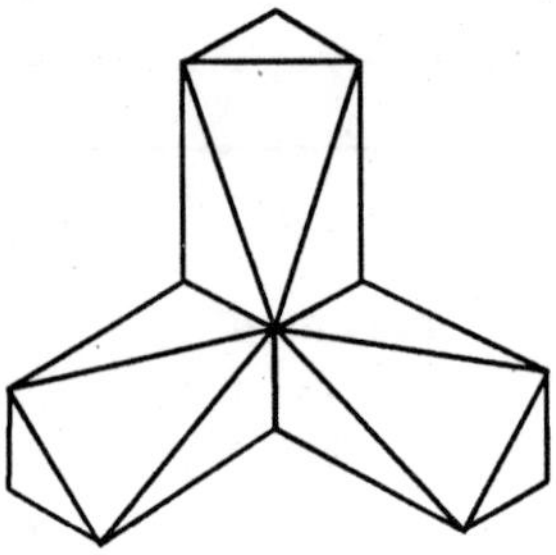

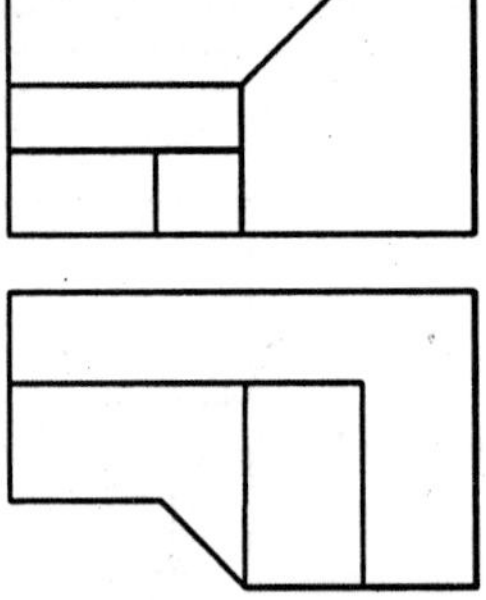

(22)

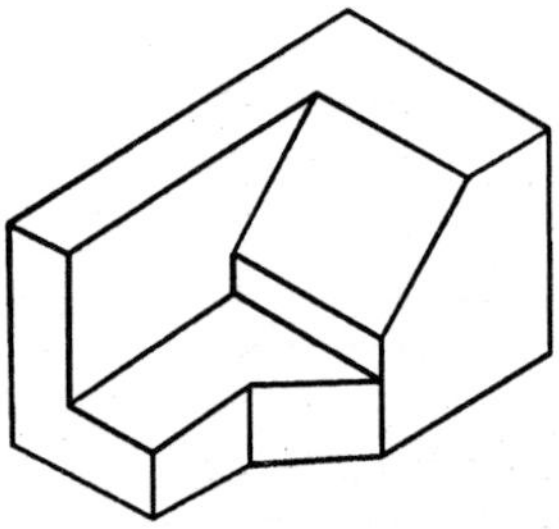

Fig. 17.36

6. What do you understand by identification of surfaces?
7. Explain the types of identification of surfaces?
8. Fig. 17.37 and 17.38 show the pictorial view of an object in which different surfaces are marked by different alphabets. Draw the orthographic projects and identify the different surfaces?

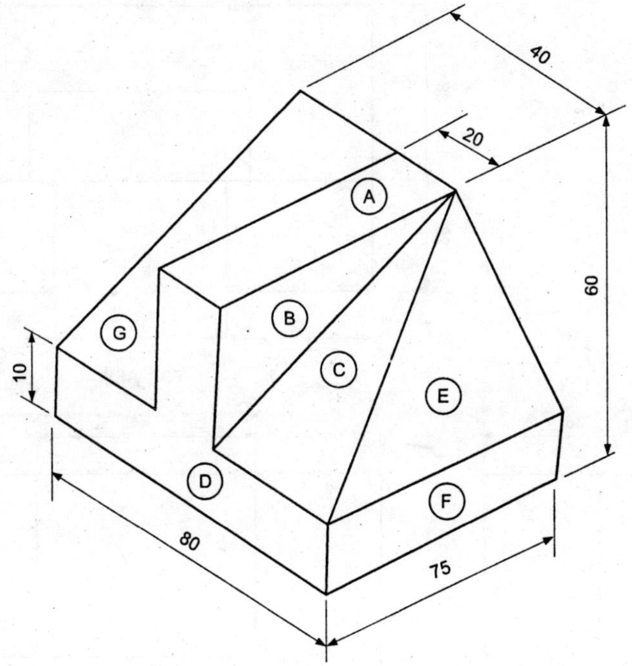

Fig. 17.37

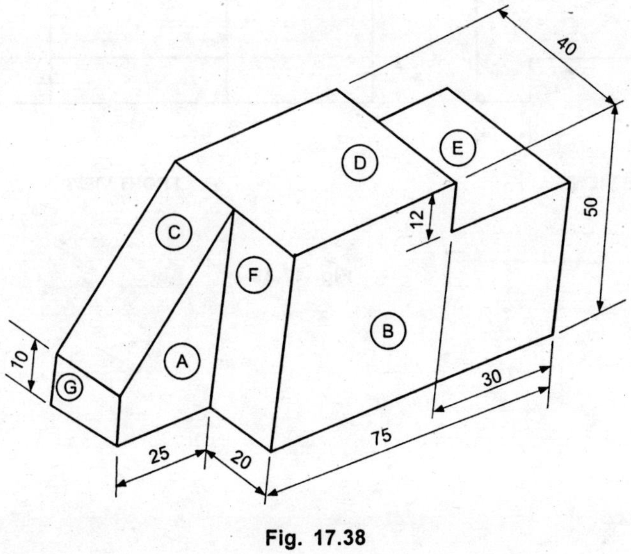

Fig. 17.38

4. Fig. 17.39 shows the orthographic views of an object in which different surfaces are marked by alphabets. Identify and mark various surfaces from the orthographic projection to the pictorial view.

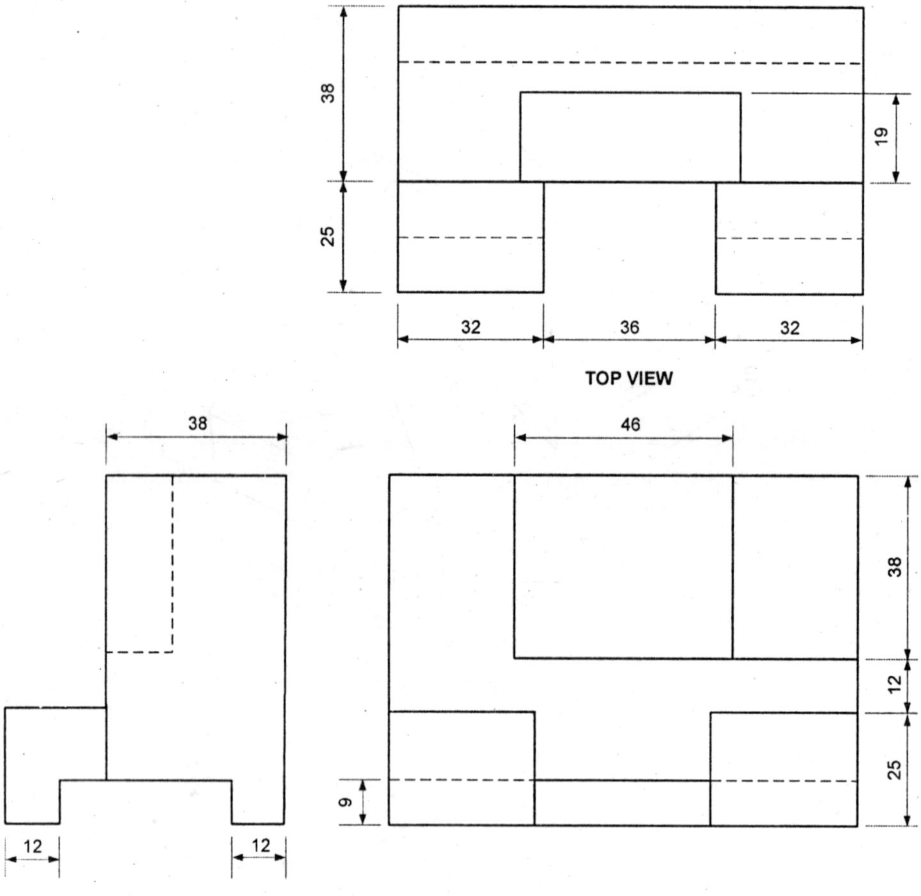

Fig. 17.39

18

SYMBOLS AND CONVENTIONS

18.1 INTRODUCTION

In engineering field, the preliminary knowledge of various types of symbols used by engineers is very important from subject point of view. Sometimes, for complicated drawing it is not convenient to show the actual details of various objects on drawing. In order to overcome this problem and for saving the time we use the shorthand notation. The shorthand notations used to represent the actual object by the engineers is known as symbols. Almost in all engineering projects including electrical, civil and mechanical we use the symbols according to requirements.

The electrical components consist of items such as fans, motors, generators, lighting, fixtures, various types of switches, cooling devices, and electronic appliances for every day comfort and convenience. This introductory chapter meets the requirement of the students. We have described mechanical, electronics, electrical and civil engineering symbols and conventions in regard to fitting.

18.2 CIVIL ENGINEERING SANITARY FITTING SYMBOLS

The civil engineering symbols are generally not drawn according to scale. However, the symbol should be drawn in a proportionate size to give better representation.

According to Indian Standard, the different types of civil engineering symbols are given in Tables 18.1 to 18.6.

Table 18.1 Symbols for Building Materials

S. No.	*Name of Object*	*Symbol*	*S. No.*	*Name of Object*	*Symbol*
1.	Plaster	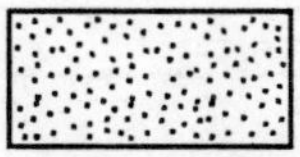	**4.**	Marble	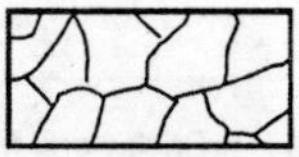
2.	Babbit Metal, Lead, White Metal	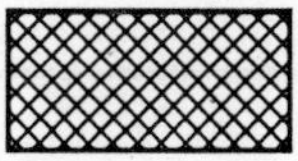	**5.**	Natural Stone	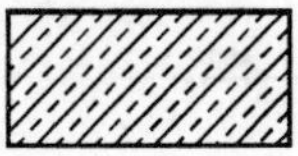
3.	Partition Blocks	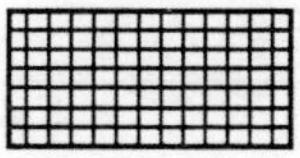	**6.**	Metal Section	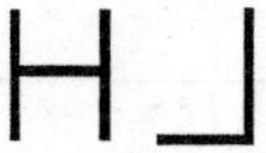

Table 18.2 Convention of Materials

S.No.	*Materials*	*Convention*
1.	Steel, Cast Iron, Copper, Aluminium and its alloys etc.	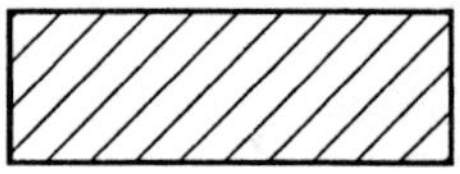
2.	Lead, Zinc, Tin, White Metal etc.	
3.	Brass, Bronze, Gun Metal etc.	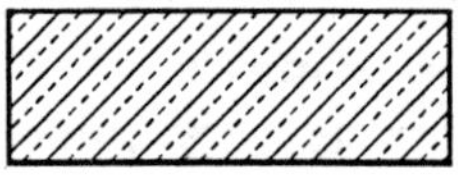
4.	Glass.	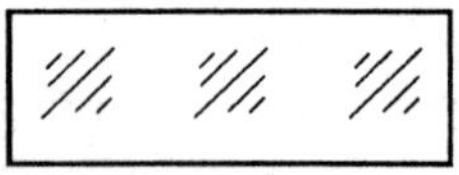
5.	Marble, Porcelain, Stoneware, Slate, etc.	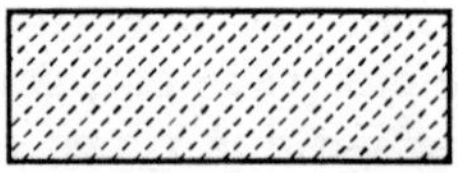
6.	Rubber, Leather, Paper, Wax, Asbestos, Fibre, Cork, etc.	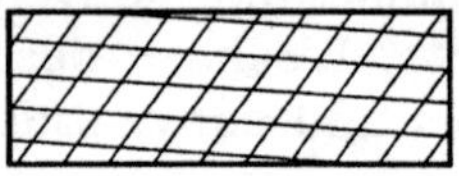
7.	Wood, Plywood, along grains	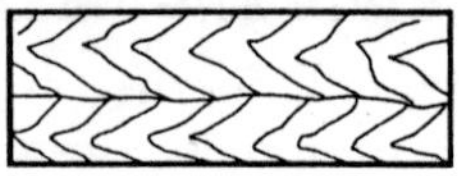
8.	Wood, Plywood, etc. across grains	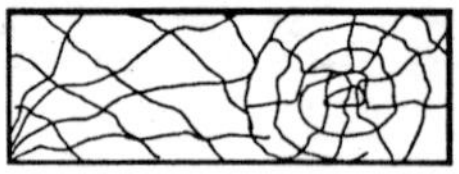
9.	Earth	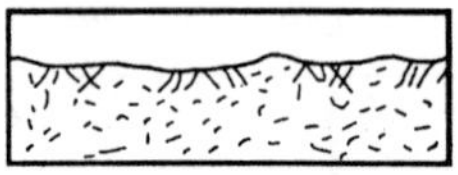
10.	Brick work, Masonary, Fire Bricks, etc.	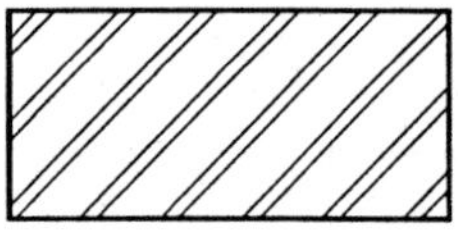
11.	Concrete.	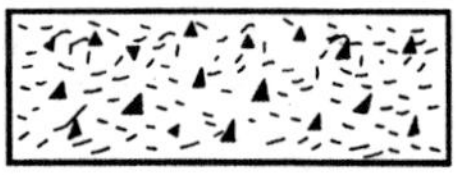
12.	Liquids such as water, Oil, Petrol, Kerosene, etc.	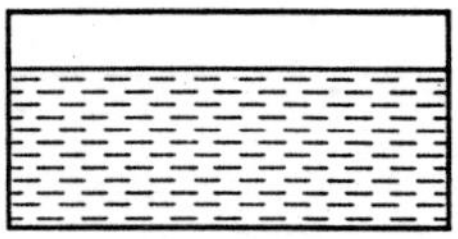

Table 18.3 Symbols of Sanitary Installation and Fitment

S.No.	Name of Object	Symbol	S.No.	Name of Object	Symbol
1.	Hot water tank		8.	Manhole	
2.	Water meter		9.	Drain cock	
3.	Cold Water Cistern		10.	Rain Water Outlet	
4.	Sluice valve or stop valve		11.	Vent Outlet	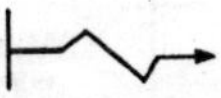
5.	Safety Valve		12.	Refrigerator	
6.	Rain Water head		13.	Heater	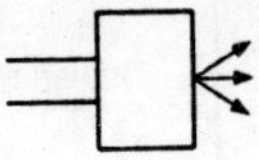
7.	Vent Inlet		14.	Towel rail	

Table 18.4 Symbols of Sanitary Installation and Fitment

S.No.	Name of Object	Symbol	S.No.	Name of Object	Symbol
1.	Kitchen Sink		9.	Floor	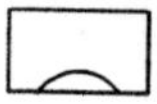
2.	Slope Sink	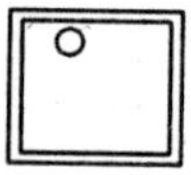	10.	Pump	
3.	Drinking fountain wall type		11.	Shower head	
4.	Water Closet (WC)		12.	Fire	
5.	Urinal Floor		13.	Galley	
6.	Indian type W C		14.	Bath roll	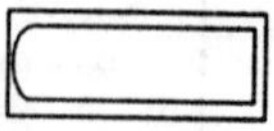
7.	Corner hung urinal	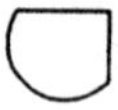	15.	Rectangular bath	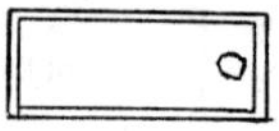
8.	Hung wall urinal	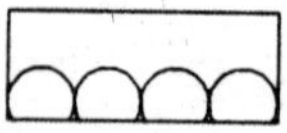	16.	Washing fountain	

Table 18.5 Application of Symbols of Pipe Fitting and Valves

Name of fitting	*Symbol*		*Name of fitting*	*Symbol*	
	Screwed	*Flanged*		*Screwed*	*Flanged*
Elbow 90°			Lateral		
Elbow 45°			Union		
Elbow Turned up			Sleeve		
Elbow Turned down			Cap		
Reducing elbow			Reducer		
Tee			Gate valve		
Tee-outlet up			Check valve		
Tee-outlet down			Globe valve		
Cross			Stop cock		

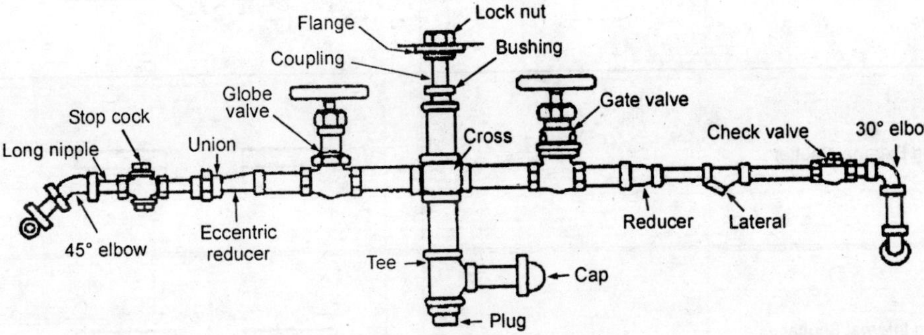

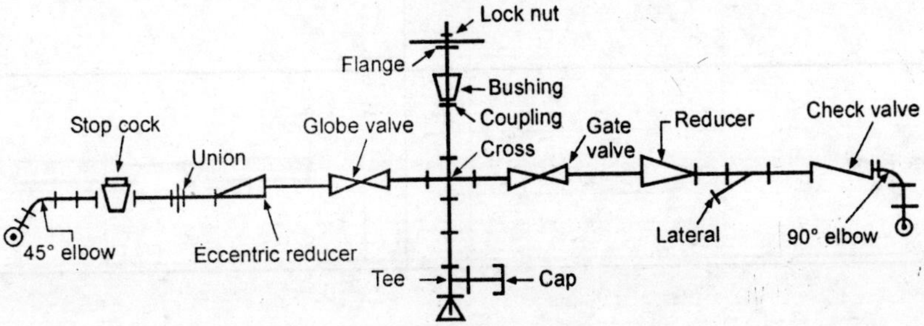

Table 18.6 Symbols of Doors

1.	Single Leaf Single Swing	
2.	Double Leaf Single Swing	
3.	Single Leaf Double Swing	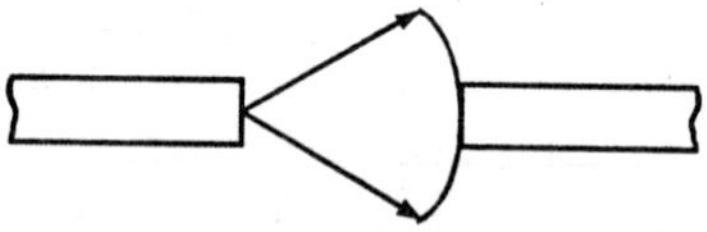
4.	Revolving Door	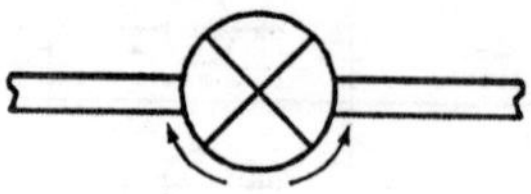
5.	Double Leaf Double Swing	
6.	Rolling External Shutter	
7.	Rolling Internal Shutter	
8.	Folding Side Hung	

18.3 MECHANICAL ENGINEERING SYMBOLS

Long parts are always difficult to draw on a drawing sheet. Material breaks are easy method of drawing these parts without reducing the scale. Meterial breaks are always drawn free hand as shown in Table 18.7. The other important mechanical engineering symbols are used in sheet metal are shown in Fig. 18.1.

Table 18.7 Symbol of Material Break

(a)	Cylindrical metal (Round Section)	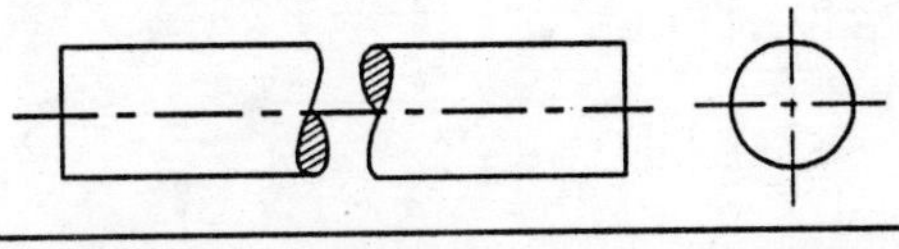
(b)	Pipe or tube	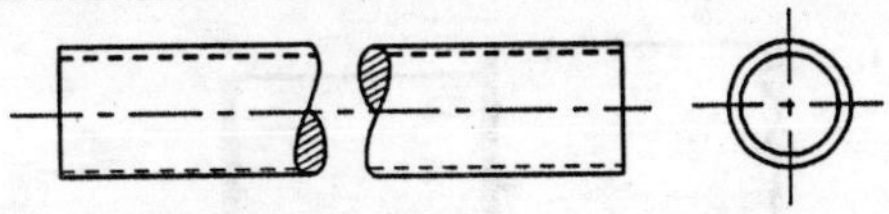
(c)	Rectangular Section	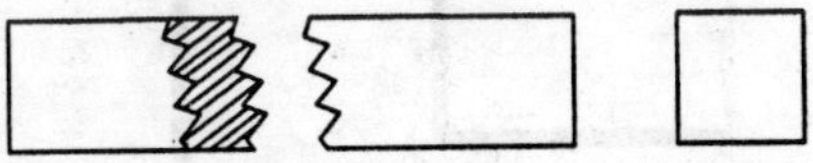
(d)	Wood (Rectangular Section)	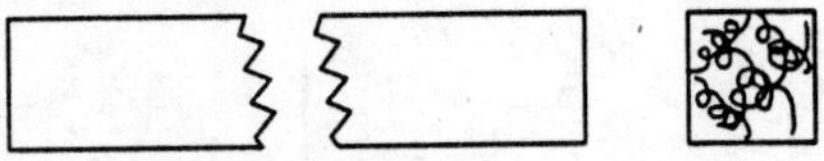
(e)	Long break for all materials	
(f)	Channel Section	
(g)	Rolled Section	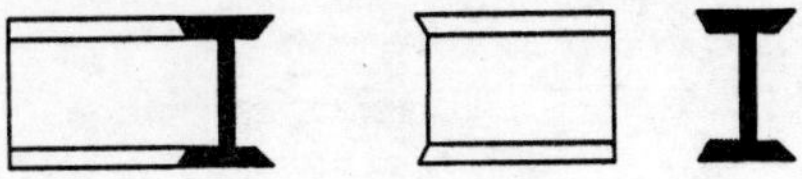

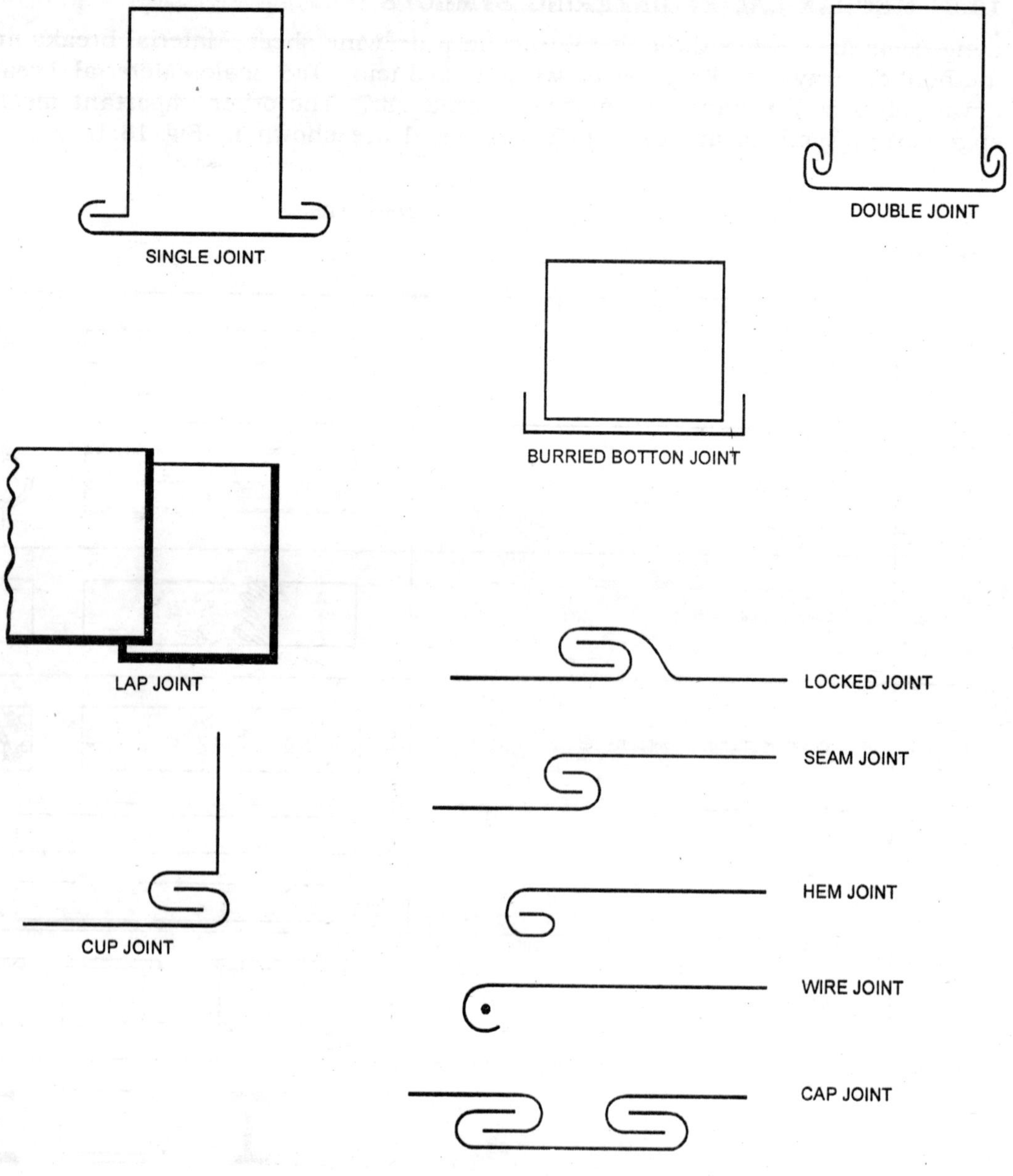

Fig. 18.1

18.4 ELECTRICAL FITTING SYMBOLS FOR DOMESTIC INTERIOR INSTALLATION

Electrical engineering symbols are generally not drawn according to scale. However, the symbol should be drawn in a proportionate size to give better representation.

According to Indian Standard, the different types of electrical engineering symbols are given in Tables 18.8 and 18.9.

Table 18.8 Electrical Engineering Symbols for Domestic Interior Installation

S.No.	*Name of Object*	*Symbol*	*S.No.*	*Name of Object*	*Symbol*
1.	Positive		**9.**	Aerial	
2.	Negative		**10.**	Loudspeaker	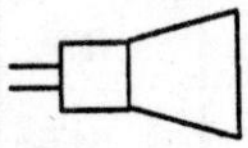
3.	Direct current		**11.**	Ceilling Fan	
4.	Alternating Current		**12.**	Meter	
5.	Push Bell Switch		**13.**	Earth Point	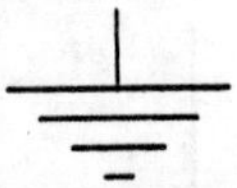
6.	Lamp		**14.**	Thyrector	
7.	Fan Regular		**15.**	Exhaust Fan	
8.	Fuse		**16.**	Bracket Fan	

Table 18.8 Contd...

S.No.	*Name of Object*	*Symbol*	*S.No.*	*Name of Object*	*Symbol*
17.	Ceiling Outlet		**25.**	Lamps in parallel	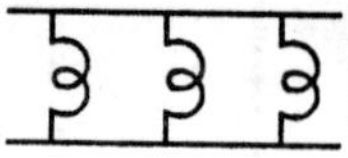
18.	Bell Push		**26.**	Two pin wall socket	
19.	Two-way Switch		**27.**	Crossed wire	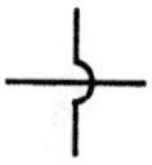
20.	Telephone Instrument		**28.**	Wall socket 3 pin	
21.	Power Plug	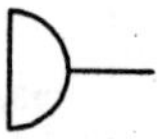	**29.**	Single phase	*1ϕ or 1* ∼
22.	Fire Alarm		**30.**	Three phase	*3ϕ or 3* ∼
23.	Automatic contact		**31.**	Ceilling rose 2 plate	
24.	Lamps in series		**32.**	Ceilling rose 3 plate	

Table 18.8 Contd...

S.No.	*Name of Object*	*Symbol*	*S.No.*	*Name of Object*	*Symbol*
33.	Buzzer		**42.**	Out side Telephone	
34.	Siren		**43.**	Light Plug	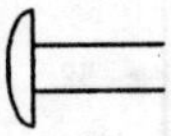
35.	Horn	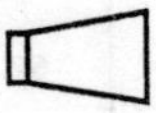	**44.**	Terminal	
36.	Battery	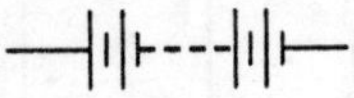	**45.**	Main Switches Power	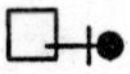
37.	Lamp on wall		**46.**	Wires cross not connected	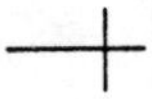
38.	Wire connection		**47.**	Amplifier	
39.	Wall Outlet (Light Bracket)	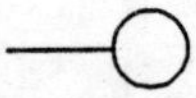	**48.**	Crystal	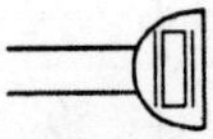
40.	One-way Switch		**49.**	Lamp or Bulb	
41.	Bell		**50.**	Single Tube Light	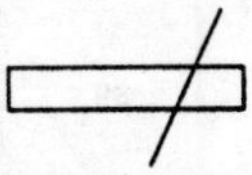

Table 18.8 Contd...

S.No.	*Name of Object*	*Symbol*	*S.No.*	*Name of Object*	*Symbol*
51.	Ammeter AC/DC II AC III DC		**60.**	Bracket lighting	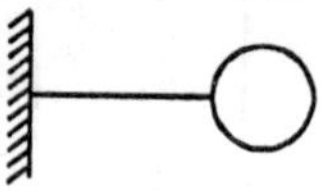
52.	Volt meter AC/DC || AC III DC		**61.**	Circuit breaker triple	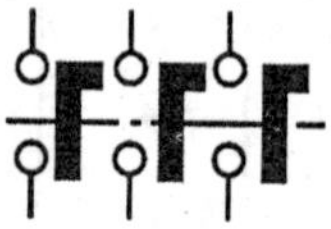
53.	Ohm meter		**62.**	Ceilling point for lighting	
54.	Multi meter		**63.**	Immersion heater	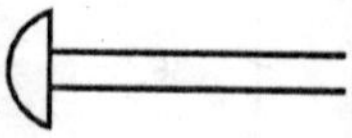
55.	Galvanometer		**64.**	Earth plate	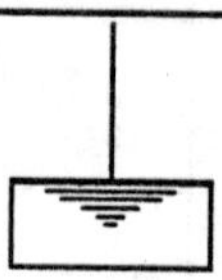
56.	Power Factor meter		**65.**	Indicator (N Denote No of waip)	
57.	Frequency meter	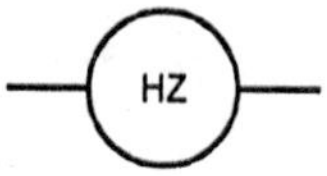	**66.**	Intermediate switch	
58.	Watt meter	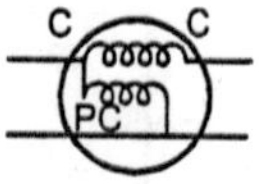	**67.**	Limit switch	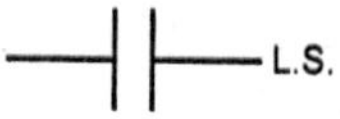
59.	Single phase energy meter	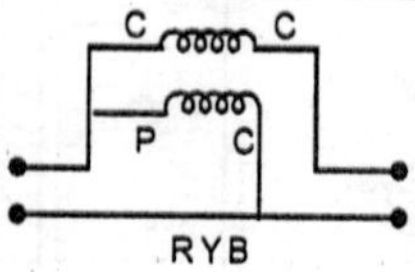	**68.**	Lighting Arrestor	

Table 18.8 Contd...

S.No.	*Name of Object*	*Symbol*	*S.No.*	*Name of Object*	*Symbol*
69.	Main switch board		**78.**	Synchronous motor	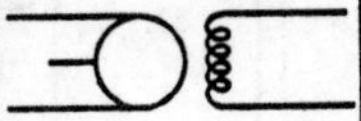
70.	Main fuse board with switches		**79.**	Wound Rotor for induction motor	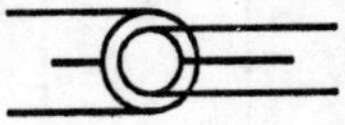
71.	Main switch for lighting		**80.**	Fan point	
72.	Ground		**81.**	Power wall socket	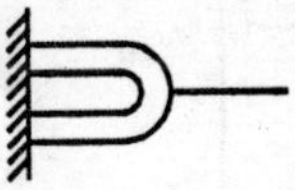
73.	Fixed capacitor	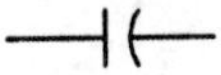	**82.**	Power wall socket with switch	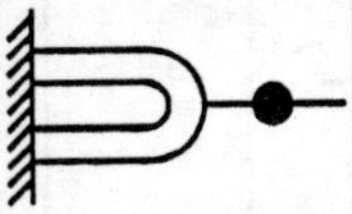
74.	Variable capacitor		**83.**	Plug	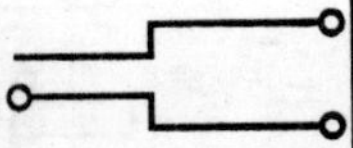
75.	Key	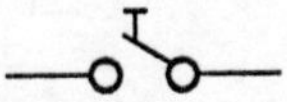	**84.**	Loop Coupling	
76.	Main cut out power		**85.**	Integrated voltage regulator (I.V.R)	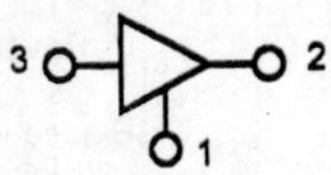
77.	Squirrel cage motor	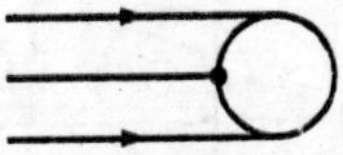	**86.**	Zener (Diode)	

Table 18.8

S.No.	Name of Object	Symbol	S.No.	Name of Object	Symbol
87.	Rectifier (DIODE)	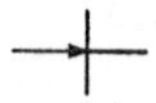	**92.**	Back diode	
88.	Crystal		**93.**	Micro phone general	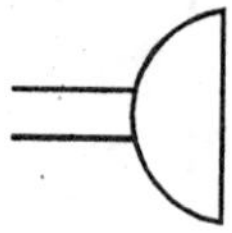
89.	Microphone		**94.**	Single Button	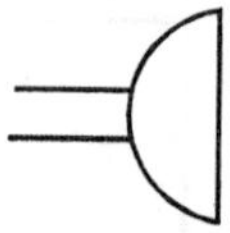
90.	Relay		**95.**	Double Button	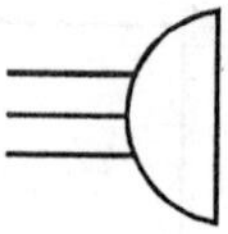
91.	Tunnel diode				

Table 18.9 Electronic Symbols

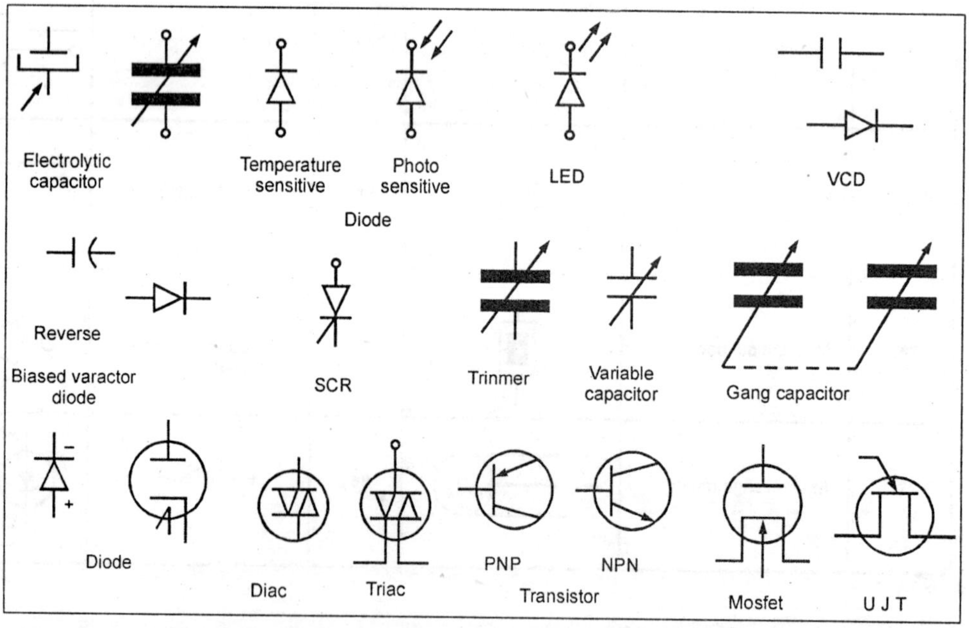

Table 18.9

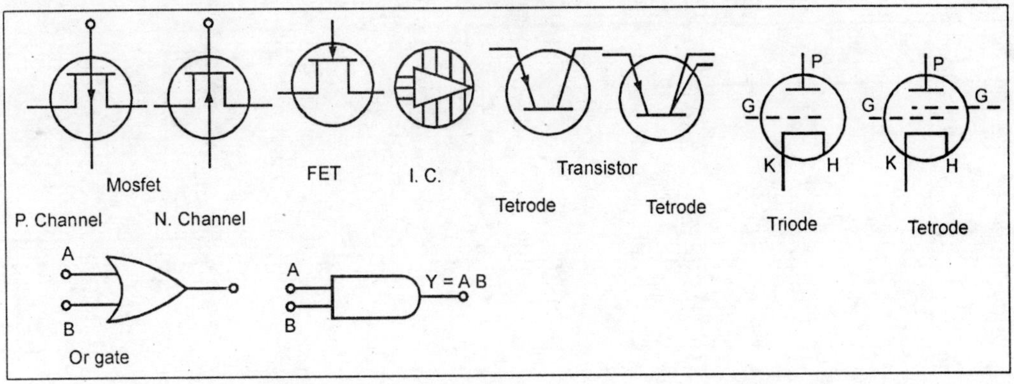
Mosfet
P. Channel
N. Channel
FET
I. C.
Transistor
Tetrode
Tetrode
P
G
K
H
Triode
P
G
G
K
H
Tetrode
A
B
Or gate
A
B
Y = A B

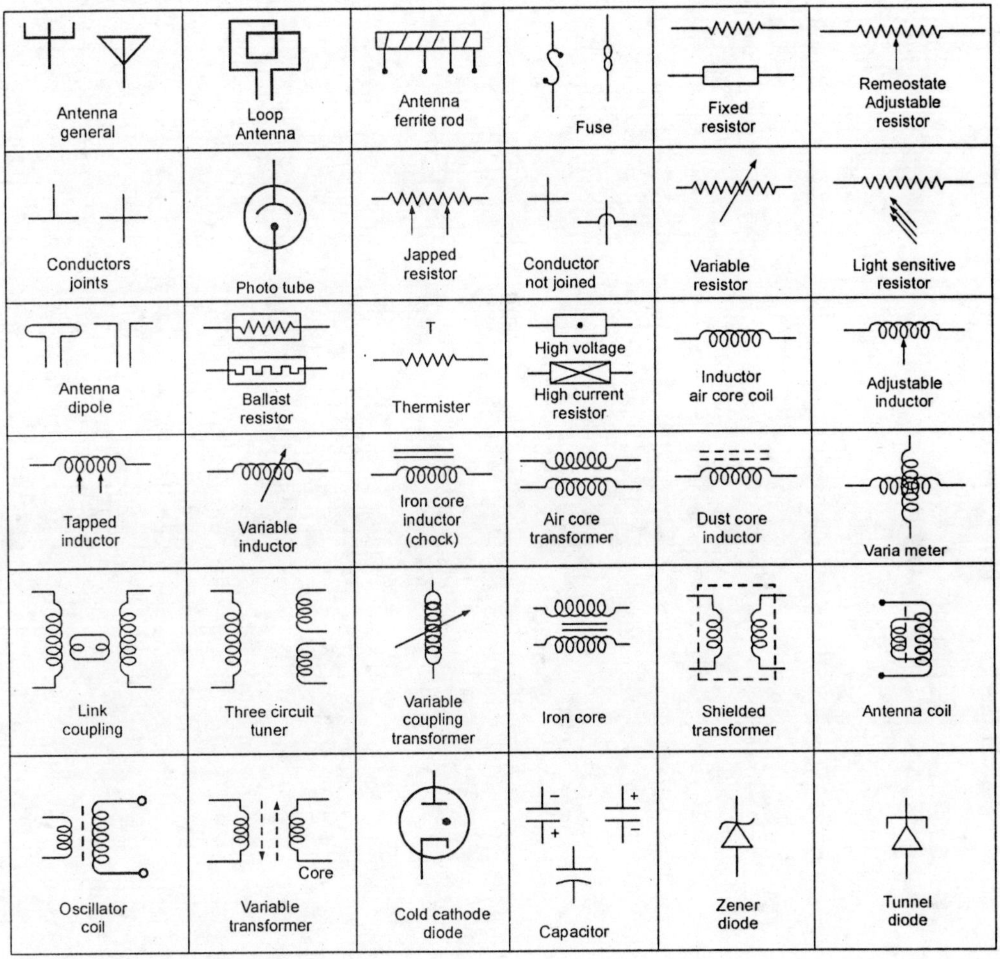
Antenna general
Loop Antenna
Antenna ferrite rod
Fuse
Fixed resistor
Remeostate Adjustable resistor
Conductors joints
Photo tube
Japped resistor
Conductor not joined
Variable resistor
Light sensitive resistor
Antenna dipole
Ballast resistor
T
Thermister
High voltage
High current resistor
Inductor air core coil
Adjustable inductor
Tapped inductor
Variable inductor
Iron core inductor (chock)
Air core transformer
Dust core inductor
Varia meter
Link coupling
Three circuit tuner
Variable coupling transformer
Iron core
Shielded transformer
Antenna coil
Oscillator coil
Core
Variable transformer
Cold cathode diode
Capacitor
Zener diode
Tunnel diode

IMPORTANT NOTES:

PART II

MECHANICAL ENGINEERING DRAWING

1

DETAIL AND ASSEMBLY DRAWING

1.1. INTRODUCTION

Before manufacturing an object, we prepare drawings which have complete information related to the manufacturing of an object such as, dimensions, surface finish etc. These drawings are very important part of manufacturing, pertaining to the drawing of machine and machine parts etc. It is commonly used by the mechanical engineers. Detail and assembly drawing is an important function of engineering drawing. In this chapter, we shall deal with the study of detailed and assembly drawing for different types of wooden joints.

1.2 DETAIL DRAWING

The drawing which provides complete information for the production of each part of a machine or structure is called detail drawing. It contains a number of parts. In a detail drawing each part is shown in the condition that gives complete and exact description of the shape, dimension, specification and title of the single part as shown in Fig. 1.1

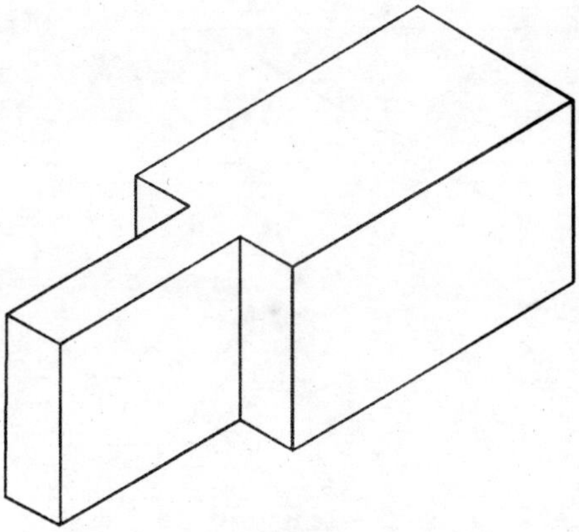

Tenon

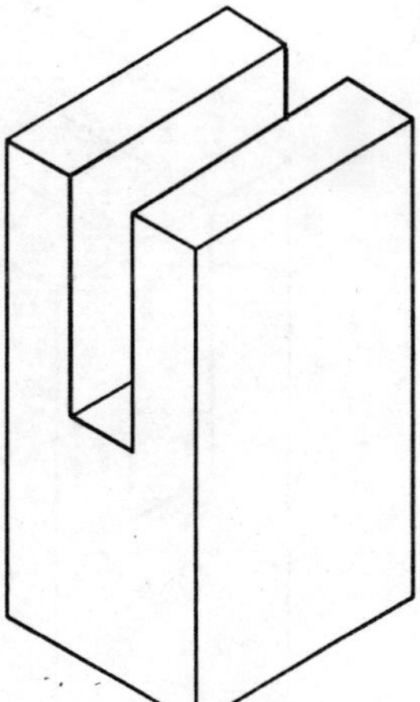

Bridle

Fig. 1.1

Detail Drawing Principles

Following steps are involved for drawing a detail drawing:

(*i*) Representation of a single part, giving an idea of location.

(*ii*) Details of all the parts in same relative position as in the assembly drawing near to each other.

(*iii*) Complete information about each single part.

(*iv*) Dimensions, limits, fits and tolerances etc. of each part.

(*v*) Specification such as surface finish, degree of hardness etc. written on each part.

(*vi*) Details of permanent joint and method of manufacturing of each part.

(*vii*) Views which are projection of each other. Such views should describe complete shape of each part including hidden details.

1.3 ASSEMBLY DRAWING

The drawing of a complete machine or structure showing all the parts assembled in their functional position is called assembly drawing. It is a design document containing a representation of all parts. It also gives the clear picture of location and relationship of different parts along with necessary data. The part list can be just directly above the title block as shown in Fig. 1.2.

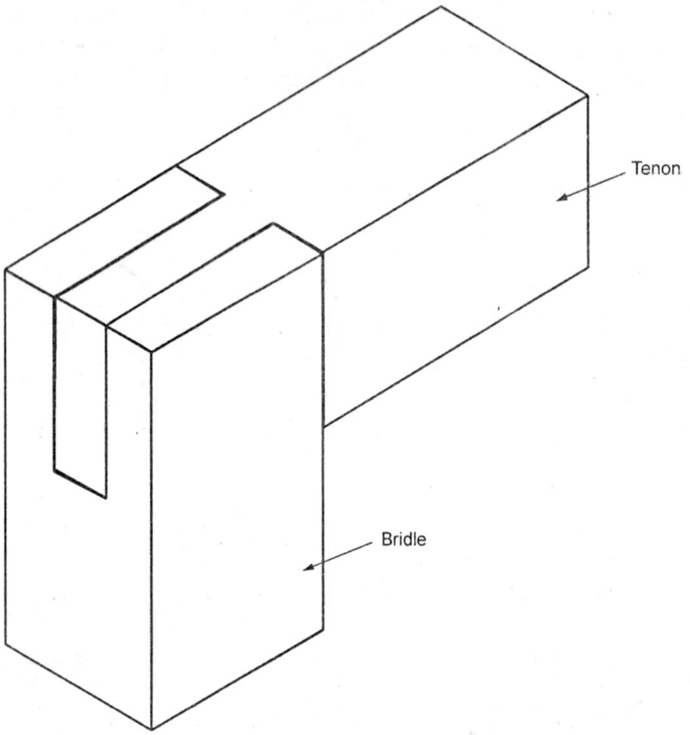

Fig. 1.2

Assembly Drawing Principles: The assembly drawing furnishes the following information are as:

(*i*) Representation of all the parts, giving an idea of location and relative position of the components which are assembled in their functional position.

(*ii*) Information enabling all the parts to be assembled.

(*iii*) Dimensions, limits, fits and tolerance etc. which are checked in accordance with the assemble drawing.

(*iv*) Specification or characteristics of the product.

(*v*) Details of permanent joints and the methods of their manufacture such as welding, soldering etc.

(*vi*) Sectional view to explain internal details, relative position and shape.

(*vii*) Views which are proper projections of each other.

(*viii*) Part list or material list indicating the component part, material, number of units and other informations.

1.4 TYPES OF ASSEMBLY DRAWING

The assembly drawings are classified according to their use are given below:

(1) Design assembly drawing.

(2) Layout assembly drawing.

(3) Installation assembly drawing.

(4) Working assembly drawing.

(5) General assembly drawing.

(1) Design Assembly Drawing: The drawing which is made at the time of design stage on large scale is known as design assembly drawing.

(2) Layout Assembly Drawing: The drawing which shows how the component or parts must be assembled to form the complete design is known as layout assembly drawing.

(3) Installation Assembly Drawing: The drawings which show how to install and erect machines are known as installation assembly drawings. They are also known as outline assembly drawings.

(4) Working Assembly Drawing: The drawings in which a complete set of working drawings of a machine that comprises of detail drawing and gives all necessary information for the production of individual parts and assembly drawing showing the location of each parts are known as working assembly drawing.

(5) General Assembly Drawing: The drawing in which detail and assembly drawing are prepared. It comprises of the detailed drawing of individual parts, sub-assembly and the assembly drawing of the machine. Accepted norms are to be observed for assembly drawings. The following information will assist you to understand the assembly drawing:

(*i*) Selection of views

(*ii*) Sectioning

(*iii*) Hidden lines

(*iv*) Dimensions

(*v*) Bills of materials (*vi*) Standard parts.

(*i*) Selection of views: One or two views drawing are generally sufficient and select only those views which show clearly how the parts are assembled together. Additional views are shown only when they add necessary information.

(*ii*) Sectioning: The part should be sectioned according to the requirement to show interior assembly details using full section or half section.

(*iii*) Hidden Lines: The lines which are used to provide additional details without the aid of section lines.

(*iv*) Dimensions: The overall dimensions and centre to centre distance showing the relationship of parts to the machine as a whole. Dimensioning of individual part should be avoided in assembly drawing.

(*v*) Bills of Materials: Each part of a machine is identified on assembly drawing by the leader line and numbers, which are used in the detail drawing.

(*vi*) Standard Parts: Standard parts such as bolts, nuts, pins, keys etc. are not shown in full details on working drawing and should be refered to their standard size.

1.5 WOODEN JOINTS

Generally detail and assembly drawings should be easily understood with the help of wooden joint. The joining of two or more wooden pieces for making various fittings, is known as wooden joint. Students should be advised that they should visualise the wooden joints assembly and after that they should visualise the machine parts assembly. There are various types of wooden joints used in engineering practice as shown in Fig. 1.3.

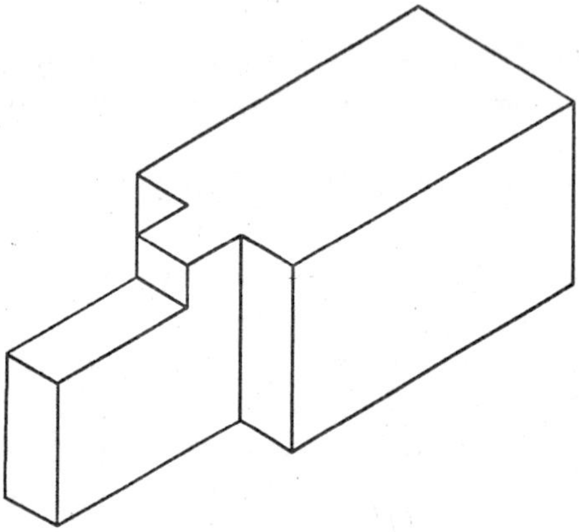

1. Haunched Tenon

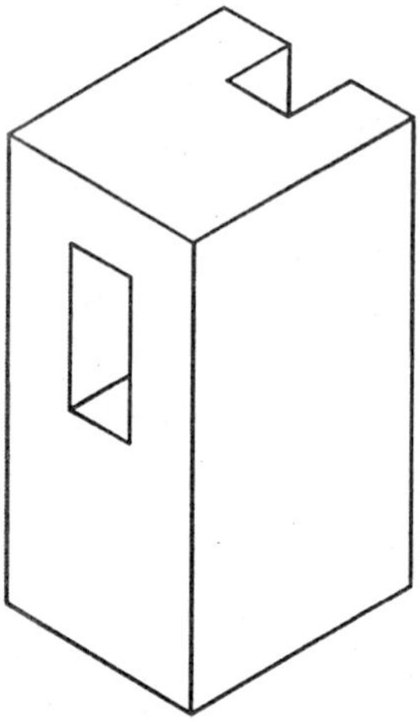

2. Haunched mortise

Fig. 1.3 Contd...

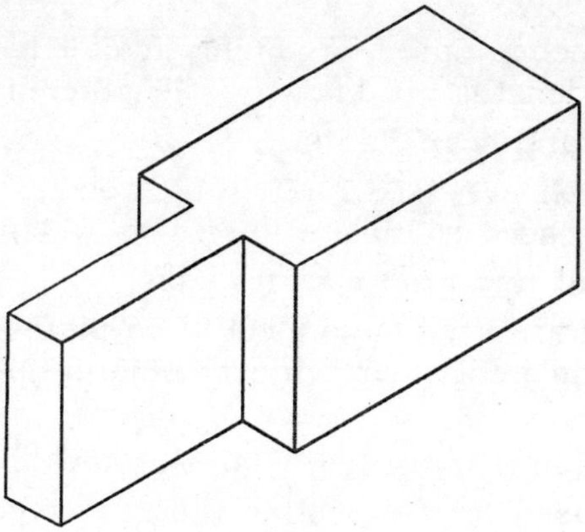

3. Tenon

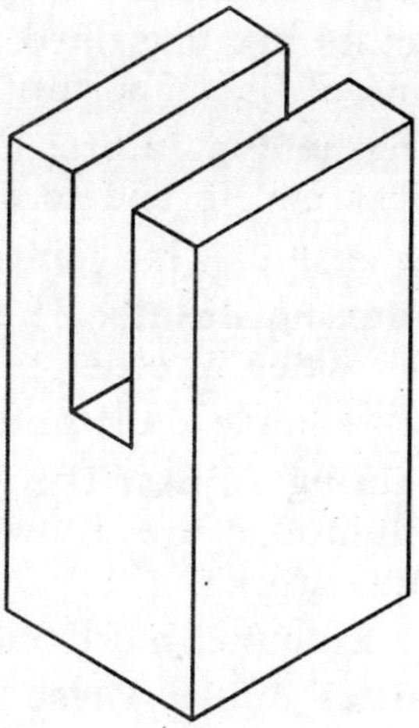

4. Bridle

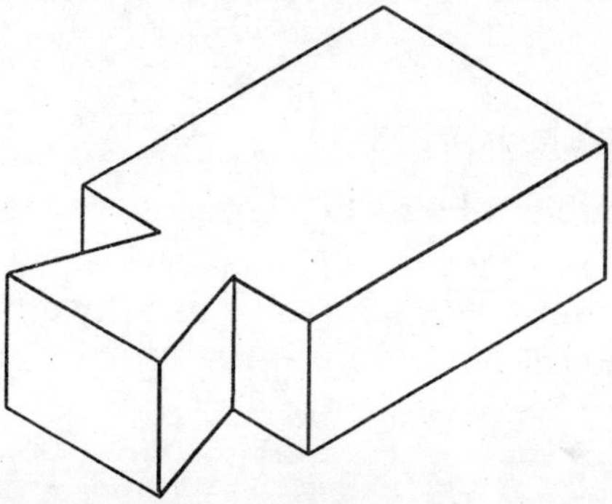

5. Dovetail

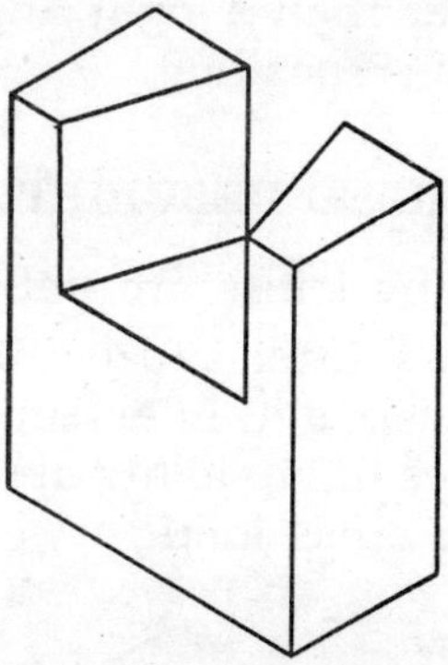

6. Pins

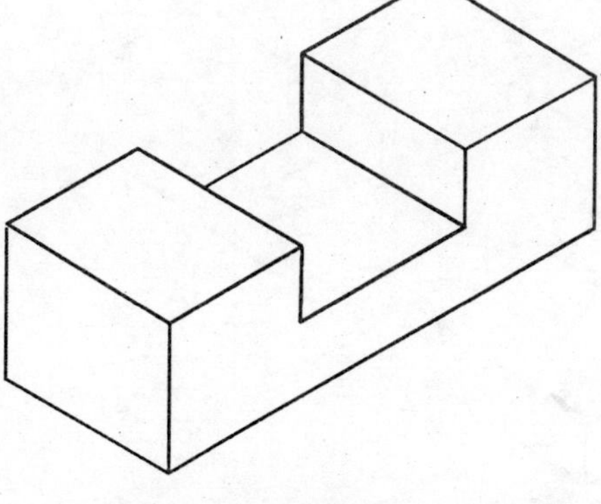

7. Halving Joint

8. Barefaced Tenon

Fig. 1.3

1.6 TYPES OF THE WOODEN JOINTS

Wooden joints are classified according to the purpose which they are intended to serve. Some of the important types of wooden joints are as follows:

1. **Lengthening Joints:** The joints which are used for joining small length of wood-pieces end to end to obtain large lengths are known as lengthening joints.
   For example, lap joint, butt joint and scarf joints.
2. **Widening Joints:** The joints which are used for joining wood pieces along their sides in order to obtain increased width are known as widening joints.
   For example, butt and tongue joint and groove joints etc.
3. **Framing Joints:** The joints which are used to connect wood pieces at desired inclinations are known as framing joints. They are commonly employed in frame work.
   For example, mortice and tenon joint, mitre joint, lap dovetail joints etc.
4. **Corner Joint:** These joints are used for connecting different types of ends and edges.
5. **Oblique Joints:** These joints are used for joining wooden pieces at an angle other than a right angle. They are widely used for the beam, timber roof and timber position.

1.7 DETAILED DESCRIPTION OF WOODEN JOINTS

The following joints are important from subject point of view:

(1) Lap joints: Lap joints are used to connect two wooden pieces to secure the corners and intersections of the framing. Lap joints are usually glued. Various types of lap joints are shown in Fig. 1.4 are T-joint, dovetail joint, corner joint and cross joint.

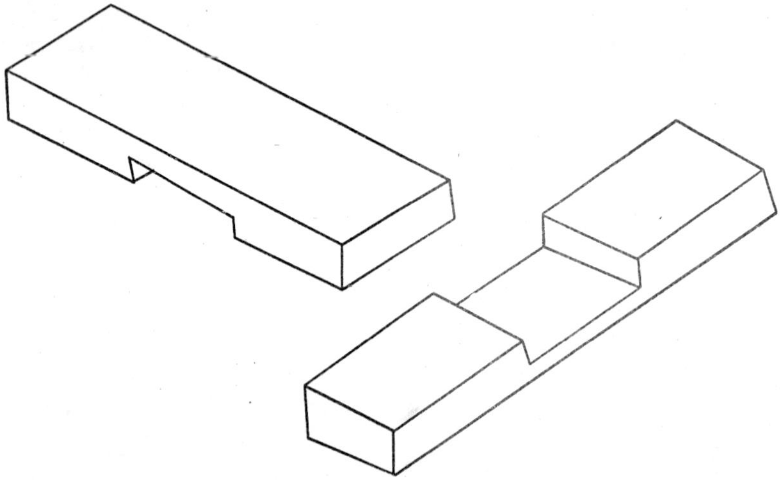

(i) Cross joint

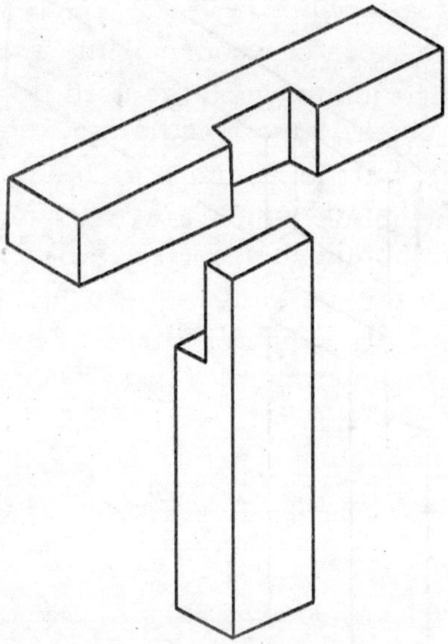

(ii) T-joint

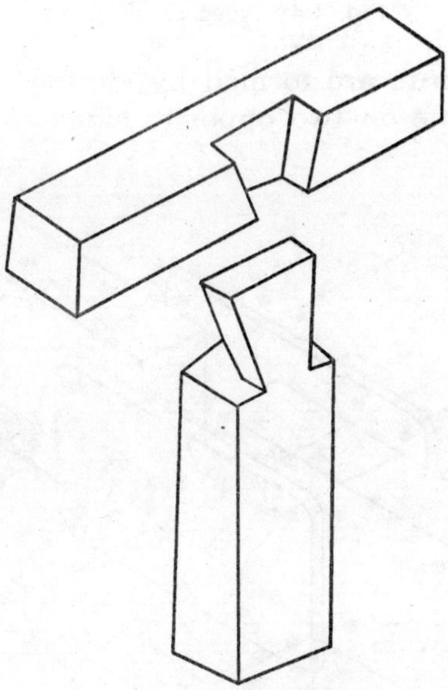

(iii) Dovetail joint

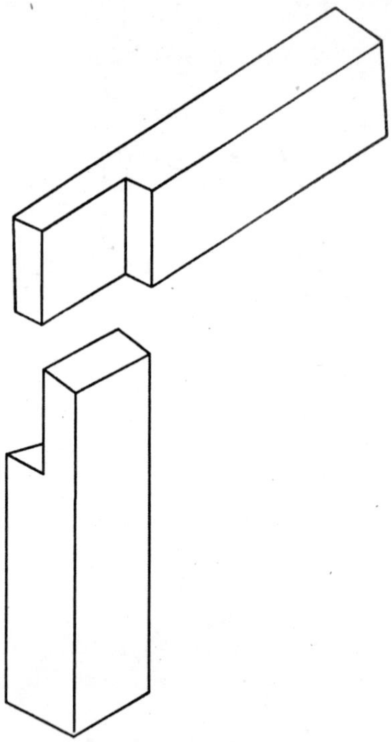

(iv) Corner joint

Fig. 1.4 Types of lap joints

(2) **Butt joints:** Butt joints are formed by joining the wooden members edge to edge by means of glue on two opposite sides as shown in Fig. 1.5

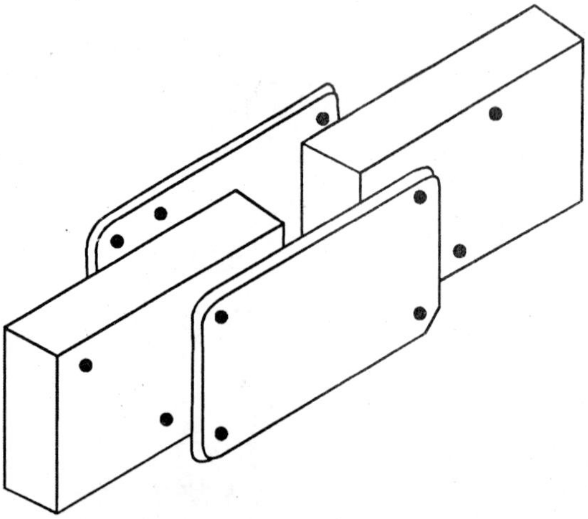

Fig. 1.5 Butt Joint

(3) Mitre joint: A mitre joint is an angle joint made by cutting the ends, of two pieces of stock at equal slant. The most common mitre joint is made by cutting each piece at an angle of 45 degree. When the pieces are put together make a right angle as shown in Fig. 1.6.

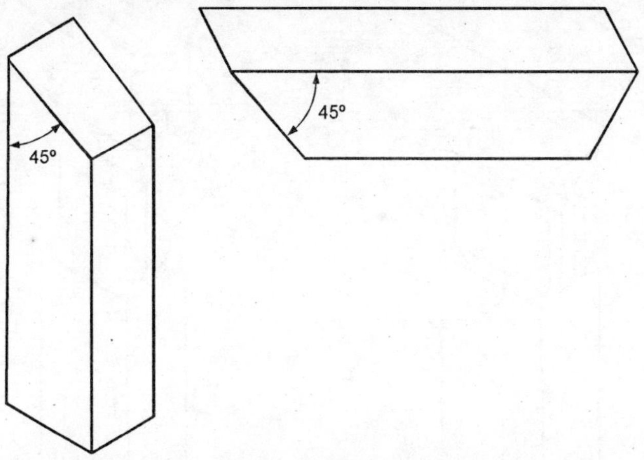

Fig. 1.6 Mitre joint

(4) Mortise and Tenon joint: This is the most common type of the joint. The mortise is the rectangular opening which is drilled out on drill press and then trimmed out with chisel whereas tenon is that part which fits into the mortise as shown in Fig. 1.7

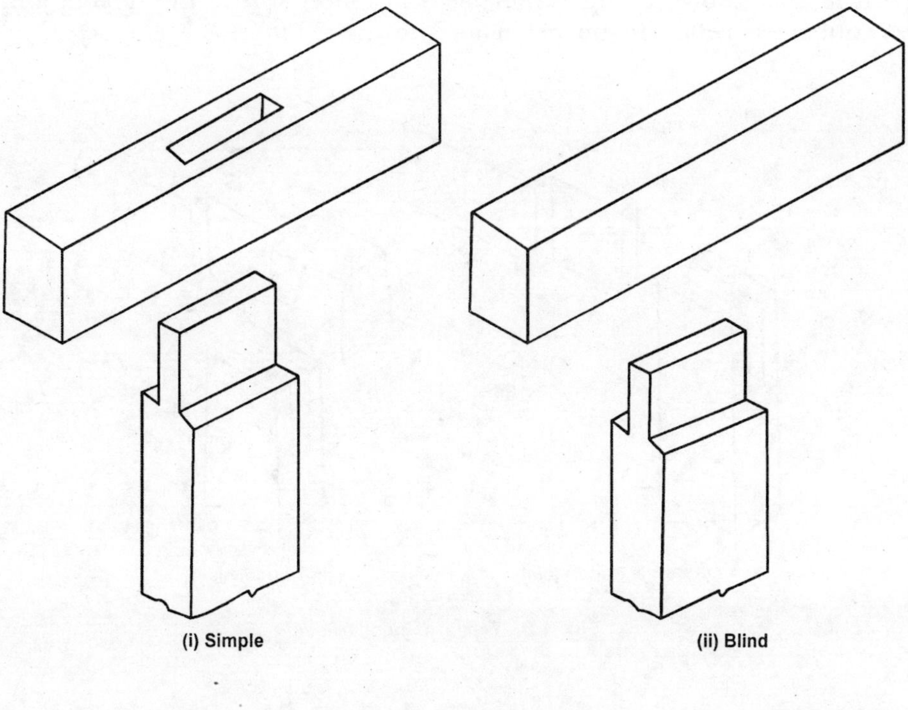

(i) Simple (ii) Blind

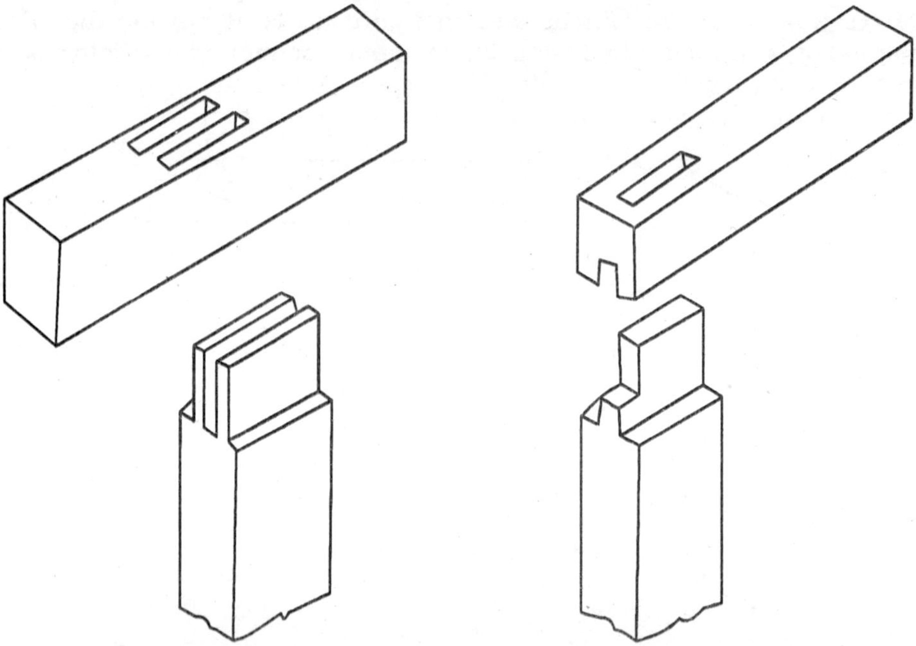

(iii) Double mortise and tenon (iv) Haunched mortise and tenon

Fig. 1.7 Types of mortise and tenon joints

(5) Briddle joint: This joint is reverse of mortise and tenon joint. This type of joint is also known as open mortise and tenon joint. This type of joint is used to connect a rafter to tie beam as shown in Fig. 1.8.

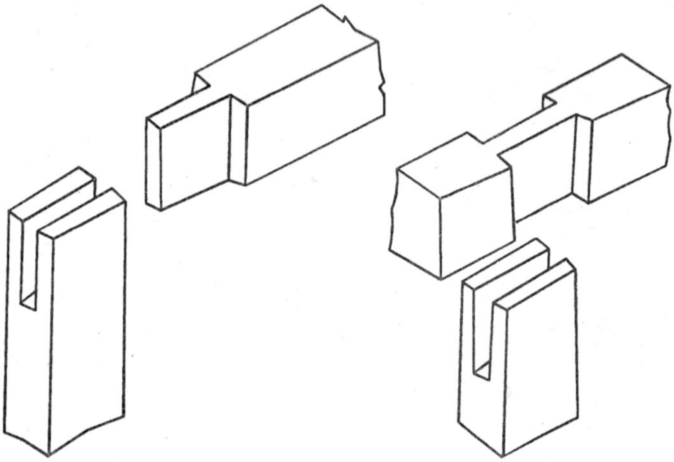

(i) Corner briddle joint (ii) T-briddle joint

Fig. 1.8 Types of briddle joint

(6) Dovetail joint: This joint is used in fine box and drawer construction. It is very difficult to made by hand. These joints are made in number of varieties and styles as shown in Fig. 1.9.

(i) Common or through devetail (ii) Lapped devetail (iii) Lapped secret devetail

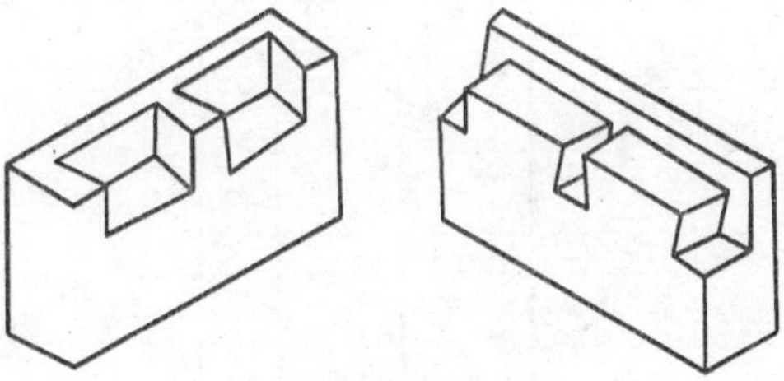

(iv) Secret devetail

Fig. 1.9 Types of devetail joint

(7) Dowel joint: Dowels are thin, small and round sticks made from hard wood and are employed in various ways. This joint is used as a substitute for mortise and tenon joints as shown in Fig. 1.10.

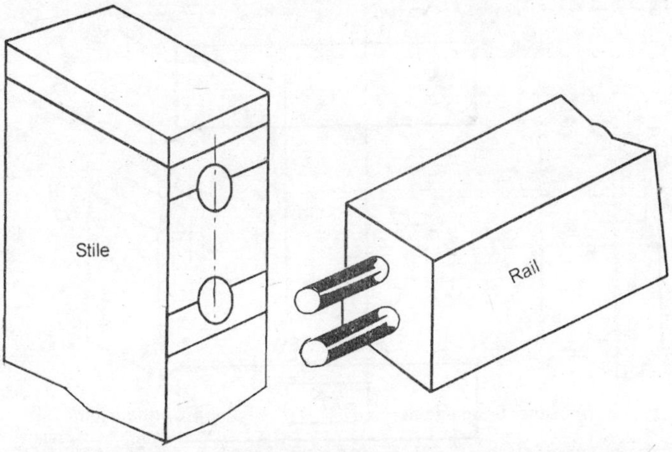

Fig. 1.10 Dowel joint

Problem 1. Fig 1.11 shows the detail drawing of a Tee-bridle joint. Assemble the parts and draw the following views:

(*i*) Front view (*ii*) Top view.

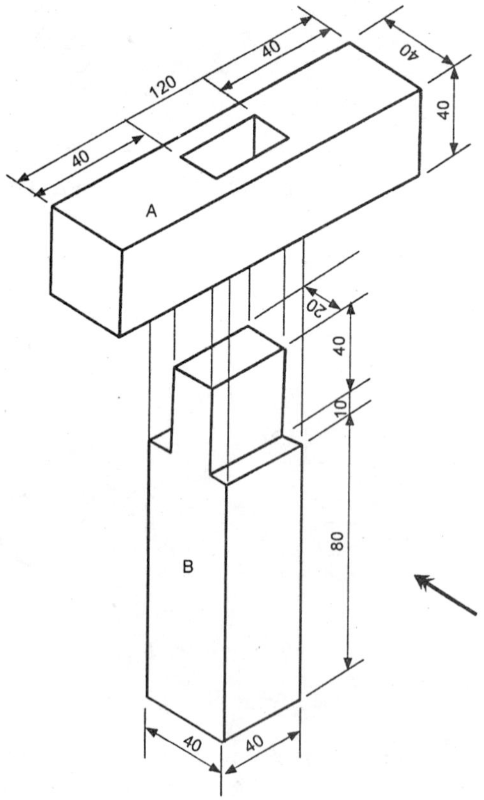

Fig. 1.11

Solution. See Fig. 1.12.

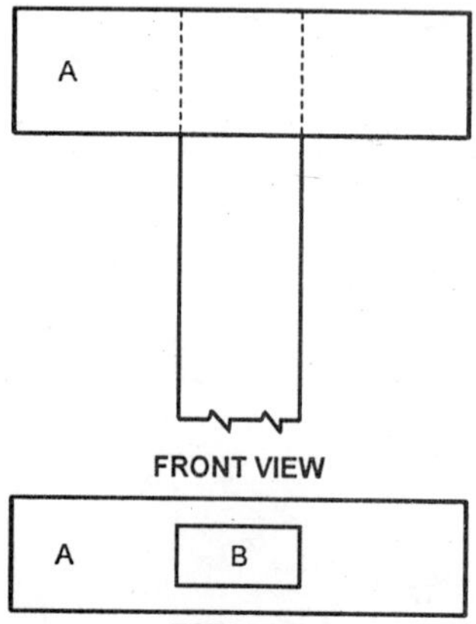

Fig. 1.12

Problem 2. Fig 1.13 shows the detail drawing of a mortise and tenon joint. Assembly the parts and draw the following views:

(*i*) Front view (*ii*) Top view.

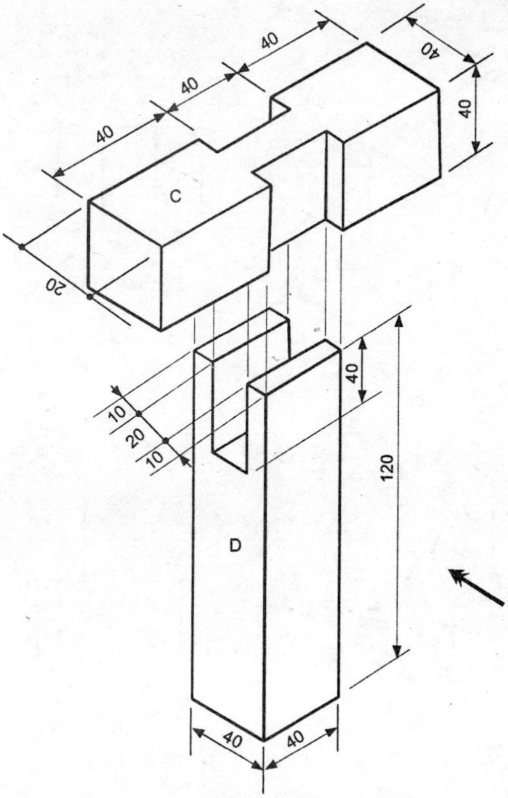

Fig. 1.13

Solution. See Fig. 1.14.

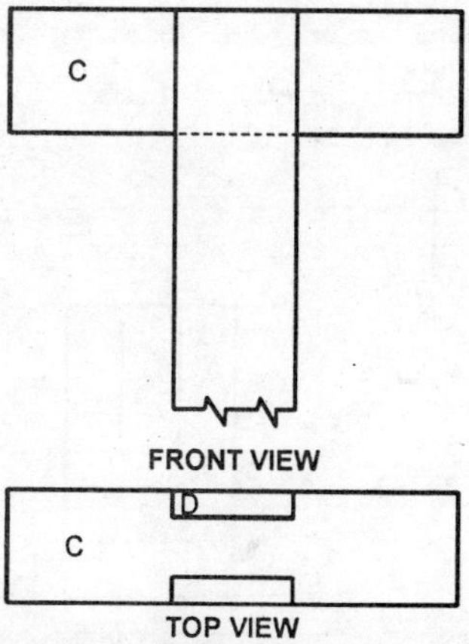

Fig. 1.14

Problem 3. Fig. 1.15 shows detail drawing of a corner bridle joint. Assemble the parts and draw the following views:

(*i*) Front view (*ii*) Side view.

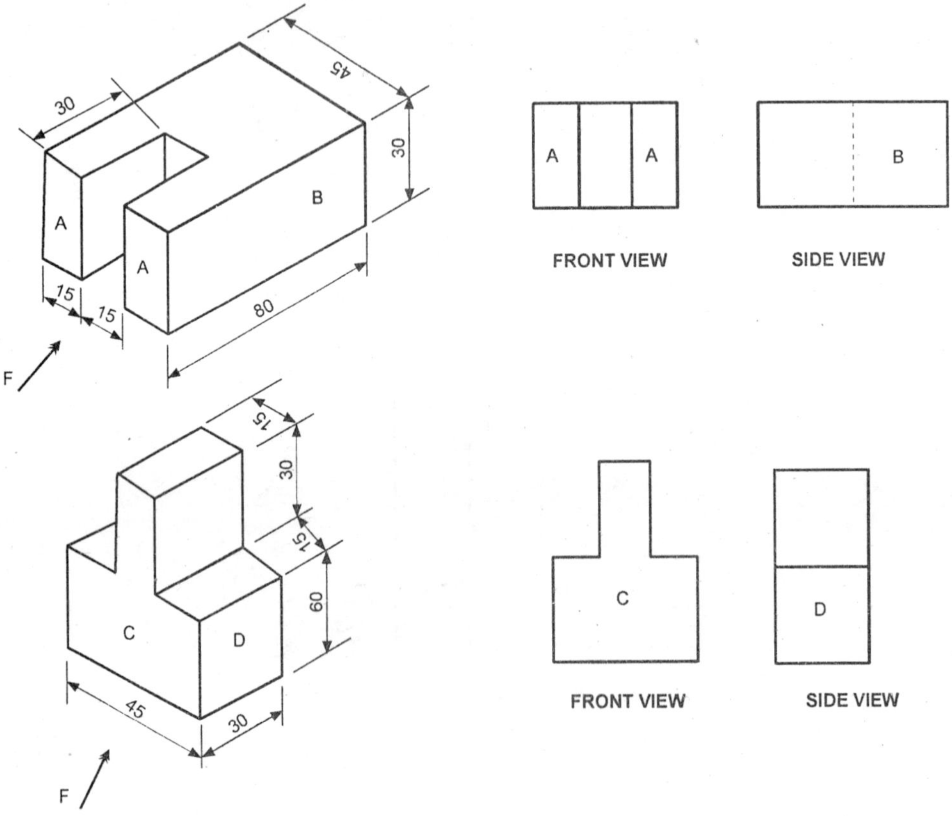

Fig. 1.15 Corner Bridle Joint (detail drawing)

Solution. See Fig. 1.16.

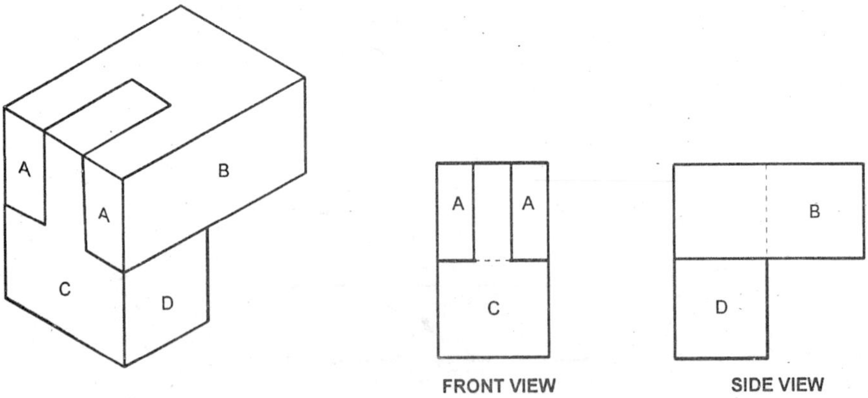

Fig. 1.16 Croner Bridle Joint (assembly drawing)

Problem 4: Assembly drawing of a Dovetail Bridle joint is shown in Fig. 1.17. Draw the detail drawing of a joint.

(i) Front view

(ii) Top view

(iii) Side view.

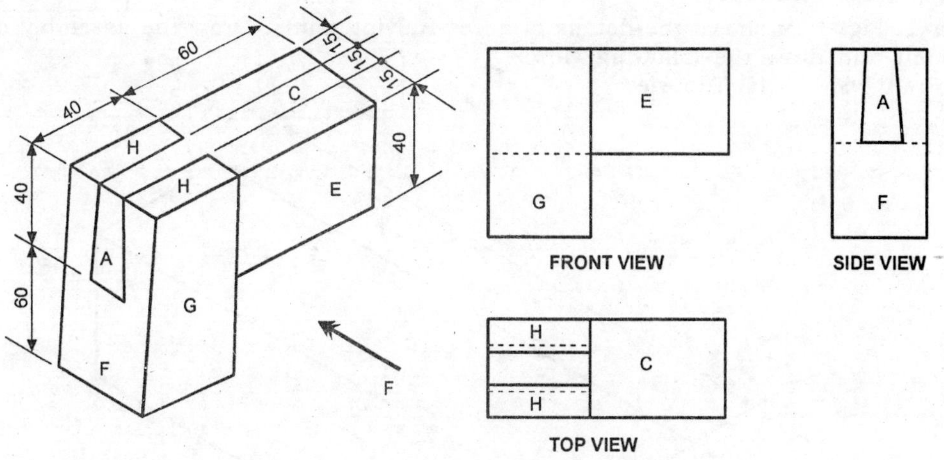

Fig. 1.17 Dovetail Bridle Joint (assembly drawing)

Solution. See Fig. 1.18.

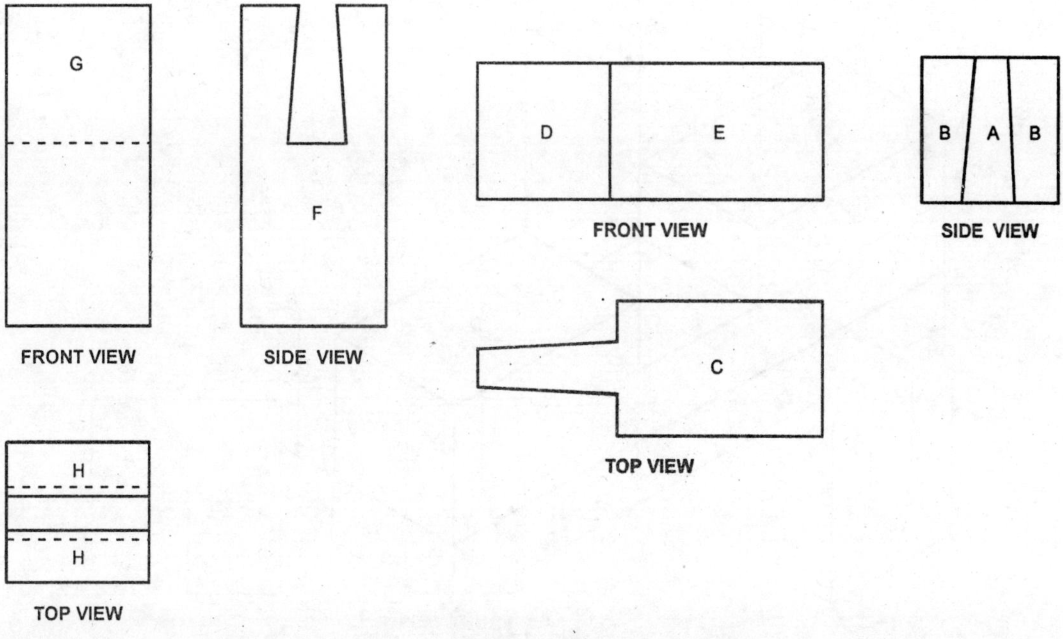

Fig. 1.18 Devetail Bridle Joint (detail drawing)

EXERCISE

1. What do you mean by a detail drawing?
2. What is the difference between detail and assembly drawing?
3. What is a part list?
4. What is wooden joint? Name at least five types of wooden joints.

PROBLEM FOR PRACTICE

Problem 1. Fig. 1.19 shows the details of a Tee-Halving joints. Draw the assembly drawing of the joint and draw the following views:

(*i*) Front view (*ii*) Top view.

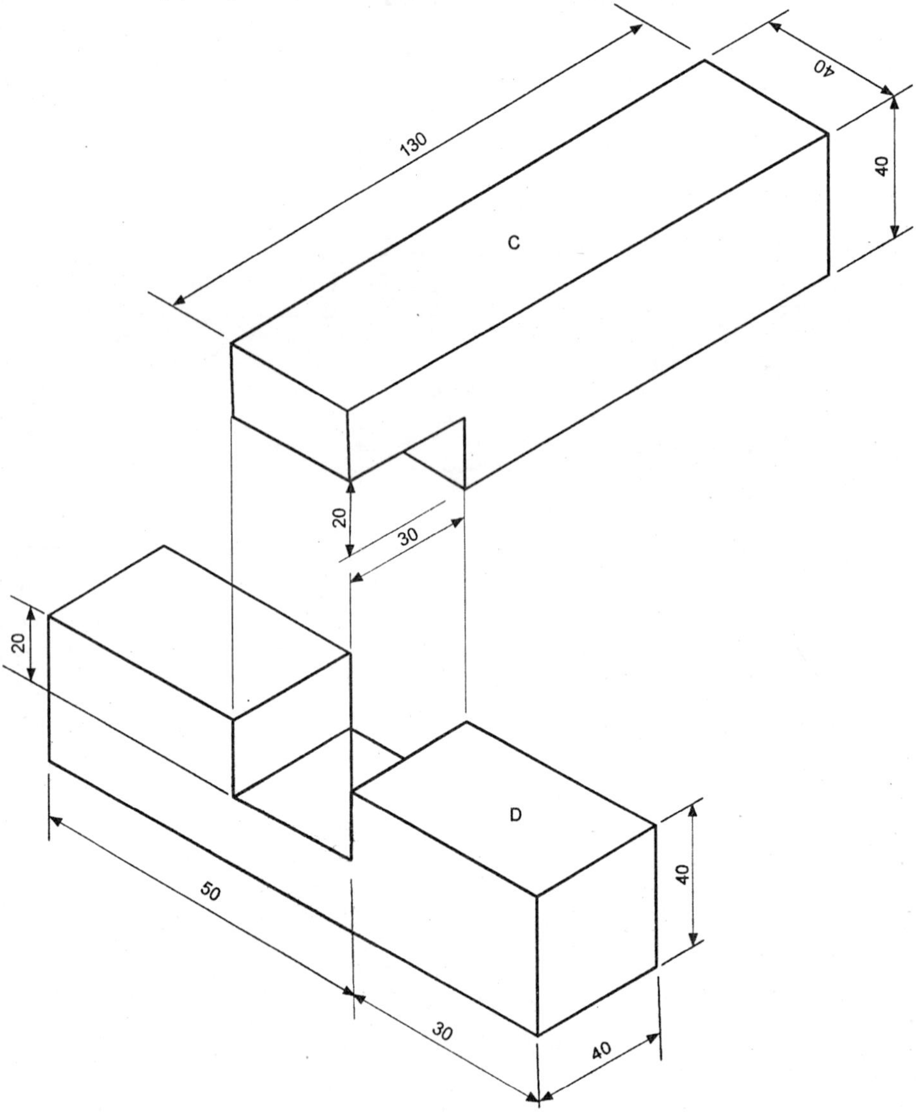

Fig. 1.19

Problem 2. Fig. 1.20 shows the details of a cross Halving joint. Draw the assembly drawing of the joint and draw the following views:

(*i*) Front view

(*ii*) Top view

(*iii*) Side view.

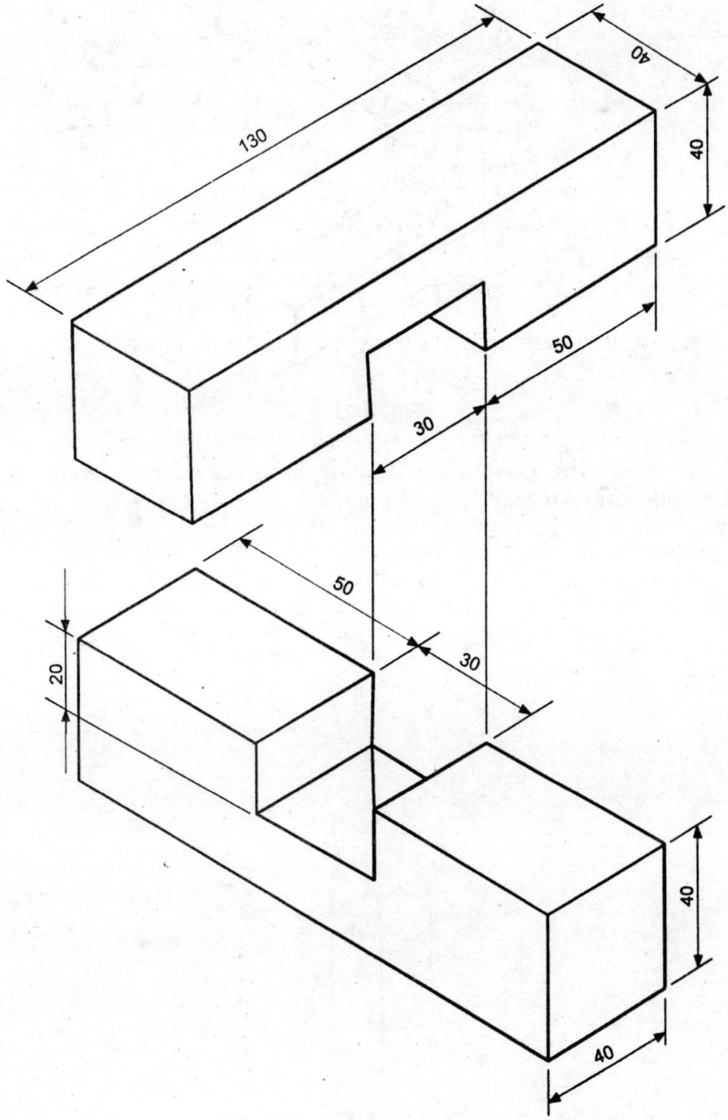

Fig. 1.20

Problem 3. Fig. 1.21 shows the corner Halving joint. Draw the assembly drawing of the joint and draw the following views:

(*i*) Front view
(*ii*) Side view.

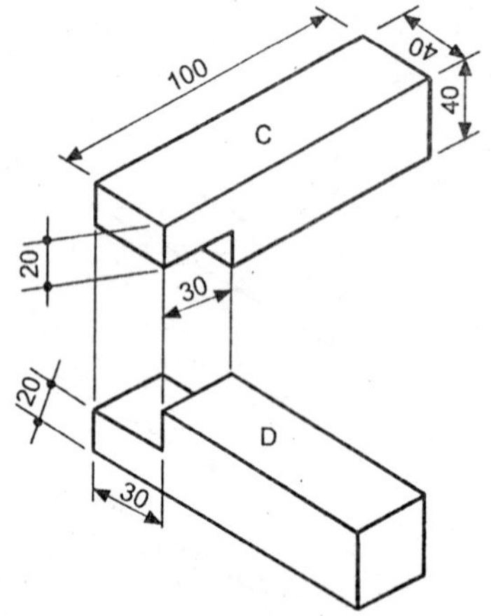

Fig. 1.21

Problem 4. Fig. 1.22 shows the Dovetailed Halving joint. Draw the assembly drawing of the joint and draw the following views:

(*i*) Front view
(*ii*) Top view.

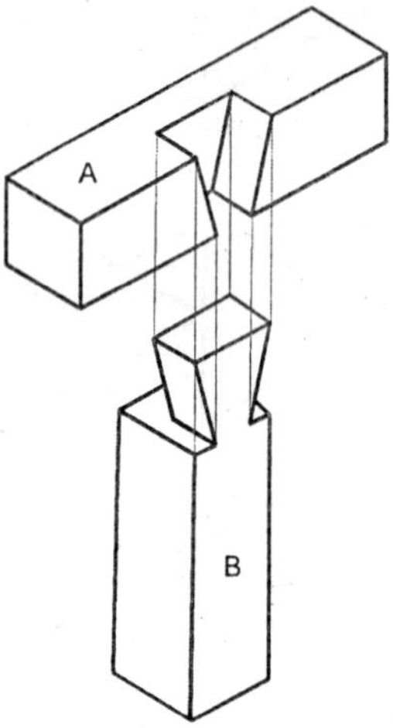

Fig. 1.22

❑❑❑

2

SCREW THREADS

2.1 INTRODUCTION

In the commercial field, the knowledge of screw threads play an important role. Screw threads are known for having advantages over welding. Different parts of steel structure, various types of machines and other engineering products are joined together by the help of fastenings. Therefore, screw threads are used for connecting two or more different parts together. A threaded piece consists of a cylindrical rod along with a projection, or thread in form of a helix. The threads are formed by cutting helical grooves on a cylindrical surface. The threaded rod is called screw.

It is an operating element of temporary fastening. It is used on bolts, nuts, screws etc. Threads are generally cut on lathe machine, whereas small size screw threads are cut by means of a die.

Applications. The main uses of threads are in steel structure, various types of machines and other engineering products such as in the construction of all types of buildings.

2.2 TERMINOLOGY OF SCREW THREADS

A screw thread is formed by cutting a continuous helical groove on a cylindrical surface. It may be single threaded or double threaded. The helical grooves may be cut either right hand or left hand.

2.3 EXTERNAL THREADS

The threads cut on the external surface of a cylinder of a male member are known as external threads as shown in Fig. 2.1.

Example: Bolts, studs and screw.

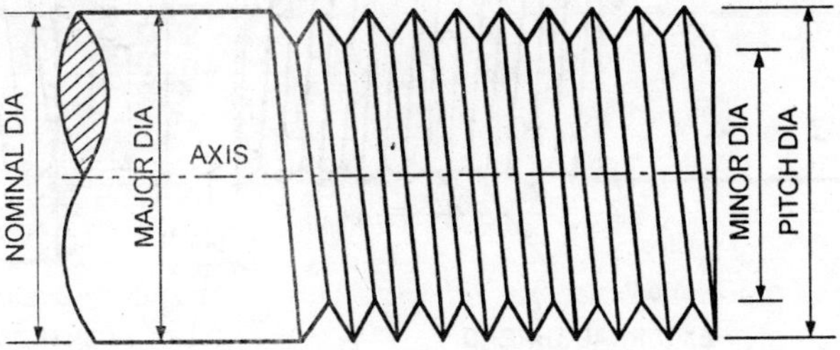

Fig. 2.1

2.4 INTERNAL THREADS

The threads cut on the internal surface of a cylinder of a female member are known as internal threads as shown in Fig. 2.2.

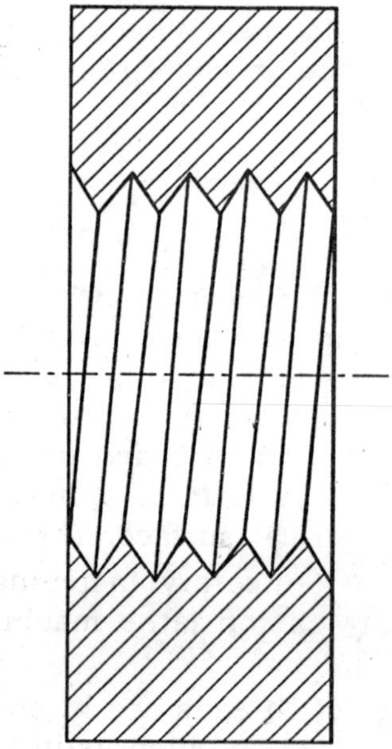

Fig. 2.2

Example: Nuts, rings and socket etc.

The terms used in screw threads are shown in Fig. 2.3. They are important from the subject point of view and are briefly described below:

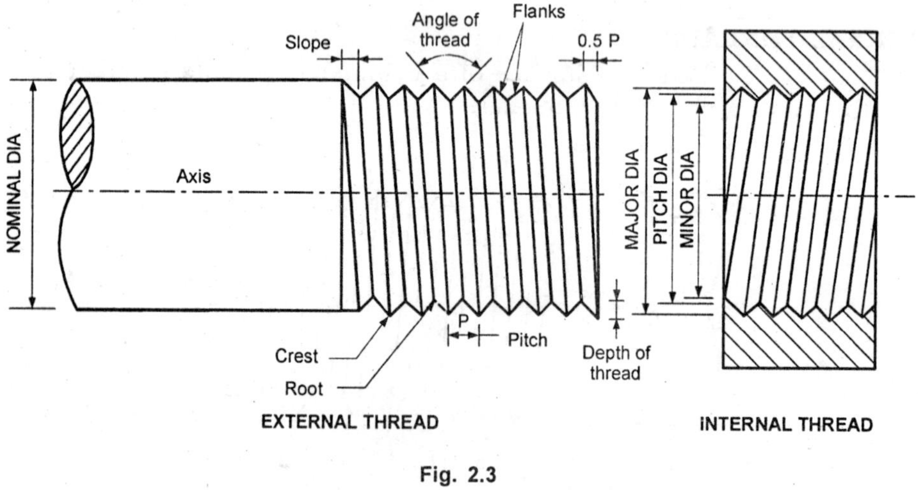

Fig. 2.3

1. Major Diameter: It is the largest diameter of an external or internal screw thread. It is also known as outside diameter or nominal diameter.

2. Minor Diameter: It is the smallest diameter of an external or internal screw thread. It is also known as core or root diameter.

3. Pitch Diameter: It is the diameter of that imaginary cylinder whose surface will intersect the threads at such point where the width of the threads will equal the adjacent width of the space between them.

4. Pitch: It is the distance measured parallel to the axis between corresponding points of adjacent thread forms.

5. Crest: It is the top surface which connects adjacent flanks of the threads.

6. Root: It is the innermost part of a thread.

7. Lead: It is the distance between two corresponding points on the same thread. Lead is equal to the pitch in case of single start threads, it is twice the pitch in double start and so on.

8. Flank: The surface between the crest and the roots of a thread is known as flank.

9. Threaded Angle: It is the angle included by the flanks of the threads.

10. Depth of thread: It is the distance between crest and root of a thread, measured normal to the axis of the screwed part.

11. Apex: The sharp corner the triangle opposite to its base.

12. Axis: The axis of the pitch cylinder of a screw thread.

2.5 RIGHT AND LEFT HAND THREADS

1. Right Hand Thread: When a threaded system winds, in a clockwise direction when seen axially is known as right hand thread. Threads are always assumed as right hand unless otherwise specified as shown in Fig. 2.4.

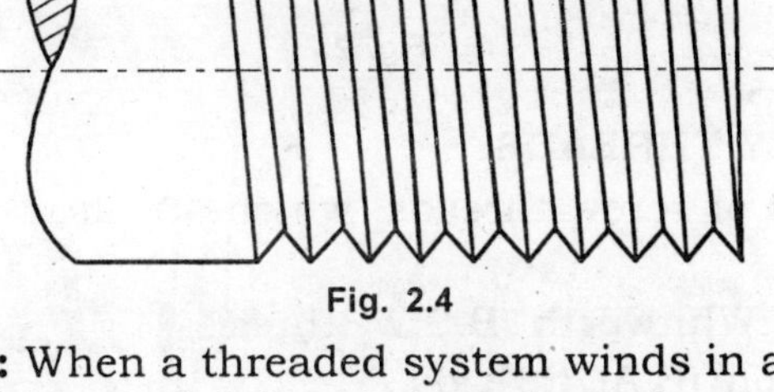

Fig. 2.4

2. Left Hand Thread: When a threaded system winds in an anticlockwise direction when seen axially is known as left hand thread as shown in Fig. 2.5.

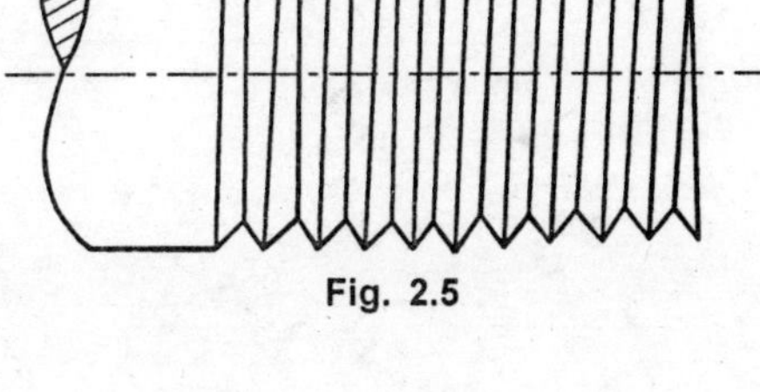

Fig. 2.5

3. Single Thread: When only one helix forms the thread, which runs on a cylinder throughout its length is called a single thread or single start thread. On a single thread the pitch is equal to its lead as shown in Fig. 2.6.

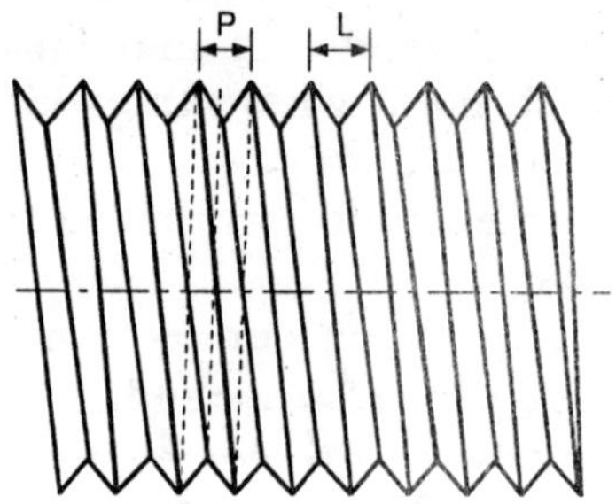

Fig. 2.6

4. Multiple Threads: When more than one helix parallel to each other, form the thread, which runs on a cylinder throughout its length is called a multiple thread or multiple start thread. Its lead is equal to number of start times its pitch as shown in Fig. 2.7.

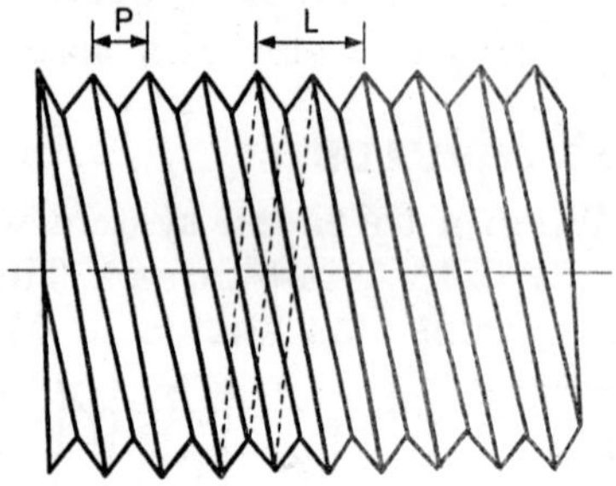

Fig. 2.7

2.6 FORMS OF SCREW THREADS

There are various forms of screw threads, which are used in engineering field. They are as follows:

1. British Standard Whitworth (B.S.W) threads.
2. British Association (B.A) threads.
3. American National Standard thread.
4. Unified Standard thread.
5. Square thread.
6. Acme thread.
7. Knuckle thread.
8. Buttres thread.
9. Metric thread.

1. British Standard Whitworth (B.S.W) Threads: This type of thread is used in great Britain. It is similar to a V-thread with only a minor difference. This thread forms an angle of 55°. These threads are found on bolts, nuts and studs etc. Now it is replaced by metric threads. The various proportion of B.S.W threads are shown in Fig. 2.8.

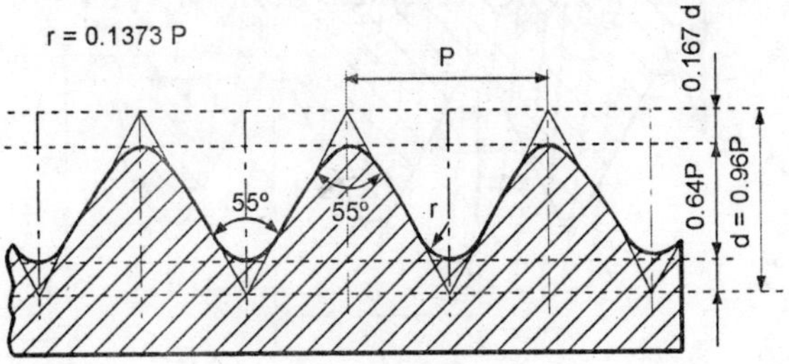

Fig. 2.8

2. British Association (B.A.) Thread: This type of thread is recommended by British Standard Association. The angle of the thread is 47.5° with both crests and roots rounded. The proportion of the B.A. threads are shown in Fig. 2.9.

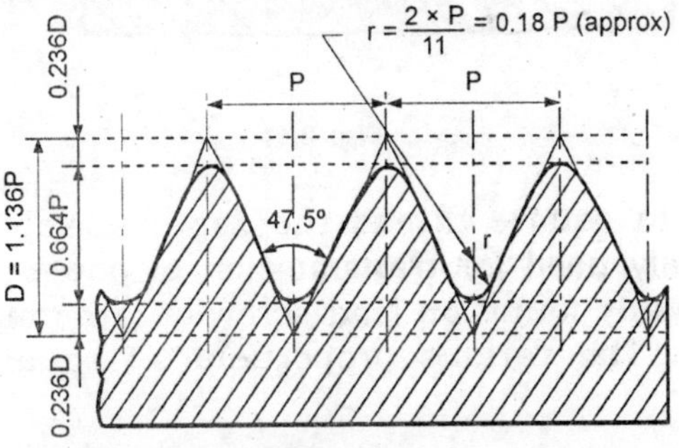

Fig. 2.9

3. American National Standard Thread: These types of threads are commonly used in United State of America with a thread angle of 60°. They are of 'V' shape and both crests and roots are flat. These threads are used for general purpose. The examples are: bolts, nuts, screw and tapped holes. The various proportions are shown in Fig. 2.10.

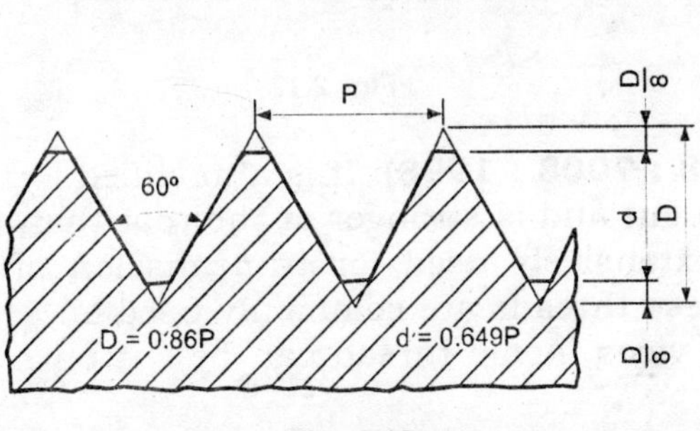

Fig. 2.10

4. Unified Standard Thread. These threads, mostly adopted by America, Britain and Canada, carry an included angle of 60°. The thread has rounded crests and roots as shown in Fig. 2.11.

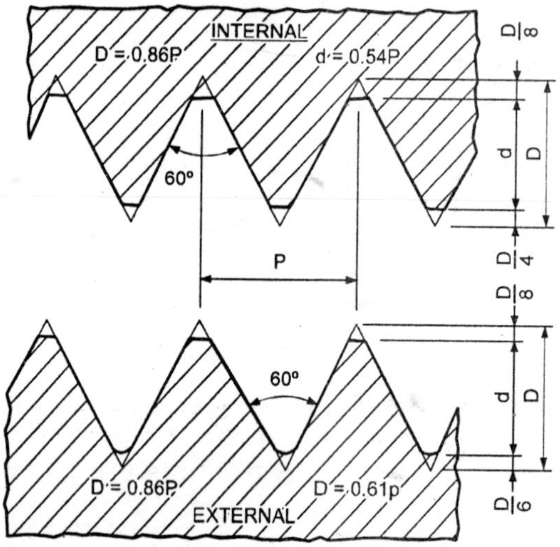

Fig. 2.11

5. Square Thread: In square thread the depth is kept half of the pitch. These square threads are widely used for transmission of power in either direction. These types of threads are usually found on lead screw of lathe machine, Jack screw, valve spindles and vices etc. The various proportions of square threads are shown in Fig. 2.12.

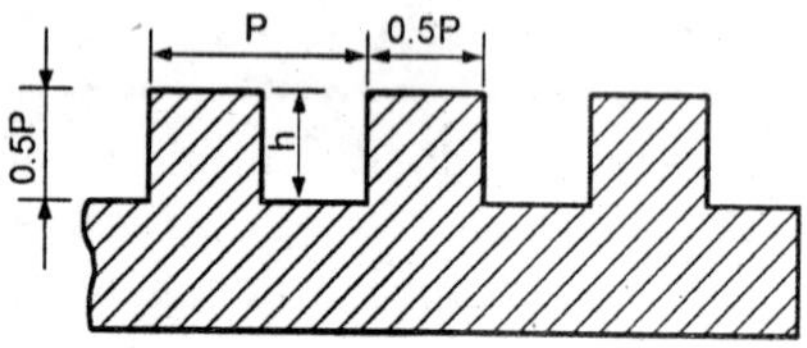

Fig. 2.12

6. ACME Thread (IS : 7008 : 1998): It is a modified form of a square thread and V-thread. It is easier to cut and is stronger at the root than the square thread. These types of threads are extensively used for transmission of power and motion. The thread angle is 29°. These threads are commonly used on screw cutting lathes, brass valves cock and bench vices. Acme thread can be cut on milling machine also. It is shown in Fig. 2.13.

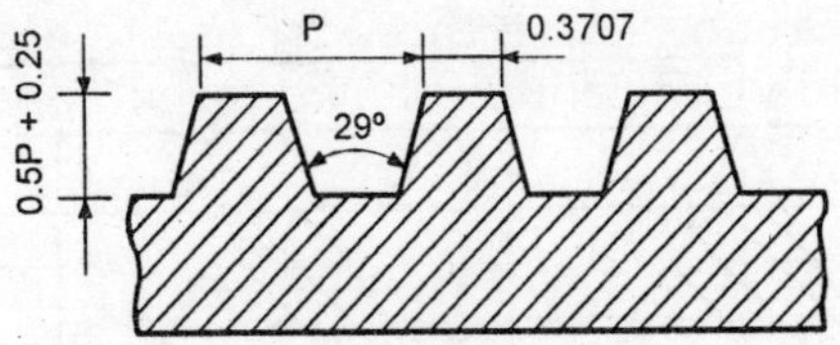

Fig. 2.13

7. Knuckle Thread: This thread is also a modified form of square thread with both crests and roots made semi-circular. It has rounded top and bottom as shown in Fig. 2.14. It can be cast easily and cannot economically be made on a machine. This type of thread is used for rough work. It is used in railway carriage couplings, electrical bulbs and necks of glass bottle etc.

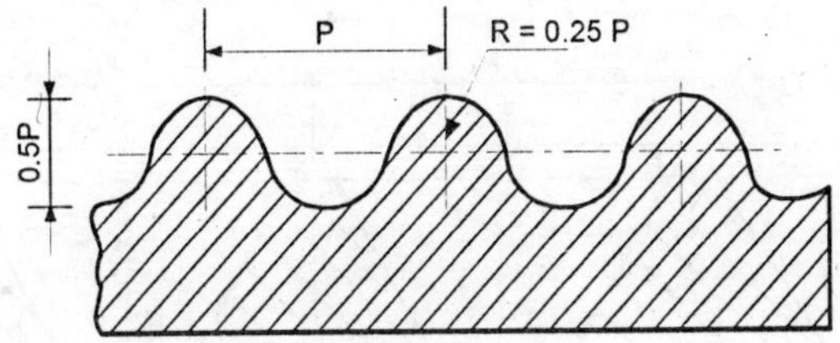

Fig. 2.14

8. Buttres Thread: Buttres thread is a combined form of 'V' and square threads with one flank of the thread perpendicular to the axis of the screw. The angle between its two flanks is 45°. It is used for transmission of power in one direction only and shown in Fig. 2.15. The application of buttres threads can be seen in carpenters vice, air plane Jacks and screw presses etc.

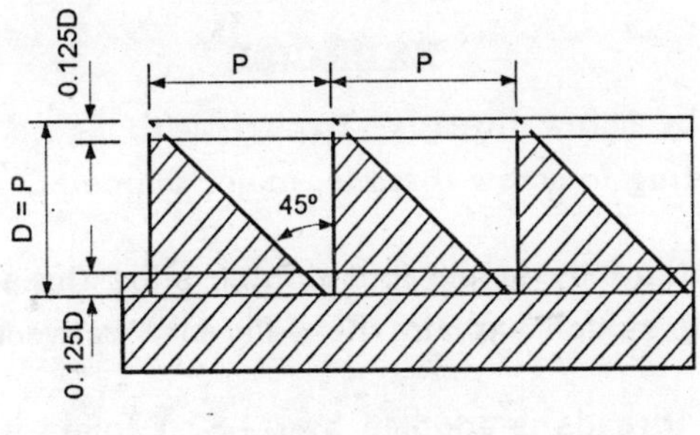

Fig. 2.15

9. Metric Thread: The Bureau of Indian Standards has recommended the adoption of the unified screw threads profile based on metric system. It is an Indian Standard thread and is similar to B.S.W. threads. It has an included angle of 60° instead of 55°. The basic profile of the thread is shown in Fig. 2.16.

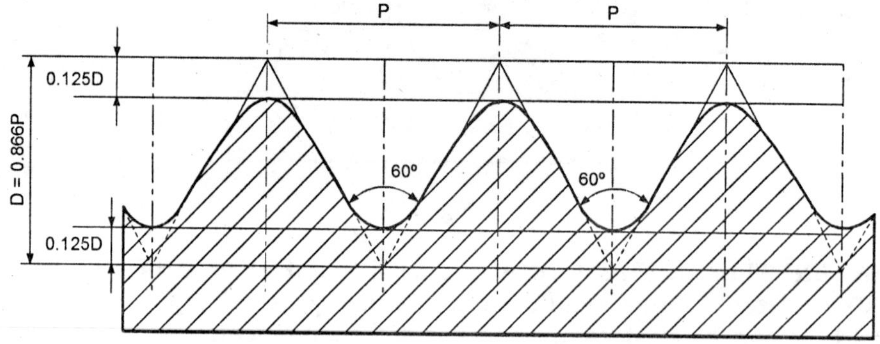

(i)

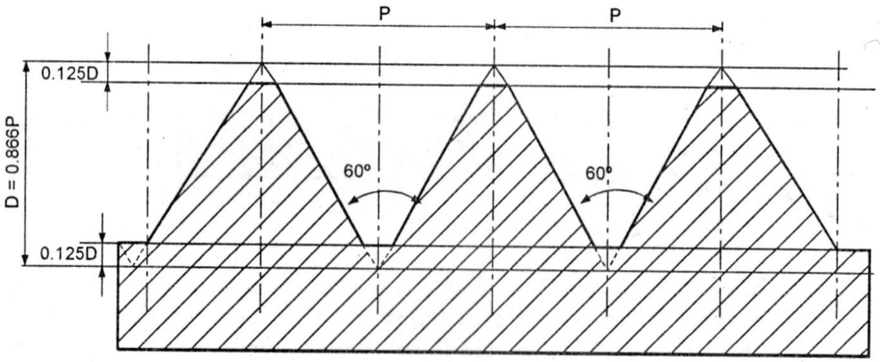

(ii)

Fig. 2.16

EXERCISE

1. What do you mean by screw threads? Explain with figure.
2. Define the terms relating to screw threads, major diameter, pitch diameter and threaded angle.
3. What do you understand by single and double start threads.
4. With the help of neat sketch explain the difference between left hand and right hand threads.
5. Which form of screw threads is adopted by B.I.S? Explain with the help of neat sketch.

3

LOCKNUTS AND LOCKING DEVICES

3.1 INTRODUCTION

As we see many different locking devices are used to prevent nuts from working loose. A screw thread holds securely unless the parts are subjected to impact and vibration, as in a railroad-track joint or an automobile engine, which may cause serious accident. In order to counter this tendency of a nut to unscrew, locking arrangements are in use.

3.2 LOCKING DEVICES

The devices which prevent nut from rotation and maintain the nut in its position are known as locking devices. The various types of locking devices are as follows:

(1) Lock nut
(2) Castle nut
(3) Slotted nut
(4) Sawn nut
(5) Locking plate nut
(6) Pin nut
(7) Simmond's locking nut
(8) Ring, penu and grooved nut
(9) Spring washer.

1. Lock Nut: It is also known as checknut, or Jambnut. It is the most common device used for locking arrangement. It has about half to two-third thickness of the standard nut. Both the surface, top and bottom of the nut are chamfered at an angle of 30° as shown in Fig. 3.1. The locking nut is always used with an ordinary nut for the locking purpose. The thin lock nut is first tightened down with ordinary force, and then the upper nut (i.e., thicker nut) is tightened down upon it. The upper nut is then held tightly while the lower one is slackened back against it. In slackening back the lock nut, a thin paper is required and it is not readily available, hence the lock nut is often placed above the ordinary nut.

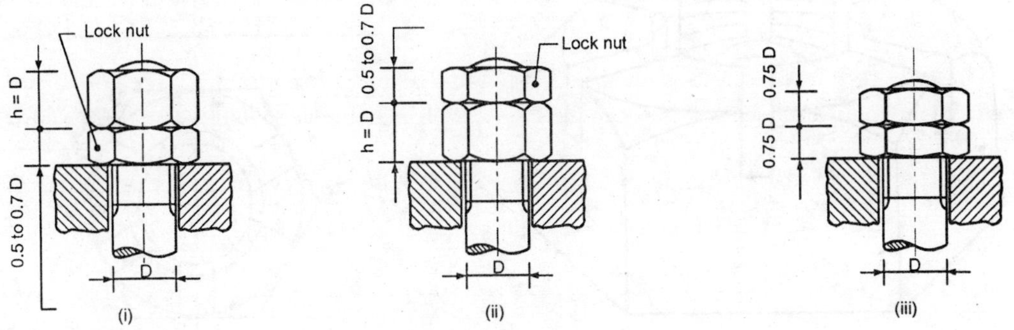

Fig. 3.1 Contd...

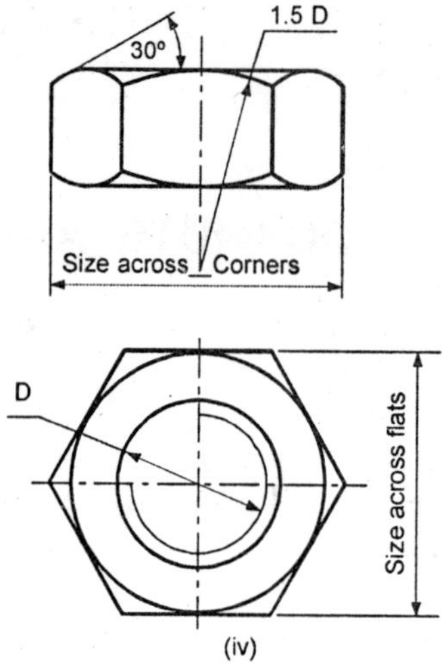

Fig. 3.1

2. Castle nut: It is variation of a slotted nut which consists of a hexagonal portion with a cylindrical collar on its upper surface which has slotted lines, with the centre of each face as shown in Fig. 3.2. A split pen passes through two slots in the nut and a hole in the bolt and keeps the nut in position. On account of additional cylindrical collar in castle nuts, there is no reduction in strength. It is extensively used where the object is subjected to sudden shocks and considerable vibration such as in automobile industry and locomotive engines.

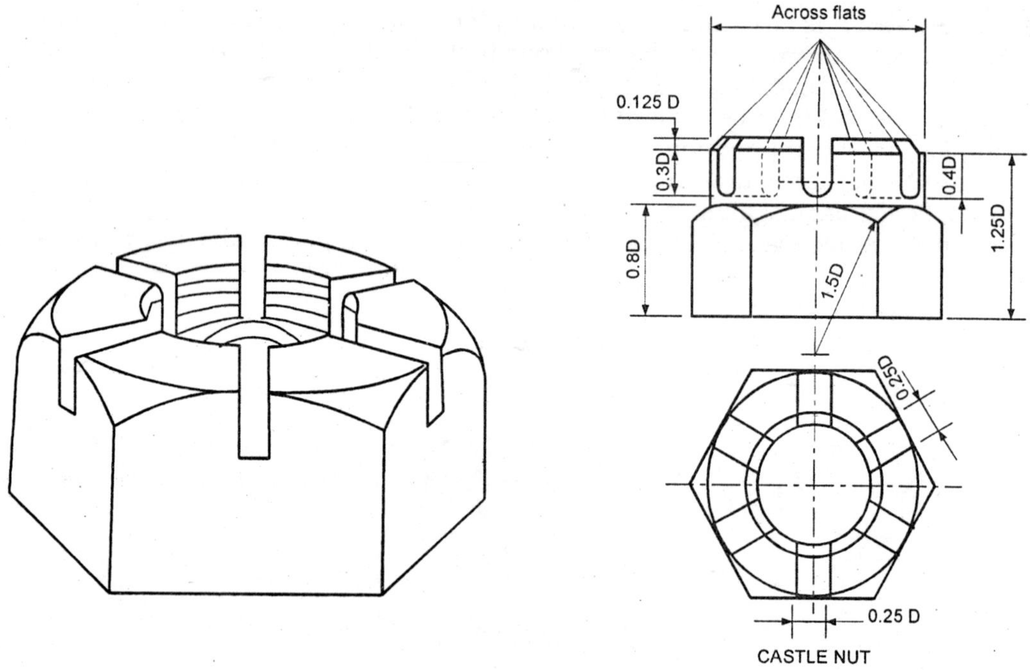

Fig. 3.2

3. Slotted Nut: The slots are cut in the upper surface and opposite faces as shown in Fig. 3.3. The depth of slots may be 5/6th and width 5/16th the diameter of the bolt. A circular hole is made in the thread at the end of the bolt. When the nut is screwed on the bolt and tightened, one of the slots comes in line with the hole. A split pin is then inserted through the slot and hole and it is opened out at its ends. This type of nut is used where the object is subjected to sudden shock such as motor car.

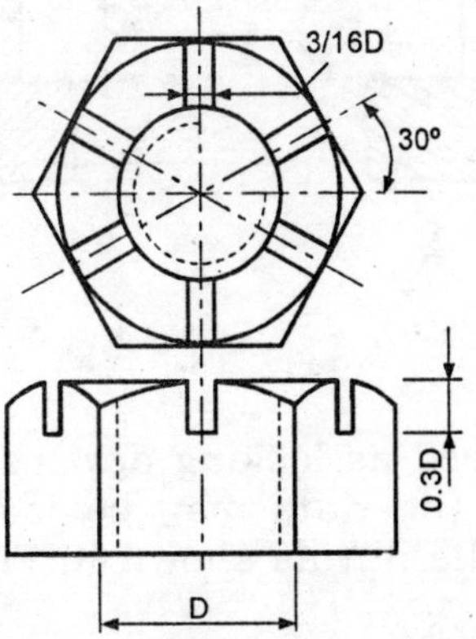

Fig. 3.3

4. Sawn Nut: It is a hexagonal nut having slot sawed about half way through as shown in Fig. 3.4. After the nut is screwed down, the small screw is tightened which produces more friction between the nut and the bolt when sawn nut is used for small diameter, the set screw is depended with and the closing up is achieved by means of a small hammer, thus the sawn nut would be more permanently fastened.

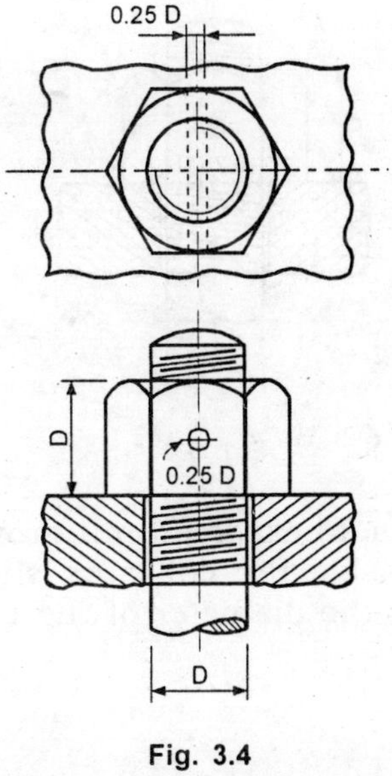

Fig. 3.4

5. Locking Plate Nut: In this case the grooves in plate are cut in side way so that the hexagonal nut fits in it through angular intervals of 30° as shown in Fig. 3.5.

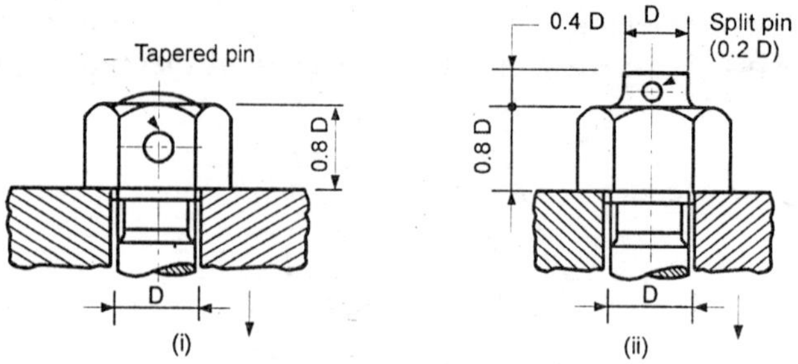

Fig. 3.5

6. Pin Nut: Pins are also used as locking devices. They are made of mild steel. In this type of locking device, the nuts may be locked by means of a taper pin passing through the middle of the nut as shown in Fig. 3.6 split pin is also used as a pin nut.

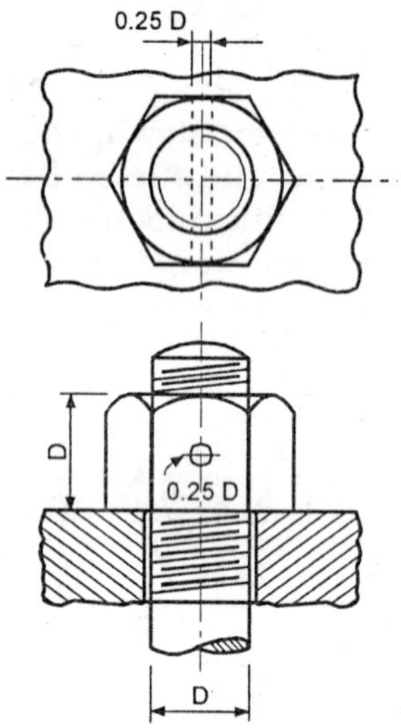

Fig. 3.6

7. Simmond's Lock Nut: It is a hexagonal nut provided with a coller at its upper surface. A fibre ring is fitted inside the coller as shown in Fig. 3.7. The internal diameter of the ring is less than the diameter of the bolt. It is not a positive locking device.

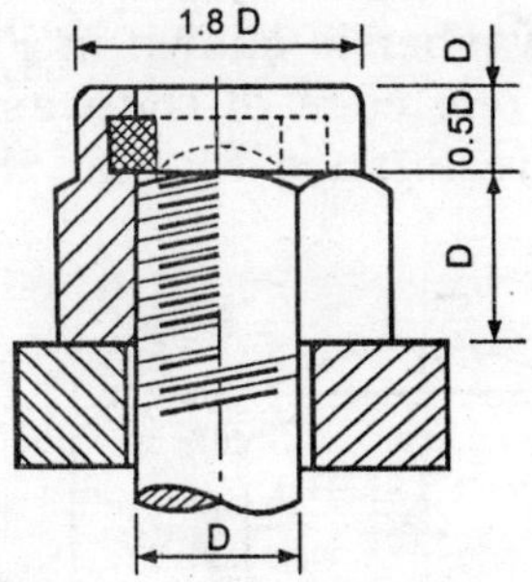

Fig. 3.7

8. Ring, Pin and Grooved Nut: It has upper portion hexagonal and a lower part cylindrical one as shown in Fig. 3.8. It fits into counter bored hole in the adjoining piece. A set screw is inserted through the nearest face of the piece. The end of the set screw enters the groove of the collar and prevents the nut from slacking. This arrangement is suitable when the bolt is placed near a face of the adjoining pieces.

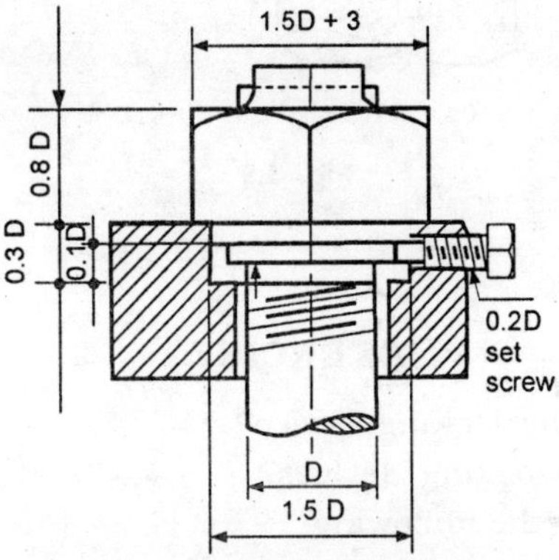

FRONT VIEW

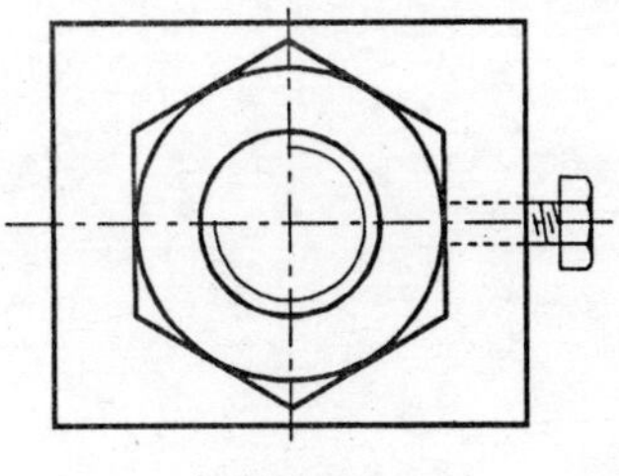

TOP VIEW

Fig. 3.8

9. Spring Washer: A spring washer is shown in Fig. 3.9. As the nut tightens the washer against the piece below, one edge of the washer is caused to dig itself into that piece, thus increasing the resistance so that the nut will not easily loosen.

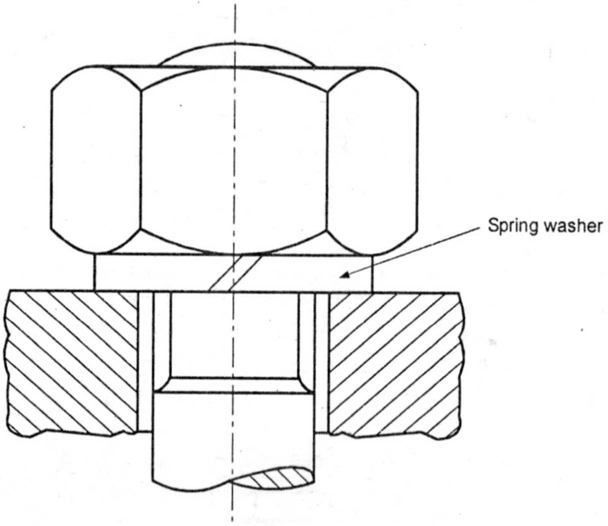

Fig. 3.9

EXERCISE

1. What do you understand by locking device?
2. For what purpose we use locking devices?
3. Write the short notes on the following:
   (*i*) Locking nut
   (*ii*) Sawn nut
   (*iii*) Pin nut
   (*iv*) Spring washer.

❑❑❑

4

THREADED FASTENERS

4.1 INTRODUCTION

Fastening devices are important in the construction of manufactured products, in the machines, fabrication and in the construction of all types of buildings.

Threaded fasteners are widely used for fastening or joining two elements temporarily by means of a screw threads. These are used in pairs for their action. The important types of screw threads are bolts and nuts, stud, screw etc. A threaded fastener is a cylindrical bar having a screw thread on one end and having a head at the other. The bolt passes through holes in two parts and is rotated into a nut at the other end. The bolt head, usually hexagonal form, is used to rotate the bolt by a wrench. Fig 4.1 shows a hexagonal bolt with nut.

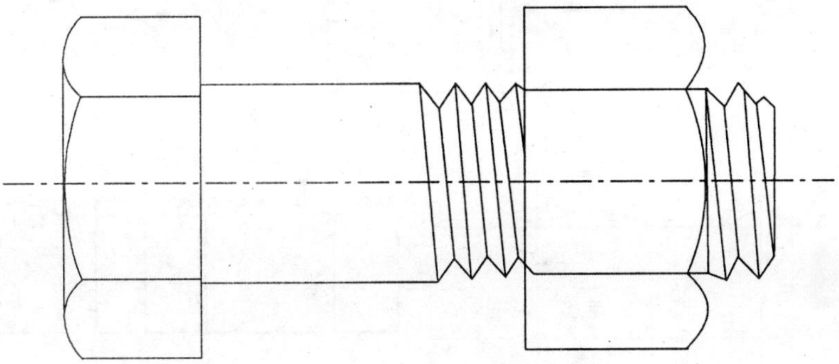

Fig. 4.1

4.2 NUTS

A device used with a bolt and capscrew to join two parts together temporarily is known nut. A nut has internal threads. It is expressed in terms of diameter of the threaded hole in the nut into which a bolt, or capscrew is fitted. These are available in two wrench type styles: square and hexagonal. In addition to the plain form usually associated with bolts, several special purpose styles are available. The top corners of a nut is chamfered at an angle of 30° to 45°.

4.3 TYPES OF NUTS

The following are the important forms of nuts used in engineering field:

(1) Hexagonal nut (2) Square nut (3) Flanged nut
(4) Cap nut (5) Dome nut (6) Capston nut
(7) Wing nut.

4.4 HEXAGONAL NUT

The following proportions are used to draw hexagonal nut:

(*i*) Thickness of nuts = TN = 0.8D to D
(*ii*) Size across flats = A/F = 1.2D + 3 mm (For bolts less than 12 mm in dia)
= 1.5 D + 3mm (For bolts more than 12 mm in dia)
(*iii*) Size across corners = 1.15 D × size across the flates
(*iv*) R = radius of front chamfer = 1.2D
(*v*) Angle of chamfer = 30°.

where, D = outer diameter of bolt.

Fig. 4.2 (*i*) and (*ii*) show the hexagonal nut.

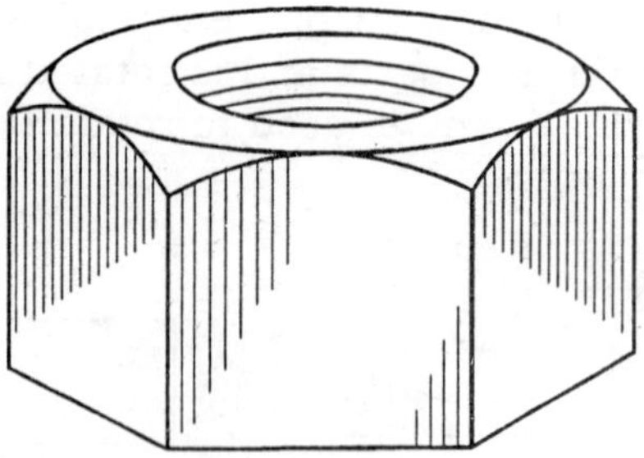

(*i*)

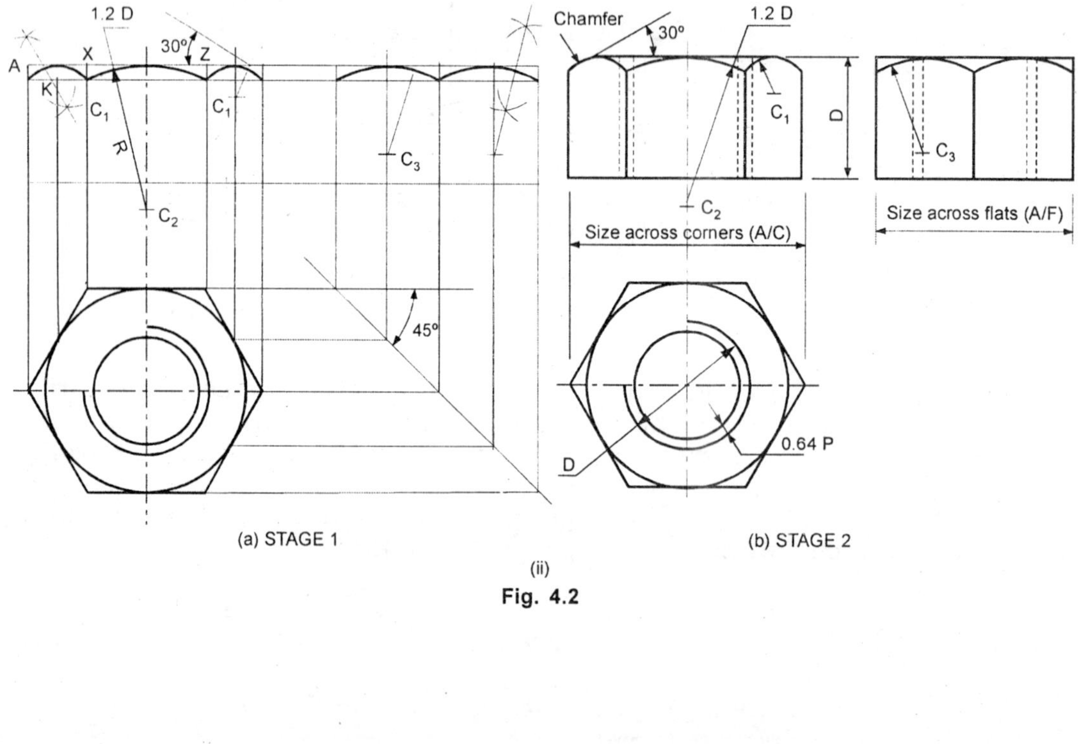

(ii)

Fig. 4.2

4.5 METHOD OF DRAWING HEXAGONAL NUT

Draw a top view containing circle of diameter A/F equal to 1.5D + 3 mm and circumscribe a regular hexagon about the circle with two sides horizontal. Next draw front elevation taking thickness equal to D. A 30° conical chamfer is recommended. Describe the arc with the radius R and centre C_2. Draw the perpendicular bisector of AX. The perpendicular bisector of AK intersects the perpendicular through K at C_1. Describe the arc AX with centre C_1, similarly, draw the side view which is a two face view.

4.6 SQUARE NUT

The nut has square sides and its corners are chamfered at 30°.

(*i*) Size across flats = 1.5D + 3mm

(*ii*) Size across corners = $\sqrt{2}$ × size A/F

(*iii*) Height of nut = 0.5D + D

(*iv*) Radius of front chamfer (R) = 1.7D to 2D.

(*v*) Angle of chamfer = 30°.

Method: Draw the circle of diameter equal to 1.5D + 3 mm and circumscribe a regular square with all its sides equally inclined to the horizontal as shown in Fig. 4.3.

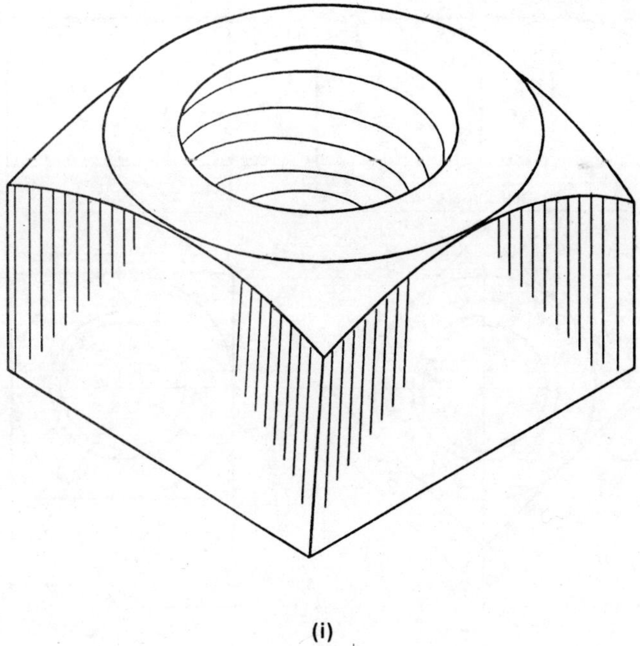

(i)

Fig. 4.3

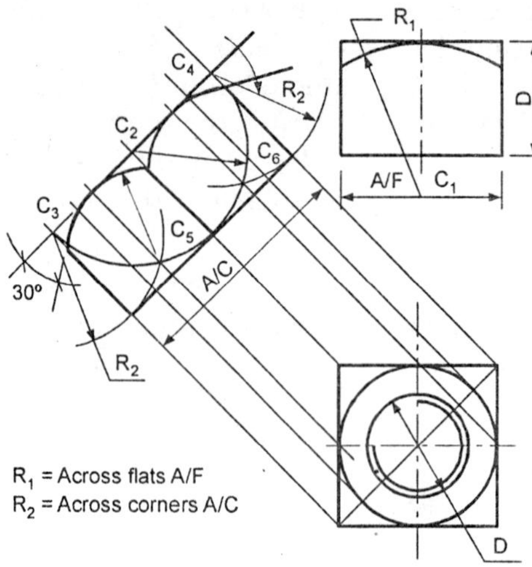

(ii)

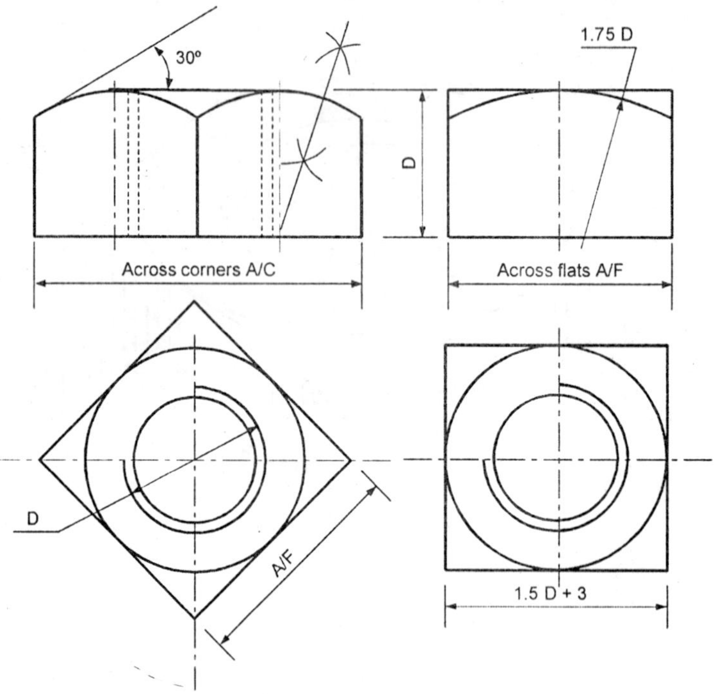

(iii) (iv)

Fig. 4.3

4.7 FLANGED NUT

The flanged nut is a hexagonal nut with washer or disc. The bearing surface of the nut increases due to the washer which provides a flat surface to contact the part to be tightened. There is no need of separate washer with this type of nut as shown in Fig. 4.4.

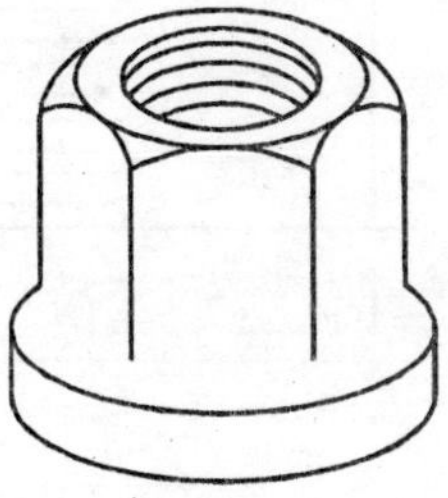

Flange nut

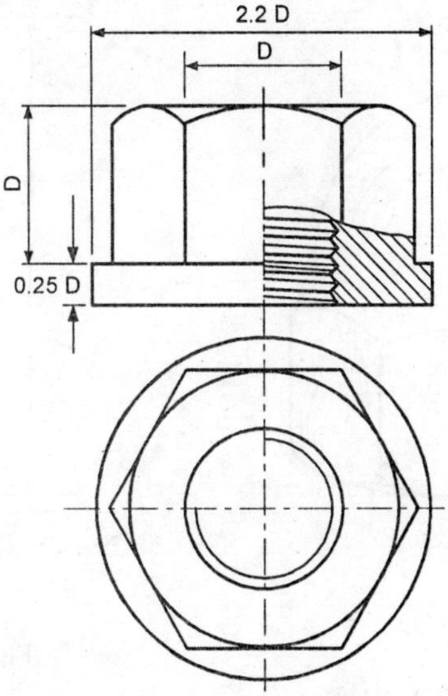

Fig. 4.4

4.8 CAP NUT

It is hexagonal, special type of nut. It is provided with an integral cylindrical cap at the top of the nut. The cap nut not only protects the bolt from corrosion but also prevents the leakage of fluid through threads as shown in Fig. 4.5.

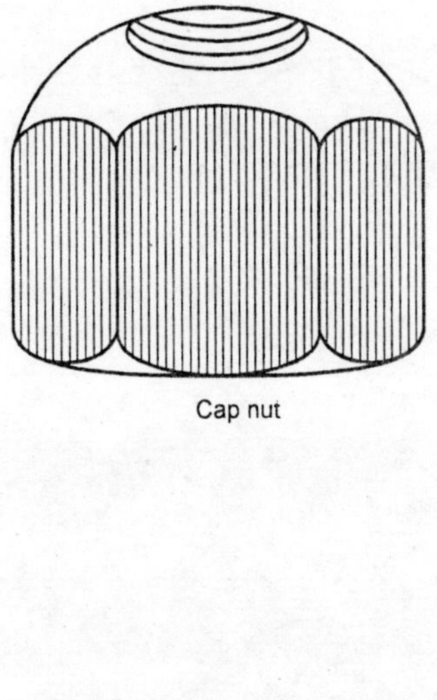

Cap nut

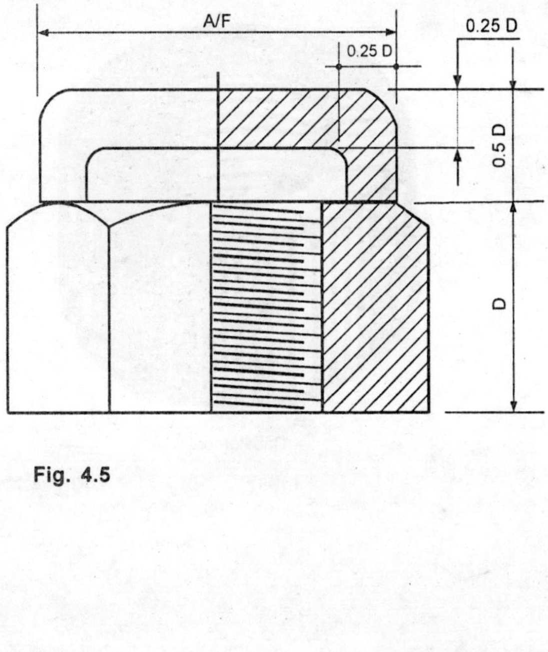

Fig. 4.5

4.9 DOME NUT

This nut is provided with an integral spherical cap at the top of the nut. It surves the same purpose as the cap nut as shown in Fig. 4.6.

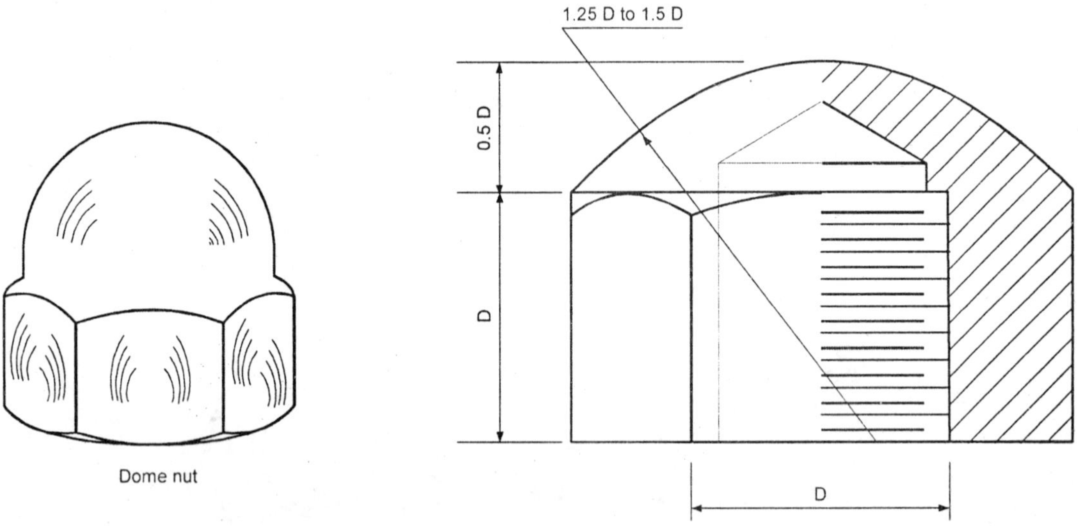

Fig. 4.6

4.10 CAPSTON NUT

It is also known as cylindrical nut as its out side is cylinder and no flats for wrench. The circular nut is provided with size equispaced circular drilled holes on the curved surface. A pin spanner is used to turn the nut as shown in Fig. 4.7.

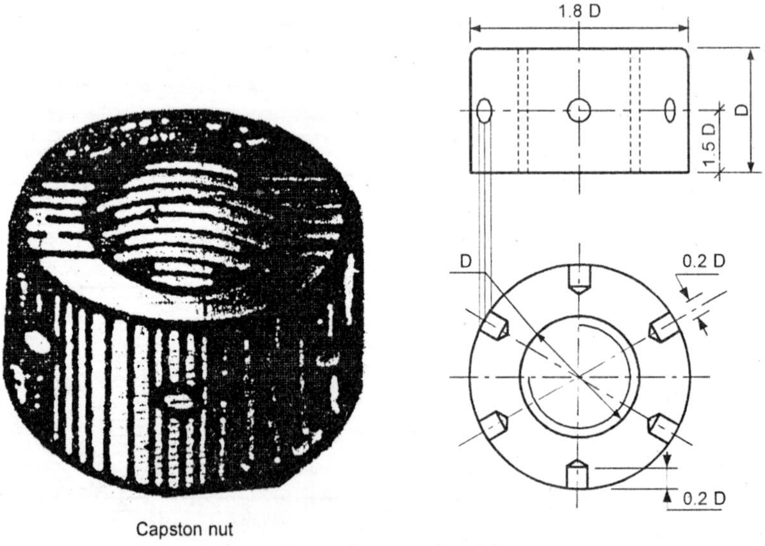

Fig. 4.7

4.11 WING NUT

It is a conical nut having two wings attached with its slant surface. It is used when they are to be tightened or loosened by hand only as shown in Fig. 4.8.

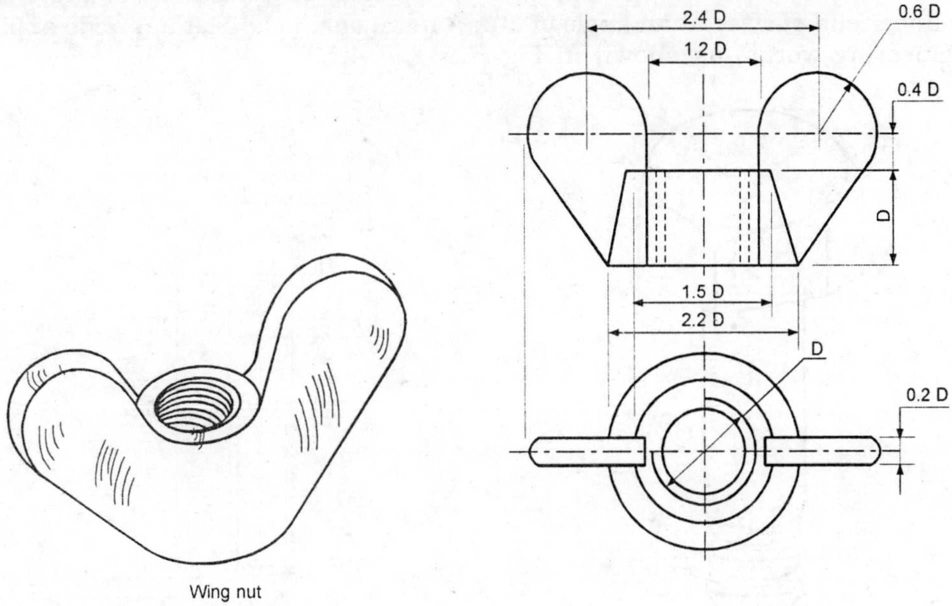

Fig. 4.8

4.12 BOLTS

A bolt is a cylindrical piece of metal, having a head on one end and Bolts are commonly made of mild steel and medium carbon steel. Thread on the other end, passed through clearance holes in two parts and draws them together by means of a nut screwed on the threaded end. The shape of the head depends upon the purpose for which the bolt is required. Bolts are available in a variety of shapes and sizes. The square and hexagonal heads are the two most important design. The bolts are available as ready to use elements in the market and depending upon method of manufacture. Bolts are commonly made of mild steel and medium carban steel. They are either black, semifinished or finished. Applications: Fabrication work, machine element, wood working, civil construction work etc.

4.13 VARIOUS TYPES OF BOLTS

There are different types of bolts are used in engineering field according to the shape of the head. Some of them are given below:

1. Hexagonal head bolt
2. Square head bolt
3. T-head bolt
4. Round Cup head bolt
5. Cheese head bolt
6. Hook bolt
7. Tap bolt
8. Eye bolt.

4.14 HEXAGONAL HEAD BOLT

A hexagonal head bolt is the most common form of bolt. It is most widely used in machine parts to tighten two or more parts together. The length and diameter of bolt depends upon the thickness of parts to be joined. The bolts are usually chamfered at the upper end surface at an angle of 30°. A hexagonal head bolt has wide applications in engineering works, as shown in Fig. 4.9 and 4.10.

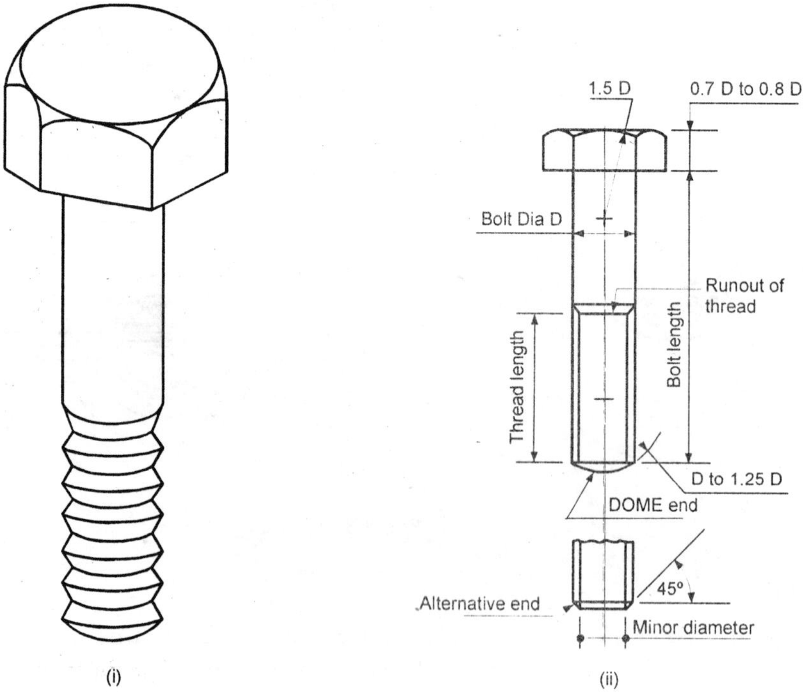

Fig. 4.9

Proportion of the hexagonal bolt:

Width across flates = S = 1.5D + 3 mm

Thickness of head = TH = 0.7D to 0.08D

Angle of chamfer = 30°

Radius of chamfer arc = R = 1.5D

Length of the bolt = L = 4D to 6D.

Length of threaded portion = L_0 = 2D + 6 mm

For length upto 150 mm = 2D + 6 mm

For length over 150 mm = 2D + 12 mm

Core diameter = d_c = 0.85 D

Radius of arc = R_1 = 0.5 × S

where, D = nominal diameter of bolt.

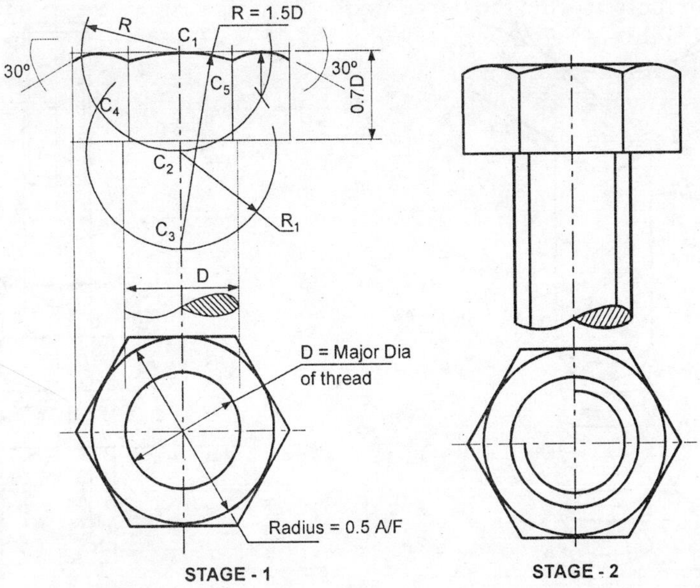

Fig. 4.10

4.15 SQUARE HEAD BOLT

It is another common form of bolts. Square head bolt is generally used when the head is to be accommodated in a recess which is itself of square form. The dimensions of the square head are the same as those of the square nut. The square bolts are usually chamfered at the upper end surface at an angle of 30°. It gives a better spanner grip than the hexagonal nut as shown in Fig. 4.11.

A square head bolt may be drawn by the following proportions:

Width across flats = S = 1.5D + 3 mm

Thickness of head = TN = 0.7D to 0.8D

Angle of chamfer = 30°

Radius of the chamfer arc = R = 2D

Length of bolt = L = 4D to 6D

Length of threaded portion L_0 = 2D + 6 mm (For length upto 150 mm)

= 2D + 12 mm (For length over 150 mm)

where, D = nominal diameter of bolt.

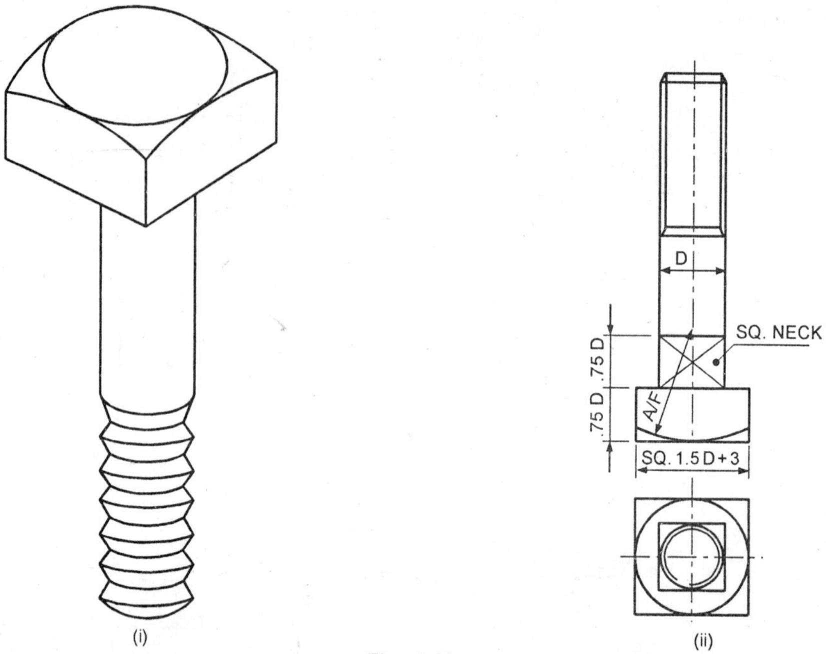

Fig. 4.11

4.16 T-HEAD BOLT

Fig. 4.12 shows a T-headed bolt. It has a head like a letter T. The bolt has square neck to prevent its rotation. It is used in machine tool tables in which T-slots are cut to accommodate the T-heads.

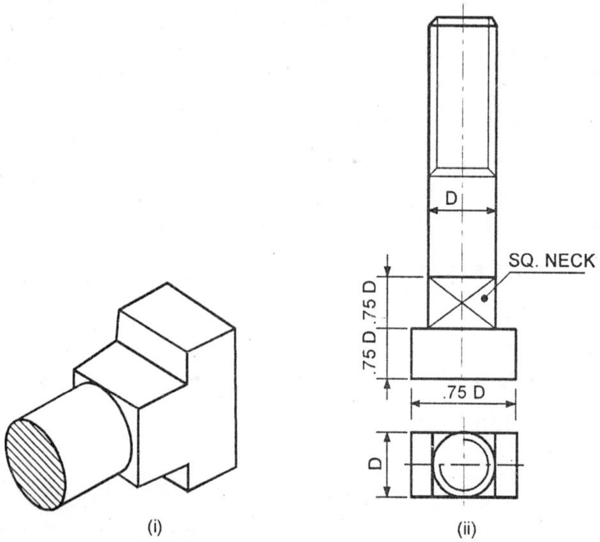

Fig. 4.12

Proportion of the T-head bolt

Width of the T-head = 1.8 D

Thickness of the head = 0.8 D

Length of the square neck = 0.8 D

where D = nominal diameter of the bolt.

4.17 ROUND CUP HEAD BOLT

It is just like a cheese headed bolt having a snug in the shank, but the head is of a cup shape and the snug is forged with the bolt. It is provided with square neck to prevent rotation of the bolt. These bolts are easy to manufacture and used mostly in tank construction and locomotive parts etc. as shown in Fig. 4.13.

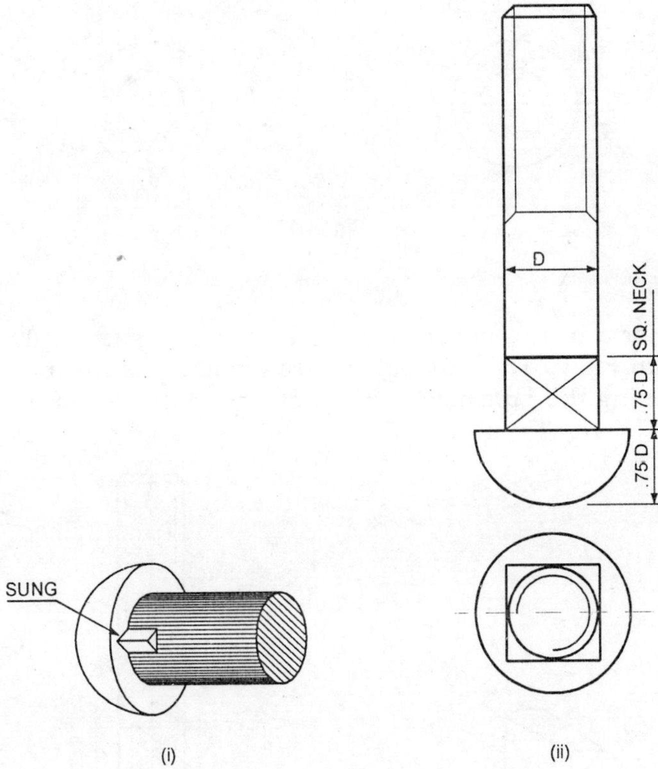

Fig. 4.13

4.18 CHEESE HEAD BOLT

Cheese head bolt is the simplest form of the bolt. It is also known as cylindrical head bolt. It is provided with a snug to prevent rotation of the bolt. It is commonly used in big ends of connecting rods, crosshead, eccentrics etc. The cylindrical or cheese head bolt is shown in Fig. 4.14.

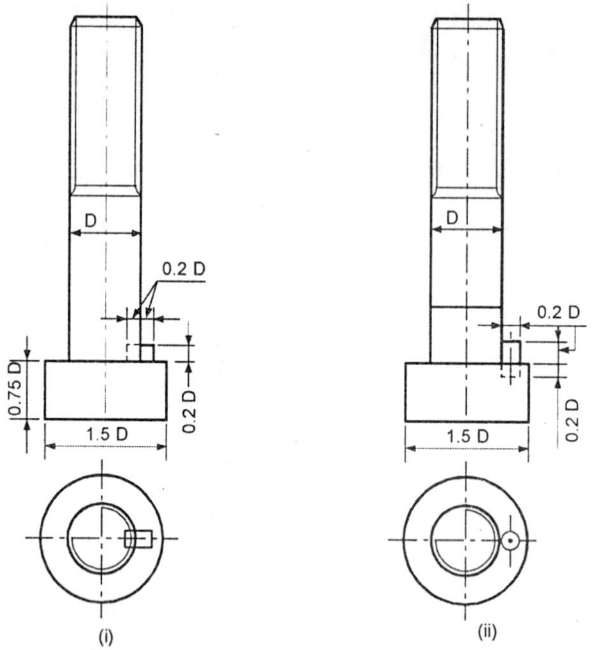

Fig. 4.14

4.19 HOOK BOLT

It is a spherical form of the bolt of which the head projects only in one side of the shank as shown in Fig. 4.15. This bolt is used when it is not possible to drill a hole in the piece adjoining the bolt head. It is provided with a square neck to prevent the rotation of bolt.

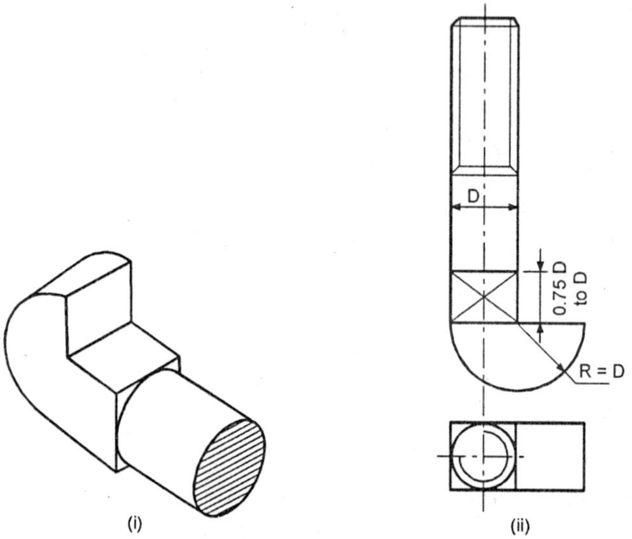

Fig. 4.15

4.20 EYE BOLT

The head of the eye bolt is circular ring of circular cross-section. It is used in lifting heavy machine parts as shown in Fig. 4.16.

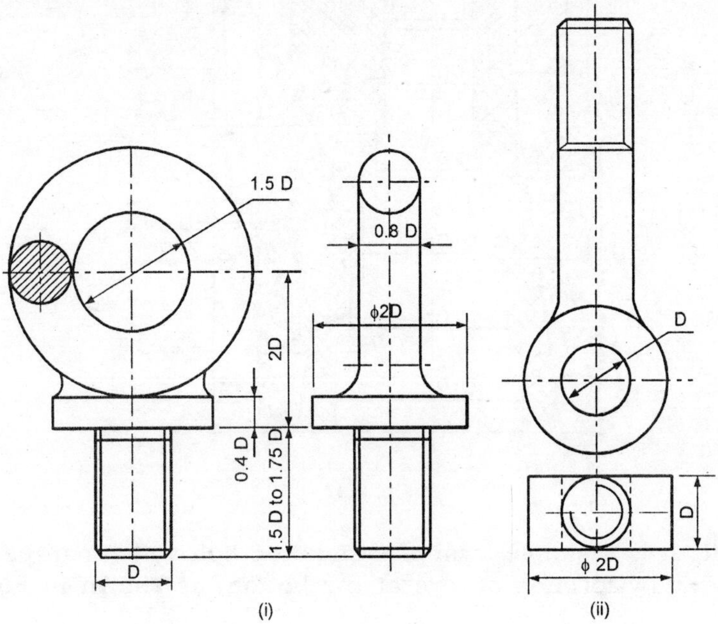

Fig. 4.16

4.21 FOUNDATION BOLTS

Foundation bolts are used for fixing heavy machines to their foundations. The bolts are suspended in the hole. The holes are filled with sand cement and concrete etc. Different types of foundation bolts are used for this purpose.

They are specially designed bolts. Various types of foundation bolts are as follows:

(*i*) Rag bolt
(*ii*) Loop bolt
(*iii*) Square head bolt
(*iv*) Curved bolt
(*v*) Lewis bolt
(*vi*) Cotter bolt.

(*i*) Rag Bolt: It is a tapered bolt of rectangular cross-section generally used for fixing heavy machines to stone or concrete foundation. The edges or sides of the bolt are grooved as shown in Fig. 4.17.

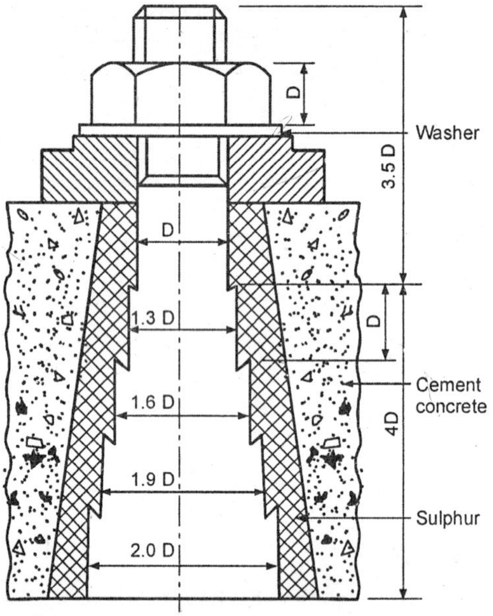

Fig. 4.17

(*ii*) Loop Bolt: It is a simple form of foundation bolt which can be quickly forged from mild steel bar by forming an eye at the bottom as shown in Fig. 4.18.

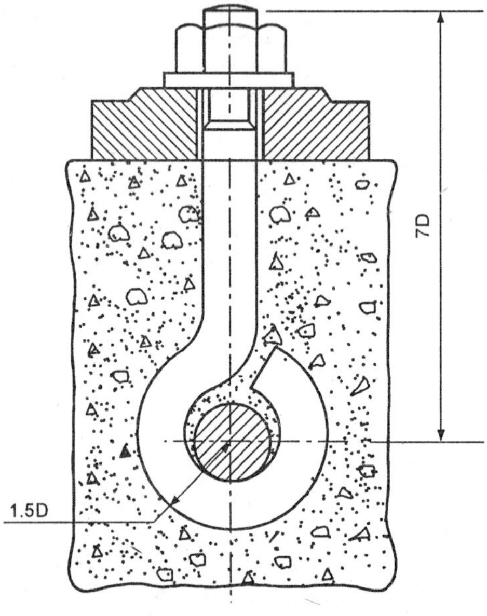

Fig. 4.18

(*iii*) Square Head Bolt: It is a square head bolt with a square neck and carrying a square plate. This square plate distributes head over a large area as shown in Fig. 4.19.

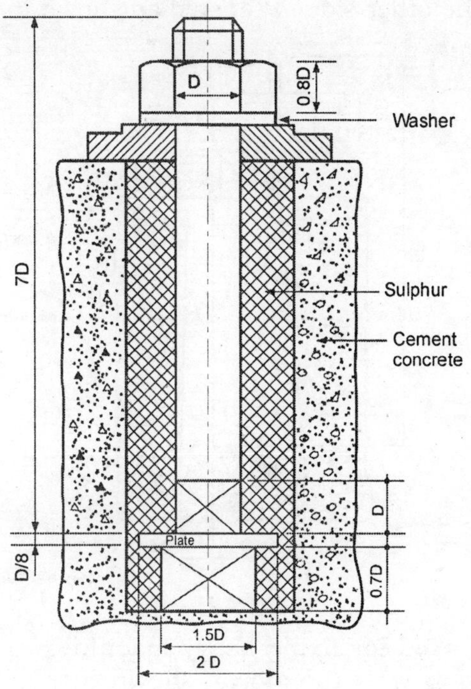

Fig. 4.19

(*iv*) Curved Bolt: It is made of simple mild steel bar with curved shank. The end of the bolt is rounded twice the shank diameter as shown in Fig. 4.20.

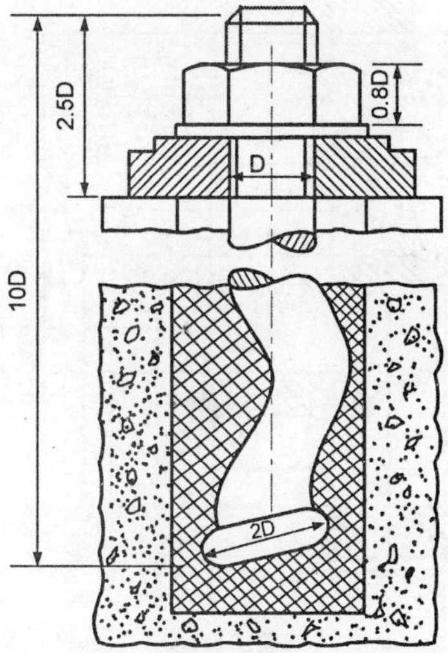

Fig. 4.20

(*v*) Lewis bolt: It is used for a temporary foundation and for slinging blocks of stone. A key is inserted with the straight side of the bolt which can be easily removed. One side of the bolt is straight while the other side in tapered as shown in Fig. 4.21.

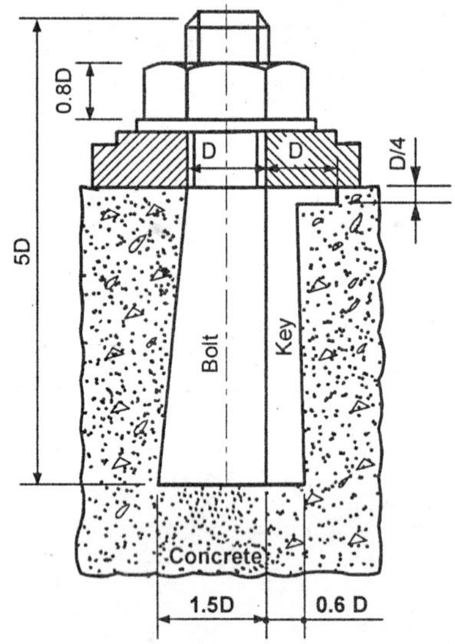

Fig. 4.21

(*vi*) Cotter bolt: It is used for fixing heavy machines to the stone foundation. It is secured below foundation with thr aid as shown in Fig. 4.22.

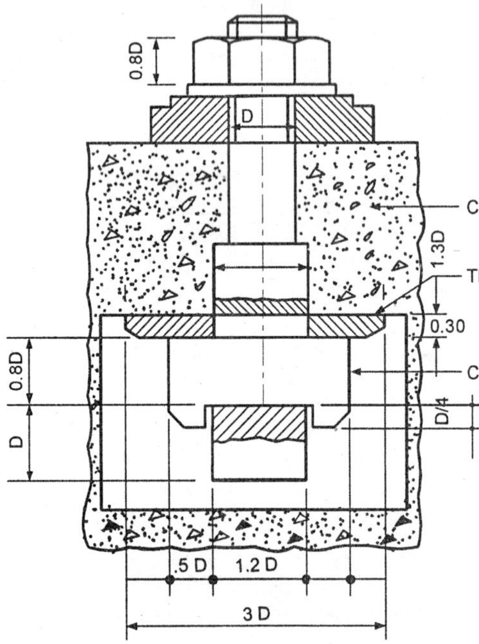

Fig. 4.22

4.22 ASSEMBLY OF BOLT, NUT AND WASHER

Assembly of all the three parts is shown in Fig. 4.23. All the dimensions of bolt, nut and washer are based on the nominal diameter of thread.

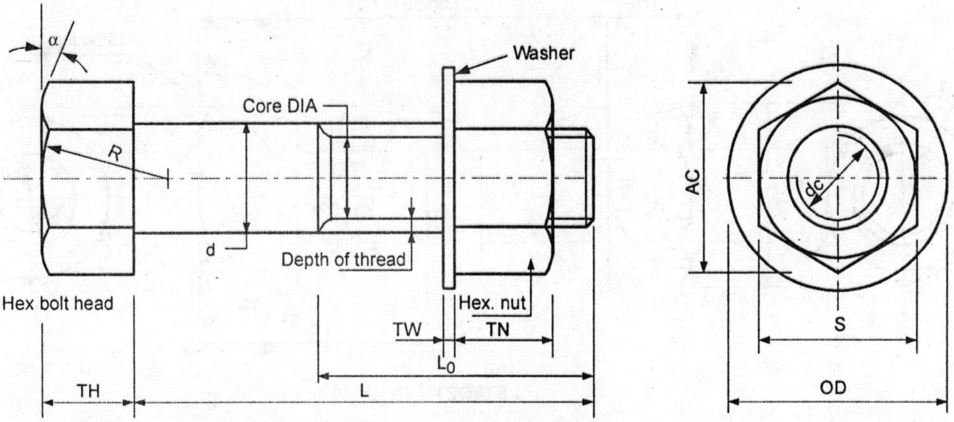

Fig. 4.23

where,

Hex — Hexagonal

M — Metric threads

N — Nut of some shape

L_0 = Threaded portion of shank = 2.5 d + 5 mm

L = Length of shank 4 d to 6 d [If not given then assume]

TH = Thickness of head = 0.7 d to 0.8 d

R = Radius of chamfer = 1.2 d

O.D = Outer dia of washer = 2 d + 3 mm

S = Distance across the flats to flat = 1.5 d + 1 mm or 3 mm.

AC = Distance across the corner = 2 d

d_c = Core dia = 0.85 d

TN = Thickness of Nut = 0.8 d to d

TW = Thickness of washer = 0.15 d

α = Angle of chamfer = 30°

R_1 = 0.5 A/F or S

where, A/F or S = 1.5 d + 3 mm

Problem 1. Draw the front view, top view and side view of a hexagonal nut, bolt with washer of the following specification:

Hex — M20 × 140 × N

Solution. See Fig. 4.24.

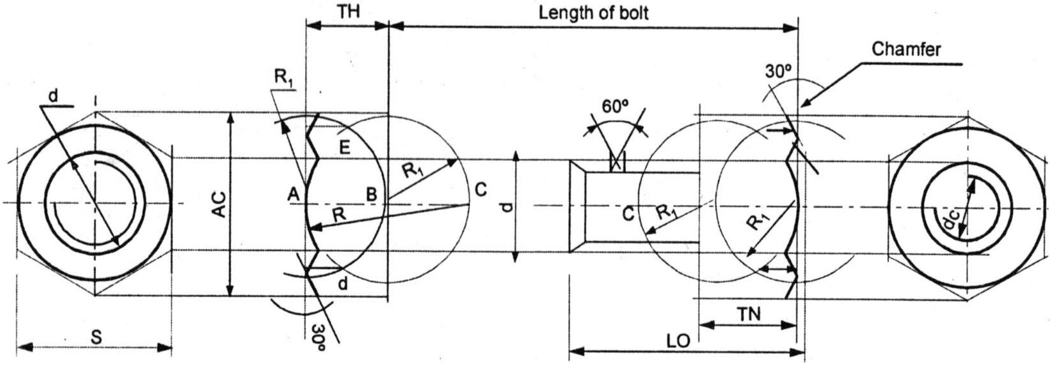

STAGE I

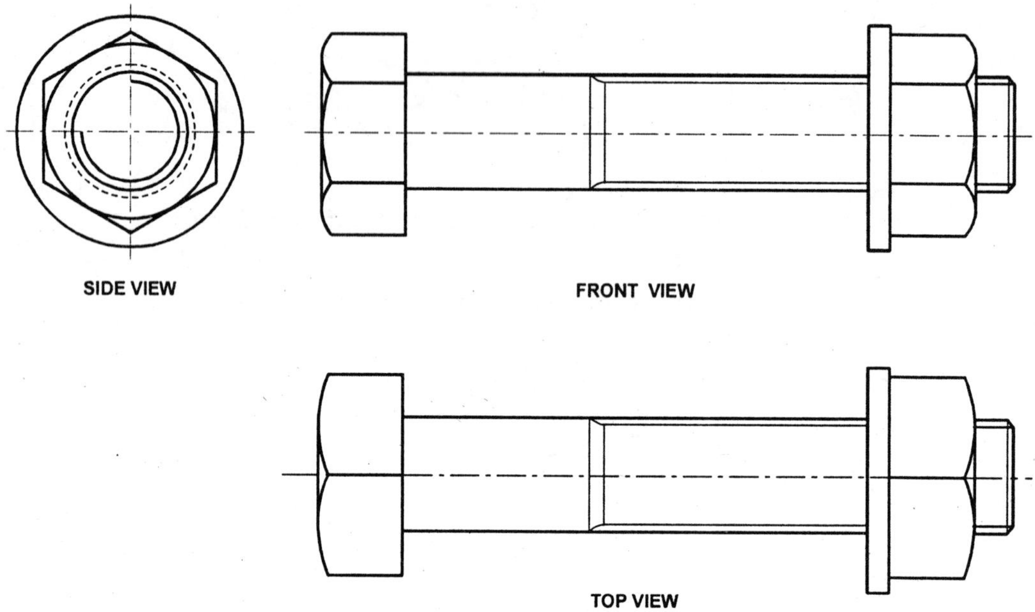

STAGE II

Fig. 4.24

Problem 2. Draw the front view and side view of a square nut and bolt of the following specification: Sq — M20 × 140 N

Solution. See Fig. 4.25.

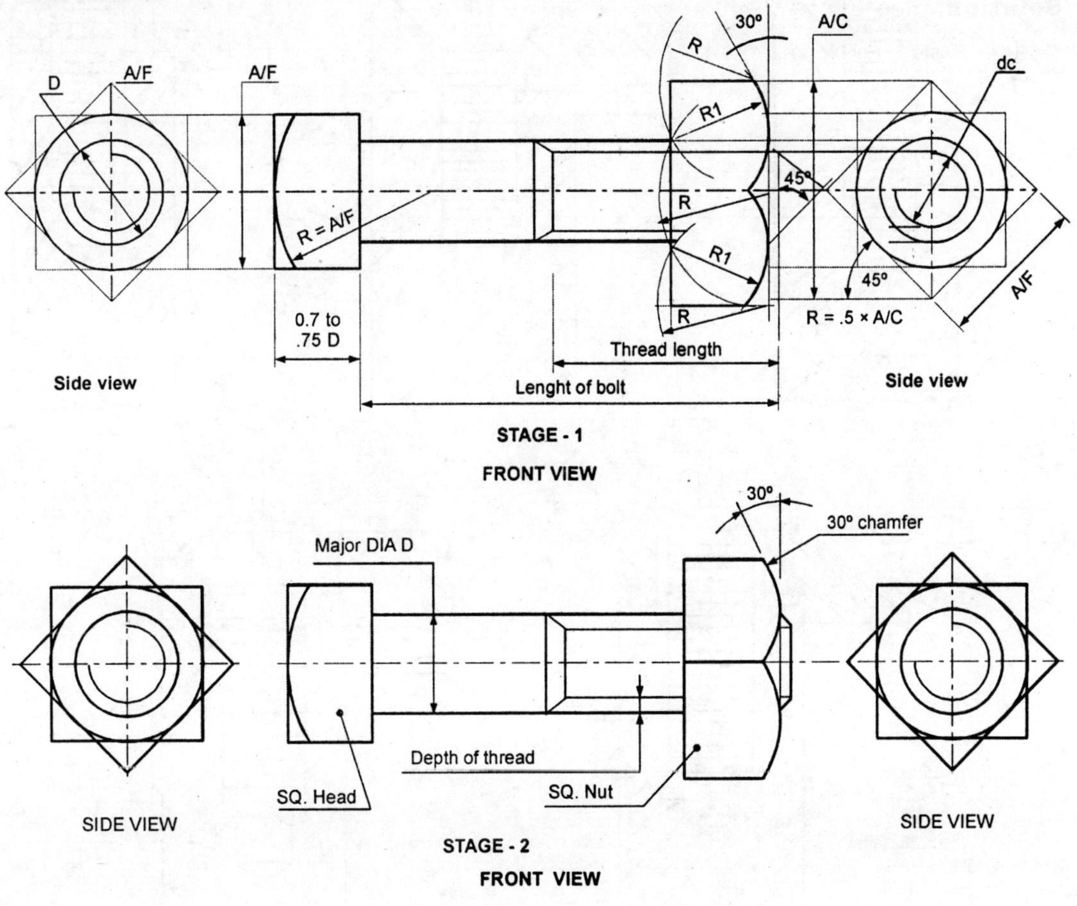

Fig. 4.25

4.23 SCREWS

There are different types of screws used in engineering field are as follows:

1. Cap screws
2. Machine screws
3. Set screws.

4.24 CAP SCREWS

A cap screw passes through a clearance hole in one piece and screws into a tapped hole in the other. Cap screws are used on machine tools. For example, the heads of the slotted and socket head screw are mechanical, and all have chamfered points. The five types of head are shown in Fig. 4.26.

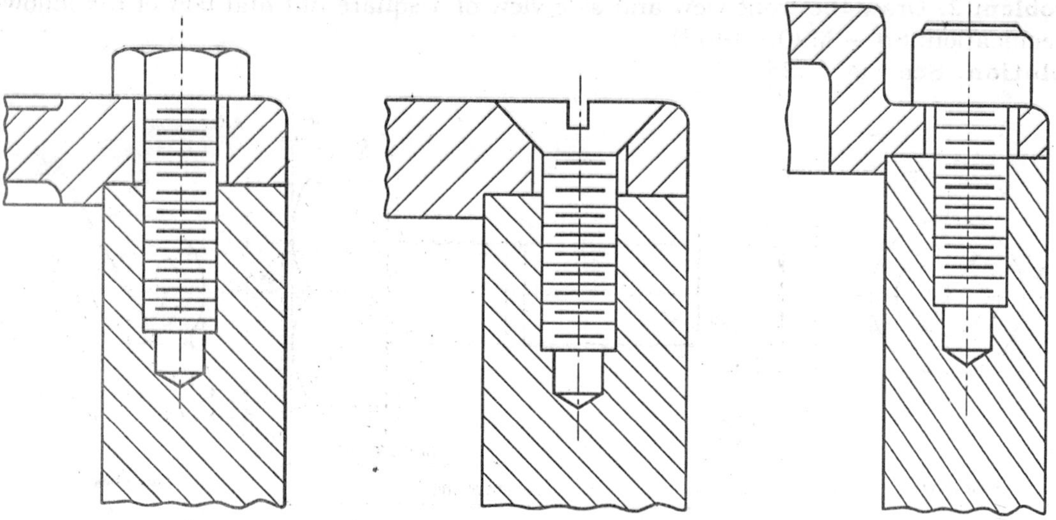

(i) (ii) (iii)

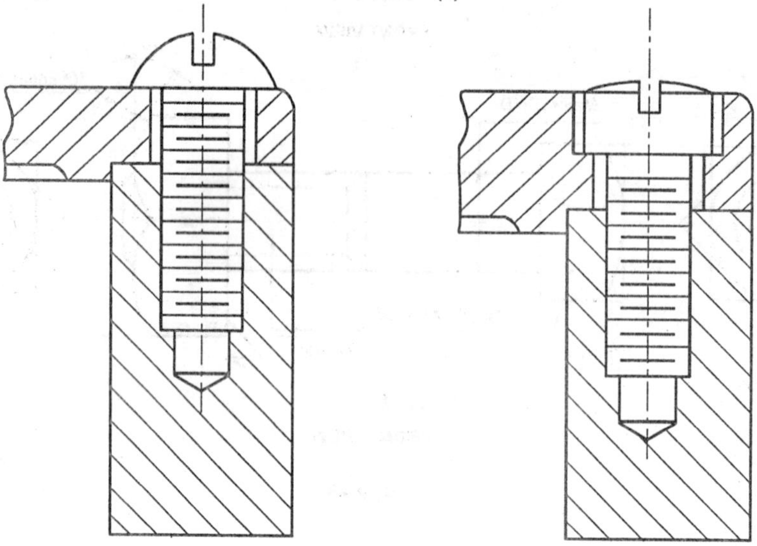

(iv) (v)

Fig. 4.26

4.25 MACHINE SCREWS

A machine screw is a small fastener, used in machines for fastening two parts together. One of the part has a tapped hole and the other part has clearance hole. Various types of heads depending upon the purpose for which a machine screw is used are shown in Fig. 4.27.

(*i*) Round head (*ii*) Cheese head
(*iii*) Counter sunk head (*iv*) Round or cup head
(*v*) Fillister head.

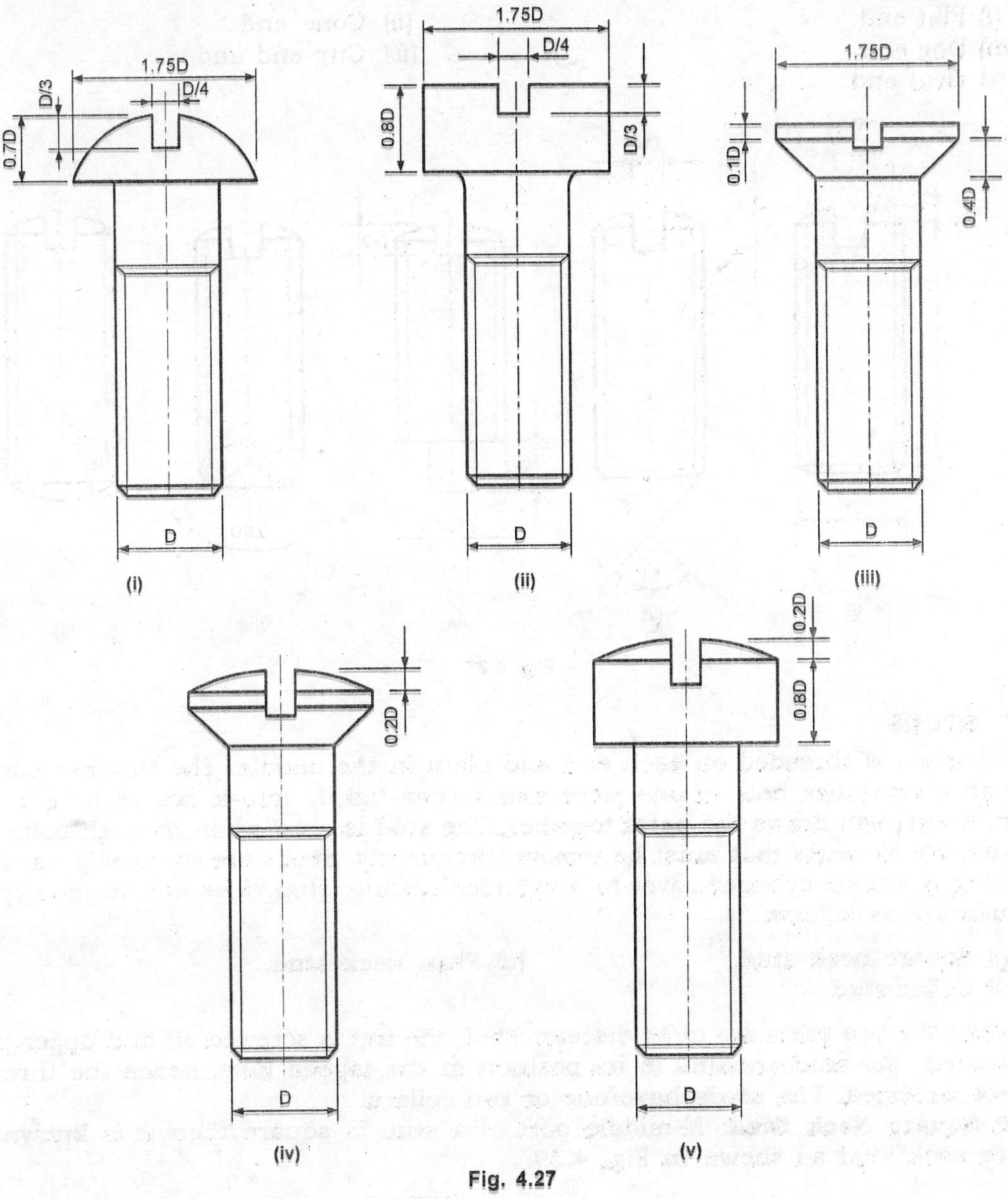

Fig. 4.27

4.26 SET SCREWS

Set screws are used as semipermanent fasteners to hold a collar, pulley etc. It should be screwed into a tapped hole in an outer part, often a hub, and bears with its points against an inner part, usually a shaft. They are mainly used for preventing relative movement between two machine parts. They are generally fully threaded and similar to tap bolt. The headless type of set screw are known as grub screws. They are made of hardened steel. The various types of set screws and their heads are shown in Fig. 4.28. are:

(*i*) Flat end
(*ii*) Cone end
(*iii*) Dog end
(*iv*) Cup end and
(*v*) Oval end.

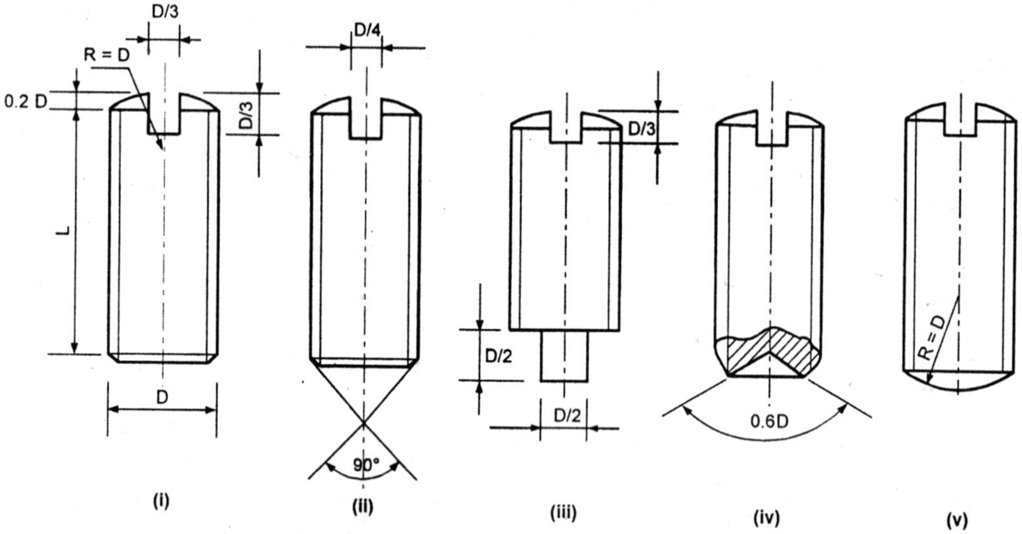

Fig. 4.28

4.27 STUDS

A stud is a rod threaded on each end and plain in the middle. The fastener passes through a clearance hole in one piece and screws tightly into a tapped hole in the other. A nut then draws the parts together. The stud is used when through bolts are not suitable for parts that must be removed frequently. Studs are commonly used for screwing of engine cylinder cover to a cylinder casting, stop valve etc. various types of studs are as follows:

(*i*) Square neck stud.
(*ii*) Plain neck stud.
(*iii*) Collar stud.

When the two parts are to be disconnected, the nut is screwed off and upper part is removed, the stud remains in its position in the tapped hole, hence the threads are not damaged. The studs have one or two collars.

(*i*) Square Neck Stud: If middle part of a stud is square then it is known as square neck stud as shown in Fig. 4.29.

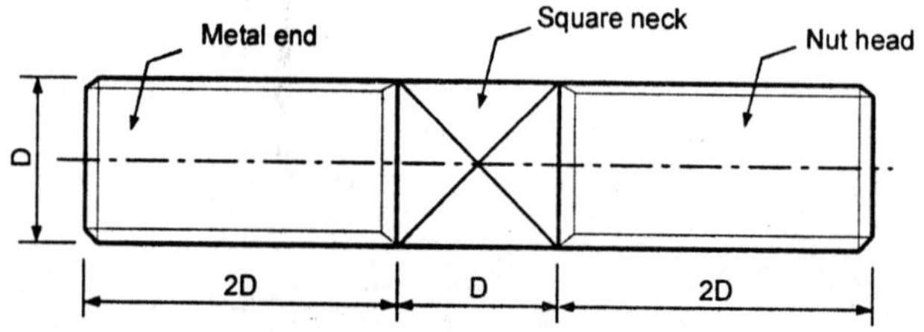

Fig. 4.29

(ii) Plain Neck Stud: If middle part of a stud is cylindrical than it is known as plain neck stud as shown in Fig. 4.30.

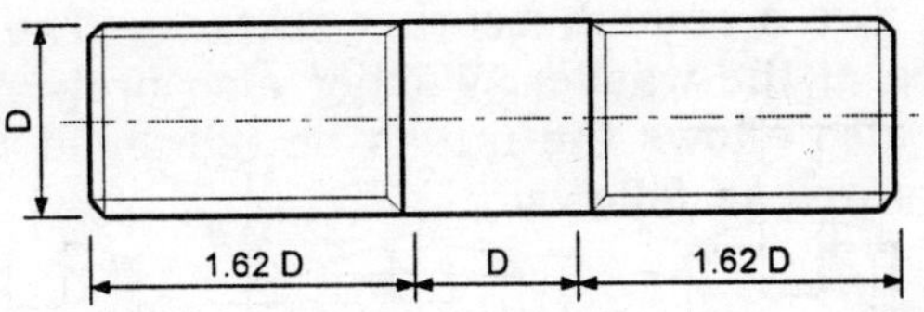

Fig. 4.30

(iii) Collar Stud: It has a collar according to design. It is used in stuffing box assembly. Collar provides a bearing surface to the stud as shown in Fig. 4.31.

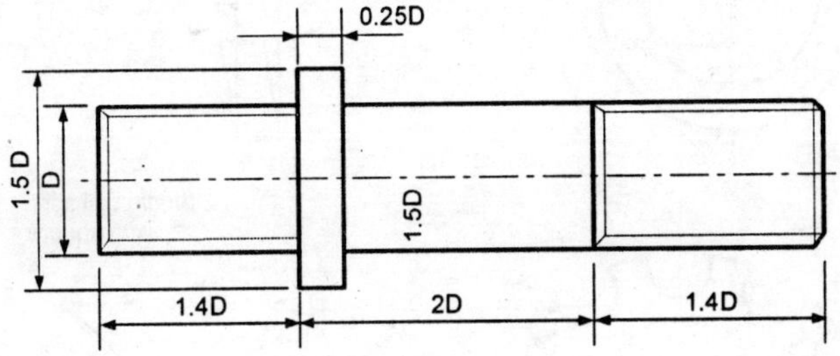

Fig. 4.31

The practical use of a stud is shown in Fig. 4.32.

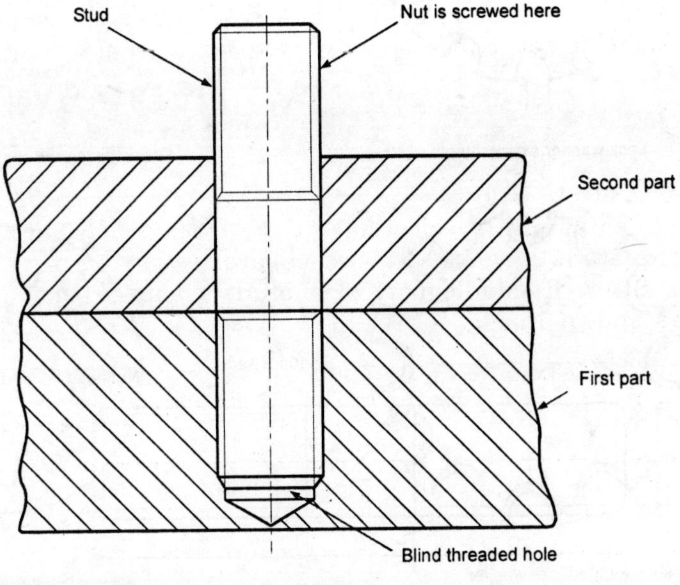

Fig. 4.32

4.28 WASHER

A washer is a circular plate having a hole in its centre. The size of washer depends upon the diameter of the bolt. Fig. 4.33 shows various types of washers. A washer is placed below the nut to give a smooth bearing surfaces. The force taken by the nut spreads over a large area of the washer. Washer also prevents the nut from cutting into the metal and this also allows the nut to be tightened to a greater extent. The various types of washers are as follows:

(*i*) Plain washer
(*ii*) Chamfered washer
(*iii*) Spring washer.

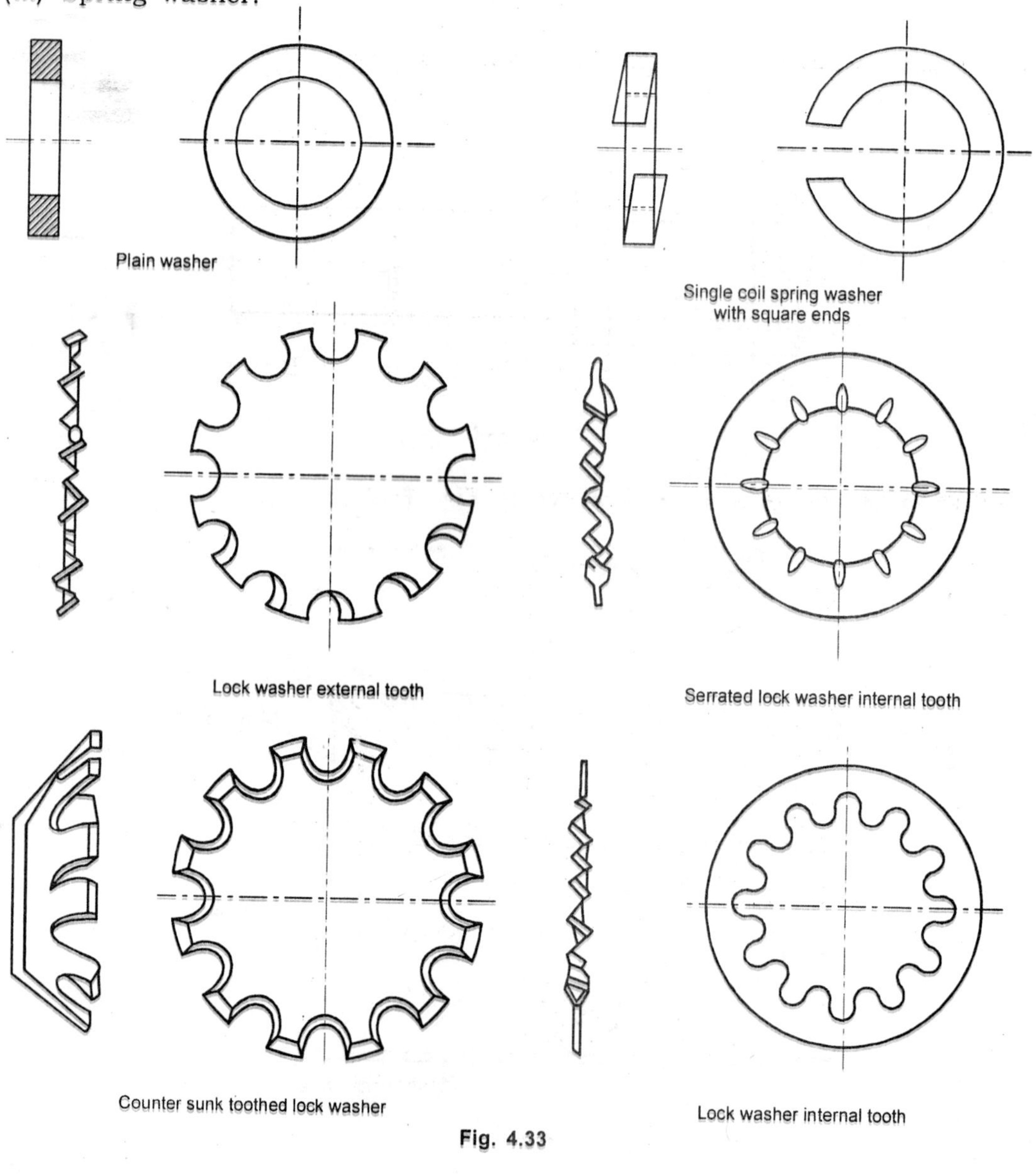

Fig. 4.33

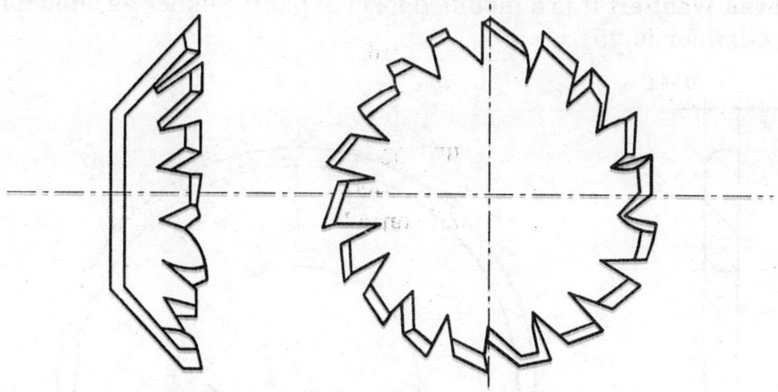

Counter sunk serrated toothed lock washer

Fig. 4.33

***(i)* Plain Washer:** Plain washers are commonly used in the assembly of nut and bolts to provide a smooth surface for the nut or bolt to turn against. It is a simple circular piece of plate as shown in Fig. 4.34.

Outer Diameter of Washer = 1.5 D + 1 mm to 2 D + 3 mm

where D = Nominal diameter of the bolt

Thickness of washer t = 0.15 D.

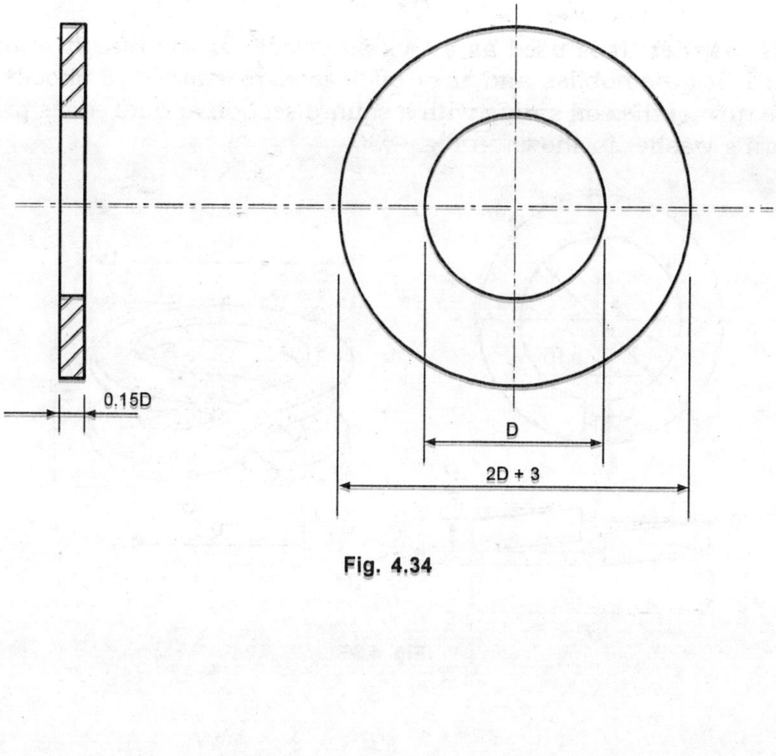

Fig. 4.34

***(ii)* Chamfered Washer:** It is a modified form of plain washer as shown in Fig. 4.35 (*b*). When angle of chamfer is 45°.

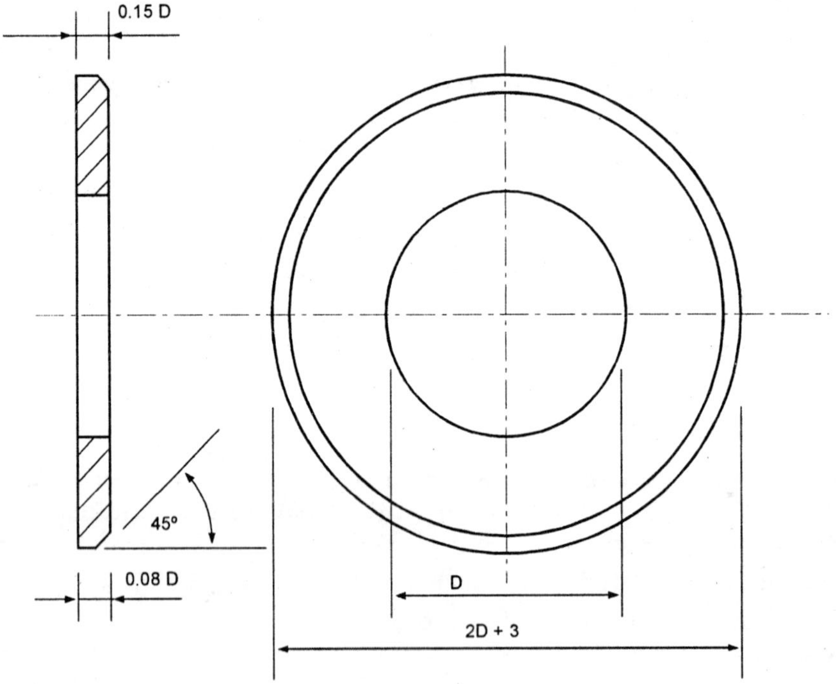

Fig. 4.35

***(iii)* Spring Washer:** It is used as a locking device for the nut. It is made of spring steel. It is used in automobiles and they offer good resistance to shocks and jerks. It represents one turn of the coil spring with a square section and its edges prevent rotation of the nut. Spring washer is shown in Fig. 4.36.

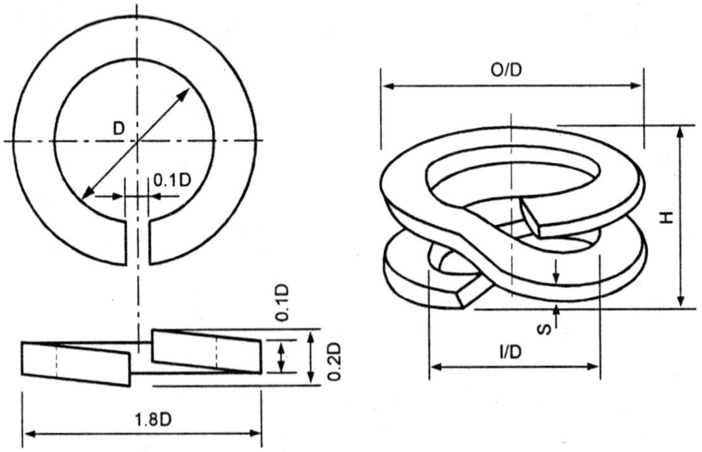

Fig. 4.36

EXERCISE

1. What is fastening?
2. What are the differences between temporary fastening and permanent fastening?
3. Sketch common types of fasteners.
4. What do you mean by nut? Sketch important types of nuts used in engineering fields.
5. What do you mean by bolt? Sketch important types of bolts used in engineering field.
6. Draw three views of a hexagonal nut for a 20 mm diameter bolt, according to approximately standard dimension.
7. What are the foundation bolts and where they are used?
8. Draw three views of the assembly of a nut, bolt and washer.
9. What do you mean by screws?
10. Explain, different types of screws used in engineering field?
11. What is the difference between set screw and machine screw?
12. Define the terms stud.
13. What do you mean by washer? Define various types of washers.

❑❑❑

IMPORTANT NOTES:

5

RIVETS AND RIVETED JOINTS

5.1 INTRODUCTION

Rivets are used to fastening and joining two or more plates of metal permanently or semi-permanently. The joints which are made by rivets are called riveted joints. Basically, a rivet is a short cylindrical bar of ductile material with a head, formed during manufacturing, at one end and tail on the other end. The cylindrical portion of the rivet is called shank as shown in Fig. 5.1. A head is formed on the tail side by forging when it is assembled to fasten the parts. They are usually made of steel (low carbon steel or nickel steel), brass, aluminium, copper. Rivets are widely used in structural work like roof, trusses, bridges, tank, ship building, air craft industry and also for pressure vessels like boilers and receivers.

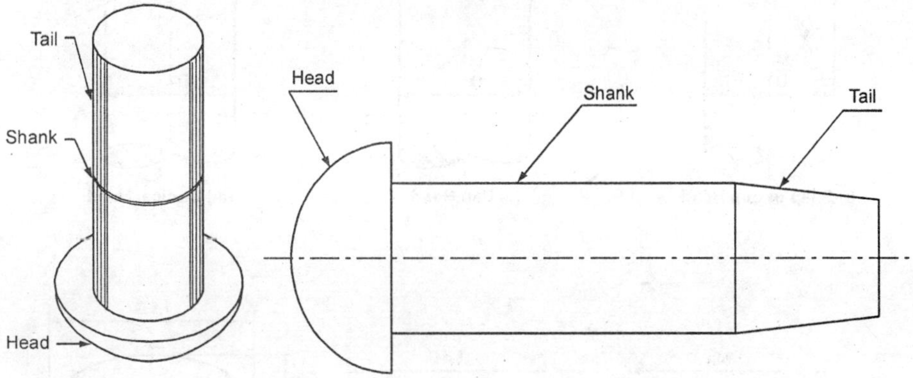

Fig. 5.1

5.2 TYPES OF RIVET HEADS

The various forms of rivet heads specified by B.I.S. are shown in Fig. 5.2. Generally, the rivet heads are classified in three types which are used for different works.

(1) Structural rivets (2) Boiler rivets (3) Small rivets.

(1) Structural Rivets: Structural rivets are used for steel structure. The diameters of rivets lies between 12 mm to 45 mm.

(2) Boiler Rivets: Boiler rivets are used for general purpose. It is generally provided with chamfer of 60° for steam tightness. The diameter of rivets lies between 12 mm to 50 mm.

(3) Small Rivets: This type of rivets are used for general purpose. The standard diameter of rivets are 2 mm to 10 mm and may be made of steel, copper brass or Aluminium (Table 5.1).

Table 5.1 Standard Diameter of Rivets

S.No.	*Types of Rivets*	*Standard Diameter*
1.	General purpose rivets below 12 mm diameter	1.6, 2.5, 3, 4, 5, 6, 8 and 10 mm
2.	General purpose and boiler rivets 12–48 mm diameter	12, 14, 16, 18, 20, 22, 27, 30, 33, 36, 39, 42 and 48

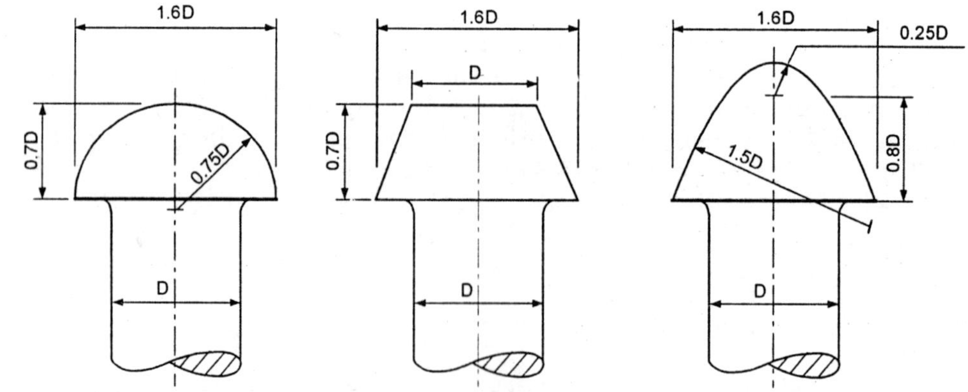

(i) Snap or cup Head (ii) Pan Head (iii) Conical Head

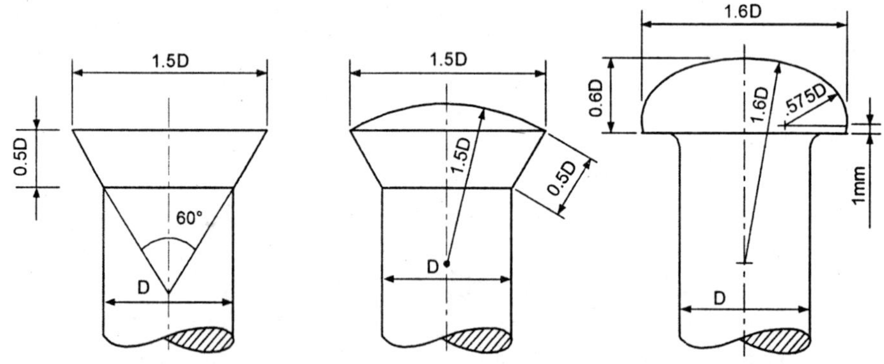

(iv) Countersunk Head (v) Rounded countersunk Head (vi) Ellipsoid Head

Fig. 5.2

The snap head is commonly used in structure work and boiler work. Counter sunk head is used where rivet surface is to be kept with a flat top such as ship building. Conical head rivets can be obtained from snap head rivets used mainly in case of hand hammering. It is not as strong as the snap head. The height of the conial head is greater than snap head. The symbols for rivets may be recommended by ISI are shown in Fig. 5.3.

SR. NO.	OBJECT	SYMBOLS
1.	Shop snap headed rivets	
2.	Shop CSK (Near side) rivets	
3.	Shop CSK (Far side) rivets	
4.	Shop CSK (Both sides) rivets	
5.	Site snap headed rivets	
6.	Site CSK (Near side) rivets	
7.	Site CSK (Far side) rivets	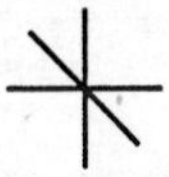
8.	Site CSK (Both sides) rivets	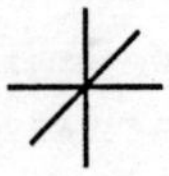
9.	Open hole	

Note:- (CSK = Counter sunk)

Fig. 5.3

5.3 METHODS OF RIVETING

The function of rivets in a joint is to make a connection that has strength and tightness. The complete process of fastening two plates by means of rivet is called riveting as shown in Fig. 5.4. The holes in the plates are punched and reamed or drilled a little larger than the diameter of a rivet. Since punching deforms the material around the hole, the drill is used. The diameter of the rivet holes is usually 1 mm to 1.5 mm larger than the diameter of the rivet. After drilling or punching the "burrs or chips" formed at the edges of the hole are removed by a little counter sinking. A cold rivet or a red hot rivet is introduced into the plates. The plates are kept in position so that the holes of the plates remain in alignment to get the rivet through them. The head of the rivet is formed by means of a tool called dolly. The tail side of the rivet is then forged to the shape of head. The riveting may be done by hand hammering or by a riveting machine depending upon the condition of work. In hand riveting the original rivet head is backed up by a hammer or heavy bar and then the die or set is placed against the end to be headed and the blows are applied by a hammer. While the machine hammering is preferable as it is more rapid and economical and is employed in large scale engineering work where a steady face forming the heads is applied by means of hydraulic or pneumatic hammers.

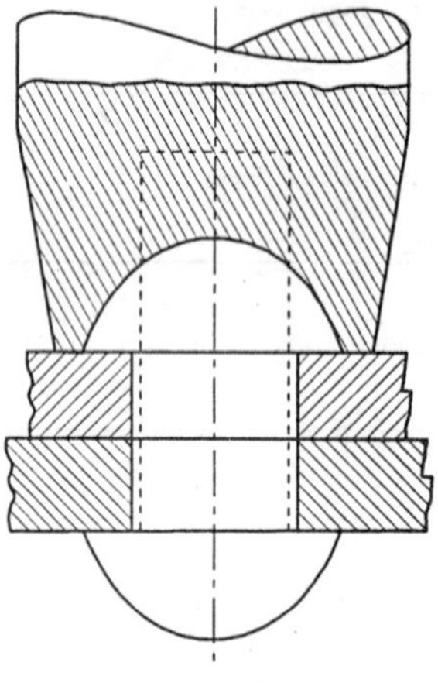

Fig. 5.4

For steel rivets upto 12 mm diameter, the cold riveting process may be used while for larger diameter rivets, hot riveting process is used and only the tail is heated and not the whole shank.

5.4 TESTING OF MANUFACTURED RIVETS

A rivet is considered fit if it withstands the following two tests:

1. Bend Test: The rivet shank is bent cold, hammering until the tail side touches the shank and does not show any cracks on the out side of the bend as shown in Fig. 5.5.

2. Flattening Test: The rivet head when flattened by hammering should spread until the diameter is 2.5 times the diameter of the shank without showing any cracks at the edge as shown in Fig. 5.6.

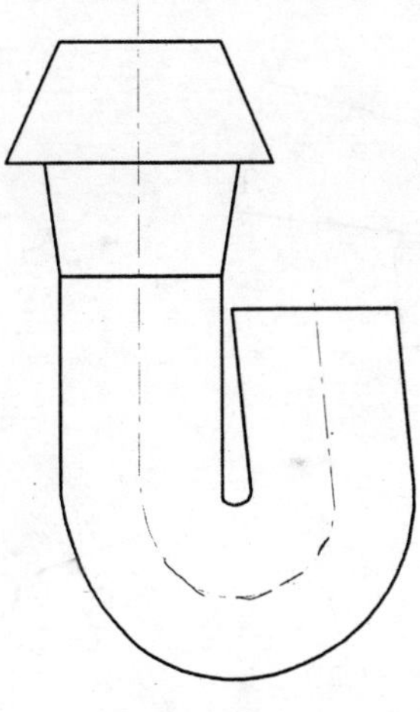

Fig. 5.5

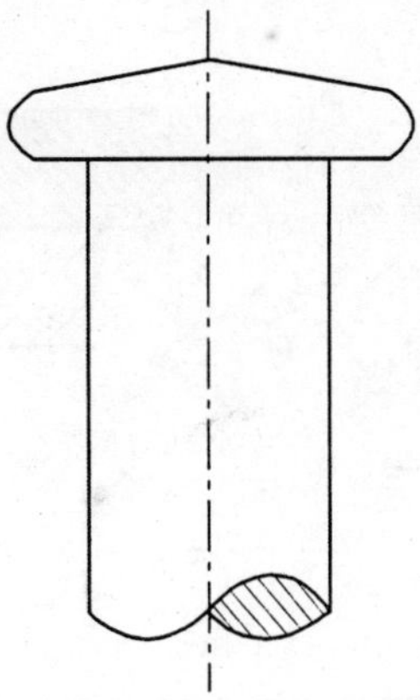

Fig. 5.6

5.5 CAULKING AND FULLERING

To prevent the leakage of steam or other fluid through the joint, the rivet heads and plates are firmly forced together by caulking or fullering operations.

In order to make the joints leak proof or fluid tight in pressure vessels like steam boilers, air receivers and tank a process known as caulking is applied. In this process, a narrow blunt tool called caulking tool which is about 5 mm thick and 35 mm in breadth is used against the edges. Caulking tool is bevelled at an angle about 80°. The rivet head is tightly pressed on the plate by a caulking tool and is hammered as shown in Fig. 5.7. Fullering is an operation of burring down the whole surface of the edges of the plate. It is a developed form of caulking. It is done by the fullening tool. When the caulking tool is about as thick, as the plate, it is call a fullering tool as shown in Fig. 5.8. Caulking and fullering must be done where perfectly fluid tight riveted joint is required.

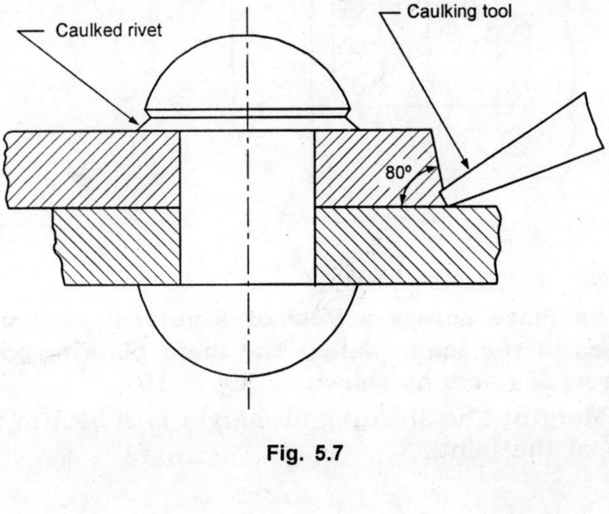

Fig. 5.7

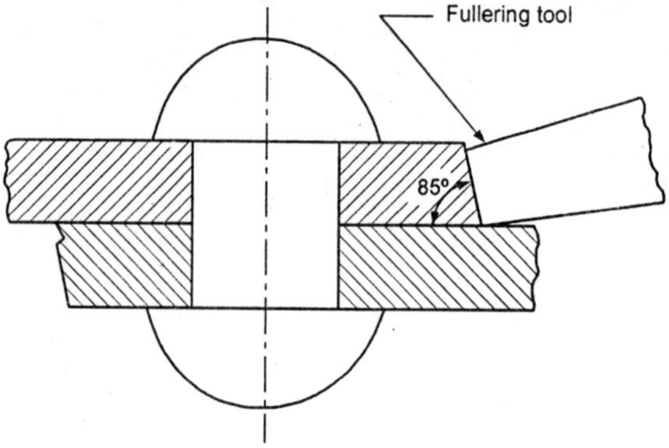

Fig. 5.8

5.6 FAILURE OF RIVETED JOINTS

A riveted joint may fail in any one of the following ways:

1. **Tearing of the Plate at an Edge:** A joint may fail due to tearing of the plate at an edge and the rivet holes as shown in Fig. 5.9. If the distance between the edge of the plate and rivet holes is not sufficient. This can be avoided by keeping the margin m = 1.5 d where d = diameter of the rivet hole.

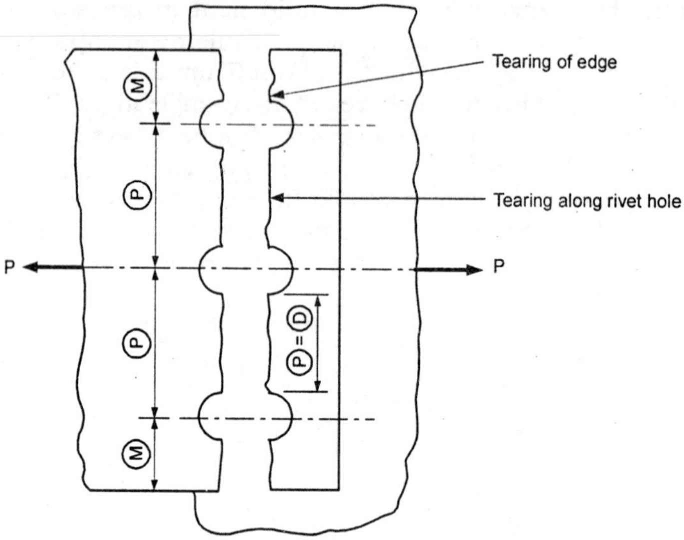

Fig. 5.9

2. **Tearing of the Plate across a Row of Rivets:** A joint may fail due to the tensile stresses in the main plates. The main plate or cover plate may tear off across a row of rivets as shown in Fig. 5.10.
3. **Shearing of Margin:** The shearing of margin is shown in Fig. 5.10. This will cause failure of the joint.

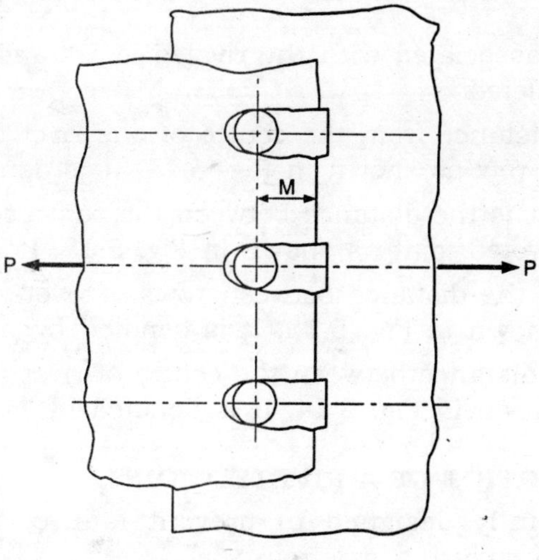

Fig. 5.10

4. **Shearing of the Rivets:** If the diameter is less than the required diameter, the joint will fail by shearing of rivets. A rivet will shear through the plane where the two plates meet together as shown in Fig. 5.11.

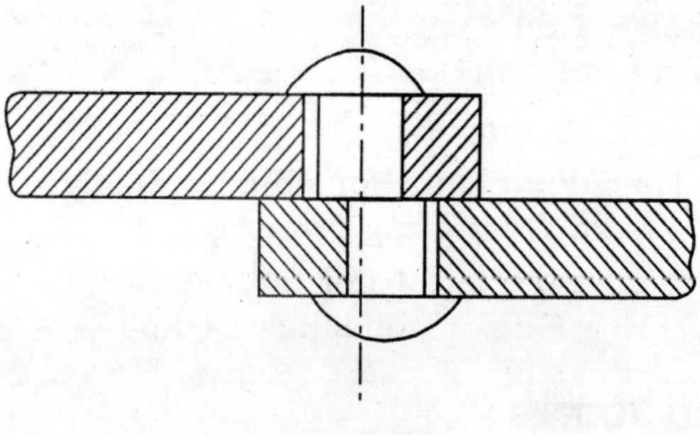

Fig. 5.11

5. **Crushing of the Plate or Rivets:** A joint may fail due to the rivet hole becoming an oval shape and hence the joint becomes loose as shown in Fig. 5.12. It occurs because the surface of hole crushes under pressure.

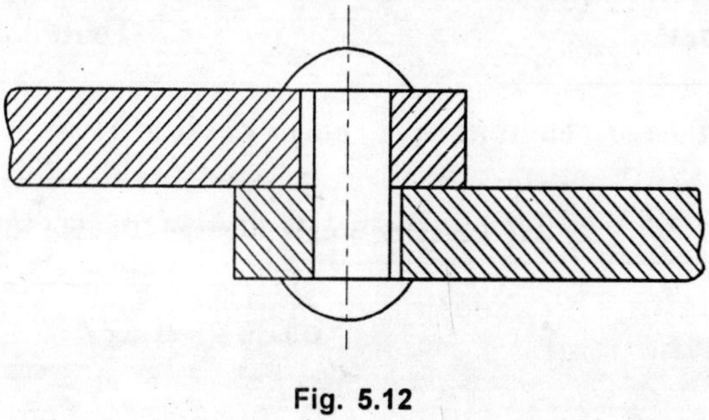

Fig. 5.12

5.7 DEFINITIONS

The following terms are associated with the riveted joints and are important after the riveting process is completed:

1. **Pitch:** It is the distance from the centre of one rivet to the centre of the next rivet in the same row as shown in Fig. 5.14. It is denoted by p where p = 3d.
2. **Diagonal Pitch:** It is the distance between the centres of the rivets in adjacent rows of zig-zag riveted joint as shown in Fig. 5.15. It is denoted by p_d.
3. **Back Pitch:** It is the distance between rows of rivets measured perpendicular to the seam as shown in Fig. 5.15. It is denoted by p_b.
4. **Margin:** It is the distance between the centre of rivet holes to the nearest edge of the plate as shown in Fig. 5.14. It is denoted by m where m = 1.5d.

5.8 GENERAL PROPORTION OF A RIVETED JOINT

Riveted joints are carefully designed to prevent failure. The following empirical proportions are taken to ensure a safe joint:

1. $d = 6\sqrt{t}$ Unwin's rules in metric units, where,
   d = dia of rivet in mm
   t = thickness of plate in mm.
   Selected standard value of *d*, which are selected from table 5.1.
2. Margin distance (m) = 1.5d
3. Maximum pitch = 3d
4. Minimum pitch = d + 30 mm
5. Diagonal pitch (p_d) = 2d + 6 mm for chain riveting
   = 2d for zig-zag riveting
6. Thickness of strap t_i = 0.6 t to t (for double strap)
   = 1.25 t (for single strap)

5.9 TYPES OF RIVETED JOINTS

Riveted joints may be divided into two types depending upon the manner in which the plates are held in relation to each other. The following flow chart shows a classification of riveted joints:

Riveted Joints

- **Lap Joint**
  - **Single Riveted**
  - **Double Riveted**
    - **Chain Riveting**
    - **Zig-Zag Riveting**
  - **Multi Riveted**
- **Butt Joint**
  - **Single Cover Plate**
  - **Double Cover Plate**
    - **Single Riveted**
    - **Double Riveted**
      - **Chain Riveting**
      - **Zig-Zag Riveting**
    - **Multi Riveted**

5.10 LAP JOINT

A lap joint is that in which one plate overlaps the other and the two plates are then riveted together as shown in Fig. 5.13.

These joints may be single riveted, double riveted and multi riveted according to one, two and three rows of rivets. Further arrangement of rivets differ in chain and zig-zag riveting as shown in Fig. 5.14 and in Fig. 5.15.

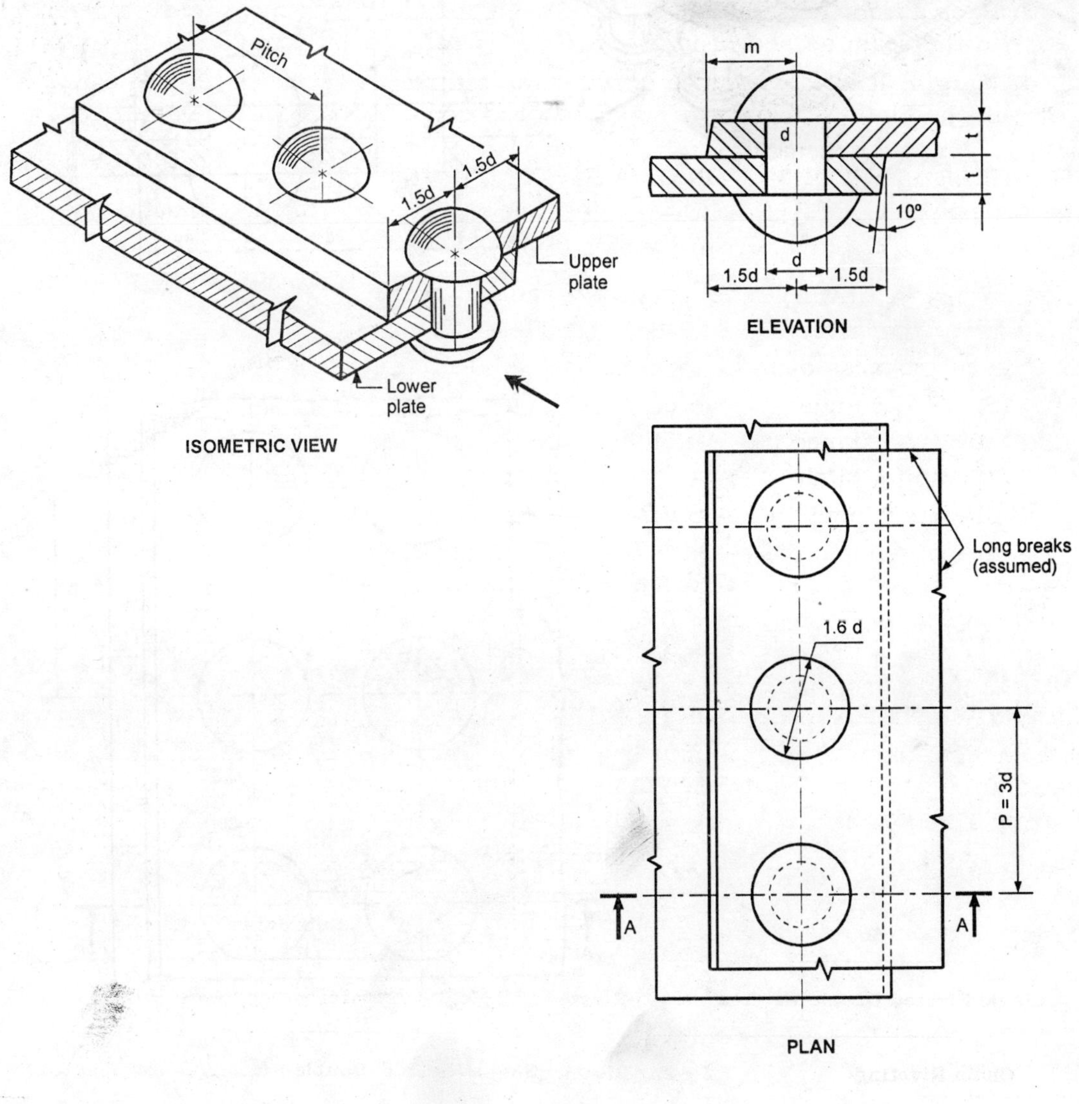

Fig. 5.13

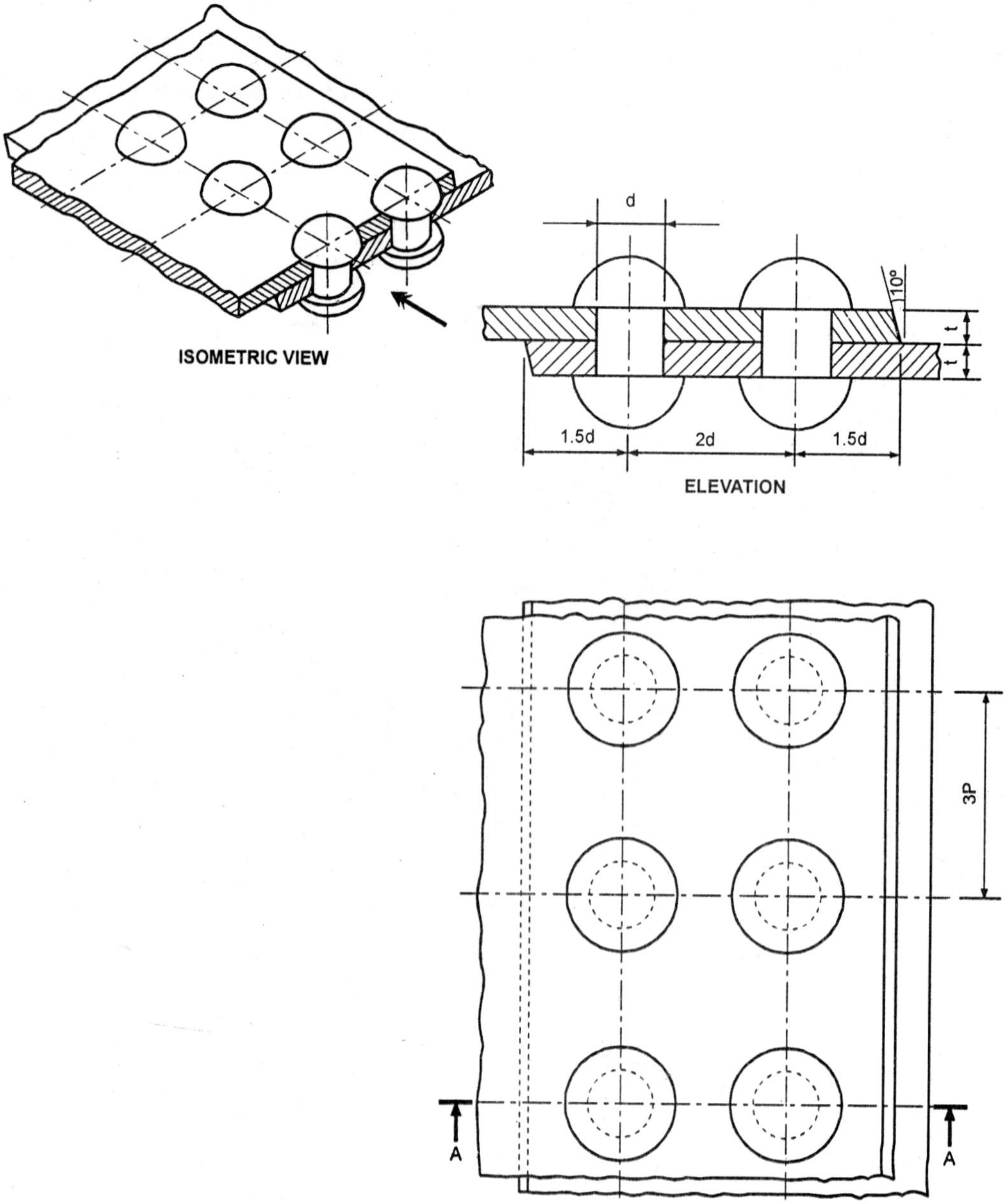

Fig. 5.14 Double-riveted Lap joint, Chain Riveting

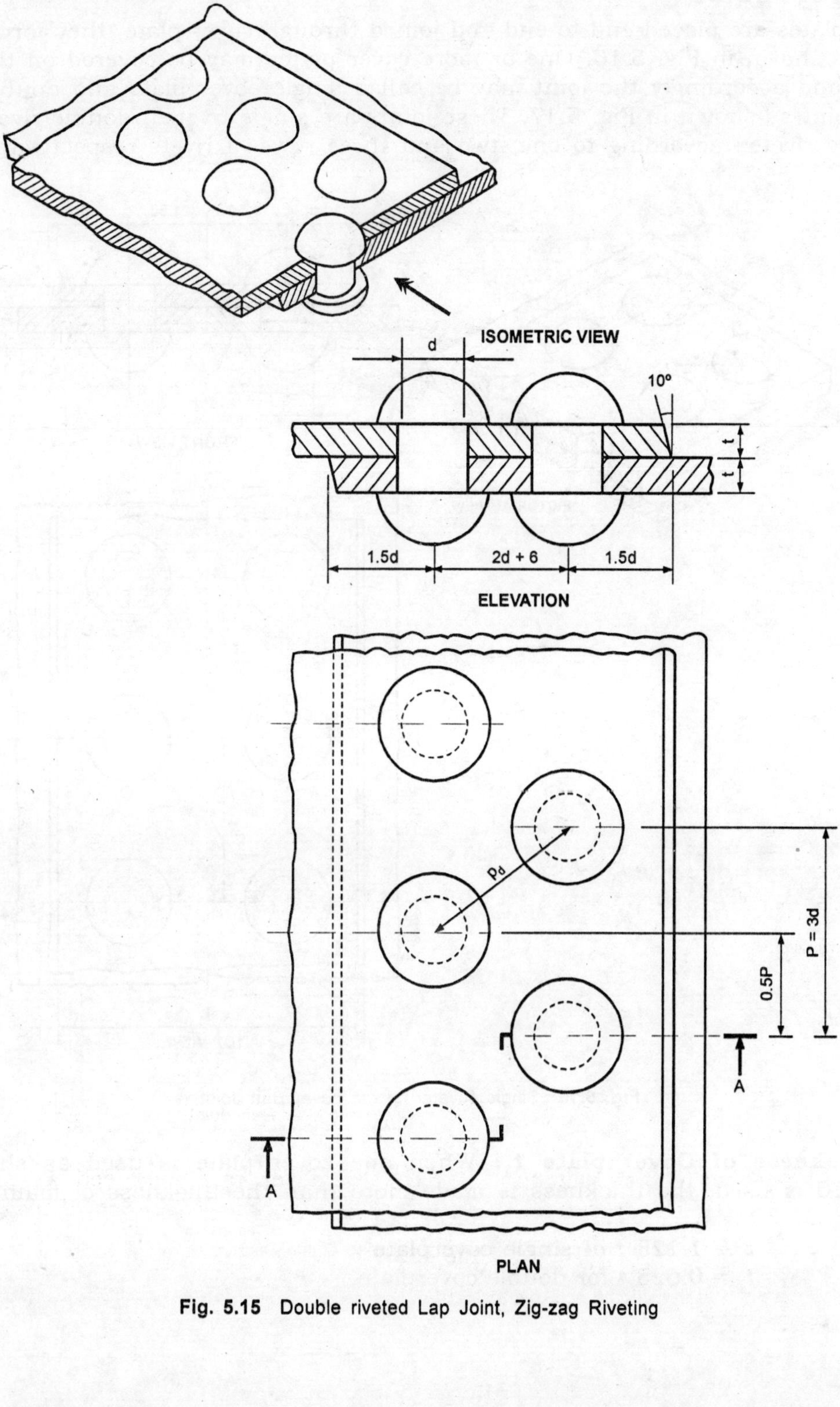

Fig. 5.15 Double riveted Lap Joint, Zig-zag Riveting

5.11 BUTT JOINT

When plates are placed end to end and joined through cover plate, they form a butt joint as shown in Fig. 5.16. One or more cover plates may be covered on the main plates and accordingly the joint may be called single cover plate and double cover plate joint as shown in Fig. 5.17. These joints are single riveted, double riveted and multiple riveted according to one, two and three rows of rivets respectively.

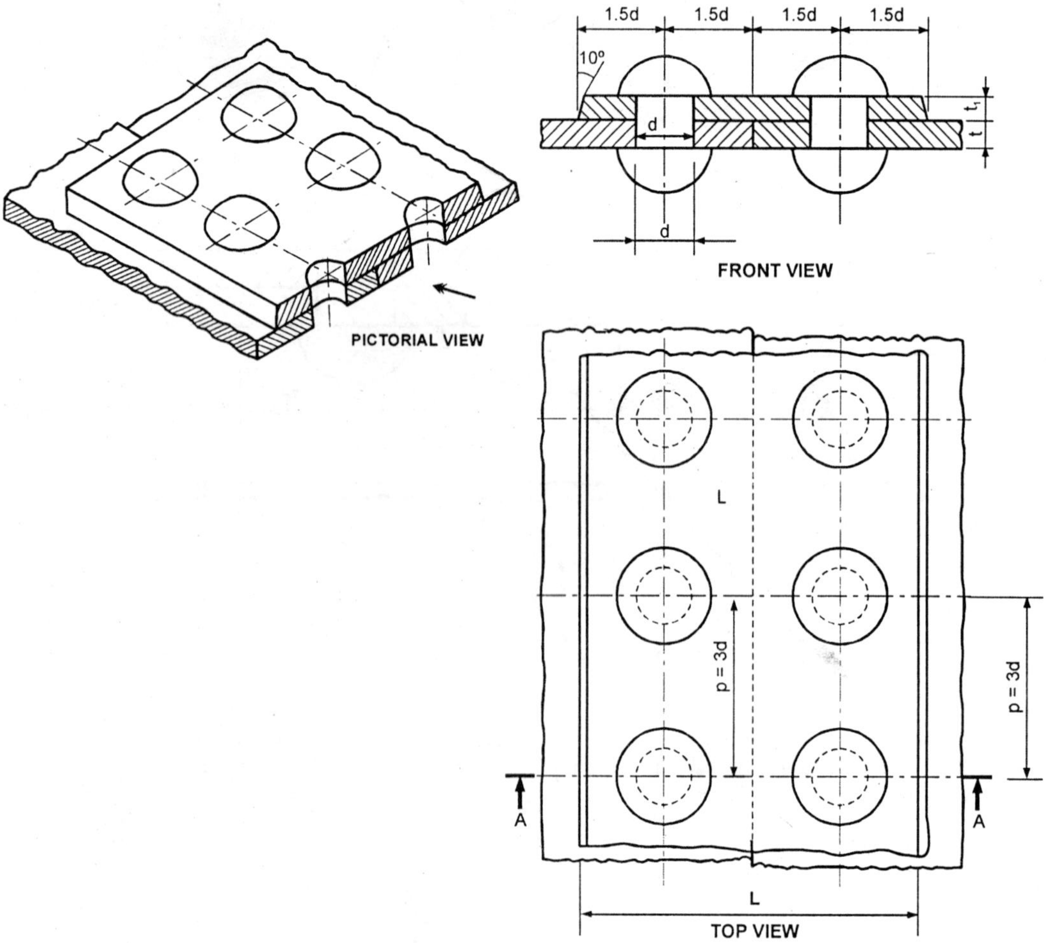

Fig. 5.16 Single Riveted single cover Butt Joint.

Thickness of Cover plate t_1: When one cover plate is used as shown in Fig. 5.16 is used, the thickness is made more than the thickness of main plates, usually

$$t_1 = 1.125\ t \text{ of single coverplate}$$
$$t_1 = 0.625\ t \text{ for double coverplate.}$$

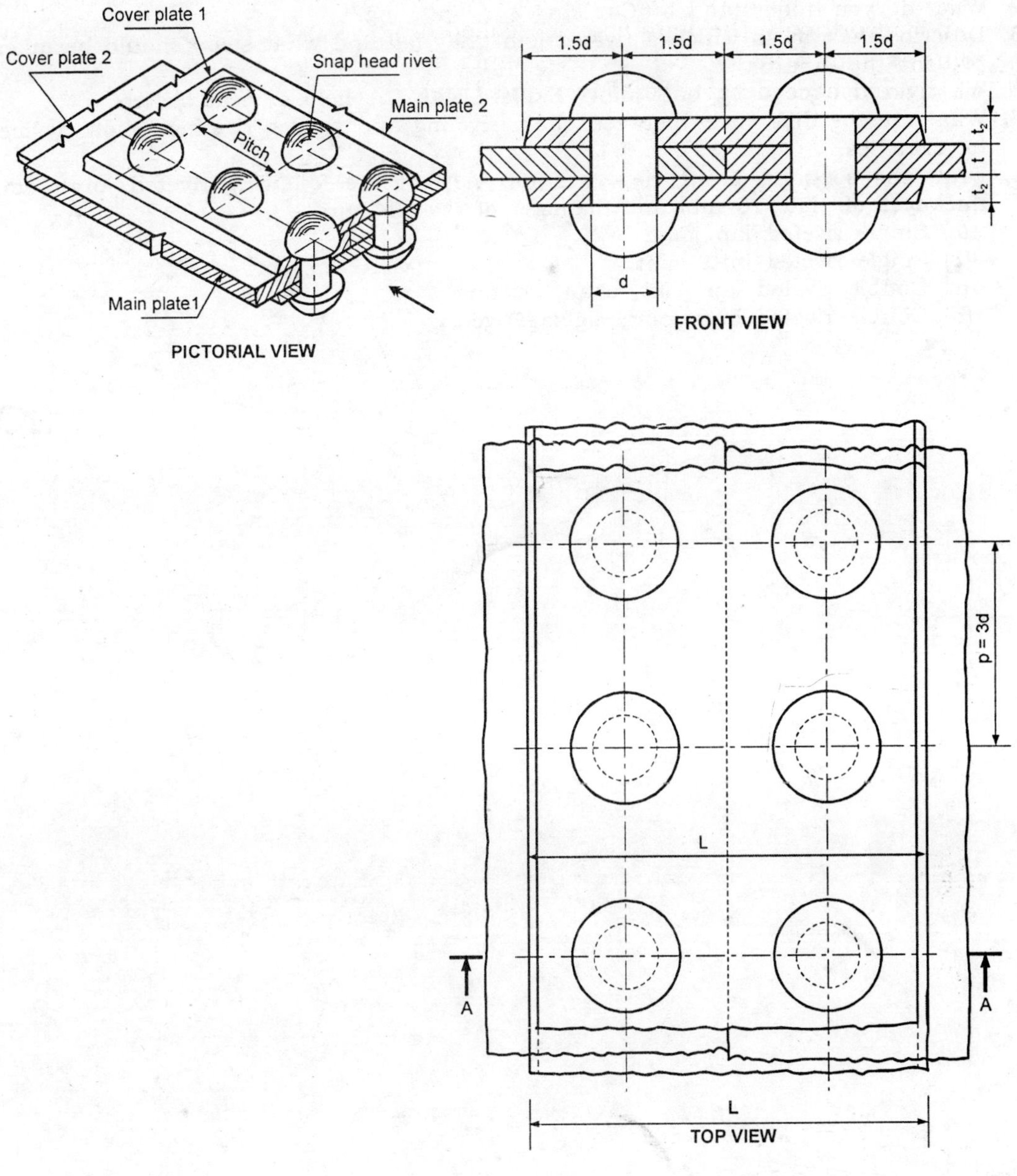

Fig. 5.17 Single Reveted Double cover Butt Joint

EXERCISE

1. Draw the different types of rivet heads.
2. What do you understand by Caulking and Fullering?
3. Describe the way in which a riveted joint may fail and what steps should be taken to prevent the failure?
4. What do you mean by butt joint? Explain with the help of neat sketch.
5. What are the differences between chain riveting and zig-zag riveting. Show by means by sketches.
6. Draw the sectional front view and top view of the following riveted joints, taken thickness of plate 16 mm and diameter of rivet 24 mm
   (*a*) Single riveted lap joint.
   (*b*) Single riveted butt joint.
   (*c*) Double riveted lap joint, chain riveting.
   (*d*) Double riveted butt joint, zig-zag riveting.

❑❑❑

6

Welded Joint

6.1 INTRODUCTION

Welding is the process of joining two or more metal parts together by the application of heat. This may be done with or without additional (filler) metal and with or without the application of pressure. It is a permanent joint.

At present time, welding has become a powerful technology. Joining of steel is done by welding. Welding has almost replaced riveting particularly in manufacturing of boilers and ships. It is extensively used in the construction of boilers, ships, bridges, steel structure etc.

6.2 WELDING PROCESSES

The welding processes may be broadly classified into the following two groups:

(1) Fusion welding

(2) Pressure welding.

(1) Fusion Welding: It is a process of welding by which the parts to be joined are held in position while the molten metal is supplied to the joint. The molten metal may come from the parts themselves or filler metal which normally have the composition of the parent metal. Fusion welding may be:

(*i*) Thermit welding

(*ii*) Gas welding

(*iii*) Electric arc welding

(*iv*) Flash welding.

(2) Pressure welding: In this method of welding two metals parts are heated to plastic condition and then hammered together. Forge welding best example of pressure welding.

6.3 TYPES OF WELDED JOINTS

Fig. 6.1 illustrates in pictorial mode, some of the various types of weld. The following types of welded joints are given below:

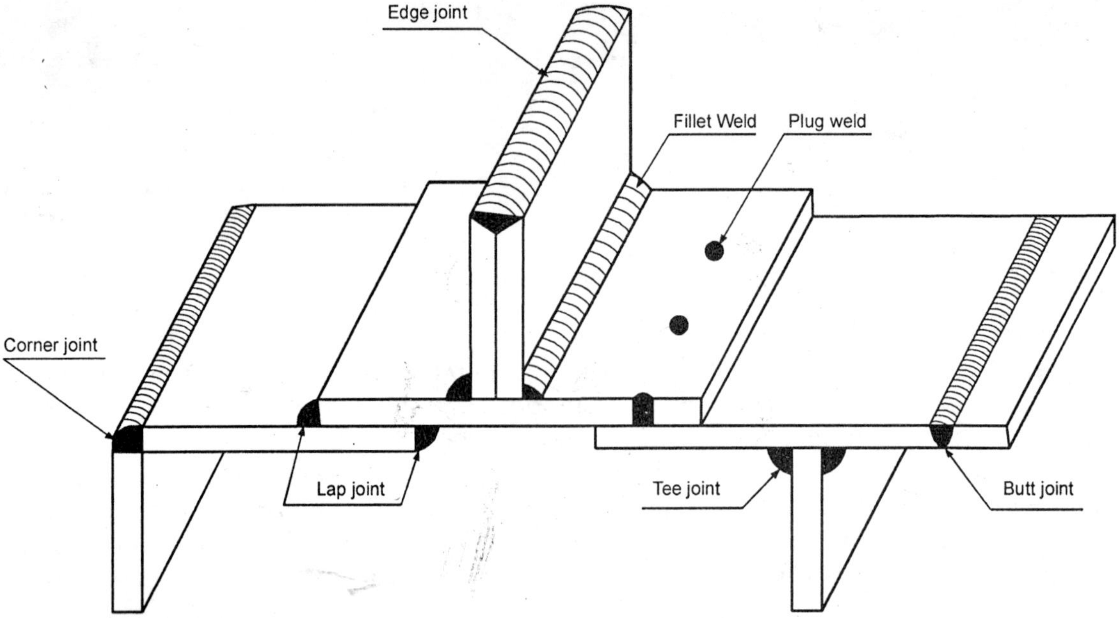

Fig. 6.1 Types of Welded Joints

1. Lap joint (Fig. 6.2).

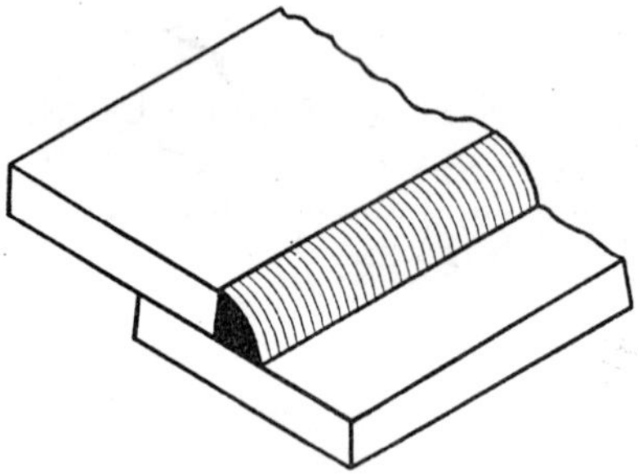

Fig. 6.2 Lap-Joint

2. Butt joint (Fig. 6.3).

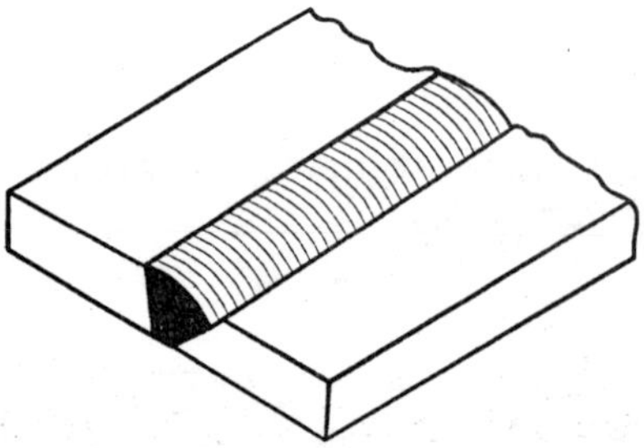

Fig. 6.3 Butt-Joint

3. Corner joint (Fig. 6.4).

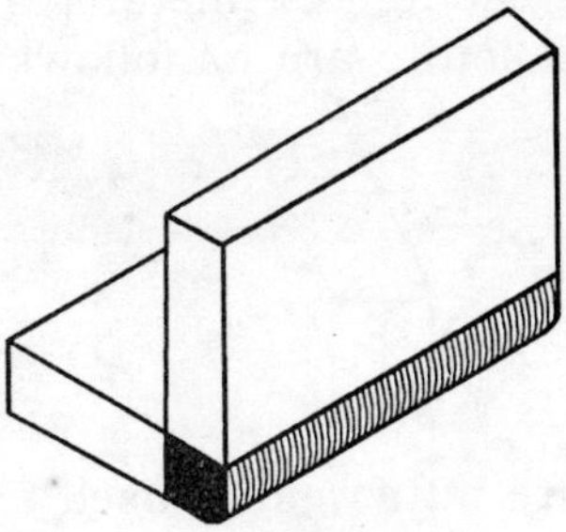

Fig. 6.4 Corner-Joint

4. Edge joint (Fig. 6.5).

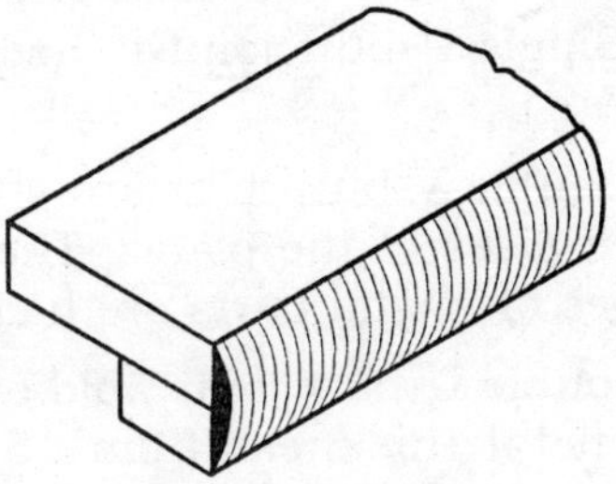

Fig. 6.5 Edge joint

5. *T*-Joint (Fig. 6.6).

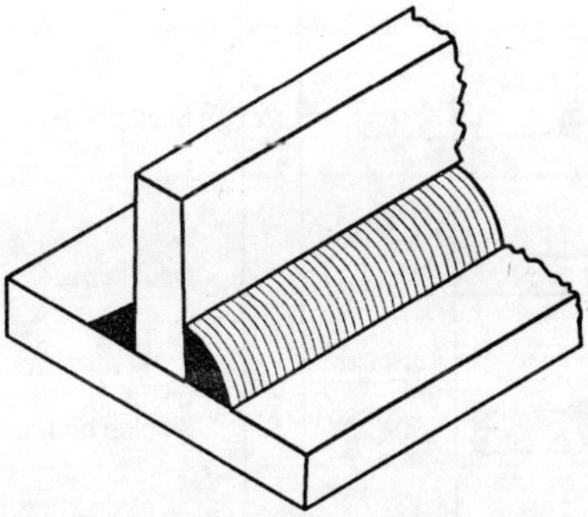

Fig. 6.6 T-Joint

6.4 LAP JOINT

Lap joint is used to join two overlapping plates. It is used when thickness of plates is less than 3 mm. The cross-section of the fillet is approximately triangular. The fillet joint may be:

(*i*) Single transverse fillet
(*ii*) Double transverse fillet
(*iii*) Parallel filled.

6.5 BUTT JOINT

The butt joint is obtained by placing the metal plates edge to edge as shown in Table 6.1. Various types of butt joints are as follows:

(*i*) Square butt joint
(*ii*) Single V-butt joint
(*iii*) Single U-butt joint
(*iv*) Double V-butt joint
(*v*) Double U-butt joint.

(*i*) Square Butt Joint: Square butt weld is used for plate thickness from 1.5 mm to 5 mm as shown in Table 6.1. The spacing between plates is about 3 mm.

(*ii*) Single V-butt Joint: Single V-butt welds is used for thickness from 6 mm to 15 mm and edges of metal parts are inclined at an angle of 55° to 70°.

(*iii*) Single U-butt Joint: Single U-butt joint is used for metal thickness from 10 mm to 20 mm.

(*iv*) Double V-butt Joint: Double V-butt joint are stronger than single V-butt joint and they are performed on both sides of the plates. They are used for plate thickness from 16 mm to 35 mm and edges of metal parts are inclined at an angle of 80° to 90°.

(*v*) Double-U-butt Joint: Double U-butt joint weld are stronger than single U-butt joints and they are used for metal thickness from 15 mm to 60 mm respectively.

Table 6.1 Welding Symbols

S. NO.	FORM OF WELD	SECTIONAL REPRESENTATION	SYMBOL	S. NO	FORM OF WELD	SECTIONAL REPRESENTATION	SYMBOL
1.	Fillet	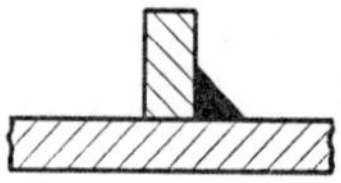		7.	Single bevel butt	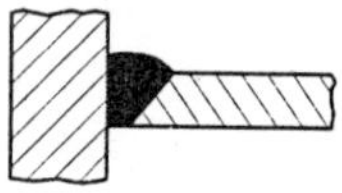	
2.	Square Butt			8.	Double bevel butt	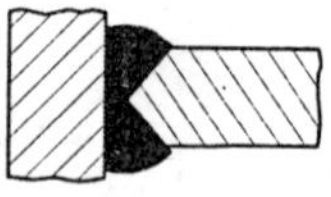	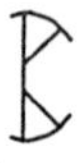
3.	Single-v Butt			9.	Single-j butt	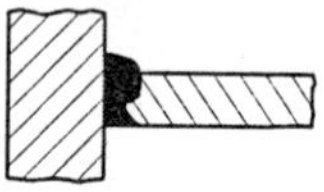	
4.	Double-v Butt			10.	Double-j Butt	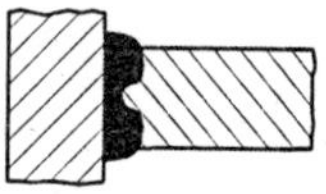	
5.	Single-u Butt			11.	Edge	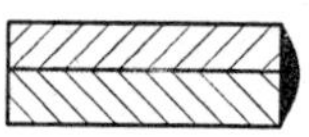	
6.	Double-u Butt		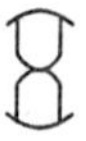	12.	Spot		

6.6 ELEMENTS OF WELDING SYMBOL

A welding symbol consists of the following eight elements as shown in Fig. 6.7:

1. Reference line
2. Arrow
3. Basic weld symbols
4. Dimensions and other data
5. Supplementary symbols
6. Finish symbols
7. Tail
8. Specification.

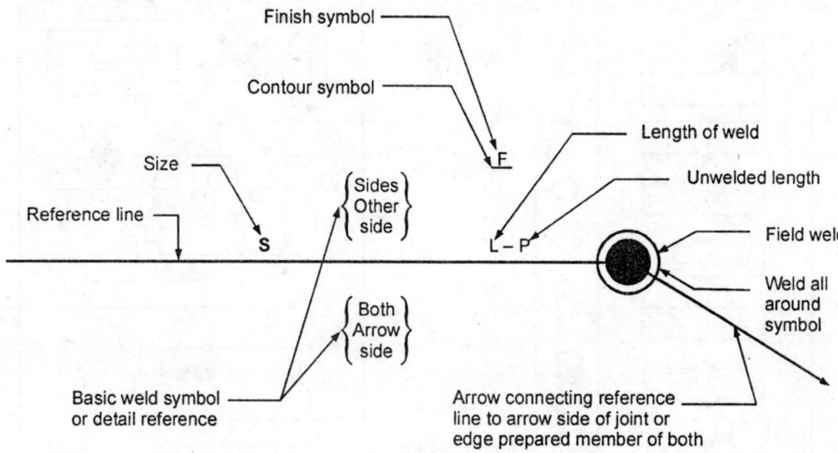

Fig. 6.7

6.7 REPRESENTATION OF A WELD

According to the ISI, elements of welding symbols shall have standard location with respect to each other as shown in Fig. 6.7.

1. The arrow point indicates the location of weld.
2. The basic symbols used to specify the type of weld.
3. The specification if any is placed in the tail of arrows.
4. Standard locations of welding symbol represented on drawing.

6.8 DEFECTS IN WELDING JOINTS

Most important defect in a joint is the presence of slags and oxide in the joint such as, inclusion, under cut and poor penetration etc.

***(i)* Inclusion:** May form a layer which will weaken the point considerably.

***(ii)* Under Cut Weld:** Develops when filled metal does not cover the parent metal at the edge.

***(iii)* Poor Penetration:** Poor penetration of filling metal leaves the lower part of the joint, unjointed. This will obviously cause the loss of section area and weaken the joint.

Different types of welding symbols are shown in Table 6.2 and 6.3.

Table 6.2 Welding Symbols

FORM OF WELD	SECTIONAL REPRESENTATION	APPROPRIATE SYMBOL	FORM OF WELD	SECTIONAL REPRESENTATION	APPROPRIATE SYMBOL
Fillet			Plug of slot		
Square butt			Backing strip		
Single 'V' butt					
Double 'V' butt			Spot		
Single 'U' butt					
Double 'U' butt			Seam		
Single bevel butt			Meshed seam	Before After	
Double bevel butt			Stich		
Single J butt			Mashed stich	Before After	
Double J butt					
Stud			Projection	Before After	
Edge weld			Flash	Rod of bar Tube	
Sealing run			Butt resistance of pressure (up set)	Rod of bar Tube	

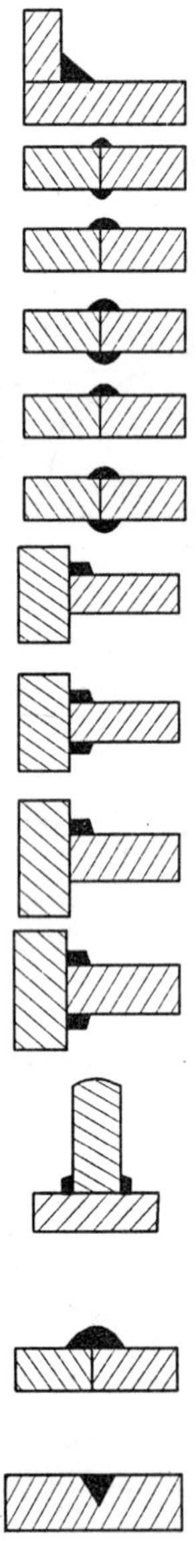

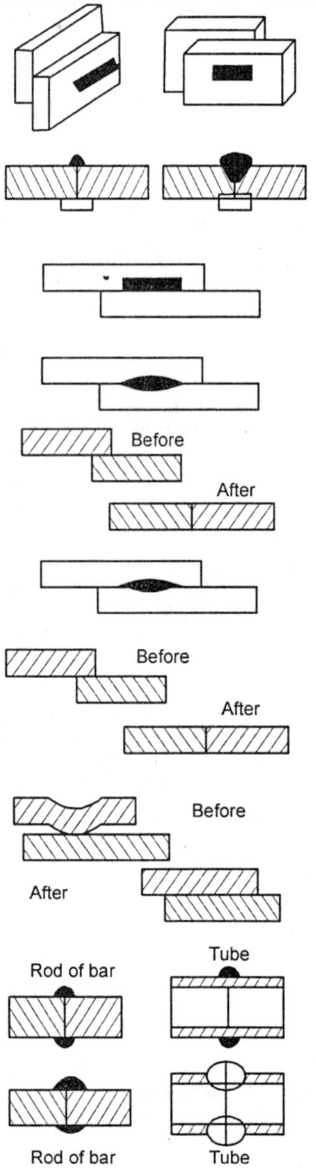

Table 6.3 Welding Symbols

S. NO	PARTICULARS	DRAWING REPRESENTATION AND SYMBOLS	
1.	Weld all round		
2.	Field of site weld	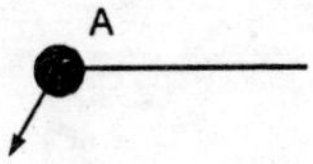	
3.	Flash contour	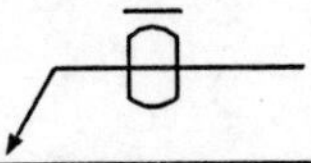	
4.	Convex contour		
5.	Concave contour		
6.	Grinding finish	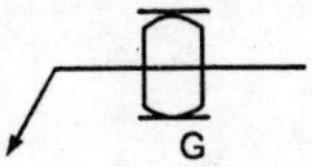	G
7.	Machining finish	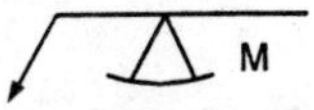	M
8.	Chipping finish	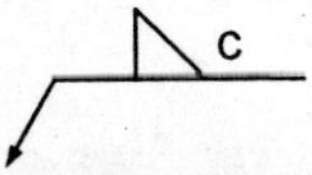	C

EXERCISE

1. What do you mean by welding?
2. What is fusion welding?
3. What are the different types of welding joints?
4. Draw free hand sketch of the following:
   (*i*) Spot weld (*ii*) Single V-Butt weld
   (*iii*) Double V-Butt weld (*iv*) Single U-Butt weld
   (*v*) Double U-Butt weld.
5. What are the various methods by which welded joints are dimensioned?

❑❑❑

IMPORTANT NOTES:

7

KEYS AND COTTER JOINTS

7.1 INTRODUCTION

Keys are temporary fasteners and are used to hold the pulleys, couplings, gears wheels, crankarms and clutches etc. on the rotating shafts. Therefore the key is define as, a device to fasten two circular parts one being around the other, in order to prevent relative rotary motion between them. It is always inserted parallel to the axis. The key is usually inserted in the recess or groove cut in the two mating surface of the parts which are to be fastened. Hence it is generally made of mild steel. They are simple in design compact and are easy to assemble and replace.

A large number of standard keys are used in engineering work. The choice of key depends upon the load being transmitted.

7.2 TYPES OF KEYS

The following types of keys are important from the subject point of view:

(1) Sunk key
(2) Saddle key
(3) Feather key
(4) Gib Head key
(5) Round key.

1. Sunk Key: The sunk keys are projected half in the key way of the shafts and half in the key way of hub of the pulley. These are suitable for heavy duty, since they roll on positive drive. It may be further classified as:

(*i*) Rectangular tapered key
(*ii*) Square tapered key
(*iii*) Parallel sunk key
(*iv*) Woodruff.

(*i*) Rectangular tapered key: A rectangular tapered key is shown in Fig. 7.1. The usual proportions are:

L = 1.5D	where, L = key length
T = D/6	T = key thickness
W = D/4	W = key width
D = Shaft diameter	

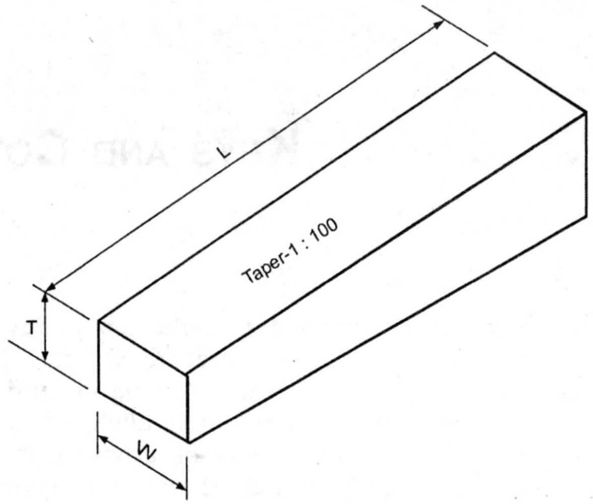

Fig. 7.1 Rectangular Tapered Key

(*ii*) Square tapered key: A square tapered key is shown in Fig. 7.2. They are same as rectangular tapered key but only the difference between them is that its width and thickness are equal. The usual proportions of these keys are:

L = 1.5 D, W = T = D/4

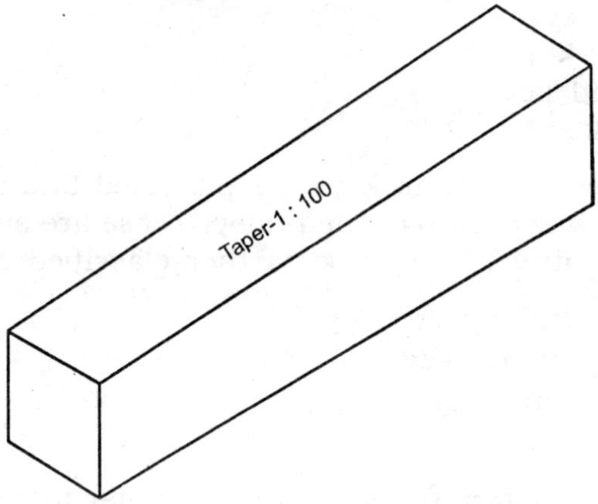

Fig. 7.2 Square Tapered Key

(*iii*) Parallel sunk key: The parallel sunk key may be rectangular or square section uniform in width and thickness throughout. Parallel key is a taper one usually 1 : 100. That is taper 1 mm in a length of 100 mm as shown in Fig. 7.3.

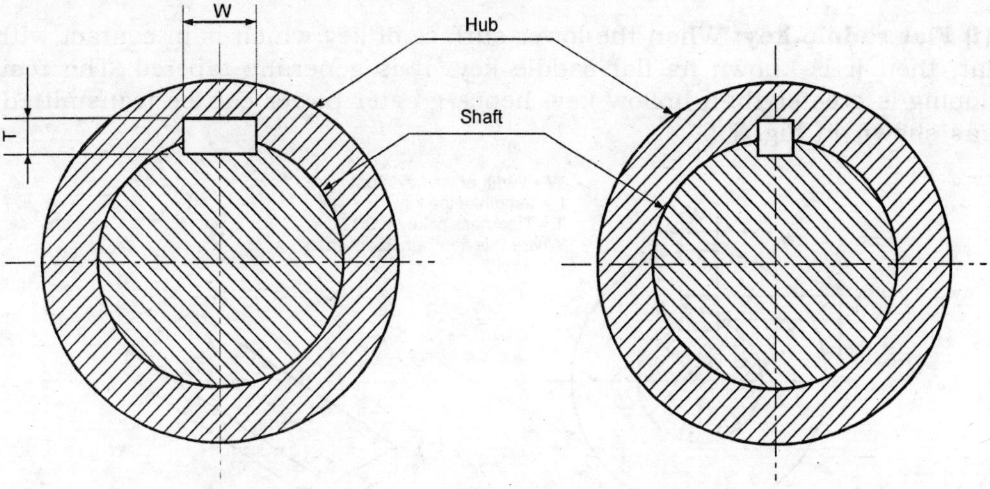

Fig. 7.3

***(iv)* Wood ruff key:** It is a semi circular in shape. It has more thickness of the key way and key seat is equal to the thickness of depth is in shaft as compared to hub. It is used in the key. The keyway is just half in the key seat. The key can be easily adjusted in the recess automobile, tractor and machine tools industries. It accommodates itself to any taper in the hub of the mating surface as shown in Fig. 7.4.

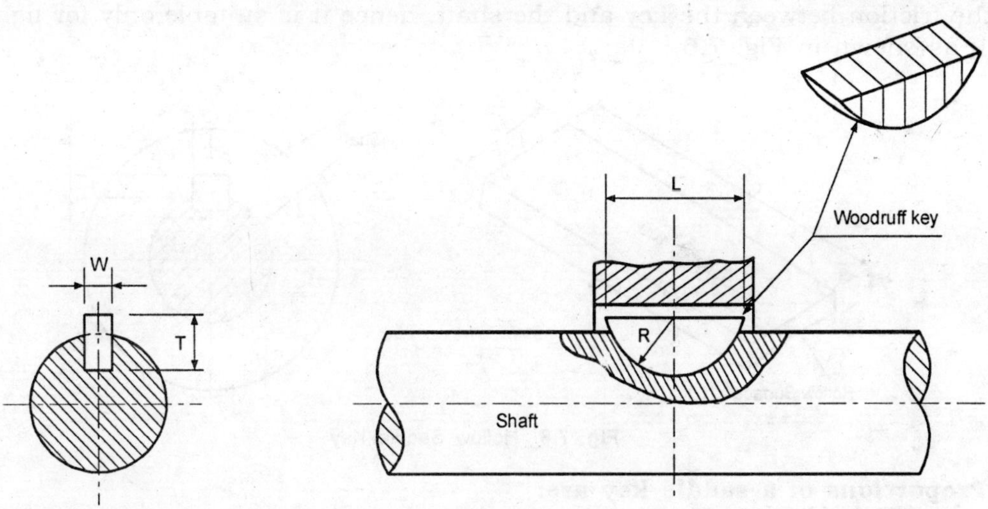

Fig. 7.4

2. Saddle Keys: Saddle keys are also taper type keys. It has tight contact between shaft and hub but it is inserted just on the outside of the shaft. No key way is made in the shaft and torque is transmitted due to friction between the bottom of the key and Shaft surface. They are of two main types:

(*i*) Flat saddle key

(*ii*) Hollow saddle key.

***(i)* Flat saddle key:** When the lower surface of key which is in contact with shaft is flat, then it is known as flat saddle key. It is generally tapered. The resistance to sloping is greater than hollow key, hence greater power can be transmitted by its use as shown in Fig. 7.5.

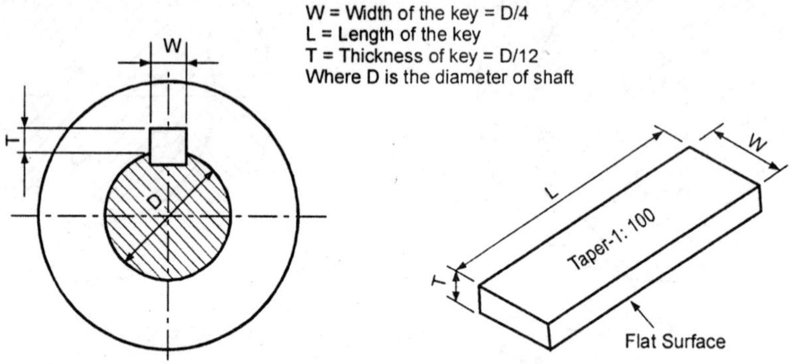

Fig. 7.5 Flat Saddle Key

***(ii)* Hollow saddle key:** When the lower surface of key is hollow that is known as hollow saddle key. It gives a saddle action on the round shaft. The key way is cut in the mating piece only. Relative rotation between the two pieces is prevented only by the friction between the key and the shaft, hence it is suitable only for light duty work as shown in Fig. 7.6.

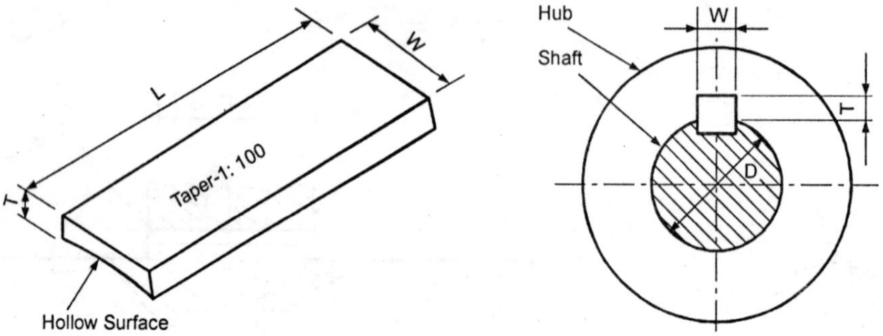

Fig. 7.6 Hollow Saddle Key

Proportions of a saddle key are:

W = D/4

T = D/12

L = D to 1.5 D

Taper on the top surface = 1 : 100

where, D = diameter of the shaft

W = Width of key

L = Key length

T = Key thickness.

3. Feather Key: A key is attached to one member of a pair and which permits relative axial movement is known as feather key. It is special type of parallel key which transmits a turning movement and also permits axial movement. It is fastened either to the shaft or hub.

Feather keys may be rectangular or square in cross-section having ends round or rectangular. Various feather keys are shown in Fig. 7.7. They are fixed to one of the two. The feather keys may be similar to parallel sink key.

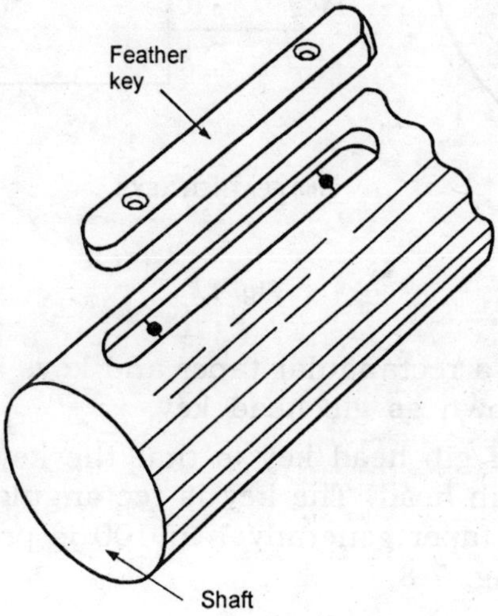

(i) FEATHER KEY

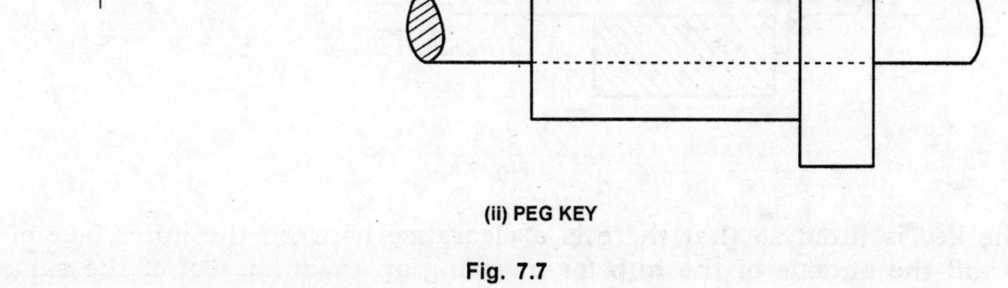

(ii) PEG KEY

Fig. 7.7

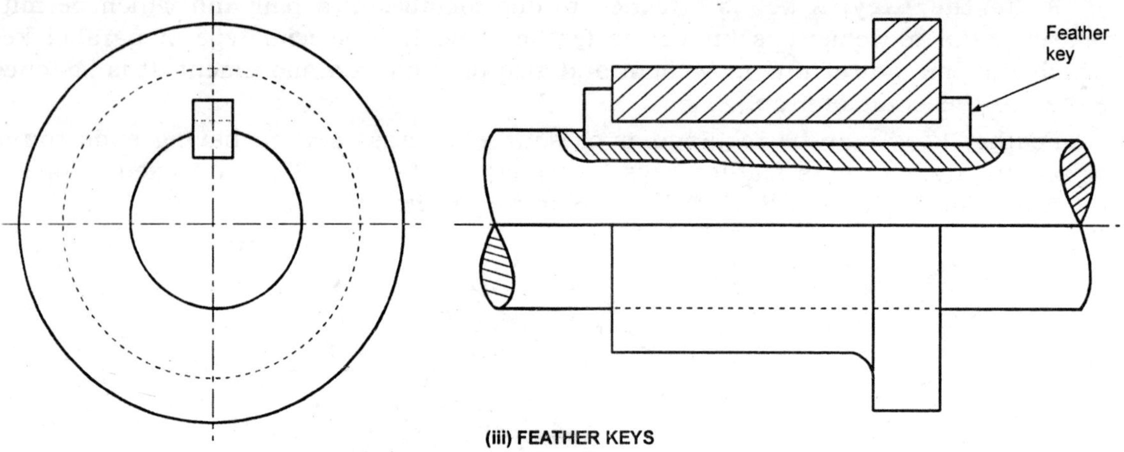

(iii) FEATHER KEYS

Fig. 7.7

4. Gib Head Key: It is a rectangular taper and keys are often provided with a gib head and such key is known as gib head key.

The main advantage of gib head key is that the key can be easily inserted and removed with the aid of gib head. The key is rectangular and uniform in width but tapered in thickness. The taper generally 1 in 100 is provided on the upper surface of the key as shown in Fig. 7.8.

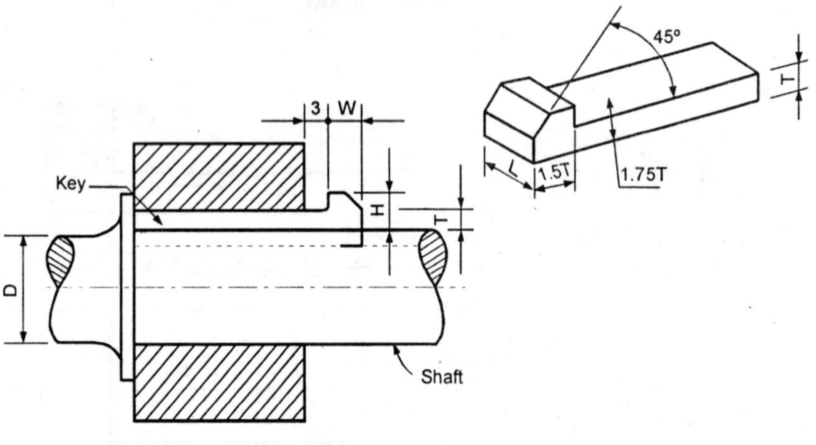

Fig. 7.8

The key is fitted so that there is a clearance between the inner face of the gib head and the outside of the hub for inserting an executor tool of the same kind.

Main dimensions of the key are as follows:

Length of gib Head = L_1= D/4

Width of gib Head = W_1 = 1.5T = T = D/6

Thickness of gib Head = T_1 = 1.75 T

Length of the key = L = 1.5D

Thickness of the key = T = D/6

Width of the key = W = D/4

Angle of chamfer on gib head = 45°

5. Round Key: It is the simplest form of a key. It is a small circular rod. The length and diameter of key depends upon the diameter of the shaft for which it is used. The key is inserted half in the hub and half in the shaft as shown in Fig. 7.9 taper is usually taken 1 : 50.

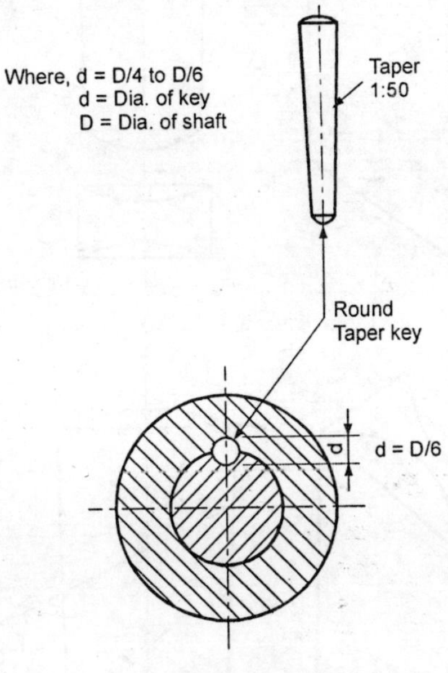

Fig. 7.9

7.3 COTTER

A cotter is a flat edge shaped piece of rectangular cross section. It is a temporary fastener and is used to hold two parts together where the parts are subjected to axial forces only. Cotters are usually made of mild steel. Keys are generally inserted parallel to the axis of the connecting shafts but a cotter is driven perpendicular to the axis of connecting parts. Cotter is uniform in thickness but taper in width on one or both sides as shown in Fig. 7.10.

The usual taper is 1 in 48 to 1 in 30. Cotter is inserted by hammering. It is usually used in connecting a piston rod to the cross-head of a reciprocating steam engine, a piston rod and its extension as a tail or pump rod etc.

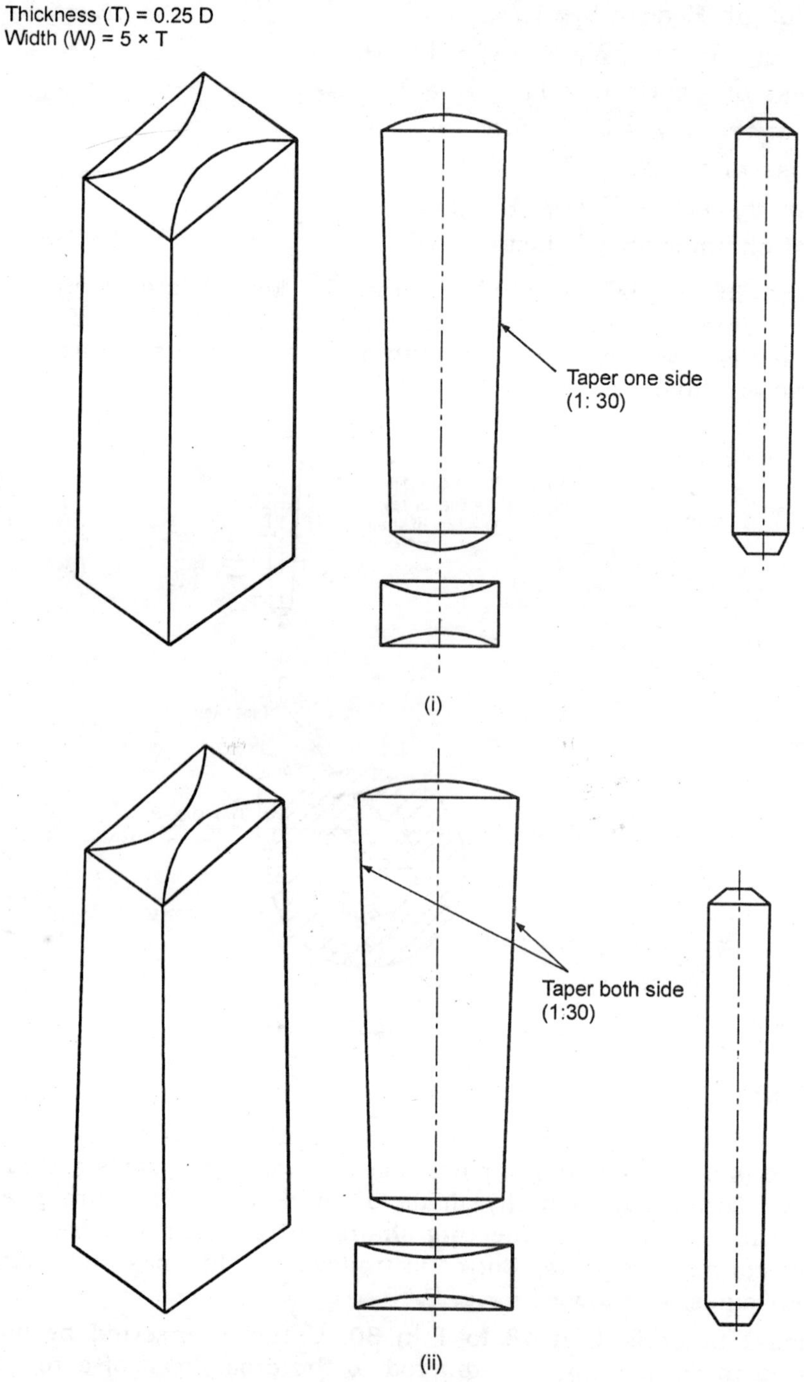

Thickness (T) = 0.25 D
Width (W) = 5 × T
Taper one side
(1: 30)
(i)
Taper both side
(1:30)
(ii)

Fig. 7.10

7.4 COTTERS JOINTS

A cotter joint is formed by using a cotter. Some important types of cotter joints are as follows:

1. Gib and cotter joint 2. Socket and Spigot joint 3. Sleeve and cotter joint.

7.5 GIB AND COTTER JOINT

Gib and cotter joints are mostly used for square rod or rectangular cross section. One end is simply slotted and other end is fork shaped. The slot in one end of the rod is adjusted in between the slots of the fork ends so that all the three slots are in line while mating assembly gib is first put into the slot and the cotter is then inserted. It should be noted that the gib is to be placed on the open side of the fork.

Problem 1. Fig. 7.11 shows pictorial details of parts of a gib and cotter joint. Assemble the parts and draw the following orthographic projection in full scale.

1. Full section front view 2. Top view 3. End view.

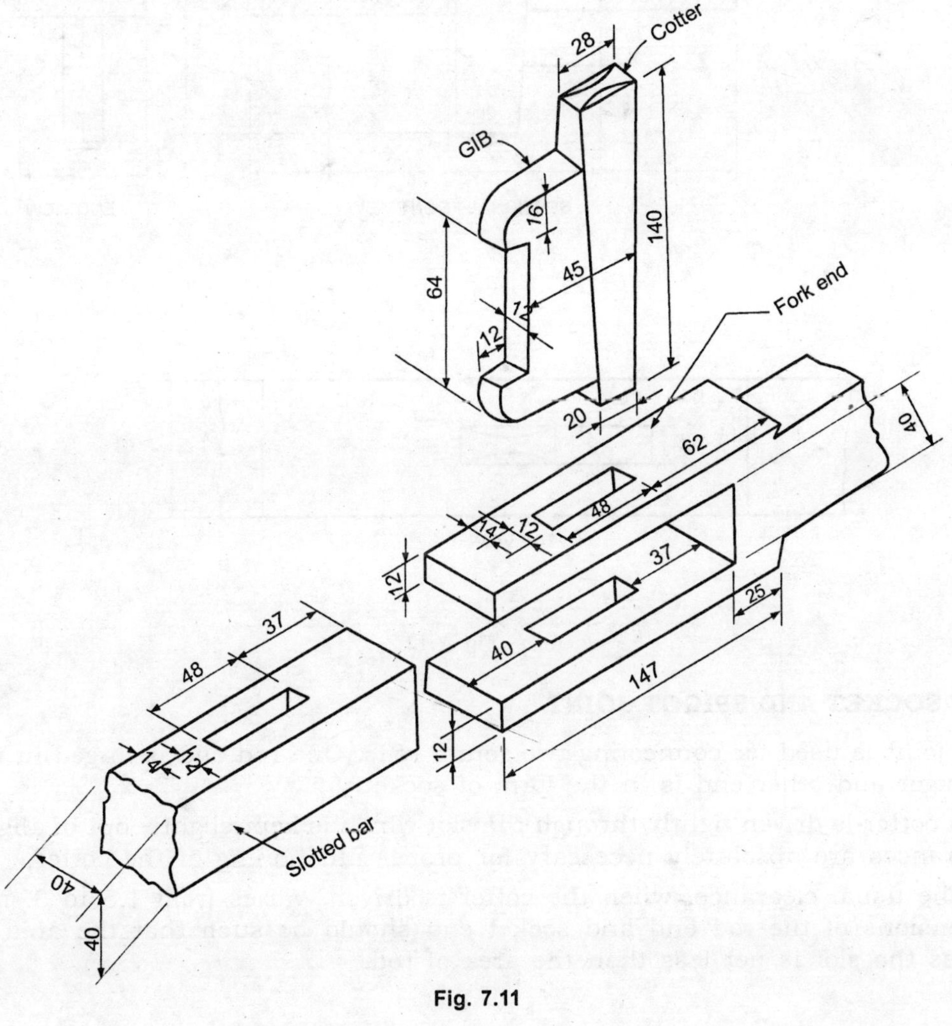

Fig. 7.11

Solution. See Fig. 7.12.

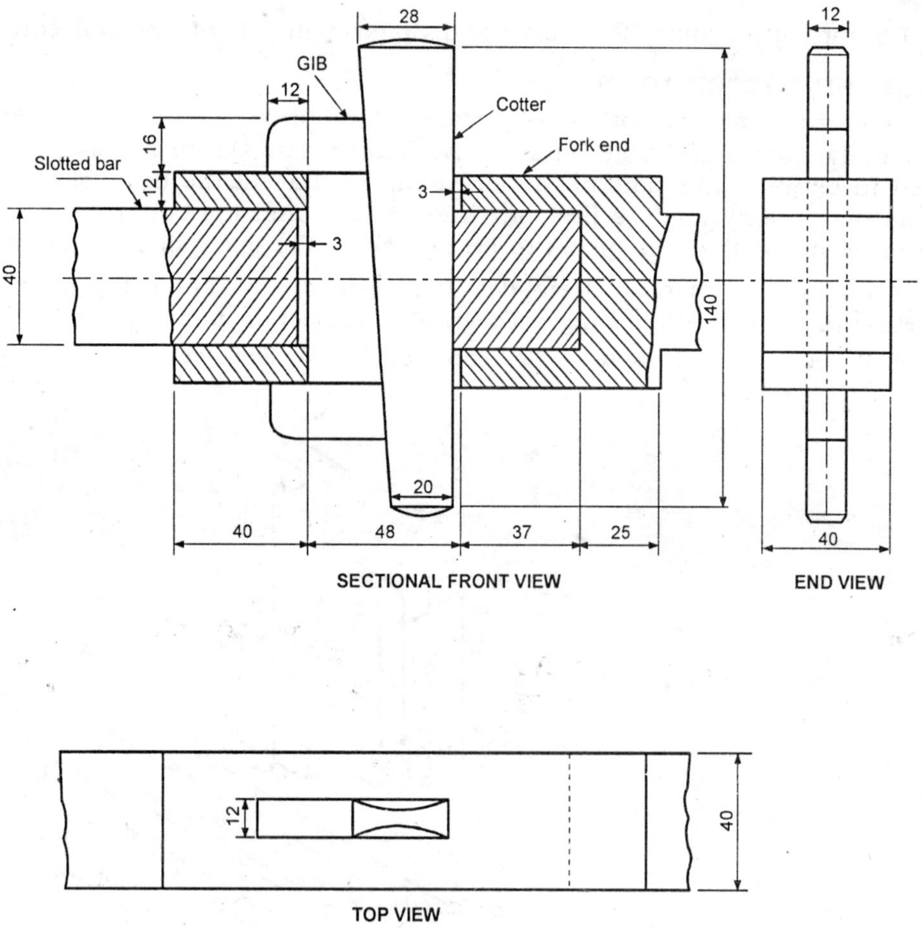

Fig. 7.12

7.6 SOCKET AND SPIGOT JOINT

This joint is used for connecting two round rods. One rod end is forged in the form of spigot and other end is in the form of socket.

A cotter is driven tightly through the slot which is kept slightly out of alignments. Clearances are absolutely necessary for proper functioning of the cotter.

The usual clearance, when the cotter is driven, varies from 1.5 to 3. mm. The dimensions of the rod end and socket end should be such that the area of each across the slot is not less than the area of rod.

Problem 2. Fig. 7.13 shows the details of parts of a socket and spigot joint. Assemble the parts and draw the following orthographic projection:

1. Full section front view
2. End view.

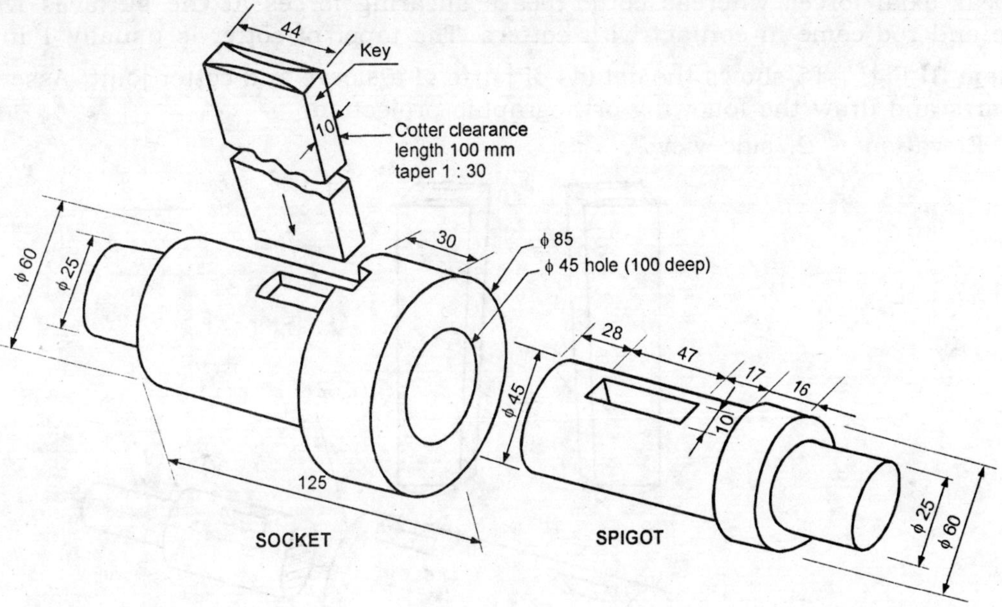

Fig. 7.13

Solution. See Fig. 7.14.

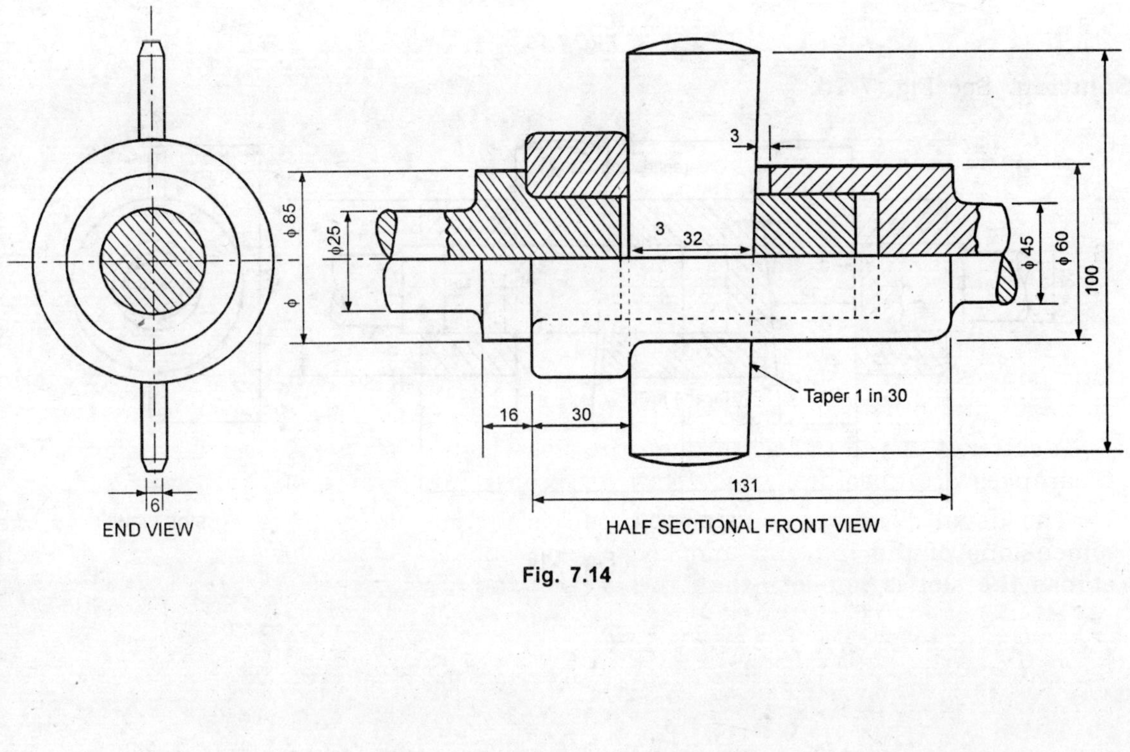

Fig. 7.14

7.7 SLEEVE AND COTTER JOINT

A sleeve and cotter joint is used to connect two round rods. In this type of joint a sleeve or muff is used over the two rods and then two cotters are inserted in the holes provided for them in the sleeve and rod to increase the length. The sleeve and rod bear axial forces whereas cotter bears shearing forces at the surfaces where sleeve and rod come in contact with cotters. The taper of cotter is usually 1 in 24.

Problem 3. Fig. 7.15 shows the details of parts of a sleeve and cotter joint. Assemble the parts and draw the following orthographic projection:

1. Elevation 2. side view.

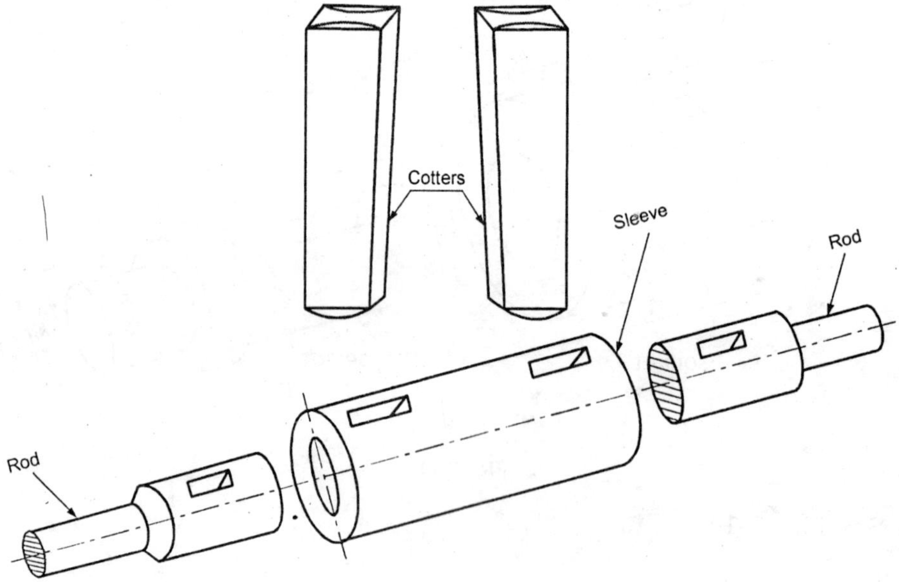

Fig. 7.15

Solution. See Fig. 7.16.

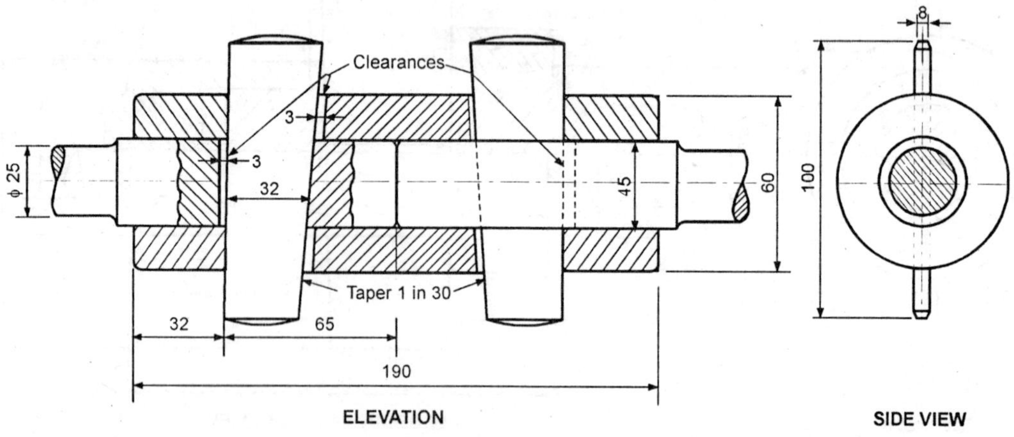

Fig. 7.16

7.8 KNUCKLE JOINT

Knuckle joint is also one of the important joint and has advantages over the cotter joint. It is also known as pin joint. A knuckle joint is used to connect two rods which are under the action of tensile or compressive loads. The joint is not rigid. It permits angular movement between the rods. Hence, it is commonly used when a reciprocating motion is to be converted into a rotatory motion or vice versa. In case of steam engine the eccentric rod is connected to the rod by means of this joint.

One end of one of the rods is made into an eye and the end of the other rod is formed into a fork with an eye in each of the fork leg. The pin is kept in position by means of a colar and a taper pin. The rods are quite free to rotate on the cylinder pin. The material used for the joint may be steel or wrought steel. A pictorial view of a knuckle joint is shown in Fig. 7.17.

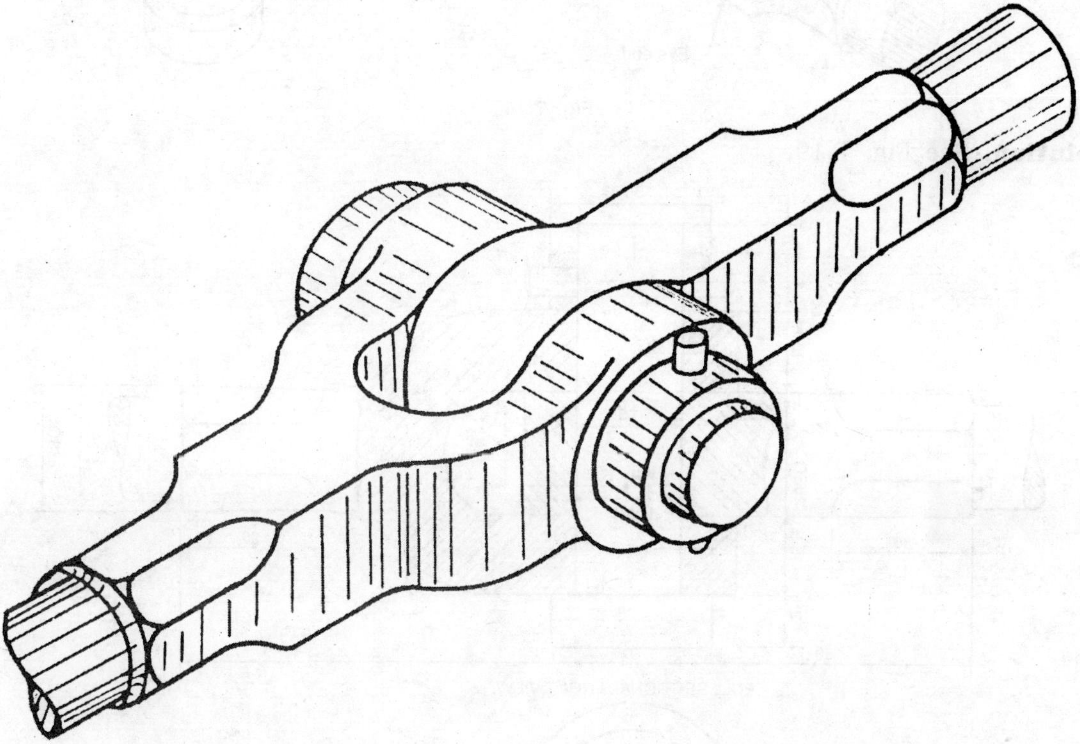

Fig. 7.17

Problem 4. Fig. 7.18 shows the details of a knuckle joint. Assemble all parts and draw the following view:

1. Full section front view
2. Top view.

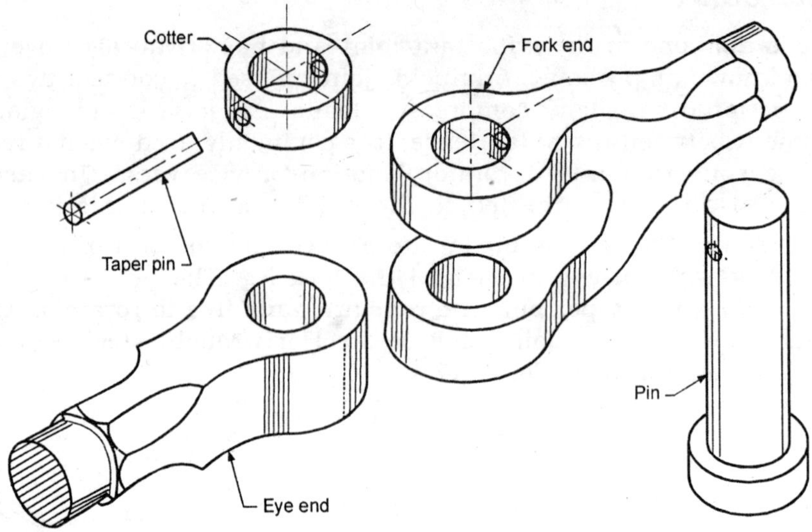

Fig. 7.18

Solution. See Fig. 7.19.

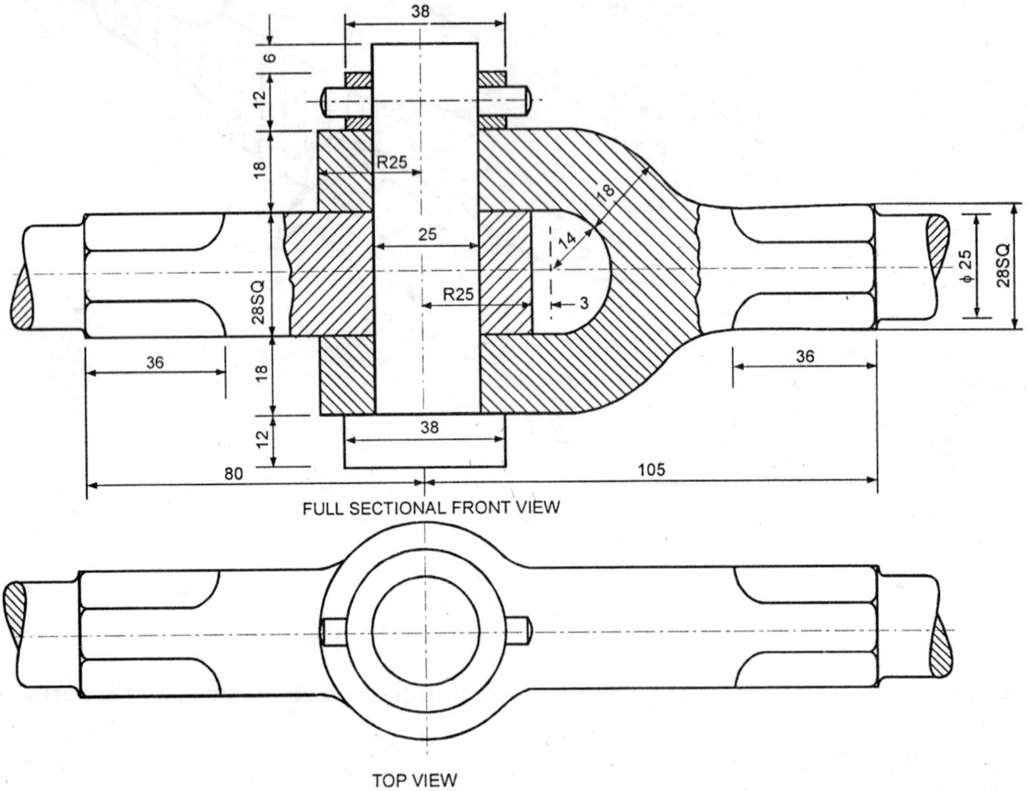

Fig. 7.19

EXERCISE

1. What is the function of a key? What is the difference between a saddle key and a sunk key?

2. Draw the neat sketch of the following keys:

(*i*) Wood ruff key
(*ii*) Hollow saddle key
(*ii*) Gib head key.

3. What do you mean by cotters and where they are used?

4. What is the difference between key and cotter?

5. Why the clearance is left in cotter joint?

6. Sketch the elevation and plan of a gib and cotter joint for two square shaft of side 45 mm.

7. Fig. 7.20 shows two views of a kunckle joint. Draw its following view to a suitable scale:
(1) Elevation (2) Plan (3) Full sectional side view.

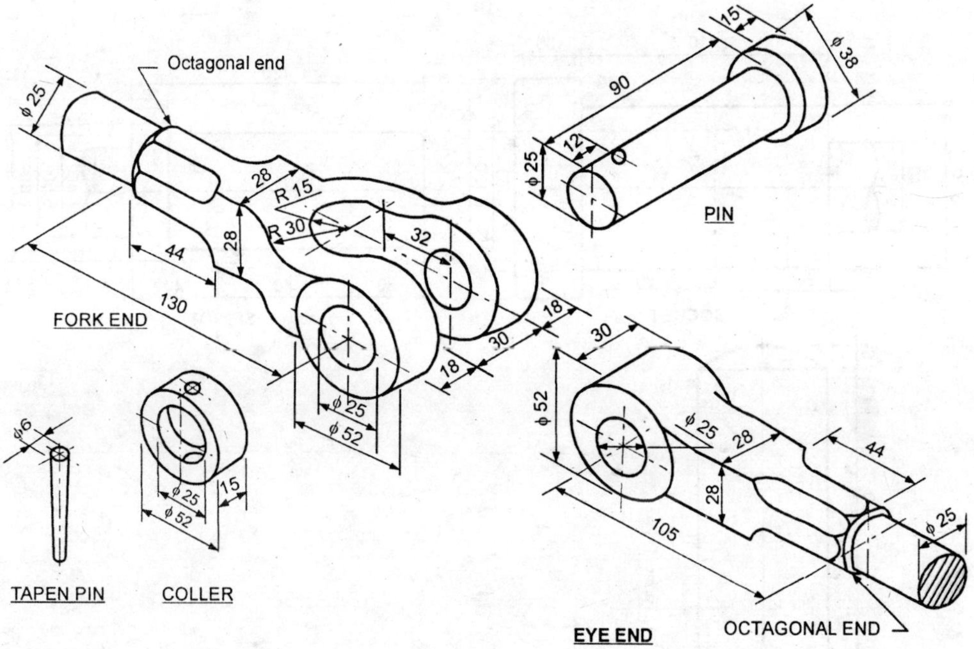

Fig. 7.20

8. Fig. 7.21 shows the pictorial view of a spigot and socket joint. Draw the following views:

(1) Elevation upper half in section
(2) Plan
(3) Side view.

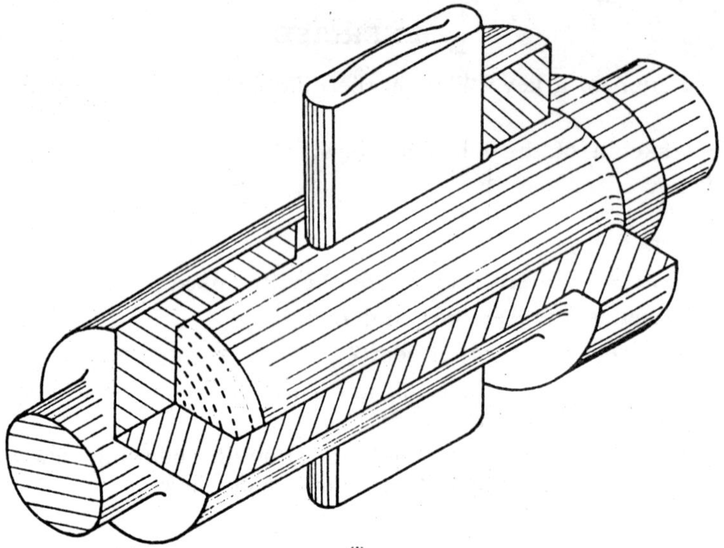

(i)

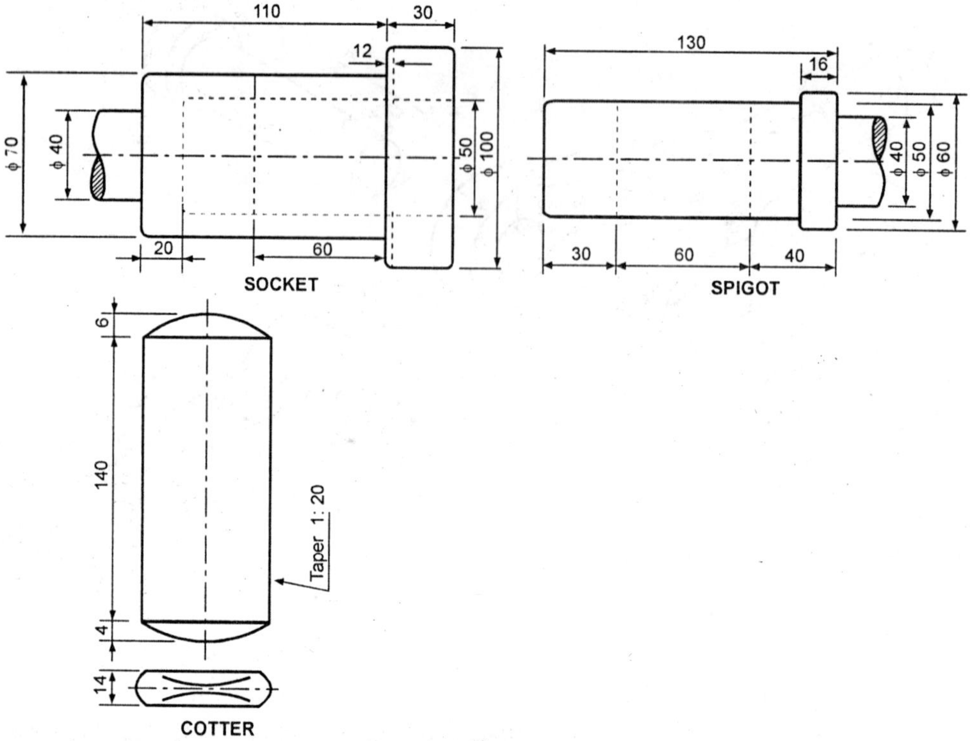
110
30
12
ϕ 70
ϕ 40
ϕ 50
ϕ 100
20
60
SOCKET
130
16
ϕ 40
ϕ 50
ϕ 60
30
60
40
SPIGOT
6
140
Taper 1: 20
4
14
COTTER

(ii)

Fig. 7.21

❑❑❑

8

COUPLINGS

8.1 INTRODUCTION

Shafts are manufactured in length varying from 6 to 10 metres due to inconveniences in transport. If we required a long line shaft then it is composed of a number of small shaft pieces put together end to end joined by couplings. Therefore, coupling is used to join two shafts.

In other words, couplings are used for joining two or more shafts to increase their length and for transmitting rotatory motion directly from one shaft to another. For example, electric motor and pump are connected by a coupling.

8.2 TYPES OF COUPLING

Couplings are divided into two groups as follows:

1. Rigid Coupling
2. Flexible Coupling.

8.3 RIGID COUPLINGS

It is used to connect two shafts which are perfectly aligned and does not permit relative motion between them.

Rigid couplings are further divided into two groups as follows:

(1) *Parallel shaft Coupling:* (*i*) Flange coupling
(*ii*) Muff coupling
(*iii*) Half lap muff coupling
(*iv*) Split muff coupling

(2) Non-parallel shaft coupling: Old coupling
(*i*) Hook's or universal coupling
(*ii*) Oldham coupling.

8.4 FLEXIBLE COUPLING

It is used to connect two shafts having both lateral and angular misalignment. The advantages of these couplings are that they have an important function of absorbing vibration, sudden shock load etc.

These couplings are of the following types:

(*i*) Pin type coupling
(*ii*) Bibley coupling
(*iii*) Belt-type coupling.

8.5 FLANGE COUPLING

It is a standard form of a coupling and is extensively used in workshop to join two coaxial shafts. It consists of two cast iron flanges, keyed to the end of two shafts to be joined and fastened together by means of nuts and bolts. Sunk taper and keys of rectangular or square cross-section are commonly used for the purpose. One of the flange has a projected portion and the other flange has a corresponding recess. This helps to bring the shaft into line and to maintain alignment. This arrangement is termed as spigot and socket centring. There is a clearance between male extension and female depression to adjust the shaft. The flange coupling is adopted to heavy loads and hence it is used in large shafting. The following two important types of flange couplings are given below:

(*i*) Unprotected type flange coupling
(*ii*) Protected type flange coupling.

(*i*) Unprotected Type Flange Coupling: Fig. 8.1 shows pictorial view of an unprotected type flange coupling, each shaft is keyed to the base of flange with a counter sunk key and the flanges are coupled together by means of bolts numbering from three, four six etc. The keys are arranged at 90° along the circumference of the shafts to divide the weakening effect caused by key ways.

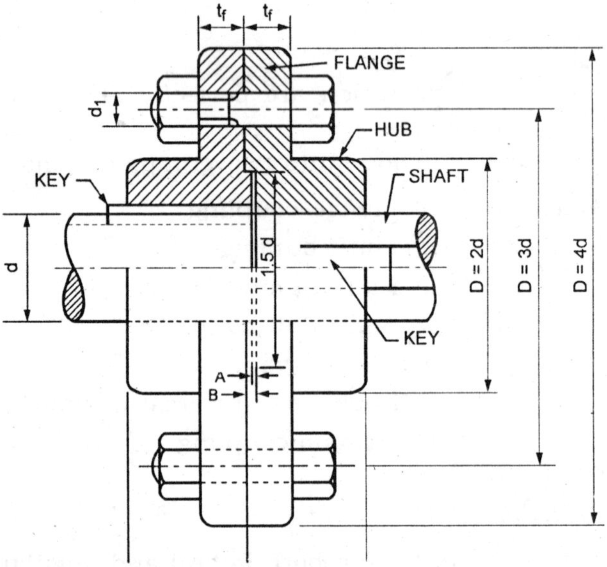

Fig. 8.1

Following standard proportions can be adopted for an unprotected type flange coupling:

Let d be the diameter of shaft. Then

(*i*) Outside diameter of hub, D = 2d

(*ii*) Length of hub, L = 1.5d

(*iii*) Pitch circle diameter of the bolts = D_1 = 2.8 to 3d

(*iv*) Outside diameter of flange, D_2 = 4d

(*v*) Thickness of the flange T = 0.5d

(*vi*) Thickness of the protective circumference flange t_1 = 0.25d

(*vii*) No. of bolts n = 3 for shaft diameter upto 40 mm

n = 4 for shaft diameter upto 100 mm

n = 6 for shaft diameter upto 180 mm

(*ii*) Protected Type of Flange Coupling: Fig. 8.2 shows pictorial view of a protected type flange coupling, in which the bolt does not project beyond the flanges in order to avoid danger to the workman. In arrangement, each flange is provided with angular projection for covering bolt heads and nuts etc. This type of coupling is sometimes used as a belt pulley. To ensure the correct alignment, one of the flange has circular projection which fits into a corresponding depression in the other flange.

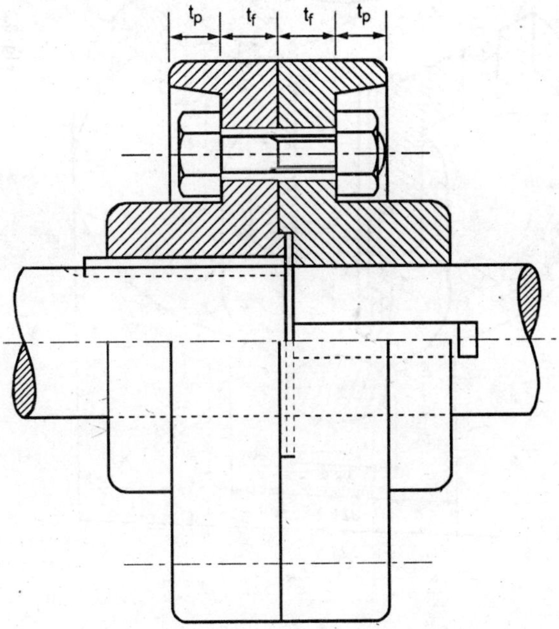

Fig. 8.2

Problem 1. Fig. 8.3 shows detail of parts of an unprotected flange coupling. Assemble the parts and draw the following projections:

(*i*) Sectional front view

(*ii*) Side view.

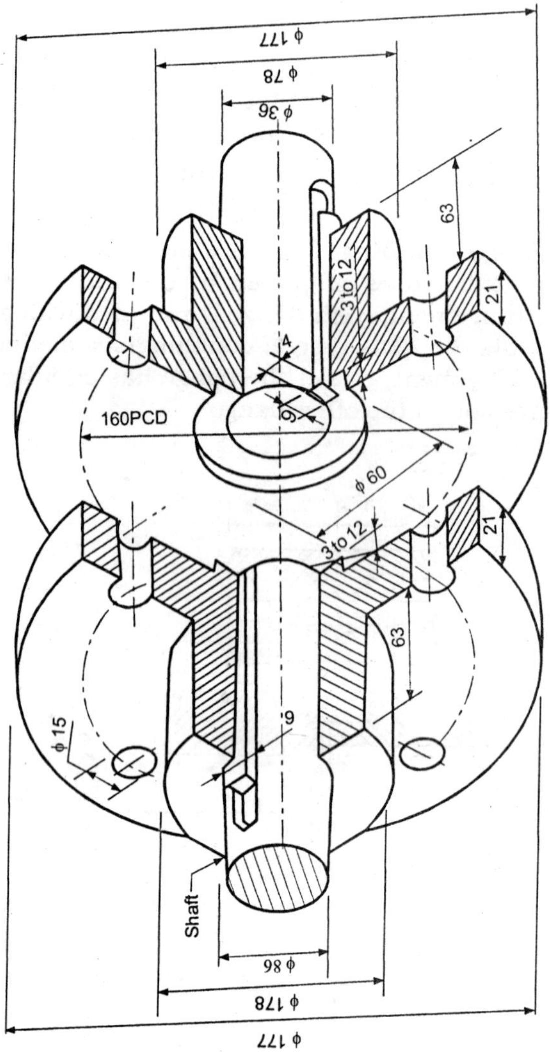

Fig. 8.3

Solution. See Fig. 8.4.

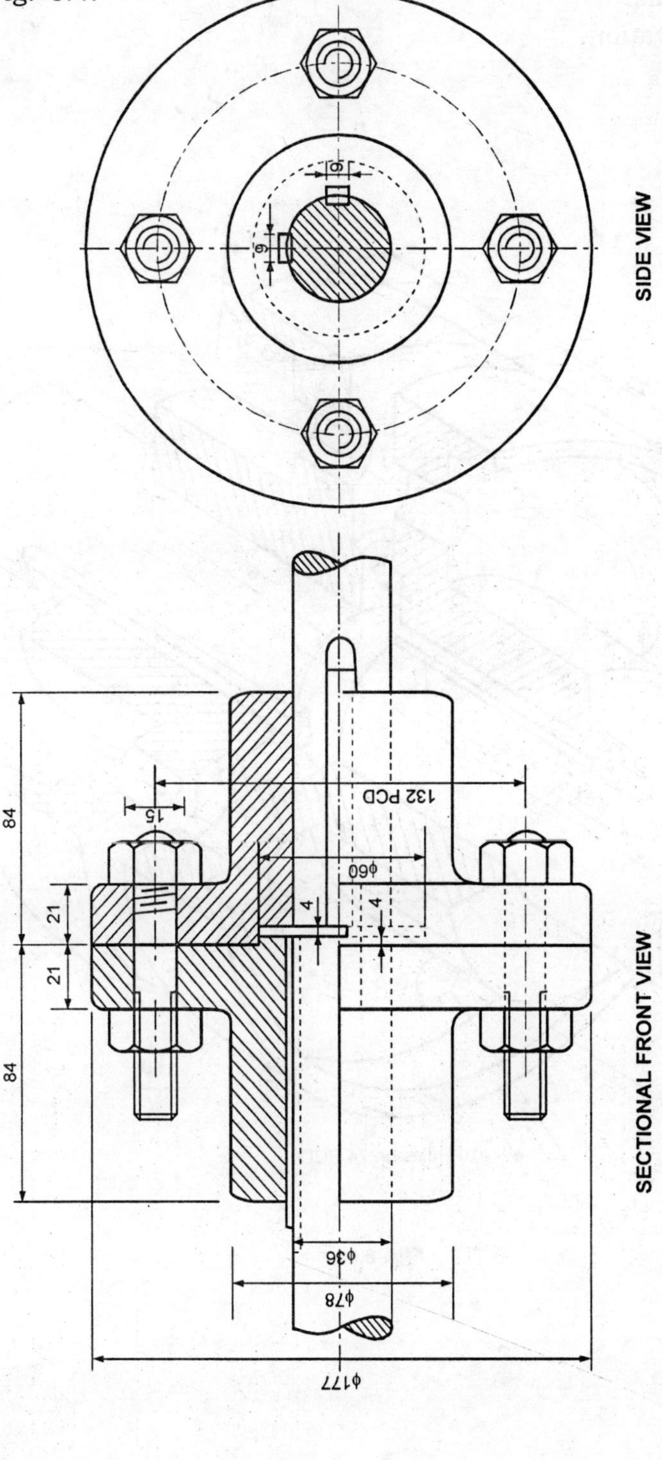

Fig. 8.4

Problem 2. Fig. 8.5 shows protected type flange coupling. Assemble the parts and draw to full size scale.

(i) Sectional elevation.

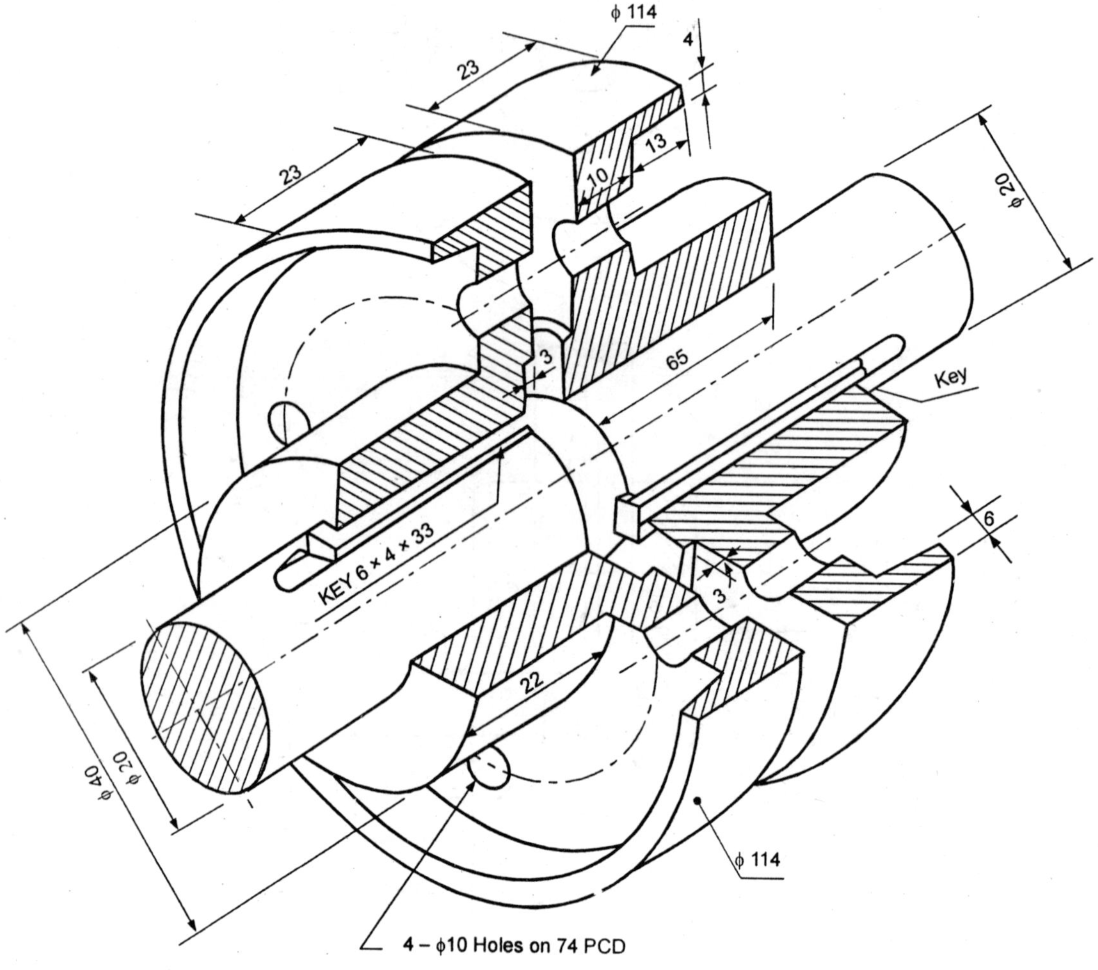

Fig. 8.5

Solution. See Fig. 8.6.

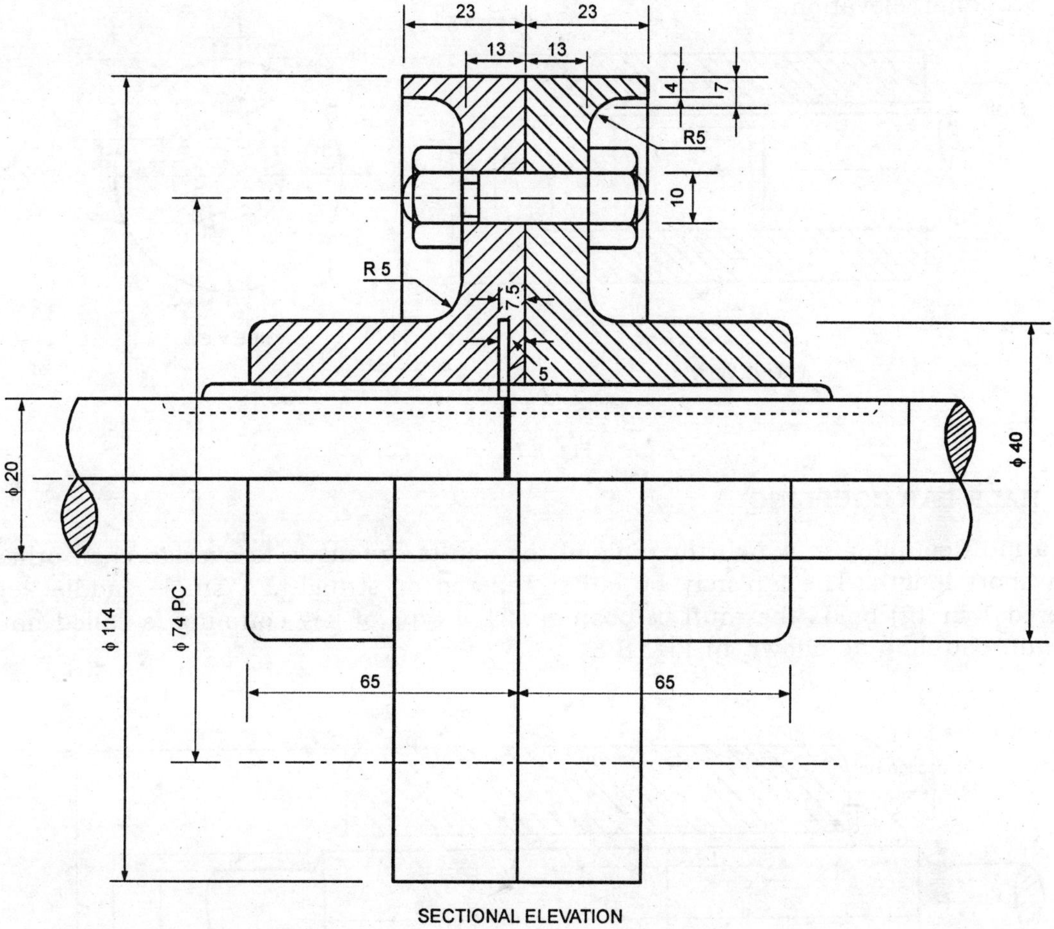

Fig. 8.6

8.6 MUFF COUPLING

It is the simplest type of rigid coupling and made of cast iron. It is also known as sleeve or Box coupling. A muff coupling consists of a hollow cylinder whose inner diameter is the same as that of the shaft. It is fitted over the end of the two shafts by means of sunk tape and key as shown in Fig. 8.7. Sometimes two separate keys are inserted from the opposite ends of the muff. The outside diameter of the muff is two times and length three times the diameter of the shaft. The usual proportions of muff coupling are as follows:

Outer diameter of the sleeve = 2d + 13 mm

Length of the sleeve L = 3.5d

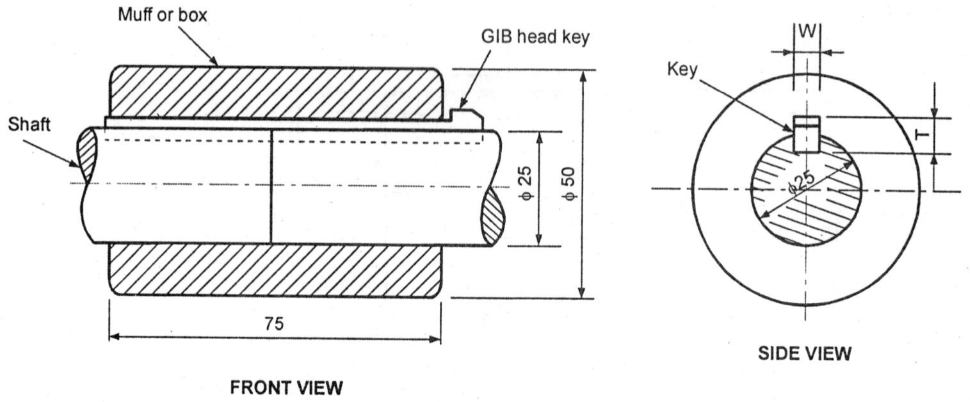

Fig. 8.7

8.7 HALF LAP COUPLING

It is a muff coupling in which the ends of the shafts are made to overlap each other for a short length. The lap may be either tapered or straight. A single saddle key (tapered 1 in 12) holds the muff in position. This type of key coupling is called half lap muff coupling as shown in Fig. 8.8.

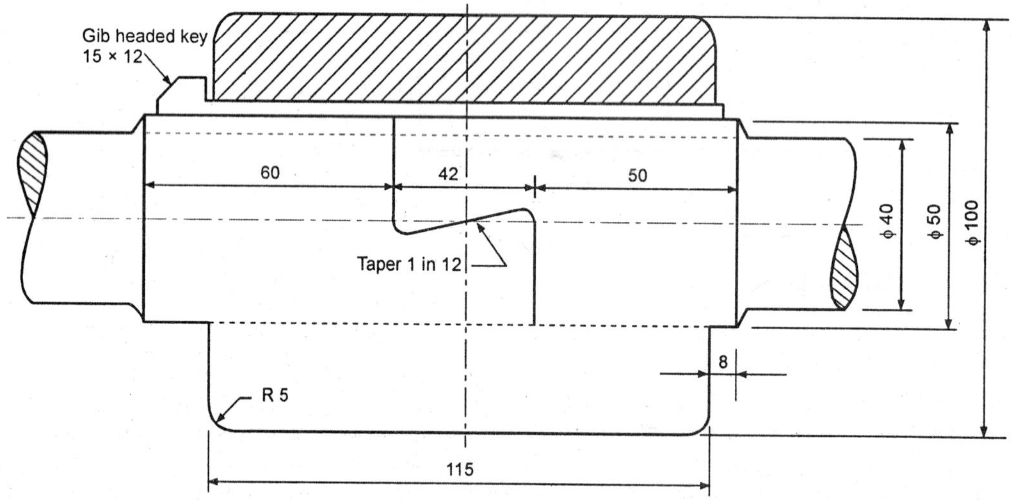

Fig. 8.8

8.8 SPLIT MUFF COUPLINGS

It is the simplest form of coupling and also known as compression coupling. In split muff coupling the muff is made into two halves which are joined together by means of nuts and bolts as shown in Fig. 8.9. The halves of the muff are made of cast iron. The shaft ends are made to each other and feather key is fitted directly in the keyways of both the shafts. One half of the muff is kept below and the other above the shaft ends and then held together by means of nuts and bolts. The advantage of this coupling is that, it can also be used as a pulley if required.

The usual proportions of the split muff coupling are:

Diameter of the muff D = 2d + 13 mm

Length of the muff L = 3.5d

where, d = diameter of the shaft.

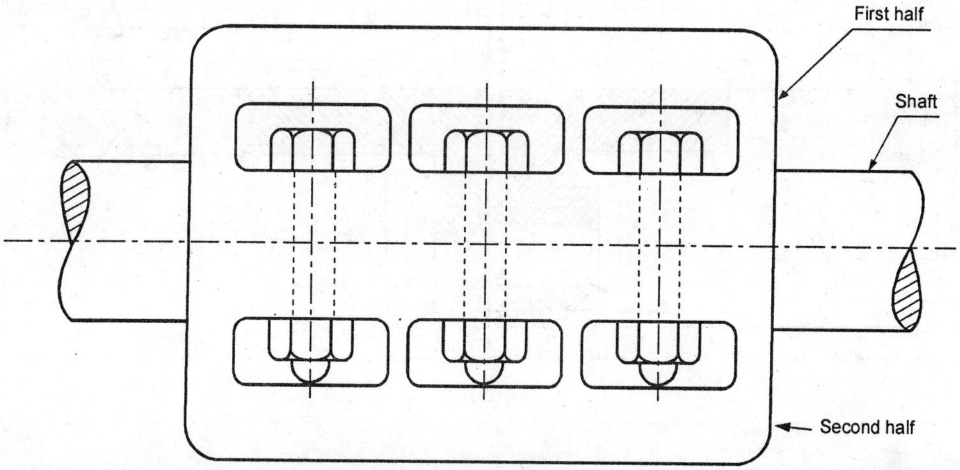

Fig. 8.9 Split Muff Coupling

8.9 FLEXIBLE COUPLING (PIN TYPE)

It is a modified form of rigid type flange coupling and used to join two shafts which are slightly out of line or requires slightly relative angular movement. The coupling bolts are known as pin. Flexible coupling uses a flexible element such as spring, rubber, leather etc. These flexible elements have the ability to absorb vibrations, shocks and jerks. A pin type flexible coupling is shown in Fig. 8.10 as four driving pins. These pins are rigidly fatened by units to one of the flange while they are covered with leathers or rubber washer and kept loose in the outer flange. These flanges are dissimilar in construction and a clearance of 5 mm is left between the face of the two flanges of the coupling.

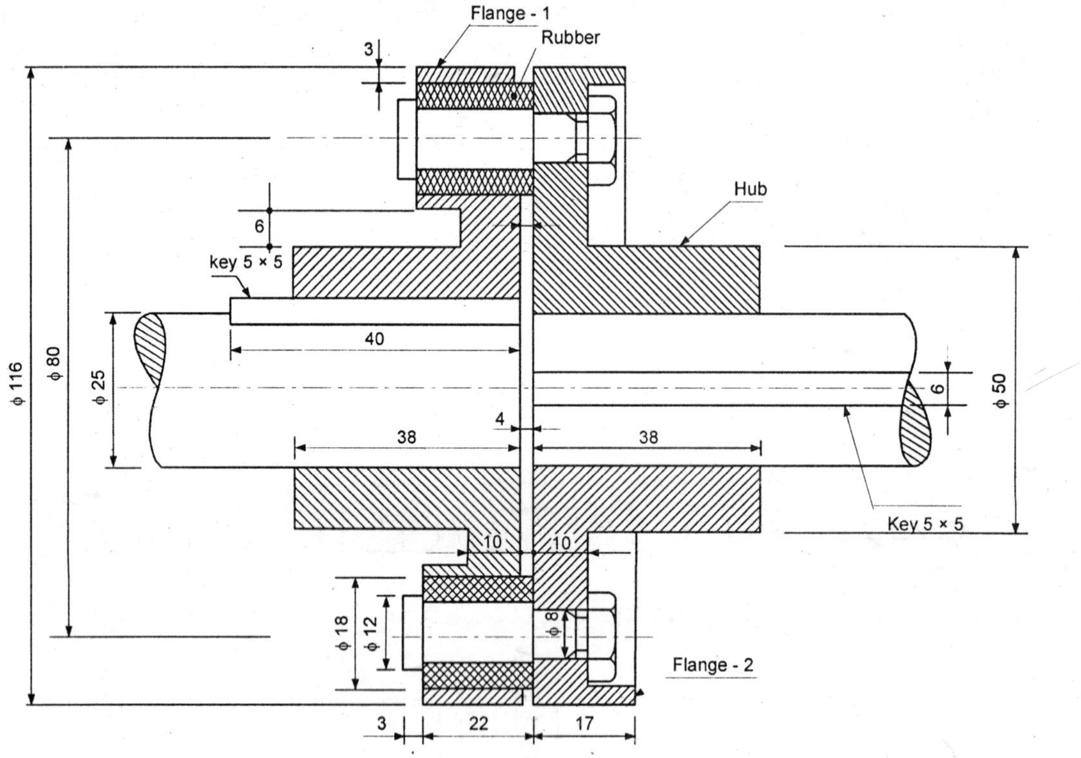

Fig. 8.10

This type of coupling is commonly used for directly connecting an electric motor to a machine.

8.10 UNIVERSAL COUPLING

This type of coupling is used when the shaft axes are intersecting. It consists of two similar forks. These forks are keyed on to the ends of the shafts. The two forks are pin joined to a centre block having two arms perpendicular to each other. In this type of coupling the angle between the shafts may be varied even when they are in motion. This coupling is widely used in agricultural machinery, machine tools and automobiles. This coupling is some times referred to as Hooke's joint, one such type of coupling is shown in Figure 8.11.

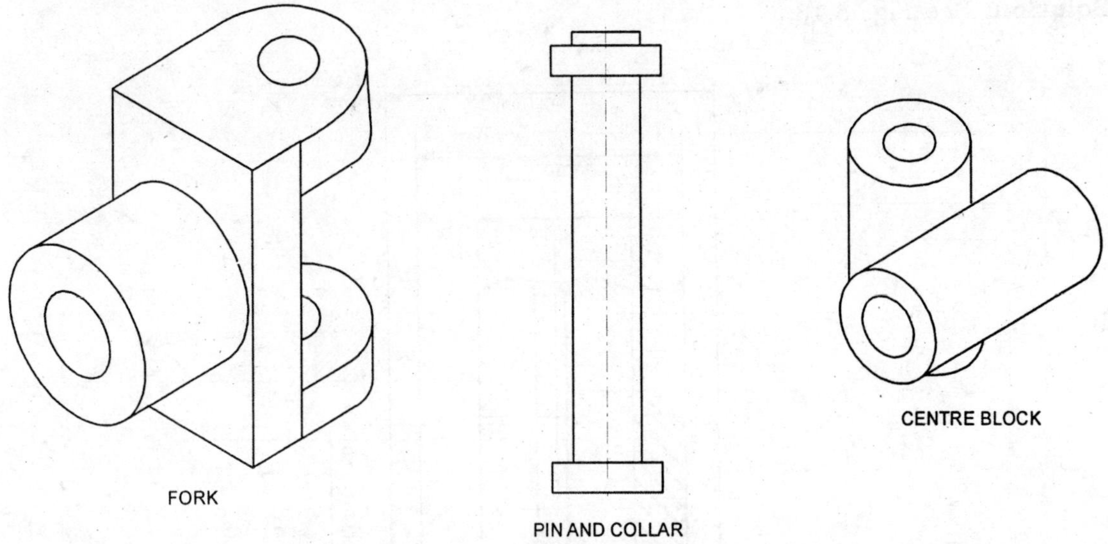

Fig. 8.11

Problem 3. Fig. 8.12 shows pictorial views of a universal coupling. Assemble the parts and draw the full size scale.

(i) Half sectional front view.

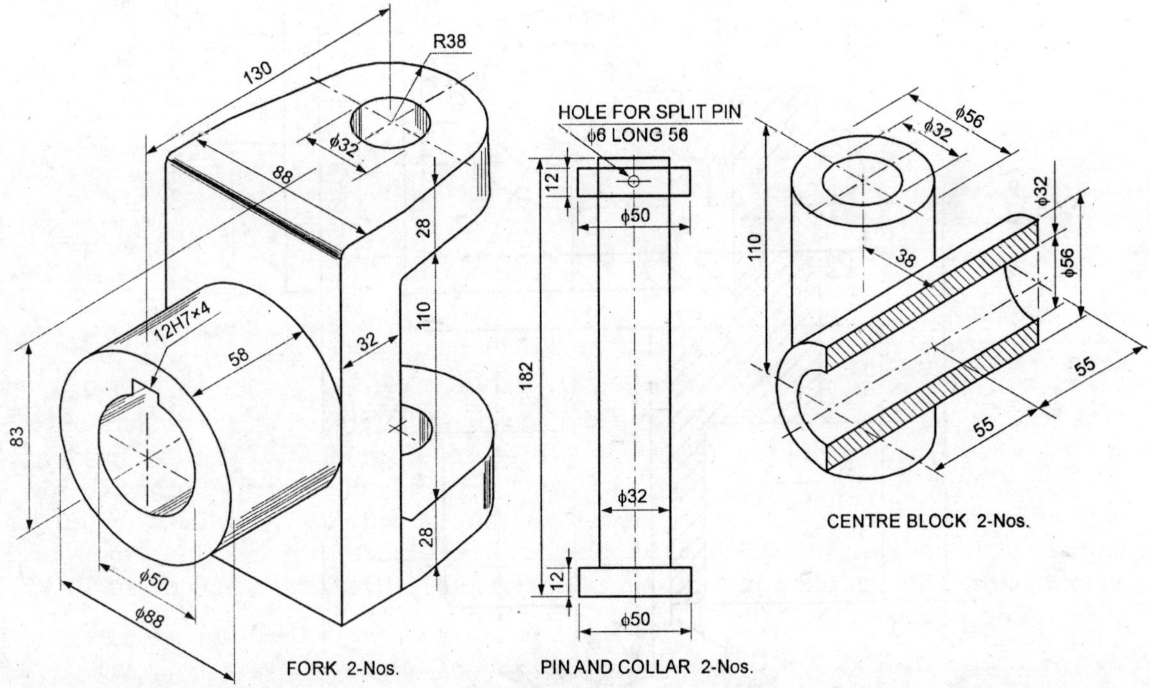

Fig. 8.12

Solution. See Fig. 8.13.

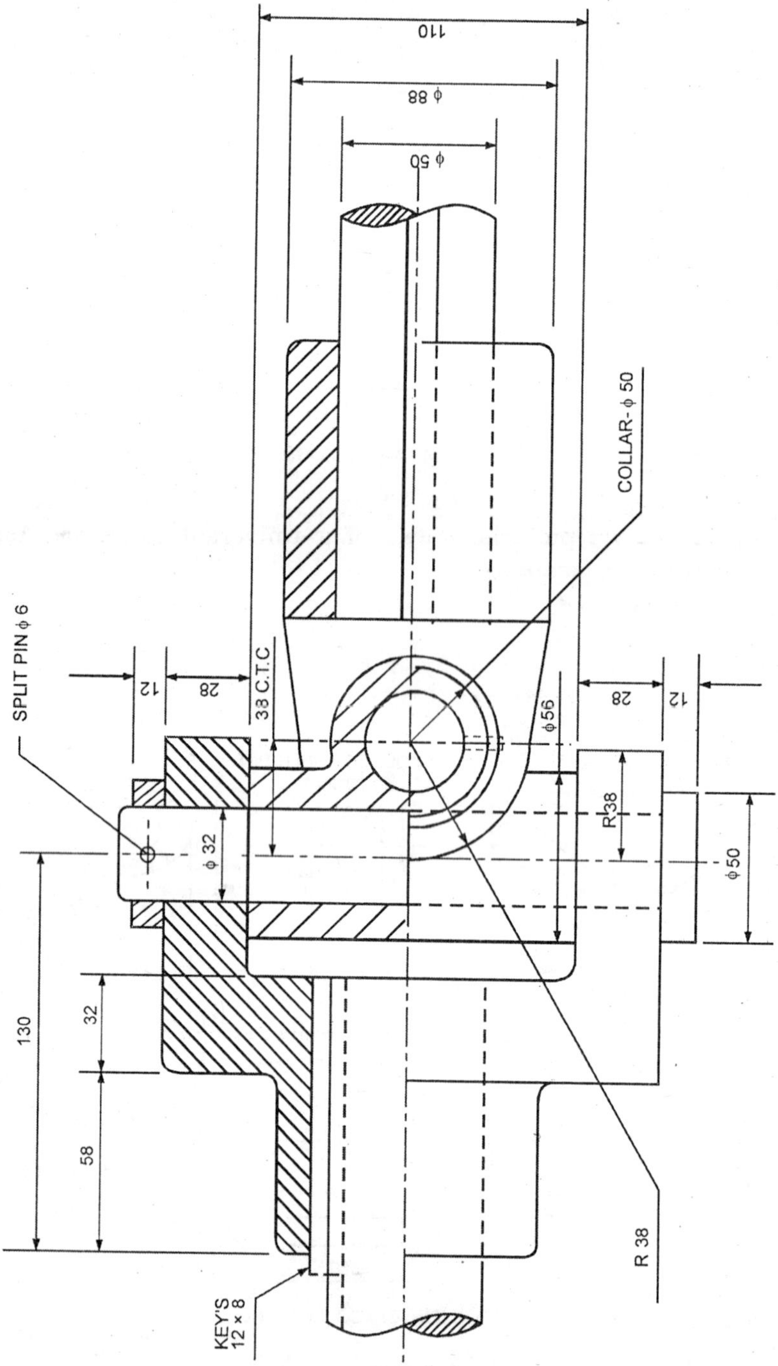

HALF SECTION FRONT VIEW

Fig. 8.13

EXERCISE

1. What do you mean by coupling? Name the different types of couplings.
2. What are the differences between rigid and non-rigid shaft couplings?
3. What do you mean by flexible couplings?
4. What are the differences between unprotected flange coupling and protected flange coupling.
5. Draw a sectional elevation and side view of a cast iron muff coupling of the following dimension?

Diameter of shaft	= 2.5 mm
Diameter of muff	= 63 mm
Length of muff	= 87.5 mm
Width of muff	= 6 mm
Depth of muff	= 4 mm
Taper of key	= 1 : 50

6. Figure 8.14 shows the details of pin type flexible coupling. Assemble the details and draw the following views:
   (*a*) Tape half-sectional front view.
   (*b*) Left side view.

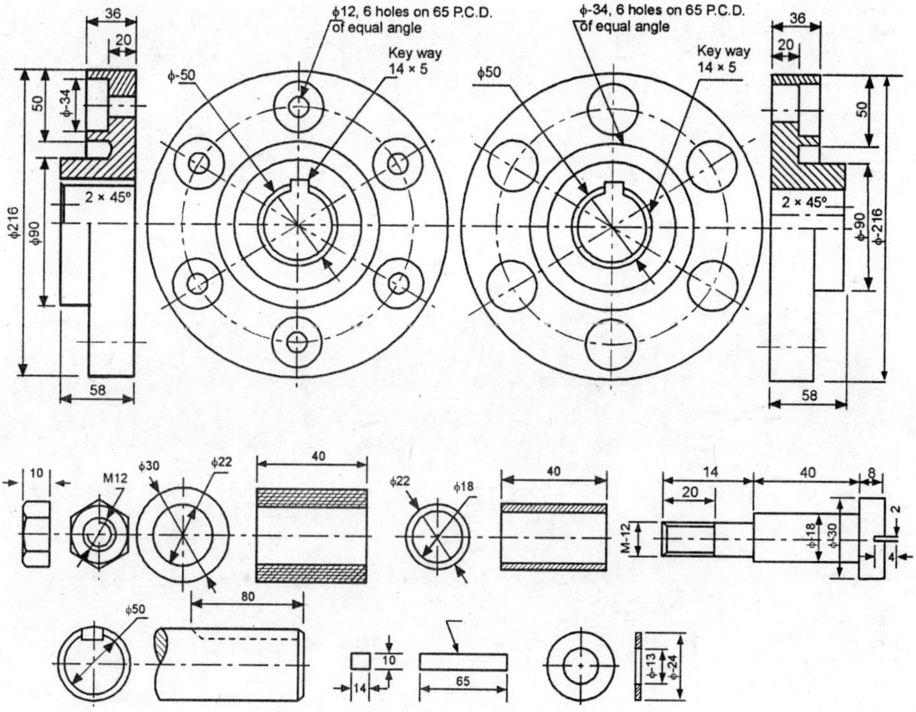

Fig. 8.14

□□□

IMPORTANT NOTES:

9

Pipes and Pipes Joints

9.1 INTRODUCTION

In engineering field, various types of pipes are used for carring fluids, e.g. steam, water, gas, oil etc. from one place to another. Sometimes they are also used as structural elements such as beams and columns.

Pipes are made of definite lengths. For getting long length pipes, it is possible to join by means of pipe joints. Type of joint used depends on the purpose for which it is required as well as material of pipe. Pipes are made of cast iron, steel, wrought iron, copper pvc, brass, lead and aluminium etc.

Selection of material for pipes depending on the nature of the fluid to be conveyed viz, pressure, velocity, tempurature and chemical properties. Pipes may be with seam or seamless. Seamless pipes are prefered for high pressure.

The size of the pipe is designated by its nominal diameter, i.e., the bore diameter.

Application:

Pipes are extensively used in water supply systems, oil refineries, chemical plant, power plant, food processing plant and sewage piping system etc.

9.2 TYPES OF PIPE JOINTS

Pipe are generally made in small lengths 2 to 6 metres. When a pipe line longer than the available lengths is required, two or more such pipes are connected, end to end. Some common forms of pipe joints are explained below.

1. Hydraulic pipe joint.
2. Flanged joint.
3. Union joint.
4. Spigot and Socket joint.
5. Expension joint.

9.3 HYDRAULIC PIPE JOINT

Fig. 9.1 shows a hydraulic joint of flanges type, which is used on high pressure water pipe, both above the ground. The flanges are cast integral with the pipe ends and are approximately ovel in shape. One end of the flange is provided with a projected part and the other flange has a corresponding depression and thus provides for better alignment, when put in assembly. Then the flanges are jointed together by means of square head nuts and bolts. For securing a perfect tight joints, placing a leak stop packing such as washer or gasket of rubber, copper, lead etc. between the two ends of flanges in order to provide a water tight joint. Important joints for hydraulic pipes are flanged joint and spigot and socket joint. Hydraulic pipe joint is mostly used for temporary pipe lines.

Problem 1. Fig. 9.1 shows a pictorial view of a flange joint. Draw the half sectional front view and sectional side view.

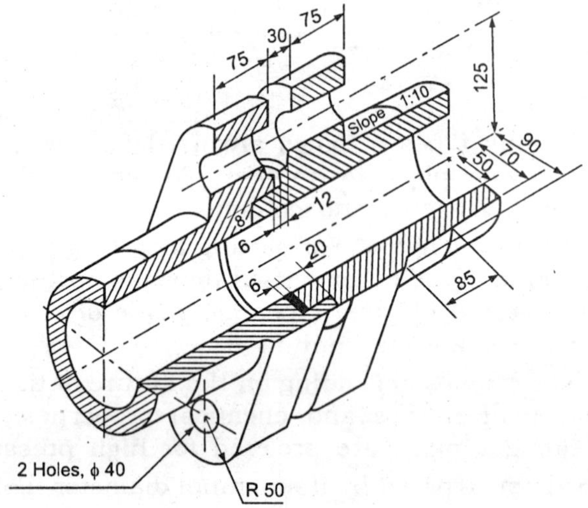

Fig. 9.1

Solution. See Fig. 9.2.

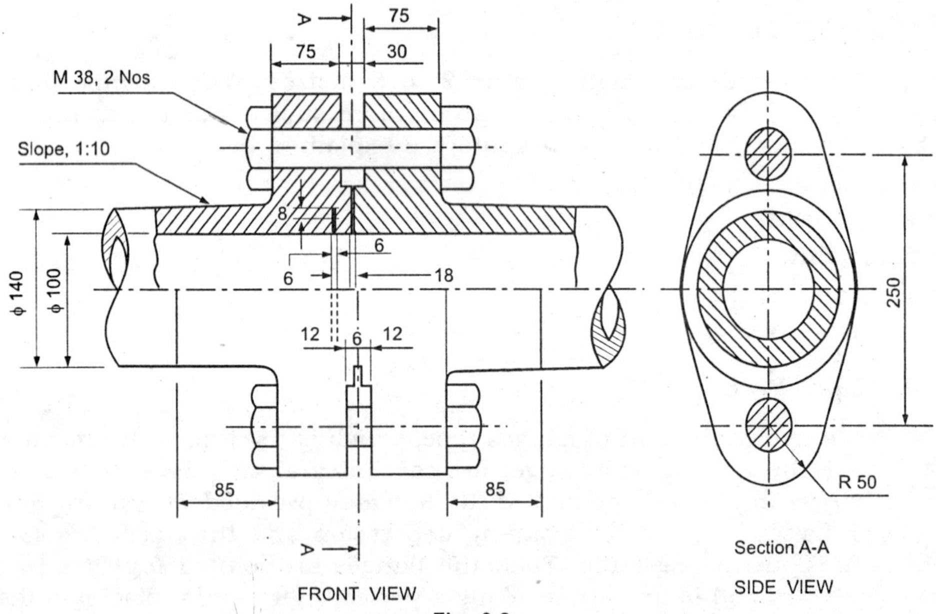

Fig. 9.2

9.4 FLANGED JOINT

It is one of the most widely used pipe joint. A flanged joint may be made with flanges cast integral with the pipes or loose flanges welded or screwed. Fig. 9.3 shows two cast iron pipes with integral flanges at their ends. The flanges are connected by means of bolts. The flange faces are machined to ensure correct alignment of the pipes. The joint may be made leakproof by placing a gasket of soft material, rubber or canvass between the flanges. The flanges are made thicker than the pipe walls, for strength. The pipes may be strengthened for high pressure duty by increasing the thickness of pipe for a short length from the flange.

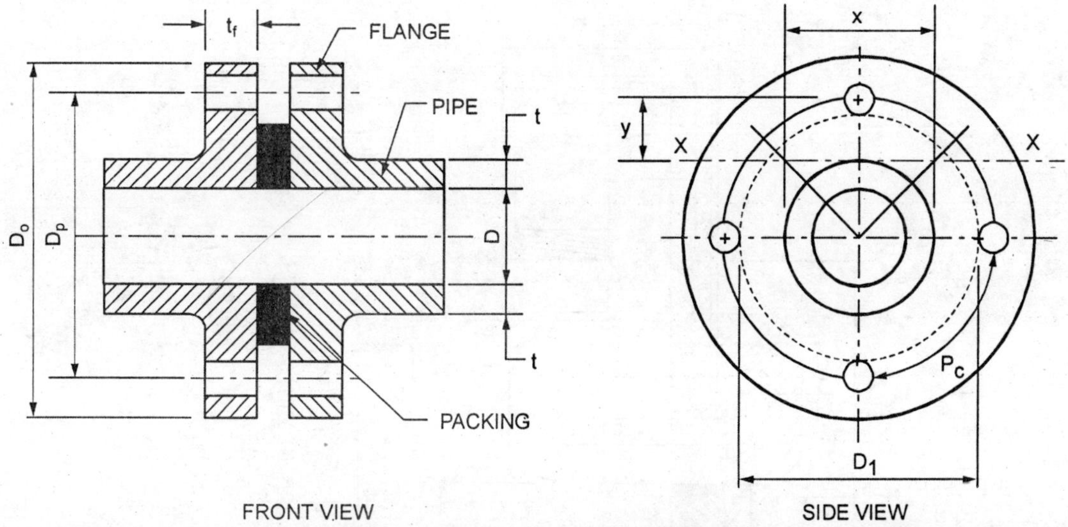

Fig. 9.3 Flanged joint

9.5 UNION JOINT

Union joint is used for connecting pipes for small diameter. copper pipes are genarally joined by this joint. This joint is a union of two couplers or sockets screwed on to the pipes ends. These couplers are drawn together by means of nut to form an air tight joint

As shown in Fig. 9.4 nut P, with external and internal threads, is screwed on to the end of one pipe. Another nut having internal threads is screwed on to the end of second pipe. The two nuts and pipes are drawn togehter by the coupler nut. For effective sealing of the joint, a packing ring may be inserted between the two, pipes to prevent leakage. For rapid disassembly this joint is used.

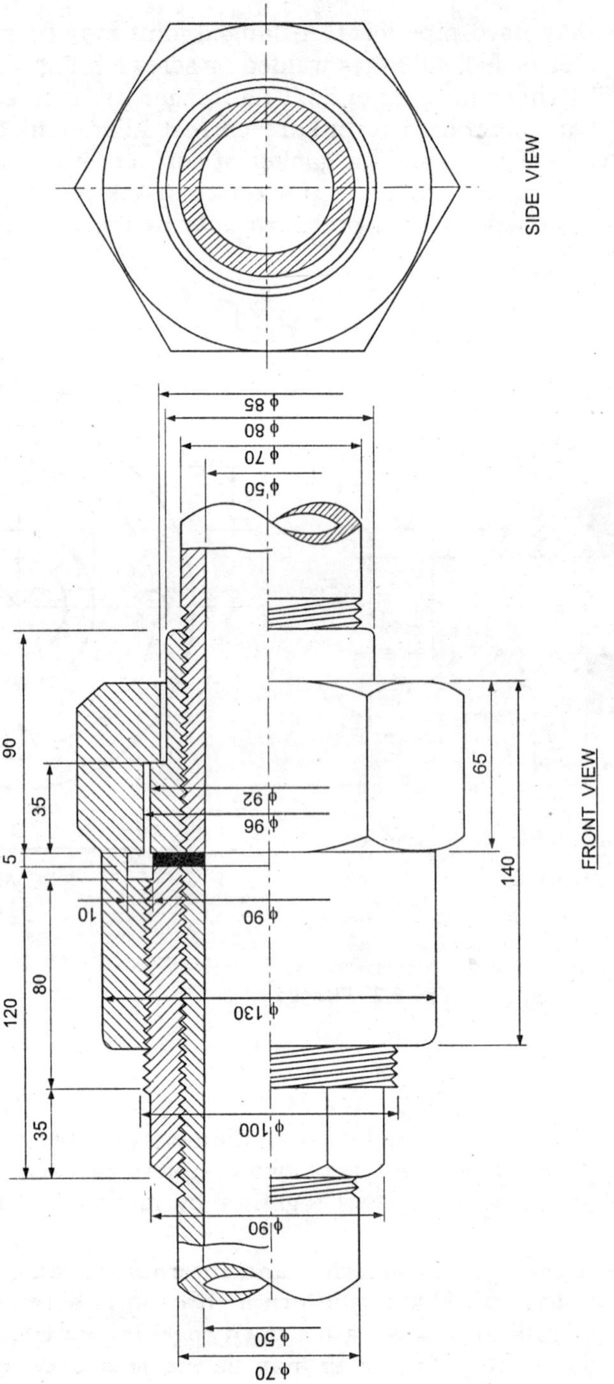
SIDE VIEW
FRONT VIEW
φ 85
φ 80
φ 70
φ 50
90
35
5
10
120
80
35
φ 92
φ 96
φ 90
φ 130
φ 100
φ 90
φ 50
φ 70
65
140

Fig. 9.4

9.6 SPIGOT AND SOCKET JOINT

Spigot and socket joints are employed for connecting underground pipe lines of large diameter, there is low pressure. The pipes are made of cast iron. This joint has little rigidity and is slightly flexible. It can, therefore, take small changes in alignment due to the settlement of the earth.

It consists of two parts spigot and socket. The spigot end of one pipe enters the socket end of the other pipe. The space between the spigot and socket is partly filled in by flexible material, such as ropes of jute and the remaining space by molten lead. This joint is used for pipes which are strictly in a straight line and commonly used for domestic sewer lines.

Problem 2. Fig. 9.5 shows the detail drawing of a spigot and socket joint. Assemble the parts and draw the front view of the joint.

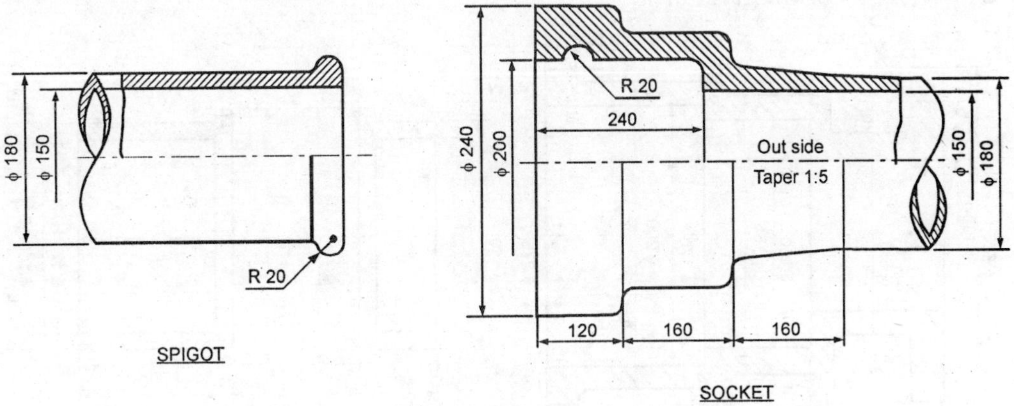

Fig. 9.5

Solution. See Fig. 9.6.

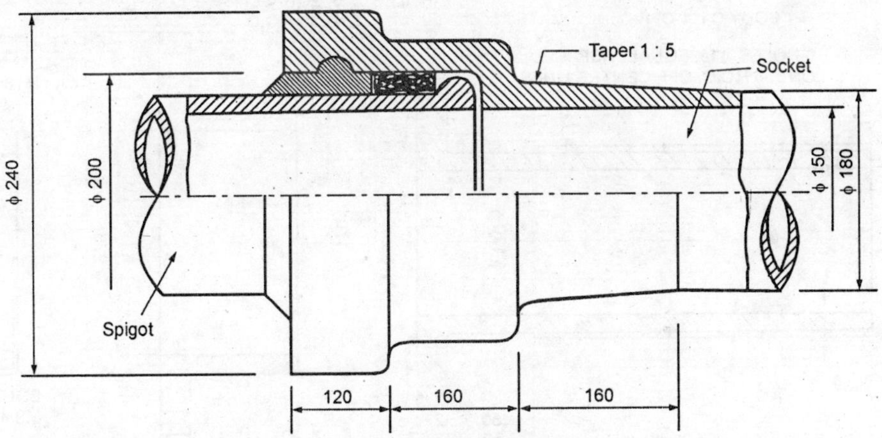

Fig. 9.6 Assembly of spigot and socket joint

9.7 EXPENSION JOINT

Expansion joint is used to carry hot fluid, such as steam at high pressure. This joint undergoes expension and contraction in axial direction due to variations of the fluid temperature.

Fig. 9.7 shows the gland and stuffing box expansion joint which is used for larger pipes. The provision of gland and stuffing box makes the joint perfectly steam tight. The pipe is free to slide in the body. For preventing the leakage of steam, asbestos packing is provided. The socket is fastened by means of nuts and bolts. To allow for free expansion in length, the pipes are not clamped rigidly, but are sespended on a hanger.

Problem 3. Fig 9.7 shows the detail drawing of an expension joint. Assemble the part and draw the full sectional front view.

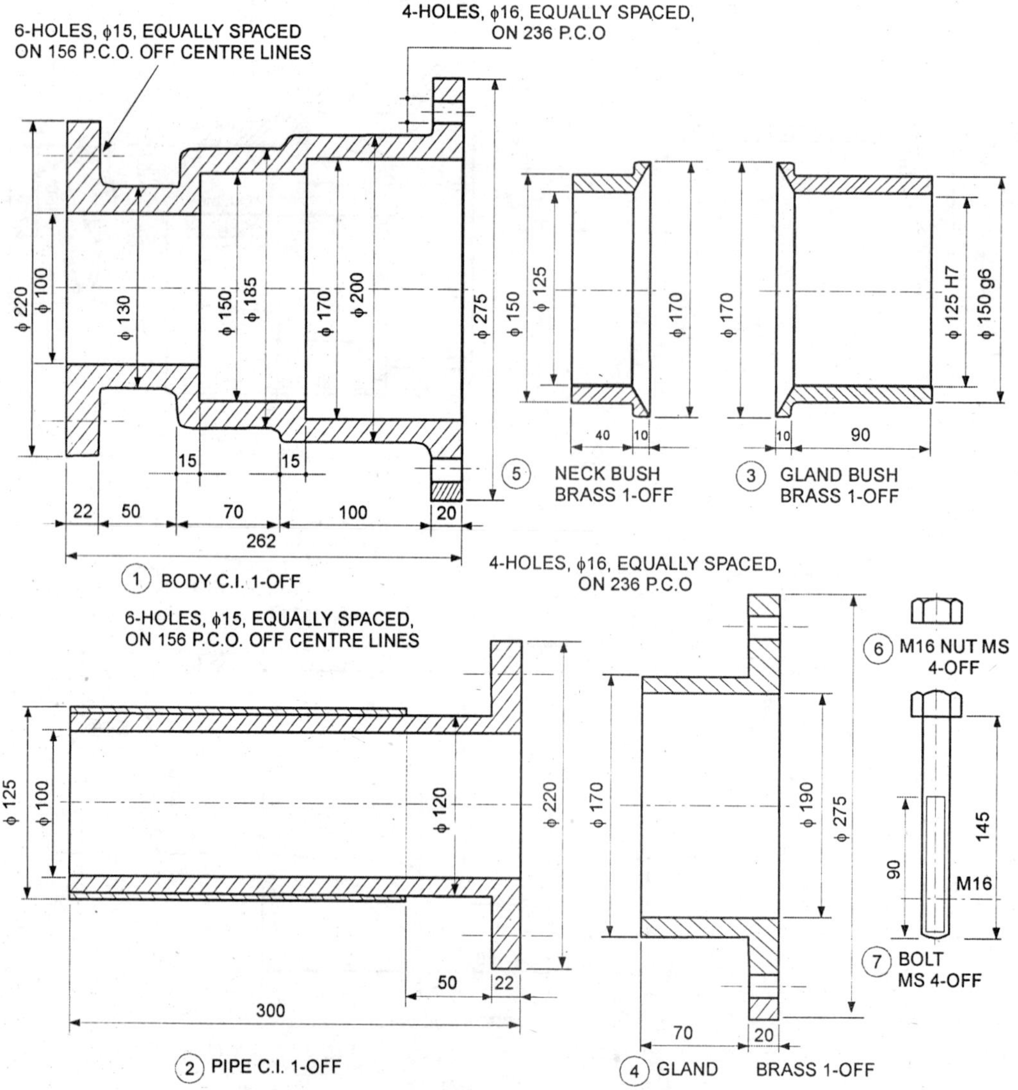

Fig. 9.7

Solution. See Fig. 9.8.

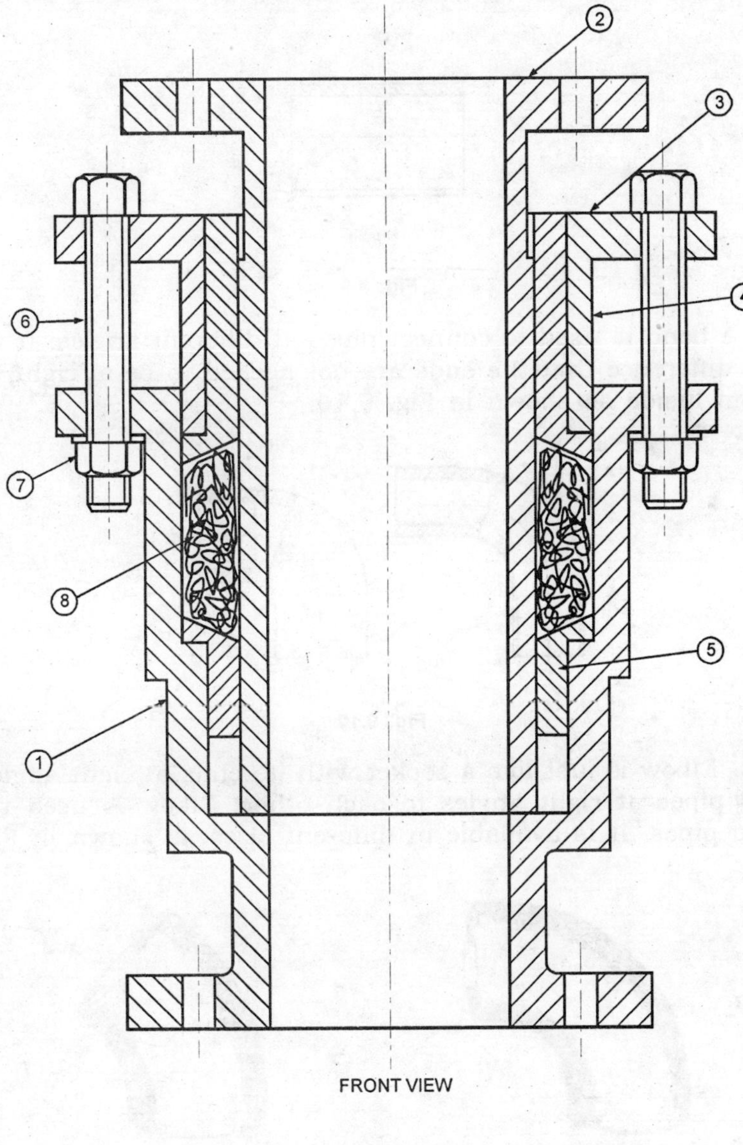

Fig. 9.8

1. Body C.I 2. Pipe C.I 3. Gland brass 4. Gland bush - Brass
5. Neck Bush Brass 6. Bolt M.S 7. Nut M.S.

9.8 PIPE FITTINGS

For joining pipes of smaller diameter, the following fittings are used:

(i) Nipple. A nipple is a short piece of pipe having external threads on its both ends. It is screwed inside the internally threaded ends of the two pipes as shown in Fig. 9.9.

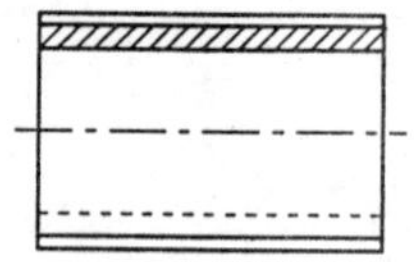

Nipple

Fig. 9.9

(ii) Bends. A bend is used to connect pipes at different angles. It is just like an elbow with the difference that the ends are not needed to be at right angle. A bend is threaded from inside as shown in Fig. 9.10.

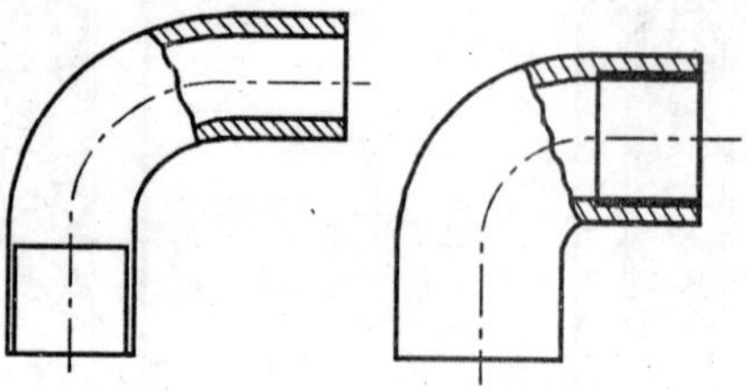

Fig. 9.10

(iii) Elbows. Elbow is just like a socket with its ends at right angle and is used to connect two pipes at right angles to each other. Elbow is used to change the direction of two pipes. It is available in different sizes as shown in Fig. 9.11.

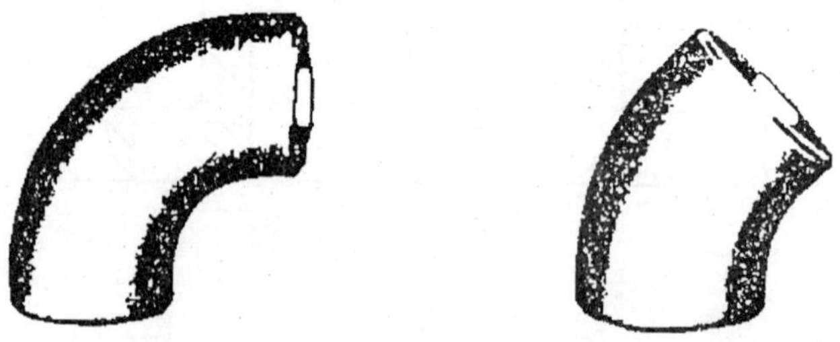

90° elbow 45° elbow

Fig. 9.11

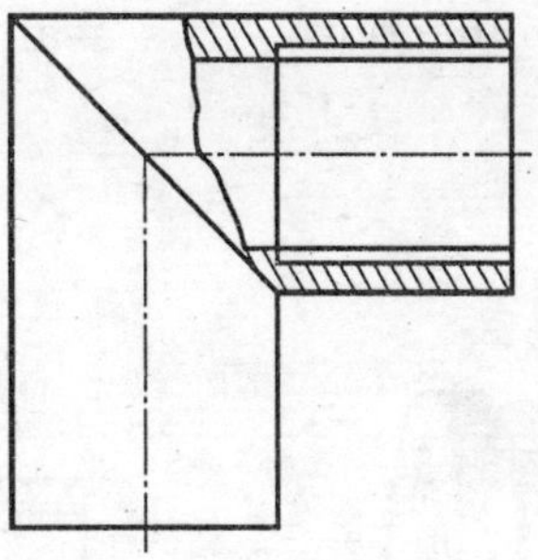

Fig. 9.11

(iv) Coupler or Socket. It is used to join two pipes of same diameters such that their axis remain in same straight line. The coupler is threaded from inside and available in different sizes as shown in Fig. 9.12.

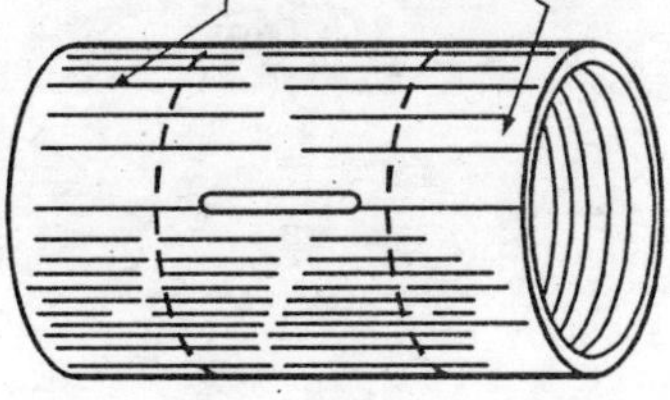

Socket

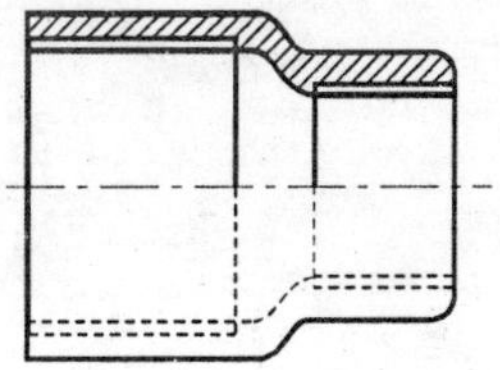

Reducing socket

Fig. 9.12

(v) Tee. A tee is used to join a branch pipe which is perpendicular to the main pipe line. A tee has three sides open and internal threads. Tees are also available in different sizes as shown in Fig. 9.13.

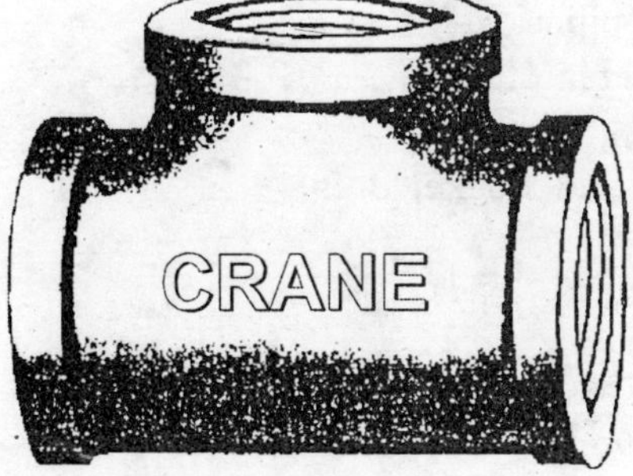

Tee

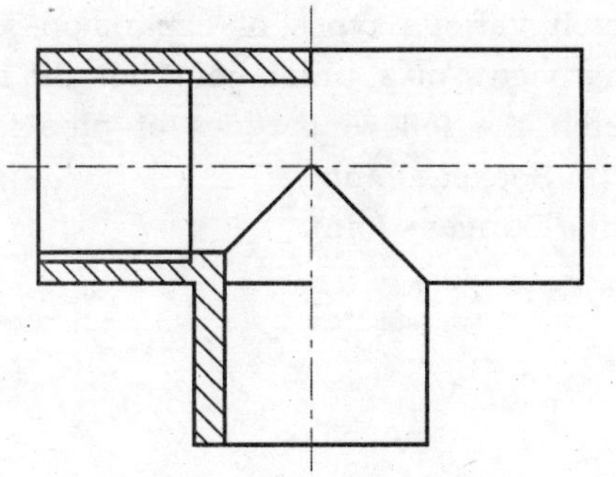

Tee

Fig. 9.13

(vi) Crosses. Crosses is used to join four pipe, with inside threads. It is connected in the main line for multiple connections. It is available in different sizes as shown in Fig. 9.14.

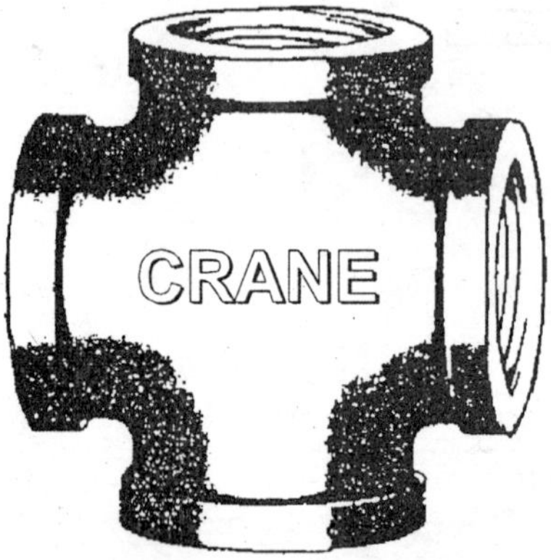

(i) Cross

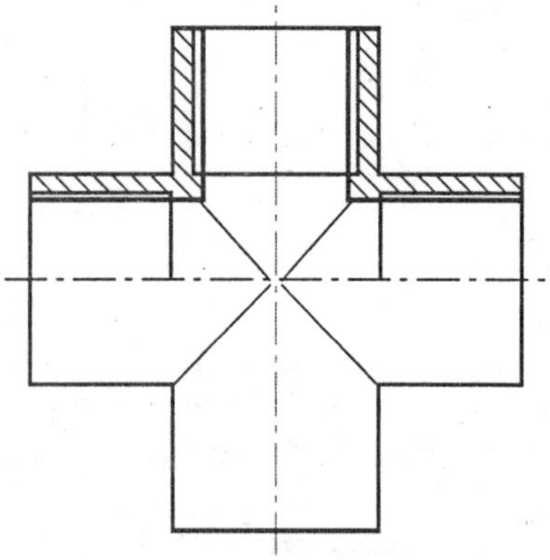

(ii) Cross

Fig. 9.14

EXERCISE

1. Explain the various types of pipes and their uses.
2. How pipe is specified according to Indian Standrards?
3. Give the symbols of the following fittings:
   (i) Elbow 90° (ii) Reducing elbow
   (iii) Tee (iv) Union
   (v) Reducer (vi) Cross.
4. Sketch various types of expansion joints for pipes.
5. Draw views of a union joint for 30 mm diameter of pipe
6. Sketch the following types of pipe joints:
   (i) Socket Joint (ii) Spigot and Socket Joint
   (iii) Flanged Joint.

❑❑❑

PART III

ELECTRICAL AND CIVIL DRAWING

1

Electrical Drawing

1.1 INTRODUCTION

Electrical drawing is an important part of engineering drawing. The art of representation of electrical objects or machines such as motors, generators, transformers, poles etc. on drawing is known as electrical machine drawing. It is commonly used by electrical engineers to express electrical engineering work and projects. In this chapter we will discuss various types of parts of Electrical Machines and their respective views.

1.2 INDUCTION MOTOR

Induction motor may be defined as "An electrical machine which converts electrical energy into mechanical energy. The motor which works on the effect of mutual induction (Transformer effect) is referred as "Induction motor".

The input power used for induction motor is A.C. (Alternating current) and according to input power supply they may be classified as under (Flowchart 1.1):

1. Single-phase induction motor.
2. Three-phase induction motor.

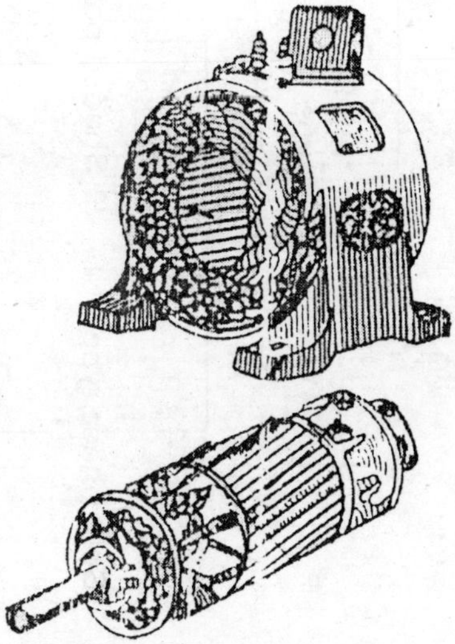

Fig. 1.1

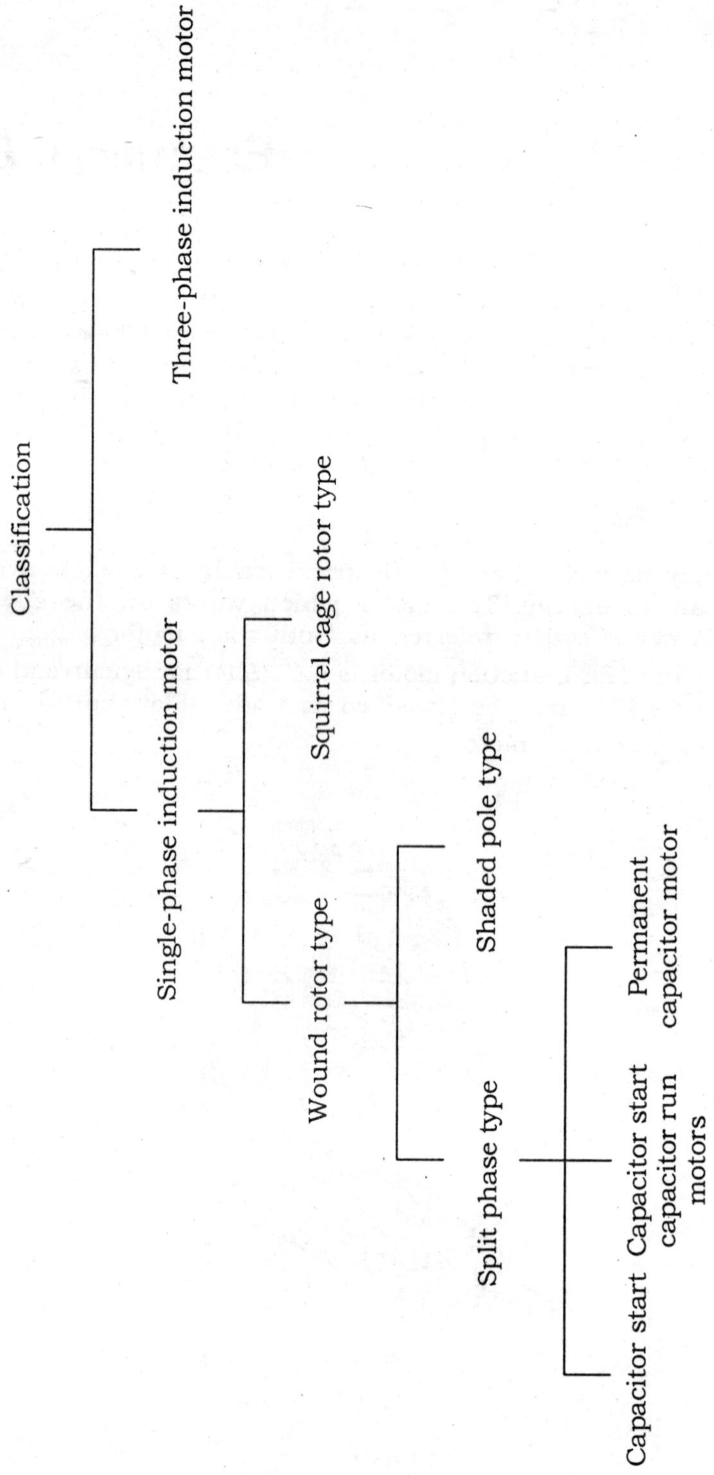

Flowchart 1.1

Three-phase Induction Motor

Three-phase induction motor is most widely used in industries for heavy load application, while single-phase induction motors are used for light load applications.

These motors have simple and rugged construction, high over load capacities and cheap in cost and available in different ratings from fractional H.P. $\left(\frac{1}{400}\text{HP}\right)$ to K.H.P's due to wide field of application. These motors are named as "Duncky of Electricity". Essential parts of an induction motor are as shown in Fig. 1.1.

Construction: Induction motor consists of the following parts:

1. Stator
2. Rotor
3. Shaft and bearing
4. End plates
5. Outer frame (yoke)

According to the rotors these motors may be classified as under:

(*i*) Squirrel cage motor

(*ii*) Wound rotor type or slip ring motor.

(*i*) Squirrel Cage Motor: In this type of motor the rotor consists of aluminium or copper bars short circuited by end rings on both sides. The rotor resistance of this type motor is fixed due to which the speed is also fixed hence the speed of this type motors can be controlled only by controlling the input voltage. Hence efficiency of this type of motors is low, but they have high overloading capacities and lower cost and mostly used in domestic purposes such as fans, pumps, drills, lathe machines etc.

(*ii*) Wound rotor type induction motor: Fig. 1.2 shows a wound rotor type induction motor. The rotor of this type of motor is wound for a fixed number of poles (as that of stator). These windings are connected to slip rings which provides a facility of speed control by controlling the rotor resistance.

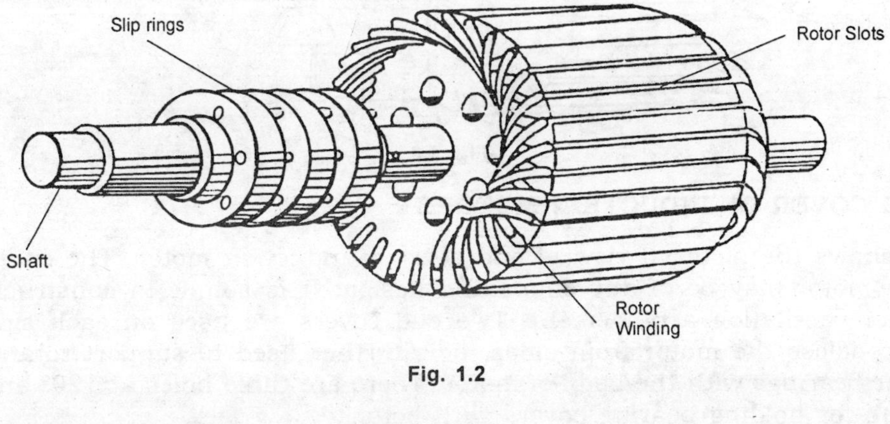

Fig. 1.2

The efficiency of this type of motor is high but cost is also high and these type of motors are used in industrial purposes where speed control is important.

The rotor speed is related to number of poles by this formula

$$N_S = \frac{120\,f}{P} \text{ (Rotor speed is slightly less than } N_S)$$

where, N_S = Synchronous speed of flux. (in r.p.m)

f = frequency of supply (in Hz)

P = No. of poles.

1.3 ROTOR OF SQUIRREL CAGE

Almost 90 percent of induction motors are squirrel-cage type because this type of rotor has the simplest and most rugged construction imaginable and is almost indestructible. The rotor consist of a cylindrical iron core and the rotor conductors. The rotor core is made of silicon steel lamination, and has a number of slot for providing the rotor winding. In squirrel cage rotors aluminium or copper bars are used as the rotor conductors. These aluminium or copper bars are fitted in the core slots and remain parallel to rotor shaft. These bars have small inclination (skewing) with the rotor slots to avoid the magnetic locking. The rotor bars are short circuited at both the ends by aluminium rings named as "End rings" and these bars acts as the short circuited winding of rotor.

The main *disadvantages of squirrel cage rotor* type induction motor are difficult to control speed and lower efficiency as shown in Fig. 1.3.

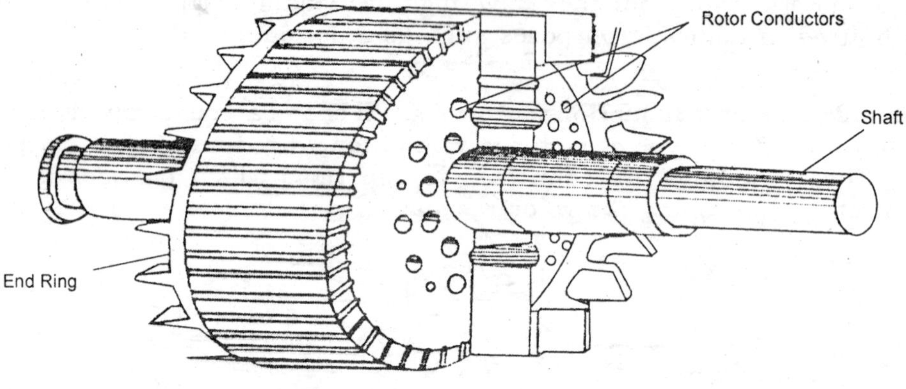

Fig. 1.3

1.4 END COVER OF INDUCTION MOTORS

Fig. 1.4 shows the pictorial view of end cover of induction motor. The end cover of induction motor may be of any shape and design. It is simple in construction and with better ventilation arrangement. Two end covers are used on each side of the motor to enclose the motor from sides. It is further used to support rotating shaft with roller bearings with the body of motor. There are three holes at 120° angle each in the hub for holding bearing covers with bolts.

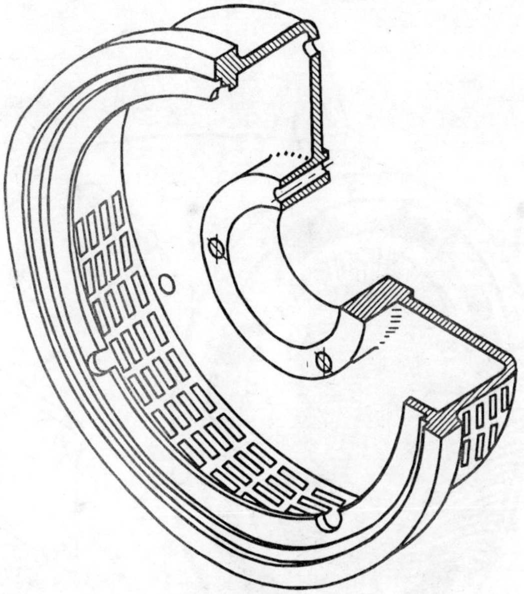

Fig. 1.4

The sides of cover which are to fit over the machined surface of the body are also machined properly so that there is not even slightest margin between two surfaces. The proper and correct fitting of end cover to the body will help to maintain uniform air gap between stator and rotor. The end cover is fitted to the body with three long studs at 120° angle each.

On one side of each end cover, there is an inward projection 3 mm thick having 3 semi-circular cuts. This projection is made to avoid reversal of circulating air in the motor. This projection comes over fan plates. The small and uniform cuts in the lower half of the end cover are for air circulation and to provide passage for air inlet from one side and exit on the other through the grooves.

1.5 MOTOR BODY

It is the outer part of machine also named as yoke. The stator poles are assembled inside the motor body with the help of bolts.

Motor body is generally made of cast iron or cast steel while the poles are made of Si steel stampings. Cast steel has higher magnetic saturation capacity and is used to reduce the weight of machine. It also has good mechanical properties.

Now-a-days rolled steel in practice for the manufacturing of yokes and frames of large and medium size machines as shown in Fig. 1.5.

Motor body has the following functions:

(*i*) Main field and commutating poles are fixed inside the frame.

(*ii*) End plates are fitted outside the frame to hold the bearings.

(*iii*) Also serves as a magnetic circuit.

(*iv*) To protect the windings from wear and tears.

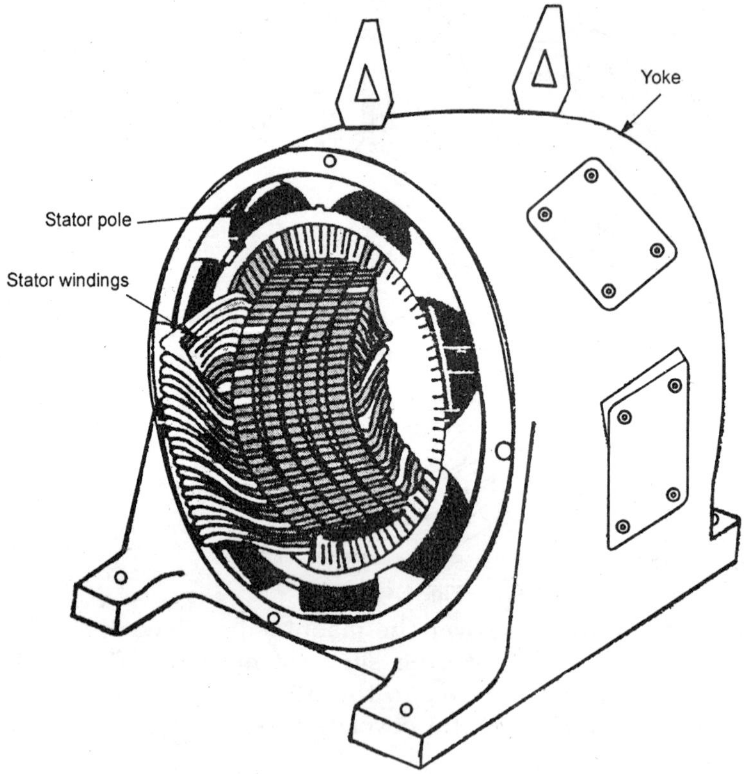

Fig. 1.5

1.6 SLIP RINGS

Slip rings are used in wound type induction motors. These are the rings by which current is taken into from the rotating parts of a machine or an external resistance can be introduced in the rotor circuit. The winding lying in rotor slots are connected to slip rings fitted at one end of rotor shaft. The carbon brushes which rub on the outer surface of the slip rings are made to carry current from and to the rotor windings. The brushes are held in brush holders mounted on insulated steel spindles, securely held with end cover of machine. Slip rings are made of brass, bronze or gun metal in single pieces insulated each other. Generally three phase induction motors are wound or slip rings type and employed where the speed controlling has prime importance. Fig. 1.6 shows a wound type rotor connected in star/delta. The diagram shows how an external resistance is inserted in each phase of rotor winding. At the time of starting, the current taken by the motor is limited for safety purposes and as the motor gradually takes up speed, the resistance is cut-off. The moment, when the motor catches its full speed, starting resistance is reduced and finally cut-off, at this time the rotor windings are short circuited automatically.

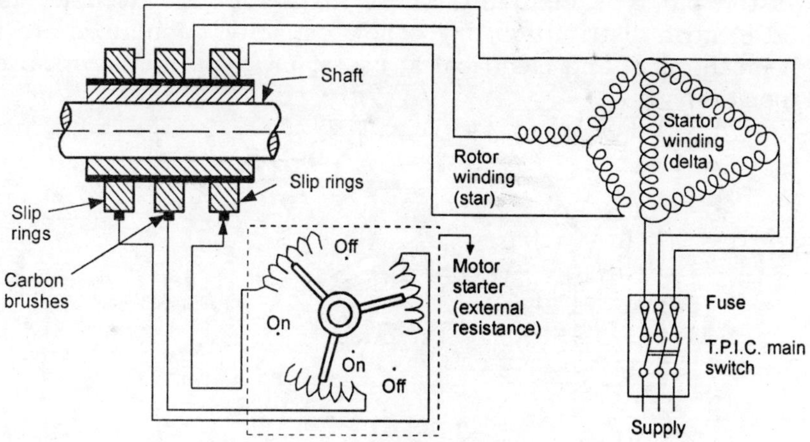

Fig. 1.6

Advantages of slip rings type motors are: best speed control, possibility of regenerative breaking higher starting torque and high efficiency. X-section of slip rings is shown in Fig. 1.7.

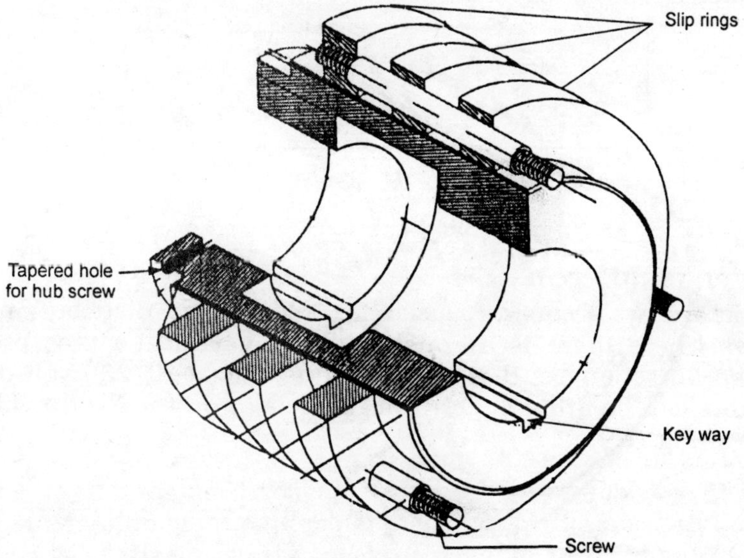

Fig. 1.7

1.7 PIN TYPE INSULATOR

Pin type insulators are used in overhead transmission and distribution lines to carry the conductors. In this type of insulators a pin of galvenised steel is available at the bottom with the help of which it may be fitted at the X-arm on the pole. On the top of this insulator a groove is available to house the conductors of overhead line. The function of insulator is to provide necessary insulation between line conductors and supports. The material used for insulators should be non-porous, free from impurities and cracks, generally "porcelain" is used but glass, steatite and composite material also used.

Fig. 1.8 shows the pin type insulator. These insulators are used for telephone lines and overhead electric distribution line of low capacity. Insulators are required to withstand high mechanical and electrical stresses. Pin type insulators are always used in vertical position.

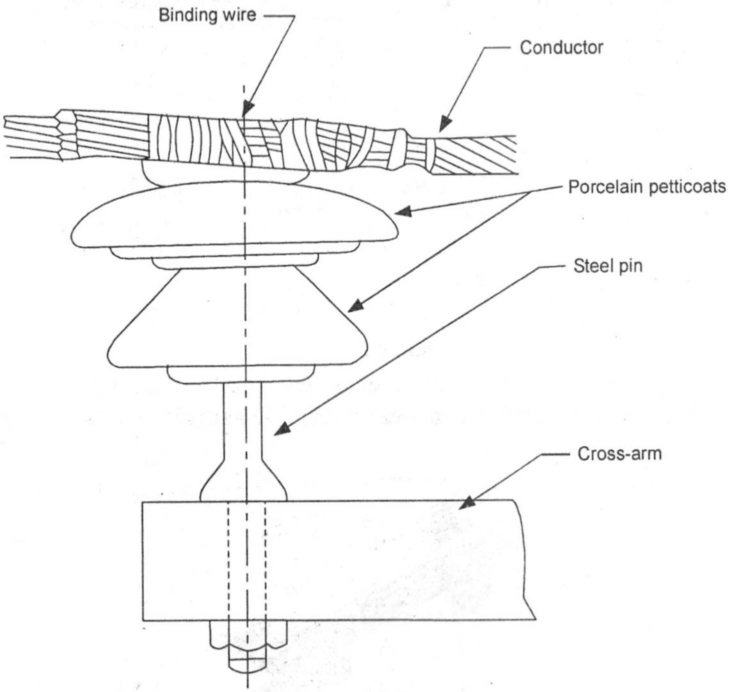

Fig. 1.8

1.8 SHACKLE TYPE INSULATOR

This type of insulators are frequently used for low voltage distribution lines, for houses or factories where there is a considerable mechanical stress or when the angle of distribution line changes. It is commonly used for 440/230 volt distribution line. These insulators can be fitted directly on the pole or on the X-arm with the help of bolts as shown in Fig. 1.9.

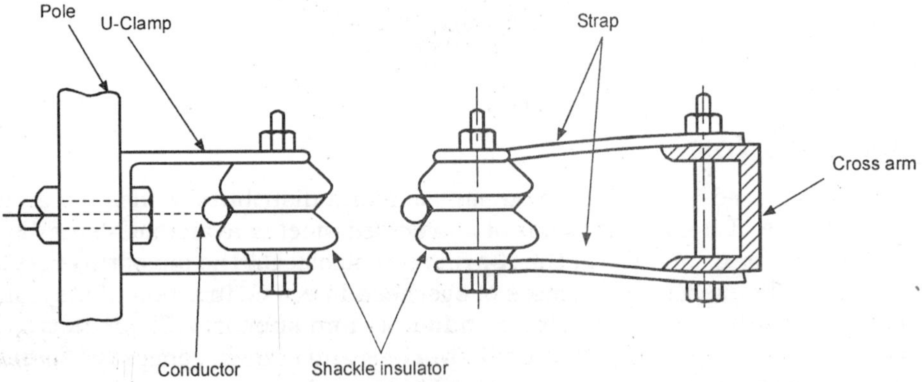

Fig. 1.9

There are two galvenised iron plates each 25 mm wide, on each side of these round insulators. A long bolt holds plates and insulator and a nut is tightened at its bottom. The other end of plates are placed around cross arm of channel iron or wood and held firmly with bolt. These insulators can be used either in horizontal or vertical position. A soft binding wire is used to fixed the conductor in the groove. The material will be under compressive force in that case.

1.9 FIELD POLES WITH COIL

The stator of A.C machines are wound for a fixed number of poles. There is a relation between number of poles and speed of motors.

$$N_S = \frac{120 f}{P}$$

where, N_S = Synchronous speed of stator field (in r.p.m)

f = frequency of A.C (in Hz)

P = No. of poles

Because frequency is constant, hence the speed of motor depends upon the number of poles direction $\left(N_S \, \alpha \, \frac{1}{P}\right)$.

Field poles are the main parts of stator and made of laminated stampings of Si-steel. The field poles consist of: (*i*) Pole shoes, (*ii*) Pole stamping and (*iii*) Pole winding.

For large machines the poles are bolted to the yoke while in small machines it may be casted with yoke. X-sectional view of pole and coil is shown in Fig. 1.10.

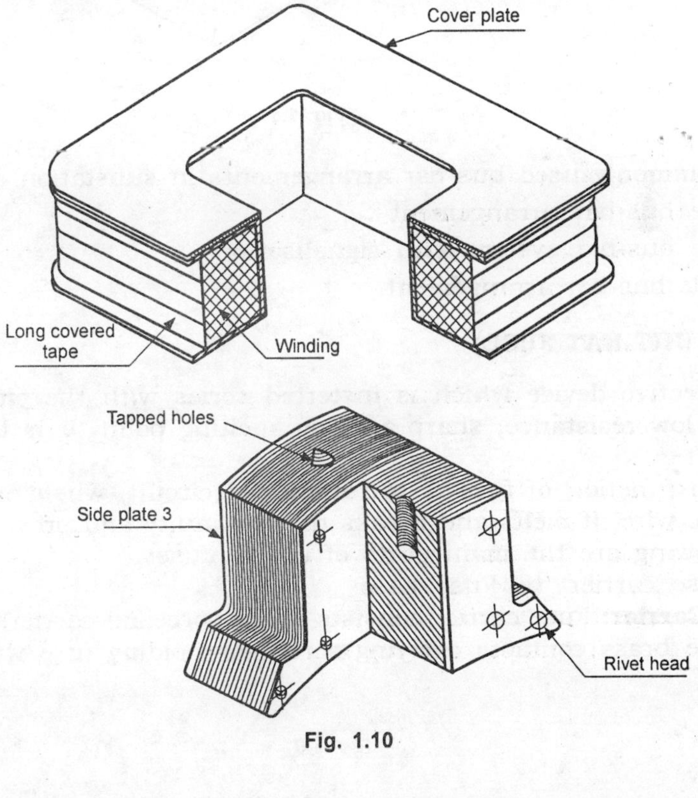

Fig. 1.10

1.10 BUS BAR POST

Bus bar is an important element of generating stations and substations which forms an important link between the incoming and outgoing lines operating at the same voltage. The incoming and outgoing lines are directly connected to the bus bars. These are generally made of copper or Aluminium bars having rectangular cross-section or thin welded tubes and operated at a constant voltage as shown in Fig. 1.11

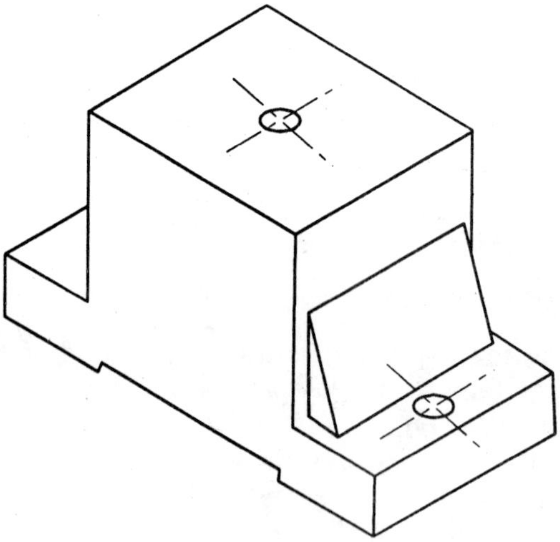

Fig. 1.11

The most commonly used bus-bar arrangements in substation are as follows:

(*i*) Single bus-bar arrangement

(*ii*) Single bus-bar system with signalisation

(*iii*) Double bus-bar arrangement.

1.11 FUSE (KIT-KAT FUSE)

Fuse is protective device which is insterted series with the circuit. It contains a thin wire of low resistance, sharp and low melting point. It is the weakest portion of the circuit.

The main function of fuse is to isolate the circuit, when excess current flows through Fuse wire. It melts and breaks the continuity and provide protection to the circuit. Following are the main parts of kit-kat fuse:

(*i*) Fuse carrier (*ii*) Fuse base

(*i*) Fuse Carrier: Fuse carrier consists of the porcelain carrier base and two brass contacts. The brass contacts carrying screw for holding fuse wire are fixed to the porcelain parts with studs. The fuse wire attached to one screw will pass through the slot on the poreclain part and be attached to the opposite clip with screw as shown in Fig. 1.12. When the fuse carrier is applied to the fuse base the current flows through the fuse wire or element. Fusing element is generally made of Lead-tin alloy, zinc, silver and copper etc.

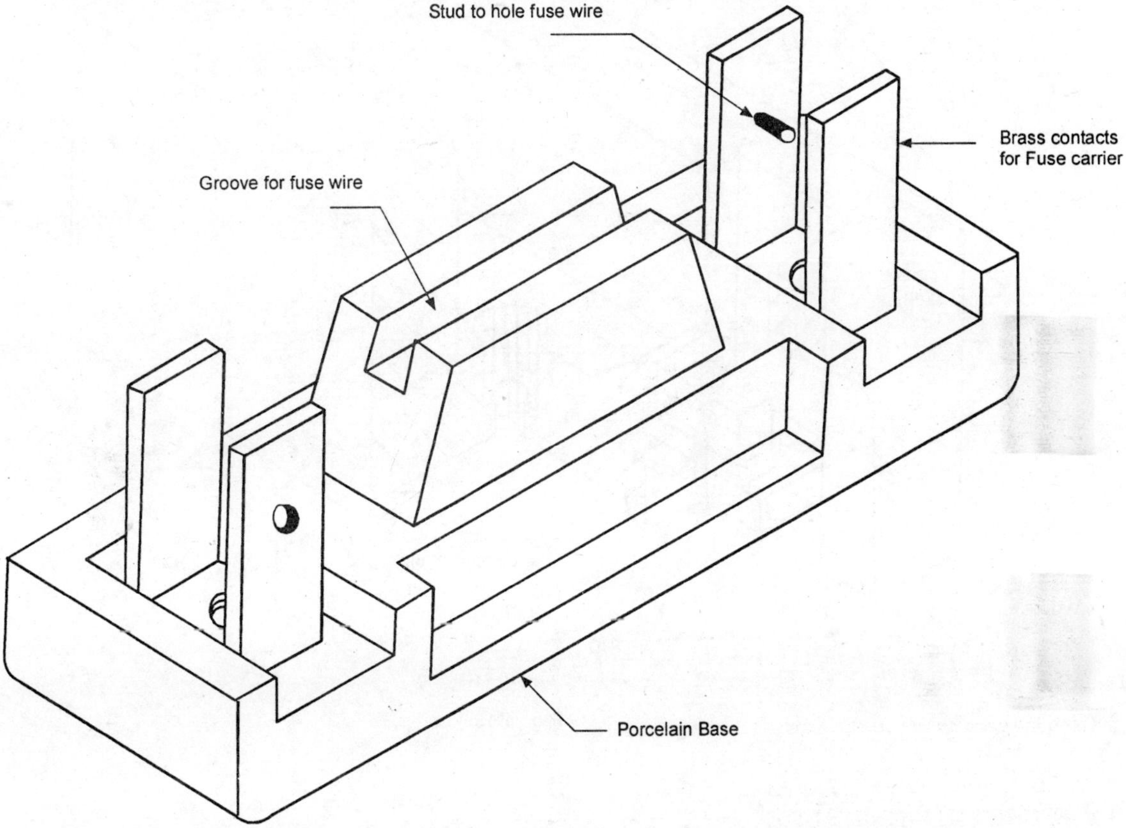

Fig. 1.12

***(ii)* Fuse Base:** The base of kit-kat fuse is made of porcelain. It has two metallic contacts generally made of brass. Fuse base is designed in such a manner that the fuse carrier can be fitted tightly between the metallic contact. The fuse base is fixed to the wooden board with the help of screw. A hole for this purpose is given in the centre. Fig. 1.13 shows a kit-kat fuse base.

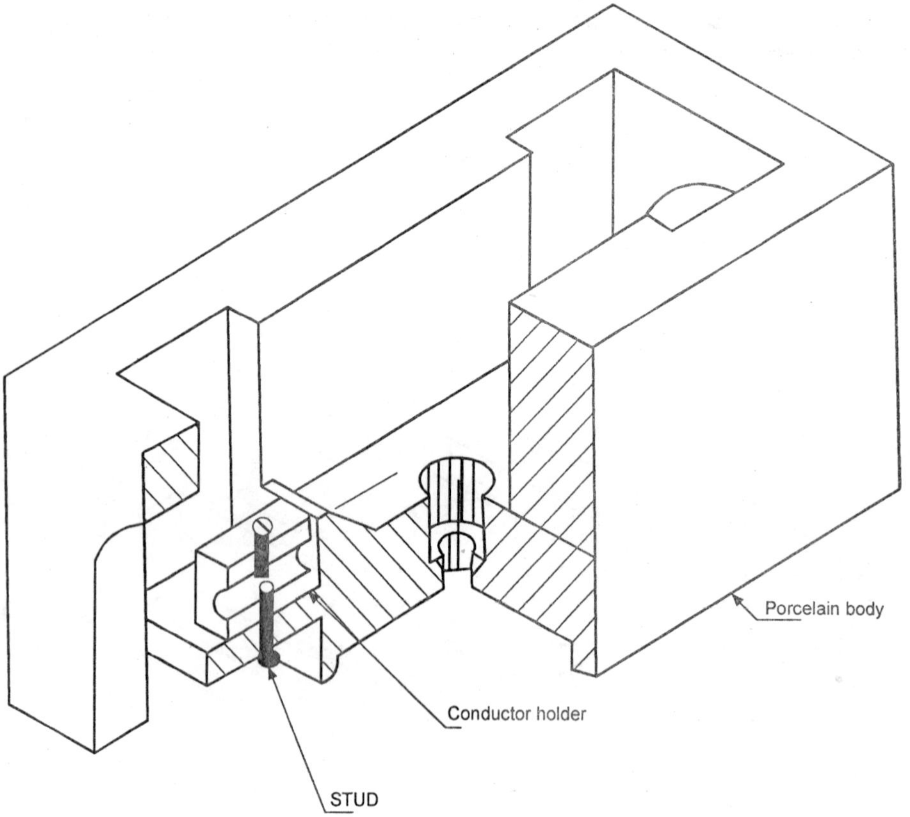

Fig. 1.13

1.12 DRY TYPE SINGLE PHASE TRANSFORMFR

Transformer is an electrical machine which transfers electrical power of one circuit to another circuit without any electrical link. The working of transformer is based on phenomenon of mutual induction in which a e.m.f. is induced in the second coil when there is any change. in the flux of first coil.

The dry type transformer is that type of transformer in which natural cooling is adopted to dissipate the heat of windings. Dry type transformer is hown in Fig. 1.14.

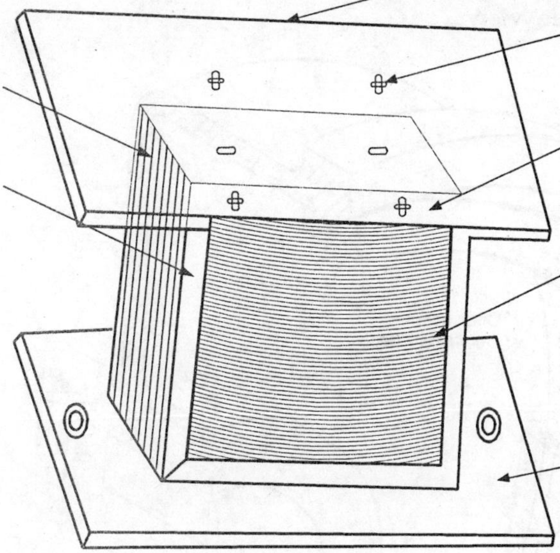

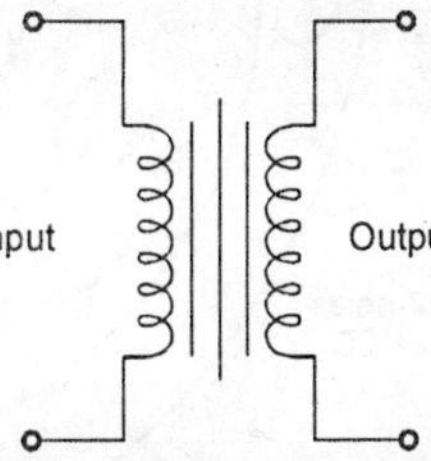

Symbolic Representation of Single Phase Transformer

Fig. 1.14

The main parts of dry type transformer are:

1. Former
2. Core
3. Windings
4. Insulation
5. Outer frame or body
6. Bushing or outer terminals.

Problem 1. Fig. 1.15 shows the isometric view of an end cover of induction motor. Draw the following views:

1. Full sectional elevation.
2. Left hand side view.

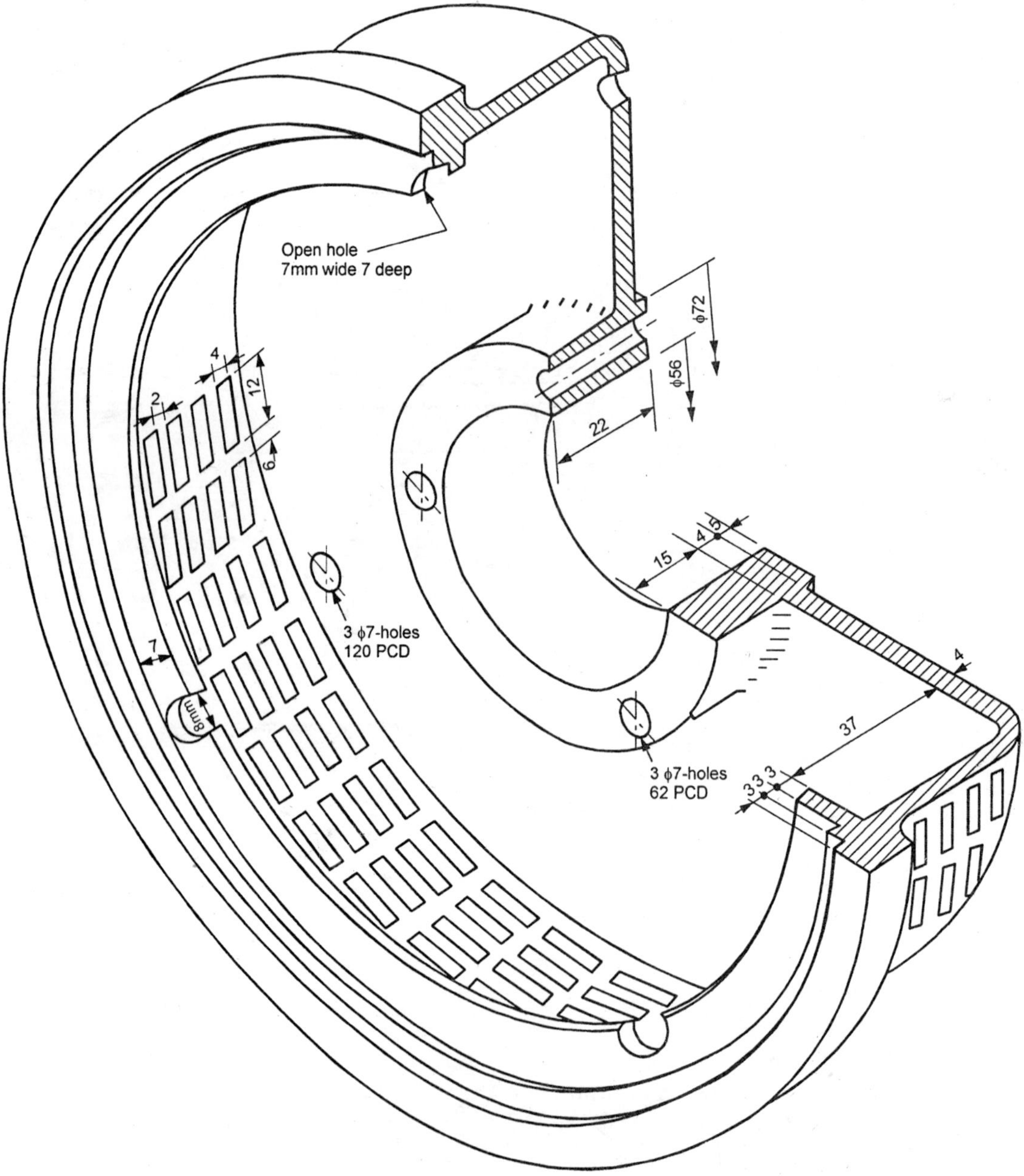

Fig. 1.15

Solution See Fig. 1.16.

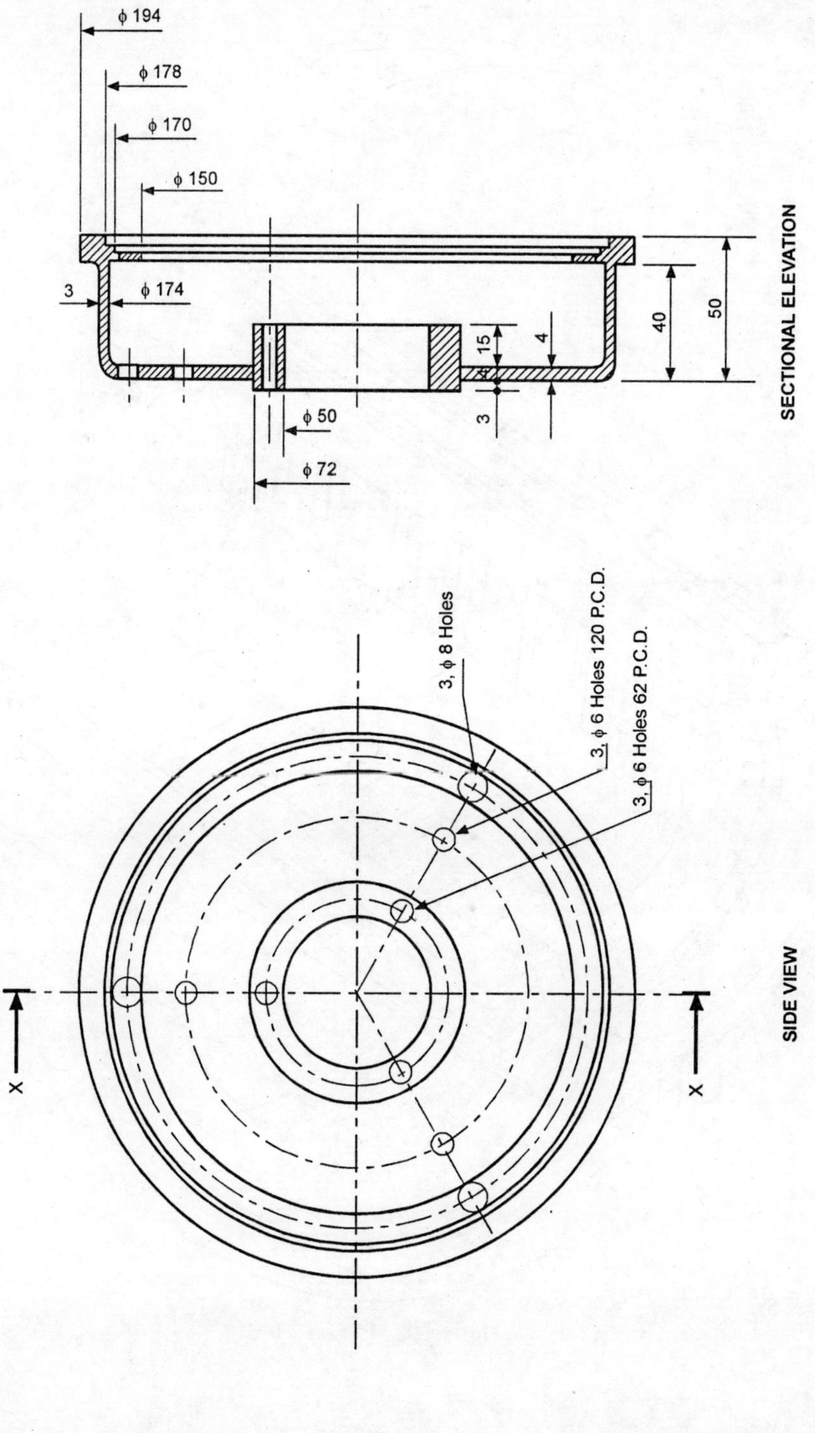

Fig. 1.16

Problem 2. Fig. 1.17 shows the pictorial view of a rotor of squirrel cage. Draw

1. Half section elevation
2. Left hand side view.

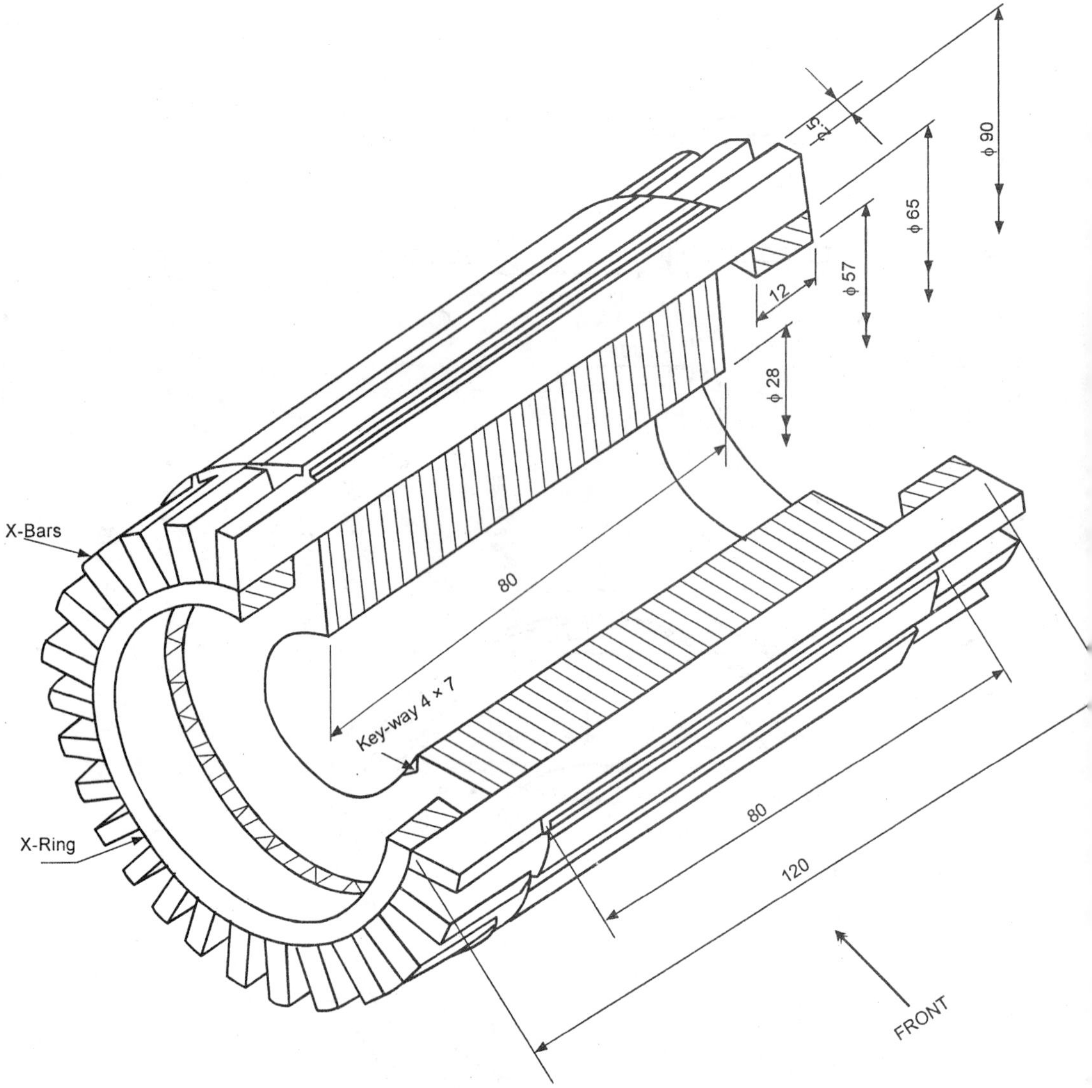

Fig. 1.17

lution. See Fig. 1.18.

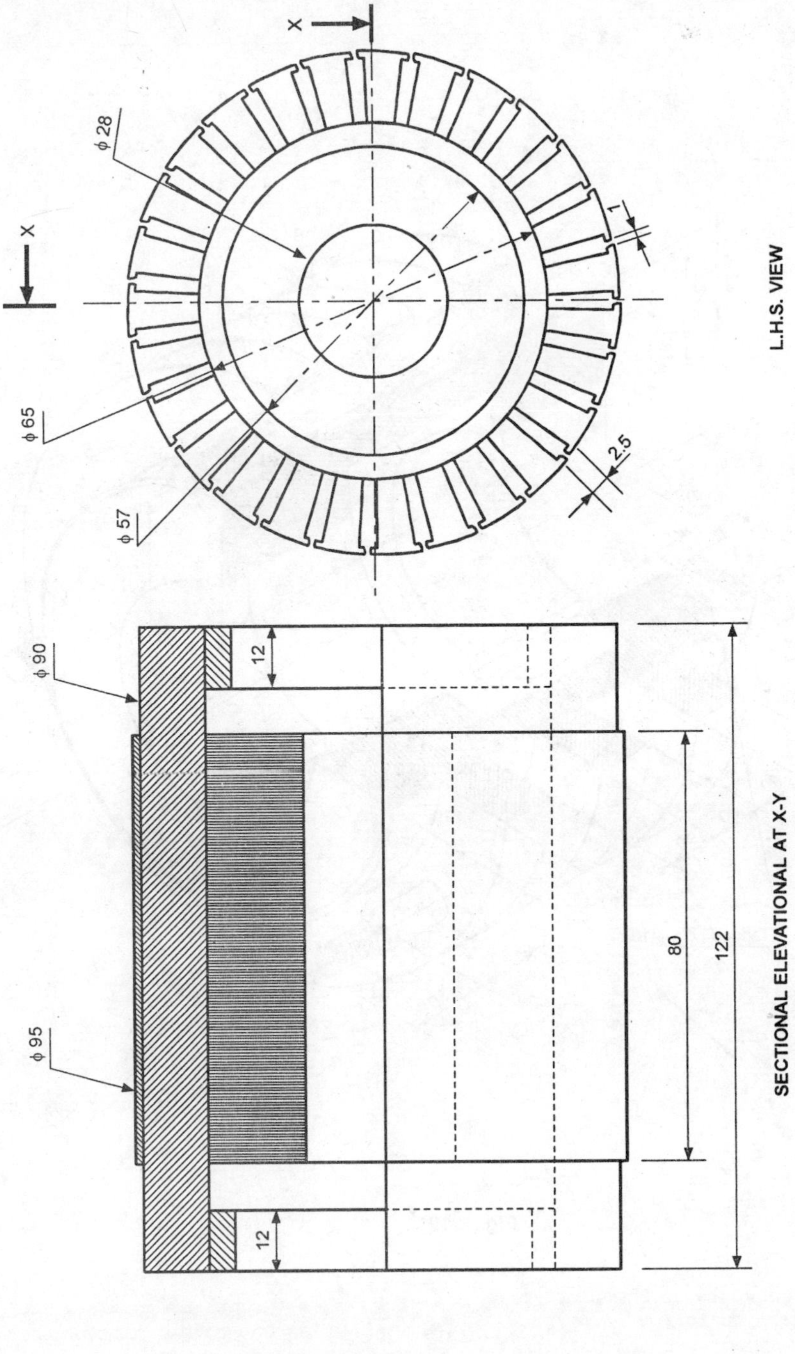

Fig. 1.18

Problem 3. Fig. 1.19 shows the isometric view of slip rings. Draw the following views:

1. Half sectional elevation.
2. Right hand side view.

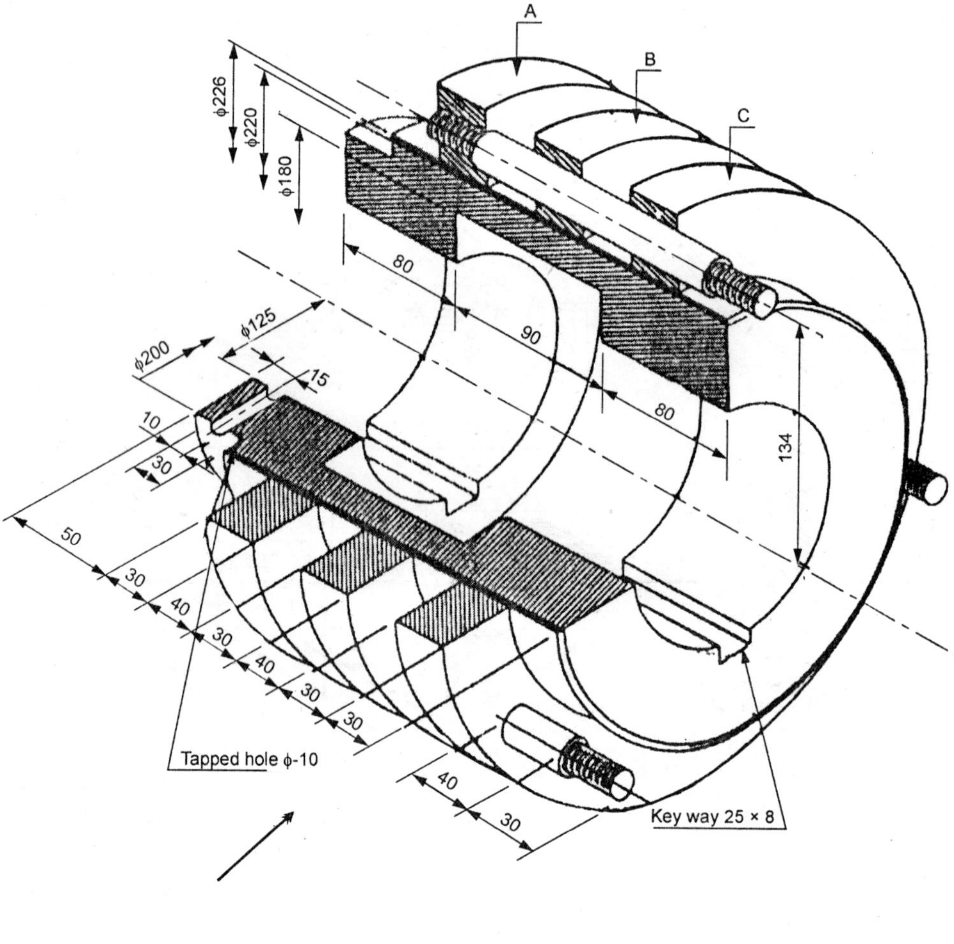

Fig. 1.19

Solution. See Fig. 1.20.

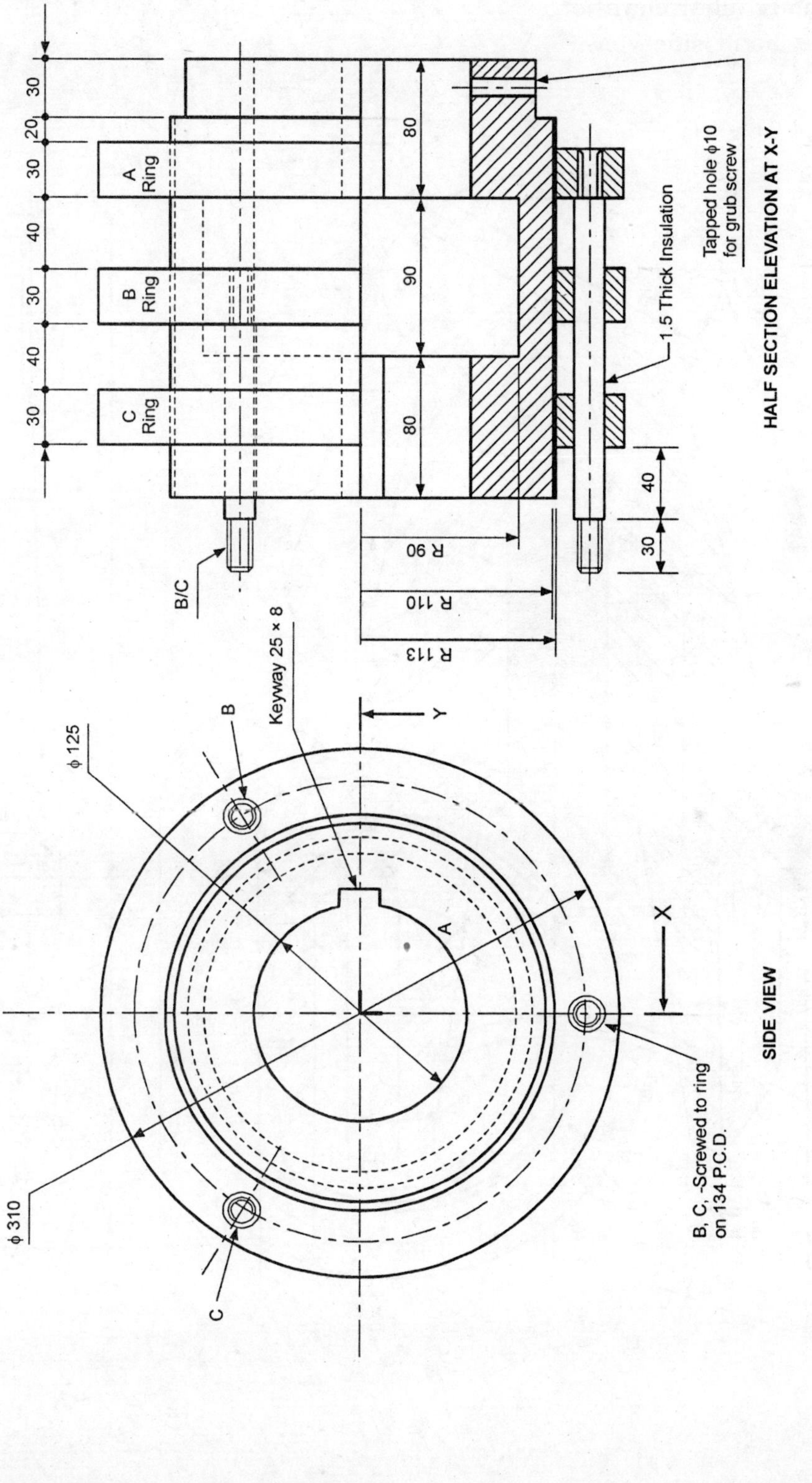

Fig. 1.20

Problem 4. Fig. 1.21 shows the isometric view of pin type insulator. Draw

1. Full sectional elevation.
2. Top view.

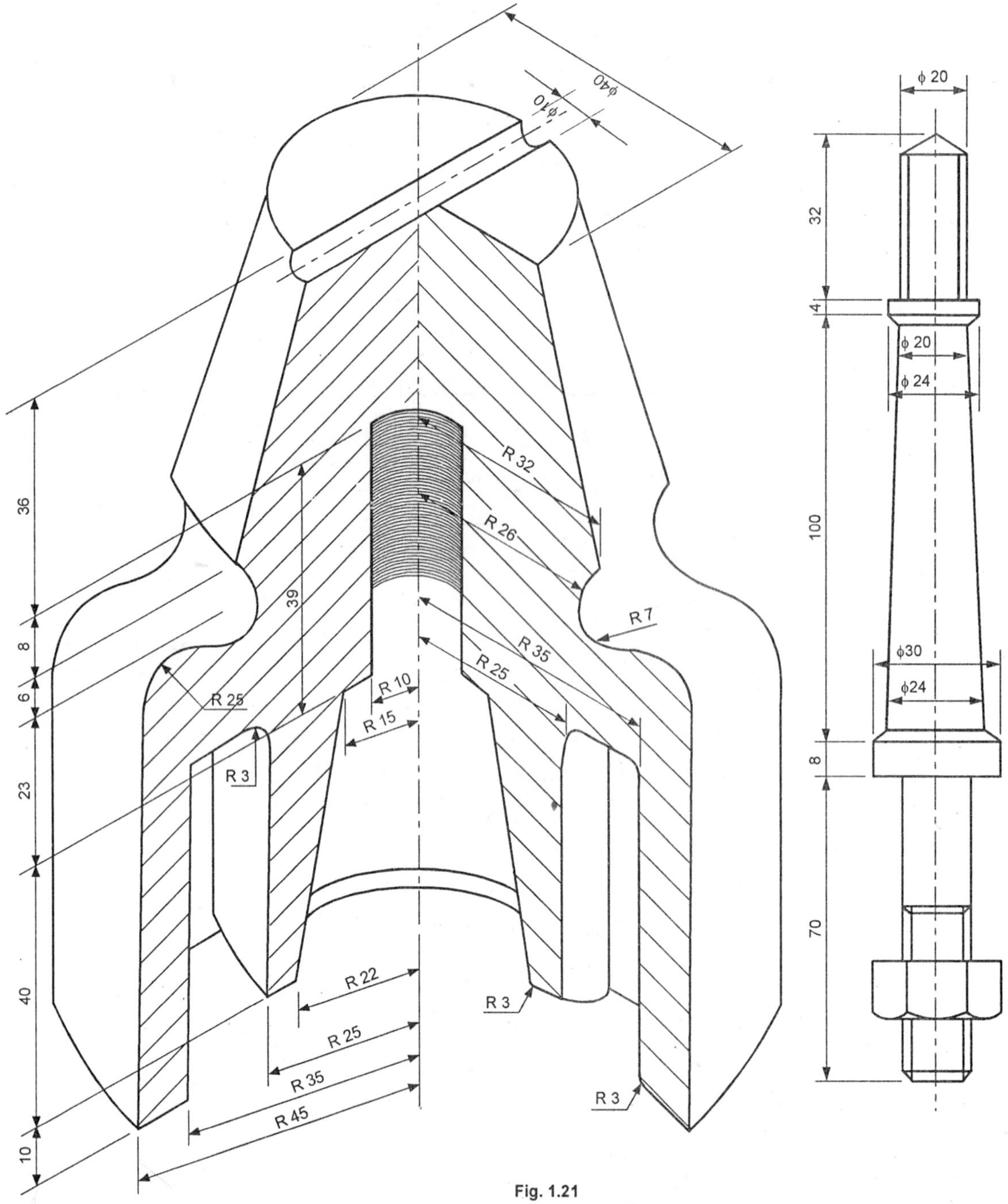

Fig. 1.21

Solution. See Fig. 1.22.

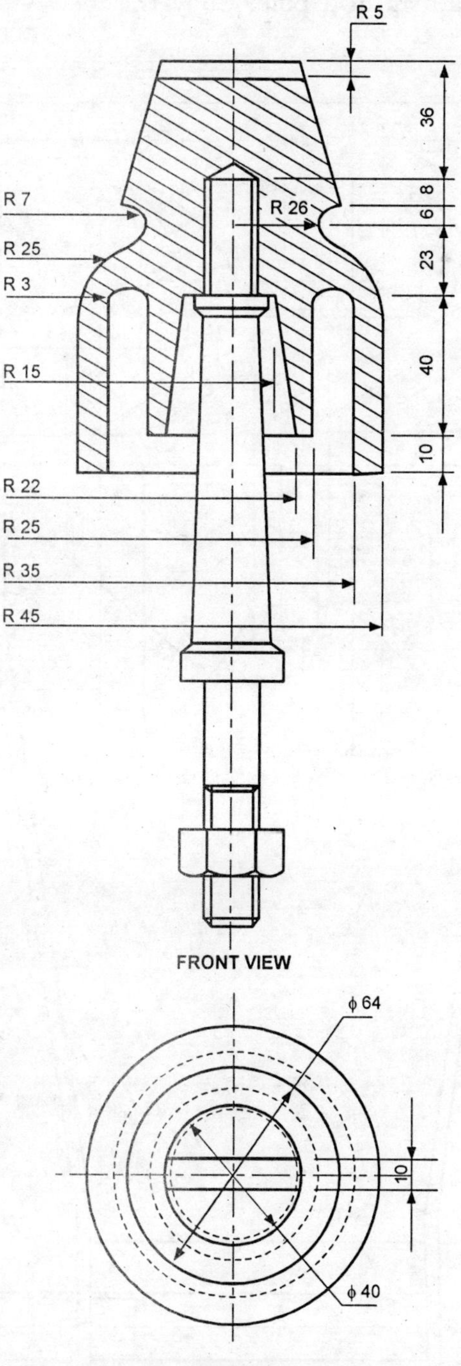

Fig. 1.22

Problem 5. Fig. 1.23 shows a shackle type insulator filled with G.I strips and bolts to be used on the cross arm of a pole. Copy the view and draw a top view to scale 1 : 1. **(B.T.E. New Delhi, June 2004)**

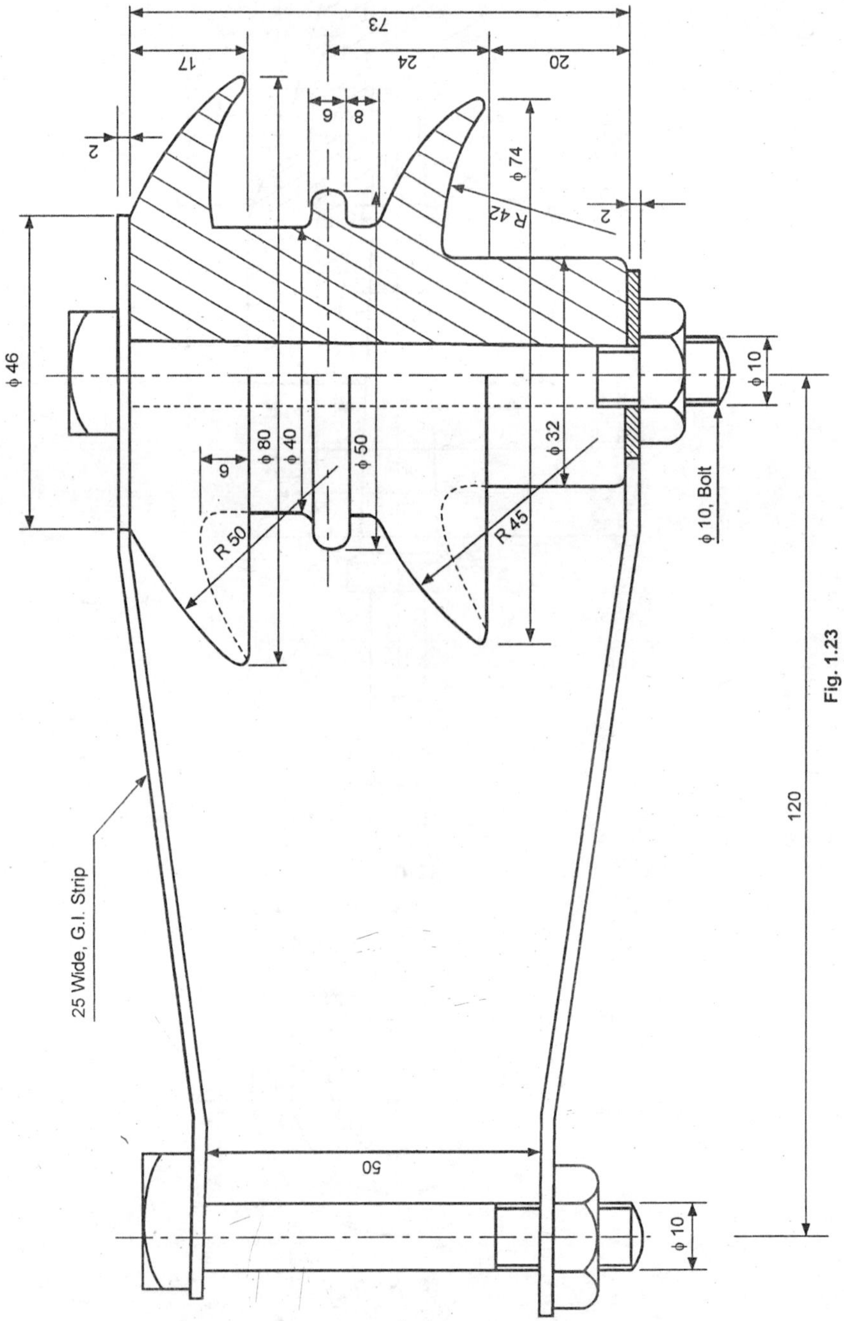

Fig. 1.23

Solution. See Fig. 1.24.

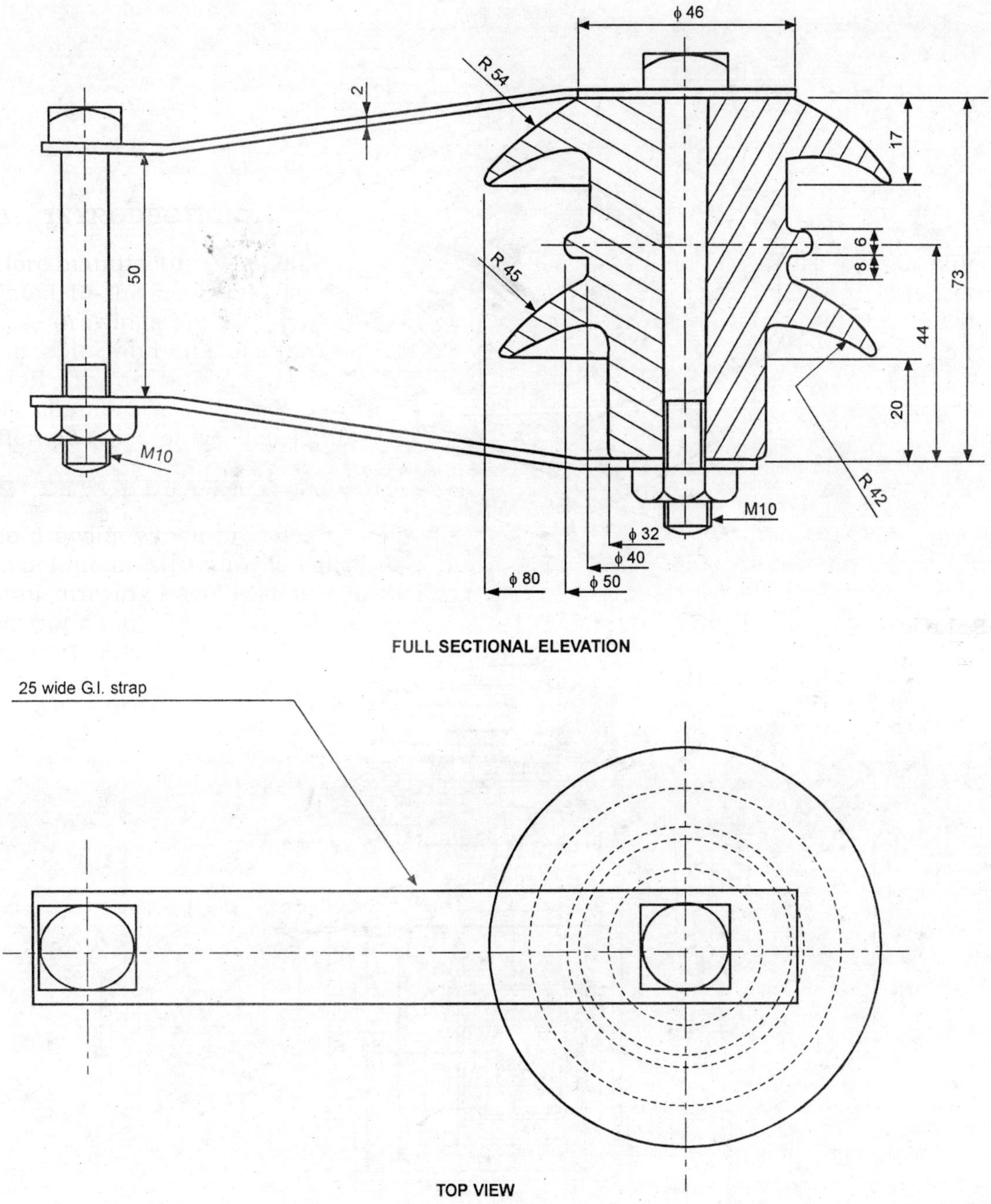

Fig. 1.24

Problem 6. Fig. 1.25 shows isometric view of field, pole and coil. Draw
1. Half sectional front view. 2. Top view. (Use first angle projection).

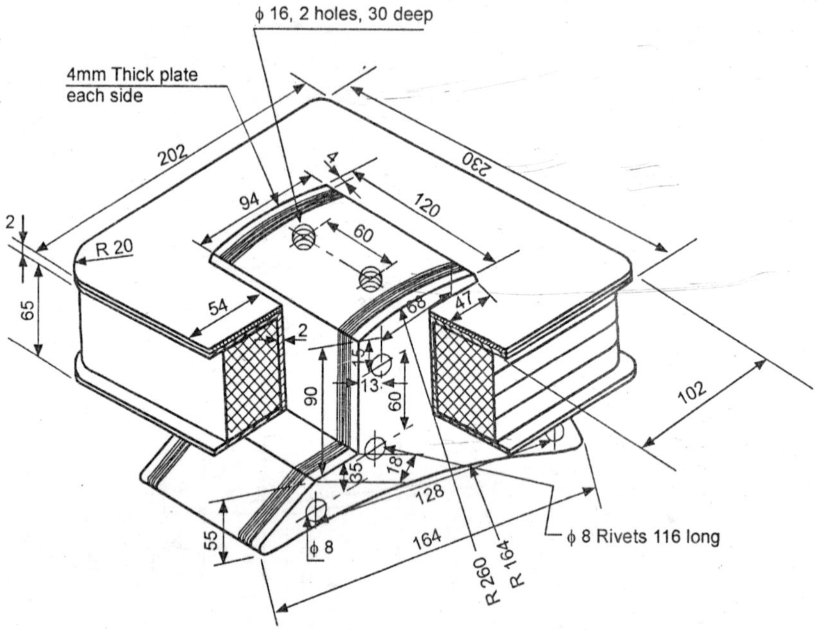

Fig. 1.25

Solution. See Fig. 1.26.

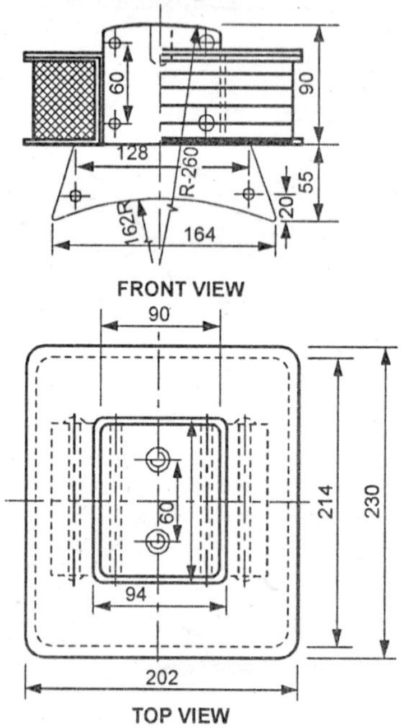

Fig. 1.26

Problem 7. Fig. 1.27 shows the isometric view of bus bar post. Draw

1. Full sectional elevation 2. Plan 3. Left hand side view.

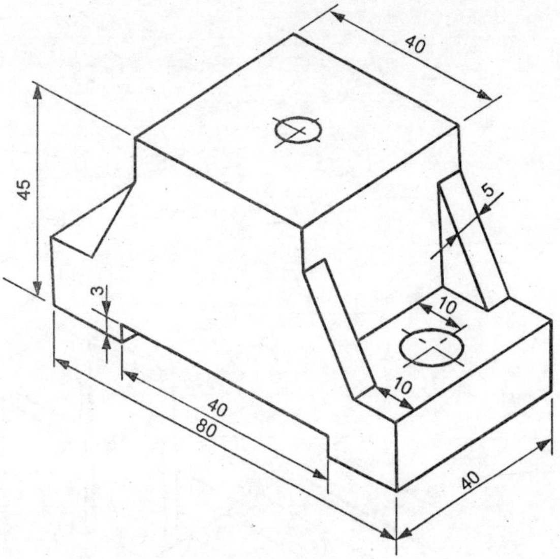

Fig. 1.27

Solution. See Fig. 1.28.

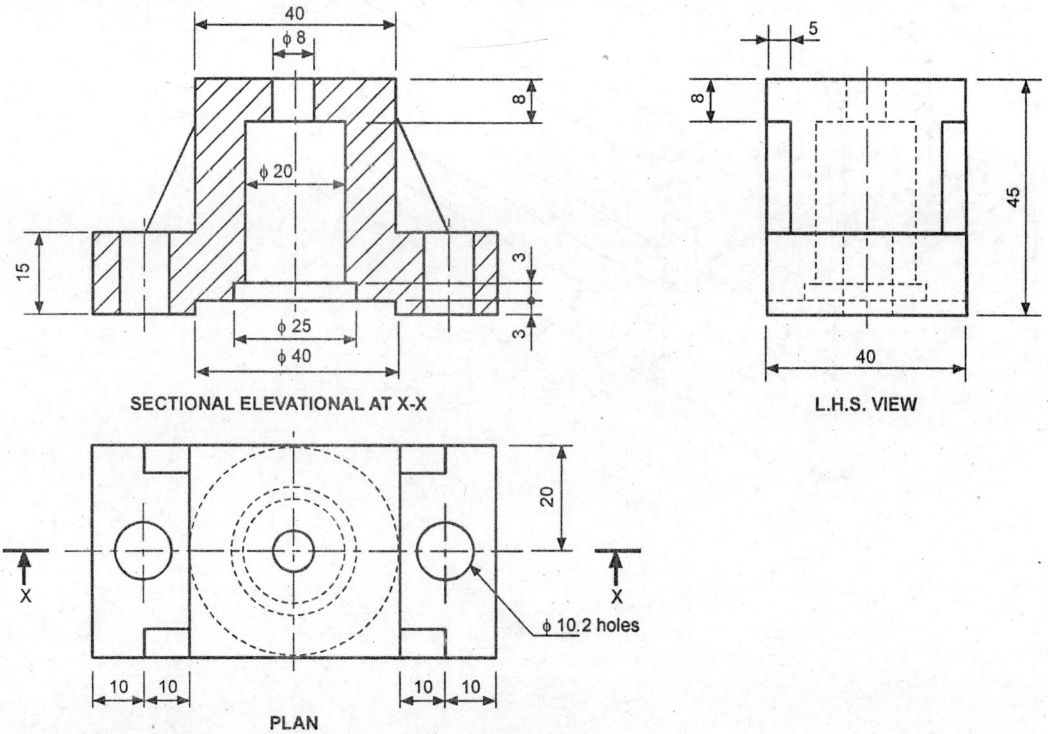

Fig. 1.28

Problem 8. Fig. 1.29 shows the pictorial view of a fuse carrier. Draw

1. Full sectional elevation.
2. Top view.
3. Left side view.

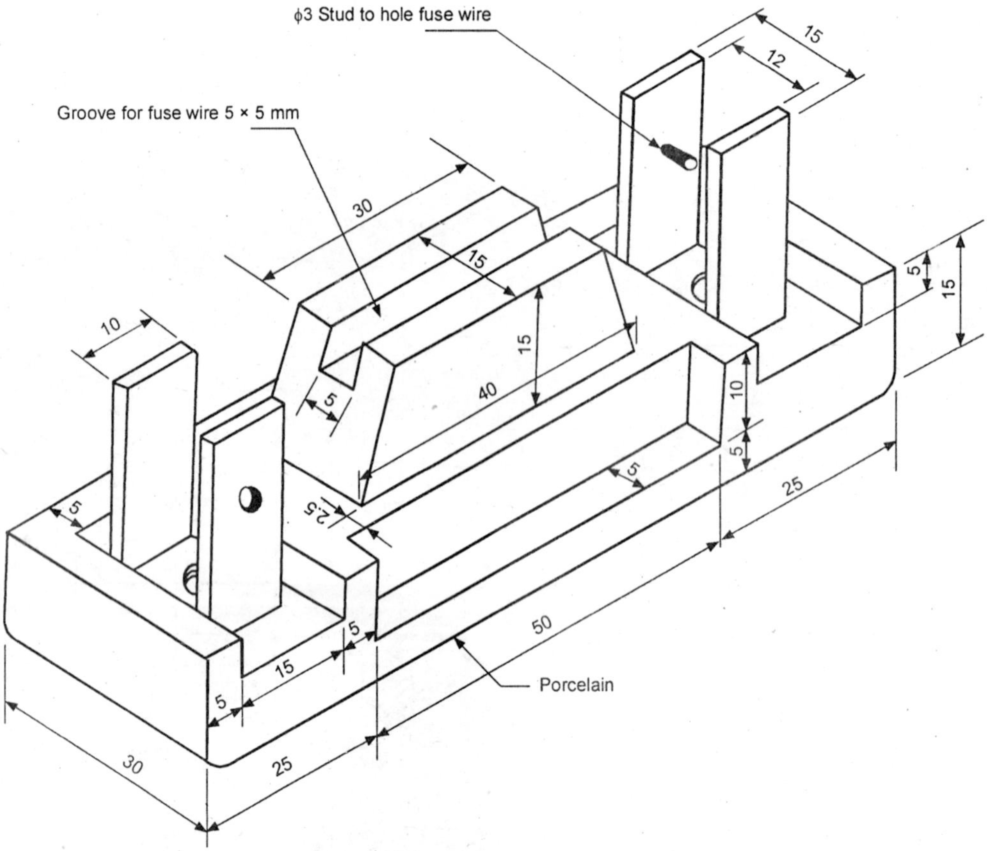

Fig. 1.29

Solution. See Fig. 1.30.

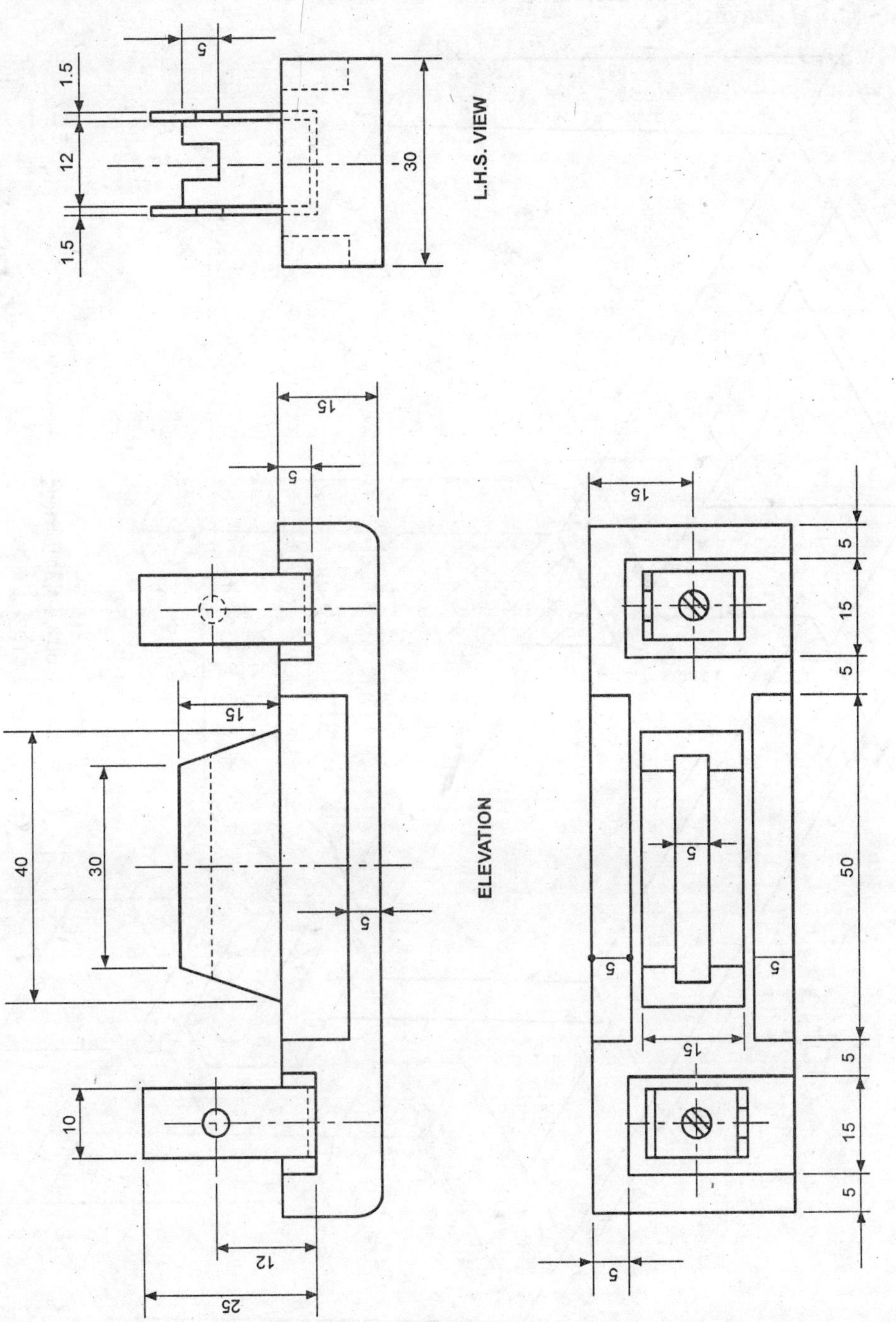

Fig. 1.30

Problem 9. Fig. 1.31 shows the pictorial view of a fuse base. Draw
1. Elevation 2. Top view. 3. Left side view.

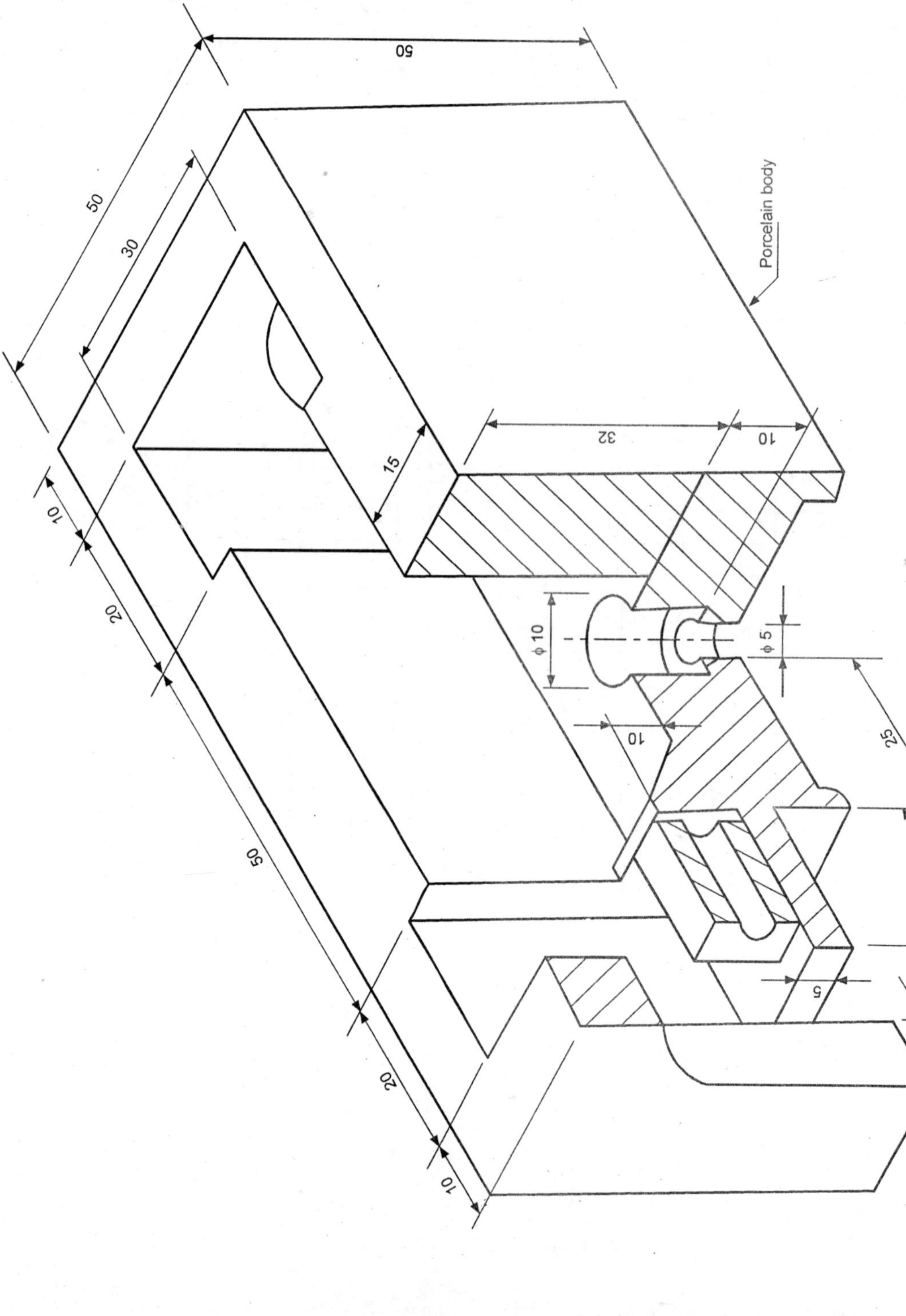

Note: STUD 4, φ-3, 15 mm long
PICTORIAL VIEW

Fig. 1 31

Solution. See Fig. 1.32.

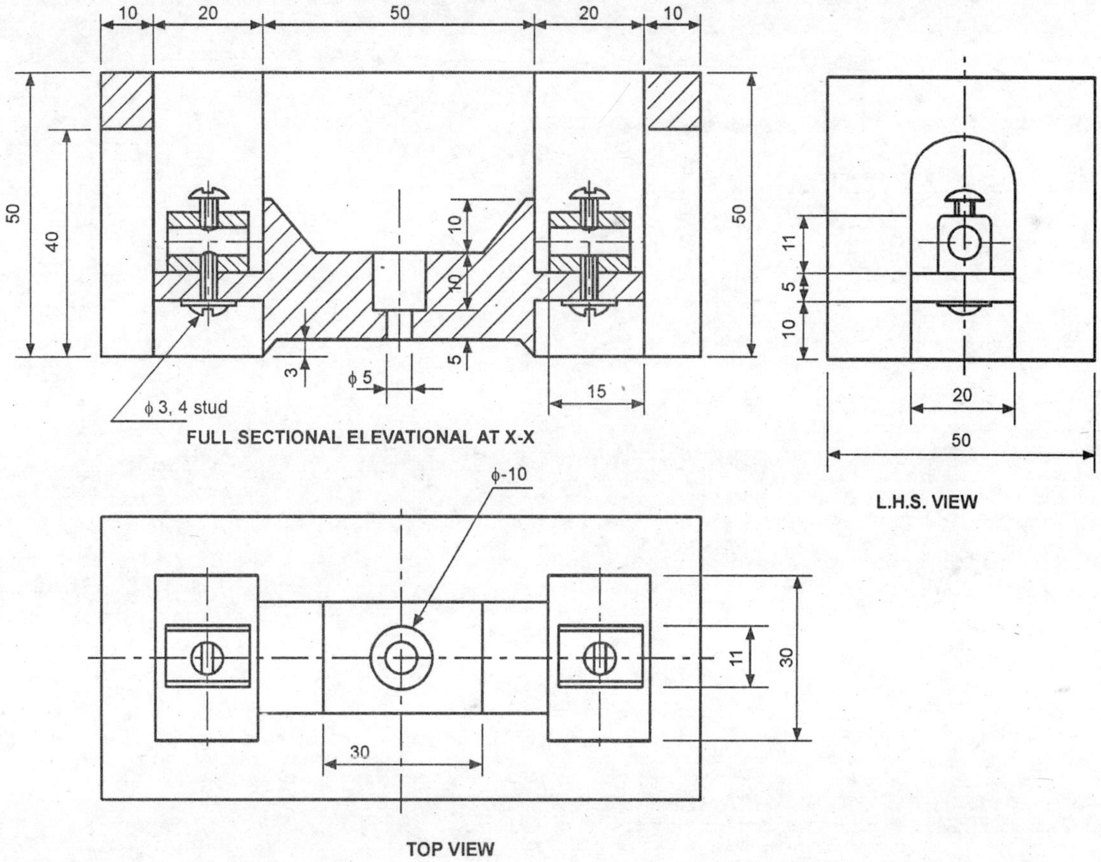

Fig. 1.32

EXERCISE

1. Define, end cover of induction motor with sketch.
2. What do you understand by the term slip rings?
3. Differentiate between pintype insulator and shackle type insulator.
4. What are the function of kit-kat fuse carrier?
5. What is the difference between dry type and oil type transformer?

❑❑❑

IMPORTANT NOTES:

2

CIVIL DRAWING

2.1 INTRODUCTION

Civil engineering drawing is a major part of civil engineering. The main aim of civil drawing is to give sufficient information by the designer to the construction engineer. In order to give sufficient informations about the building following views are drawn such as plan, elevation and section along any particular plane. Basically, civil drawing is a type of technical drawing that shows information about grading, landscaping or other side details.

Civil drafters prepare drawings and topographical and relief maps used in major construction or civil engineering projects, such as highways, bridges, pipelines, flood control projects and water and sewage systems.

2.2 BUILDING PLAN DRAWING WITH ELECTRICAL AND CIVIL ENGINEERING SYMBOLS

A building layout is the arrangement of different portion of a building such as room, bed room, living room dining hall, drawing hall, kitchen, bathroom, store room, balcony etc. The architect draws several types of drawing in preparing the plans of a house. A building plan drawing is an important part for building the houses. By the help of building plan drawings the engineers, supervisors and workers can complete their work easily and timely. A building plan drawing is developed in various stages such as:

(*i*) Prepare building layout as per requirement. The plan is drawn in single line showing various positions of rooms with dimensions.

(*ii*) Prepare the floor plan which contains the necessary dimensions which helps in the construction of a house. It includes overall size, wall thickness, location of walls, windows, doors, stairs, electrical details and plumbing work etc.

(*iii*) After the completion of floor plan drawing architect starts working on the elevation. These are front, right side, rear and left side. The details of drawings are -prepared for the supervisor as well as the worker by which they should start the construction as per specification of architect.

Problem 1. Draw the plan of a low income group house showing one room janta flat (size 22½ m^2) along with civil and electrical engineering symbols.

Solution. See Fig. 2.1.

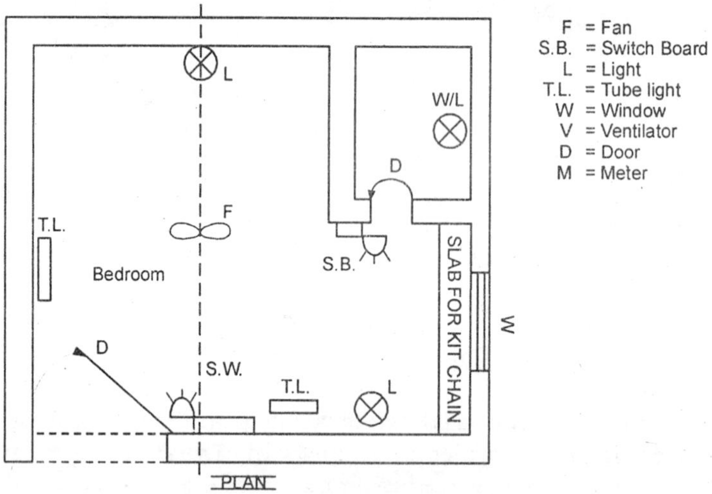

Fig. 2.1 One room janta flat

Problem 2. Draw the plan of a room (3.4 m × 5.5 m) with specification:

Window: 1 m × 1.5 m, Door 1 meter

Also show, the electrical and civil engineering symbol on it.

Solution. See Fig. 2.2.

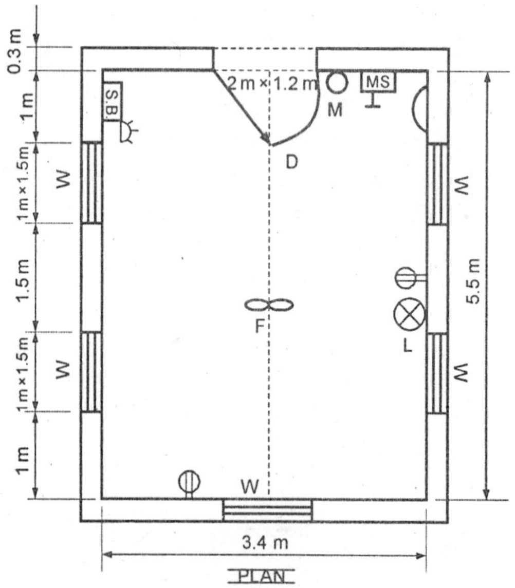

Fig. 2.2

Problem 3. Draw a plan of a middle income group house, showing one bed room, living room, kitchen and bath room of size 77.38 square metre, along with its necessary civil and electrical engineering symbols.

Solution. See Fig. 2.3.

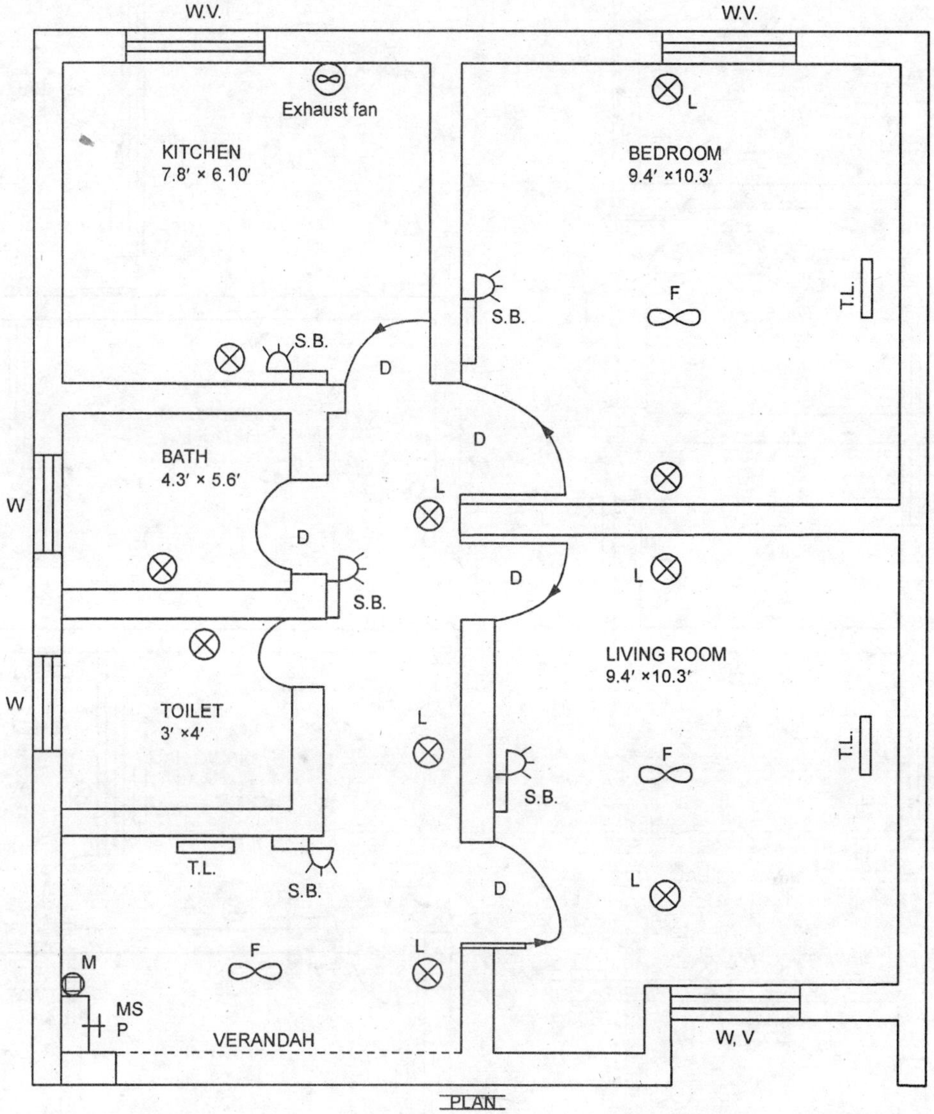

D = Door L = Light M = Meter
W = Window T.L. = Tube light M.S. = Main Switches, Power
V = Ventilator S.B. = Switch Board F = Fan

Fig. 2.3 Middle Income Group (Size 77.38 Sq Mt)

Problem 4. Draw the plan of 2 bedroom type C flat size 107 square meter along with its necessary civil and electrical engineering symbols.

Solution. See Fig. 2.4.

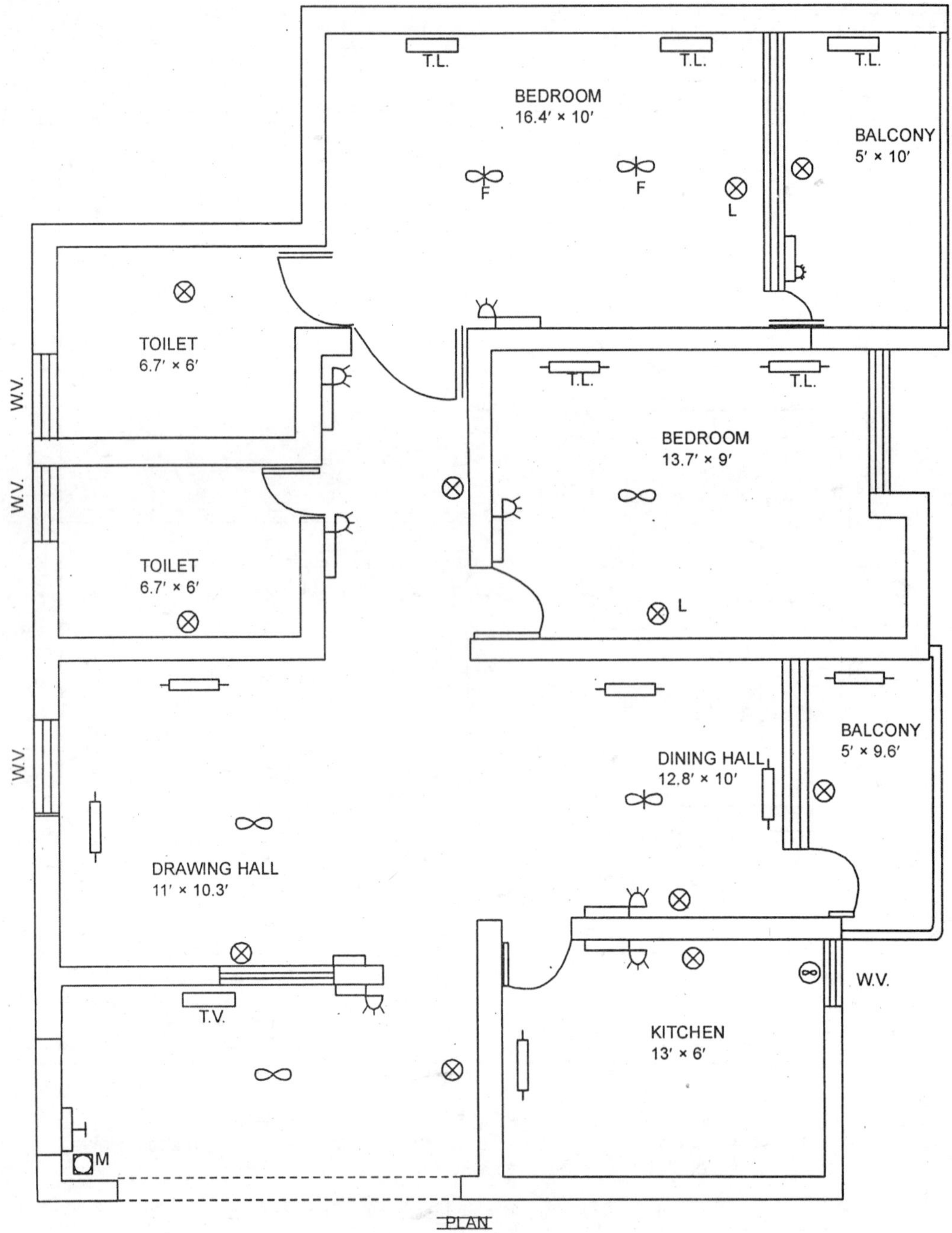

Fig. 2.4

Problem 5. Prepare a floor plan of a conference hall of an engineering college size 20 m × 12 m along with electrical and civil engineering symbols.

Solution. See Fig. 2.5.

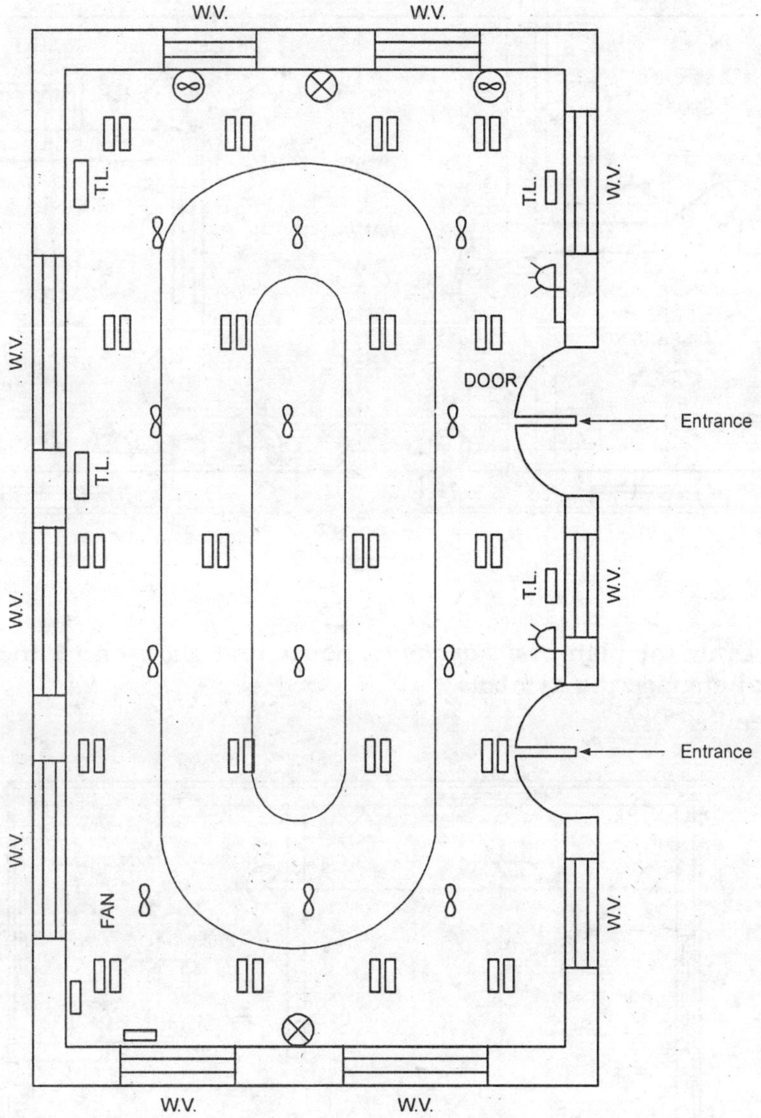

Fig. 2.5

Problem 6. Draw the plan of a dispensary for students hostel showing waiting room, doctor room, toilet, store and dispensing room alongwith necessary civil and electrical engineering symbols.

Solution. See Fig. 2.6.

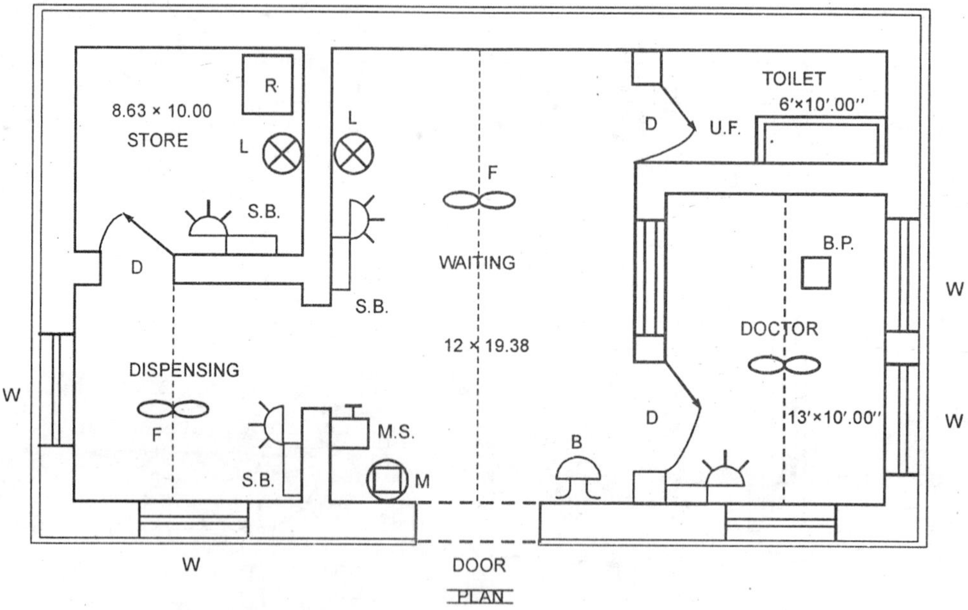

Fig. 2.6

Problem 7. Draw the plan of a *Panchayat* house and show on its the necessary civil and electrical engineering symbols.

Solution. See Fig. 2.7.

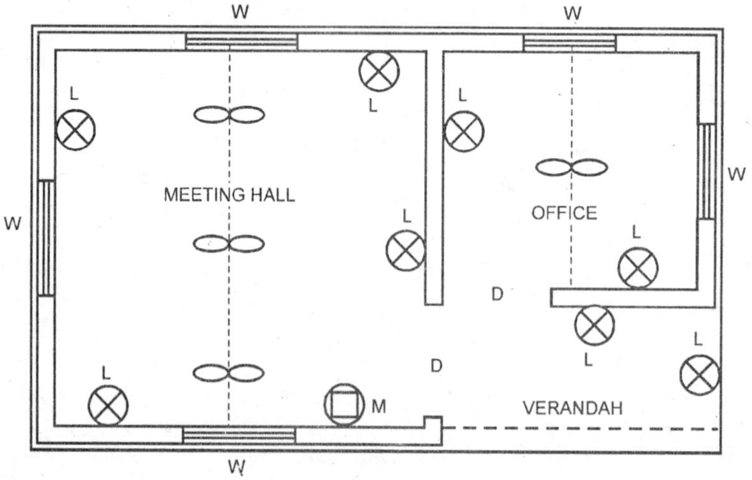

Fig. 2.7

Problem 8. Draw a plan for a canteen for students and staff of a engineering college along with civil and electrical engineering symbols.

Solution. See Fig. 2.8.

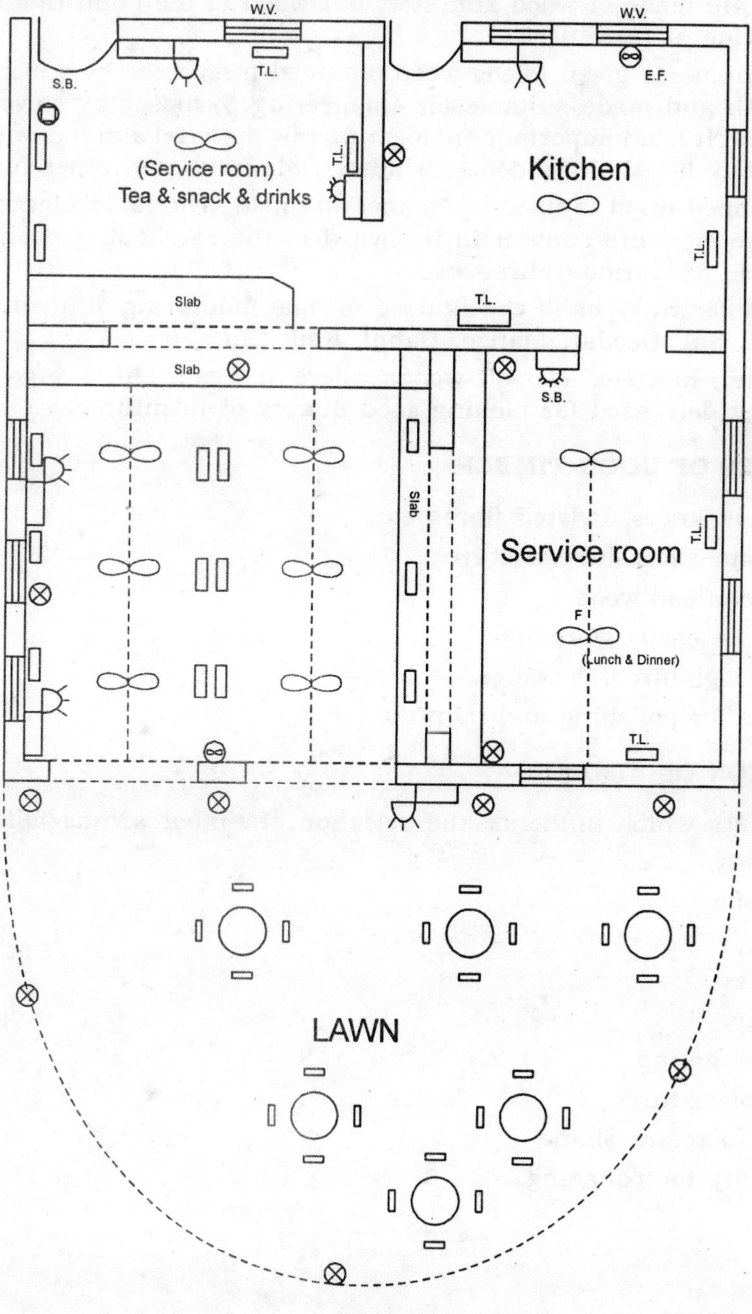

Fig. 2.8

2.3 FURNITURES

Furnitures are manufactured in a wide range for offices, institutions, hostels, houses etc. and using various quality of raw materials.

Furnitures are made of wood and steel but wood is the main raw material used for manufacturing of furnitures.

Timber is the name given to the wood obtained from trees by cutting these trees after full growth and made suitable for engineering purposes by sawing. It is chief product of forest. It is an important engineering raw material and has wide application in our day to day life such as doors, windows, almirahs and other furnitures etc.

A well seasoned wood is used in engineering field. The main object of seasoning is to reduce the moisture content in the wood to the extent it is desirable so as to make it suitable for various purposes.

There are different types of woods used for manufacturing of furnitures such as, Teak, Shisham, Sal, Deodar, Mango, Babul, Kail, Chid etc.

Deodar, Chid, Kail etc. are soft woods where as Teak, Sal, Mango etc. are hard wood. Teak is widely used for making good quality of furnitures.

2.4 QUALITIES OF GOOD TIMBER

- Free from knots, twisted fibres etc
- Free from excessive moisture
- Absence of sap wood
- Should be easily workable
- Posses high fire resistance
- Suitable for polishing and painting.

2.5 SELECTION OF TIMBERS

The main factors which influence the selection of timber are as follows:

- Durability
- Workability
- Weight
- Hardness
- Elasticity
- Types of grains
- Types of textures
- Ability to retain shape
- Suitability for polishing.

Problem 9. Fig. 2.9 shows the isometric view of a dining table. Draw to scale 1 : 10 the following. **(B.T.E. New Delhi, June 2004)**

(*i*) Front view (Looking from A)

(*ii*) Top view.

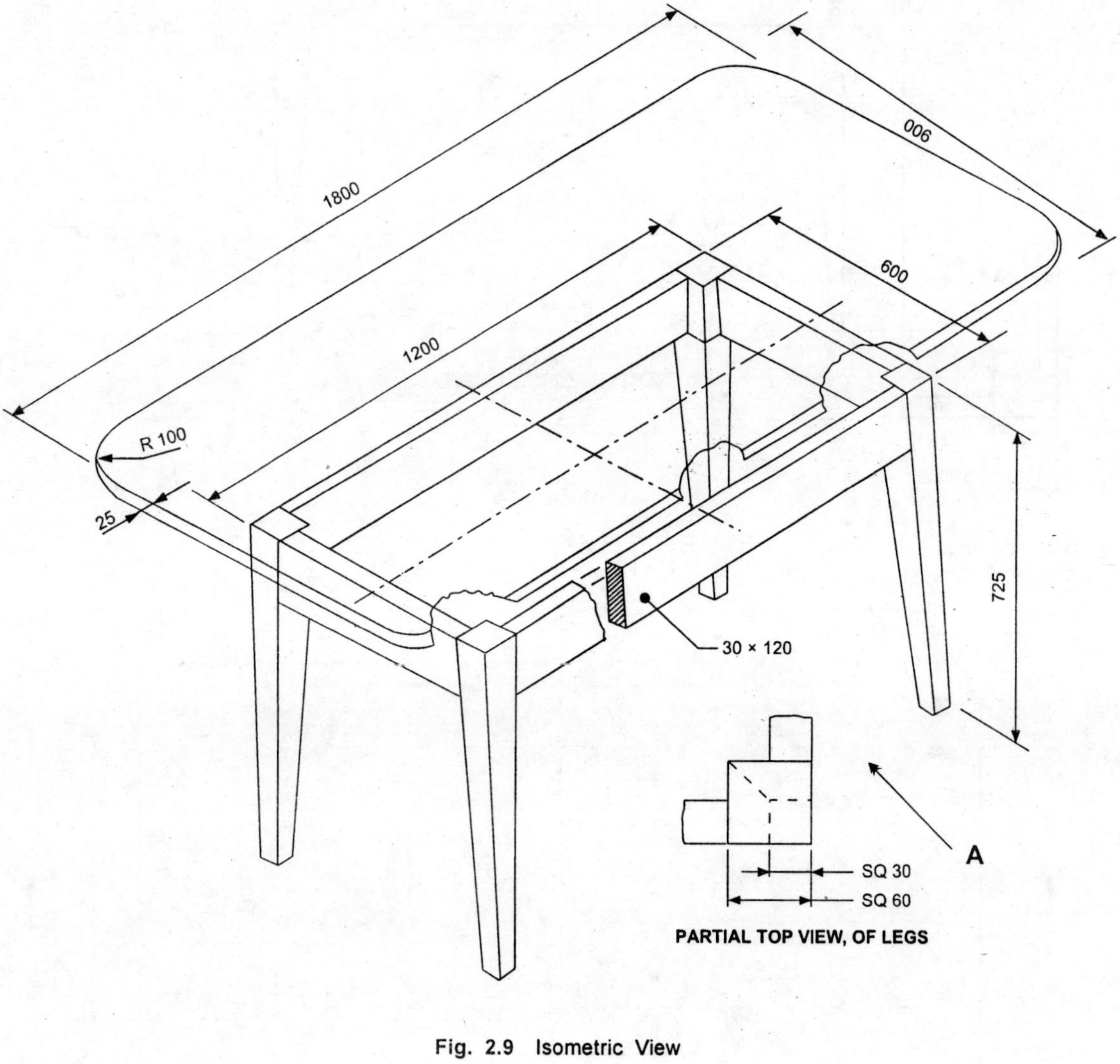

Fig. 2.9 Isometric View

Solution. See Fig. 2.10.

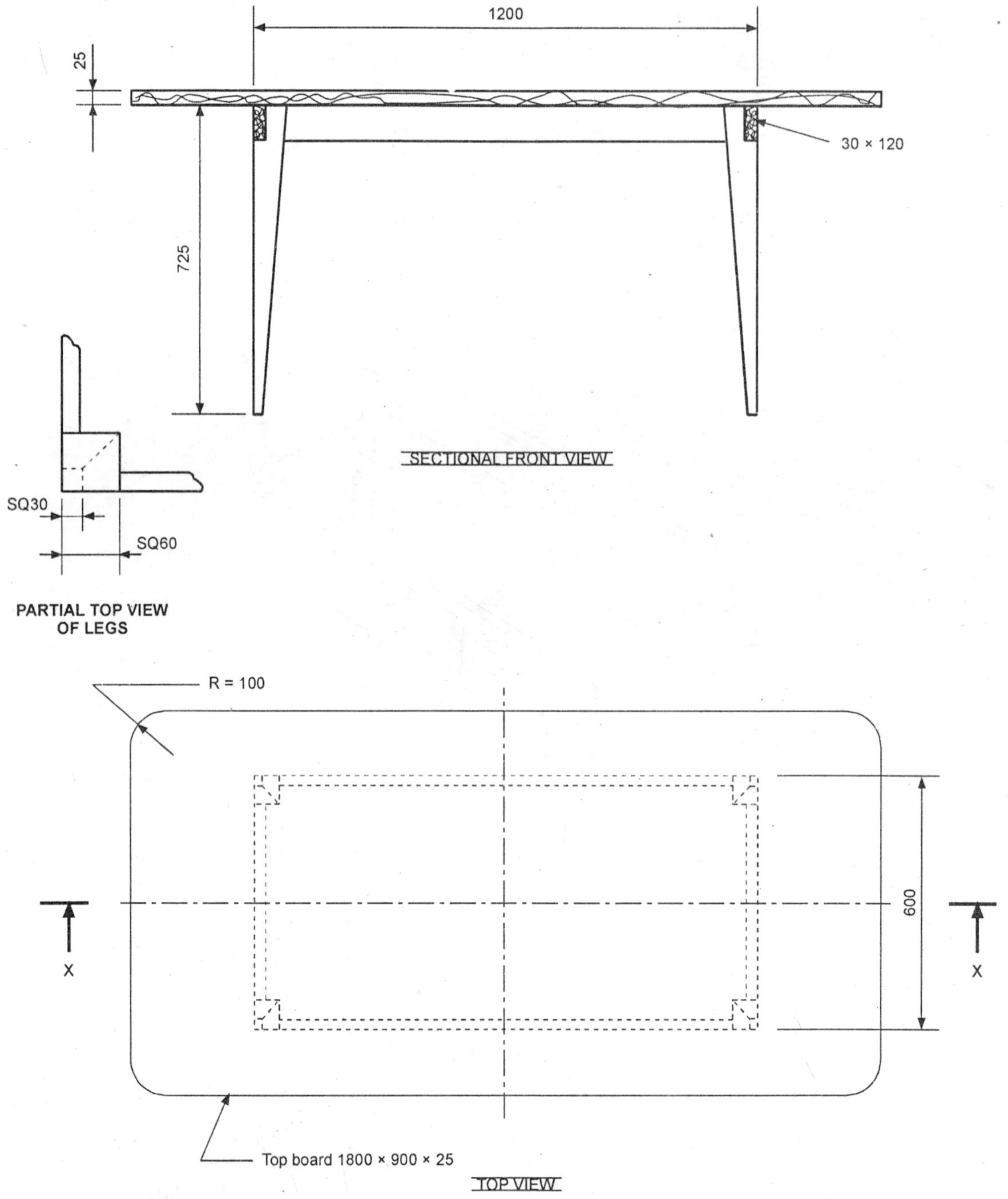

Fig. 2.10

Problem 10. Fig. 2.11 shows the orthographic views of a dining table. Draw the isometric view of the dining table.

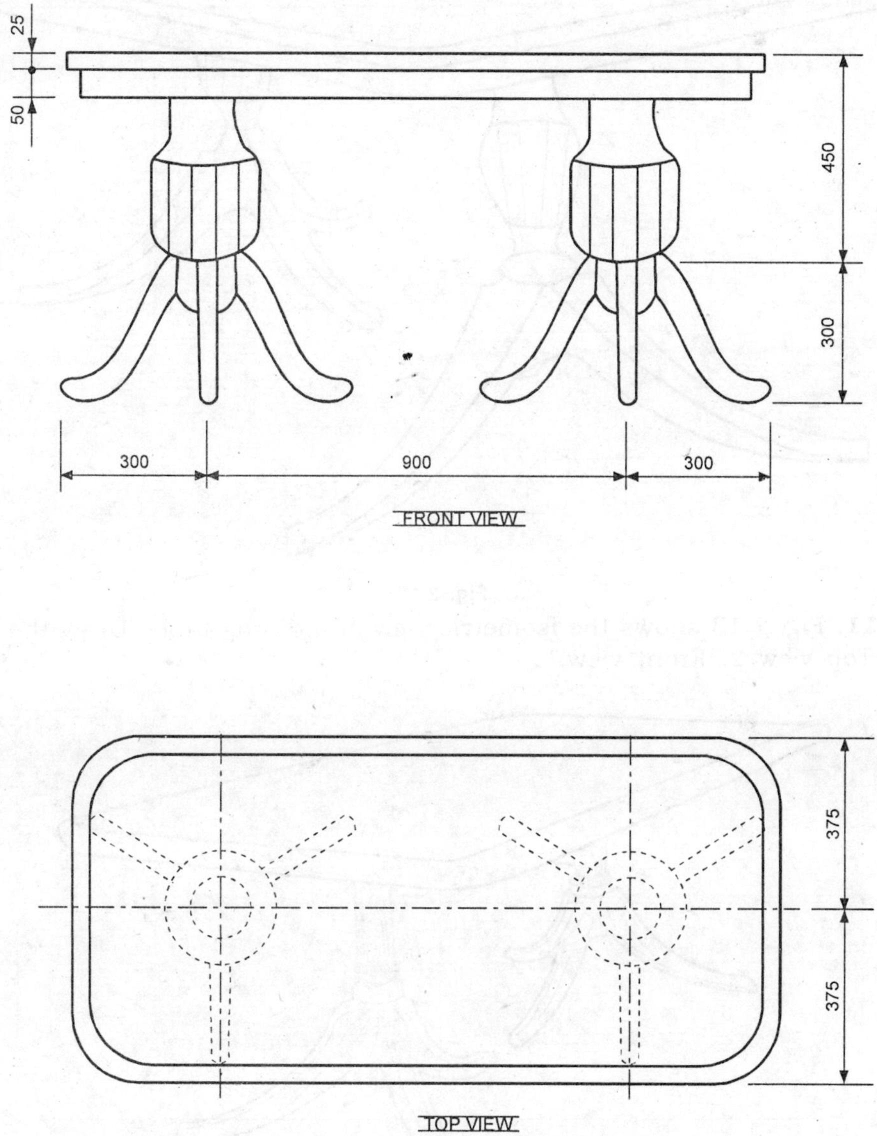

Fig. 2.11

Solution. See Fig. 2.12.

Fig. 2.12

Problem 11. Fig. 2.13 shows the isometric view of a dining table. Draw the following views: 1. Top view 2. Front view.

Fig. 2.13

Solution. See Fig. 2.14.

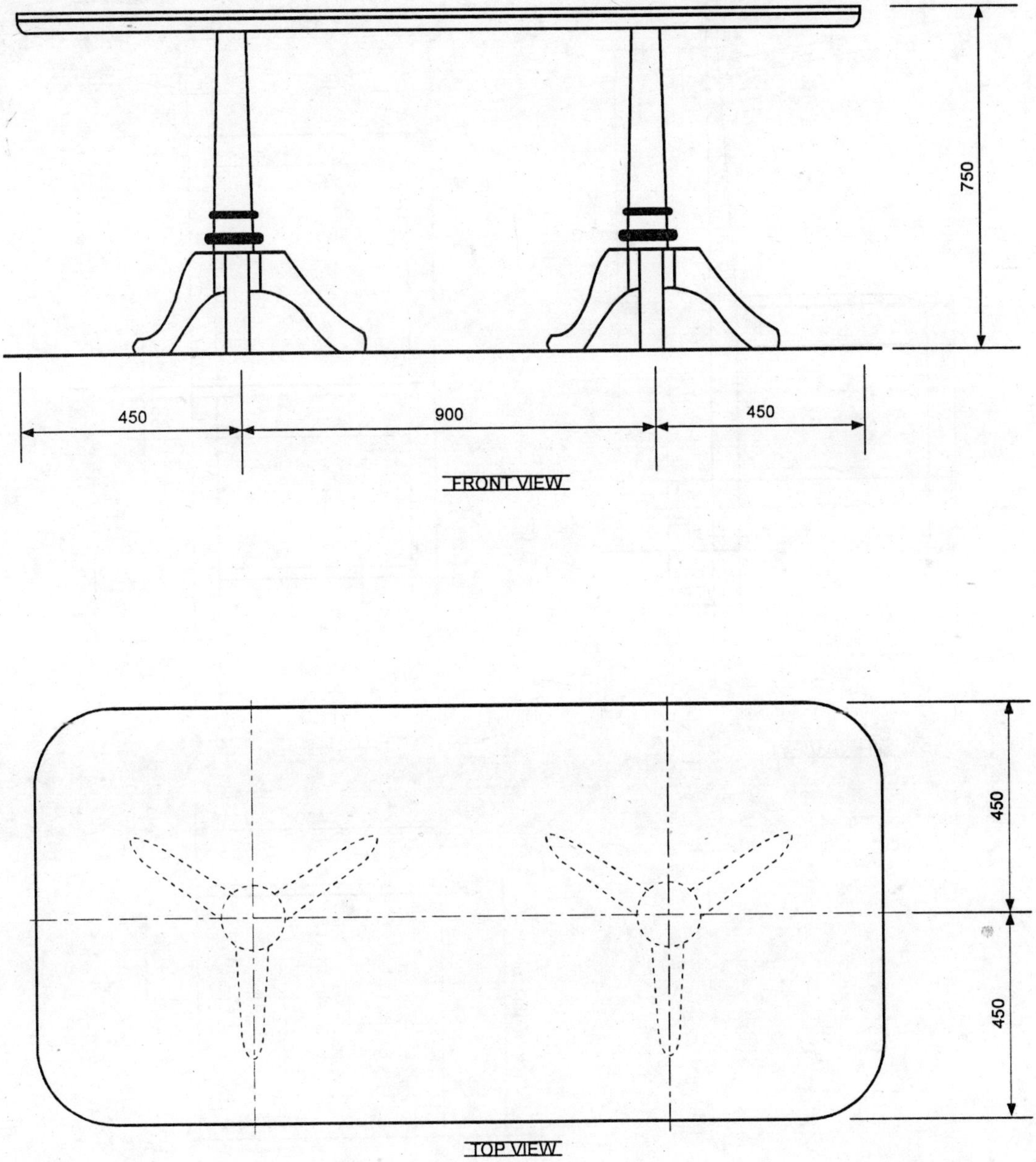

Fig. 2.14

Problem 12. Fig. 2.15 shows the orthographic views of a chair without arms. Draw the isometric view.

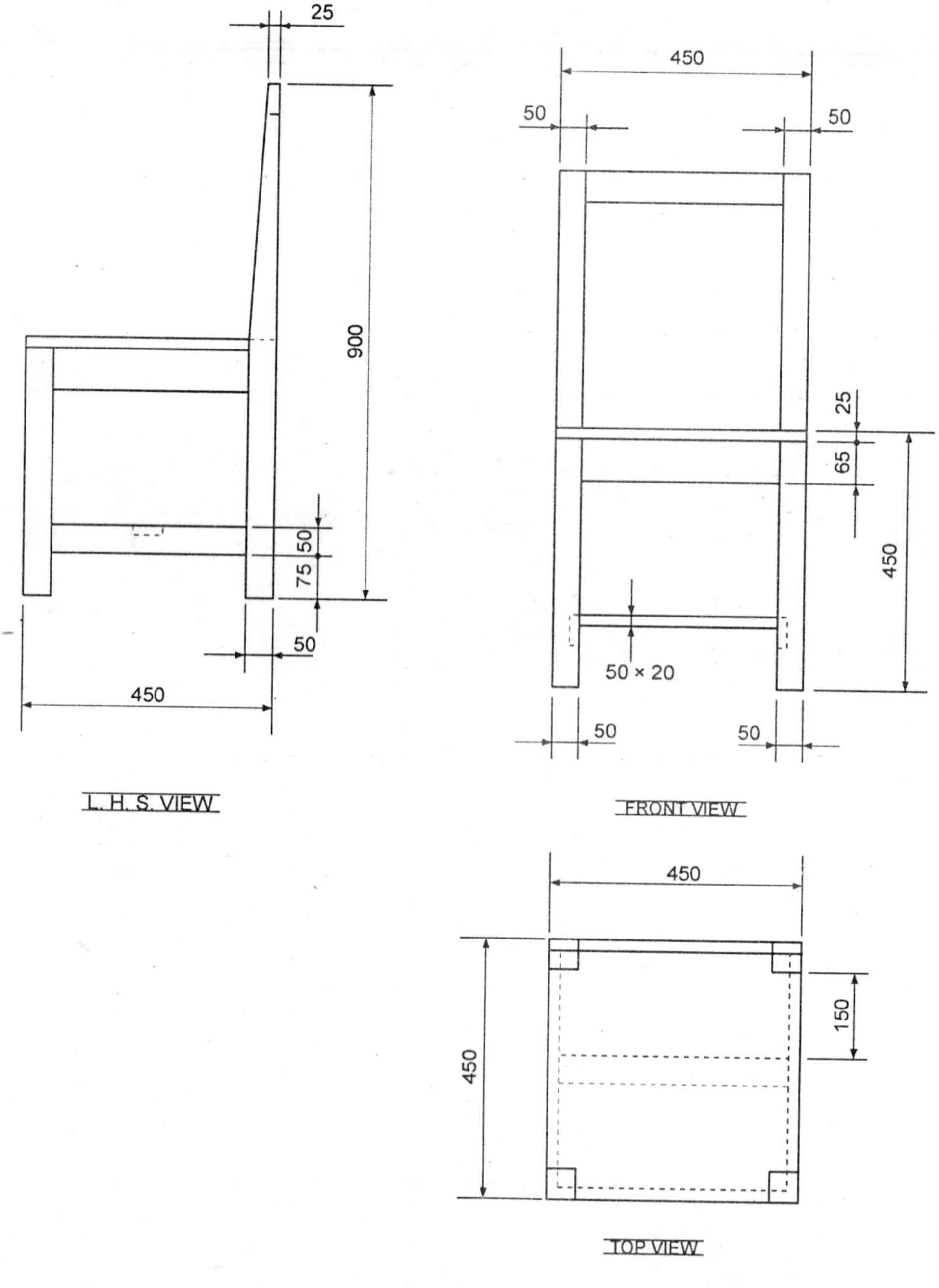

Fig. 2.15

Solution. See Fig. 2.16.

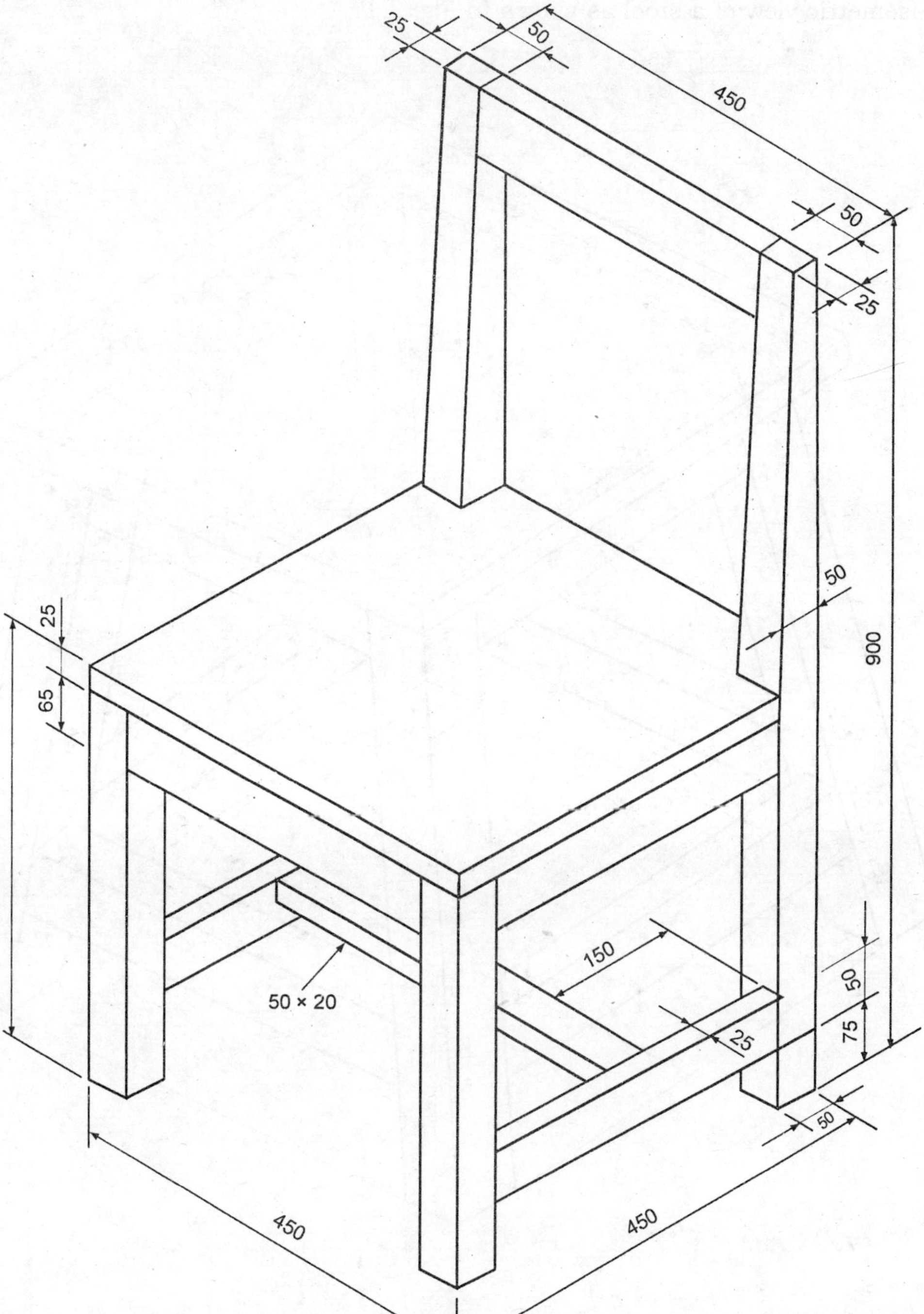

Fig. 2.16

Problem 13. Draw a plan and elevation of a stool having a square top and four legs from a given isometric view of a stool as shown in Fig. 2.17.

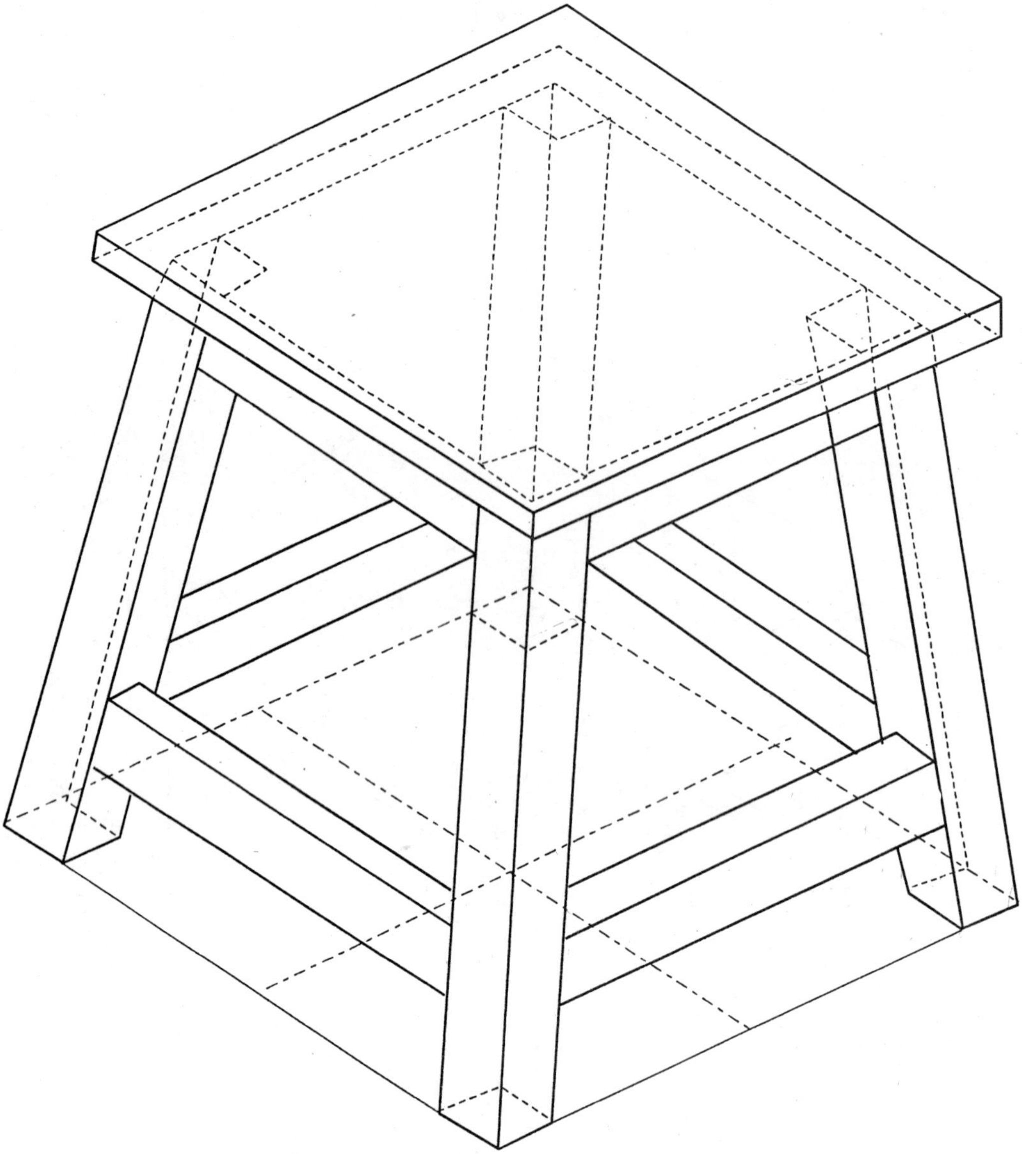

Fig. 2.17

Solution. See Fig. 2.18.

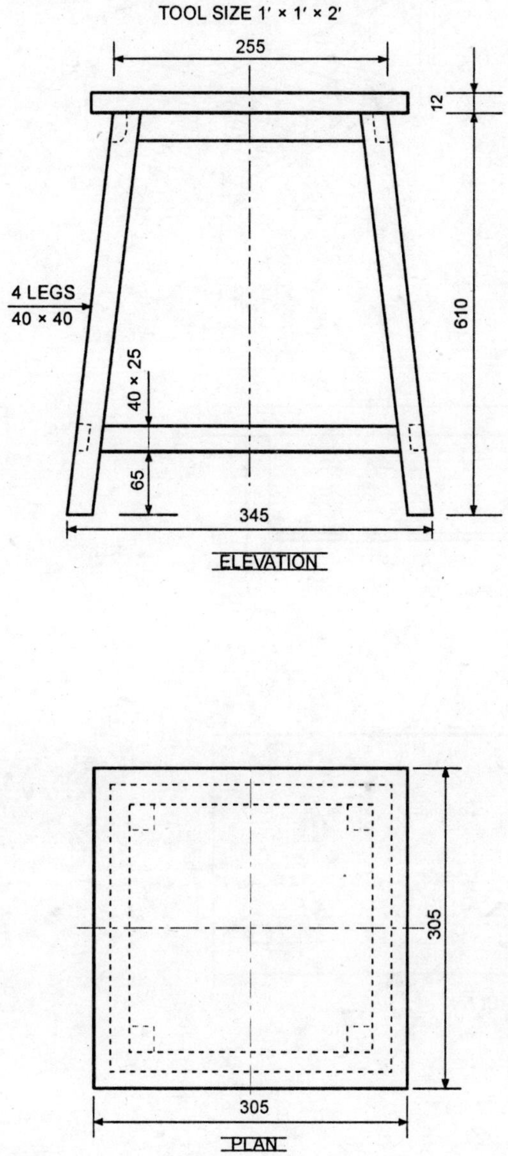

Fig. 2.18

Problem 14. Draw a plan, elevation and side view of a centre table having a rectangular top and four legs from a given isometric view as shown in Fig. 2.19.

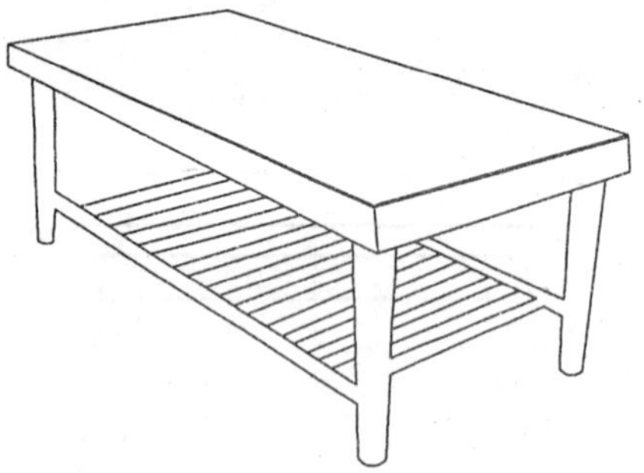

Fig. 2.19

Solution. See Fig. 2.20.

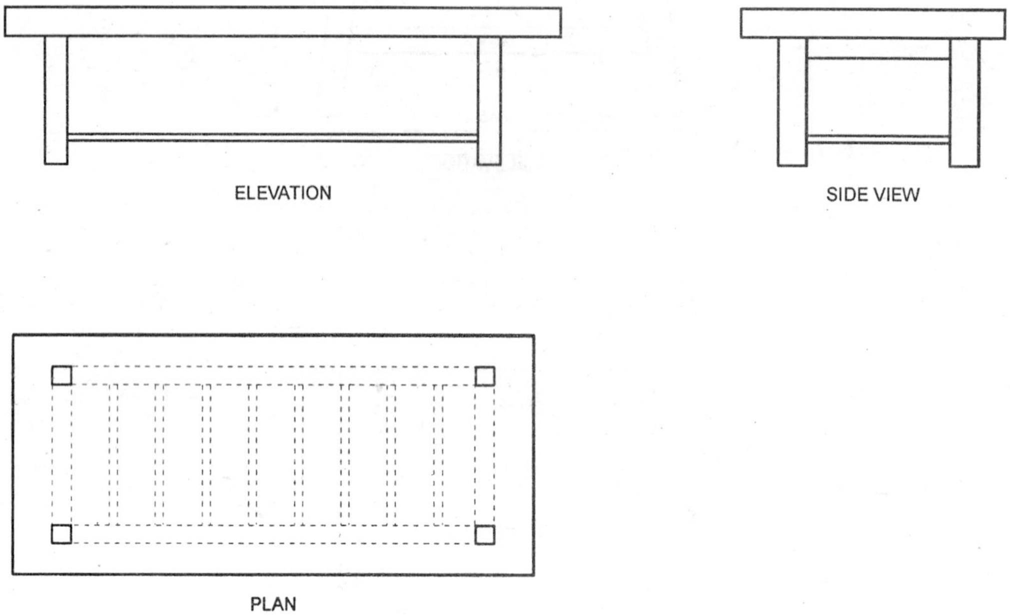

Fig. 2.20

EXERCISE

1. What are the different types of symbols used in electrical engineering?
2. What do you mean by building plan drawing?
3. Why do we prepare furniture drawing?
4. Fig. 2.21 shows the orthographic views of a table. Draw the isometric view of the given Fig. 2.21

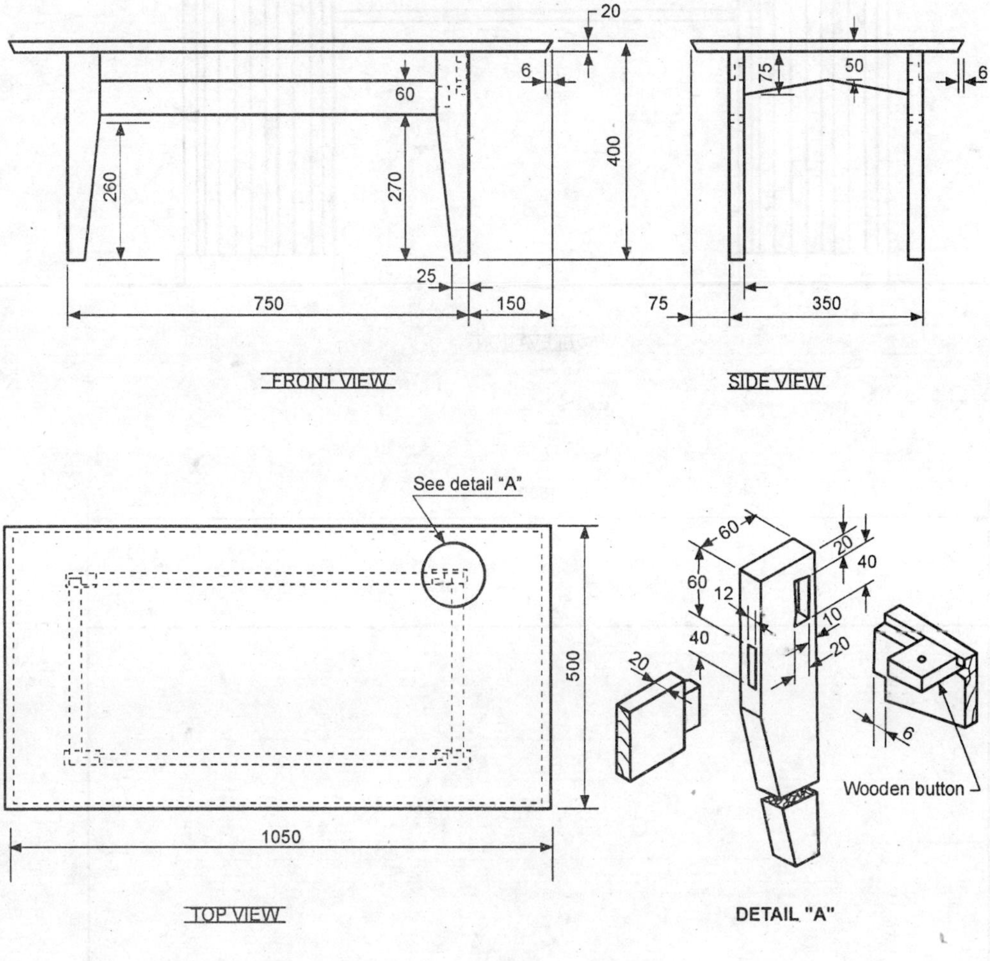

Fig. 2.21

5. Fig. 2.22 shows the orthographic views of a table. Draw the isometrics view of the dining table.

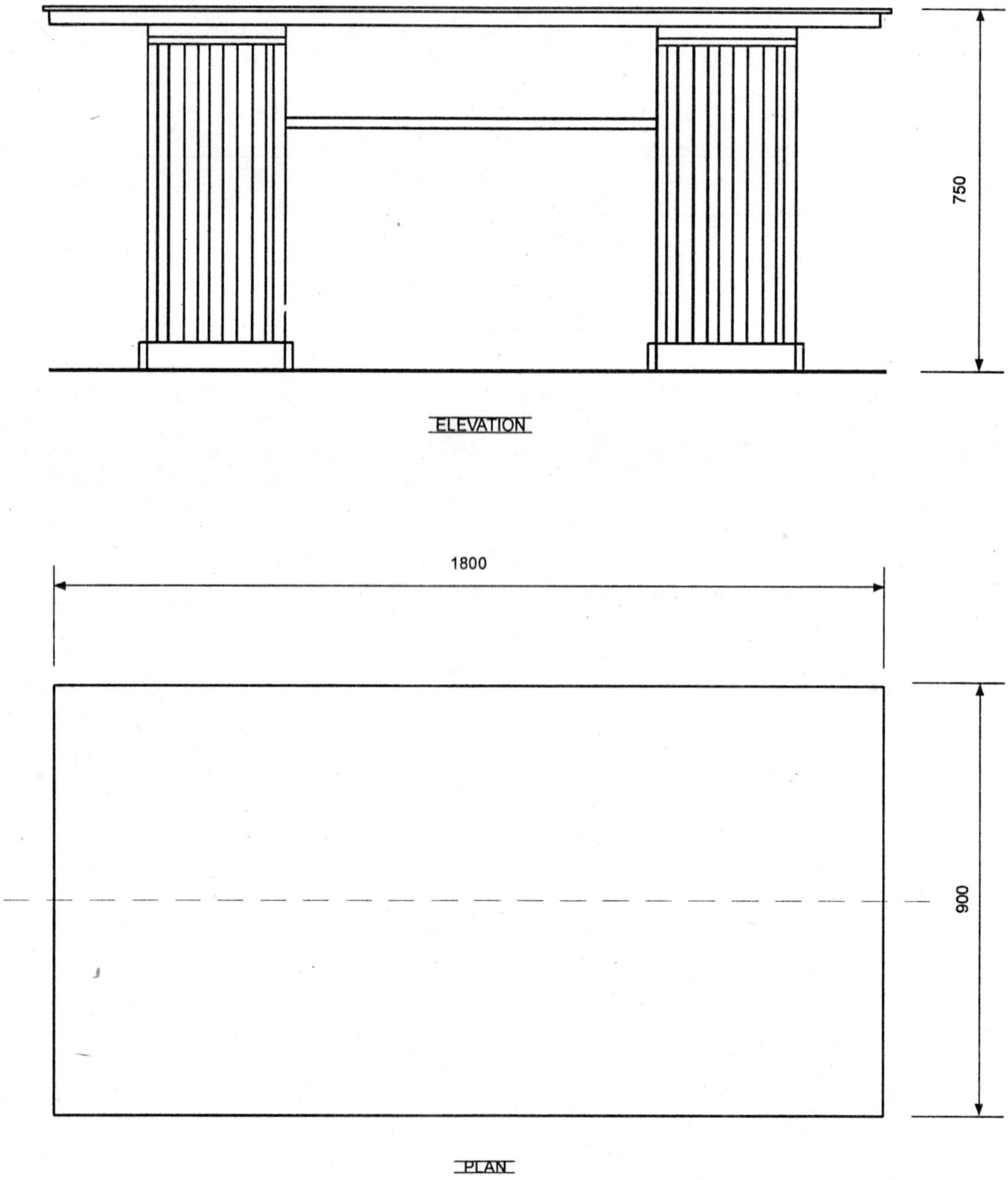

Fig. 2.22

6. Fig. 2.23 shows the isometric view of "TABLE". Draw the scale 1 : 5, the following view:

(a) Front view looking the direction of arrow 'A'.

(b) Top view.

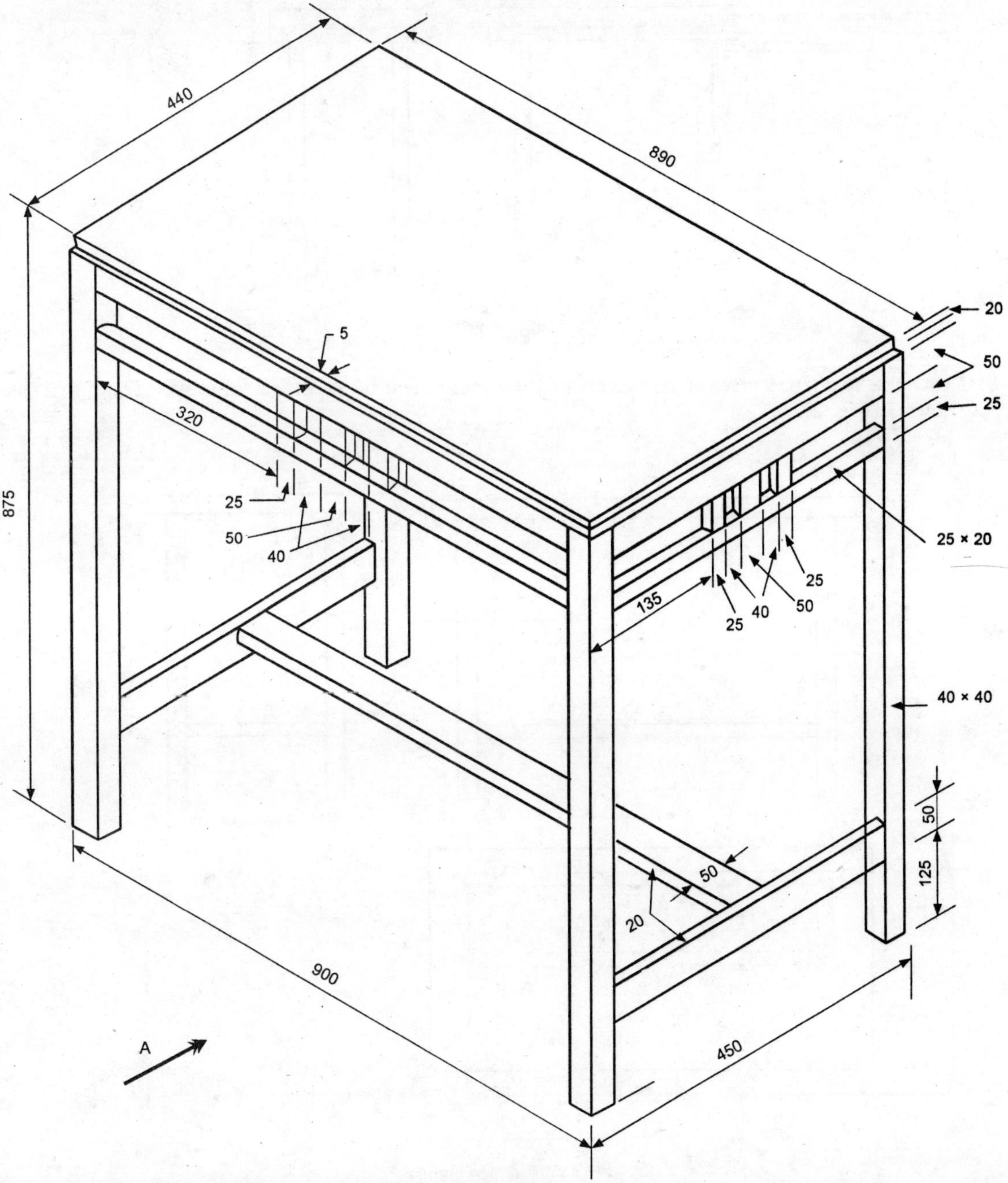

Fig. 2.23

7. Draw the isometric view of the given orthographic view of a stool as shown in Fig. 2.24.

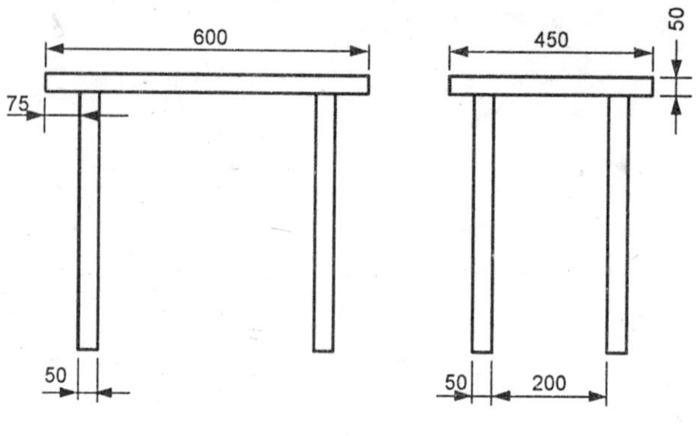

Fig. 2.24

8. Draw the isometric view of the given orthographic view of an office table 4′ × 2′-6″ × 2′ as shown in Fig. 2.25.

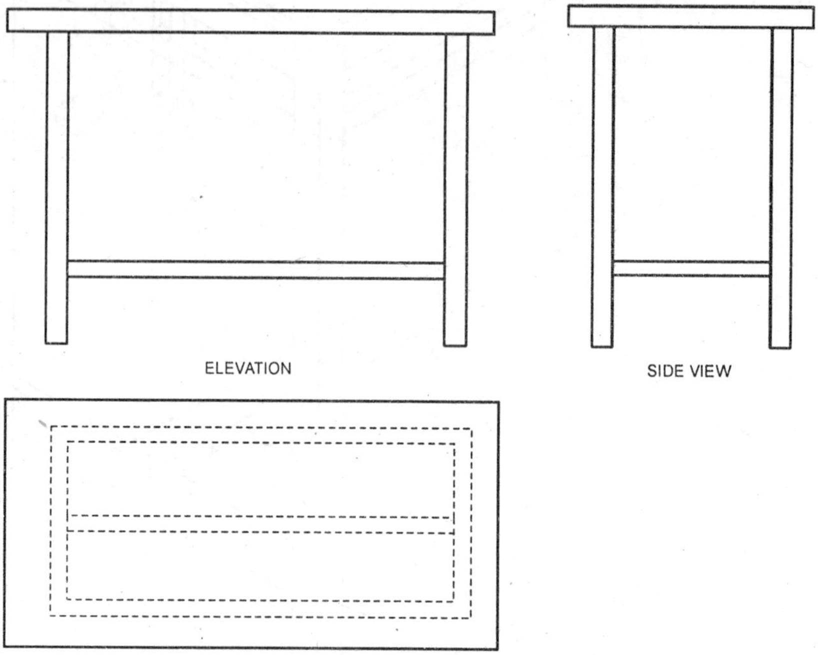

Fig. 2.25 Office Table

9. Fig 2.26 shows an isometric view of a stool. Draw the following in suitable scale:
(i) Front view
(ii) Top view isometric.

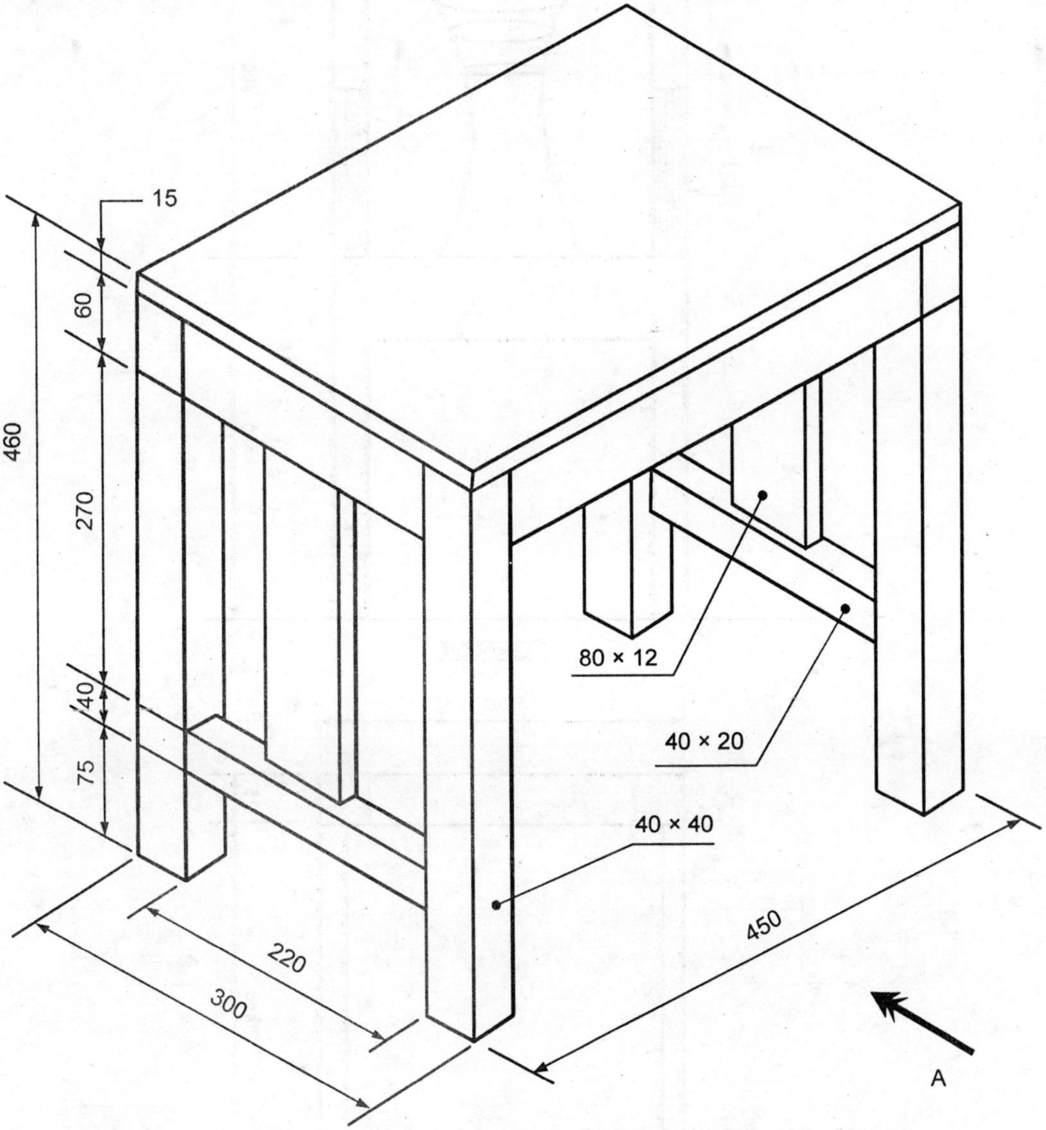

Fig. 2.26

10. Fig. 2.27 shows the orthographic views of a chair with arm. Draw its isometric view.

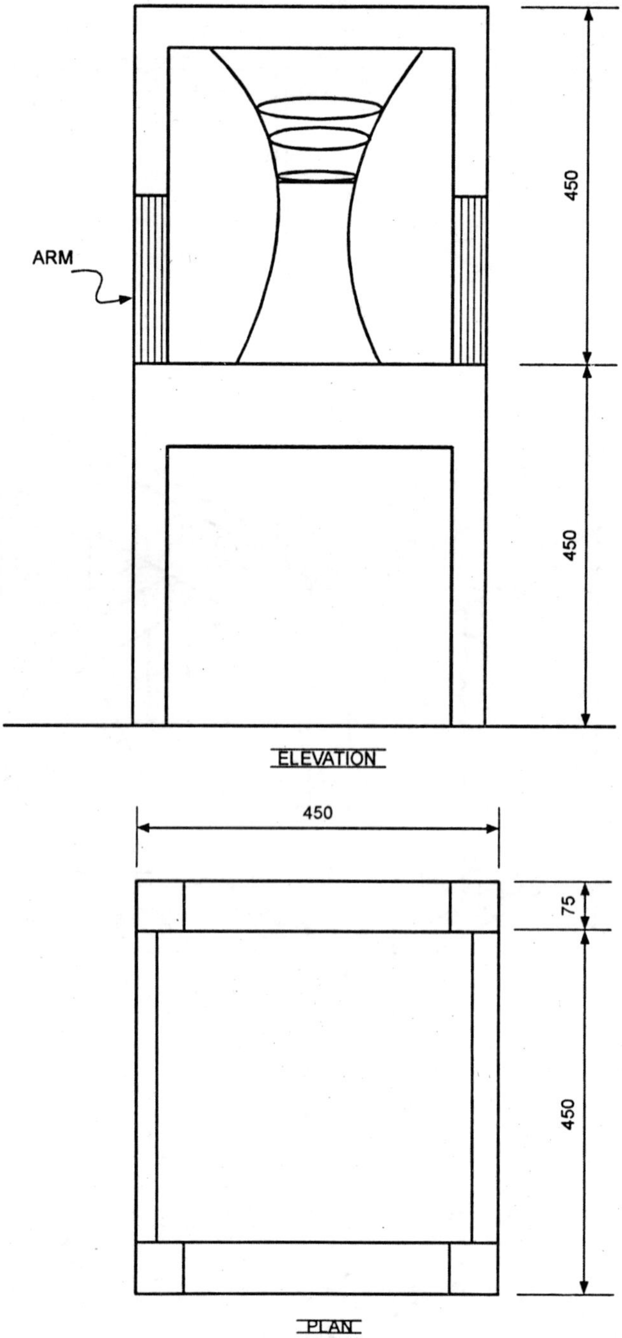

Fig. 2.27

11. Fig. 2.28 shows the orthographic views of a simple book rack. Draw it isometric view.

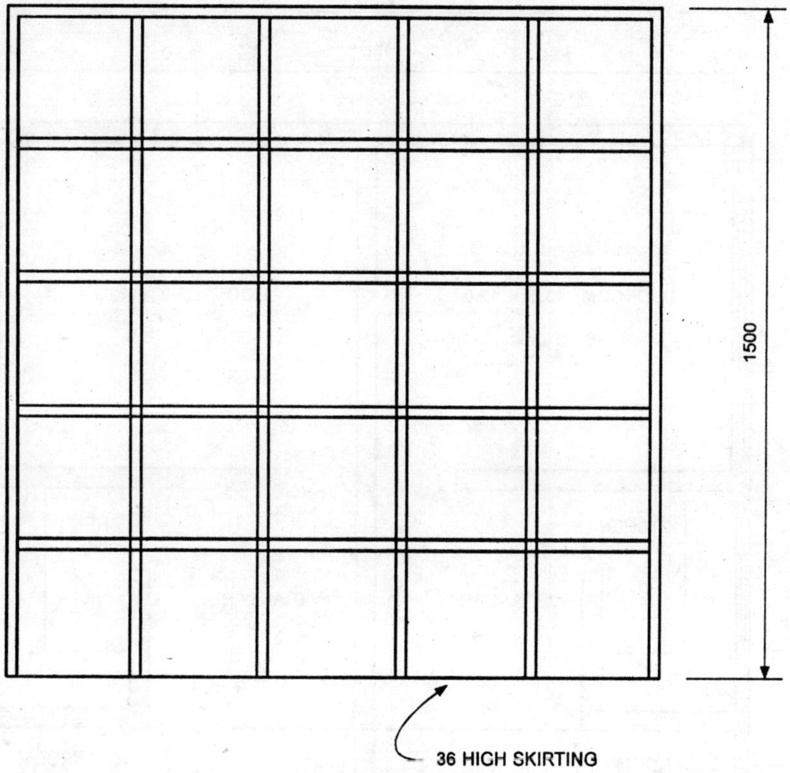

ELEVATION

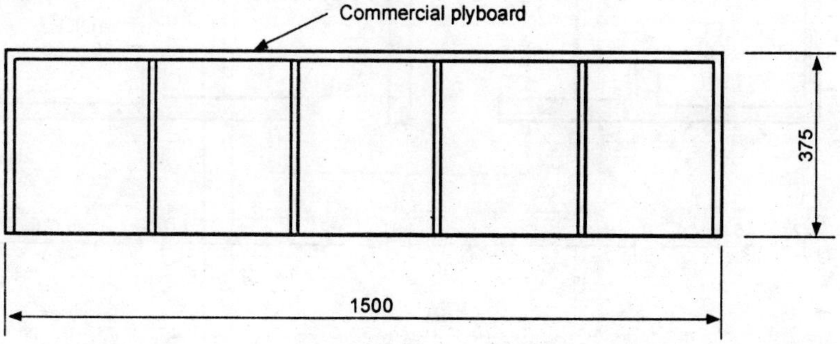

PLAN

Fig. 2.28

12. Fig. 2.29 shows the plan of one bedroom with Toilet, bathroom and verndah. Show necessary civil and electrical engineering symbols.

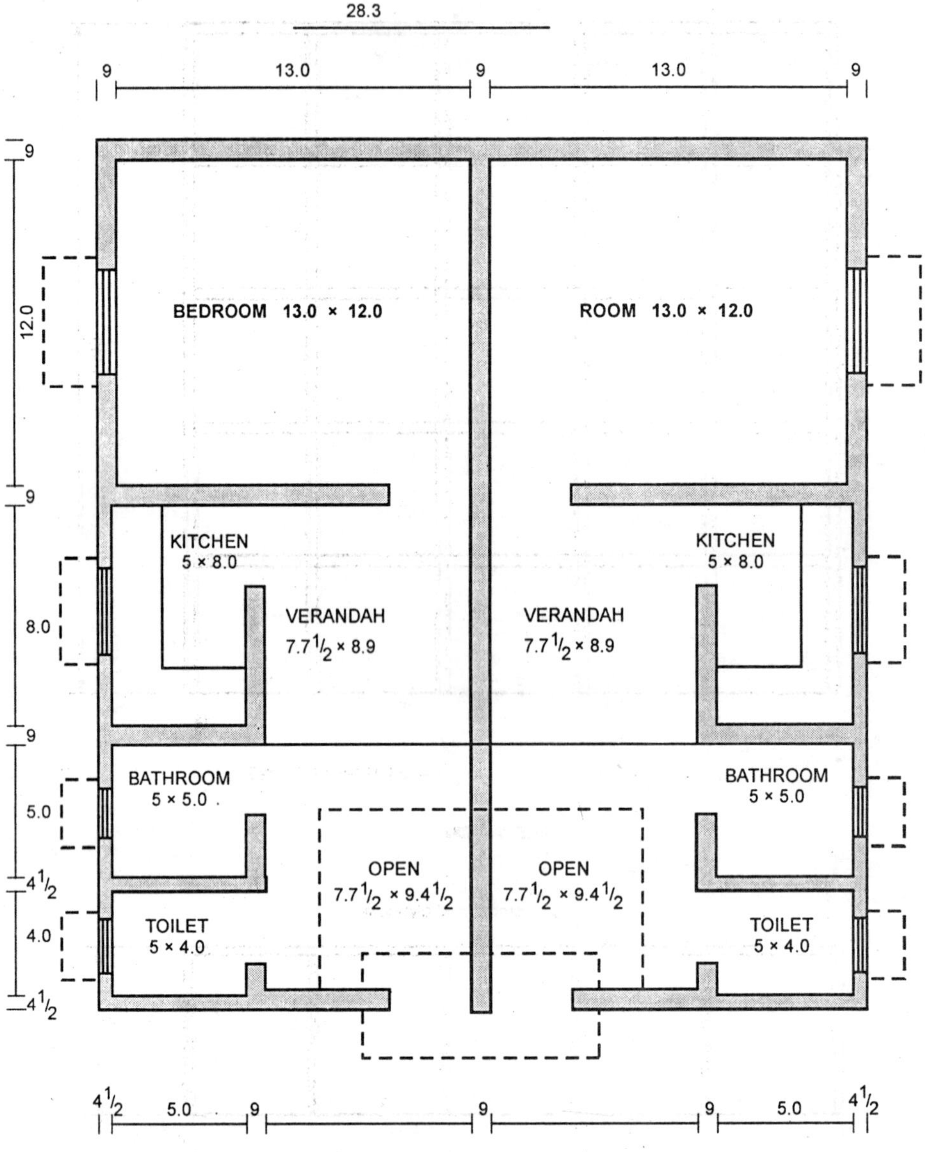

Fig. 2.29

❑❑❑

3

INDIAN STANDARD CODES FOR DRAWING

IS 46 : 1988	Engineering drawing practice for schools & colleges
IS 696 : 1972	Code of practice for general engineering drawings (revised)
IS 813 : 1986	Scheme of symbols for welding
IS 919 : Part 1 : 1963	Recommendation for limits and fits for engineering : Part 1 General engineering
IS 1076 : Part 1 : 1985 ISO 3 : 1973	Preferred numbers : Part 1 Series of preferred numbers
IS 1076 : Part 2 : 1985 ISO 17 : 1973	Preferred numbers : Part 2 Guide to the use of preferred numbers and series of preferred numbers
IS 1076 : Part 3 : 1985 ISO 497 : 1973	Prefered numbers Part 3 Guide to the choice of series of preferred numbers and series containing more rounded values of preferred numbers
IS 2102 : Part 1 : 1980	General tolerance for dimensions and form and position : Part 1 General tolerances for linear and angular dimensions
IS 2709 : 1982	Guide for selection of fits
IS 3073 : 1967	Assessment of surfacc roughness
IS 3403 : 1981	Dimensions for knurls
IS 4218 : Part 1 : 1976	ISO metric screw threads : Part 1 Basis and design profiles
IS 4218 : Part 2 : 1976	ISO metric screw threads : Part 2 Diameter pitch combination
IS 4218 : Part 3 : 1974	ISO metric screw threads : Part 3 Basic dimensions for design profile
IS 4210 : Part 4 : 1976	ISO metric screw threads : Part 4 Tolerancing system
IS 4218 : Part 5 : 1979	ISO metric screw threads : Part 5 Tolerances
IS 4218 : Part 6 : 1978	ISO metric screw threads : Part 6 Limits of sizes for commercial bolts and nuts
IS 7283 : 1974	Hot rolled bars for productin of bright bars
IS 8000 : Part 1 : 1985 ISO 1101 : 1983	Geometrical tolerancing on technical drawings : Part 1 Tolearances of form, orientation, location and run-out and appropriate geometrical definitions

IS 8000 : Part 2 : 1976	Geometrical tolerancing on tachnical drawing : Part 2 Maximum materical principles
IS 8000 : Part 3 : 1985	Geometrical tolerancing on technical drawings : Part 3
ISO 1960 : 1982	Dimensioning and tolerancing of profiles
IS 8000 : Part 4 : 1976	Geometrical tolerancing on technical drawings : Part 4 Practical examples of indication on drawings
IS 9606 : Part 1 : 1983 ISO 3098/1 : 1974	Lettering on technical drawings : Part 1 English characters
IS 9609 : Part 2 : 1985 ISO 3098/2 : 1984	Lettering on technical drawings : Part 2 Greek characters
IS 10164 : 1985 ISO 6428 : 1982	Requirements to execute technical drawings for microcopying
IS 10711 : 1983 ISO 5457 : 1980	Sizes of drawing sheet
IS 10712 : 1983 ISO 6433 : 1981	Presentation of item references on technical drawings
IS 10713 : 1983 ISO 5455 : 1979	Scales for use on technical drawings
IS 10714 : 1983 ISO 6433	General principles of presentation on technical drawings
IS 10715 : 1983 ISO 6410 : 1981	Presentation of threaded parts on technical drawintgs
IS 10716 : 1973 ISO 2162 : 1973	Rules for presentation of springs on techincal drawings
IS 10717 : 1983 ISO 2203 : 1973	Conventional representation of gears on technical drawings
IS 10718 : 1983 ISO 3040 : 1974	Method of dimensioning and tolerancing cones on tachnical drawings
IS 10719 : 1983 ISO 1302 : 1978	Method of indicating surface texture on technical drawings
IS 10720 : 1983 ISO 5261 : 1981	Technical drawings for structural metal work
IS 10721 : 1985	Datum and datum systems for geometrical toleracing on technical drawings
IS 10990 : 1984	Code of practice for industrical piping diagram
IS 11065 : Part 1 : 1984	Drawing practice for axonometric projection : Part 1 Isometric projection

IS 11065 : Part 2 : 1985	Drawing practice for axonometric projection : Part 2 Dimetric projection
IS 11663 : 1986	Conventional representation of common features
IS 11664 : 1986	Folding of drawing sheet
IS 11665 : 1985 ISO 7200 : 1984	Technical drawings-Title blocks
IS 11666 : 1985 ISO 7573 : 1983	Technical drawings-Item lists
IS 11667 : 1985 ISO 406 : 1982	Technical drawings-Linear and angular toleracing indications on drawings
IS 11669 : 1986 ISO 129 : 1985	General principles of dimensioning on techincal drawings
IS 11670 : 1986	Abbreviations for use in technical drawings

INDIAN STANDARDS CODES FOR GEARS

1. IS 4059 : 1967 Accuracy requirements for medium quality medium speed gears
2. IS 4725 : 1968 Accuracy requirements for precision gears
3. IS 4702 : 1968 Accuracy requirements for high precision gears
4. IS 2535 : 1969 Basic rack and modules of cylindrical gears for general engineering and heavy engineering (first revision).
5. IS 4058 : 1967 Accuracy required for coarse quality low speed gears
6. IS 2458 : 1965 Glossary of terms for toothed gearing
7. IS 5257 : 1969 Glossary for terms for worm gearing
8. IS 2467 : 1963 National for toothed gearing
9. IS 3681 : 1966 General plan for spur and helical gears.

ABBREVIATIONS SYMBOLS AND NOTATIONS

These are given below:

Terms	*Abb. and/or Symbols*	*Terms*	*Abb. and/or Symbols*
A		Approximate	APPROX
Abbreviation	ABB	Arrangement	ARRGT
Across comers	A/C	Assembly	ASSY
Acros flats	A/F	At	@
Alteration	ALT	Auxiliary	AUX
Angle	Angle, ∠	Auxiliary ground Plane	AGP
		Auxiliary inclined Plane	AIP
		Auxiliary reference Plane	X_1Y_1, X_2Y_2
Approved	APPD	Auxiliary vertical Plane	AVP

(Contd...)

Terms	*Abb. and/or Symbols*	*Terms*	*Abb. and/or Symbols*
B		**D**	
Bearing	BRG	Degree	Deg
British Standard	BRG	Diameter	dia, d, D, Dia, ϕ
British Standard Fine	BSF	Diametral Pich	DP
British Standard Pipe	BSP	Dimension	Dim
British Standard Whitworth	BSW	Drawing	Drg
British Association	BA	**E**	
British Standard Cycle	BS CYCLE	East	E
C		Etcetra	etc.
Centimetre	cm or CM	**F**	
Centre Line	CL	Figure	Fig. fig.
Centre plane	CP	Foot, or Feet	Ft. ft
Centres	CRS	**G**	
Centre of Centre	C to C or C/C	General	GEN
Cente of Gravity	CG	Ground level	GL
Centre of vision	C	Ground line	GL
Chamfered	CHMED	Ground Plane	GP
Channel	[	**H**	
Checked	CHKD	Head	HD
Cheese head	CH HD	Hexagon or Hexagonal	Hex
Circle	Cire	Hexagonal Head	Hex HD
Circular Pitch	CP	Horizontal	Horz
Circumference	Circ, Oce	Horizontal Plane	HP
Column	COL	Horizontal Trace	HT
Constant	CONST	Horizontal Line	HL
Compared	COMP	Hydraulic	HYD
Contined	CONTD	**I**	
Counterbore	C BORE	Imperical Standard Wire Gauge	SWG
Countersunk	CSK	Inch or Inches	in
Countersunk head	CSK HD	Indian Standard	IS
Cube or Cubic	CU	Inside Diameter	ID I/D
Cylinder of Cylinderical	Cyl	Inspection	INSP
		Insulation	INSUL

(Contd...)

Terms	*Abb. and/or Symbols*	*Terms*	*Abb. and/or Symbols*
It is recommended that the word 'ditto' or its equivalent abbreviations should not be used on drawings.		**R**	
		Radius	rad, r, R, Rad, RAD
L		Reference	Ref
Left Hand	LH	Reference line	XY
Length	Li	Required	Reqd
Long	LG	Right angle	Rt. angle, L
M		Right Hand	RH
Machine/Machinary	M/C	Rivet	rvt
Machined	M/cd	Round	RD
Manufacturing	MFG	Round Head	Rd Hd
Material	MATL	Rolled Steel Joist or Section	RSJ or I
Maximum	Max.	**S**	
Mechanical	MECH	Screw/Screwed	SCR
Metre	m	Screw Threads	
Millimetre	mm	Serial number	SL NO.
Minute (or angle)		Sheet	SH
Modification	MOD	Sketch	SK
N		South	S
Nominal	NOM	Specification	SPEC
Not to scale	NTS	Spot face	SF
Number	NO	Square	sq or Sq
North	N	Square Head	Sq HD
O		Standard	STD
Opposite	OPP	Standard Wire Gauge	SWG
Outside Diameter	OD	Station Point	SP
P		Symetrical (in a note)	SYM
Perpendicular	PA, ⊥	System International	SI
Pitch Circle	PC	**T**	
Pitch Circle Diameter	PCD	Tee	T
Picture Plane, Profile Plane	PP	Temperature	TEMP
Plate	PL	Thick	THK
Q		Thread	THD
Quantity	QTY	Thread per centimetre	TPC

(Contd...)

Terms	*Abb. and/or Symbols*	*Terms*	*Abb. and/or Symbols*
Through	THRU	US National Coarse (Sellers)	USNC
Tolerance	TOL	US National Fine (SAE)	USNF
Traced	ted	**V**	
Typical	TYP	Vartical Plane	VP
U		Vertical Trace	VT
Undercut (in a note)	U/C	**W**	
Unified Coarse	UNC	Weight	WT
Unified Fine	UNF	West	W
Unified Special	UNS	With reference toss	
		With reference to (in a note)	WRT

MATERIALS

Metals (Ferrous)		*Metals (Ferrous)*	
Cast Iron	CI	Brass	Br
Cast Steel	CS	Bronze	Bronze
Forged Steel	FS	Copper	Cpr/Cu
Mild Steel	MS	Gun Metal	GM
Spring Steel	Sp. S	Phosphor Bronze	Phor. B
Aluminium	Al	White Metal	WM
		Zinc	Zn

A, B, C, etc. To represent a point/line ends/solid corners in space

a, b, c, etc. To represent top view of a point/line ends/solid corners

a′, b′, c′, etc. To represent front view of a point/line ends/solid corners

A′, B′, C′, etc. To represent perspective view of a point/line ends/solid corners

θ-True inclination of a line with HP

ϕ-True inclination of a line with VP

α-Apparent inclination of a line with HP

β-Apparent inclination of a line with VP

OTHER IMPORTANT ABBREVIATIONS

AC	Alternating current
DC	Direct current
C/S	Cycle Per Second
DB	Distribution Board
DPIC	Double pole Iron Clad
EMF	Electromotive Force
HT	High Tension
HP	Horse Power
KW	Kilo Watt
KVA	Kilo volt Ampere
KWH	Kilo Watt Hour
LV	Low Voltage
LT	Low Tension
MV	Medium Voltage.
MW	Megha Watt
NL	Neutral Link
RPM	Revolution Per minute
Sh	Shunt
Se	Series.
T.P.IC	Triple Pole iron clad
P.d.	Potential difference
V	Volt
A	Ampere
MMF	Magnets Motive force
PH	Phase.

WEIGHTS AND MEASURE

LINEAR MEASURE	*LINEAR MEASURE*
	SQUARE MEASURE
10 millimetres = 1 centimetre	100 sq. millimetres = 1 sq. centimetre
10 centimetres = 1 decimetre	100 sq. centimetres = 1 sq. decimetre
10 decimetres = 1 metre	100 sq. decimetres = 1 sq. metre
10 metres = 1 decametre	100 sq. metres = 1 sq. decimetre
10 decametres = 1 hectometre	100 sq. decametres = 1 sq. hectometre
10 hectometres = 1 kilometre	100 sq. hectometres = 1 sq. kilometres

(Contd...)

LINEAR MEASURE			*LINEAR MEASURE*		
CUBIC MEASURES			1 sq. kilometre	=	247.105 acres
1000 cu. millimetres		1 cu. centimetre	1 sq. kilometre	=	0.3861 sq. miles.
1000 cu. centimetres		1 cu. decimetre			
1000 cu. decimetres		1 cu. metre	12 inches	=	1 foot
LIQUID MEASURES			3 feet	=	1 yard
10 milliletres	=	1 centilitre	22 yards	=	1 chain
10 centilitres	=	1 decilitre	10 chains	=	1 furlong
10 decilitres	=	1 litre	10 furlongs	=	1 mile
10 litres	=	1 decalitre	*SQUARE MEASURE*		
10 decalitres	=	1 hectalitre	144 sq. inches	=	1 sq. ft.
10 hectolitres	=	1 kilolitre	9 sq. feet	=	1 sq. yard
WEIGHTS			1210 sq. yards	=	1 rood
10 milligrams	=	1 centigram	4 roods	=	1 aeres (4840 sq. yards)
10 centigrams	=	1 decigram			
10 decigrams	=	1 gram	640 acres	=	1 sq. mile
10 grams	=	1 decagram	*CUBIC MEASURE*		
10 decagrams	=	1 hectogram	1728 cu. inches	=	1 cu. Foot
10 hectograms	=	1 kilograms	27 cu. feet	=	1 cu. Yard
10 kilograms	=	1 quintal	128 cu. feet	=	1 cord (Wood)
10 quintal	=	1 ton	40 cu. feet	=	1 ton (Shipping)
1000 kilograms	=	1 ton	215042 cu. inches	=	1 U.S Standard Gal
METRIC QUIVALENTS (LENGTH)			1 cu. foot	=	About 4/5 of a Bushel
1 millimetre	=	0.03937 inches	*LIQUID MEASURE*		
1 centimetre	=	0.3937 inches	60 minims	=	1 fluid drachm
1 metre	=	39.3701 inches	8 fluid drachms	=	1 fluid ounce
1 metre	=	3.808 ft.	40 fluid ounces	=	1 pint
1 metre	=	1.0936 yards	2 pints	=	1 quart
1 metre	=	0.54681 fathoms	4 quarts	=	1 gallon
1 kilometre	=	0.62137 miles (land)	*AVOIRDUPOIS WEIGHT*		
AREA			16 drams	=	1 ounce
1 sq. millimetre	=	0.00155 sq. inches	16 ounces	=	1 pound
1 sq. centimetre	=	0.155 sq. inches	14 pounds	=	1 stone
1 sq. metre	=	10.7639 sq. ft.	28 pounds	=	1 quarter
1 sq. metre	=	1.19399 sq. yards	4 quarters	=	1 cwt
1 hectare	=	2.17105 acres	20 cwts	=	1 ton (2240 Ibs)
			2000 pounds	=	1 short ton
			2240 pounds	=	1 longs ton

❑❑❑

PART IV

AUTOCAD

1

COMPUTER-AIDED DRAFTING

1.1 INTRODUCTION TO COMPUTER

Computer is an electronic machine that can perform mathematical and logical calculations and data processing functions in accordance with a predetermined programme of instructions.

Computer is now affecting every sphere of human activities and have become an indispensible necessity in contemporary society. It brings many changes in industries, government agencies, education society, medicine, scientific research, social science and even in art like music and painting. The areas of computer applications are almost literally too numerous to mention. Computers have become an integeral part of men in every day life. Engineers and scientists make use of the high speed computing capability of computer to solve their research, design buildings, bridges and machines etc. It helps in automation of many industrial and business system. They are extensively used in manufacturing and processing industries power distribution system, air lines control and railway reservation system and banking system. Trunk monitoring (ATMs) let us conduct banking transaction, anywhere in the world. Computer-aided design (CAD) and computer-aided manufacturing (CAM) are becoming popular among the large industrial establishment. Modelling and simulation is another area where computers are widely used.

1.2 COMPUTER-AIDED DRAFTING

In engineering field, computer-aided drafting (CADr) or computer-aided design (CAD) has been utilized in different fields of engineering and science. Use of computers to accomplish the task of producing drawings originated in 1960s by launching a sketching programme called sketch pad. Sketch pad is the first computer package that allowed engineers for the first time to generate drawings using an interactive computer graphic terminal with the help of key board and light pen. Computer Aided-Design has become a significent and necessary factor in modern engineering industries. It is almost impossible to think of any engineering project without involving this technology. Manufacturing of a product is the main activity in engineering profession. The design of a product may start with trial design in the form of sketches on the paper. As the design improves and under goes changes, the final form of design must be the scaled manufacturing drawing with finer details included. These drawings are two-dimensional and three-dimensional.

An engineering drawing may be prepared by means other than the use of conventional tools. Traditionally, drafting instruments have been used. The popular alternative now is to prepare the drawing with the aid of a computer. This method is known as computer-aided design or computer aided drafting.

Definition of CAD: Computer-Aided Design can be defined as, the process of preparing a drawing of an object on the screen of a computer. In other words, it can be defined as the use of computer system to assist in creation, modification, analysis or optimization of design.

CAD is not suitable for design/drawing concept. It is only a tool that can be used to supplement traditional tools. The underlying basic concept in engineering practice are orthographic projection, isometric projection, section of solids etc. There are various types of drawings required in engineering practice such as in the field of mechanical engineering drawing, the drawing of machine components and layout are prepared. The use of CADr process provides enhanced graphics capabilities which allows any designer to:

- Concept utilize his ideas
- Modify the design very easily
- Perform animation
- Make design calculation.

In latest CAD system, intreractive computer graphic (ICG) is used. The ICG denotes a user oriental system in the computer is employed to create, transform and display data in the form of picture. The image is constructed out of the basic geometric element points, lines, circles etc. It can be modified according to the commands, enlarged, reduced in size, moved to another location on screen, rotated and other transformation are also performed.

Application of CAD: CADr applications in various fields of engineering are as follows:

- Mechanical : Design of machine elements, CNC machine tools, Robots etc.
- Automotive : Kinematics, Hydroulics, Steering etc.
- Electrical : Circuit layout, Panel design, Control system etc.
- Electronics : Schematic diagrams of PCs, ICs etc.
- Communication : Communication network, Satellite transmitting picture etc.
- Civil and architectural : Mapping, Building drawing, Structural design, Town planning, Interior decorations, Multi-storeyed complex etc.
- Aerospace : Design of spacecraft, Flight simulator lofting etc.
- Automated-design : Automatic dimensioning, Generation of cross-hatched area, Scaling of drawing, Developed section view and Enlarged view in details etc.
- Geometric modelling : Generation of points, Lines and Circles, Rotation of objects etc.

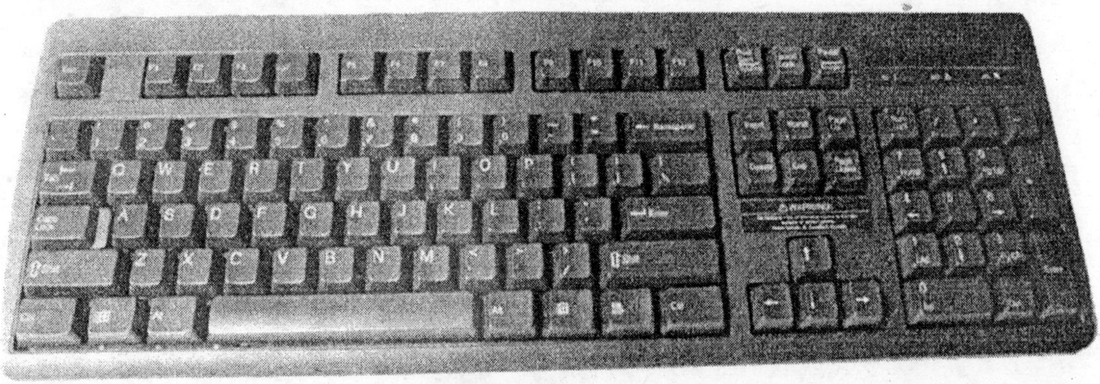

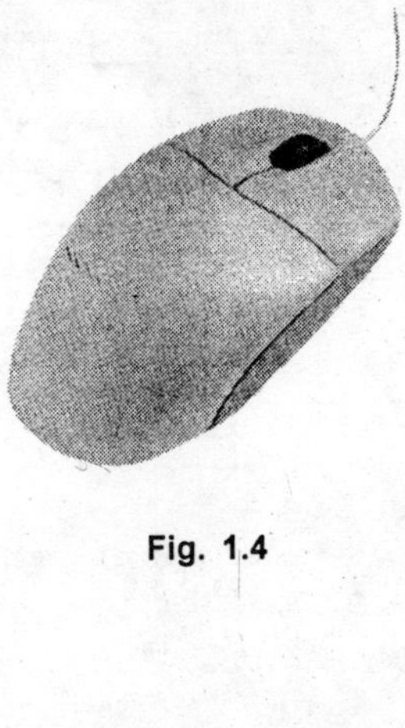

1.3 ELEMENTS OF A COMPUTER

The computer system consists of the hardware and software to perform the specialized design function required by the particular user firm.

The CAD hardware typically includes the computer graphics display terminal, key-board, mouse, touch pad, touch screen and other peripheral equipments.

The CAD software consists of the computer program to implement computer graphics on the system plus application programes to facilitate the engineering functions of the user company.

1.4 HARDWARE

For a computer to be of any use there must be a means of giving to it information to process (input), instructions for the method of processing (programs) and a means of retrieving the results (output).

A typical CAD system will include one or more input, output and storage devices, as well as the central processing unit, the arrangement at which an engineer works is known as a "workstation". Workstation are usually net-worked together so that everyone works with a common and readily accessible catalog of drawing and design data as shown in Fig. 1.1.

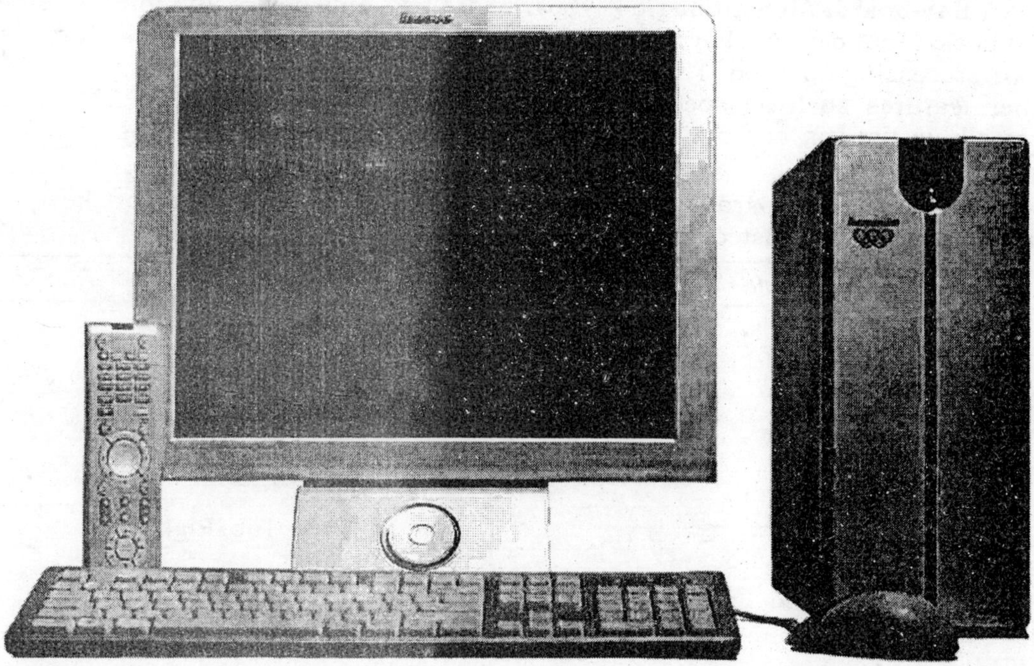

Fig. 1.1

Fig. 1.2 shows a block diagram of hardware element of a computer.

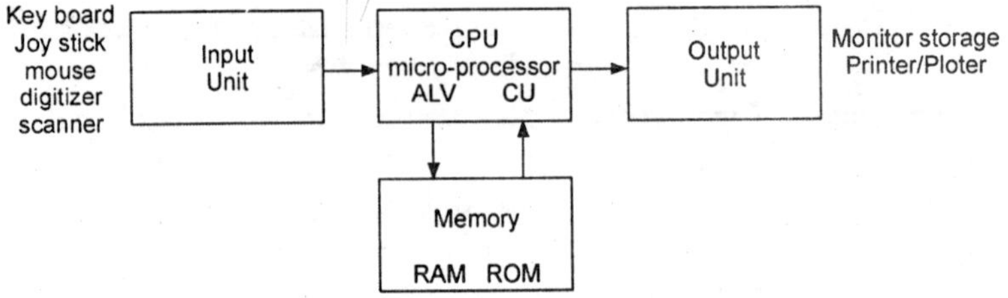

Fig. 1.2

1.5 INPUT DEVICE

The computer can only accept electronic signals as information, but there are a surprising number of ways of producing the necessary signals. Some of these devices are as follows:

- Key board (Alphanumeric)
- Mouse
- Joy stick
- Digitzer
- Scanner.

(i) Key-board: Alphanumeric keyboards are text-only device and form an essential and basic input device. They are typically employed to create/edit programs to perform word processing function. They are usually similar to a typewriter, but it may include other features such as special function keys or a number keypad. The keyboard typically is used in one or two ways. It is used for writing-either programs or word processing.

There are some extra keys in keyboard which are called function keys. These functional keys are listed below.

Function Key	*Description*
F_1	Online Help
F_2	Text/Graphics screen
F_3	Running snap
F_4	Tablet On/Off
F_5	Isoplane Top/Right/Left
F_6	Coordinates On/Off
F_7	Grid On/Off
F_8	Ortho On/Off
F_9	Snap On/Off

These function keys are used to perform some special functions in particular softwares. For example, F1 is used for help in most of the softwares, F9 is used to control snap in AutoCAD.

The speed of the inputting data with the keyboard is a function of the ability to use the keyboard as shown in Fig. 1.3.

Fig. 1.3

***(ii)* Mouse:** Mouse is another graphics input device. This simple device usually has two or three buttons. The mouse is moved on a flat surface known as "mouse pad". It consists of two small wheels which rotate when the mouse moves on the surface. Nowadays most of the mouse we are using are optical mouse. They have a sensor at their bottom which controls its speed and precision. In laptops, the alternative of mouse is touchpad. The functions of the touchpad is same as mouse. Touch screen monitors are also used nowadays as input devices. Although they are not extensively used in CAD systems today.

In Auto-CAD, button one (left button) on mouse device is the pick button. We use the pick button to select the commands from the side screen or pull down menus. Select menu items and select the dialog box items as shown in Fig. 1.4.

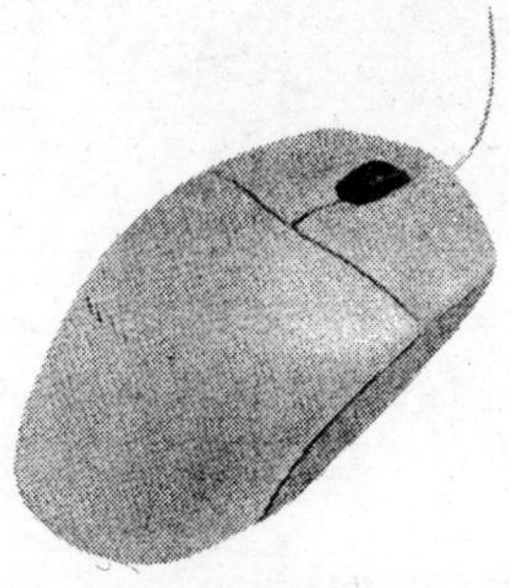

Fig. 1.4

(*iii*) Joystick: Basically it is a device used to locate the position of the cursor on the screen. It should be moved in the same direction as you wish the cursor. Their concept of operation is very similar to that of the mechanical mouse discussed in the above section. Joystics are suitable for faster display system and have become very popular in the home computer market. In CAD system they are most effectively used in conjunction with screen-display type menu facilities as shown in Fig. 1.5.

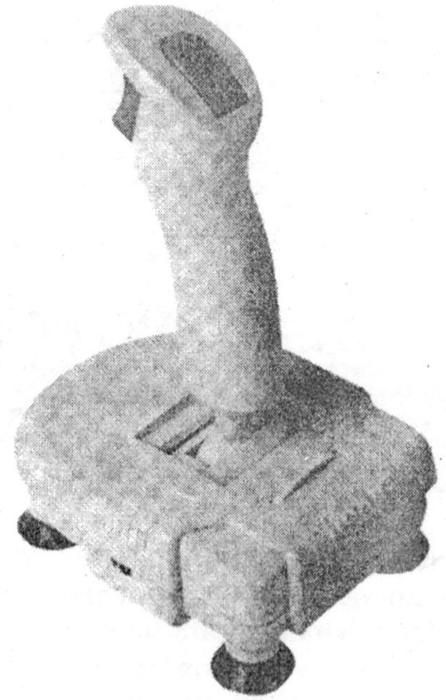

Fig. 1.5

(*iv*) Scanner: The scanner is an input device. It is used to make an exact copy of a picture or photograph which is displayed on the monitor as shown in Fig. 1.6.

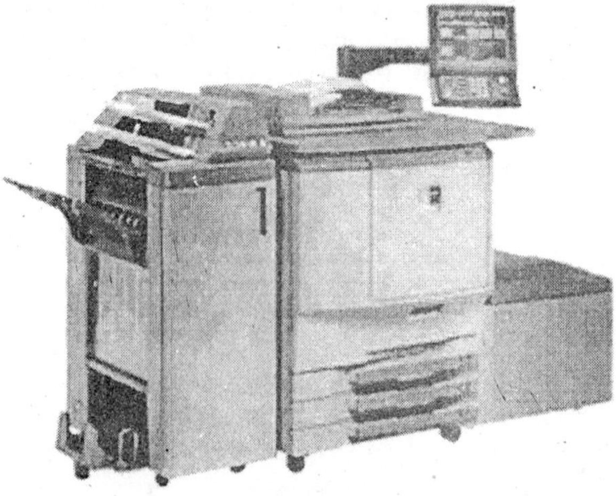

Fig. 1.6

1.6 PROCESSOR UNIT

***(i)* Central Processing Unit (CPU):** All the arithmetic operations, taking decision and control of all computer devices is done by central processing unit. It comprises of an arithmetic section for computations and a primary storage section for holding the instruction and related data for processing.

***(ii)* Arithmetic Logic Unit (ALU):** It does all calculations and makes decisions on the given information. It is that part of the central processing unit that performs arithmetic and logic operations. This comprises of a number of registers. A register is placed within the arithmetic, logic unit, where instructions or data are held temporarily.

***(iii)* Control Unit:** It controls all the computer devices. It interprets source information to target information. It controls input and output devices and also memory units. It is that part of the processors which is responsible for controlling sequence of operations.

(iv) Memory: A memory or store is required in a computer to store programs and the data processed by programmes. A memory is made up of a large number of cells, with each cell capable of storing on bit. The memory unit is called by different names, such as storage, internal storage, primary storage, main memory or simple memory. It can be classified into two groups.

(*a*) Main memory

(*b*) Storage memory.

***(v)* Read Only Memory (ROM):** These are random access memories in which data words are permanently written during fabrication.

A word can later be read from the memory by specifying its address. The content of the word cannot, however be altered such a memory reading from a ROM should be non-destruction the memory also should be non-volatile.

***(vi)* Random Access Memory (RAM):** It is a volatile memory used for temporary storage once the computer is shut off, everything stored in the memory is wiped out.

RAM is also the working memory and the primary memory since all the data and information goes to the memory chip first before being sent to the ALU for further work.

***(vii)* Output Device:** The purpose of this unit is to produce the results of the software. The output from a computer is usually either on the screen (soft copy) or on paper (hard copy) Hard copy may be on a printer on plotter etc. There are various types of output devices used for CAD are as follows:

1. Monitor
2. Plotter or Printers
3. Storage.

***(viii)* Monitor:** Monitor looks like a home television system. Various sizes of the monitor are available in the market as (30/35/48cm). The monitor screens may be monochrome or colour. They are used in text mode or graphics mode although some terminals and a few micro-computers do not have a graphics mode. Various display technologies are now available to the user to choose from among the available technologies, the CRT (Cathode ray tube) is the most dominating and has produced a wide range of extremely effective graphic displays. Other technologies such as LCD (Liquid Crystal Display) which produces low energy 'Low-glave, space efficiency flat screens.

The screen is divided into horizontal and vertical directions into a large number of picture element called pixels, the higher the number of pixel, the better will be the appearance of the picture as shown in Fig. 1.7.

Fig. 1.7

(*ix*) Printers or Plotters: Printer or plotters are used for printing of final drawing and documentation on paper. It gives a hard copy for permanent record of alpha-numeric commands on paper. Several types of plotters have been developed for CAD systems, the most popular variety of printer is laser printer as shown in Fig. 1.8.

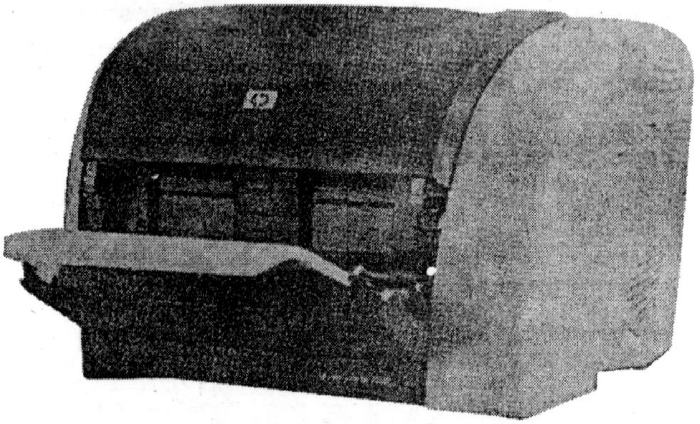

Fig. 1.8

(*x*) Storage: The computer uses primary and secondary storage systems for the information that it processes. The primary system consists of solid-state chips which are volatile, that is the information is stored as electrical charges which are lost when the power is turned off. Other types of primary memory chips are PROMS and EPROMS. Both are ROM chips, which may be programmed by the user. The secondary storage system differs from the primary storage by being more or less permanent.

Secondary storage is also much larger, and takes longer to access, when compared to primary storage, secondary storage is also shared by different users of course.

A RAM disk is a hybrid memory form. It is a volatile memory installed on a board in chip form like RAM, unlike RAM it is used as a temporary secondary storage because it can be accessed much more quickly than any disk system.

1.7 CADD SOFTWARE

Software communication is a pattern of code called a language. The most primitive language is called machine code, which speaks, directly to the hardware equipment in either binary (two digit) signals. The writing of software is made much less involved with the aid of high level languages which are used in most areas of CADD.

Software usually consists of a number of separate application package to perform the desired function. The size of computer depends on the number and size of packages and number of workstations.

A wide range of standard software is available and generally it is not worth developing users own software. Basically a software is an interpreter which allows the user to perform specific type of application related to CAD software. There are a number of 2D drafting software packages available in the market. AutoDesk, makers of AutoCAD is a leader in the 2D engineering CADD software industry. Although this course will focus on AutoCAD, there are other CADD software, packages available. They include:

1. Corel Draw
2. CAD Std
3. Pro CAD$^+$
4. Accucadd
5. CADD5
6. CADD 2002
7. Vector Engineer
8. Dexterpen
9. Corel CAD.

All the above software are capable of creating drafting, but many of them do not have as many features as AutoCAD. The most important characteristic of CAD software is its three dimensional associative centralized and integrated data base known as 3D drafting. Such a data base is always rich in information needed in design. Various 3D modeling packages are:

1. Pro\E
2. Unigraphics
3. CATIA
4. Ideas
5. SolidWorks
6. Solidedge.

Application software includes drafting and dimensioning software. 3D geometric modelling, surface modelling, solid modelling etc.

1.8 AUTOCAD

AutoCAD is a very popular software package that provides computer-aided design and drafting (CADD) capabilities for micro computers. It is a comprehensive software application that facilitates almost all varieties of 2D drawing, such as electrical, mechanical, plumbing, Air-conditioning, architectural etc. AutoCAD has introduced 3D drawings and has started in corporating the internet and network support.

AutoCAD is accepted as the industry standard and it is preferred by a large community of CAD users in the world. Although AutoCAD is available for a variety of computer systems, majority of AutoCAD implementations are available on IBM or compatible personal computers with MS-DOS operating system. AutoCAD can be used with many engineering design programmes and can be used separately if needed.

Autodesk, US based developer of "AutoCAD software" is the world leading supplier of computer-aided design and drawing software packages. Since its inception in 1982, the company has introduced a family of software packages for use in a wide range of industries. It has hit the technical world like a shock wave, revolutionizing the manner of drawing preparation.

Application: AutoCAD package is suitable for accurate and perfect drawing of engineering designs. The design of machine parts, isometric views and assembly drawings are possible in AutoCAD. This package is also suitable for 2D and 3D drawings etc.

Various Versions of AutoCAD: The first release of AutoCAD version 1.0 was in 1982 many updates and improvements were done constantly. Release of AutoCAD version-12 was introduced in 1992 and AutoCAD release-14 introduced in 1998, AutoCAD 2000 in 1999, AutoCAD 2002, upto AutoCAD 2009.

Recently AutoCAD 2008 has been launched which offers a higher level of speed, accuracy ease of use. AutoCAD 2009 is strictly a windows XP/Vista program.

1.9 SYSTEM REQUIREMENTS FOR AUTOCAD 2009

Listed below are the hardware requirements for running AutoCAD 2009 on any system.

1. Pentium 133 MHz or better
2. 64 MB RAM (32 MB minimum)
3. Windows versions, like XP, 2000, 98 and Vista.
4. 1024 × 768 VGA video display (800 × 600 VGA video display minimum)
5. 150 MB free hard-disk space (64 MB swap space).
6. Pointing device (mouse or digitizer with wintab driver)
7. 4 × CD-ROM drive
8. Printer or plotter
9. Modem (connection to Inernet).
10. Sound Card for multimedia learning.

❑❑❑

2

GETTING STARTED WITH AUTOCAD

2.1 INTRODUCTION

This chapter explains the various aspects of the AutoCAD 2008 for Window drawing screen and shows how they can be manipulated. Launching AutoCAD 2008 is very easy. Just double-click the AutoCAD shortcut. After few seconds, you would see the AutoCAD desktop in which top line displays the Window pulldown menus for exiting a program and changing program. The second line is the standard toolbar, contains a group of commands. The third line contains some command icons and an area that shows the current, or docked, object properties that are active. The line just above the drawing portion of the screen displays the name of current drawing. The bottom left corner of the screen shows the co-ordinete display position of the horizontal, vertical crosshairs in terms of an X, Y co-ordinate value. The commands listed on the bottom line display the horizontal and vertical scroll bars that can be used to move the drawing screen up and down, left and right etc.

2.2 STARTING AUTOCAD

When a user start the computer, the operating systems such as Microsoft, Windows Vista™, Windows XP Home and Window Vista 64-bit will be automatically loaded on it and the Windows screen will be displayed with a number of application icons. Start AutoCAD by double-clicking on the AutoCAD 2008 icon on the desktop of the computer as shown in Fig. 2.1. After a few moments, AutoCAD 2008 Windows appear on screen as shown in Fig. 2.2.

2.3 AUTOCAD SCREEN COMPONENTS

The various components of the initial AutoCAD screen are the drawing area, command windows, menu bar, several toolbars, model and the states bar as shown in Fig. 2.2.

1. Drawing Area

It covers the major portion of the screen as shown in Fig. 2.2. Here, user can draw the objects and use the commands. To draw the objects, user need to define the coordinate points which can be selected by using pointing device. The position of the pointing device is represented on the screen by the help of cursor. There is a coordinate system icon at the lower left corner of the drawing area. The window also has the standard Window buttons such as close, minimize and so on the top right corner.

2. Command Window

The command window is at the bottom of the drawing area has the command prompt where we can enter the commands. It also display the subsequent prompt sequences and the massages as shown in Fig. 2.2.

3. Pull-down Menus

We can also select commands from the menu. The menu bar that displays the menu bar is at the top of the screen. If we move the cursor over the menu bar, different titles are *highlighted*. These menu hold all the commands and functions that are the heart of the AutoCAD.

These menus hold all the commands and functions that are the heart of the AutoCAD.

The best example of that are shown in Fig. 2.3. These menus can be used by clicking on menu item and then selecting appropriate commands such as:

(*i*) **File:** This menu includes file new, file open, file save, print, copy, paste etc.

(*ii*) **Edit:** This menu provides commands from interfacing with the other windows application.

(*iii*) **View:** Shows the most commonly used display commands.

(*iv*) **Insert:** Lets you to insert various blocks.

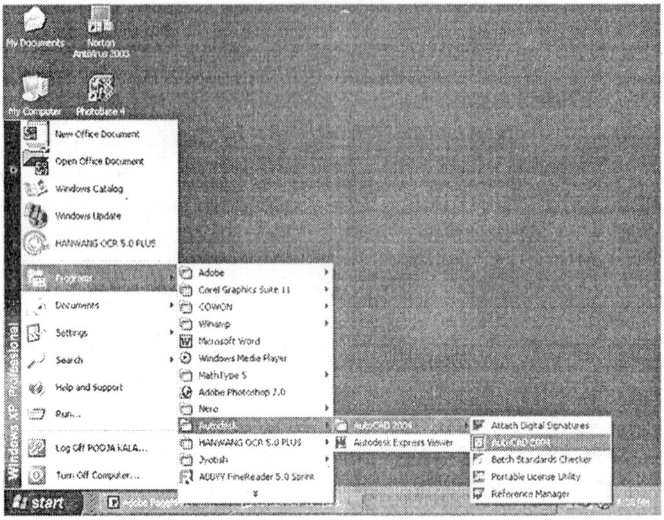

Fig. 2.1

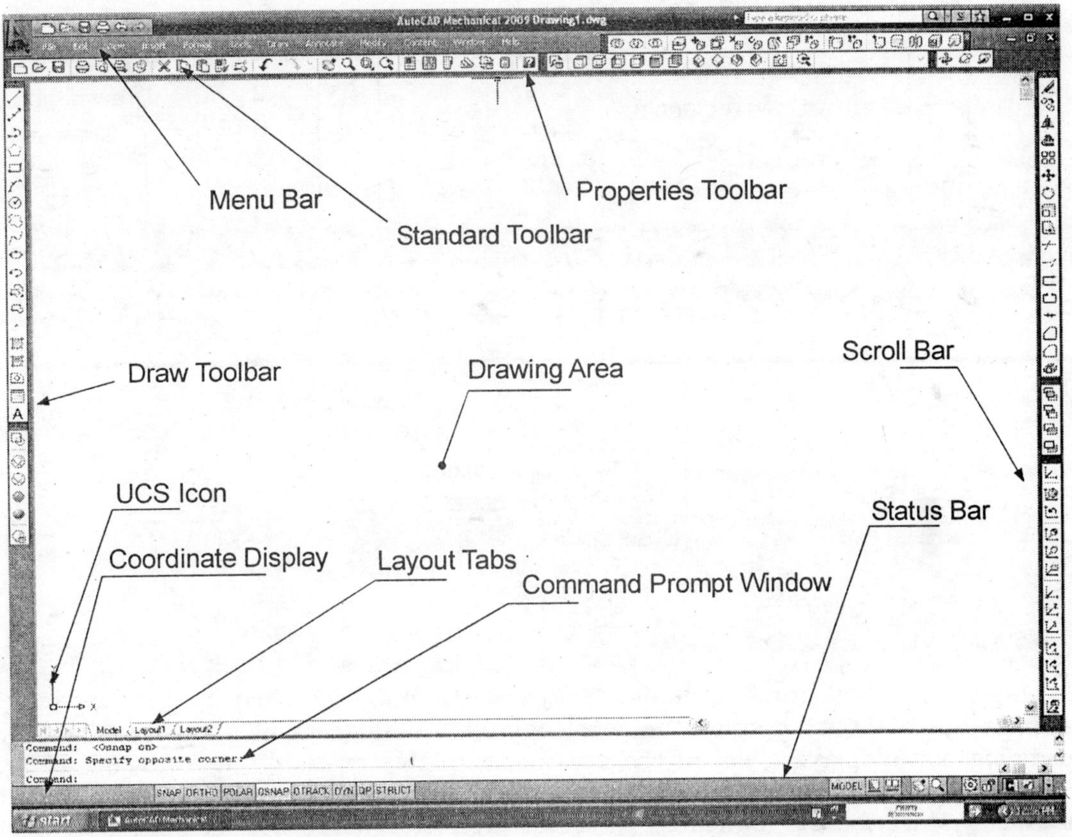

Fig. 2.2

(*v*) **Format:** You can change fonts.

(*vi*) **Tool:** Various tools available which support drawing.

(*vii*) **Draw:** Lets you to select various draw commands.

(*vii*) **Dimension:** It provides dimension to the existing drawing.

(*ix*) **Modify:** Provision of changes in the existing drawing.

(*x*) **Help:** It has on the line help for AutoCAD. The entire manual is contained in this context sensitive windows based help system.

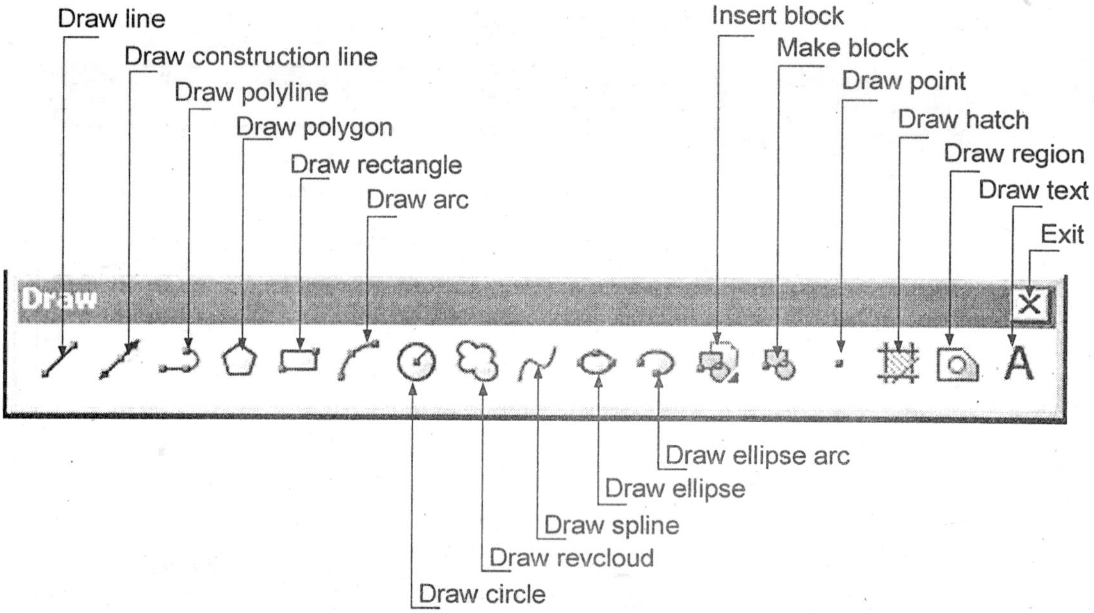

Fig. 2.3

2.4 STARTING A NEW DRAWING

User can open a new drawing using the Q New Command. When a user invoke it, by default AutoCAD will display the select template dialog box as shown in Fig. 2.4. This dialog box displays a list of the default templates available in AutoCAD 2009. The default template is acad.dwt, which starts the 2D drawing or select the acad3D.dwt template to start the 3D modeling. Alternatively, select any other template to start a new drawing, which will use the settings of the selected templates.

Quit/Exit: Quits AutoCAD if there have been no changes in all opened drawing since the drawing were last saved. If the drawing has been modified, AutoCAD displays the drawing modification dialog box to prompt user to save or discard the changes before quiting.

2.5 SAVING

In AutoCAD or any computer system, save same your work before exit from the drawing editor or turnoff the system. It is also recommended to save your drawings after regular time of internal, so that in the event of a power failure.

AutoCAD has provided the SAVE commands that allows the user to save their work on the hard disk of the computer. User may choose save from the file menu, or the save button in the standard toolbar. If the current drawing is unnamed and the user save the drawing for the first time, the SAVE command will prompt the user to enter the file name in the Save Drawing. As dialog box shown in Fig. 2.5. User can enter the name for the drawing and then choose the save button. This allows the user to do a quick save.

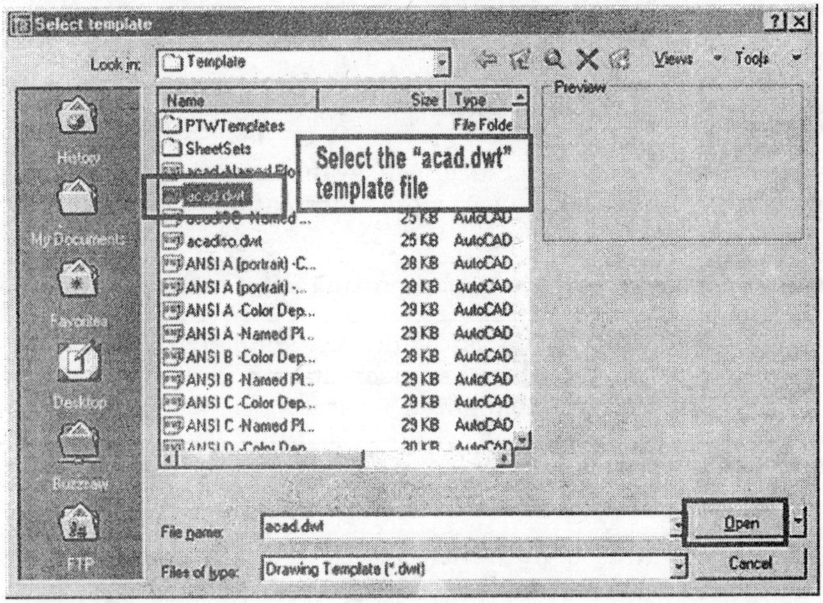
Select template
Look in:
Template
Views
Tools
Name
Size
Type
Preview
PTWTemplates
File Folde
SheetSets
Select the "acad.dwt" template file
acad.dwt
acadiso.dwt
25 KB
AutoCAD
ANSI A (portrait) -C...
28 KB
AutoCAD
ANSI A (portrait) -...
28 KB
AutoCAD
ANSI A -Color Dep...
29 KB
AutoCAD
ANSI A -Named Pl...
29 KB
AutoCAD
ANSI B -Color Dep...
28 KB
AutoCAD
ANSI B -Named Pl...
29 KB
AutoCAD
ANSI C -Color Dep...
29 KB
AutoCAD
ANSI C -Named Pl...
29 KB
AutoCAD
History
My Documents
Favorites
Desktop
Buzzsaw
FTP
File name:
acad.dwt
Open
Files of type:
Drawing Template (*.dwt)
Cancel

Fig. 2.4

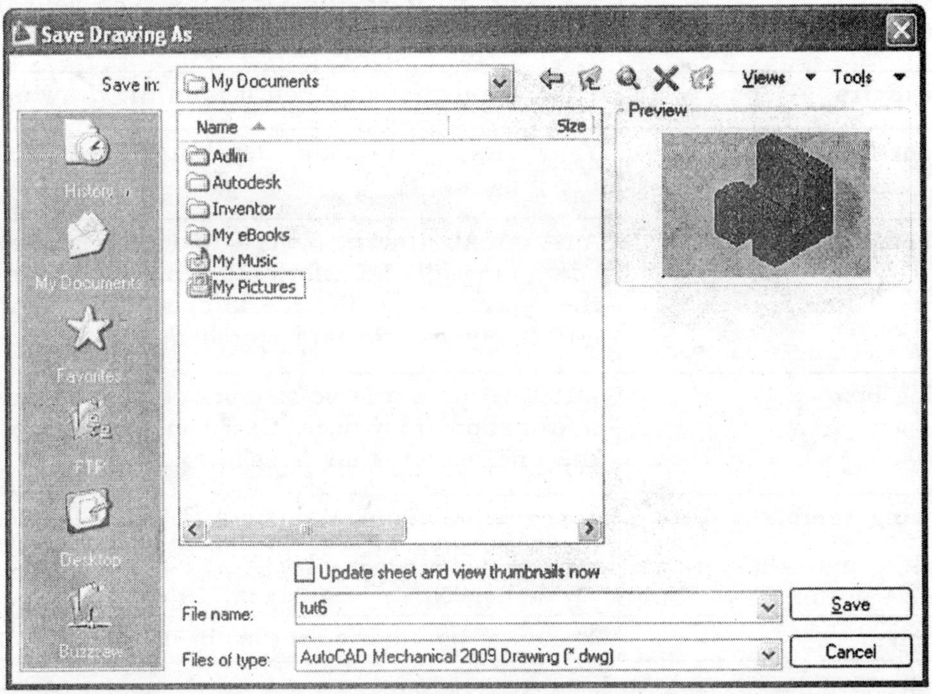
Save Drawing As
Save in:
My Documents
Views
Tools
Name
Size
Preview
Adlm
Autodesk
Inventor
My eBooks
My Music
My Pictures
History
My Documents
Favorites
FTP
Desktop
Buzzsaw
Update sheet and view thumbnails now
File name:
tut6
Save
Files of type:
AutoCAD Mechanical 2009 Drawing (*.dwg)
Cancel

Fig. 2.5

Close: AutoCAD closes the current drawing if there have been no changes since the drawing was last saved. If user should modify the drawing, user to save or discard the changes.

2.6 BASIC AUTOCAD TERMINOLOGY

There are some basic terms that user will want to review before using AutoCAD. Some terms have links to give user more information.

Absolute co-ordinates	A way of inputting points based on AutoCAD's origin.
Acad.dwt	This is the default template that automatically loads whenever user start a drawing session. It can be customized to suit your needs.
Associated Dimensioning	Dimensions that are associated with specific points will update as that point is moved.
Backup file	AutoCAD can be set to automatically backup your drawing and save it. This is a safeguard in case your file gets corrupted. It is saved with a .BAK extension
Block	A pre-drawn image user can insert in your drawing to save time and make your file size smaller.
Crosshairs	This is your cursor when it is in the drawing space.
Cursor	Your cursor will change depending on where it is in the program.
Database	An AutoCAD drawing file is actually one large database containing all the information needed to reproduce the objects when the file is opened. Info for layers and linetypes, etc. are stored in this manner.
Dialog box	AutoCAD uses a large number of dialog boxes to get information from user. User must know how input the information that it asks for.
Drawing template file	This is a file that contains preset values for frequently used setting. AKA a prototype drawing. The file extension in DWT.
Extents	The outer boundaries of the objects user have drawn.

Grid	This is pattern of dots displayed on the screen to guide user. It can be toggled on and off by pressing the F7 key.
Layer	All objects are drawn on a layer. User can group objects (such as electrical) on a single layer and organize your drawing.
Layout Tabs	A space used for plotting your drawings (formerly called Paper Space).
Limits (Grid)	A setting to impose an 'artificial' boundary on your drawing that sets the area of the grid, and when turned on, limits user to drawing in the grid area.
Linetype	All objects are drawn with a particular linetype. Examples would be solid, centre, dashed, etc.
Model space	The drawing space where user 'model' the objects.
Modify	A generic term used for changing your objects.
Object	Any item that is in the AutoCAD database. Also known as an entity.
Origin	The (0, 0) point of your current co-ordinate system.
Orthomode	This is a drawing mode that allows user to draw only perpendicular lines. It is toggled on and off by pressing the F8 key.
Osnap-Object Snap	This is a method of 'snapping' to certain, precise points on an object.
Pan	To move around drawing by dragging the drawing area around your screen.
Path	The specific folder where AutoCAD looks for, or saves files.
Pick	To select an object by 'left-clicking' on it.
Plot	Also known as print. To make a hard copy of your drawing.
Polar co-ordinates	A way of inputting points based on distance and angle.

Property	Any specific characteristic of an object such as layer, scale, linetype, start point, etc.
Relative co-ordinates	A way of inputting points based on a starting point.
Selection set	The current group of objects selected for modifying.
Snap	This is a drawing mode that allows user to snap your cursor to precise points laid out in a grid pattern. Toggle with the F9 key.
Styles	Formatting that defines the look of text, dimensions, etc.
Units	The basic drawing unit set for your drawing. For example, user can use inches or millimeters depending on your needs. User can also set the precision you want displayed, such nearest 1/4", 1/2" 1/64", etc.
User co-ordinate system (UCS)	Modifications made to the World Co-ordinate System (WCS) results in a User Co-ordinate System (UCS)
View	A particular arca of your drawing.
Viewport	A separate 'window' on your drawing. User may have more than one viewport visible to see different areas of your drawing at the same time.
Wizard	An easy step-by-step instruction set to help user set-up certain aspects of your drawing.
World Co-ordinate System (WCS)	This is the common X-Y co-ordinate system that is the default. If it is modified, it becomes a User co-ordinate System (UCS)
Zoom	To view either a smaller section of your drawing (zoom in) or a larger section (zoom out).

2.7 BASIC AUTOCAD COMMANDS

This chapter demonstrates how to work with AutoCAD commands. AutoCAD commands are operated by using command tools, tool bars and a series of prompts. The prompts appear in the command: line box and ask for a selection or numerical input so that a command sequence can be completed. Most of the commands are contained in the draw and modify tool bars are demonstrated in this chapter. The purpose is to present enough commands for the students to be able to create simple 2-D drawings.

There are three methods of giving command to AutoCAD.

(*i*) First is on the command line

(*ii*) Second is the side screen

(*iii*) Third is from the top drop down menu.

For a beginner it is recommended to use the command line.

2.8 LIMITS

In AutoCAD, the drawings must be drawn full scale and therefore, the limits are needed to size up a drawing area. The limits of the drawing area are usually determined by the following factors.

(*i*) The actual size of the drawing.

(*ii*) The space needed for putting down the dimensions, notes, bill of materials.

(*iii*) The space for the borders and title block.

The limits command allows the user to change the upper and lower limits of the drawing area. Turn limits, checking ON or OFF.

Command: Limits (Press Enter↵)

Specify lower left corner or [ON/OFF] < 0.0000, 0.0000 > : (Press Enter↵)

Specify upper right corner < 12.0000, 9.0000 > :

Type 297,210 (Press Enter↵)

Type zoom (Press Enter↵)

Type all (Press Enter↵).

2.9 ZOOM

The zoom all command magnifies the drawing on the screen. This command is to follow limits, command in order to apply selected limits.

This command enlarges or reduces the view of the drawing on the screen, but it does not affect the actual size of the objects. In this way, the zoom command functions like the zoom lens on a camera. When the user magnify the apparent size of a section of the drawing, seen that area in greater detail. On the other hand, if the user reduce the apparent size of the drawing, seen a layer area.

Command: Zoom (press ENTER↵)

[All/centre/Dynamic/Extents/previous/scale/Window/< Real time > : All (Press Enter↵)

2.10 ENDING AUTOCAD

When user finishes using AutoCAD, Select exit from the file menu to turnoff the windows programme. Before exiting, AutoCAD if user would like to save the work discard the work or cancel command. Select the discard to exit from the AutoCAD window.

❑❑❑

IMPORTANT NOTES:

Starting with the Advanced Sketching

3.1 INTRODUCTION

Starting with the advanced sketching with 2D systems recognise only flate shapes defined by points, lines, curves contained with two-dimensional plane. 2D systems are primitive by compression with 3D system, but 2D system is sufficient for a wide variety applications and at its lower cost, is an attractive choice for many companies. The majority of CAD orthographic engineering drawings and electrical circuit drawing are created on 2D system as shown in Fig. 3.1.

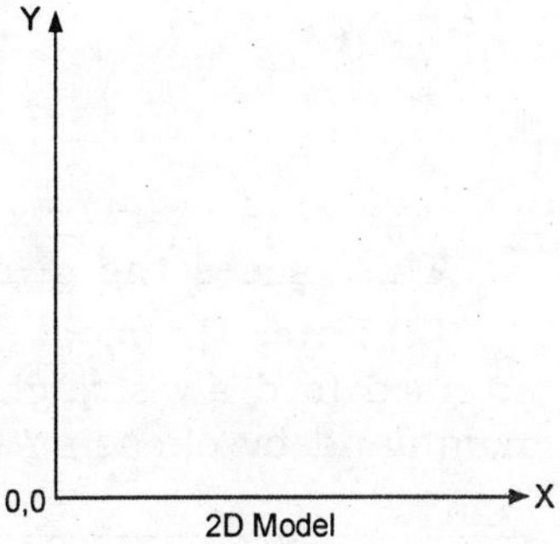

Fig. 3.1

3.2 VARIOUS COMMANDS OF 2D SYSTEM

1. Point: AutoCAD uses points to determine where an object is located. There is an origin where it begins counting from. This point is (0, 0). Every object is located in relation to the origin. If user were to draw a line straight out to the right from the origin, this would be considered the positive X-axis. If user were to draw a line straight up, this would be the positive Y-axis. Fig. 3.2 shows a point located at (8, 5). This means that the point is 8 units over in the axis and 5 units up in the Y-axis. When user are working with points, X always comes first.

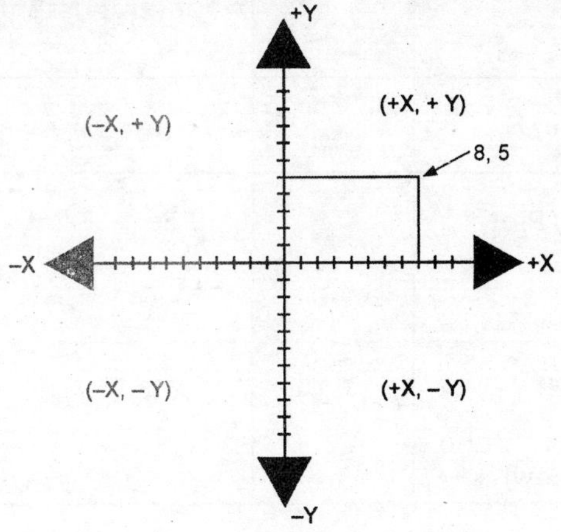

Fig. 3.2

Problem 1: Plot a point at the location (12, 10).

Solution: See Fig 3.3.

Command: Point

point (12, 10)

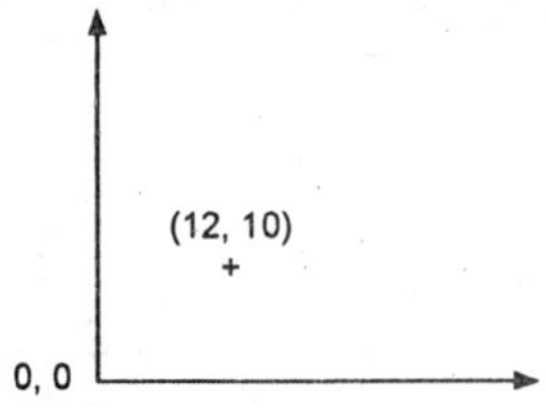

Fig. 3.3

This places the given point in the drawing at location (12, 10).

(2) Line: The most fundamental object in a drawing is the line. The line command is used to draw straight lines between two defined points. User can invoke the line command by choosing the line button from the drawn toolbar as shown in Fig. 3.4.

Command	**Keystroke**	**Icon**	**Menu**	**Result**
Line	Line/L		Draw > Line	Draw a straight line segment from one point to the next
Circle	Circle/C		Draw > Circle > Centre, Radius	Draws a circle based on a centre point and radius
Erase	Erase/E		Modify > Erase	Erases an object
Print	Print/Plot Ctrl+P		File > Print	Enables the Print/Plot Configuration Dialog Box
Undo	U (Don't use 'Undo' for now)		Edit > Undo	Undoes the last command

Fig. 3.4

Command: Line

From Point: Specify a point-P_1 or [undo]

Specify a point P_2 or [close/undo]

Press enter at the end of the LINE command.

***(i)* Undo:** User can undo the most recently drawn, line segment by entering the option U when prompts to specify next point. User can undo all the line segments drawn in reverse till the first point of the first line segment.

***(ii)* Close:** Close option joins the very last point entered with the very first point that is picked in a series of line segment that user had draw by a straight line.

Line can be drawn by anyone of the following three methods using LINE commands

(*i*) Absolute co-ordinate system

(*ii*) Relative co-ordinate system

(*iii*) Polor co-ordinate system.

(*i*) Absolute Co-ordinate System (X, Y) Symbol (Fig. 3.5)

COMMAND: LINE

Specify first point: 5, 5↵

Specify next point: 8, 5↵

Specify next point: 6, 6↵

Specify next point: C↵

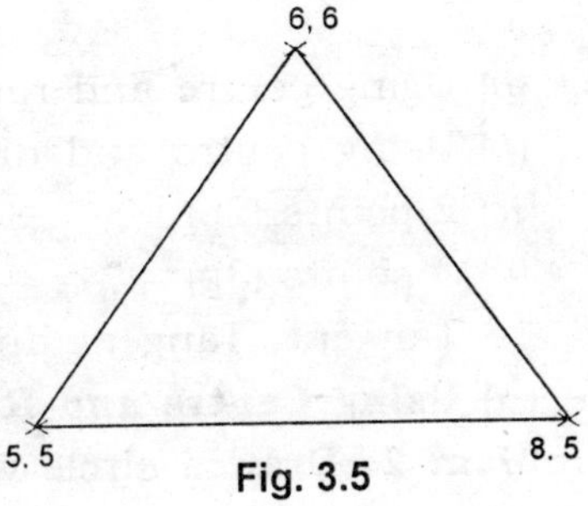

Fig. 3.5

(*ii*) Relative Co-ordinate System @ X Distance, Y Distance (Fig. 3.6)

COMMAND : LINE

Specify first point; 3, 3.↵

Specify next point: @ 6, 0↵

Specify next point: @ 0, 5↵

Specify next point: @ −3, 0↵

Specify next point: @ 0, −2↵

Specify next point: @ −3, 0↵

Specify next point: c ↵

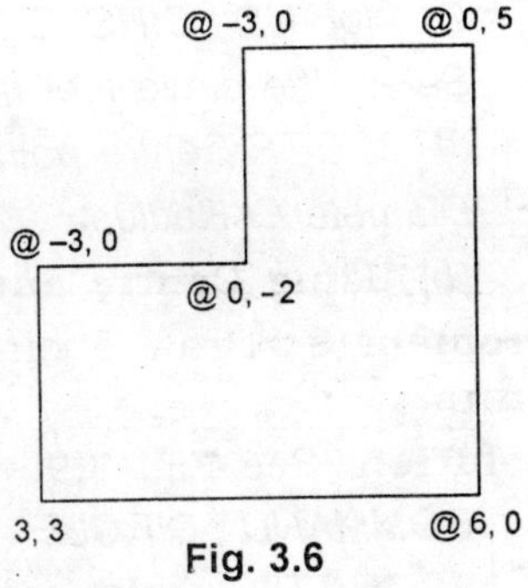

Fig. 3.6

(*iii*) Polar Co-ordinate system @ distance (angle)

Polar co-ordinate system uses a distance and an angle with reference to a previous point to locate a point. Angles are measured in anticlock direction, taking 0° towards right [Fig. 3.7].

COMMAND : LINE

Specify first point : 3, 3

Specify next point : @ 6 < 0

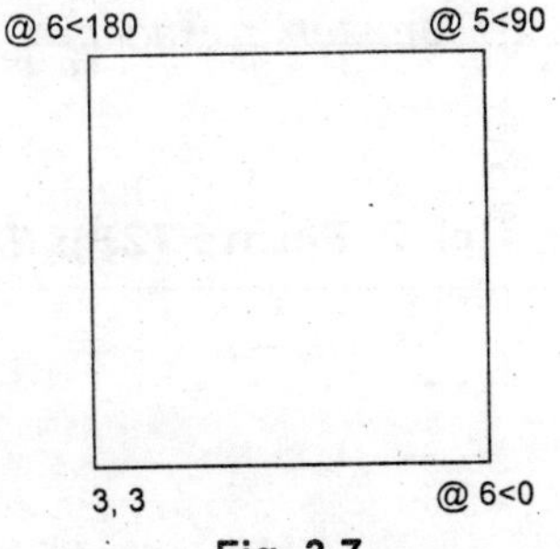

Fig. 3.7

Specify next point : @ 5 < 90

Specify next point : @ 6 < 180

Specify next point : c

(3) Curves: Following are the various types of curves used in engineering drawing:

(*i*) Circle

(*ii*) Arc

(*iii*) Ellipse

(*iv*) Regular or any other type.

(*i*) CIRCLE: With this command user can draw a circle as required. User can also invoke the circle command from the draw, toolbar, from the DASHBOARD. Circle may be defined by a center point and either a radius or diameter; by two or three points on the diameter, arc and a radius value. Following are the various methods to draw circles:

(*a*) Using centre and radius

(*b*) Using centre and diameter

(*c*) 2 points (2p)

(*d*) 3 points (3p)

(*e*) Tangent, Tangent and Radius (TTR).

(*a*) Using Centre and Radius:

Problem 2: Draw a circle with centre (5, 5) and radius 16 units

Solution: See Fig. 3.8.

COMMAND : CIRCLE

Select the circle tool from the Draw toolbar.

3P/2P/TTR/Centre point > : 5.5 ↵

Diameter/ <Radius> : 16 ↵

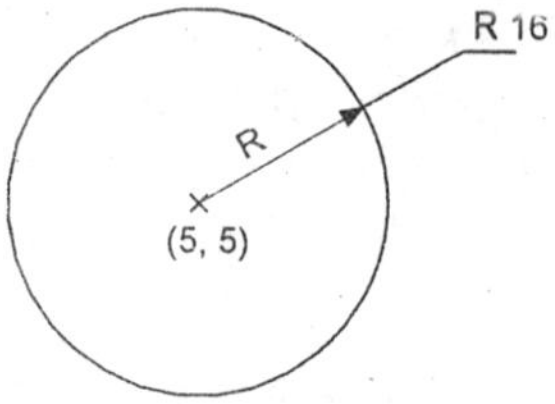

Fig. 3.8

(*b*) Using Centre and Diameter:

Problem 3: Draw a circle with centre (8, 15) and diameter 16 units

Solution: See Fig. 3.9.

COMMAND : CIRCLE

3P/2P/TTR/<centre point > : 8, 15 ↵

Diameter/ < Radius > : 16 ↵

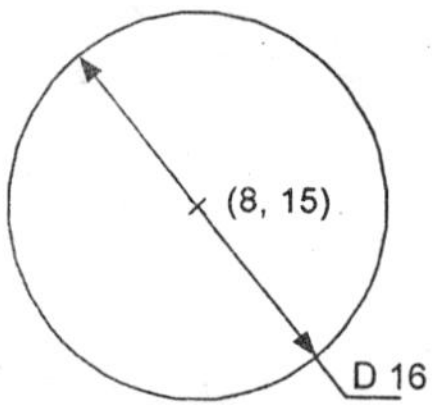

Fig. 3.9

(c) 2 Points (2P): This allows to enter two diametrically opposite points of the circle.

Problem 4: Draw a circle using the given 2 points (8, 32) and (8, 45) by entering 2nd points of the circle diameter.

Solution: See Fig. 3.10.

COMMAND : CIRCLE

3P/2P/TTR/< centre point> 16p ↵

First point on diameter: 8, 32 ↵

Second point on diameter 8, 45 ↵

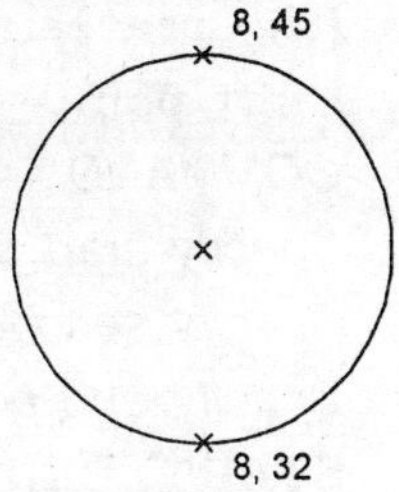

Fig. 3.10

***(d)* 3 Points:** This allows to enter any three points on the circumference of the circle.

Problem 5: Draw a circle using the given 3 points (5, 20), (5, 25) and (10, 20).

Solution: See Fig. 3.11

COMMAND : CIRCLE

3p/2p/TTR/<centre point> : 3p ↵

First point: 5, 20 ↵

Second point: 5, 25 ↵

Third point: 10, 20 ↵

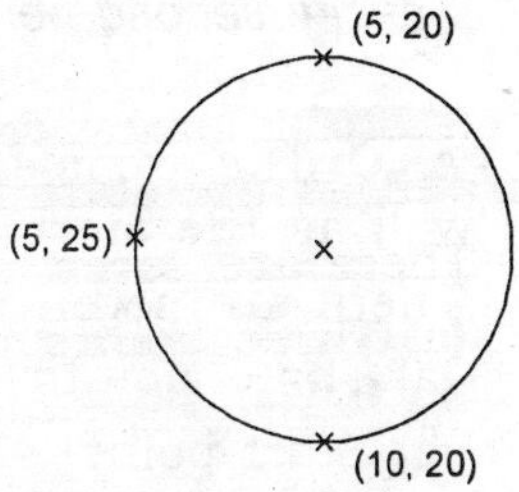

Fig. 3.11

***(e)* TTR: (Tangent, Tangent and Radius):** The tangent and radius option allows to select two objects as tangent and fits a circle between them for a specified radius.

Problem 6: Draw a circle with radius 13 units and two existing lines as tangent.

Solution: See Fig. 3.12.

Take: For line 1, from point (17, 5) to point (20, 10)

For Line 2, from point (20, 2) to point (20, 6)

COMMAND : CIRCLE

3p/2p/ TTR < centre point > : TTR ↵

Enter tangent specification : Select first object T_1, Enter second tangent specification: Select second object T_2 ↵

Radius < current > : 13 ↵

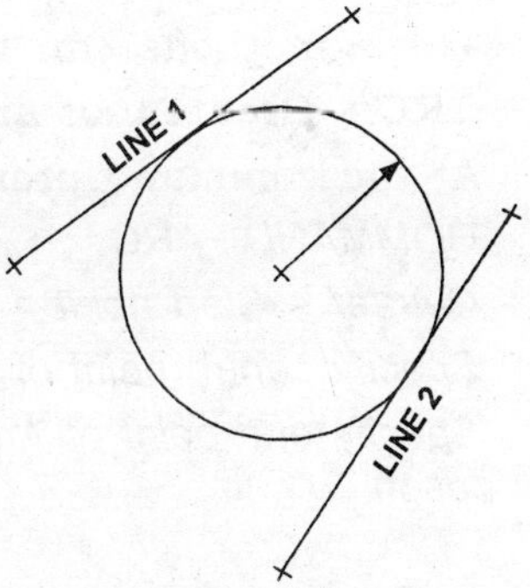

Fig. 3.12

Three points method (3 Points)

This draws an arc using three specific point along the circumference of the arc. The first and the third points form the end points of the arc. The second points can be any point on the circumference of the arc.

Solution: See Fig. 3.13.

COMMAND : ARC

Centre / < Start point > : Specify start point ↵

Centre/End/ < Second point > specify second point ↵

End point : Specify third point ↵

Fig. 3.13

(*ii*) Creates an Arc

Start point— This specifies the start point of an arc.

COMMAND : ARC

Specify start point of Arc or [centre]: use one of the point fixing method ↵

Specify second point of Arc or [centre/End]: use one of the point fixing methods ↵

Specify end point of Arc: use one of the point fixing method ↵

START, CENTRE METHOD

• *CENTRE – specifies the centre of the arc segment [Fig. 3.14].*

COMMAND : ARC

Specify second point of Arc or [Centre/End] : CE ↵

ARC: The arc is a curve specified of centre and radius as well as the start angles and end angles.

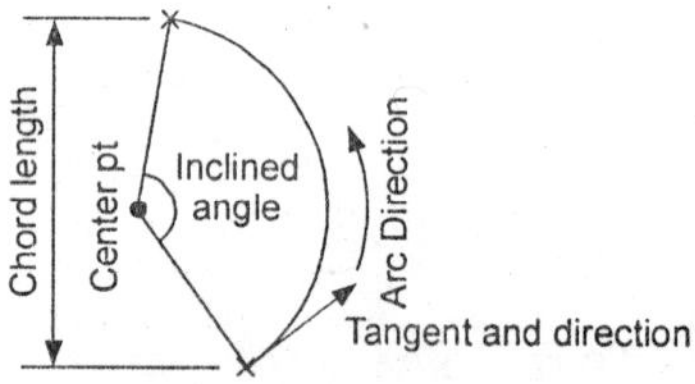

Fig. 3.14

There are seven methods used for drawing an arc.

(a) Three points method

(b) Start point — Centre point — End point

(c) Start point — Centre point — Length of chord

(d) Start point — End point — Angle of inclusion

(e) Start point — End point — Direction

(f) Start point — Centre point — Angle of inclusion

(g) Start point — End point — Radius.

These methods can be used by executing the arc command.

ARC - Creates an arc

At the command prompt, enter ARC [Fig. 3.15]

COMMAND : ARC

Centre/ < Start point > : specify a point, entre c, or press enter ↵

Specify centre point of Arc: use one of the point fixing method ↵

Specify end point of Arc or [Angle/chord length]: specify a point or enter an option ↵

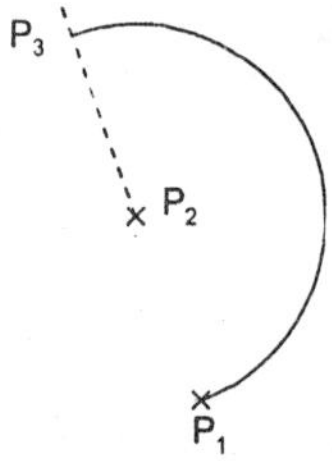

Fig. 3.15

END POINT: Draw-ARC-start, centre, end using the centre point (P_2) as shown in Fig. 3.16. Draw an arc counter clockwise from the start point (P1) to a point that falls on an imaginary ray drawn from the centre point through the end point (P_3).

The end point determines the angle at which the arc ends. The arc does not necessarily pass through this third point.

ANGLES: Draw → Arc → Start, Centre Angle

The angle option draws an arc counter clockwise from the start point (P_1) using a centre (P_2) with a specified included angle.

Specify included angle: Specify an angle.

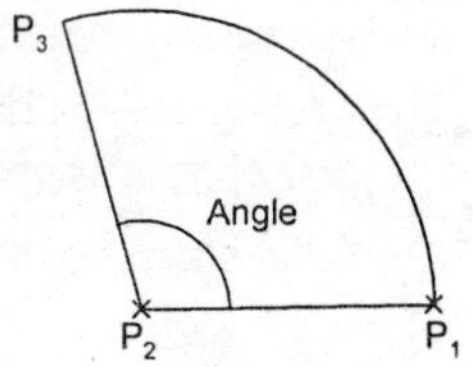

Fig. 3.16

Note: If angle is negative (–ve), then version of AutoCAD 2008 draws an arc clockwise.

(iii) **ELLIPSE:** There are three options associated with the Ellipse tool. These three options allow the user to define the Ellipse.

1. Ellipse is defined as the full length of one axis and half length of the other axis.
2. Define as the centre point of ellipse and half length of other two axis.

COMMAND : ELLIPSE

Specify axis end point of ellipse or (ARC/CENTRE): use one of the point fixing method or enter an option. Ellipse can be drawn by anyone of the following methods:

AXIS END POINTS

Defines the first axis by two specified end points. The angle of the first axis determines the angle of the ellipse. The first axis can be defined either by the major or minor axis as shown in Fig. 3.17.

COMMAND : ELLIPSE

Specify axis end point of ellipse or [Arc/centre] using one of the point fixing method ↵

Specify distance to the other axis or [Rotation]: specify distance ↵

Specify rotation around major axis: specify an angle ↵

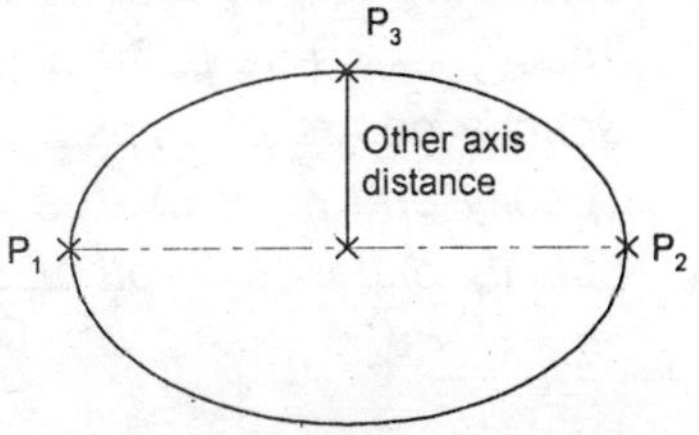

Fig. 3.17

Problem 7: Draw an ellipse using major axis end point (12, 22) (65, 25) and minor axis endpoint (30, 30)

Solution: See Fig. 3.18.

COMMAND : ELLIPSE

Specify axis end point of ellipse or [Arc/centre]: 12, 22 ↵

Specify other end point of axis : 65, 25 ↵

Specify distance to other axis or [Rotation]: 30, 30 ↵

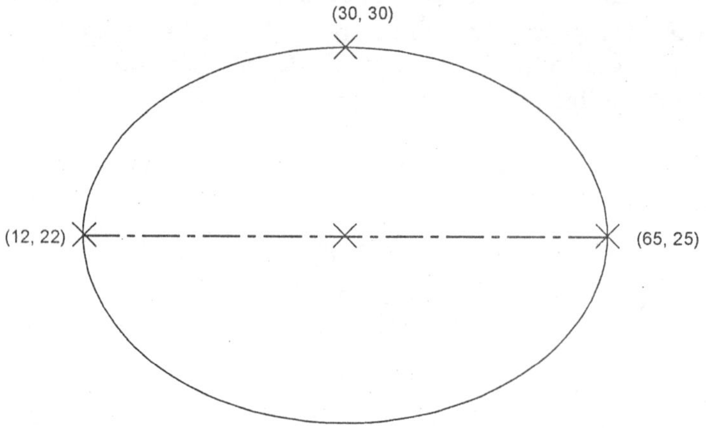

Fig. 3.18

CENTRE AXIS END POINTS

User can start from the centre point of an ellipse as specified below [Fig. 3.19].

COMMAND : ELLIPSE

Select the ellipse tool from the draw toolbar

Specify axis end point of ellipse or [Arc/centre]:c ↵

Specify centre of ellipse: specify a distance ↵

Specify end point of axis: specify a distance ↵

Specify distance to other axis or [Rotation]: Specify a distance or angle ↵

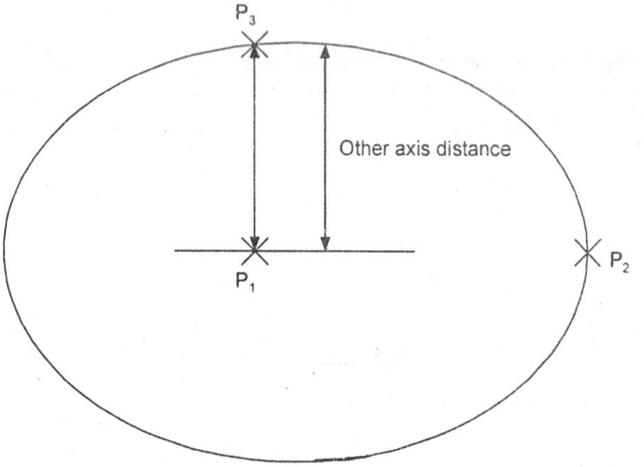

Fig. 3.19

Problem 8: Draw an ellipse with centre (100, 20) major axis end point (120, 25) and minor axis end point (90, 30).

Solution: See Fig. 3.20.

COMMAND : ELLIPSE

Select the ellipse tool from the draw toolbar

Specify axis end point of ellipse or [Arc/centre]:c ↵

Specify centre of ellipse: 100, 20 ↵

Specify centre of axis : 120, 25 ↵

Specify centre of distance to the other axis or [Rotation]: (90, 30) ↵

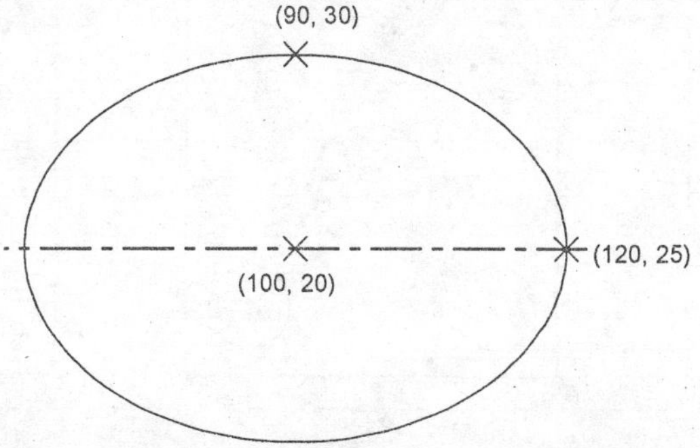

Fig. 3.20

(4) Polygon: Polygon is a geometric figure with equal sides. Polygon command creates a regular polygon with 3 to 1024 sides. For example, a triangle is a three sides polygon and pentagon is a five sides polygon. In AutoCAD, the POLYGON command is used to draw regular 2D polygon [Fig. 3.21].

COMMAND : POLYGON

Enter number of sides < current > : Enter a positive integer specify centre of polygon or [edge] : use one of the point fixing method ↵

Specify first endpoint of edge use one of the point fixing method ↵

Specify second point of edge: use one of the point fixing method ↵

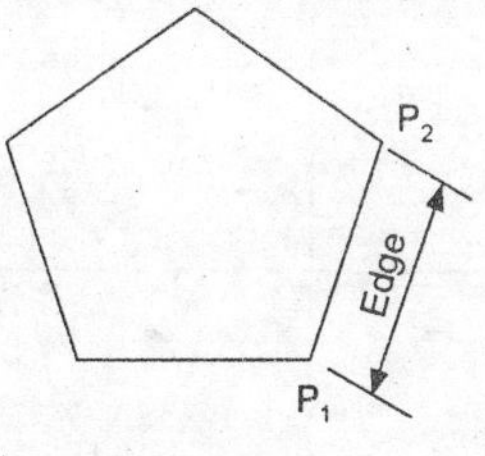

Fig. 3.21

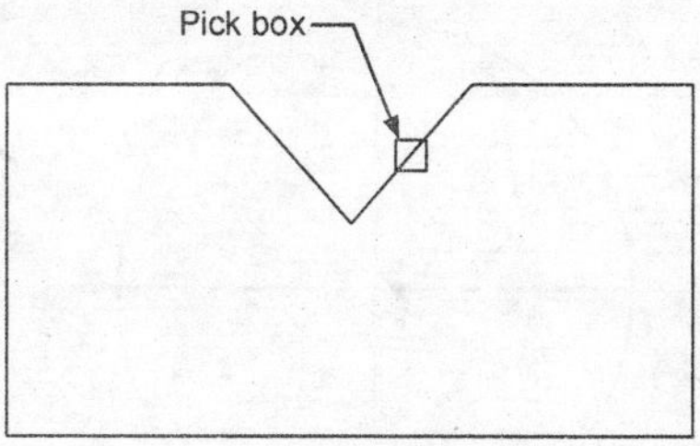

Fig. 3.22

(5) Erase: Erasing means to remove unwanted part of a drawing ERASE command is used to remove a single entity or group of entities from the drawing screen. This command is used exactly the same way as in erase is used in manual drafting to remove the unwanted the user invoke the ERASE command, a small box, known as the pick box, replaces the screen cursor. To erase an object, move the pick box so that it touches the object user can select the object by pressing the pick button of the pointing device as shown in Fig. 3.22.

COMMAND : ERASE

Select the object : Use any object selection method ↵

(6) OOPS: Oops command is used to restore the erased entity immediately. The following illustration narrates the above situation. First, the circle at the centre is removed using ERASE command. The same is restored after using oops command [Fig. 3.23].

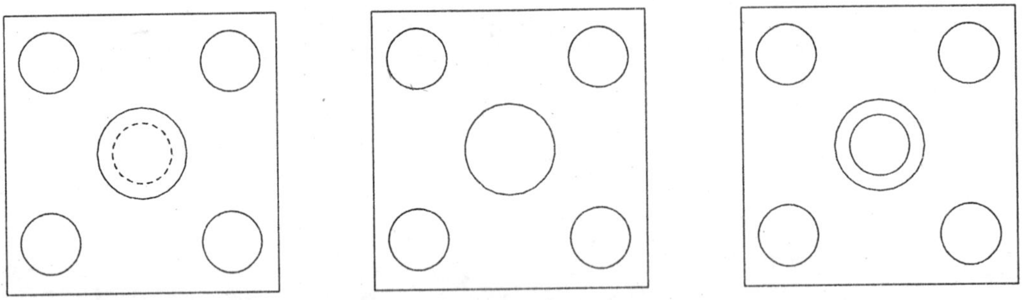

Fig. 3.23

(7) Move: Sometimes object should not be located at the actual position where they actually needed. In these situations, user can use the MOVE command. This command allows to move one or more objects from their current position to a new position. This change in the position of the objects does not change their size as shown in Fig. 3.24.

COMMAND : MOVE

Select objects: use one of the object selection method ↵

Specify base point or displacement: use one of the point fixing method or, enter the displacement ↵

Specify second point of displacement or < use first point as displacement > : use one of the point fixing method of press enter ↵

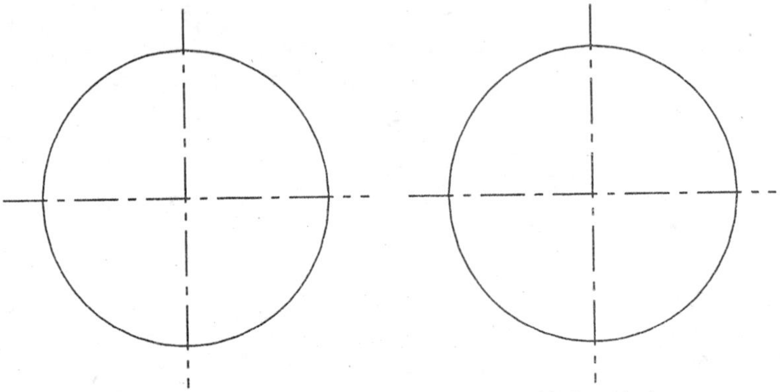

Fig. 3.24

(8) Copy: This command is similar to the MOVE command is the sense that it makes copies of the selected objects and places them at a specified location as shown in Fig. 3.25.

COMMAND : COPY

Select objects: Specify base point or displacement or enter option M ↵

Select second point of displacement or < use first point as displacement > : use one of the point as displacement > : use one of the point fixing method or press enter ↵

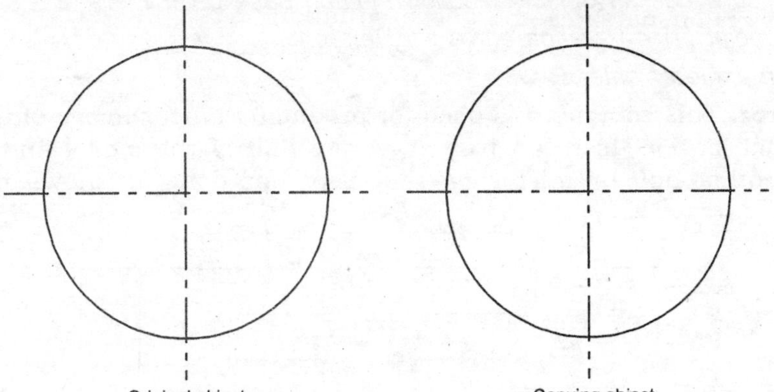

Fig. 3.25

(9) ARRAY: If the user needs to make multiple copies of an object but at a regular interval, copy command is a little cumbersome. ARRAY command comes in handy in such situations, where prompts user for the number of rows and columns.

COMMAND : ARRAY

Select objects: use any object selection method ↵

(10) RECTANGULAR ARRAY: This is a method of creating a rectangular array, define by a number of rows and columns that forms a matrix an objects [Fig. 3.26].

COMMAND : ARRAY

Selection of object ↵

ENTER the type of array [Rectangular/polar] <R> : R ↵

ENTER the number of rows (- -) < 1 > : Enter a positive integer ↵

ENTER the number of columns (III) < 1 > : Enter a positive integer ↵

Enter the distance between rows or specify unit cell (- -) : specify a distance ↵

Specify the distance between columns (III) : specify a distance ↵

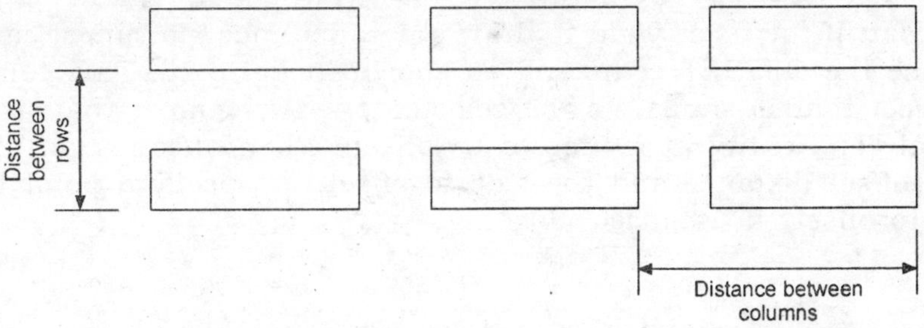

Fig. 3.26

(11) Rotate: Sometimes when making drawing, user may need to rotate an object or group of an objects. In these situation, user can use the ROTATE command. ROTATE command moves an object about a base point.

COMMAND : ROTATE

Select Object : use an object selection method base point ↵

Specify a point (1) < Rotation angle > / Reference ↵

Specify an angle or enter R ↵

(12) Mirror: This command is used for producing mirror image of the symmetrical object. In such cases, user can just draw one half of the model and AutoCAD, can produce the other half by mirroring what user has done as shown in Fig. 3.27.

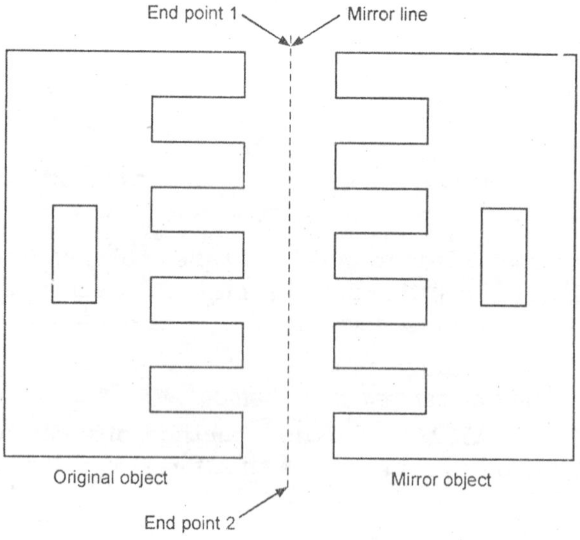

Fig. 3.27

COMMAND : MIRROR

Select objects: use any object selection method ↵

Specify first point of mirror line: use any of the point fixing methods ↵

Specify second point of mirror line: use any of the fixing methods ↵

Delete source object? [Yes/No] <N> : Enter an option. ↵

(13) Offset: If the user, want to draw a parallel lines, polylines, circles, arcs etc., user can use the OFFSET command as shown in fig. 3.28. This command creates another object that is similar to the selected one. Remember that user are allowed to select only one entity at a time to be offset. When offseting an object user can specify the offset distance and the side to offset, or specify a point through which user want to offset the selected object.

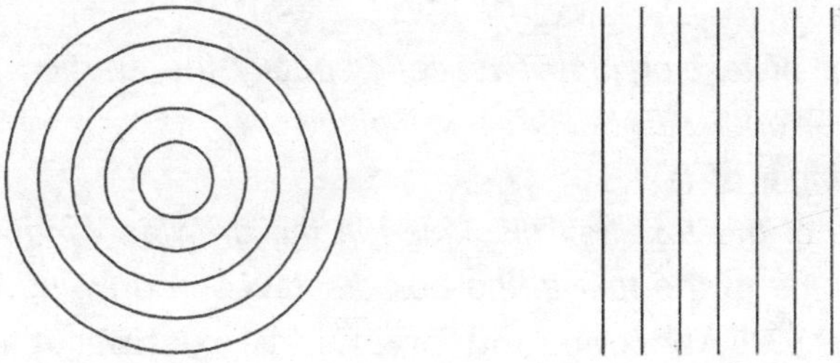

Fig. 3.28

Command : OFFSET

Specify offset distance or [through] <current> ↵

Specify a distance or press enter ↵

(14) TRIM: When creating a design, there are a number of places where user have to remove the unwanted and extending edges of an object. In such cases, user can use the TRIM command. This command trims the objects that extend beyond a required point of instruction.

Command : TRIM

Current setting: Projection = UCS ; Edge = None ↵

Select cutting edge ↵

Select objects: use an object selection method or press enter ↵

(15) EXTEND: The EXTEND command may be considered the opposite of the TRIM command. In TRIM command user trim the objects, but in the EXTEND command user can extend lines, rays, arcs and polylines to meet other object. This command does not extend closed loops. In EXTEND command user are required to select the boundary edges firstly. The boundary edges are those objects that are selected lines or arcs extend to meet.

Command : EXTEND

Current setting: Projection= UCS ↵

Edge = Extend ↵

Select boundary edges ↵

Select object: use an object selection method or press enter ↵

(16) TEXT: The TEXT command is used to write a single line text in the drawing. Although user can write more than one lines of text using this command, but each line will be a separate text entity. After invoking this command user need to specify the start point, height and rotation angle for the text. The character appear on the screen, as user enter them. When user press enter after typing a line, the cursor automatically places itself at the start of the next line and repeats the prompt for entering another line. User can end the command by pressing the enter key and the backspace key is use to edit the text on the screen while writing it. The prompt sequence is given next.

COMMAND : TEXT

Specify start point of text or [Justify/style] : specify the starting point of the text.

Specify height <current> : Enter the text height

Specify rotation angle of text <0> ↵

Exter the first line of the text box displaced in the drawing window ↵

Exter the second line of the text in the box displayed in drawing window ↵

(17) Break: The BREAK command breaks an existing object into two or erases portions of the objects. This command can be used to remove a part of the selected objects or to break objects such as lines, arcs, circles, ellipses and polylines. There are two methods of BREAK commands.

(*i*) 1 Point option.

(*ii*) 2 Point option.

The 2 point method allows, to break an object between two selected points as shown in Fig. 3.29. In this method the portion of the object between the two selected point is removed. The point at which, selected the object becomes the first break point and then user are prompted to enter the second break point.

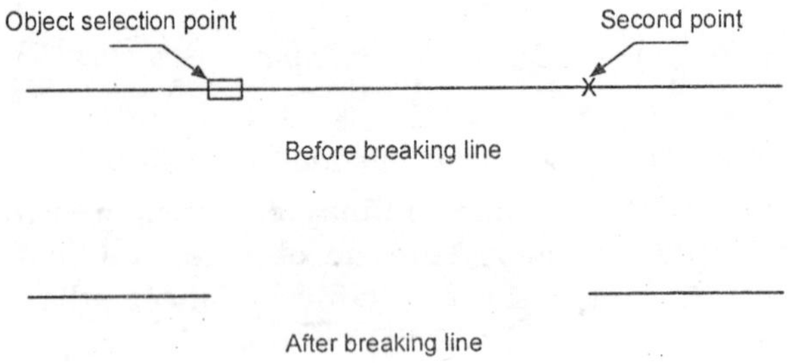

Fig. 3.29

Select object: Select the object to be broken

Specify second break point or [First point] : Specify the second break point on the object.

The object is between these two points and the in between portion of the object is removed as shown in Fig. 3.29.

(18) Chamfer: The chamfer command is used to bevel the edges of the solid. This command is also used to reduce the area of the stress concentration in the solid. In simple words, chamfer is defined as, the taper provided on a surface of an object. A beveled line connects two separate objects to create a chamfer as shown in Fig. 3.30.

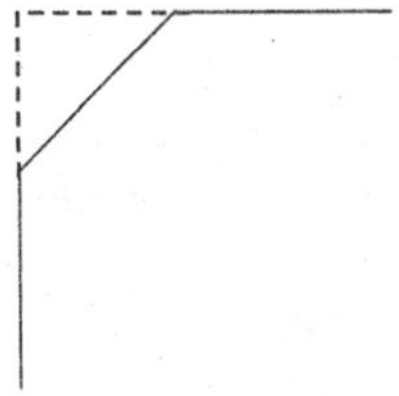

Fig. 3.30

The size of a chamfer depends on its distance from the corner. If a chamfer is equidistance from the corner in both the directions, it is 45-degree chamfer. In AutoCAD, the chamfer can be created using two methods, by defining two distances or by defining one distance or and the chamfer angle.

(TRIM mode) current chamfer Dist 1 = 0.0000,

Dist 2 = 0.0000

Select first line or [Undo/Polyline/Distance/Angle/Trim/Method/Multiple]:

Chamfering the model using the distance option are shown in fig. 3.31.

Select first line or [Undo/Polyline/Distance/Angle/Trim/Method/Multiple]: D ↲

Specify first chamfer distance <0.0000>: Enter a distance value or specifying two points.

Specify second chamfer distance <0.0000>: Enter a distance value or specify two points.

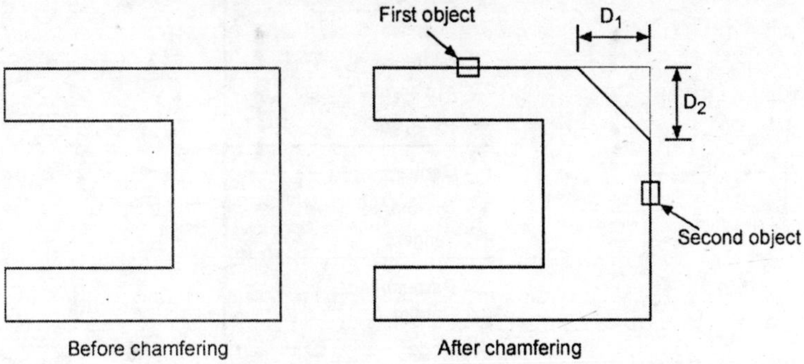

Fig. 3.31

(19) FILLET: The edges in the design are generally filleted to reduce the area of stress concentration. The FILLET command helps to form round corners between any two entities by allowing to define two entities that form a sharp vertex.

The result is that a smooth round arc is created that connects the two object as shown in Fig. 3.32.

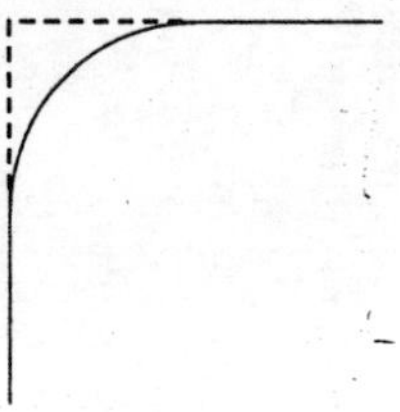

Fig. 3.32

A fillet can also be created between two intersecting or parallel lines as well as nonintersecting and nonparallel lines, polylines, rays, circles and true ellipses.

Current settings: Mode = TRIM, Radius = 0.0000

Select first object or [Undo/Polyline/Radius/TRIM/Multiple]

(20) Quit: This exists AutoCAD

At the command prompts, enter quit

or at the right top of the screen click (X) to exit from AutoCAD.

3.3 OBJECT SNAPS

Object snaps are one of the most useful features of AutoCAD. They improve the performance and accuracy of the drawing and make drafting much simpler than it normally would be. The term object snap refers to the cursor's ability to snap exactly to a geometric point on an object. The *advantage* of using object snaps is that user do not have to specify an exact point. For example, to place a point at the midpoint of a line, may not be able to specify the exact point. Using the MID point object snap, move the cursor somewhere on the object. User will notice a marker (in the form of a geometric shape, a triangle for Midpoint) is automatically displayed at the middle point (snap point) [Fig. 3.33].

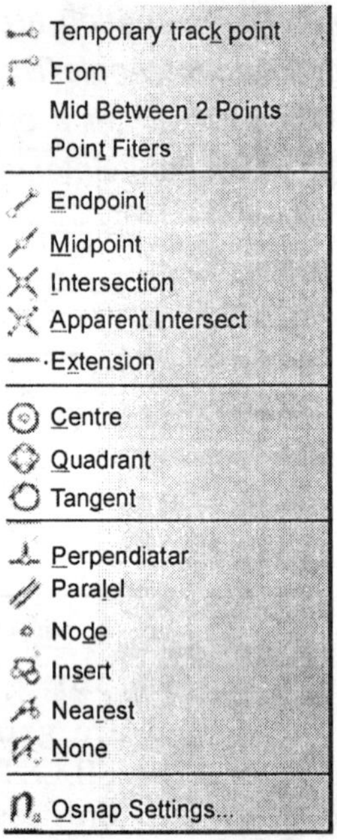

(*i*) Object snap modes shortcut menu

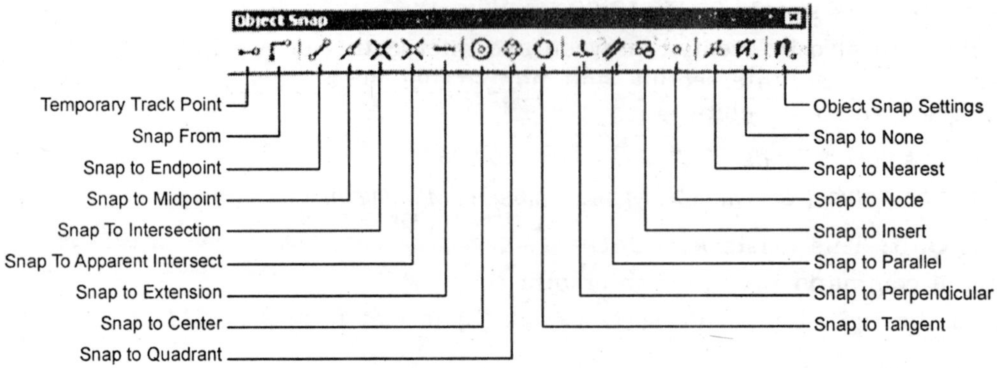

(*ii*) The Object Snap Toolbar

Fig. 3.33

The following are the object snap modes in AutoCAD:

ENDpoint
MIDpoint
Nearest
Centre
Tangent
Quadrant

Intersection
Perpendicular
Parallel

(1) Endpoint

 The ENDpoint Object Snap mode **snaps to the closest endpoint of a line or an** arc. To use this Object Snap mode, select **the Endpoint button, and move the cursor** (crosshairs) anywhere close to the endpoint of the object. **The marker will be displayed** at the endpoint; click to specify that point. **AutoCAD will grab the endpoint of the** object. If there are several objects **near the cursor crosshairs. AutoCAD will grab the** endpoint of the object that is closest **to the crosshairs, or if the Magnet is on, user** can move to grab the desired endpoint. Fig. 3.34 invoke the LINE command from the Draw toolbar.

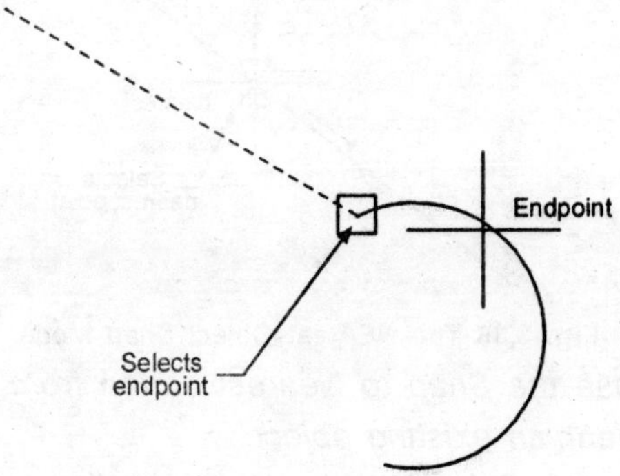

Fig. 3.34 The ENDpoint Object Snap Mode

*Specify first point: Select the Snap **Endpoint button from the Object Snap toolbar.***
*endp of Move the crosshair and select **arc.***
*Specify next point or [Undo]: Select the **endpoint of the line.***

(2) Midpoint

 The MIDpoint Object Snap mode **snaps to** the midpoint of a line or an arc. To **use this** Object Snap mode, select Midpoint osnap **and** select the object anywhere. AutoCAD **will grab** the midpoint of the object. Fig. 3.35 **invoke the** LINE command from the Draw toolbar.

*Specify first point: Select the starting **point of the** line.*

*Specify next point or [Undo]: Choose the **Snap to** Midpoint button from the Object Snap toolbar.*

*mid of Move the cursor and select the **original line.***

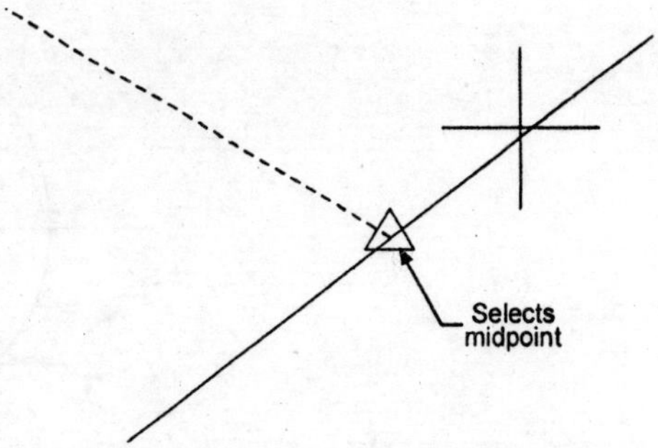

Fig. 3.35 The MIDpoint Object Snap Mode

(3) Nearest

 The NEArest Object Snap mode selects a point on an object (line, arc, circle, or ellipse) that is visually closet to the graphics cursor (crosshairs). To use this mode, enter the command, and then choose the Nearest object snap. Move the crosshairs near the intended point on the object so as to display the marker at the desired point and then select the object. AutoCAD will grab a point on the line where the marker was displayed. Fig. 3.36 invoke the LINE command from the Draw toolbar.

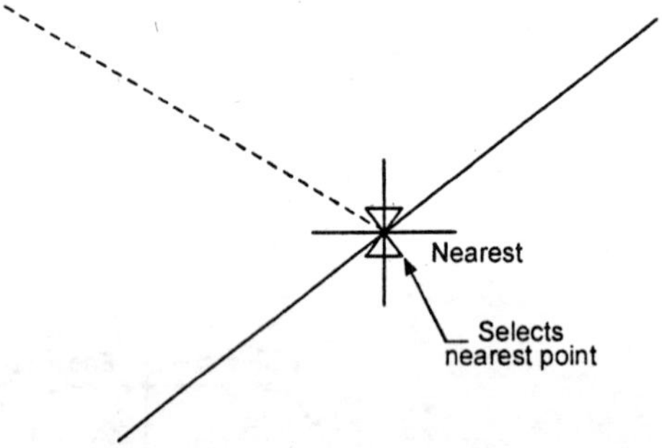

Fig. 3.36 The NEArest Object Snap Mode

Specify first point: Choose the Snap to Nearest button from the Object Snap toolbar.
Idea to Select a point near an existing object.
Specify next point-or [Undo]: Select end points of the line.

(4) Centre

 The CENtre Object Snap mode allows user to snap to the centre point of an ellipse, circle, or arc. After selecting this option, user must point to the visible part of the circumference of a circle or arc. Fig. 3.37 invokes the LINE command from the Draw toolbar.

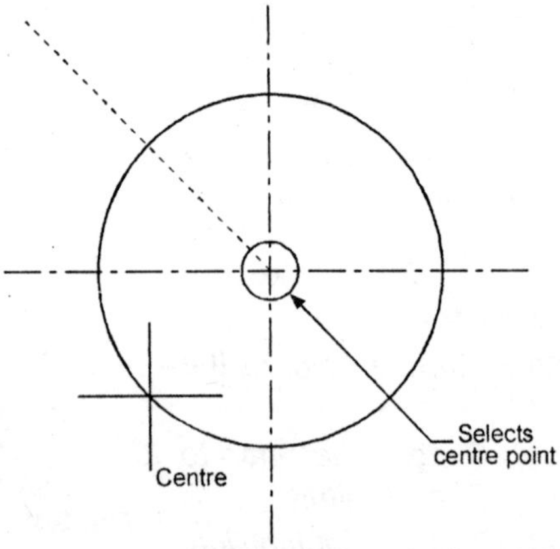

Fig. 3.37 The Centre Object Snap Mode

(5) Tangent

 The TANgent Object Snap allows user to draw a tangent to or from an existing ellipse, circle, or arc. To use this object snap, place the cursor on the circumference of the circle or arc to select it. Fig. 3.38 invokes the LINE command from the Draw toolbar.

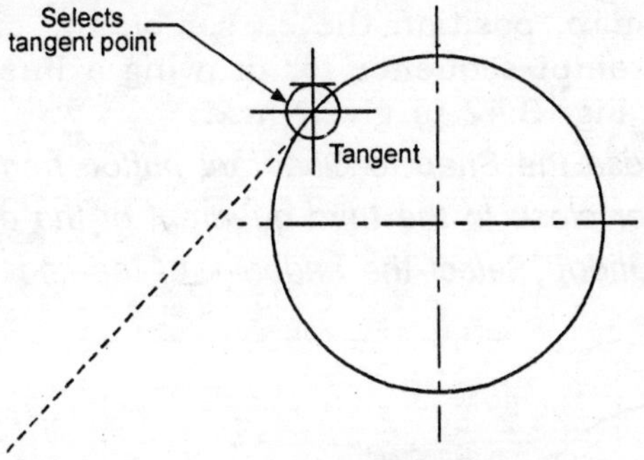

Fig. 3.38

Specify first point: Select the starting point of the line.

Specify next point or [Undo]: Choose the Snap to Tangent button from the Object Snap toolbar.

_tan to Move the cursor and select the circle.

Specify next point or [Undo]: Select the endpoint of the line (tangent of the circle).

Fig. 3.39 shows the use of NEArest, ENDpoint, MIDpoint, and TANgent Object Snap modes.

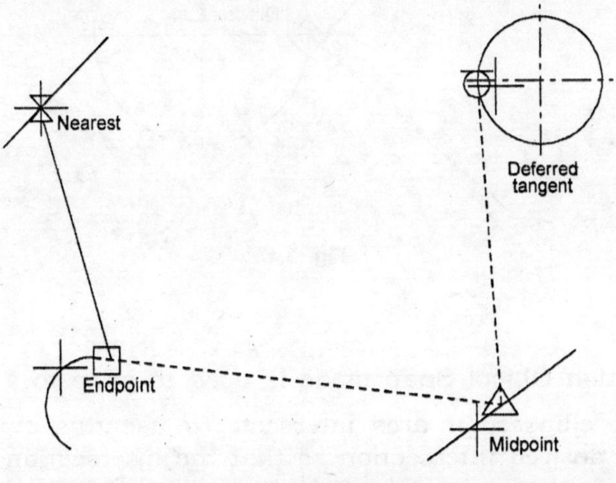

Fig. 3.39

(6) Quadrant

The QUAdrant Object Snap mode is used when user need to snap to a quadrant point of an ellipse, arc, or a circle. A circle has four quadrants, and each quadrant subtends an angle of 90-degree. The quadrant points are located at 0, 90, 180, and 270-degree positions. If the circle is inserted as a block, that is rotated, the quadrant points are also rotated by the same amount, [Fig. 3.40 and 3.41].

The use this object snap, position the cursor on the circle or arc closert to the desired quadrant. The prompt sequence for drawing a line from the third quadrant of a circle, as shown in Fig. 3.42 is given next.

Specify first point: Choose the Snap to Quadrant button from the Object Snap toolbar.

_qua of Move the cursor close to the third quadrant of the circle and select it.

Specify next point or [Undo]: Select the endpoint of the line.

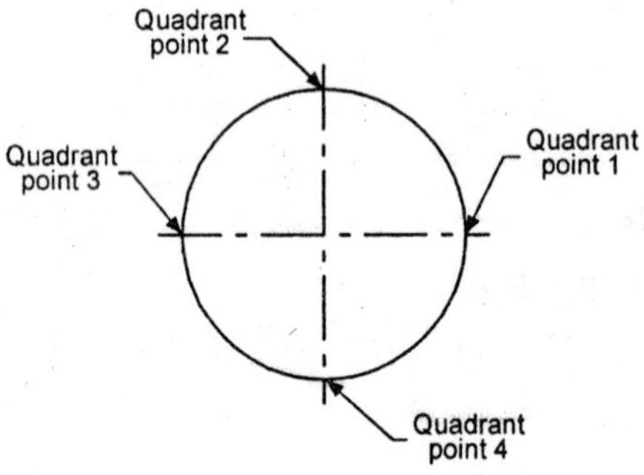

Fig. 3.40 Location of the circle quadrants

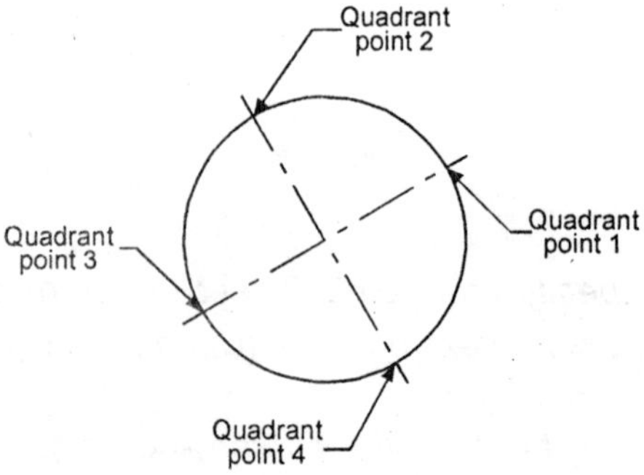

Fig. 3.41 Quadrants in a rotated circle

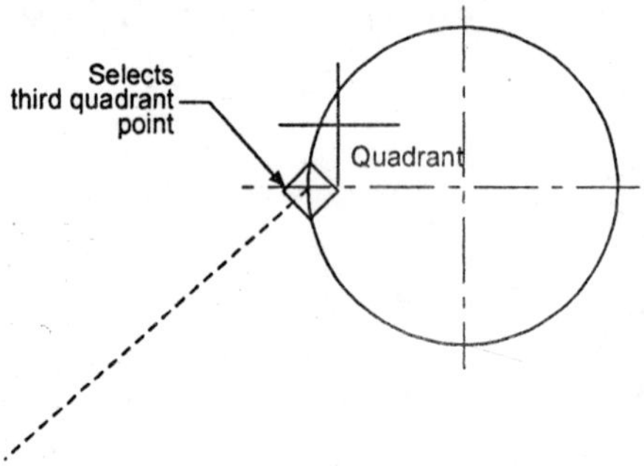

Fig. 3.42

(7) Intersection

The INTersection Object Snap mode is used to snap to a point where two or more lines, circles, ellipses, or arcs intersect. To use this object snap, move the cursor close to the desired intersection so that the intersection is within the target box, and then specify that point. Fig. 3.43 invokes the LINE command. The prompt sequence is given text.

Specify first point: Choose the Snap to Intersection button from the Object Snap toolbar.

_into of Position the cursor near the intersection and select it.

Specify next point or [Undo]: Select the endpoint of the line.

After selecting the Intersection Object Snap, if your cursor is close to an object and not close to an actual intersection, the tooltip displays Extended Intersection. If user select this object now, AutoCAD prompts and, for the selection of another object. If your cursor is close to another object, AutoCAD marks the extended intersection point between these two objects. This mode selects extended or visual intersections of lines, arcs, circles, or ellipses as shown in Fig. 3.44. The extended intersection are the intersections that do not exist at present, but are imaginary and formed if the line or arc is extended.

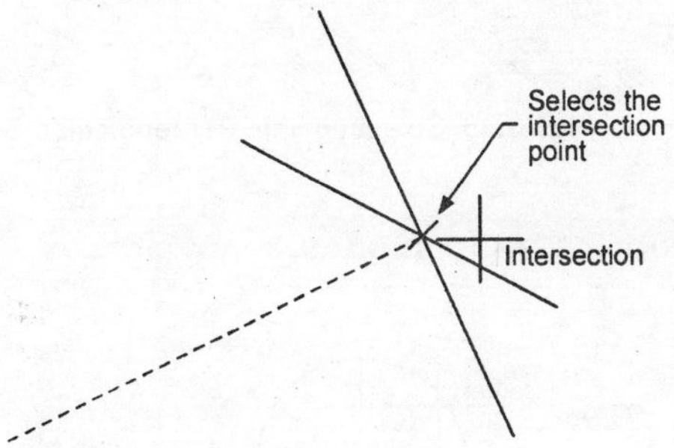

Fig. 3.43 The INTersection Object Snap Mode

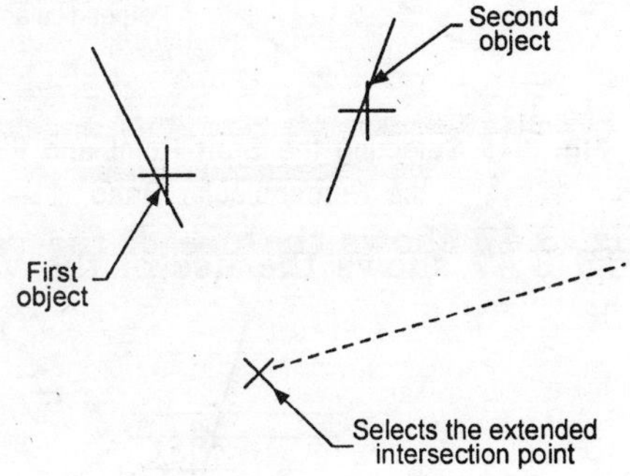

Fig. 3.44 Extended Intersection Object Snap Mode

(8) Perpendicular

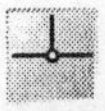

The PERpendicular Object Snap mode is used to draw a line perpendicular to or from another line, or normal to or from an arc or circle, or to an ellipse. When user use this mode and select an object, AutoCAD calculates the point on the selected object so that the previously selected point is perpendicular to the line. The object can be selected by positioning the cursor anywhere on the line. First invoke the LINE command: the prompt sequence to draw a line perpendicular to a given line is given next. [Fig. 3.45]

Specify first point: Select the starting point of the line.

Specify next point or [Undo]: Choose the Snap to Perpendicular button from the Object Snap toolbar.

_per to Select the line on which user want to draw perpendicular.

When user select the line first, the rubber-band feature of the line in disabled. The line will appear only after the second point is selected. Invoke the LINE command. The prompt sequence for drawing a line perpendicular from given the line is given next. [Fig. 3.46.]

Specify first point: Choose the Snap to Perpendicular button from the Object Snap toolbar.
_per to Select the line on which user want to draw perpendicular.
Specify next point or [Undo]: Select the endpoint of the line.

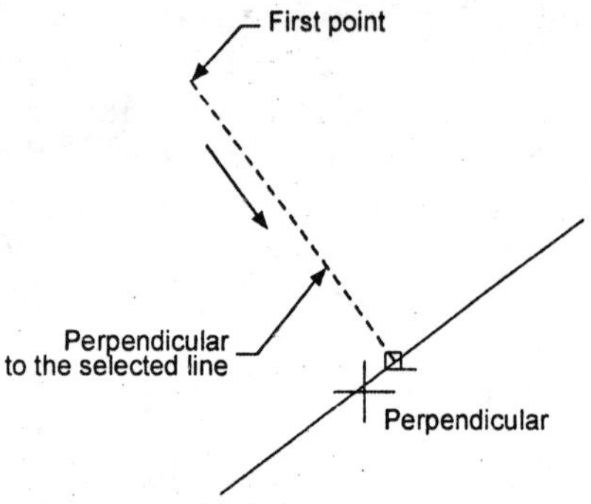

Fig. 3.45 Selecting the Start Point and then the the Perpendicular Snap

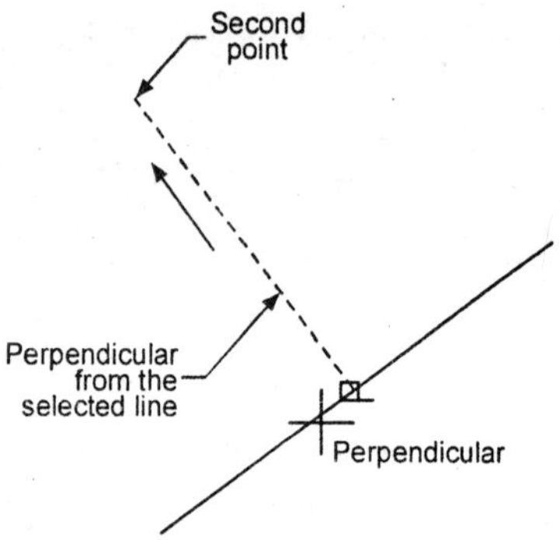

Fig. 3.46 Selecting the Perpendicular Snap

Fig. 3.47 shows the use of the various object snap modes.

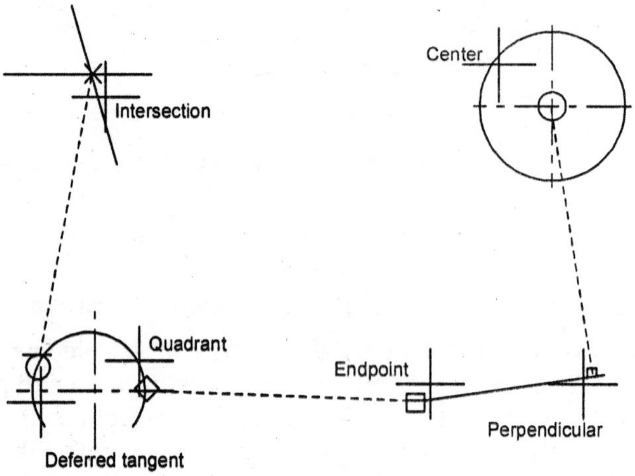

Fig. 3.47 Using Various Object Snap Modes to Locate Points

(9) Parallel

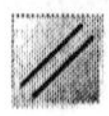

When user need to draw a line parallel to a line or polyline on the screen, user can use the PARallel Object Snap as shown in Fig. 3.48. For example, when user are in the middle of the LINE command, and user have to draw a line parallel to the one already on the screen, user can use the PARallel object snap as follows.

Command: Choose Line from the Draw toolbar.

Specify first point: Select a point on the screen.

Specify next point or [Undo]: *Choose the Parallel bottom from the Object Snap toolbar.*
_par to *Specify object to which parallel is to be drawn.*

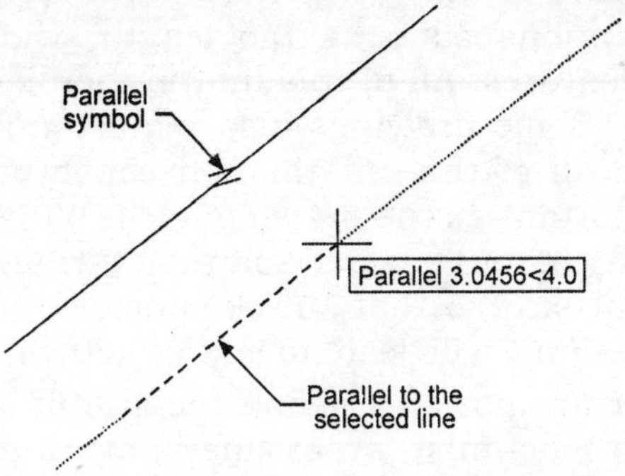

Fig. 3.48 Using the Parallel Object Snap

When user specify the reference object, a parallel sign is displayed. User should briefly pause on that line so that a small plus sign appears on it to indicate that it has been selected. Now, on moving the cursor close to an angle parallel to the line, an imaginary parallel line appears, on which user can select the next point. A tooltip which has the relative polar coordinate is displayed with the cursor as user move it on the construction line. This helps user to select the next point. This line which has been drawn is parallel to the selected object.

(10) Extension

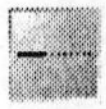

The EXTension Object Snap gives user an option to locate a point on the extension path of a line or an arc as shown in Fig. 3.49. It can also be used with intersection to determine the point of the extended intersection. To use the extension, choose the Line button from the Draw toolbar and then choose the Snap to Extension button from the Object Snap toolbar. Briefly pause at the end of the line or arc user want to use. A small plus sign (+) appears at the end of the line or arc, indicating that it has been selected. If user move the cursor along the extension path, a temporary extension path is displayed and the tooltip displays relative polar coordinates from the end of the line. Select a point or enter a distance to begin a line and then select another point to finish the line.

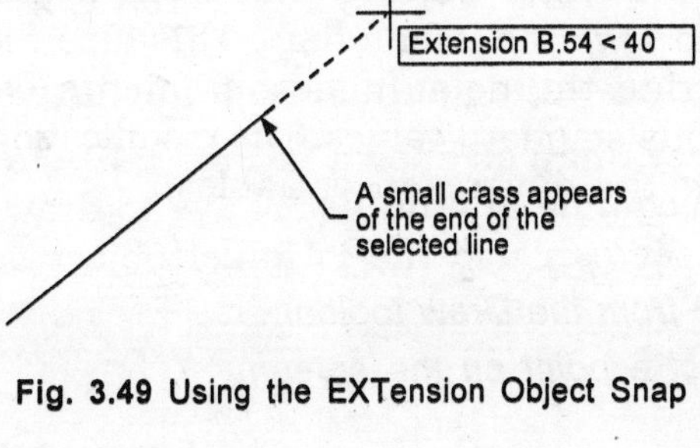

Fig. 3.49 Using the EXTension Object Snap

3.4 NEED FOR DIMENSIONING

To make designs more informative and practical, the drawing must convey more than just the graphic picture of the product. To manufacture an object, the drawing must contain size descriptions such as the length, width, height, angle, radius, diameter and location of features. All of this information is added to the drawing with the help of dimensioning. Some drawings also require information about tolerances with the size of features. All of this information conveyed through dimensioning is vital and often just as important as the drawing itself. With the advances is computer-aided design/drafting and computer-aided manufacturing, it has become mandatory to draw the part to actual size so that the dimension reflect the actual size of the features. Incorrect dimensions will lead to manufacturing errors.

By dimensioning, user are not only giving the size of a part, user are also giving series of instructions to a machinist, an engineer, or an architect. The way the part is positioned in a machine, the sequence of machining operations, and the location of different features of the part depend on how user dimension the part. For example, the number of decimal places in a dimension (2.000) determines the type of machine that will be used to do that machining operation. The machining cost of such an operation is significantly higher than for a dimension that has only one digit after the decimal (2.0). Similarly, whether a part is to be forged or cast, the radii of the edges and the tolerance user provide to these dimensions determine the cost of the product, the number of defective parts, and the number of parts user get from a single die.

(1) Dimensioning in AutoCAD

The objects that can be dimensioned in AutoCAD range from straight lines to arcs. The dimensioning commands provided by AutoCAD can be classified into four categories:

(*i*) Dimension Drawing Commands
(*ii*) Dimension Style Commands
(*iii*) Dimension Editing Commands
(*iv*) Dimension Utility Commands.

While dimensioning an object, AutoCAD automatically calculates the length of the object or the distance between two specified points. Also, settings like a gap between the dimension text and the dimension line, the space between two consecutive dimension lines, arrow size, and text size are maintained and used when the dimensions are being generated for a particular drawing. The generation of arrows, lines (dimension lines, extension lines), and other objects that form a dimension are automatically performed by AutoCAD to save the user's time. This also results in uniform drawings. However, user can override the default measurements computed by AutoCAD and change the setting of various standard values. The modification of dimensioning standards can be achieved through the dimension variables.

(2) Fundamental Dimensioning Terms

Before studying AutoCAD's dimensioning commands, it is important to know and understand various dimensioning terms that are common to linear, angular, radius, diameter, and ordinate dimensioning. Fig. 3.50 shows some dimensioning objects.

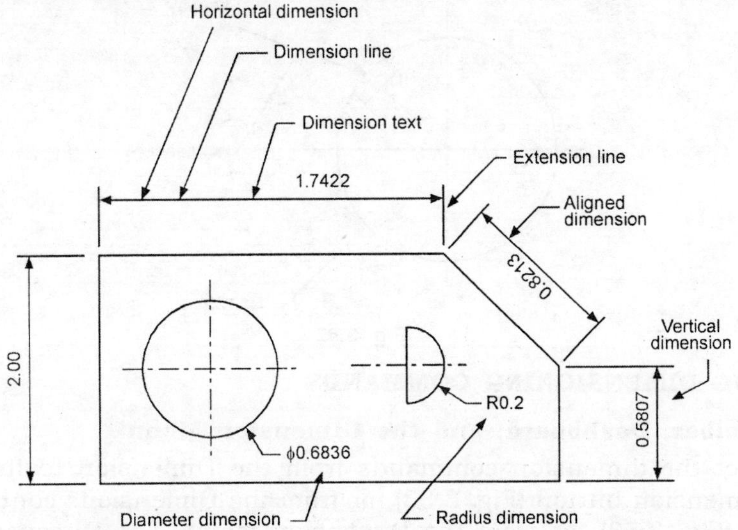

Fig. 3.50

(3) Extension Lines

Extension lines are drawn from the object measured to the dimension line as shown in Fig. 3.51. These lines are also called witness lines. Extension lines are used in linear and angular dimensioning. Generally, extension lines are drawn perpendicular to the dimension line. However, user can make extension lines incline at an angle by using the DIMEDIT command (Oblique option) or by selecting Dimension Edit from the Dimension toolbar. AutoCAD also allows user to suppress either one or both extension lines in a dimension.

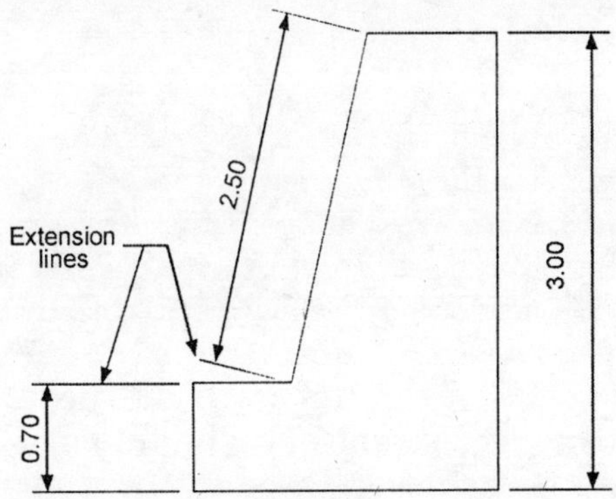

Fig. 3.51

(4) Leader Line

A leader line is a line that stretches from the dimension text to the object being dimensioned. Sometimes the text for dimensioning and other annotations does not adjust properly near the object. In such cases, user can use a leader and place the text at the end of the leader line. Fig 3.52 shows the circle, has a keyway slot that is too small to be dimensioned. In this situation, a leader can be drawn from the text to the keyway feature. Also, a leader can be used to attach annotations such as part numbers, notes, and instructions to an object.

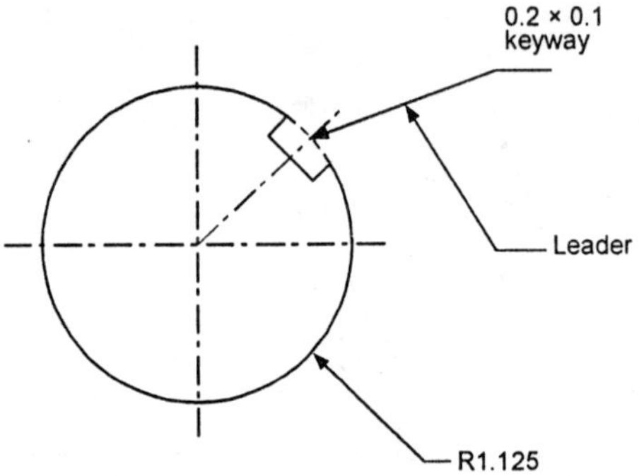

Fig. 3.52

(5) SELECTING DIMENSIONING COMMANDS

Using the Toolbar, Dashboard, and the Dimension Menu

User can select the dimension commands from the Dimension toolbar by choosing the desired dimension button (Fig. 3.53), or from the Dimensions control panel of the DASHBOARD (Fig. 3.53), or from the Dimension menu. The Dimension toolbar can displayed by right-clicking on any toolbar and choosing Dimension from the shortcut menu.

Fig. 3.53

4

Getting Started with 3D

4.1 INTRODUCTION

One of the latest enhancements in AutoCAD is directly start in the 3D modelling environment. All commands and options required to create the 3D design are displayed by default in environment as shown in Fig. 4.1.

Today, CADD technology has provided us the power to build typical types of 3D-objects on the screen and visualise the object without spending much time, money and efforts. Using AutoCAD the industry standard for computer aided design and drafting software student can build and visualize 3D models easily. These 3D objects are generated by the process of geometric modelling.

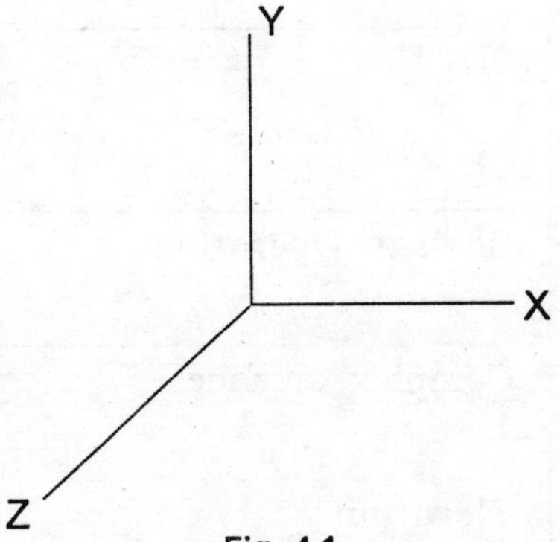

Fig. 4.1

4.2 TYPES OF 3D MODELS

1. Wireframe Modelling
2. Surface Modelling
3. Solid Modelling.

1. Wireframe Modelling: It is the simplest of the three Models. It is a skeletal description of a 3D object. There are no surfaces in a wireframe mode; it consists only of points, lines and curves that describe the edge of the object. With AutoCAD user can create wireframe models by positioning 2D objects anywhere in 3D space. Basically these are generated continuous line segments.

2. Surface Modelling: In the surface technique the objects are created by use of surfaces attached to fireframe constructions. The surfaces are useful for preventing mass flows and allows storage of quantities because of the hollowness of the object. The AutoCAD surface modeler defines faceted surfaces using a polygonal mesh. Mechanical desktop, user can create true curved surface.

3. Solid Modelling: Solid Modelling is the simplest type 3D modelling. With the help of AutoCAD solid modeler, studies can make 3D objects by creating basic 3D shapes such as boxes, prism, cones, cylinder, spheres, wedges and tori etc. It is the process of creating objects which is similar to actual solid object. In the solid modelling technique, the object is completely filled with solid material. The creation of solid models on the screen allows calculation of the mass, properties, engineering properties like volume area, mass, centre of gravity etc. With mechanical desktop, user can also define solids parametrically and maintain associatively between 3D Models and the 2D views that student generate from them.

4.3 3D CAD TERMINOLOGY

2D	A concept of displaying real-world objects on a flat surface showing only height and width. This system uses only the *X* and *Y* axes.
3D	A way of displaying real-world object in a more natural way adding depth to the height and width. This system uses the *X*, *Y* and *Z* axes.
Boolean Operations	Commands that allow user to add, subtract or intersect solid objects in AutoCAD.
Complex surface	Generally a curved surface. Examples: car fender, landscape contour.
Elevation	The difference between an object being at zero on the Z-axis and the height that it is above zero.
Extrude	The extrude command raises the shape of a 2D outline into a 3D solid. For example, a circle would be extruded into a cylinder.
Face	The simplest true 3D surface.
Facet	A three or four sided polygon that represents a piece (or section) of a 3D surface.
Hidden line removal	A way of hiding lines that would not be visible if user were viewing the actual object user have drawn in AutoCAD. (Command: HIDE)
Isometric Drawing	A simple way of achieving a 3D appearance using 2D drawing methods.
Plan View	Also known as the top view, a plan view looks directly down the WCS *Z*-axis to the *X*-*Y* axis.
Primitive	A basic solid building block. Examples: boxes, cones, cylinders.

Region	A 2D area consisting of lines, arcs, etc.
Rendering	A complex way of adding photo-realistic qualities to a 3D model user have created.
Shading	A quick way of adding color to a 3D object user have drawn. (Command: SHADE)
Solid Model	A 3D model creating using solid 'building blocks'. This is the most accurate way of representing real-world objects in CAD.
Surface Model	A 3D model defined by surfaces. The surface consists of polygons.
Thickness	A property of lines and other objects that gives them a 3D like appearance.
UCS	The user co-ordinate system. This is defined by the person drawing to have easier access to portions of a 3D model.
View	A particular view of the object user have created.
Viewport	A window into your drawing showing a particular view. User can have several viewports on your screen. Different from the viewports used in plotting.
Wireframe Modcl	A 3D shape that is defined by lines and curves. A skeletal representation. Hidden line removal is not possible with this model.
Z-Axis	The third axis that defines the depth.

4.4 BASIC AutoCAD COMMAND FOR 3D DRAWING

AutoCAD absolute coordinate system is called the world coordinate system (WCS). The default setting for the WCS in a viewing position located so that student are looking at the system at 90° to its *X*, *Y* plane. (see Fig. 4.1).

The *Z*-axis is also perpendicular to the *X*, *Y* plane or directly aligned with student view point. This set up is ideal for 2D drawings and is called a plan view. All these 2D drawings are done relative to these coordinates until a new UCS (user coordinate system) is defined or the user switches back to the WCS.

1. View Points: The orientation of the WCS may be changed by changing the drawings view points. There are two ways to change the view point.

(*i*) View pull down menu

(*ii*) View tool bar.

2. View Pull-down Menu: The grid serves to help define a visual orientation

(i) Select the view pull-down menu

(ii) Select 3D views

(iii) Select SE isometric.

The SE Isometric view can also be created using the SE isometric tool on the view tool bar.

(iv) Select south east isometric from the current view list.

(iv) Select Set current, then OK.

3. To Return to the Original WCS Orientation

(i) Select the view pull-down menu

(ii) Select 3D views, plan views, world UCS.

(iii) Type zoom; press enter [All centre/dynamic/extents/Previews/scale/window/]<real time>:

(iv) Type 75; Press enter.

For wire frame mode.

Solids commands: The AutoCAD package allows drawing of solid models such as box, wedge, cylinder, sphere etc.

4. Section: The section command is very similar the SLICE command. The only difference is that the command does not chop the solid. Instead, it creates a cross-section along the selected section plane. The cross-section thus created is a region.

Select objects: select the object to section

Select objects: ↵

specify first point on section plane by [object/Z axis/view/XY/YZ/ZX/3 points] < 3 points >:

4.5 CREATING SOLID MODELS

The solid modeling is the process of building objects that have all the attributes of an actual solid object. The predefined solid primitives that can be used to construct a solid model such as box, wedge, cone, cylinder, sphere and torus.

1. BOX: User can use the box command to create a solid rectangular box or cube. Start a new file by the acad3D.dwt template file. In 3D drawing templates, dynamically preview the operations that are perform.

(i) By two corner option [Fig. 4.2]

Specify first corner or [centre] <0, 0, 0> : 2, 2, 0

Specify other corner or [Cube/Length] : @ 5, 4, 0

Specify height or [2 point] : 3

(ii) Centre length option [Fig. 4.3]

Specify first corner or [centre] <0, 0, 0> : C

Specify other centre <0, 0, 0> : 4, 4

Specify corner or [cube/length] : L

Specify length : 7

Specify width : 5

Specify height : 3

[length = 5
width = 4]

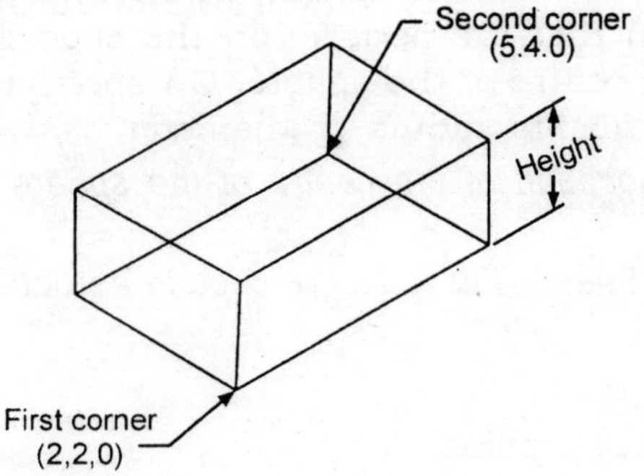

Fig. 4.2

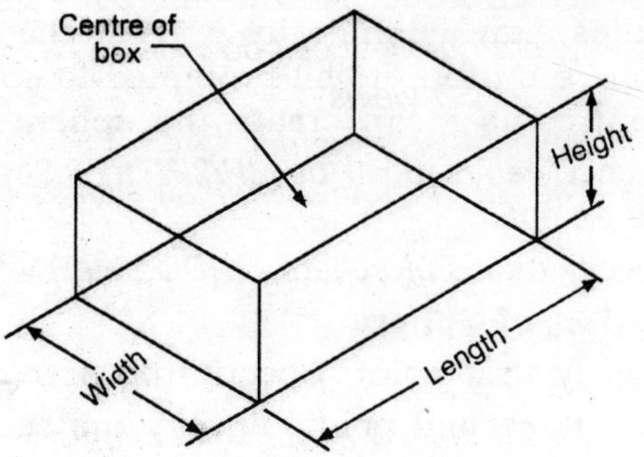

Fig. 4.3

2. CONE: The CONE command creates a solid cone with an elliptical or circular base. This command provides, with the option of defining the cone height or the location of the cone apex. Defining the location of the apex will also define the height of the cone and the orientation of the cone base from the XY plane as shown in Fig. 4.4.

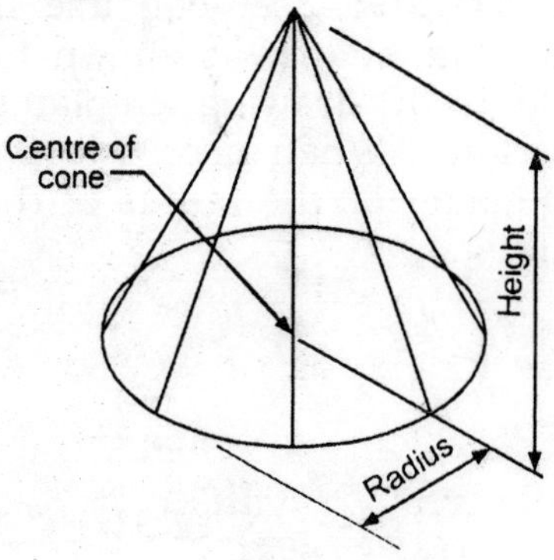

Fig. 4.4

Specify centre point for base or [3P/2P/Ttr/Elliptical] <0, 0, 0> : specify the centre of the base.

Specify base radius or [Diameter] < default > : specify the radius or Enter D to specify the diameter of the cone specify height or [2 Point/Axis/end point/Top radius] <default>:

Specify the height of the cone or enter an option or press the ENTER KEY to accept the default value.

3. CYLINDER: The CYLINDER command is used to create a solid cylinder. Similar to the CONE command, this command provides, with two options for creating the cylinder. Circular cylinder and elliptical cylinder. This command also allows to define the height of the cylinder or choose from the 2 point or Axis end point options.

Circular cylinder [Fig. 4.5]

Specify centre point of base or [3P/2P/Ttr/Elliptical]<0, 0, 0>: Specify the location of the centre point or choose one of the options

Specify base radius or [Diameter] <default> : Specify the radius or choose the option for specifying the diameter.

Specify height of the cylinder or [2 Point/Axis/end point]< default > : specify the height of the cylinder or choose an option.

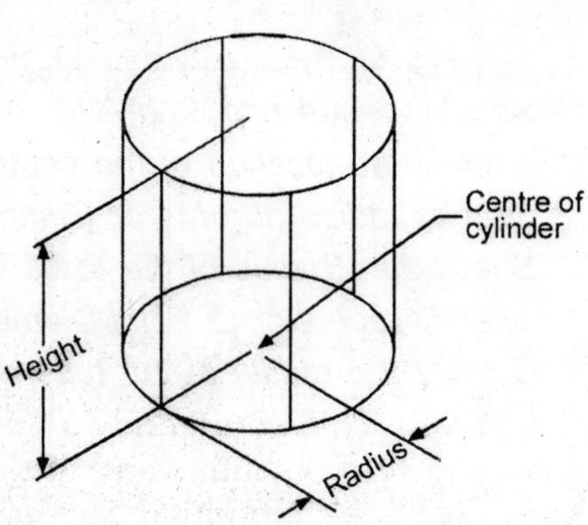

Fig. 4.5

4. SPHERE: The SPHERE command is used to create a solid sphere. In 3D drawing templates, can dynamically preview the operation that are perform on the choosing the sphere button, it will prompted to specify the centre of the sphere. On specifying the centre, user can create the sphere by defining its radius or diameter.

Specify centre point or [3P/2P/Ttr] : Specify the location of the centre of the sphere or choose an option.

Specify radius of sphere or [Diameter] <default> : Specify the radius or choose an option.

3P Option of Sphere

Specify first point: Specify the first through point.

Specify second point: Specify the second through point.

Specify third point: Specify the third through point.

5. TORUS: User can use the TORUS command to create a torus that is a tyre-tubelike shape, as shown in Fig. 4.6. Start a new file by the *acad3D.dwt* template file. In 3D drawing templates, user can dynamically preview the operations that user perform. When user select this command, AutoCAD will prompt user to enter the diameter or the radius of the torus and the diameter or radius of tube as shown in Fig. 4.7.

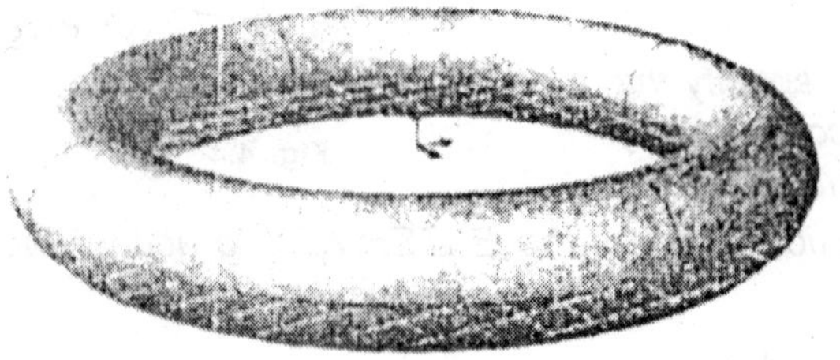

Fig. 4.6 Dynamically Created Torus

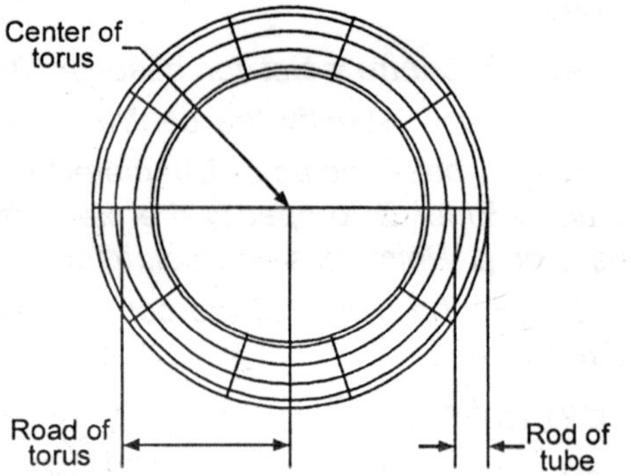

Fig. 4.7 Parameters Associated with a Torus

Specify centre or [3P/2P/Ttr]:

Specify the location of the centre of the torus or choose an option.

Specify radius of torus or [Diameter]:

Specify the radius of the torus or Enter D.

Specify radius or [2 Point/Diameter]:

Specify the radius of the tube or choose an option.

6. WEDGE: This command is used to create a solid wedge and is similar to the BOX command. This means that this command provides user with the options of creating the wedge that is similar to those of the BOX command.

7. POLYSOLID: The POLYSOLID command is similar to the POLYLINE command with the difference that this command creates a solid with a rectangular cross-section of a specified width and height. This command can also convert existing lines, 2D polylines, arcs, and circles to a polysolid feature. The prompt sequence, when user will invoke the POLYSOLID command, is given next.

COMMAND: POLYSOLID

Height = current, Width = current, Justification = current

*Specify start point or [Object/Height/Width/Justify]<Object>: **Specify the start point for the profile of the polysolid. Else, press the ENTER key to specify an object to convert into a polysolid or enter an option.***

Next Point of Polysolid: When user specify the start point for the profile of the solid, this option is displayed. This option is used to specify the next point of the current polysolid segment. If additional polysolid segments are added to the first polysolid, AutoCAD automatically makes the endpoint of the previous polysolid the start point of the next polysolid segment.

COMMAND: POLYSOLID

Height = current, Width = current, Justification = current

*Specify start point or [Object/Height/Width/Justify] <Object>: **Specify the start point of the polysolid.***

*Specify next point or [Arc/Undo]: **Specify the endpoint of the first polysolid segment.***

*Specify next point or [Arc/Close/Undo]: **Specify the endpoint of second polysolid segment or press the ENTER key to exit the command.***

8. SLICE: SLICE command is used to slice the selected solid with the help of a specified plane. User will be given an option to select the portion of the sliced solid that has to be retained. User can also retain both the portions of the sliced.

*Select objects to slice : **Select the object to slice select objects to slice:** ↵*

Specify first point on the slicing plane or [Planer object/surface/Z axis/View/XY/YZ/ZX/3 points] <3 points>:

3 Points

This option is used to slice a solid using a plane defined by three points as shown in Fig. 4.8.

*Select objects to slice: **Select the object to be sliced.***

Select objects to slice: ↵

*Specify first point on slicing plane or **[Planer object/surface/Z axis/view/XY/YZ/ZX/3 points]** <3 points>:* ↵

*Specify first point on plane: **Specify the point P_1 on the slicing plane as shown in Fig. 4.9.***

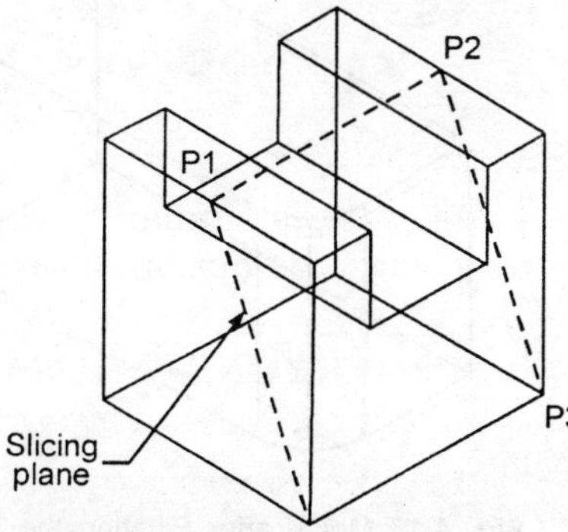

Fig. 4.8 Defining the Slicing Plane

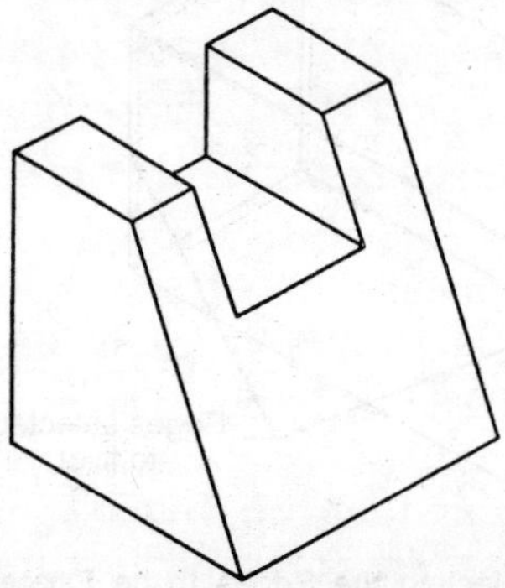

Fig. 4.9 Model after Slicing

Specify second point on plane: Specify the point P_2 on the slicing plane.

Specify third point on plane: Specify the point P_3 on the slicing plane.

Specify a point on desired side of the plane or [keep both sides]. Select the portion of the solid to retain or enter B to retain both the portions of the sliced solid.

10. FILLET: As mentioned earlier, the FILLET command is used to round the edges or corners of the models. This is generally done to reduce the stress concentration area in the model. The behaviour of this command is different while working with 2D entities from the behaviour while working with solid models. Therefore, it is very important for the user to first understand the use of this command to fillet the edges of the solid models. Fig. 4.10 shows two lines that are selected to be filleted. Now, as these lines are nothing but 2D entities, when user select these two lines to fillet, the result will be as shown in Fig. 4.11.

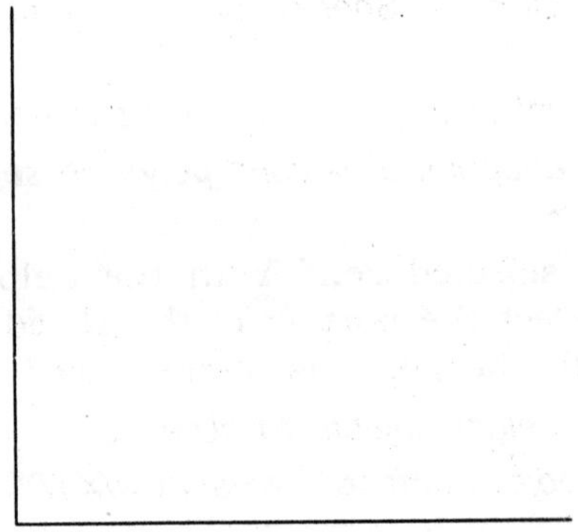

Fig. 4.10 Lines before Filleting

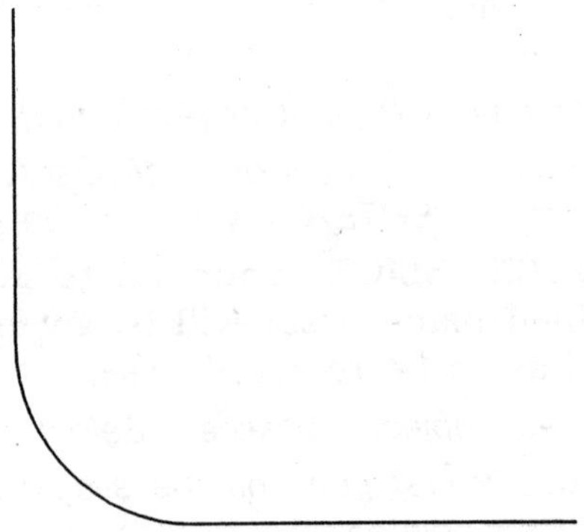

Fig. 4.11 Lines after Filleting

This shows that if actually there was a vertical edge at the corner of the lines shown in Fig. 4.10, then it would have been filleted. However, in 3D models, user directly have the vertical edges and therefore, user have to select the vertical edge to be filleted. Fig. 4.12 shows a solid model. To fillet this model, user just need to select the vertical edges, as shown in Fig. 4.13.

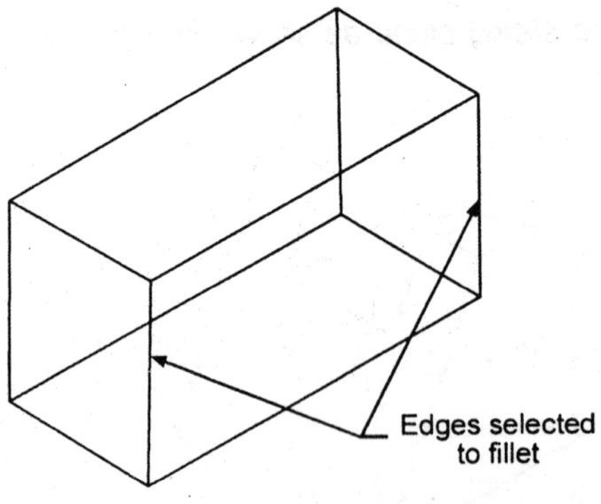

Fig. 4.12 Selecting the Edges to be Filleted

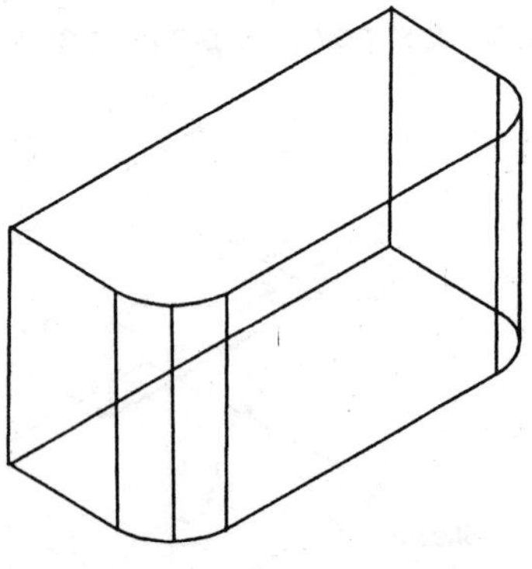

Fig. 4.13 Model after Filleting the Edges

11. CHAMFER: The CHAMFER command is used to bevel the edges of the solid models. This command is also used to reduce the area of the stress concentration in the solid models. The working of this command is also different while working with solid model.

(TRIM mode) Current chamfer Dist 1 = current, Dist 2 = current

Select first line or [Undo/Polyline/Distance/Angle/Trim/mEthod/Multiple]: Select the edge to chamfer. One of the faces associated with the edge will be selected and highlighted.

Base surface selection...

Enter surface selection option [Next/OK(current)]<OK>: Give a null response if user want to make this face as the base surface. Otherwise enter N at this prompt.

Specify base surface chamfer distance <default value>: Specify the distance.

Specify other surface chamfer distance <default value>: Specify the distance.

Select an edge or [Loop]: Select the edge to fillet.

Fig. 4.14 and 4.15 show the solid model before and after chamfering, respectively.

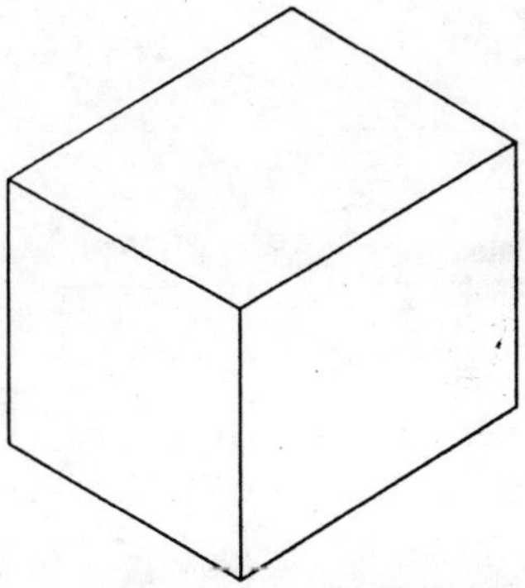

Fig. 4.14 Solid Model before Chamfering

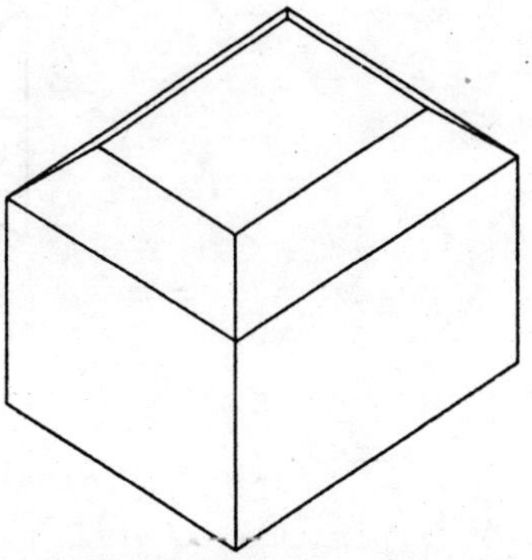

Fig. 4.15 Solid Model after Chamfering

12. ROTATE: The ROTATE3D command is used to rotate the selected solid model in the 3D space about a specified axis. Once again the right-hand thumb rule will be used to determine the direction of rotation of the solid model in 3D space. The prompt sequence that will follow when user choose this command from the Modify menu is given next.

Current positive: ANGDIR = counterclockwise ANGBASE = 0

Select objects: Select the solid model.

Select objects: ↵

Specify first point on axis or define axis by
[Object/Last/View/Xaxis/Yaxis/Zaxis/2points]:

2points Option

This is the default option for rotating solid models. This option allows user to rotate the solid model about an axis specified using two points. The direction of the axis will be from the first point of the second point. Using this direction of the axis, user can calculate the direction of rotation of the solid model by applying the right-hand thumb rule.

[Object/Last/View/Xaxis/Yaxis/Zaxis/2points]: ↵

Specify first point on axis: Specify the first point of the rotation axis. [Fig. 4.16.]

Specify second point on axis: Specify the second point of the rotation axis.

Specify rotation angle or [Reference]: Specify the angle of rotation.

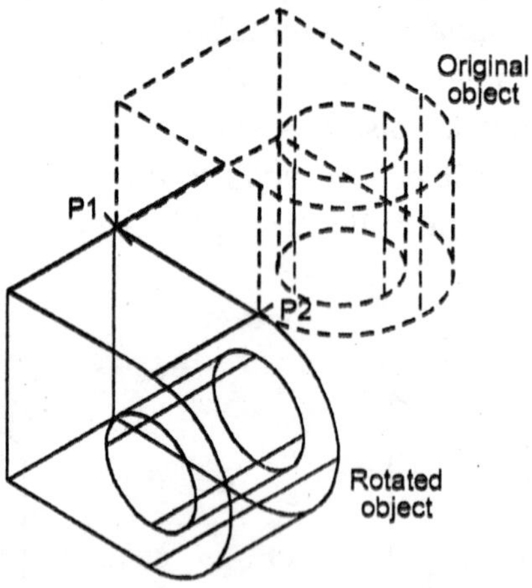

Fig. 4.16

13. MIRROR: The MIRROR3D command is used to mirror the solid models about a specified plane in the space. The prompt sequence that will follow when user choose this command from the Modify menu is given next.

Sect objects: Select the solid model to be mirrored.

Select objects: ↵

Specify first point of mirror plane (3 points) or [Object/Last/Zaxis/XY/YZ/ZX/3points] < 3points >:

3points Option

This is default option for mirroring the solid models. As discussed earlier, a line can be defined by the two points from which the line passes. Similarly, a plane can be defined by the three points through which it passes. This option alloys user to specify the three points from which the mirroring plane passes.

Specify first point of mirror plane (3 points) or [Object/Last/Zaxis/View/XY/YZ/ZX/3points] < 3points >: ↵

Specify first point on mirror plane: Specify the first point on the plane.

Specify second point on mirror plane: Specify the second point on the plane. [Fig 4.12]

Specify third point on mirror plane: Specify the third point on the plane. [Fig. 4.17]

Delete source objects? [Yes/No] <N>: ↵

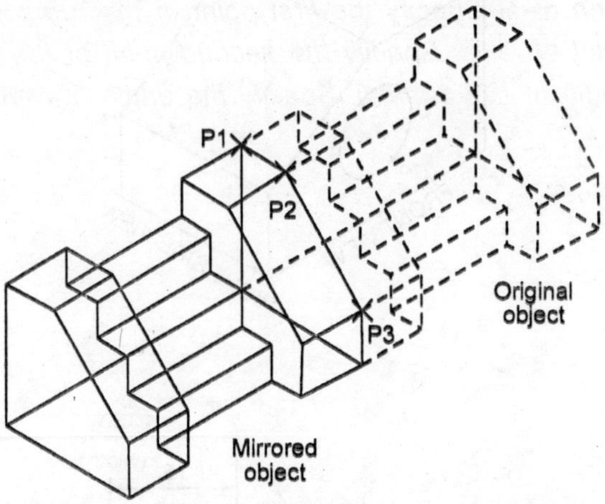

Fig. 4.17

14. MATERIAL: This option is used to apply material to the selected face.

Select faces or [Undo/Remove]: Select one or more faces to apply the material

Select faces or [Undo/Remove/ALL]: Select one or more faces, enter an option, or ↵

Enter new material name <By Layer>: Enter the name of the material or ↵

4.6 ISOMETRIC DRAWING

Using isometric commands is one of the simplest ways to give a 3D representation when using only 2D commands. This has been the usual way of doing things before CAD allow true 3D work to be done. Many times an isometric drawing is used to compliment a 3 view orthographic drawing as shown in fig. 4.18.

User can see that it is a very simple drawing. This basic isometric drawing of the object gives a very good idea of what it looks like If this is all that is needed then isometric works. Unfortunately, as soon as user change anything, like the block's height, user will need to red all four views.

AutoCAD has a command called ISOPLANE which allows user to easily draw at a 30 degree angle as needed for an isometric drawing. User can switch between the three 'isoplanes' (top, right, left) by using this command or by pressing the F5 key.

Command: ISOPLANE <ENTER>

Current isoplane: Right

Enter isometric plane setting [Left/Top/Right] <Left>: T <ENTER>

Current isoplane: Top

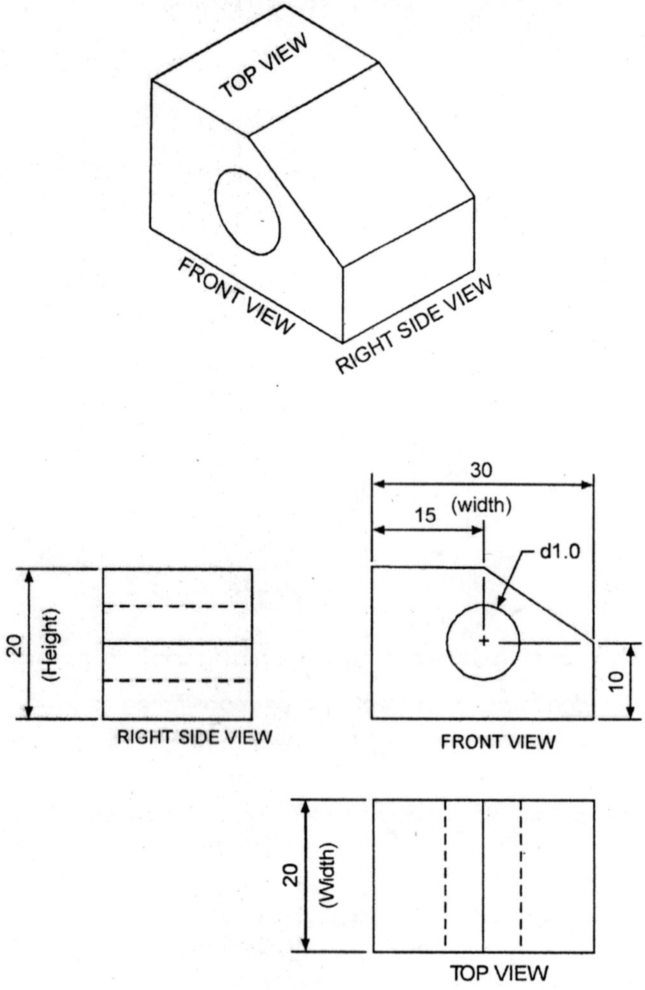
TOP VIEW
FRONT VIEW
RIGHT SIDE VIEW
30
15
(width)
d1.0
20
(Height)
10
RIGHT SIDE VIEW
FRONT VIEW
20
(Width)
TOP VIEW

Fig. 4.18

JANUARY EXAMINATION 2009

Engineering Drawing–I

Time: 4 hrs *M.M. 100*

Note: (1) Attempt all questions.
(2) Assuming missing data, if any.
(3) All first Angle projection.
(4) All dimensions are in mm.

1. For the isometric view shown in Fig. 1, draw the following views in scale FULL SIZE:

(a) Front view looking in the direction of arrow shown
(b) Top view
(c) Left side view. (14 + 14 + 12 = 40)

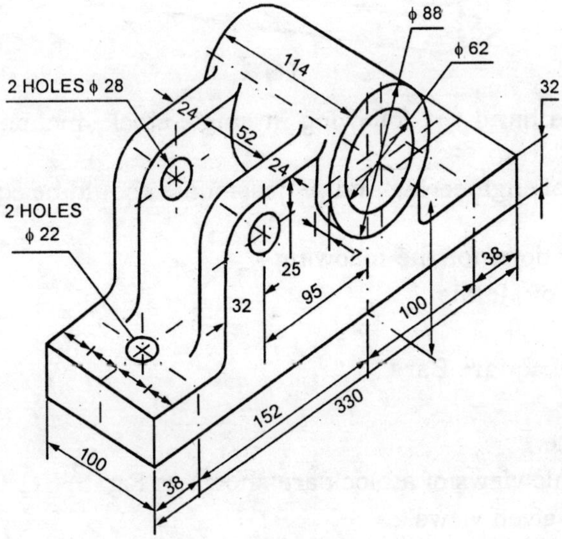

Fig. 1

OR

From the pictorial view shown in Fig. 2, draw to full scale, the following views :

(a) Top view
(b) Sectional front view at A-A. (18 + 22 = 40)

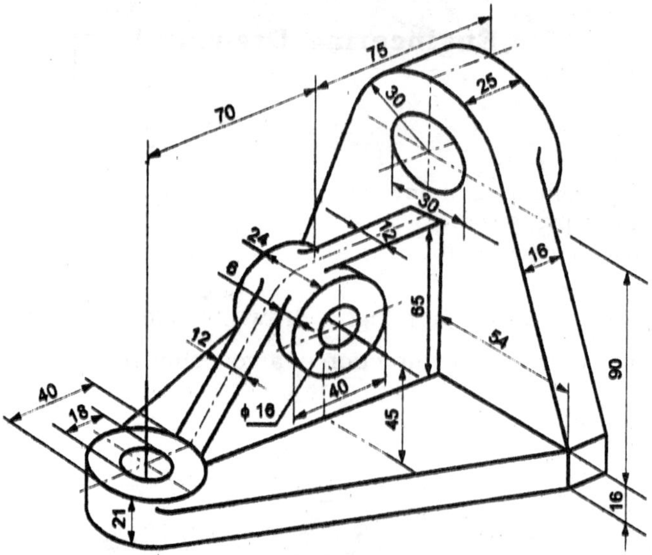

Fig. 2

2. (a) Print in free hand the following in single-stock, inclined capital letters, using the ratio 6 : 5—

"A student of engineering and professionals should be equipped with good quality pencils".

(b) Give conventions for the following :

(1) Section of Metals

(2) Liquids

(3) Break of square Bars

(4) Wood

(5) Concrete. (10 + 10 = 20)

3. Two orthographic views of a block are shown in Fig. 3:

(a) Redraw the given views.

(b) Add the missing view.

(c) Draw its isometric view. (4 + 6 + 10 = 20)

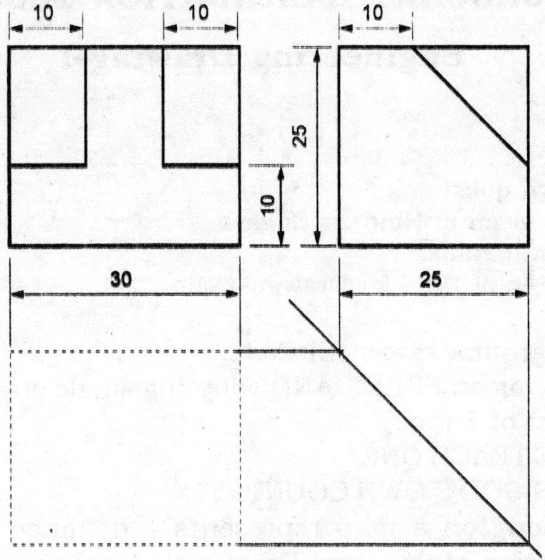

Fig. 3

4. Construct a diagonal scale to read meters, decimeters and centimeters for a R.F. of $\frac{1}{50}$ and long enough to measure upto 5 metres. Show on it a length of 2.89 metres, 3.67 metres and 4.44 meters. 20

❑❑❑

JANUARY EXAMINATION 2009

Engineering Drawing–I

Time: 4 hrs *M.M. 100*

Note: (1) Attempt any five questions.
(2) Answer may be given in Hindi or English.
(3) Assume missing details.
(4) Follow BIS S.P. 46 of 1988 for Drawing Code.

1. (a) Draw the line groups as per ISI Code. 10
(b) Print the following on FREE HAND adopting single stroke, vertical capital letters having a height of 5 mm : 10
(1) "EACH ONE TEACH ONE"
(2) "KERALA IS GOD'S OWN COUNTRY"

2. A line of 20 cm long on a map represents a distance of 400 meters. Find the representative fraction of the map. Draw a diagonal scale so as to measure upto a single metre and long enough to measure a distance of 400 metres. Measure and mark distances of 356 metres and 108 metres on the scale. 20

OR

Draw a Vernier scale of meters when 1 cm represents 2.5 metres. Find the R.F. of this scale and show a distance of 35.2 metres on this scale.

3. A right regular square pyramid is resting on the HP with its axis perpendicular to HP and parallel to V.P. The side of base is 15 mm and height 30 mm. Once of its bases is parallel to VP and 15 mm in front of it. Draw the projections of the pyramid in H.P. and V.P. 20

4. Draw the development of a square pyramid of base 30 mm and height 65 mm. 20

5. An 'ISOMETRIC' view of Bevel is given in Fig. 1 Draw to full size of following orthographic views, in First Angle projection, looking from 'Arrow A': 20
(a) Front view
(b) Top view.

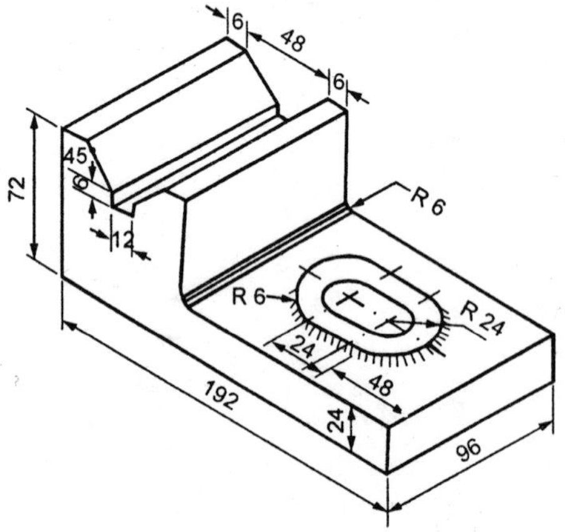

Fig. 1

6. Two views of an object is given in Fig. 2. Draw the missing top view and also draw the isometric view of the object. 20

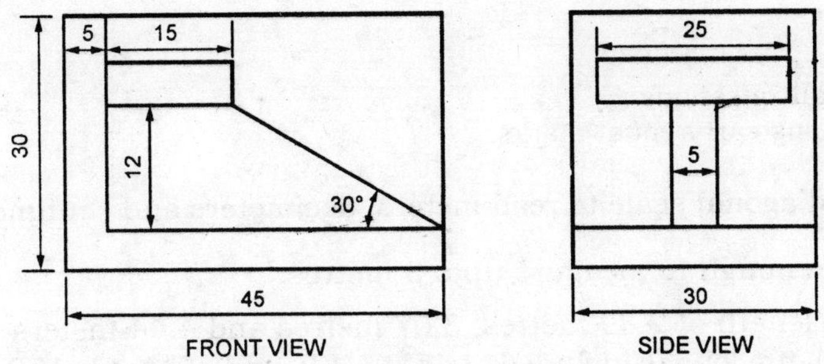

Fig. 2

7. A cylinder of 30 mm diameter and 60 mm length is lying with its axis at an angle of 45° to the V.P. It is cut by a horizontal sectional plane V.T. at a distance of 12 mm in front of the axis. Draw the true sectional plan of the cylinder. 20

8. Construct a parabola when the distance of focus is 50 mm from the directrix. Draw tangent and normal at any point of the curve. 20

OR

Construct an ellipse whose major axis = 70 mm and minor axis = 50 mm.

□□□

JANUARY EXAMINATION 2009

Engineering Drawing–I

Time: 4 hrs *M.M. 100*

Note: (1) Attempt all questions.
(2) All questions carry equal marks.

1. Construct a diagonal scale to read meters, decimeters and centimeters for a R.F. of $\frac{1}{50}$ and long enough to measure upto 5 metres.
   Show on it a length of 2.89 metres, 3.67 metres and 4.44 meters.
2. A line AB 120 mm long is included at 45° to H.P. and 30° to the V.P. Its mid point VC is in V.P. and 20 mm above H.P. The end A is the 3rd quadrant and B is in the 1st quadrant. Draw the projections of the line AB.
3. A pentagonal pyramid, edge of base 25 mm and axis 55 mm long is resting on a corner of its base on horizontal plane in such a way that the slant edge contained by that corner makes an angle of 60° to H.P. and 45° to V.P. Draw its projections.
4. A right regular triangular pyramid side of base 40 mm and axis 65 mm long is lying on H.P. on one of its triangular slant faces such that the axis is parallel to the V.P. cuts the pyramid cutting plane, parallel to the V.P. cuts the pyramid and is at a distance of 10 mm from the axis. Draw its sectional front view, top view and develop its lateral surface.
5. The front view of an object is shown in Fig. 1. Draw the isometric projection of the object.

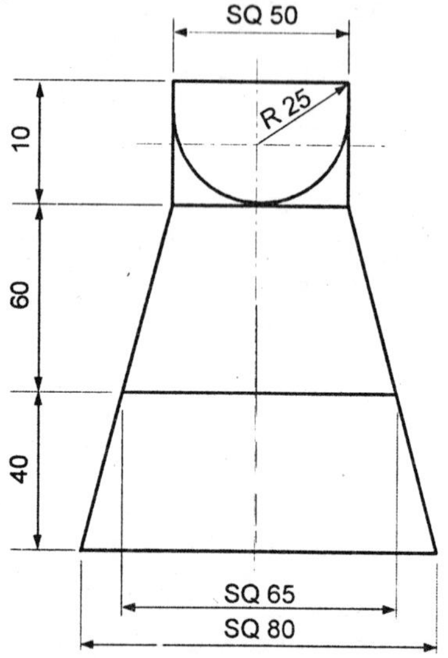

Fig. 1

All dimension are in mm.

❑❑❑

MAY EXAMINATION 2007

Engineering Drawing–II

Time: 4 hrs *M.M. 100*

Note: [1] Attempt all questions.
[2] Answer any missing data.
[3] This question paper contains one sketch.

1. Details of a protected flange coupling are shown in Fig. 1 Draw the following views of the assembly to a suitable scale given dimensions:
   (a) Front elevation top half in section,
   (b) Side view looking from left.
2. (a) Draw the following revet heads, having nominal diameter 24 mm:
   Snap head, pan head, conical head and flat countersank head.
   (b) Draw the following keys in position in a shaft of diameter 50 mm
   Give head key and feather key. 20
3. (a) Draw the views of the assembly of a square headed bolt with a hexagonal nut and washer with the nominal diameter of 24 mm and shank length 100 mm.
   (b) Draw the conventional representation of internal threads in section and without section of nominal diameter of 24 mm.
4. (For Mechanical, Automobile and Production Engineering Students only)
   A cylinder of 40 mm diameter, axial height 60 mm is resting on the circular base on H.P. The cylinder is cut by a section plane perpendicular to V.P. and at 45° to H.P. in the middle of the axis. Draw the development of lower portion of the cylinder surface. 20

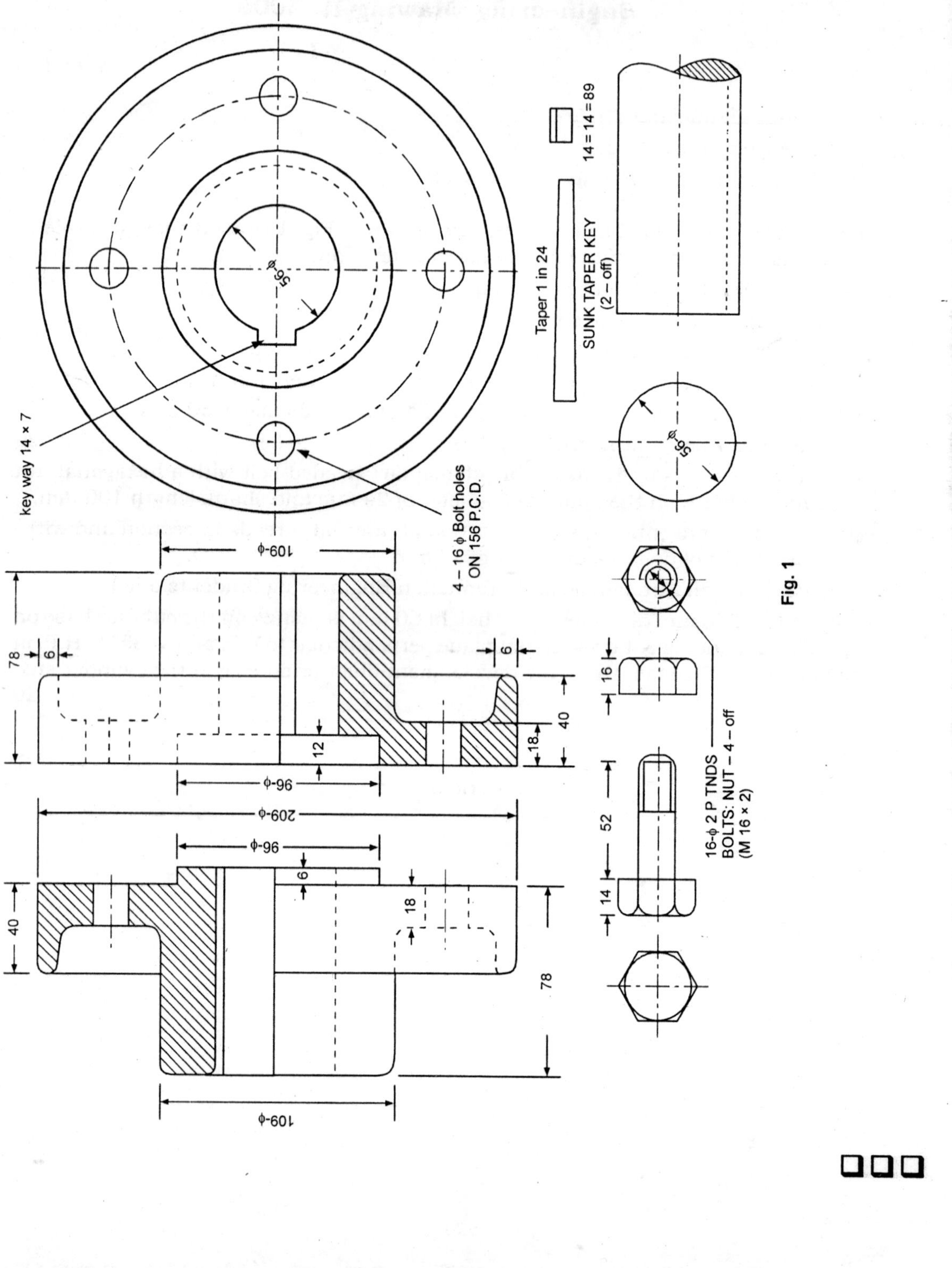
key way 14 × 7
4 – 16 ϕ Bolt holes
ON 156 P.C.D.
ϕ-56
Taper 1 in 24
SUNK TAPER KEY
(2 – off)
14 = 14 = 89
16-ϕ 2 P TNDS
BOLTS: NUT – 4 – off
(M 16 × 2)
109-ϕ
96-ϕ
209-ϕ
78
40
18
12
6
16
52
14

Fig. 1

□□□

DECEMBER EXAMINATION 2006

Engineering Drawing–I

Time: 4 hrs *M.M. 100*

Note: [1] Attempt all questions.

[2] Answer may be given in English

[3] Assume any missing or mismatching demension.

1. (a) Give the symbols and conventions for the following: 5

(i) Electric Fan

(ii) Electric Flourescent Tube light

(iii) Earthing

(iv) Fan regulator

(v) W.C.

(b) Prepare a drawing of a stool having top surface 400 mm × 600 mm and having a thickness of 30 mm. There are 4 legs, each of 40 mm × 40 mm square section. Assume the remaining dimensions for connecting the legs at top and bottom. 15

2. Draw a plain scale to show kilometers. A rectangular plot of 25 square kilometer is represented on a map by a similar rectangle of area 1 square cm. Measure a distance of 65 km on it. 20

3. Fig. 1 shows the pictorial view of an object. Draw to a suitable scale the following views: 35

(a) Fron view

(b) Right side view

(c) Sectional top view at AA.

4. Fig. 2 shows the two views of an object. Draw these two views and add the third missing view. Also draw the isometric drawing of the object. 25

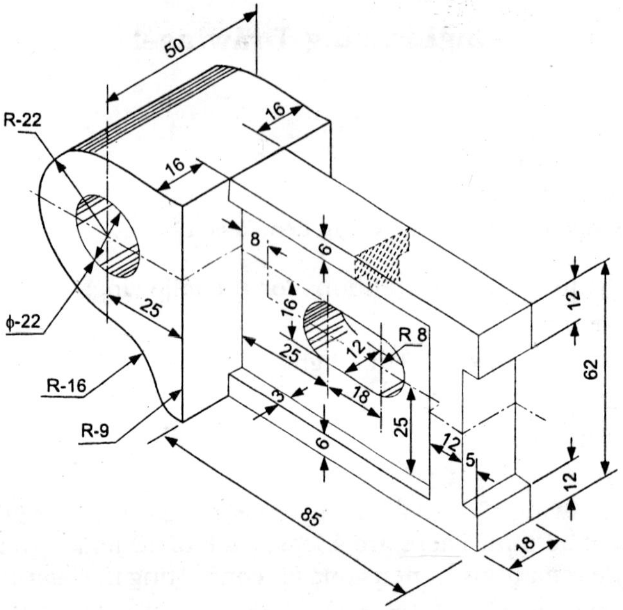
50
16
R-22
16
8
6
ϕ-22
25
16
R 8
12
25
R-16
3
18
25
R-9
6
12
5
62
12
12
85
18

Fig. 1

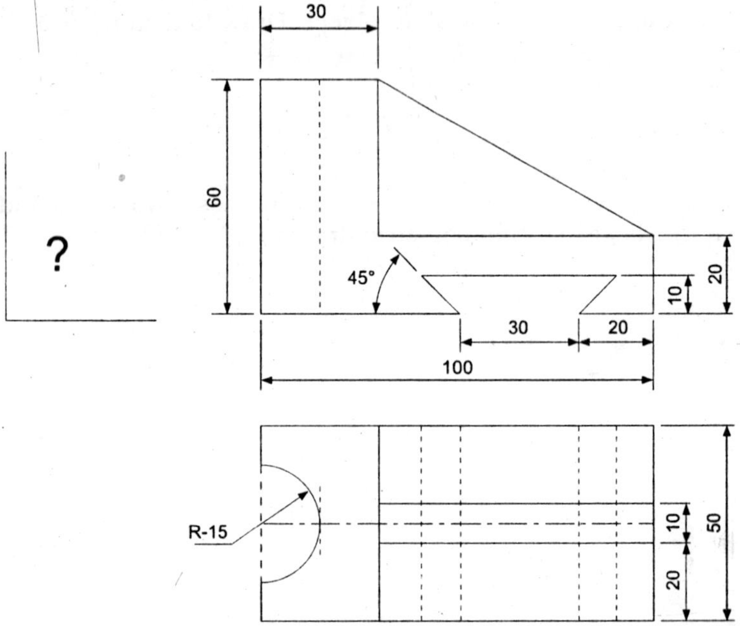
30
60
?
45°
10
20
30
20
100
R-15
10
50
20

Fig. 2

□□□

DECEMBER EXAMINATION 2006

Engineering Drawing–I

Time: 4 hrs *M.M. 100*

Note: [1] Attempt all questions.
[2] Answer may be given in English
[3] Assume any missing or mismatching dimensions.

1. (a) What type of line is indicated to show the following? Given the name and also draw the required lines 10
(i) Visible boundary
(ii) Line of symmetry
(iii) Hidden outline
(iv) Cutting plane
(v) Leader line

(b) Print single stroke free hand lower and supper case with a height of 7 mm the following:
"Scrap was imported from Iran by ship and trucks to cover a total distance of 5675245 metres".

2. Draw a diagonal scale to represent kilometers for a representative fraction of $\frac{1}{5,00,000}$ and long enough to read upto 900 kilometers and having spaces of 150 kilometers as a unit. Measure a distance of 515 km on the scale. 20

3. Fig. 1 shows the pictrorial view of an object. Draw the following views of the object to a suitable scale: 35
(a) Sectional front view at AA
(b) Left side view
(c) Plan.

4. Fig. 2 shows two views of an object. Draw these views and add the third missing view. Also draw the isometric drawing of the object.

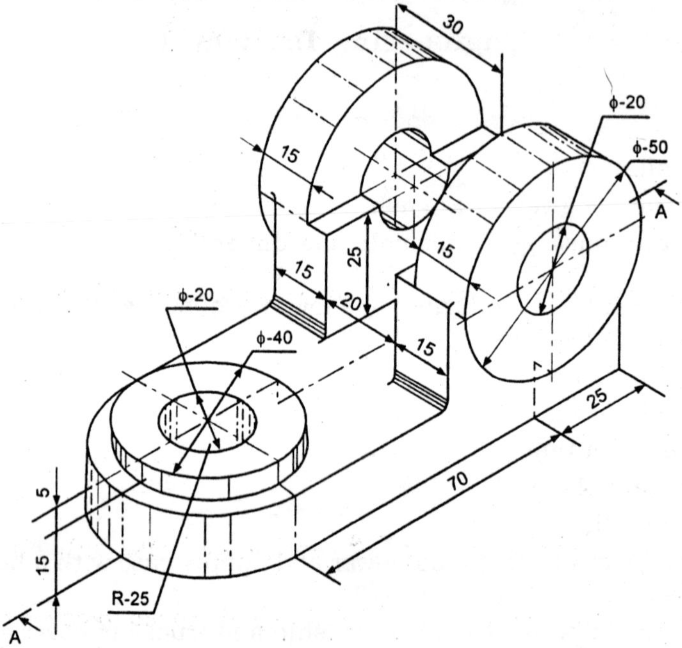
30
ϕ-20
ϕ-50
15
A
25
15
15
ϕ-20
20
ϕ-40
15
25
5
70
15
R-25
A

Fig. 1

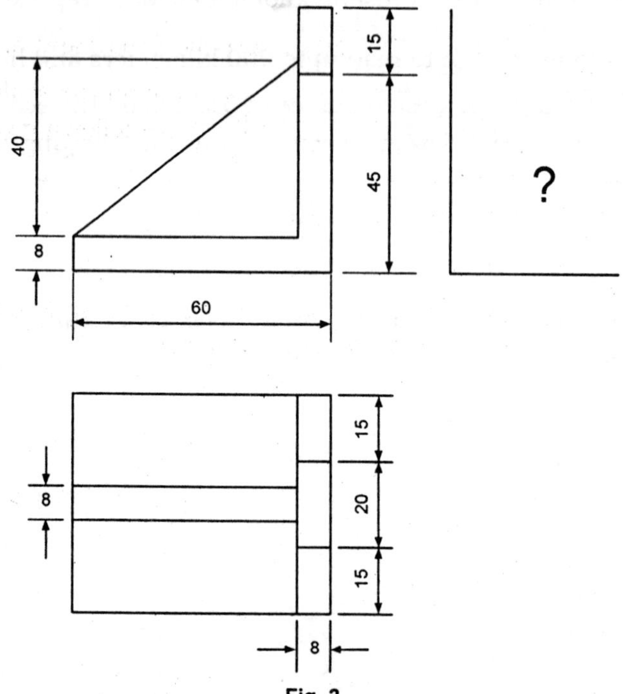
15
40
45
?
8
60
15
8
20
15
8

Fig. 2

□□□

MAY/JUNE EXAMINATION 2005

Engineering Drawing–II

Time: 4 hrs *M.M. 100*

Note : (1) Write your Roll No. on the top immediately on receipt of this question paper.

(2) This question paper contains two sections, Section — A and Section — B.

(3) Attempt Section — B which is compulsory and any three questions from Section — A

(4) Assume missing data, if any. All dimensions are in millimeters.

(5) Use First Angle projection system.

(6) Answer may be given in Hindi or English.

[Section—A]

1. Sketch in proportion the following: 5 + 5 + 10 = 20

(a) Conventional representation of International Metric threads size M24 without section.

(b) Fillister head machine screw of size M10.

(c) Two views of a Castle Nut of size M24.

2. (a) Keeping the axis horizontal draw two views of a Hexagonal headed bolt and nut with washer. Take the nominal size of bolt M24 and length 100 mm.

(b) Draw two views of woodruff key, suitable for 60 mm diameter shaft.

3. Figure 1 shows the details of Knuckle Joint (pictorial). Assemble the details and draw the following views of the assembly in scale full size. 8 + 8 + 4 = 20

(a) Top half-sectional front view

(b) Left side view. Give dimensions.

4. Draw two views of double riveted, double cover plate, butt joint suitable for 9 mm plate thickness. (Main plates) 10 + 10 = 20

[Section—B]

(For Electrical Engineering Students Only)

5. (a) Left half sectional front view of a Pin Type Insulator fitted with a pin is shown in Figure 2. Copy the given view and draw a Plan/Top view to scale 1 : 1. Give dimensions. 40

(For Civil Engineering Students Only)

(b) Figure 3 shows an Isometric view of a Stool. Draw to scale 1 : 2 the following: 40

(i) Front view in direction A.

(ii) Top View

(For Plastic Technology Students Only)

(c) Figure 4 shows sectional view of a mould. Draw the following views of the parts to a suitable scale by scaling the dimensions : 40

(i) Two views of the side blocks (Fig. 4a)

(ii) Two views of the injection side of mould (Fig. 4c)

(iii) Two vies of the conical seat frame block. (Fig. 4d)

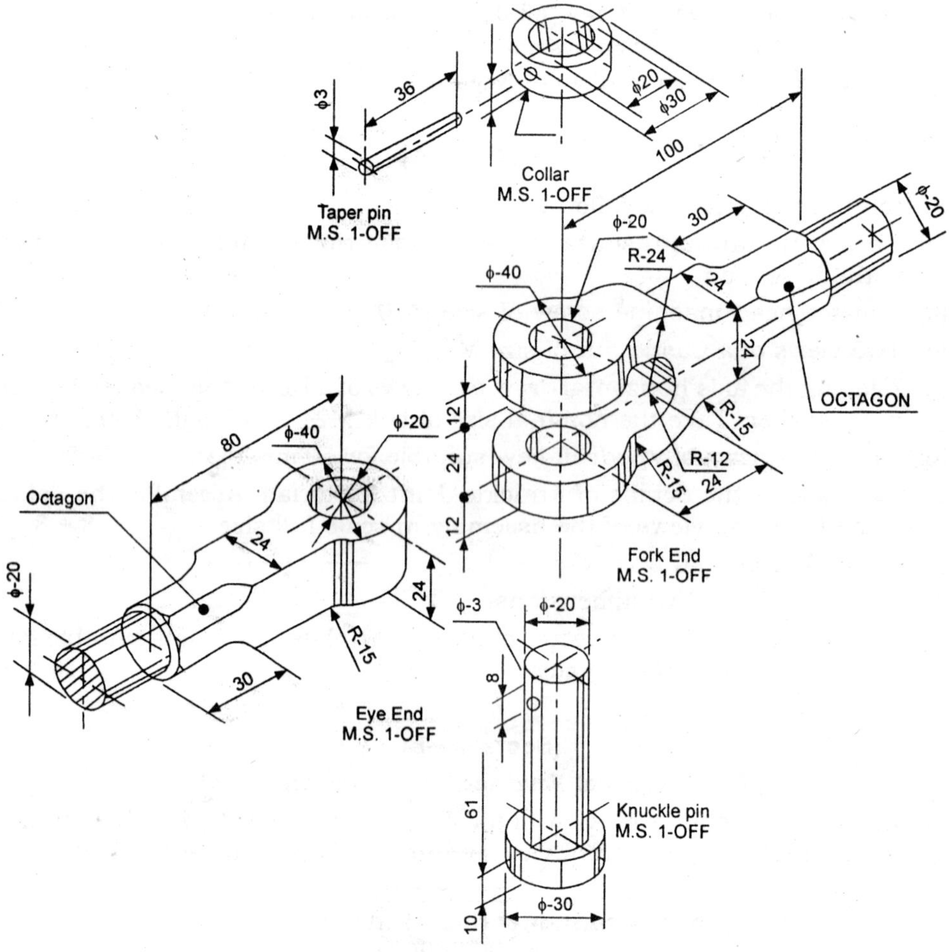

Fig. 1

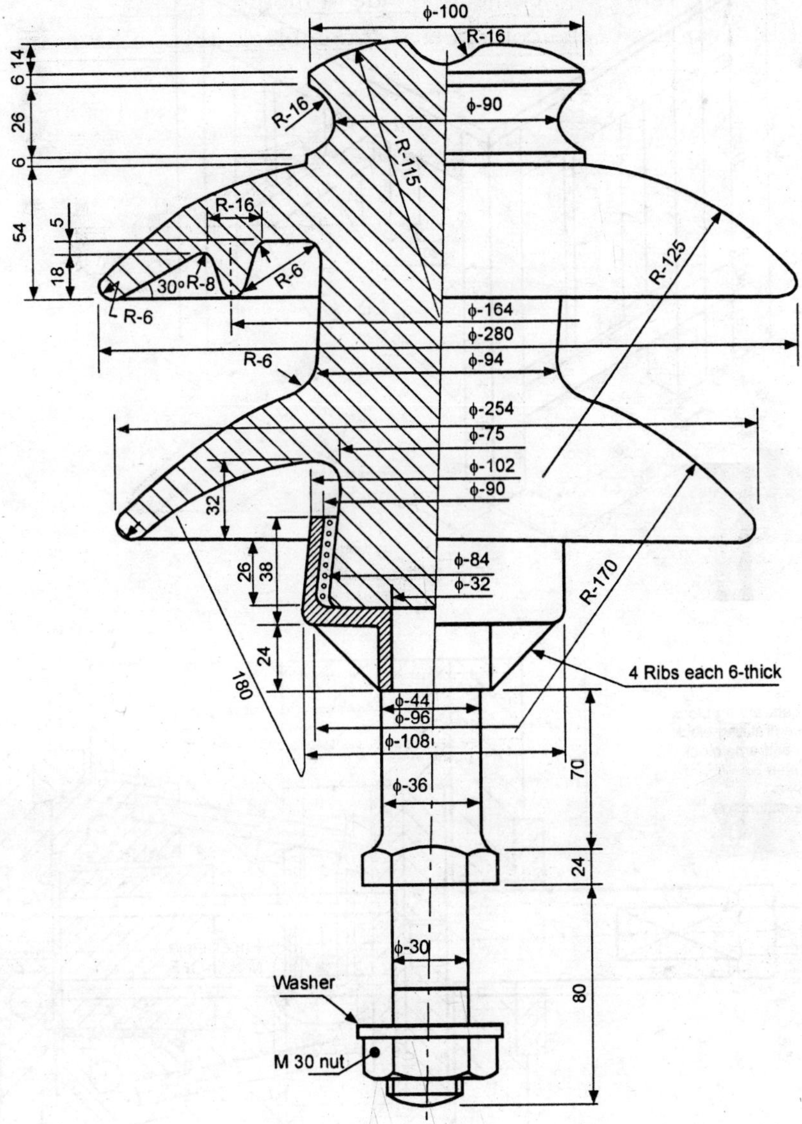
φ-100
R-16
R-16
φ-90
R-115
R-16
R-6
30°
R-8
R-6
R-125
φ-164
φ-280
R-6
φ-94
φ-254
φ-75
φ-102
φ-90
φ-84
φ-32
R-170
4 Ribs each 6-thick
180
φ-44
φ-96
φ-108
φ-36
φ-30
Washer
M 30 nut
6
14
6
26
6
54
5
18
32
26
38
24
70
24
80

Fig. 2

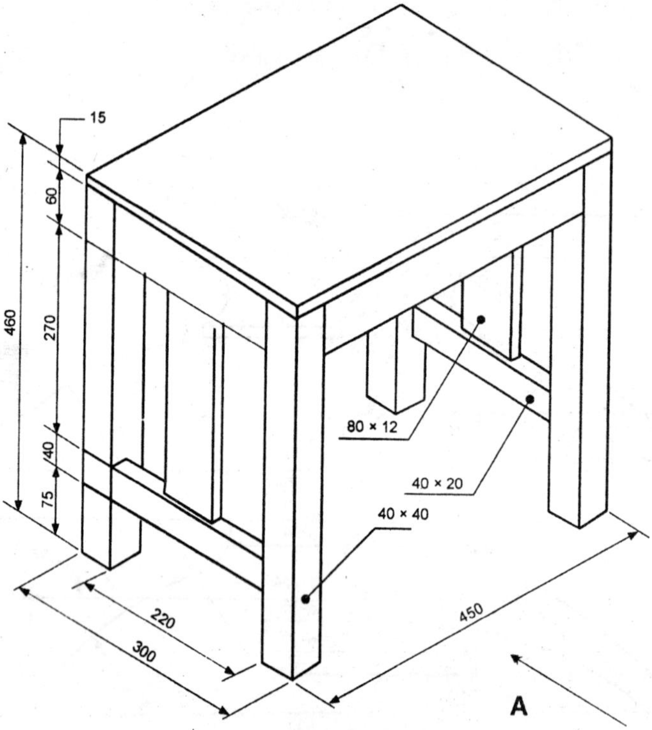
15
60
460
270
40
75
80 × 12
40 × 20
40 × 40
220
300
450
A

Fig. 3

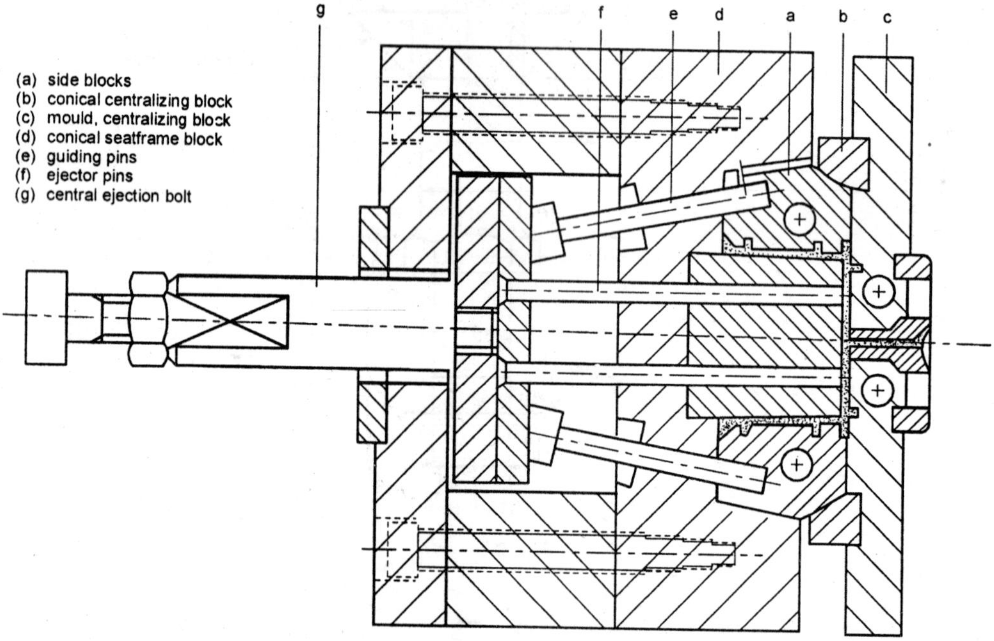
(a) side blocks
(b) conical centralizing block
(c) mould, centralizing block
(d) conical seatframe block
(e) guiding pins
(f) ejector pins
(g) central ejection bolt
g
f
e
d
a
b
c

Fig. 4

❑❑❑

DECEMBER EXAMINATION 2004

Engineering Drawing–I

Time: 4 hrs *M.M. 100*

General Instructions

[1] Attempt any four questions.
[2] All questions carry equal marks.
[3] Make use of first-angle projection.

1. (a) Print the given sentence in single stroke vertical gothic and in 7 mm, height.

"IN SECTIONS OF SOLIDS CUTTING PLANES ARE REPRESENTED BY THEIR TRACES".

(b) Draw the following conventionally:

(i) Section for insulated material.
(ii) Break for a pipe.
(iii) Line showing extreme position of movable parts.
(iv) Cutting plane line.

2. (a) Draw a regular pentagon of 10 mm, side and inscribe 5 circles in it, each touching one side and two circles.

(b) Construct a diagonal scale to measure metres, when 10 cm on the drawing represents 250 metres. The scale should be long enough to measure 200 metres and show a length of 173 metres on the scale.

3. Fig. 1 shows pictorial view of an object. Draw the following views in scale full size:

(a) Front view through — A
(b) Top view through — B
(c) Right side view through — D

4. Fig. 2 shows pictorial view of an object. Draw the following views in scale full size.

(a) Sectional front view at — AA', through — X
(b) Top view

5. Fig. 3, shows three incomplete views of an object. Complete the missing lines in the views and also draw the isometric drawing of the object.

6. (a) Given the conventions for the following:

(i) Pendant switch, (ii) Three pin plug,
(iii) Sliding door, (iv) Window (upper hung).

(b) Sketch free hand a standard dimension wooden stool in pictorial view.

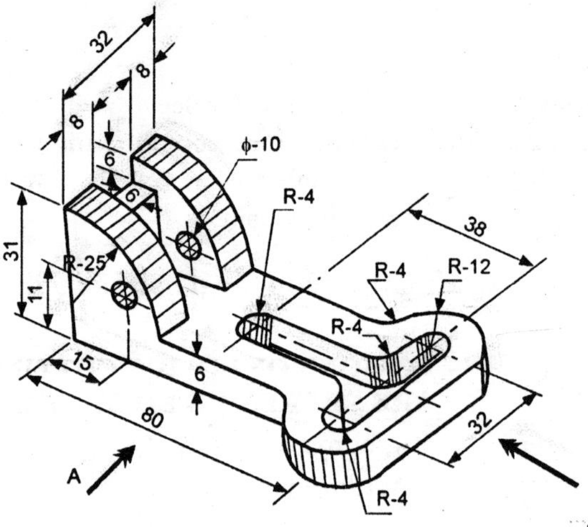

Fig. 1

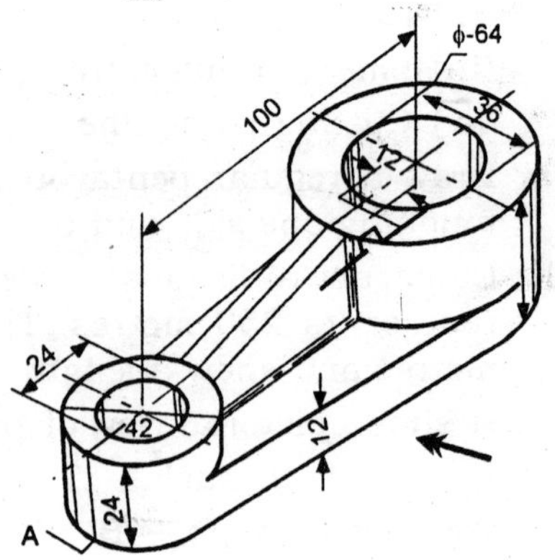

Fig. 2

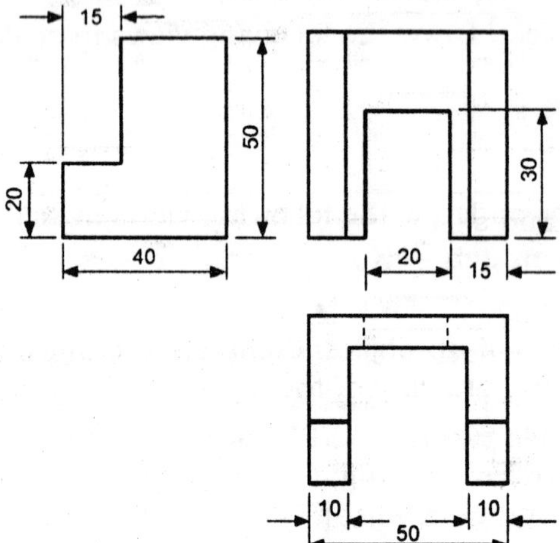

Fig. 3

□□□

MAY/JUNE EXAMINATION 2004

Engineering Drawing–II

Time: 4 hrs *M.M. 100*

Note: [1] This question paper contains TWO Sections, Section A and Section B.
[2] Attempt section B which is compulsory and any three questions from section A.
[3] Assume missing data, if any. All dimensions in millimetres.
[4] Use First Angle projection system.
[5] Answer may be given in Hindi or English.

SECTION–A

1. Sketch in proportion the following : 5 + 5 + 10 = 20

(a) Conventional representation of International Metric threads size M24 in section

(b) Countersunk head machine screw of size M-10.

(c) Two views of a Hexagonal Nut of size M-24.

2. (a) Keeping the axis horizontal draw two views of a Square headed bolt and nut with washer of size M24 and length 100 mm.

(b) Draw two views of peg feather key, suitable for 60 mm diameter shaft. 15 + 5 = 20

3. Figure 1 shows the details of Gib and Cotter Joint for Square rods (pictorial), assemble the details and draw the following views of the assembly in scale 1 : 1

(a) Top half sectional front view, and

(b) Top view. Give dimensions. 8 + 8 + 4 = 20

4. (a) Draw two views of double riveted, single cover plate, butt joint suitable for 9 mm plate thickness (Main plates).

(b) Give the symbols or seam weld and single-J butt weld. 10 + 10 = 20

SECTION–B

(For Mechanical, Automobile and Production Engineering Students only)

5. A pentagonal pyramid base edges 25 mm and axial height 60 mm is resting on its base on the HP with one rear base edge parallel to VP, it is cut by an inclined plane which is perpendicular to VP and making 45° to the HP, through the mid point on the axis. Draw the development in one piece of the lateral surface of the remaining pyramid. 40

(For Electrical Engineering Students Only)

6. Figure 2 shows a Shackle Type Insulator filled with G.I. straps and bolts to be used on the cross arm of a pole. Copy the view and draw a Plan/Top view to scale 1 : 1. Give dimensions.

(For Civil Engineering Students Only)

7. Figure 3 shows the isometric view of a Dining Table. Draw to scale 1 : 10 the following: 40

(a) Front view looking from A, and

(b) Top view.

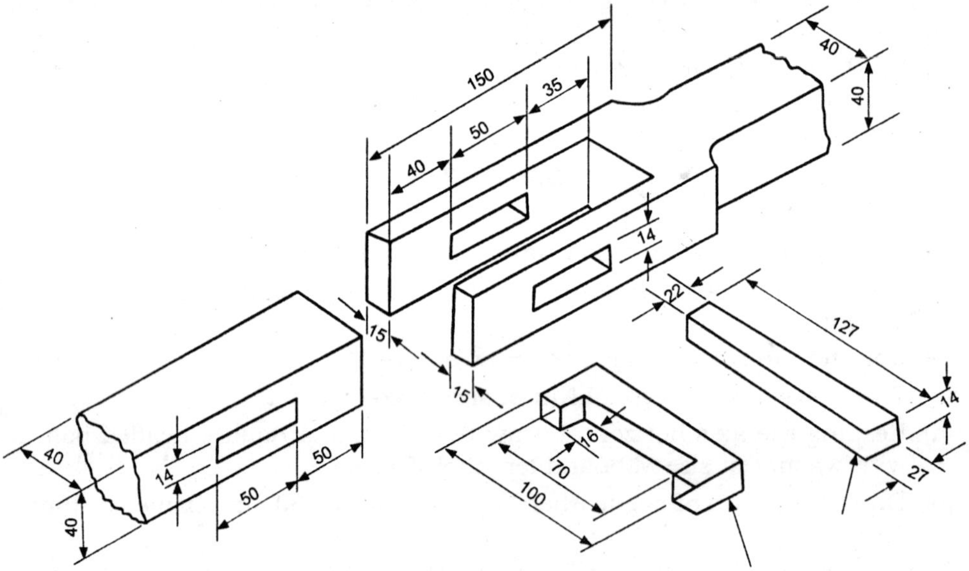

Fig. 1

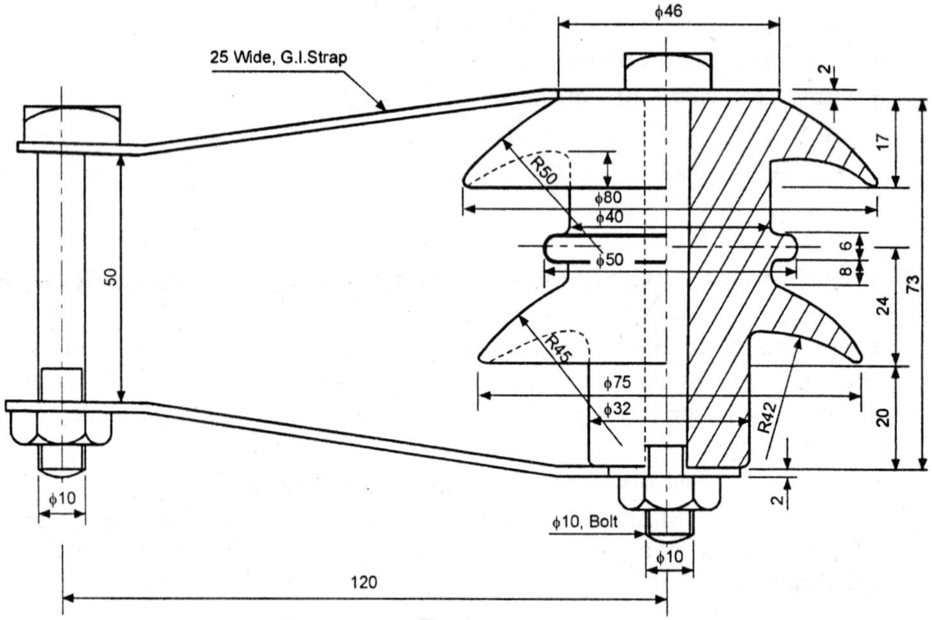

Fig. 2